PASS THE CLASS MEDIA GUIDE

Chapter Test Videos will help you prepare for your next test.

Every end-of-chapter test question from the textbook has an accompanying video, featuring actual instructors.

Step-by-step solutions follow the problem-solving methods used in the text.

Rewind, play, and pause buttons allow you to review at your own pace.

The solutions include interactive questions with immediate feedback on your answer.

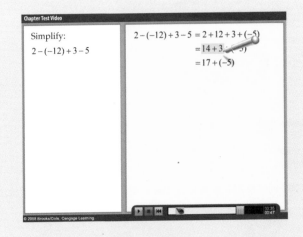

The Chapter Test Video icon in your textbook indicates that the chapter test videos are available online via:

✔ The **Online Study Center**.

✔ The **Online Multimedia eBook**.

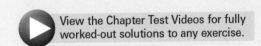
View the Chapter Test Videos for fully worked-out solutions to any exercise.

PASS THE CLASS MEDIA GUIDE

WebAssign allows you to access your assignments from anywhere, at any time of day or night.

Get what you need, when you need it.

Your **Home Page** for your Beginning Algebra class allows you to:

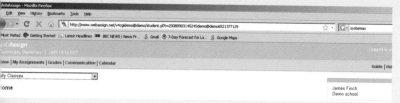

✔ Access a list of your **Current Assignments, Past Assignments,** and **Upcoming Assignments**.

✔ View your **Calendar**, including personalized due dates.

✔ View your **Grades**.

✔ Access the **Communication** page, containing Forums and Messages from your instructor.

Keep track of due dates.

Your **My Assignments** page includes:

✔ The name and description of your assignment.

✔ The date and time your assignment is due—the *last* moment you can submit work done on the assignment.

✔ Scores you have received on your assignments.

Use the **calendar** to keep track of your homework, quizzes, tests, and more.

Visit www.webassign.net to access the WebAssign homework for this textbook.

PASS THE CLASS MEDIA GUIDE

Your homework, calendar, and grades—all in one convenient place. That's the power of **WebAssign.**

Complete your homework.

Once you click on an assignment, your **Assignment Page** appears. Your assignments will give you immediate and unlimited practice and allow you to:

✔ Submit your **answers**.

✔ Keep track of your **current score** as you're working.

✔ Record notes using the **notes box.**

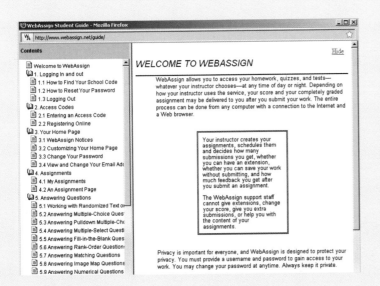

Need help?

The WebAssign **Student Guide** provides step-by-step help for:

✔ Logging in.

✔ Viewing and completing assignments.

✔ Accessing your grades.

Visit www.webassign.net/guide/index.html to access these instructions and more.

PASS THE CLASS MEDIA GUIDE

You'll be set for success with this suite of online multimedia tools.

Get one-on-one help in a hurry.

Smarthinking® Live, Online Tutoring provides an easy-to-use and effective online tutoring service. A dynamic Whiteboard and a Graphing Calculator function will allow you to collaborate easily with your experienced, trained e-structor.

Smarthinking® is available when you need it! Submit questions 24 hours a day, 7 days a week, or chat live with an e-structor up until 1 AM EST.

Want a textbook that understands your learning style?

The **Online Multimedia eBook** is an electronic version of your textbook, with links to interactive study tools:

✔ Chapter Test videos provide step-by-step solutions to every end-of-chapter test question.

✔ Video Lessons feature short video clips of core topics.

✔ Glossary flashcards will help you refresh on key terms.

✔ Tutorials allow you to:
  - Study a Concept.
  - Try an Example.
  - Practice an Exercise.

Visit www.cengage.com/math/aufmann to access the Online Study Center for this textbook.

Beginning Algebra with Applications with a Trigonometry Supplement

Richard N. Aufmann | Vernon C. Barker | Joanne S. Lockwood

CENGAGE
Learning™

Australia • Brazil • Japan • Korea • Mexico • Singapore • Spain • United Kingdom • United States

CENGAGE
Learning™

Beginning Algebra with Applications with a Trigonometry Supplement

Beginning Algebra with Applications with a Trigonometry Supplement
Aufmann, Barker, Lockwood

© 2010 Cengage Learning. All rights reserved.

ACP TRIG CHAPTERS
AUFMANN | LOCKWOOD

© 2009 Cengage Learning. All rights reserved.

Executive Editors:
 Maureen Staudt
 Michael Stranz

Senior Project Development Manager:
 Linda deStefano

Marketing Specialist:
 Courtney Sheldon

Senior Production/Manufacturing Manager:
 Donna M. Brown

PreMedia Manager:
 Joel Brennecke

Sr. Rights Acquisition Account Manager:
 Todd Osborne

Cover Image:
Getty Images*

*Unless otherwise noted, all cover images used by Custom Solutions, a part of Cengage Learning, have been supplied courtesy of Getty Images with the exception of the Earthview cover image, which has been supplied by the National Aeronautics and Space Administration (NASA).

For product information and technology assistance, contact us at
Cengage Learning Customer & Sales Support, 1-800-354-9706
For permission to use material from this text or product,
submit all requests online at **cengage.com/permissions**
Further permissions questions can be emailed to
permissionrequest@cengage.com

This book contains select works from existing Cengage Learning resources and was produced by Cengage Learning Custom Solutions for collegiate use. As such, those adopting and/or contributing to this work are responsible for editorial content accuracy, continuity and completeness.

Compilation © 2010 Cengage Learning
ISBN-13: 978-1-111-47027-2

ISBN-10: 1-111-47027-8
Cengage Learning
5191 Natorp Boulevard
Mason, Ohio 45040
USA
Cengage Learning is a leading provider of customized learning solutions with office locations around the globe, including Singapore, the United Kingdom, Australia, Mexico, Brazil, and Japan. Locate your local office at:
international.cengage.com/region.

Cengage Learning products are represented in Canada by Nelson Education, Ltd.
For your lifelong learning solutions, visit **www.cengage.com/custom.**
Visit our corporate website at **www.cengage.com.**

Printed in the United States of America

Contents

3 Solving Equations and Inequalities   105

4 Solving Equations and Inequalities: Applications 165

5　Linear Equations and Inequalities　246

6   Systems of Linear Equations   327

7   Polynomials   368

8 Factoring   417

Preface

**Welcome to
*Beginning Algebra
with Applications*!**

The seventh edition of *Beginning Algebra with Applications* provides mathematically sound and comprehensive coverage of the topics considered essential in a first-year algebra course. The text has been designed not only to meet the needs of the traditional college student but also to serve the needs of returning students whose mathematical proficiency may have declined during years away from formal education.

In this new edition of *Beginning Algebra with Applications*, we have continued to integrate some of the approaches suggested by AMATYC. Each chapter opens by illustrating and referencing a mathematical application within the chapter. At the end of each section there are "Applying Concepts" exercises that include writing, synthesis, critical thinking, and challenge problems. At the end of each chapter there is a "Focus on Problem Solving" section that introduces students to various problem-solving strategies. This is followed by "Projects and Group Activities," which can be used for cooperative learning activities.

**Changes to the
Seventh Edition**

✔ **NEW! Interactive Exercises** These exercises test students' understanding of the basic concepts presented in a lesson. Included when appropriate, these exercises:

- Generally appear at the beginning of an objective's exercise set.
- Provide students with guided practice on some of the objective's underlying principles.
- Test students' knowledge of the terms associated with a topic OR provide fill-in-the-blank exercises in which students are given part of a solution to a problem and are asked to complete the missing portions.
- Act as stepping stones to the remaining exercises for the objective.

✔ **NEW! Think About It Exercises** These exercises are conceptual in nature. They generally appear near the end of an objective's exercise set and ask the students to think about the objective's concepts, make generalizations, and apply them to more abstract problems. The focus is on mental mathematics, not calculation or computation, and they are designed to help students synthesize concepts.

✔ **REVISED! Chapter 1** This chapter has been expanded and reorganized. The title is now "Prealgebra Review" to reflect the content and intent.

- In Section 1.3, the presentation of operations on fractions has been changed from presenting addition and subtraction of rational numbers first, followed by multiplication and division, to presenting multiplication and division of rational numbers first, followed by addition and subtraction.
- Section 1.5, "Concepts from Geometry," is new and has been added to provide students with a review of angle measurement and the perimeter and area of plane geometric figures.

✔ **REVISED! Chapter 11** This chapter now includes a section on complex numbers. Section 11.4 presents simplifying complex numbers, operations on complex numbers, and solving quadratic equations with complex number solutions.

Changes to the Media Enhanced Edition

✔ **Media Enhancements** This updated seventh edition has been enhanced with a variety of multimedia tools to help students succeed in algebra:

- **NEW! Chapter Test Videos** Every chapter test question in the text has an accompanying chapter test video, featuring step-by-step solutions that follow the problem-solving methods used in this textbook. These solutions are presented by real instructors and also feature interactive questions to keep students engaged. Students can access these videos through the Online Study Center.

- **NEW! WebAssign®** Developed by teachers, for teachers, WebAssign allows instructors to focus on what really matters—teaching rather than grading. Instructors can create assignments from a ready-to-use database of algorithmic questions based on end-of-section exercises, or write and customize their own exercises. With WebAssign, instructors can create, post, and review assignments; deliver, collect, grade, and record assignments instantly; offer practice exercises, quizzes, and homework; and assess student performance to keep abreast of individual progress.

- **NEW! Online Multimedia eBook** This electronic version of the textbook includes links to chapter test videos, video lessons, tutorials, and glossary flashcards to expand upon and reinforce concepts as they appear in the text.

✔ **Student Support Resources** This textbook features new tools to support student learning, including:

- **NEW! Pass the Class Media Guide** This student-focused guide provides an overview of the many varied media tools available to students, including Chapter Test Videos, WebAssign, Smarthinking® online tutoring, the Online Multimedia eBook, and more.

- **AIM for Success: Getting Started** This updated student preface encourages students to interact with the textbook. Students are asked to fill in the blanks, answer questions, prepare a weekly time schedule, find information within the text and on the class syllabus, write explanations, and provide solutions. This approach will ensure their understanding of how the textbook works and what they need to do to succeed in this course.

  - **AIM for Success PowerPoint Slide Show** This PowerPoint Presentation is available on the Online Teaching Center and offers a lesson plan for *AIM for Success: Getting Started* in the text. Visit www.cengage.com/math/aufmann to access this content and more.

Acknowledgments

We would especially like to thank users of the previous edition for their helpful suggestions on improving the text. Also, we sincerely appreciate the suggestions and the time and effort of the following people who reviewed this manuscript and/or its previous edition in preparation for the seventh edition.

Joe Archuleta, *Imperial Valley College, Imperial, CA*

Kevin Argo, *Halifax Community College, Weldon, NC*

Don K. Brown, *Georgia Southern University, Statesboro, GA*

Kai S. Chuang, *New Mexico State University, Carlsbad, NM*

Wil Clarke, *La Sierra University, Riverside, CA*

Andres Delgado, *Orange County Community College, Middletown, NY*

Sudhir Goel, *Valdosta State University, Valdosta, GA*

Anne Haney

Kenneth S. Hirschel, *Orange County Community College, Middletown, NY*

Kathryn Lavelle, *Westchester Community College, Valhalla, NY*

Yash Manchanda, *Saddleback Community College, Mission Viejo, CA*

Roger Martin, *Louisiana State University, Shreveport, LA*

Terri Seiver, *San Jacinto College, Pasadena, TX*

Gail Ulager, *Robert Morris College, Moon Township, PA*

Tom Wheeler, *Georgia Southwestern State University, Americus, GA*

Jean Wilberg, *SUNY Morrisville College, Morrisville, NY*

Michael D. Young, *Pitt Community College, Winterville, NC*

STUDENT SUCCESS

Beginning Algebra with Applications is designed to foster student success through an integrated text and media program.

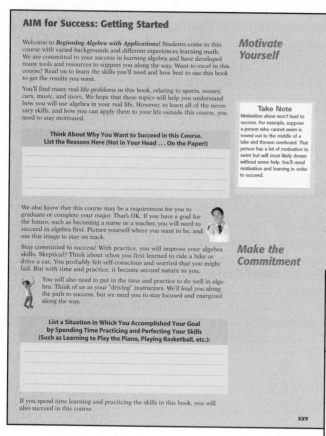

page xxv

AIM for Success: Getting Started

This preface helps students develop the study skills necessary to achieve success in college mathematics.

It also provides students with an explanation of how to effectively use the features of the text.

AIM for Success: Getting Started can be used as a lesson on the first day of class or as a student project. A lesson plan, with accompanying PowerPoint slides, is available for instructors on the Online Teaching Center.

Objective-Based Approach

All lessons, exercise sets, tests, and supplements are organized around a carefully constructed hierarchy of objectives. This organization serves as a framework for a complete learning system, allowing students to remediate their learning independently at any point in the process.

Each chapter's objectives are listed on the chapter opener page, which serves as a road-map to student learning.

A numbered objective describes the topic of each lesson.

page 246

5.3 **Slopes of Straight Lines**

OBJECTIVE **1** **Find the slope of a straight line**

page 276

xvi

All exercise sets correspond directly to objectives.

page 283

Answers to the Prep Tests, Chapter Review Exercises, Chapter Tests, and Cumulative Review Exercises refer students back to the original objectives for further study.

5.3 Exercises

1 Find the slope of a straight line

1. Explain how to find the slope of a line when you know two points on the line.

2. What is the difference between a line that has zero slope and a line whose slope is undefined?

Answers to Chapter 5 Selected Exercises

PREP TEST

1. -3 [1.4.2] 2. -1 [2.1.1] 3. $-3x + 12$ [2.2.4] 4. -2 [3.2.1]

6. -2 [3.2.1] 7. 13 [2.1.1] 8. $\frac{3}{4}x - 4$ [2.2.4] 9. a, b, c [3.3.1]

page A14

Prep Test

1. Simplify: $\dfrac{5 - (-7)}{4 - 8}$

2. Evaluate $\dfrac{a - b}{c - d}$ when $a = 3$, $b = -2$, $c = -3$, and $d = 2$.

3. Simplify: $-3(x - 4)$

4. Solve: $3x + 6 = 0$

5. Solve $4x + 5y = 20$ when $y = 0$.

6. Solve $3x - 7y = 11$ when $x = -1$.

7. Given $y = -4x + 5$, find the value of y when $x = -2$.

8. Simplify: $\dfrac{1}{4}(3x - 16)$

9. Which of the following are solutions of the inequality $-4 < x + 3$?
   a. 0   b. -3 c. 5   d. -7 e. -10

page 247

Assessment and Review

Prep Tests assess students' mastery of prerequisite skills for the upcoming chapter.

The Answers found at the back of the book refer them to the appropriate section objective for review.

The **end-of-chapter material** includes:

Chapter Summary

Chapter Review Exercises

Chapter Test

These resources help students prepare for tests.

Chapter 5 Summary

Key Words

A **rectangular coordinate system** is formed by two number lines, one horizontal and one vertical, that intersect at the zero point of each line. The number lines that make up a rectangular coordinate system are called the **coordinate axes**, or simply the **axes**. The **origin** is the point of intersection of the two coordinate axes. Generally, the horizontal axis is labeled the **x-axis**, and the vertical axis is labeled the **y-axis**. A rectangular coordinate system divides the plane determined by the axes into four regions called **quadrants**. [5.1.1, pp. 247]

Examples

page 316

Cumulative Review Exercises help students maintain skills learned in previous chapters.

Cumulative Review Exercises

1. Simplify: $12 - 18 \div 3 \cdot (-2)^2$

2. Evaluate $\dfrac{a - b}{a^2 - c}$ when $a = -2$, $b = 3$, and $c = -4$.

3. Simplify: $4(2 - 3x) - 5(x - 4)$

4. Solve: $2x - \dfrac{2}{3} = \dfrac{7}{3}$

page 325

AUFMANN INTERACTIVE METHOD (AIM)

Beginning Algebra with Applications uses an interactive style that engages students in trying new skills and reinforcing learning through structured exercises.

EXAMPLE 1 Multiply: $(2xy)(3x^2y)$

 Solution $(2xy)(3x^2y)$
$= (2 \cdot 3)(x \cdot x^2)(y \cdot y)$ • Use the Commutative and Associative Properties of Multiplication to rearrange and group factors.
• Multiply variables with the same base by adding the exponents.

$= 6x^{1+2}y^{1+1}$

$= 6x^3y^2$

PROBLEM 1 Multiply: $(3x^2)(6x^3)$

 ■ Solution   See page S16.

EXAMPLE 2 Multiply: $(2x^2y)(-5xy^4)$

 Solution $(2x^2y)(-5xy^4)$
$= [2(-5)](x^2 \cdot x)(y \cdot y^4)$ • Use the Properties of Multiplication to rearrange and group factors.

$= -10x^3y^5$ • Multiply variables with the same base by adding the exponents.

PROBLEM 2 Multiply: $(-3xy^2)(-4x^2y^3)$

 ■ Solution   See page S16.

page 375

An Interactive Approach

• Each section of the text is divided into objectives, and every objective contains one or more sets of matched-pair examples. The first example in each set is worked out.

• The second example, called "Problem," is for the student to work. By solving this problem, the student actively practices concepts as they are presented in the text.

SECTION 7.2

Problem 1

$(3x^2)(6x^3) = (3 \cdot 6)(x^2 \cdot x^3) = 18x^5$

Problem 2

$(-3xy^2)(-4x^2y^3)$
$= [(-3)(-4)](x \cdot x^2)(y^2 \cdot y^3)$
$= 12x^3y^5$

page S16

• *Complete worked-out* solutions to these Problems appear at the back of the book for students to check their work.

NEW! Interactive Exercises

Placed at the beginning of an objective's exercise set (when appropriate), these exercises provide guided practice and test students' understanding of the underlying concepts in a lesson. They also act as stepping-stones to the remaining exercises for the objective.

---

1 Multiply monomials

1.   Explain how to multiply two exponential expressions with the same base. Provide an example.

2. Use the Rule for Multiplying Exponential Expressions to multiply:
$(x^7)(x^2) = x^{\underline{2}+\underline{2}} = \underline{\quad?\quad}$.

3. Multiply: $(5a^6b)(2a^5b^3)$
$(5a^6b)(2a^5b^3)$
$= (5 \cdot \underline{\quad?\quad})(a^6 \cdot \underline{\quad?\quad})(b \cdot \underline{\quad?\quad})$ • Use the Commutative and Associative Properties of Multiplication to rearrange and group factors.

$= (\underline{\quad?\quad})(a^{\underline{2}+\underline{2}})(b^{\underline{2}+\underline{2}})$ • Multiply variables with the same base by $\underline{\quad?\quad}$ the exponents.

$= 10a^{\underline{2}}b^{\underline{2}}$ • Simplify.

page 377

CONCEPTUAL UNDERSTANDING

Beginning Algebra with Applications helps students understand the course concepts through the textbook exposition and feature set.

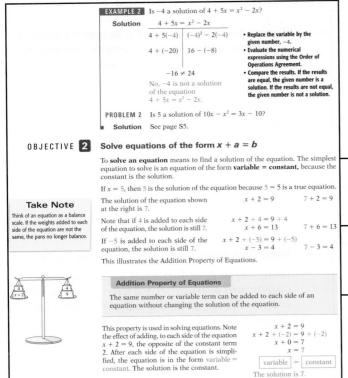

page 107

Features in the Exposition

- Key terms, in bold, emphasize important vocabulary.

- Margin notes titled Take Note amplify the concept under discussion or alert students to points requiring special attention.

- Key concepts are presented in orange boxes in order to highlight them and provide for easy reference.

In solving an equation, the goal is to rewrite the given equation in the form variable = constant. The Addition Property of Equations can be used to rewrite an equation in this form. The Addition Property of Equations is used to remove a term from one side of an equation by adding the opposite of that term to each side of the equation.

- Important points are now highlighted, to help students recognize what is most important and to study more effectively.

EXAMPLE 3 Solve and check: $y - 6 = 9$

Solution $y - 6 = 9$ • The goal is to rewrite the equation in the form variable = constant.

$y - 6 + 6 = 9 + 6$ • Add 6 to each side of the equation (the Addition Property of Equations).

$y + 0 = 15$ • Simplify using the Inverse Property of Addition.

$y = 15$ • Simplify using the Addition Property of Zero. Now the equation is in the form variable = constant.

Check $y - 6 = 9$
$15 - 6 \mid 9$
$9 = 9$ • This is a true equation. The solution checks.

The solution is 15.   • Write the solution.

PROBLEM 3 Solve and check: $x - \dfrac{1}{3} = -\dfrac{3}{4}$

Solution See page S5.

page 108

xix

CONCEPTUAL UNDERSTANDING (*continued*)

Beginning Algebra with Applications helps students understand the course concepts through the textbook exposition and feature set.

Features in the Exercise Sets

3.1 Concept Review

Determine whether the statement is always true, sometimes true, or never true.

1. Both sides of an equation can be multiplied by the same number without changing the solution of the equation.

2. Both sides of an equation can be divided by the same number without changing the solution of the equation.

3. For an equation of the form $ax = b$, $a \neq 0$, multiplying both sides of the equation by the reciprocal of a will result in an equation of the form $x = constant$.

4. Use the Multiplication Property of Equations to remove a term from one side of an equation.

page 118

• **Concept Review** exercises appear at the beginning of each exercise set and are designed to test a student's understanding of the topic.

---

31.   Without solving the equation $x + \frac{13}{15} = -\frac{21}{43}$, determine whether x is less than or greater than $-\frac{21}{43}$. Explain your answer.

32.   Without solving the equation $x - \frac{11}{16} = \frac{19}{24}$, determine whether x is less than or greater than $\frac{19}{24}$. Explain your answer.

page 119

• **NEW! Think About It Exercises** are conceptual in nature. They ask the students to think about the objective's concepts, make generalizations, and apply them to more abstract problems. The focus is on mental mathematics, and they are designed to help students synthesize concepts.

---

2 Solve equations of the form $x + a = b$

27. How is the Addition Property of Equations used to solve an equation?

28. Explain why the goal in solving an equation is to write the equation in the form *variable = constant*.

page 119

• **Writing Exercises** require students to verbalize concepts, which is a crucial step in learning them.

3.1 Applying Concepts

Solve.

226. $\frac{2m + m}{5} = -9$

227. $\frac{3y - 8y}{7} = 15$

228. $\frac{\frac{1}{1}}{x} = 5$

229. $\frac{1}{\frac{1}{x}} + 8 = -19$

230. $\frac{\frac{4}{3}}{b} = 8$

231. $\frac{\frac{5}{7}}{a} - \frac{\frac{3}{7}}{a} = 6$

232. Solve for x: $x \div 28 = 1481$ remainder 25

233. Geometry Find the value of x in the diagram shown at the right.

234. Consumerism Your bill for dinner, including a 7.25% sales tax, was $92.74. You want to leave a 15% tip on the cost of the dinner before the sales tax. Find the amount of the tip to the nearest dollar.

235. Consumerism The total cost for a dinner was $97.52. This included a 15% tip calculated on the cost of the dinner after a 6% sales tax. Find the cost of dinner before the tip and tax.

page 128

• **Applying Concepts** are more challenging problems involving multiple concepts that require interpretation, analysis, and critical thinking. They are designed to help students to apply and internalize concepts.

XX

PROBLEM SOLVING

Beginning Algebra with Applications emphasizes applications, problem solving, and critical thinking.

58. Education One method used to "curve" the grades on an exam is to use the formula $R = 10\sqrt{O}$, where R is the revised score and O is the original score. Use this formula to find the original score on an exam that has a revised score of 75. Round to the nearest whole number.

59. Physics A formula used in the study of shallow-water wave motion is $C = \sqrt{32H}$, where C is the wave velocity in feet per second and H is the depth in feet. Use this formula to find the depth of the water when the wave velocity is 20 ft/s.

60. **Sports** The infield of a baseball diamond is a square. The distance between successive bases is 90 ft. The pitcher's mound is on the diagonal between home plate and second base at a distance of 60.5 ft from home plate. Is the pitcher's mound more or less than halfway between home plate and second base?

61. **Sports** The infield of a softball diamond is a square. The distance between successive bases is 60 ft. The pitcher's mound is on the diagonal between home plate and second base at a distance of 46 ft from home plate. Is the pitcher's mound more or less than halfway between home plate and second base?

page 571

Integrated Real-Life Applications

Wherever appropriate, the last objective of a section presents applications that require students to use problem-solving strategies, along with the skills covered in that section, to solve practical problems. This carefully integrated applied approach generates student awareness of the value of algebra as a real-life tool. Applications are taken from many disciplines and are emphasized through sourced data.

EXAMPLE 4 A guy wire is attached to a point 22 m above the ground on a telephone pole that is perpendicular to the ground. The wire is anchored to the ground at a point 9 m from the base of the pole. Find the length of the guy wire. Round to the nearest hundredth.

Strategy To find the length of the guy wire, use the Pythagorean Theorem. One leg is the distance from the bottom of the wire to the base of the telephone pole. The other leg is the distance from the top of the wire to the base of the telephone pole. The guy wire is the hypotenuse. Solve the Pythagorean Theorem for the hypotenuse.

Solution
$c = \sqrt{a^2 + b^2}$
$c = \sqrt{(22)^2 + (9)^2}$
$c = \sqrt{484 + 81}$
$c = \sqrt{565}$
$c \approx 23.77$

The guy wire has a length of 23.77 m.

PROBLEM 4 A ladder 12 ft long is resting against a building. How high on the building will the ladder reach when the bottom of the ladder is 5 ft from the building? Round to the nearest hundredth.

Solution See page S25.

EXAMPLE 5 How far would a submarine periscope have to be above the water for the lookout to locate a ship 5 mi away? The equation for the distance in miles that the lookout can see is $d = \sqrt{1.5h}$, where h is the height in feet above the surface of the water. Round to the nearest hundredth.

Strategy To find the height above water, replace d in the equation with the given value. Then solve for h.

Solution
$d = \sqrt{1.5h}$
$5 = \sqrt{1.5h}$
$5^2 = (\sqrt{1.5h})^2$
$25 = 1.5h$
$\dfrac{25}{1.5} = h$
$16.67 \approx h$

The periscope must be 16.67 ft above the water.

PROBLEM 5 Find the length of a pendulum that makes one swing in 1.5 s. The equation for the time of one swing is $T = 2\pi\sqrt{\dfrac{L}{32}}$, where T is the time in seconds and L is the length in feet. Round to the nearest hundredth.

Solution See page S25.

page 567

Problem-Solving Strategies

A carefully developed approach to problem solving emphasizes the importance of *strategy* when solving problems.

- Students are encouraged to develop their own strategies as part of their solutions to problems.

- Model strategies are always presented as guides for students to follow as they attempt the parallel Problems that accompany each numbered Example.

Problem 5

Strategy To find the length of the pendulum, replace T in the equation with the given value and solve for L.

Solution
$T = 2\pi\sqrt{\dfrac{L}{32}}$

$1.5 = 2\pi\sqrt{\dfrac{L}{32}}$

$\dfrac{1.5}{2\pi} = \sqrt{\dfrac{L}{32}}$

$\left(\dfrac{1.5}{2\pi}\right)^2 = \left(\sqrt{\dfrac{L}{32}}\right)^2$

$\left(\dfrac{1.5}{2\pi}\right)^2 = \dfrac{L}{32}$

$32\left(\dfrac{1.5}{2\pi}\right)^2 = L$ • Use the π key on your calculator.

$1.82 \approx L$

The length of the pendulum is 1.82 ft.

page S25

xxi

81. **Geometry** A circular fountain is being designed for a triangular plaza in a cultural center. The fountain is placed so that each side of the triangle touches the fountain as shown in the diagram at the right. Find the area of the fountain. The formula for the radius of the circle is given by

$$r = \sqrt{\frac{(s-a)(s-b)(s-c)}{s}}$$

where $s = \frac{1}{2}(a + b + c)$ and a, b, and c are the lengths of the sides of the triangle. Round to the nearest hundredth.

82. Can the Pythagorean Theorem be used to find the length of side c of the triangle at the right? If so, determine c. If not, explain why the theorem cannot be used.

83. What is a Pythagorean triple? Provide at least three examples of Pythagorean triples.

84. Complete the statement using the symbol $<$, $=$, or $>$. Explain how you determined which symbol to use.
   a. For an acute triangle with side c the longest side, $a^2 + b^2$ _____ c^2.
   b. For a right triangle with side c the longest side, $a^2 + b^2$ _____ c^2.
   c. For an obtuse triangle with side c the longest side, $a^2 + b^2$ _____ c^2.

Focus on Problem Solving

Deductive Reasoning   Deductive reasoning uses a rule or statement of fact to reach a conclusion. In the section Equations Containing Fractions in the "Rational Expressions" chapter, we established the rule that if two angles of one triangle are equal to two angles of another triangle, then the two triangles are similar. Thus any time we establish this fact about two triangles, we know that the triangles are similar. Two examples of deductive reasoning follow.

Given that ΔΔΔ = ◊◊◊◊ and ◊◊◊◊ = ÓÓ, then ΔΔΔΔΔΔ is equivalent to how many Ós?

Because 3 Δs = 4 ◊s and 4 ◊s = 2 Ós, 3 Δs = 2 Ós.

6 Δs is twice 3 Δs. We need to find twice 2 Ós, which is 4 Ós.

Therefore, ΔΔΔΔΔΔ = ÓÓÓÓ.

Lomax, Parish, Thorpe, and Wong are neighbors. Each drives a different type of vehicle: a compact car, a sedan, a sports car, or a station wagon. From the

page 573

Focus on Problem Solving

Students are introduced to various successful problem-solving strategies within the end-of-chapter material. Strategies include:

• drawing a diagram,

• applying solutions to other problems,

• working backwards,

• inductive reasoning,

• and trial and error.

NEW! Think About It Exercises

These exercises focus on concepts, not on calculation or computation, and will help develop students' critical thinking skills.

41. Without actually solving the equations, identify which equation has no solution.
   a. $-\sqrt{2x-5} = -3$ **b.** $\sqrt{2x} - 5 = -3$ **c.** $\sqrt{2x-5} = -3$

42. How many times will the Property of Squaring Both Sides of an Equation be used in the solving of each equation? Do not solve.
   a. $\sqrt{x-3} = \sqrt{4x-7}$ **b.** $\sqrt{x-6} = \sqrt{x} - 3$

page 569

Additional Resources—Get More Value from Your Textbook!

INSTRUCTOR RESOURCES

Instructor's Annotated Edition (IAE)

This edition contains a replica of the student text and additional items just for the instructor. Answers to all exercises are provided.

Online Teaching Center

This website offers instructors a variety of resources, including instructor's solutions, digital art and figures, course sequences, drill sheets, printed test bank, and more.

Computerized Testing

Computerized Testing provides instructors with a wide array of new algorithmic exercises along with improved functionality and ease of use. Instructors can create, author/edit algorithmic questions, customize, and deliver multiple types of tests.

STUDENT RESOURCES

Student Solutions Manual

Contains complete solutions to all odd-numbered exercises and all of the solutions to the end-of-chapter material.

Math Study Skills Workbook, Third Edition, by Paul Nolting

Helps students identify their strengths, weaknesses, and personal learning styles in math. Nolting offers study tips, proven test-taking strategies, a homework system, and recommendations for reducing anxiety and improving grades.

Online Study Center

This free website gives students access to Chapter Test Videos, the Online Multimedia eBook, ACE practice tests, glossary flashcards, and other study resources.

Instructional DVDs

Hosted by Dana Mosely, these text-specific DVDs cover all sections of the text and provide explanations of key concepts, examples, exercises, and applications in a lecture-based format. DVDs are now close-captioned for the hearing-impaired.

Online Study and Teaching Centers

Instructors and students have powerful course management tools and text-specific content to support all of their online teaching and learning needs. The Online Study and Teaching Centers now include:

- **NEW! WebAssign®** Developed by teachers, for teachers, WebAssign allows instructors to create assignments from an abundant ready-to-use database of algorithmic questions, or write and customize their own exercises. With WebAssign, instructors can create, post, and review assignments 24 hours a day, 7 days a week; deliver, collect, grade, and record assignments instantly; offer more practice exercises, quizzes, and homework; assess student performance to keep abreast of individual progress; and capture the attention of online or distance learning students.

- **SMARTHINKING® Live, Online Tutoring** SMARTHINKING provides an easy-to-use and effective online, text-specific tutoring service. A dynamic **Whiteboard** and a **Graphing Calculator** function enable students and e-structors to collaborate easily.

Online Course Management Content for Blackboard®, WebCT®, and eCollege®

Deliver program- or text-specific content online using your institution's local course management system. Cengage Learning offers homework, tutorials, videos, and other resources formatted for Blackboard, WebCT, eCollege, and other course management systems. Add to an existing online course or create a new one by selecting from a wide range of powerful learning and instructional materials.

For more information, visit www.cengage.com/math/aufmann or contact your local Cengage sales representative.

AIM for Success: Getting Started

Welcome to *Beginning Algebra with Applications*! Students come to this course with varied backgrounds and different experiences learning math. We are committed to your success in learning algebra and have developed many tools and resources to support you along the way. Want to excel in this course? Read on to learn the skills you'll need and how best to use this book to get the results you want.

You'll find many real-life problems in this book, relating to sports, money, cars, music, and more. We hope that these topics will help you understand how you will use algebra in your real life. However, to learn all of the necessary skills, and how you can apply them to your life outside this course, you need to stay motivated.

Take Note
Motivation alone won't lead to success. For example, suppose a person who cannot swim is rowed out to the middle of a lake and thrown overboard. That person has a lot of motivation to swim but will most likely drown without some help. You'll need motivation **and** learning in order to succeed.

**Think About Why You Want to Succeed in this Course.
List the Reasons Here (Not in Your Head . . . On the Paper!)**

We also know that this course may be a requirement for you to graduate or complete your major. That's OK. If you have a goal for the future, such as becoming a nurse or a teacher, you will need to succeed in algebra first. Picture yourself where you want to be, and use this image to stay on track.

Stay committed to success! With practice, you will improve your algebra skills. Skeptical? Think about when you first learned to ride a bike or drive a car. You probably felt self-conscious and worried that you might fail. But with time and practice, it became second nature to you.

You will also need to put in the time and practice to do well in algebra. Think of us as your "driving" instructors. We'll lead you along the path to success, but we need you to stay focused and energized along the way.

**List a Situation in Which You Accomplished Your Goal
by Spending Time Practicing and Perfecting Your Skills
(Such as Learning to Play the Piano, Playing Basketball, etc.):**

If you spend time learning and practicing the skills in this book, you will also succeed in this course.

Think You Can't Do Math? Think Again!

You can do math! When you first learned the skills you just listed, you may have not done them well. With practice, you got better. With practice, you will be better at math. Stay focused, motivated, and committed to success.

We can't emphasize enough how important it is to overcome the "I Can't Do Math Syndrome." If you listen to interviews of very successful athletes after a particularly bad performance, you will note that they focus on the positive aspect of what they did, not the negative. Sports psychologists encourage athletes to always be positive—to have a "Can Do" attitude. Develop this attitude toward math and you will succeed.

Skills for Success

Get the Big Picture   If this were an English class, we wouldn't encourage you to look ahead in the book. But this is algebra—go right ahead! Take a few minutes to read the table of contents. Then, look through the entire book. Move quickly: scan titles, look at pictures, notice diagrams.

Getting this big picture view will help you see where this course is going. To reach your goal, it's important to get an idea of the steps you will need to take along the way.

As you look through the book, find topics that interest you. What's your preference? Horse racing? Sailing? TV? Amusement parks? Find the Index of Applications in the back and pull out three subjects that interest you. Then, flip to the pages in the book where the topics are featured, and read the exercises or problems where they appear. Write these topics here:

Write the Topic Here	Write the Corresponding Exercise/Problem Here

You'll find it's easier to work at learning the material if you are interested in how it can be used in your everyday life.

Use the following activities to think about more ways you might use algebra in your daily life. Flip open your book to the exercises below to answer the questions.

✔ (see p. 95, #112) I am moving across the country and want to maintain my current cost of living, but I'm unsure of what my salary will be. I need algebra to . . .

✔ (see p. 203, #27) I want to buy a tennis racket, but they're very expensive. Luckily, I've found one that's on sale. I need algebra to . . .

✔ (see p. 128, #240) I am planning to buy a house and have been offered two different mortgage interest rates. I need algebra to . . .

_____

_____

You know that the activities you just completed are from daily life, but do you notice anything else they have in common? That's right—they are **word problems**. Try not to be intimidated by word problems. You just need a strategy. It's true that word problems can be challenging because we need to use multiple steps to solve them:

✔ Read the problem.

✔ Determine the quantity we must find.

✔ Think of a method to find it.

✔ Solve the problem.

✔ Check the answer.

In short, we must come up with a *strategy* and then use that strategy to find the *solution*.

We'll teach you about strategies for tackling word problems that will make you feel more confident in branching out to these problems from daily life. After all, even though no one will ever come up to you on the street and ask you to solve a multiplication problem, you will need to use math every day to balance your checkbook, evaluate credit card offers, etc.

Take a look at the example below. You'll see that solving a word problem includes finding a *strategy* and using that strategy to find a *solution*. If you find yourself struggling with a word problem, try writing down the information you know about the problem. Be as specific as you can. Write out a phrase or a sentence that states what you are trying to find. Ask yourself whether there is a formula that expresses the known and unknown quantities. Then, try again!

page 350

Get the Basics   On the first day of class, your instructor will hand out a **syllabus** listing the requirements of your course. Think of this syllabus as your personal roadmap to success. It shows you the *destinations* (topics you need to learn) and the *dates* you need to arrive at those destinations (when you need to learn the topics by). Learning algebra is a journey. But, to get the most out of this course, you'll need to know what the important stops are, and what skills you'll need to learn for your arrival at those stops.

You've quickly scanned the table of contents, but now we want you to take a closer look. Flip open to the table of contents and look at it next to your syllabus. Identify when your major exams are and what material you'll need to learn by those dates. For example, if you know you have an exam in the second month of the semester, how many chapters of this text will you need to learn by then? What homework do you have to do during this time? Write it down using the chart below:

Take Note

Take a look at your syllabus to see if your instructor has an **attendance policy** that is part of your overall grade in the course.

The attendance policy will tell you:

- How many classes you can miss without a penalty.
- What to do if you miss an exam or quiz.
- If you can get the lecture notes from the professor, if you miss a class.

Chart Your Progress			
Write the dates of your exams in this column.	Write the chapters you'll need to learn by each exam.	Write the homework you need to do by each exam.	Write the grades you receive on your exams here.

Managing these important dates will help keep you on track for success.

Manage Your Time   We know how busy you are outside of school. Do you have a full-time or a part-time job? Do you have children? Visit your family often? Play basketball or write for the school newspaper? It can be stressful to balance all of the important activities and responsibilities in your life. Making a **time management plan** will help you create a schedule that gives you enough time for everything you need to do.

Let's get started! Use the grid on the next page to fill in your weekly schedule.

First, fill in all of your responsibilities that take up certain set hours during the week. Be sure to include:

> **Take Note**
> We realize that your weekly schedule may change. Visit www.cengage.com/math/ aufmann to print out additional blank schedule forms, if you need them.

✔ Each class you are taking

✔ Time you spend at work

✔ Any other commitments (child care, tutoring, volunteering, etc.)

Then, fill in all of your responsibilities that are more flexible. Remember to make time for:

✔ **Studying** You'll need to study to succeed, but luckily you get to choose what times work best for you. Keep in mind:

▶ Most instructors ask students to spend twice as much time studying as they do in class. (3 hours of class = 6 hours of study)

▶ Try studying in chunks. We've found it works better to study an hour each day, rather than studying for 6 hours on one day.

▶ Studying can be even more helpful if you're able to do it right after your class meets, when the material is fresh in your mind.

✔ **Meals** Eating well gives you energy and stamina for attending classes and studying.

✔ **Entertainment** It's impossible to stay focused on your responsibilities 100% of the time. Giving yourself a break for entertainment will reduce your stress and help keep you on track.

✔ **Exercise** Exercise contributes to overall health. You'll find you're at your most productive when you have both a healthy mind **and** a healthy body.

> **Take Note**
> When planning your schedule, give some thought to how much time you realistically have available each week.
>
> For example, if you work 40 hours a week, take 15 units, spend the recommended study time given at the right, and sleep 8 hours a day, you will use over 80% of the available hours in a week. That leaves less than 20% of the hours in a week for family, friends, eating, recreation, and other activities.
>
> Visit www.cengage.com/math/ aufmann and use the Interactive Time Chart to see how you're spending your time—you may be surprised.

Here is a sample of what part of your schedule might look like:

	8–9	9–10	10–11	11–12	12–1	1–2	2–3	3–4	4–5	5–6
Monday	History class Jenkins Hall 8-9:15	Eat 9:15-10	Study/Homework for History 10-12 AM		Lunch & Nap! 12-1 PM		Work 2-6 PM			
Tuesday	Sleep!	Math class Douglas Hall 9-9:45	Study/Homework for Math 10-12 AM		Eat 12-1 PM	English Class Scott Hall 1-2 PM	Study/Homework for English 2-4 PM		Hangout with Alli & Mike 4 until whenever!	

	MORNING						**AFTERNOON**								**EVENING**					
	8–9	9–10	10–11	11–12	12–1	1–2	2–3	3–4	4–5	5–6	6–7	7–8	8–9	9–10	10–11
Monday															
Tuesday															
Wednesday															
Thursday															
Friday															
Saturday															
Sunday															

Tear along the dotted line to remove.

Features for Success in This Text

Organization   Let's look again at the table of contents. There are 11 chapters in this book. You'll see that every chapter is divided into **sections**, and each section contains a number of **learning objectives**. Each learning objective is labeled with a number from 1 to 5. Knowing how this book is organized will help you locate important topics and concepts as you're studying.

Preparation   Ready to start a new chapter? Take a few minutes to be sure you're ready, using some of the tools in this book.

✔ **Cumulative Review Exercises:** You'll find these exercises after every chapter, starting with Chapter 2. The questions in the Cumulative Review Exercises are taken from the previous chapters. For example, the Cumulative Review for Chapter 3 will test all of the skills you have learned in Chapters 1, 2, and 3. Use this review to test what you know before a big exam.

Here's an example of how to use the Cumulative Review:

▶ Turn to page 244 and look at the questions for the Chapter 4 Cumulative Review, which are taken from the current chapter and the previous chapters.

▶ We have the answers to all of the Cumulative Review exercises in the back of the book. Flip to page A13 to see the answers for this chapter.

▶ Got the answer wrong? We can tell you where to go in the book for help. For example, scroll down page A13 to find the answer for the first exercise, which is -12, -6. You'll see that after this answer, there is an **objective reference** [1.1.1]. This means that the question was taken from Chapter 1, Section 1, Objective 1. Go here to re-study the objective.

✔ **Prep Tests:** These tests are found at the beginning of every chapter, and will help you see if you've mastered all of the skills needed for the new chapter.

Here's an example of how to use the Prep Test:

▶ Turn to page 166 and look at the Prep Test for Chapter 4.

▶ All of the answers to the Prep Tests are in the back of the book. You'll find them in the first set of answers in each answer section for a chapter. Turn to page A10 to see the answers for this Prep Test.

▶ Re-study the objectives if you need some extra help.

✔ Before you start a new section, take a few minutes to read the **Objective Statement** for that section. Then, browse through the objective material. Especially note the words or phrases in bold type—these are important concepts that you'll need as you're moving along in the course.

✔ As you start moving through the chapter, pay special attention to the **rule boxes**. These rules give you the reasons certain types of problems are solved the way they are. When you see a rule, try to rewrite the rule in your own words.

Multiplication Property of Equations

Each side of an equation can be multiplied by the same nonzero number without changing the solution of the equation.

---

page 109

Knowing what to pay attention to as you move through a chapter will help you study and prepare.

Interaction   We want you to be actively involved in learning algebra and have given you many ways to get hands-on with this book.

✔ **Instructional Examples** Take a look at page 108 below. See the blue lines above and below the example? These indicate an instructional example that usually has explanatory remarks to the left of the solution. These examples provide additional examples of important concepts and examine important techniques or principles that can be used to solve other types of problems.

Solve: $y + \dfrac{1}{2} = \dfrac{5}{4}$

The goal is to rewrite the equation in the form *variable = constant*.

Add the opposite of the constant term $\dfrac{1}{2}$ to each side of the equation. This is equivalent to subtracting $\dfrac{1}{2}$ from each side of the equation.

$$y + \frac{1}{2} = \frac{5}{4}$$

$$y + \frac{1}{2} - \frac{1}{2} = \frac{5}{4} - \frac{1}{2}$$

$$y + 0 = \frac{5}{4} - \frac{2}{4}$$

$$y = \frac{3}{4}$$

The solution $\dfrac{3}{4}$ checks.

The solution is $\dfrac{3}{4}$.

page 108

Grab a paper and pencil and work along as you're reading through each example. When you're done, get a clean sheet of paper. Write down the problem and try to complete the solution without looking at your notes or at the book. When you're done, check your answer. If you got it right, you're ready to move on to the next section.

✔ **Example/Problem Pairs** You'll need hands-on practice to succeed in algebra. Use the Example/Problem pairs to get the practice you need.

Take a look below at page 109, Example 4 and Problem 4:

EXAMPLE 4   Solve: $\dfrac{1}{2} = x + \dfrac{2}{3}$

Solution

$$\frac{1}{2} = x + \frac{2}{3}$$

$$\frac{1}{2} - \frac{2}{3} = x + \frac{2}{3} - \frac{2}{3}$$ • Subtract $\dfrac{2}{3}$ from each side of the equation.

$$-\frac{1}{6} = x$$ • Simplify each side of the equation.

The solution is $-\dfrac{1}{6}$.

PROBLEM 4   Solve: $-8 = 5 + x$

Solution   See page S5.

page 109

You'll see that each Example is fully worked-out. Study this Example carefully by working through each step. Then, try your hand at it by completing the Problem. If you get stuck, the solutions to the Problems are provided in the back of the book. There is a page number following the Problem, which shows you where you can find the completely worked-out solution. Use the solution to get a hint for the step on which you are stuck. Then, try again!

When you've finished the solution, check your work against the solution in the back of the book. Turn to page S5 to see the solution for Problem 4.

Remember that sometimes there can be more than one way to solve a problem. But, your answer should always match the answers we've given in the back of the book. If you have any questions about whether your method will always work, check with your instructor.

Review We have provided many opportunities for you to practice and review the skills you have learned in each chapter.

✔ **Section Exercises** After you're done studying a section, flip to the end of the section and complete the exercises. If you immediately practice what you've learned, you'll find it easier to master the core skills. Want to know if you answered the questions correctly? The answers to the odd-numbered exercises are given in the back of the book.

✔ **Chapter Summary** Once you've completed a chapter, look at the Chapter Summary. This is divided into two sections: *Key Words* and *Essential Rules and Procedures*. Flip to page 157 to see the Chapter Summary for Chapter 3. This summary shows all of the important topics covered in the chapter. See the page number following each topic? This shows you the page in the text where you can find more information on the concept.

✔ **Chapter Review Exercises** You'll find the Chapter Review Exercises after the Chapter Summary. Flip to page 159 to see the Chapter Review Exercises for Chapter 3. When you do the review exercises, you're giving yourself an important opportunity to test your understanding of the chapter. The answer to each review exercise is given at the back of the book, along with the objective the question relates to. When you're done with the Chapter Review Exercises, check your answers. If you had trouble with any of the questions, you can re-study the objectives and re-try some of the exercises in those objectives for extra help.

✔ **Chapter Tests** The Chapter Tests can be found after the Chapter Review Exercises and can be used to prepare for your exams. Think of these tests as a "practice run" for your in-class tests. Take the test in a quiet place and try to work through it in the same amount of time you will be allowed for your exam.

Here are some strategies for success when you're taking your exams:

▶ Scan the entire test to get a feel for the questions (get the big picture).

▶ Read the directions carefully.

▶ Work the problems that are easiest for you first.

▶ Stay calm, and remember that you will have lots of opportunities for success in this class!

Features for Success Online

Practice   The Online Study Center includes a link to **WebAssign®**, which features practice problems for every chapter in the book. These practice problems provide even more opportunities to help you master the core skills. Each practice problem also includes a link to the **Online Multimedia eBook**, which brings you directly to the appropriate objective to review if you need extra help.

Excel   We have tools online to help you as you're working through the text. Visit the Online Study Center for:

✓ **Chapter Test Videos** featuring step-by-step solutions to every chapter test question in the text.

✓ **DVD clips** hosted by Dana Mosely. These short segments are a quick way to get a better handle on topics that are giving you trouble. If you find the DVD clips helpful and want even more coverage, find out how to get a comprehensive set of DVDs for the entire course at www.cengage.com/math/aufmann.

✓ Live, online tutoring with **SMARTHINKING®**

✓ **Glossary Flashcards**, which will help refresh you on key terms.

Get Involved

Have a question? Ask! Your professor and your classmates are there to help. Here are some tips to help you jump into the action:

✓ See something you don't understand? There are a few ways to get help:

▶ Raise your hand in class.

▶ Your instructor may have a website where students can write in with questions, or your professor may ask you to email or call him or her directly. Take advantage of these ways to get your questions answered.

▶ Visit a **math center**. Ask your instructor for more information about the math center services available on your campus.

▶ Your instructor will have **office hours** where he or she will be available to help you. Take note of where and when your instructor holds office hours. Use this time for one-on-one help, if you need it. Write down your instructor's office hours here:

Office Hours: _____

Office Location: _____

✔ Form a **study group** with students from your class. This is a great way to prepare for tests, catch up on topics you may have missed, or get extra help on problems you're struggling with. Here are a few suggestions to make the most of your study group:

> ▶ **Test each other by asking questions.** Have each person bring a few sample questions when you get together.
>
> ▶ **Practice teaching each other.** We've found that you can learn a lot about what you know when you have to explain it to someone else.
>
> ▶ **Compare class notes.** Couldn't understand the last five minutes of class? Missed class because you were sick? Chances are someone in your group has the notes for the topics you missed.
>
> ▶ **Brainstorm test questions.**
>
> ▶ **Make a plan for your meeting.** Agree on what topics you'll talk about, and how long you'll be meeting for. When you make a plan, you'll be sure that you make the most of your meeting.

It takes hard work and commitment to succeed, but we know you can do it! Doing well in algebra is just one step you'll take along the path to success.

Ready, Set, Succeed!

We want you to check the box below once you have accomplished your goals for this course.

☐ I succeeded in Beginning Algebra!

Take Note
Visit www.cengage.com/math/aufmann to create your very own customized certificate celebrating your accomplishments!

We are confident that if you follow our suggestions, you will succeed. Good luck!

1 Prealgebra Review

DVD

SSM

Online Study Center

Need help? For online student resources, such as section quizzes, visit the Online Study Center at www.cengage.com/math/aufmann.

How do investment bankers know which shares of stock to buy or sell? They decide based on each stock's price and whether it is likely to increase or decrease over time. Positive or negative numbers are used to express the amount of change in the price of a share of stock. Stock market analysts calculate the moving average of a stock, which averages the changes in a stock's price over several days. The moving average is used every day to discover trends in the movement of the price and to create investment strategies. **Exercises 156 and 157 on page 22** involve calculating moving averages for different stocks.

Prep Test

1. What is 127.1649 rounded to the nearest hundredth?

2. Add: $49{,}147 + 596$

3. Subtract: $5004 - 487$

4. Multiply: 407×28

5. Divide: $456 \div 19$

6. What is the smallest number into which both 8 and 12 divide evenly?

7. What is the greatest number that divides evenly into both 16 and 20?

8. Without using 1, write 21 as a product of two whole numbers.

9. Represent the shaded portion of the figure as a fraction.

 1.1   # Introduction to Integers

OBJECTIVE 1   Order relations

It seems to be a human characteristic to group similar items. For instance, a botanist places plants with similar characteristics in groups called species. Nutritionists classify foods according to food groups; for example, pasta, crackers, and rice are among the foods in the bread group.

Mathematicians place objects with similar properties in groups called sets. A **set** is a collection of objects. The objects in a set are called **elements** of the set.

The **roster method** of writing sets encloses a list of the elements in braces. The set of sections within an orchestra is written {brass, percussion, strings, woodwinds}.

When the elements of a set are listed, each element is listed only once. For instance, if the list of numbers 1, 2, 3, 2, 3 were placed in a set, the set would be {1, 2, 3}.

The numbers that we use to count objects, such as the number of students in a classroom or the number of people living in an apartment house, are the natural numbers.

Natural numbers = {1, 2, 3, 4, 5, 6, 7, 8, 9, 10, . . .}

The three dots mean that the list of natural numbers continues on and on and that there is no largest natural number.

The natural numbers do not include zero. The number zero is used for describing data such as the number of people who have run a two-minute mile and the number of college students at Providence College who are under the age of 10. The set of whole numbers includes the natural numbers and zero.

$$\text{Whole numbers} = \{0, 1, 2, 3, 4, 5, 6, 7, \ldots\}$$

The whole numbers do not provide all the numbers that are useful in applications. For instance, a meteorologist also needs numbers below zero.

$$\text{Integers} = \{\ldots, -5, -4, -3, -2, -1, 0, 1, 2, 3, 4, 5, \ldots\}$$

Each integer can be shown on a number line. The integers to the left of zero on the number line are called **negative integers.** The integers to the right of zero are called **positive integers** or natural numbers. Zero is neither a positive nor a negative integer.

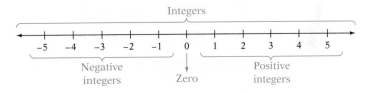

The **graph of an integer** is shown by placing a heavy dot on the number line directly above the number. The graphs of -3 and 4 are shown on the number line below.

Consider the following sentences.

   The quarterback threw the football, and the receiver caught *it*.

   A student purchased a computer and used *it* to write English and history papers.

In the first sentence, *it* is used to mean the football; in the second sentence, *it* means the computer. In language, the word *it* can stand for many different objects. Similarly, in mathematics, a letter of the alphabet can be used to stand for a number. Such a letter is called a **variable.** Variables are used in the following definition of inequality symbols.

Definition of Inequality Symbols

If a and b are two numbers and a is to the left of b on the number line, then a **is less than** b. This is written $a < b$.

If a and b are two numbers and a is to the right of b on the number line, then a **is greater than** b. This is written $a > b$.

Negative 4 is less than negative 1.

$-4 < -1$

5 is greater than 0.

$5 > 0$

There are also inequality symbols for **is less than or equal to** ($\leq$) and **is greater than or equal to** ($\geq$).

$7 \leq 15$ 7 is less than or equal to 15. $6 \leq 6$ 6 is less than or equal to 6.
              This is true because $7 < 15$.   This is true because $6 = 6$.

EXAMPLE 1   Use the roster method to write the set of negative integers greater than or equal to -6.

Solution $A = \{-6,-5,-4,-3,-2,-1\}$ • A set is designated by a capital letter.

PROBLEM 1   Use the roster method to write the set of positive integers less than 5.

Solution   See page S1.

EXAMPLE 2   Given $A = \{-6, -2, 0\}$, which elements of set A are less than or equal to -2?

Solution $-6 < -2$ • Find the order relation between each element of set A and -2.

$-2 = -2$

$0 > -2$

The elements -6 and -2 are less than or equal to -2.

PROBLEM 2   Given $B = \{-5, -1, 5\}$, which elements of set B are greater than -1?

Solution   See page S1.

OBJECTIVE **2**   **Opposites and absolute value**

Two numbers that are the same distance from zero on the number line but are on opposite sides of zero are **opposite numbers** or **opposites.** The opposite of a number is also called its **additive inverse.**

The opposite of 5 is -5.

The opposite of -5 is 5.

The negative sign can be read "the opposite of."

$-(2) = -2$ The opposite of 2 is -2.

$-(-2) = 2$ The opposite of -2 is 2.

EXAMPLE 3   Find the opposite number.   **A.** 6   **B.** -51

Solution   **A.** -6 **B.** 51

PROBLEM 3   Find the opposite number.   **A.** -9 **B.** 62

Solution   See page S1.

The **absolute value** of a number is its distance from zero on the number line. Therefore, the absolute value of a number is a positive number or zero. The symbol for absolute value is two vertical bars, $|\ |$.

The distance from 0 to 3 is 3. Therefore, the absolute value of 3 is 3.

$$|3| = 3$$

The distance from 0 to -3 is 3. Therefore, the absolute value of -3 is 3.

$$|-3| = 3$$

Absolute Value

The absolute value of a positive number is the number itself. The absolute value of zero is zero. The absolute value of a negative number is the opposite of the negative number.

EXAMPLE 4   Evaluate.   **A.** $|-4|$ **B.** $-|-10|$

Solution   **A.** $|-4| = 4$

B. $-|-10| = -10$ • The absolute value sign does not affect the negative sign in front of the absolute value sign. You can read $-|-10|$ as "the opposite of the absolute value of negative 10."

PROBLEM 4   Evaluate.   **A.** $|-5|$ **B.** $-|-9|$

Solution   See page S1.

1.1   Concept Review

Determine whether the statement is always true, sometimes true, or never true.

1. The absolute value of a number is positive.

2. The absolute value of a number is negative.

3. If x is an integer, then $|x| < -3$.

4. If x is an integer, then $|x| > -2$.

5. The opposite of a number is a positive number.

6. The set of positive integers is {0, 1, 2, 3, 4, . . .}.

7. If a is an integer, then $a \leq a$.

8. If a and b are integers and $a > b$, then $a \geq b$.

9. If x is a negative integer, then $|x| = -x$.

10. Suppose a and b are integers and $a < b$. Then $|a| < |b|$.

1.1 Exercises

1. Order relations

1. How do the whole numbers differ from the natural numbers?

2. Explain the difference between the symbols $<$ and $\leq$.

3. Another name for the set of positive integers is the set of ___?___ numbers.

4. The inequality $-5 < -1$ is read "negative five ___?___ negative one."

5. The inequality $0 \geq -4$ is read "zero ___?___ negative four."

6. Which number is greater, -10 or -3?

Place the correct symbol, $<$ or $>$, between the two numbers.

7. -2 -5 **8.** -6 -1 **9.** -16 1 **10.** -2 13

11. 3 -7 **12.** 5 -6 **13.** 0 -3 **14.** 8 0

15. -42 27 **16.** -36 49 **17.** 21 -34 **18.** 53 -46

19. -27 -39 **20.** -51 -20 **21.** -131 101 **22.** 127 -150

23. A number n is to the right of the number 5 on the number line. Which of the following is true?
a. n is positive.   **b.** n is negative.   **c.** n is 0.
d. n can be positive, negative, or 0.

24. A number n is to the left of the number 5 on the number line. Which of the following is true?
a. n is positive.   **b.** n is negative.   **c.** n is 0.
d. n can be positive, negative, or 0.

25. Do the inequalities $6 \geq 1$ and $1 \leq 6$ express the same order relation?

26. Use the "$\leq$" inequality symbol to rewrite the order relation expressed by the inequality $-2 \geq -5$.

Use the roster method to write the set.

27. the natural numbers less than 9

28. the natural numbers less than or equal to 6

29. the positive integers less than or equal to 8

30. the positive integers less than 4

31. the negative integers greater than -7

32. the negative integers greater than or equal to -5

Solve.

33. Given $A = \{-7, 0, 2, 5\}$, which elements of set A are greater than 2?

34. Given $B = \{-8, 0, 7, 15\}$, which elements of set B are greater than 7?

35. Given $D = \{-23, -18, -8, 0\}$, which elements of set D are less than -8?

36. Given $C = \{-33, -24, -10, 0\}$, which elements of set C are less than -10?

37. Given $E = \{-35, -13, 21, 37\}$, which elements of set E are greater than -10?

38. Given $F = \{-27, -14, 14, 27\}$, which elements of set F are greater than -15?

39. Given $B = \{-52, -46, 0, 39, 58\}$, which elements of set B are less than or equal to 0?

40. Given $A = \{-12, -9, 0, 12, 34\}$, which elements of set A are greater than or equal to 0?

41. Given $C = \{-23, -17, 0, 4, 29\}$, which elements of set C are greater than or equal to -17?

42. Given $D = \{-31, -12, 0, 11, 45\}$, which elements of set D are less than or equal to -12?

43. Given that set A is the positive integers less than 10, which elements of set A are greater than or equal to 5?

44. Given that set B is the positive integers less than or equal to 12, which elements of set B are greater than 6?

45. Given that set D is the negative integers greater than or equal to -10, which elements of set D are less than -4?

46. Given that set C is the negative integers greater than -8, which elements of set C are less than or equal to -3?

2 Opposites and absolute value

47. What is the additive inverse of a number?

48. What is the absolute value of a number?

49. The opposite of a negative number is a ___?___ number.

50. The additive inverse of 7 is ___?___.

51. The equation $|-5| = 5$ is read "the ___?___ of negative five is five."

52. Write the statement "the opposite of negative nine is nine" in symbols.

Find the opposite number.

53. 22

54. 45

55. −31

56. −88

57. −168

58. −97

59. 630

60. 450

Evaluate.

61. $-(-18)$

62. $-(-30)$

63. $-(49)$

64. $-(67)$

65. $|16|$

66. $|19|$

67. $|-12|$

68. $|-22|$

69. $-|29|$

70. $-|20|$

71. $-|-14|$

72. $-|-18|$

73. $-|0|$

74. $|-30|$

75. $-|34|$

76. $-|-45|$

Solve.

77. Given $A = \{-8, -5, -2, 1, 3\}$, find
  a. the opposite of each element of set A.
  b. the absolute value of each element of set A.

78. Given $B = \{-11, -7, -3, 1, 5\}$, find
  a. the opposite of each element of set B.
  b. the absolute value of each element of set B.

79. True or false? The absolute value of a negative number n is greater than n.

80. A number n is positive. In order to make the statement $|n|$ ___?___ n a true statement, which symbol must replace the question mark?
  a. > **b.** < **c.** ≤ **d.** =

Place the correct symbol, < or >, between the two numbers.

81. $|-83|$ $|58|$

82. $|22|$ $|-19|$

83. $|43|$ $|-52|$

84. $|-71|$ $|-92|$

85. $|-68|$ $|-42|$

86. $|12|$ $|-31|$

87. $|-45|$ $|-61|$

88. $|-28|$ $|43|$

1.1 Applying Concepts

Write the given numbers in order from least to greatest.

89. $|-5|, 6, -|-8|, -19$

90. $-4, |-15|, -|-7|, 0$

91. $-(-3), -22, |-25|, |-14|$

92. $-|-26|, -(-8), |-17|, -(5)$

Meteorology A meteorologist may report a wind-chill temperature. This is the equivalent temperature, including the effects of wind and temperature, that a person would feel in calm air conditions. The table below gives the wind-chill temperature for various wind speeds and temperatures. For instance, when the temperature is 5°F and the wind is blowing at 15 mph, the wind-chill temperature is −13°F. Use this table for Exercises 93 and 94.

Wind Chill Factors														
Wind Speed (in mph)	Thermometer Reading (in degrees Fahrenheit)													
	25	20	15	10	5	0	−5	−10	−15	−20	−25	−30	−35	−40	−45
5	19	13	7	1	−5	−11	−16	−22	−28	−34	−40	−46	−52	−57	−63
10	15	9	3	−4	−10	−16	−22	−28	−35	−41	−47	−53	−59	−66	−72
15	13	6	0	−7	−13	−19	−26	−32	−39	−45	−51	−58	−64	−71	−77
20	11	4	−2	−9	−15	−22	−29	−35	−42	−48	−55	−61	−68	−74	−81
25	9	3	−4	−11	−17	−24	−31	−37	−44	−51	−58	−64	−71	−78	−84
30	8	1	−5	−12	−19	−26	−33	−39	−46	−53	−60	−67	−73	−80	−87
35	7	0	−7	−14	−21	−27	−34	−41	−48	−55	−62	−69	−76	−82	−89
40	6	−1	−8	−15	−22	−29	−36	−43	−50	−57	−64	−71	−78	−84	−91
45	5	−2	−9	−16	−23	−30	−37	−44	−51	−58	−65	−72	−79	−86	−93

93. Which of the following weather conditions feels colder?
  a. a temperature of 5°F with a 20 mph wind or a temperature of 10°F with a 15 mph wind
  b. a temperature of −25°F with a 10 mph wind or a temperature of −15°F with a 20 mph wind

94. Which of the following weather conditions feels warmer?
  a. a temperature of 5°F with a 25 mph wind or a temperature of 10°F with a 10 mph wind
  b. a temperature of −5°F with a 10 mph wind or a temperature of −15°F with a 5 mph wind

Complete.

95. On the number line, the two points that are four units from 0 are _____ and _____.

96. On the number line, the two points that are six units from 0 are _____ and _____.

97. On the number line, the two points that are seven units from 4 are _____ and _____.

98. On the number line, the two points that are five units from −3 are _____ and _____.

99. If a is a positive number, then $-a$ is a _____ number.

100. If a is a negative number, then $-a$ is a _____ number.

101. An integer that is its own opposite is _____.

102. True or False. If $a \geq 0$, then $|a| = a$.

103. True or False. If $a \leq 0$, then $|a| = -a$.

104. Give examples of some games that use negative integers in the scoring.

105. Give some examples of English words that are used as variables.

106. Write an essay describing your interpretation of the data presented in the table at the right.

The Twenty-First Century: An Easier Ladder to Climb Number of 30- to 34-year-olds competing for jobs			
	1992	*1999*	*2005*
Men	10.3 million	9.2 million	8.5 million
Women	8.3 million	7.9 million	7.8 million
Total	18.6 million	17.1 million	16.3 million

1.2 Operations with Integers

OBJECTIVE 1 **Add integers**

A number can be represented anywhere along the number line by an arrow. A positive number is represented by an arrow pointing to the right, and a negative number is represented by an arrow pointing to the left. The size of the number is represented by the length of the arrow.

Addition is the process of finding the total of two numbers. The numbers being added are called **addends.** The total is called the **sum.** Addition of integers can be shown on the number line. To add integers, find the point on the number line corresponding to the first addend. At that point, draw an arrow representing the second addend. The sum is the number directly below the tip of the arrow.

$4 + 2 = 6$

$-4 + (-2) = -6$

$-4 + 2 = -2$

$4 + (-2) = 2$

The pattern for addition shown on the preceding number lines is summarized in the following rules for adding integers.

Addition of Integers

Integers with the same sign
To add two numbers with the same sign, add the absolute values of the numbers. Then attach the sign of the addends.

$$2 + 8 = 10$$
$$-2 + (-8) = -10$$

Integers with different signs
To add two numbers with different signs, find the absolute value of each number. Then subtract the smaller of these absolute values from the larger one. Attach the sign of the number with the larger absolute value.

$$-2 + 8 = 6$$
$$2 + (-8) = -6$$

EXAMPLE 1   Add.   **A.** $162 + (-247)$ **B.** $-14 + (-47)$
   C. $-4 + (-6) + (-8) + 9$

Solution   **A.** $162 + (-247) = -85$

• The signs are different. Subtract the absolute values of the numbers (247 − 162). Attach the sign of the number with the larger absolute value.

B. $-14 + (-47) = -61$

• The signs are the same. Add the absolute values of the numbers (14 + 47). Attach the sign of the addends.

C. $-4 + (-6) + (-8) + 9$
$= -10 + (-8) + 9$
$= -18 + 9$
$= -9$

• To add more than two numbers, add the first two numbers. Then add the sum to the third number. Continue until all the numbers have been added.

PROBLEM 1   Add.

   A. $-162 + 98$ **B.** $-154 + (-37)$ **C.** $-36 + 17 + (-21)$

Solution   See page S1.

OBJECTIVE **2**   **Subtract integers**

Subtraction is the process of finding the difference between two numbers. Subtraction of an integer is defined as addition of the opposite integer.

Subtract $8 - 3$ by using addition of the opposite.

Subtraction → Addition of the Opposite

$$8 \; - \; (+3) \; = \; 8 \; + \; (-3) \; = \; 5$$

Opposites

To subtract one integer from another, add the opposite of the second integer to the first integer.

first number	−	second number	=	first number	+	the opposite of the second number		
40	−	60	=	40	+	(−60)	=	−20
−40	−	60	=	−40	+	(−60)	=	−100
−40	−	(−60)	=	−40	+	60	=	20
40	−	(−60)	=	40	+	60	=	100

EXAMPLE 2   Subtract: $-12 - 8$

Solution $-12 - 8 = -12 + (-8)$ • Rewrite subtraction as addition of the opposite.

$= -20$ • Add.

PROBLEM 2   Subtract: $-8 - 14$

Solution   See page S1.

When subtraction occurs several times in a problem, rewrite each subtraction as addition of the opposite. Then add.

EXAMPLE 3   Subtract: $-8 - 30 - (-12) - 7 - (-14)$

Solution $-8 - 30 - (-12) - 7 - (-14)$

$= -8 + (-30) + 12 + (-7) + 14$ • Rewrite each subtraction as addition of the opposite.

$= -38 + 12 + (-7) + 14$ • Add the first two numbers.
$= -26 + (-7) + 14$ Then add the sum to the third number. Continue until all the numbers have been added.
$= -33 + 14$
$= -19$

PROBLEM 3   Subtract: $4 - (-3) - 12 - (-7) - 20$

Solution   See page S1.

OBJECTIVE 3   Multiply integers

Point of Interest

The cross × was first used as a symbol for multiplication in 1631 in a book titled The Key to Mathematics. *In that same year, another book,* Practice of the Analytical Art, *advocated the use of a dot to indicate multiplication.*

Multiplication is the process of finding the product of two numbers.

Several different symbols are used to indicate multiplication. The numbers being multiplied are called **factors;** for instance, 3 and 2 are factors in each of the examples at the right. The result is called the **product.** Note that when parentheses are used and there is no arithmetic operation symbol, the operation is multiplication.

$3 \times 2 = 6$
$3 \cdot 2 = 6$
$(3)(2) = 6$
$3(2) = 6$
$(3)2 = 6$

When 5 is multiplied by a sequence of decreasing integers, each product decreases by 5.

$$(5)(3) = 15$$
$$(5)(2) = 10$$
$$(5)(1) = 5$$
$$(5)(0) = 0$$

The pattern developed can be continued so that 5 is multiplied by a sequence of negative numbers. The resulting products must be negative in order to maintain the pattern of decreasing by 5.

$$(5)(-1) = -5$$
$$(5)(-2) = -10$$
$$(5)(-3) = -15$$
$$(5)(-4) = -20$$

This illustrates that the product of a positive number and a negative number is negative.

When -5 is multiplied by a sequence of decreasing integers, each product increases by 5.

$$(-5)(3) = -15$$
$$(-5)(2) = -10$$
$$(-5)(1) = -5$$
$$(-5)(0) = 0$$

The pattern developed can be continued so that -5 is multiplied by a sequence of negative numbers. The resulting products must be positive in order to maintain the pattern of increasing by 5.

$$(-5)(-1) = 5$$
$$(-5)(-2) = 10$$
$$(-5)(-3) = 15$$
$$(-5)(-4) = 20$$

This illustrates that the product of two negative numbers is positive.

This pattern for multiplication is summarized in the following rules for multiplying integers.

Multiplication of Integers

Integers with the same sign
To multiply two numbers with the same sign, multiply the absolute values of the numbers. The product is positive.

$$4 \cdot 8 = 32$$
$$(-4)(-8) = 32$$

Integers with different signs
To multiply two numbers with different signs, multiply the absolute values of the numbers. The product is negative.

$$-4 \cdot 8 = -32$$
$$(4)(-8) = -32$$

EXAMPLE 4   Multiply.   **A.** $-42 \cdot 62$ **B.** $2(-3)(-5)(-7)$

Solution   **A.** $-42 \cdot 62$ • The signs are different. The product is negative.
$$= -2604$$

B. $2(-3)(-5)(-7)$ • To multiply more than two numbers, multiply
$$= -6(-5)(-7)$$ the first two numbers. Then multiply the
$$= 30(-7)$$ product by the third number. Continue until all
$$= -210$$ the numbers have been multiplied.

PROBLEM 4   Multiply.   **A.** $-38 \cdot 51$ **B.** $-7(-8)(9)(-2)$

Solution   See page S1.

OBJECTIVE **4**   **Divide integers**

For every division problem there is a related multiplication problem.

$$\text{Division: } \frac{8}{2} = 4 \qquad \text{Related multiplication: } 4 \cdot 2 = 8$$

This fact can be used to illustrate the rules for dividing signed numbers.

The quotient of two numbers with the same sign is positive.

$\dfrac{12}{3} = 4$ because $4 \cdot 3 = 12$.

$\dfrac{-12}{-3} = 4$ because $4(-3) = -12$.

The quotient of two numbers with different signs is negative.

$\dfrac{12}{-3} = -4$ because $-4(-3) = 12$.

$\dfrac{-12}{3} = -4$ because $-4 \cdot 3 = -12$.

Division of Integers

Integers with the same sign
To divide two numbers with the same sign, divide the absolute values of the numbers. The quotient is positive.

Integers with different signs
To divide two numbers with different signs, divide the absolute values of the numbers. The quotient is negative.

Note that $\dfrac{-12}{3} = -4$, $\dfrac{12}{-3} = -4$, and $-\dfrac{12}{3} = -4$. This suggests the following rule.

$$\text{If } a \text{ and } b \text{ are two integers, and } b \neq 0, \text{ then } \frac{a}{-b} = \frac{-a}{b} = -\frac{a}{b}.$$

Read $b \neq 0$ as "b is not equal to 0." The reason why the denominator must not be equal to 0 is explained in the following discussion of zero and one in division.

Zero and One in Division

Zero divided by any number other than zero is zero.	$\dfrac{0}{a} = 0, a \neq 0$	because $0 \cdot a = 0$.
Division by zero is not defined.	$\dfrac{4}{0} = ?$	$? \times 0 = 4$ There is no number whose product with zero is 4.
Any number other than zero divided by itself is 1.	$\dfrac{a}{a} = 1, a \neq 0$	because $1 \cdot a = a$.
Any number divided by 1 is the number.	$\dfrac{a}{1} = a$	because $a \cdot 1 = a$.

EXAMPLE 5   Divide.   **A.** $(-120) \div (-8)$ **B.** $\dfrac{95}{-5}$ **C.** $-\dfrac{-81}{3}$

Solution   **A.** $(-120) \div (-8) = 15$

B. $\dfrac{95}{-5} = -19$

C. $-\dfrac{-81}{3} = -(-27) = 27$

PROBLEM 5   Divide.   **A.** $(-135) \div (-9)$ **B.** $\dfrac{84}{-6}$ **C.** $-\dfrac{36}{-12}$

Solution   See page S1.

OBJECTIVE **5**   **Application problems**

In many courses, your course grade depends on the *average* of all your test scores. You compute the average by calculating the sum of all your test scores and then dividing that result by the number of tests. Statisticians call this average an **arithmetic mean.** Besides its application to finding the average of your test scores, the arithmetic mean is used in many other situations.

Stock market analysts calculate the **moving average** of a stock. This is the arithmetic mean of the changes in the value of a stock for a given number of days. To illustrate the procedure, we will calculate the 5-day moving average of a stock. In actual practice, a stock market analyst may use 15 days, 30 days, or some other number.

The table below shows the amount of increase or decrease, in cents, in the closing price of a stock for a 10-day period.

Day 1	Day 2	Day 3	Day 4	Day 5	Day 6	Day 7	Day 8	Day 9	Day 10
+50	−175	+225	0	−275	−75	−50	+50	−475	−50

To calculate the 5-day moving average of this stock, determine the average of the stock for days 1 through 5, days 2 through 6, days 3 through 7, and so on.

Days 1–5	Days 2–6	Days 3–7	Days 4–8	Days 5–9	Days 6–10
+50	−175	+225	0	−275	−75
−175	+225	0	−275	−75	−50
+225	0	−275	−75	−50	+50
0	−275	−75	−50	+50	−475
−275	−75	−50	+50	−475	−50
Sum = −175	Sum = −300	Sum = −175	Sum = −350	Sum = −825	Sum = −600
$= \dfrac{-175}{5}$	$= \dfrac{-300}{5}$	$= \dfrac{-175}{5}$	$= \dfrac{-350}{5}$	$= \dfrac{-825}{5}$	$= \dfrac{-600}{5}$
Average = −35	Average = −60	Average = −35	Average = −70	Average = −165	Average = −120

The 5-day moving average is the list of means: $-35, -60, -35, -70, -165,$ and $-120.$ If the numbers in the list tend to increase, the price of the stock is showing an upward trend; if they decrease, the price of the stock is showing a downward trend. For the stock shown here, the price of the stock is showing a downward trend. These trends help analysts determine whether to recommend a stock.

EXAMPLE 6   The daily low temperatures, in degrees Celsius, during one week were recorded as follows: $-8°$, $2°$, $0°$, $-7°$, $1°$, $6°$, $-1°$. Find the average daily low temperature for the week.

Strategy   To find the average daily low temperature:

▶ Add the seven temperature readings.

▶ Divide the sum by 7.

Solution

$-8 + 2 + 0 + (-7) + 1 + 6 + (-1)$
$= -6 + 0 + (-7) + 1 + 6 + (-1)$
$= -6 + (-7) + 1 + 6 + (-1)$
$= -13 + 1 + 6 + (-1)$
$= -12 + 6 + (-1)$
$= -6 + (-1)$
$= -7$

$-7 \div 7 = -1$

The average daily low temperature was $-1°C$.

PROBLEM 6   The daily high temperatures, in degrees Celsius, during one week were recorded as follows: $-5°$, $-6°$, $3°$, $0°$, $-4°$, $-7°$, $-2°$. Find the average daily high temperature for the week.

Solution   See page S1.

1.2   Concept Review

Determine whether the statement is always true, sometimes true, or never true.

1. The sum of two integers is larger than either of the integers being added.

2. The sum of two nonzero integers with the same sign is positive.

3. The quotient of two integers with different signs is negative.

4. To find the opposite of a number, multiply the number by -1.

5. To find the opposite of an integer, divide the integer by -1.

6. To perform the subtraction $a - b$, add the opposite of a to b.

7. $4(-8) = -4$

8. If x and y are two integers and $y = 0$, then $\frac{x}{y} = 0$.

9. If x and y are two different integers, then $x - y = y - x$.

10. If x is an integer and $4x = 0$, then $x = 0$.

1.2 Exercises

1 Add integers

1. Explain how to add two integers with the same sign.

2. Explain how to add two integers with different signs.

3. In the addition equation $8 + (-3) = 5$, the addends are ____?____ and ____?____, and the sum is ____?____.

4. Use the diagram at the right to complete this addition equation: ____?____ + ____?____ = ____?____.

Add.

5. $-3 + (-8)$ **6.** $-12 + (-1)$ **7.** $-4 + (-5)$ **8.** $-12 + (-12)$

9. $6 + (-9)$ **10.** $4 + (-9)$ **11.** $-6 + 7$ **12.** $-12 + 6$

13. $2 + (-3) + (-4)$ **14.** $7 + (-2) + (-8)$ **15.** $-3 + (-12) + (-15)$

16. $9 + (-6) + (-16)$ **17.** $-17 + (-3) + 29$ **18.** $13 + 62 + (-38)$

19. $-3 + (-8) + 12$ **20.** $-27 + (-42) + (-18)$

21. $13 + (-22) + 4 + (-5)$ **22.** $-14 + (-3) + 7 + (-6)$

23. $-22 + 10 + 2 + (-18)$ **24.** $-6 + (-8) + 13 + (-4)$

25. $-126 + (-247) + (-358) + 339$ **26.** $-651 + (-239) + 524 + 487$

Complete Exercises 27 and 28 without actually finding the sums.

27. Is the sum $812 + (-537)$ positive or negative?

28. Is the sum of -57 and -31 positive or negative?

2 Subtract integers

29. Explain the meaning of the words *minus* and *negative*.

30. Explain how to rewrite $6 - (-9)$ as addition of the opposite.

31. $-10 - 4 = -10 +$ ___?___   • Rewrite subtraction as addition of the opposite.
$\quad\quad\quad = $ ___?___   • Add.

32. $8 - (-5) = 8 +$ ___?___   • Rewrite subtraction as addition of the opposite.
$\quad\quad\quad = $ ___?___   • Add.

Subtract.

33. $16 - 8$

34. $12 - 3$

35. $7 - 14$

36. $7 - (-2)$

37. $3 - (-4)$

38. $-6 - (-3)$

39. $-4 - (-2)$

40. $6 - (-12)$

41. $-12 - 16$

42. $-4 - 3 - 2$

43. $4 - 5 - 12$

44. $12 - (-7) - 8$

45. $-12 - (-3) - (-15)$

46. $4 - 12 - (-8)$

47. $13 - 7 - 15$

48. $-6 + 19 - (-31)$

49. $-30 - (-65) - 29 - 4$

50. $42 - (-82) - 65 - 7$

51. $-16 - 47 - 63 - 12$

52. $42 - (-30) - 65 - (-11)$

53. $-47 - (-67) - 13 - 15$

54. $-18 - 49 - (-84) - 27$

Complete Exercises 55 and 56 without actually finding the difference.

55. Is the difference $-25 - 52$ positive or negative?

56. Is the difference 8 minus -5 positive or negative?

3 Multiply integers

57. Explain how to multiply two integers with the same sign.

58. Explain how to multiply two integers with different signs.

59. Name the operation in each expression. Justify your answer.
  a. $8(-7)$ **b.** $8 - 7$ **c.** $8 - (-7)$ **d.** $-xy$ **e.** $x(-y)$ **f.** $-x - y$

60. Name the operation in each expression. Justify your answer.
  a. $(4)(-6)$ **b.** $4 - (6)$ **c.** $4 - (-6)$ **d.** $-ab$ **e.** $a(-b)$ **f.** $-a - b$

61. In the equation $(-10)(7) = -70$, the factors are ___?___ and ___?___, and the product is ___?___.

62. In the equation $15(-3) = -45$, the 15 and -3 are called the ___?___, and -45 is called the ___?___.

63. For the product $(-4)(-12)$, the signs of the factors are the same. The sign of the product is _____?_____ . The product is _____?_____ .

64. For the product $(10)(-10)$, the signs of the factors are different. The sign of the product is _____?_____ . The product is _____?_____ .

Multiply.

65. $14 \cdot 3$

66. $62 \cdot 9$

67. $5(-4)$

68. $4(-7)$

69. $-8(2)$

70. $-9(3)$

71. $(-5)(-5)$

72. $(-3)(-6)$

73. $(-7)(0)$

74. $-32 \cdot 4$

75. $-24 \cdot 3$

76. $19(-7)$

77. $6(-17)$

78. $-8(-26)$

79. $-4(-35)$

80. $-5(23)$

81. $5 \cdot 7(-2)$

82. $8(-6)(-1)$

83. $(-9)(-9)(2)$

84. $-8(-7)(-4)$

85. $-5(8)(-3)$

86. $(-6)(5)(7)$

87. $-1(4)(-9)$

88. $6(-3)(-2)$

89. $4(-4) \cdot 6(-2)$

90. $-5 \cdot 9(-7) \cdot 3$

91. $-9(4) \cdot 3(1)$

92. $8(8)(-5)(-4)$

93. $-6(-5)(12)(0)$

94. $7(9) \cdot 10(-1)$

95. Is the product of three negative integers positive or negative?

96. Is the product of four positive numbers and three negative numbers positive or negative?

4   Divide integers

97. Write the division expression $\dfrac{-15}{3}$ using the division symbol: _____?_____ $\div$ _____?_____ .

98. Write the division expression $8 \div (-4)$ as a fraction: $\dfrac{?}{?}$. The quotient is _____?_____ .

Write the related multiplication problem.

99. $\dfrac{-36}{-12} = 3$

100. $\dfrac{28}{-7} = -4$

101. $\dfrac{-55}{11} = -5$

102. $\dfrac{-20}{-10} = 2$

Divide.

103. $12 \div (-6)$ **104.** $18 \div (-3)$ **105.** $(-72) \div (-9)$

106. $(-64) \div (-8)$ **107.** $0 \div (-6)$ **108.** $-49 \div 0$

109. $45 \div (-5)$ **110.** $-24 \div 4$ **111.** $-36 \div 4$

112. $-56 \div 7$ **113.** $-81 \div (-9)$ **114.** $-40 \div (-5)$

115. $72 \div (-3)$ **116.** $44 \div (-4)$ **117.** $-60 \div 5$

118. $144 \div 9$ **119.** $78 \div (-6)$ **120.** $84 \div (-7)$

121. $-72 \div 4$ **122.** $-80 \div 5$ **123.** $-114 \div (-6)$

124. $-128 \div 4$ **125.** $-130 \div (-5)$ **126.** $(-280) \div 8$

127. $-132 \div (-12)$ **128.** $-156 \div (-13)$ **129.** $-182 \div 14$

130. $-144 \div 12$ **131.** $143 \div 11$ **132.** $168 \div 14$

Complete Exercises 133 and 134 without using a calculator.

133. State whether the quotient $-\dfrac{520}{-13}$ is positive or negative.

134. State whether each quotient is positive, negative, zero, or undefined.
   a. $-61 \div 0$ **b.** $0 \div 85$ **c.** $-172 \div (-4)$ **d.** $-96 \div 4$

5 Application problems

135. At 2:00 P.M. the temperature was 85°F. By 10:00 P.M. the temperature had dropped by 20°F. Which expression can be used to find the temperature, in degrees Fahrenheit, at 10:00 P.M.?
   a. $85 + 20$ **b.** $85 - 20$ **c.** $20 - 85$ **d.** $85 \div 20$

136. After three tests, a student's test average was 82. After the fourth test, the student's test average was 84. Was the student's grade on the fourth test higher or lower than 82?

137. Temperature Find the temperature after a rise of 9°C from −6°C.

138. Temperature Find the temperature after a rise of 7°C from −18°C.

139. Temperature The high temperature for the day was 10°C. The low temperature was −4°C. Find the difference between the high and low temperatures for the day.

140. *Temperature* The low temperature for the day was −2°C. The high temperature was 11°C. Find the difference between the high and low temperatures for the day.

141. *Chemistry* The temperature at which mercury boils is 360°C. Mercury freezes at −39°C. Find the difference between the temperature at which mercury boils and the temperature at which it freezes.

142. *Chemistry* The temperature at which radon boils is −62°C. Radon freezes at −71°C. Find the difference between the temperature at which radon boils and the temperature at which it freezes.

Geography The elevation, or height, of places on Earth is measured in relation to sea level, or the average level of the ocean's surface. The following table shows height above sea level as a positive number and depth below sea level as a negative number. (*Source: Information Please Almanac*)

Continent	Highest Elevation (in meters)		Lowest Elevation (in meters)	
Africa	Mt. Kilimanjaro	5895	Qattara Depression	−133
Asia	Mt. Everest	8844	Dead Sea	−400
Europe	Mt. Elbrus	5634	Caspian Sea	−28
North America	Mt. McKinley	6194	Death Valley	−86
South America	Mt. Aconcagua	6960	Salinas Grandes	−40

Mt. Aconcagua

143. Use the table to find the difference in elevation between Mt. Elbrus and the Caspian Sea.

144. Use the table to find the difference in elevation between Mt. Aconcagua and Salinas Grandes.

145. Use the table to find the difference in elevation between Mt. Kilimanjaro and the Qattara Depression.

146. Use the table to find the difference in elevation between Mt. McKinley and Death Valley.

147. Use the table to find the difference in elevation between Mt. Everest and the Dead Sea.

148. *Temperature* The daily low temperatures, in degrees Celsius, during one week were recorded as follows: 4°, −5°, 8°, 0°, −9°, −11°, −8°. Find the average daily low temperature for the week.

149. *Temperature* The daily high temperatures, in degrees Celsius, during one week were recorded as follows: −8°, −9°, 6°, 7°, −2°, −14°, −1°. Find the average daily high temperature for the week.

150. Temperature On January 22, 1943, the temperature at Spearfish, South Dakota, rose from −4°F to 45°F in two minutes. How many degrees did the temperature rise during those two minutes?

151. Temperature In a 24-hour period in January of 1916, the temperature in Browning, Montana, dropped from 44°F to −56°F. How many degrees did the temperature drop during that time?

Aviation The table at the right shows the average temperatures at different cruising altitudes for airplanes. Use the table for Exercises 152 and 153.

Cruising Altitude	Average Temperature
12,000 ft	16°F
20,000 ft	−12°F
30,000 ft	−48°F
40,000 ft	−70°F
50,000 ft	−70°F

152. What is the difference between the average temperature at 12,000 ft and the average temperature at 40,000 ft?

153. How much colder is the average temperature at 30,000 ft than at 20,000 ft?

154. Education To discourage random guessing on a multiple-choice exam, a professor assigns 5 points for a correct answer, −2 points for an incorrect answer, and 0 points for leaving the question blank. What is the score for a student who had 20 correct answers, had 13 incorrect answers, and left 7 questions blank?

155. Education To discourage random guessing on a multiple-choice exam, a professor assigns 7 points for a correct answer, −3 points for an incorrect answer, and −1 point for leaving the question blank. What is the score for a student who had 17 correct answers, had 8 incorrect answers, and left 2 questions blank?

156. The Stock Market The value of a share of eBay stock on November 15, 2005, was $43.05. The table below shows the amount of increase or decrease, to the nearest 10 cents, from the November 15 closing price of the stock for a 10-day period. Calculate the 5-day moving average for this stock.

Day 1	Day 2	Day 3	Day 4	Day 5	Day 6	Day 7	Day 8	Day 9	Day 10
−50	+130	+90	+150	+60	−10	+10	−130	−90	+30

157. The Stock Market The value of a share of Disney stock on November 15, 2005, was $26.06. The table below shows the amount of increase or decrease, to the nearest 10 cents, from the November 15 closing price of the stock for a 10-day period. Calculate the 5-day moving average for this stock.

Day 1	Day 2	Day 3	Day 4	Day 5	Day 6	Day 7	Day 8	Day 9	Day 10
−20	+10	−80	−20	−10	+10	0	+10	0	+20

1.2   Applying Concepts

Simplify.

158. $|-7 + 12|$

159. $|13 - (-4)|$

160. $|-13 - (-2)|$

161. $|18 - 21|$

Assuming the pattern is continued, find the next three numbers in the pattern.

162. $-7, -11, -15, -19, \ldots$

163. $16, 11, 6, 1, \ldots$

164. $7, -14, 28, -56, \ldots$

165. $1024, -256, 64, \ldots$

Solve.

166. 32,844 is divisible by 3. By rearranging the digits, find the largest possible number that is still divisible by 3.

167. 4563 is not divisible by 4. By rearranging the digits, find the largest possible number that is divisible by 4.

168. How many three-digit numbers of the form 8__4 are divisible by 3?

In each exercise, determine which statement is false.

169. a. $|3 + 4| = |3| + |4|$ **b.** $|3 - 4| = |3| - |4|$ **c.** $|4 + 3| = |4| + |3|$ **d.** $|4 - 3| = |4| - |3|$

170. a. $|5 + 2| = |5| + |2|$ **b.** $|5 - 2| = |5| - |2|$ **c.** $|2 + 5| = |2| + |5|$ **d.** $|2 - 5| = |2| - |5|$

Determine which statement is true for all real numbers.

171. a. $|x + y| \le |x| + |y|$ **b.** $|x + y| = |x| + |y|$ **c.** $|x + y| \ge |x| + |y|$

172. a. $||x| - |y|| \le |x| - |y|$ **b.** $||x| - |y|| = |x| - |y|$ **c.** $||x| - |y|| \ge |x| - |y|$

173. Is the difference between two integers always smaller than either one of the numbers in the difference? If not, give an example for which the difference between two integers is greater than either integer.

174. If $-4x$ equals a positive integer, is x a positive or a negative integer? Explain your answer.

175. Explain why division by zero is not allowed.

Rational Numbers

OBJECTIVE **1**   **Write rational numbers as decimals**

A **rational number** is the quotient of two integers. Therefore, a rational number is a number that can be written in the form $\frac{a}{b}$, where a and b are integers, and b is not zero. A rational number written in this way is commonly called a **fraction.**

$a \leftarrow$ an integer
$\overline{b} \leftarrow$ a nonzero integer

$\left. \dfrac{2}{3}, \quad \dfrac{-4}{9}, \quad \dfrac{18}{-5}, \quad \dfrac{4}{1} \right\}$ Rational numbers

Because an integer can be written as the quotient of the integer and 1, every integer is a rational number.

$$5 = \frac{5}{1} \qquad -3 = \frac{-3}{1}$$

A number written in **decimal notation** is also a rational number.

three-tenths $0.3 = \dfrac{3}{10}$

thirty-five hundredths $0.35 = \dfrac{35}{100}$

negative four-tenths $-0.4 = -\dfrac{4}{10}$

A rational number written as a fraction can be written in decimal notation.

Take Note

The fraction bar can be read "divided by."

$\frac{5}{8} = 5 \div 8$

EXAMPLE 1   Write $\dfrac{5}{8}$ as a decimal.

Solution

$$\begin{array}{r} 0.625 \\ 8\overline{)5.000} \\ -4\,8 \\ \hline 20 \\ -16 \\ \hline 40 \\ -40 \\ \hline 0 \end{array}$$

$\leftarrow$ This is called a **terminating decimal.**

$\leftarrow$ The remainder is zero.

$$\frac{5}{8} = 0.625$$

Take Note

Dividing the numerator by the denominator results in a remainder of 0. The decimal 0.625 is a terminating decimal.

PROBLEM 1   Write $\dfrac{4}{25}$ as a decimal.

Solution   See page S1.

EXAMPLE 2 Write $\frac{4}{11}$ as a decimal.

Solution

$$
\begin{array}{r}
0.3636\ldots \leftarrow \text{This is called a \textbf{repeating decimal.}}\\
11)\overline{4.0000}\\
-33\\
\hline
70\\
-66\\
\hline
40\\
-33\\
\hline
70\\
-66\\
\hline
4 \leftarrow \text{The remainder is never zero.}
\end{array}
$$

$\dfrac{4}{11} = 0.\overline{36}$ ← The bar over the digits 3 and 6 is used to show that these digits repeat.

Take Note

No matter how far we carry out the division, the remainder is never zero. The decimal $0.\overline{36}$ is a repeating decimal.

PROBLEM 2 Write $\frac{4}{9}$ as a decimal. Place a bar over the repeating digits of the decimal.

Solution See page S1.

Rational numbers can be written as fractions, such as $-\frac{6}{7}$ or $\frac{8}{3}$, where the numerator and denominator are integers. But every rational number also can be written as a repeating decimal (such as 0.25767676 . . .) or a terminating decimal (such as 1.73). This was illustrated in Examples 1 and 2.

Numbers that cannot be written either as a repeating decimal or as a terminating decimal are called **irrational numbers.** For example, 2.45445444544445... is an irrational number. Two other examples are $\sqrt{2}$ and π.

$$\sqrt{2} = 1.414213562\ldots \quad \pi = 3.141592654\ldots$$

The three dots mean that the digits continue on and on without ever repeating or terminating. Although we cannot write a decimal that is exactly equal to $\sqrt{2}$ or to π, we can give approximations of these numbers. The symbol $\approx$ is read "is approximately equal to." Shown below are $\sqrt{2}$ rounded to the nearest thousandth and π rounded to the nearest hundredth.

$$\sqrt{2} \approx 1.414 \quad \pi \approx 3.14$$

The rational numbers and the irrational numbers taken together are called the **real numbers.**

OBJECTIVE **2** **Multiply and divide rational numbers**

The sign rules for multiplying and dividing integers apply to multiplication and division of rational numbers.

The product of two fractions is the product of the numerators divided by the product of the denominators.

EXAMPLE 3   Multiply: $\dfrac{3}{8} \cdot \dfrac{12}{17}$

Solution $\dfrac{3}{8} \cdot \dfrac{12}{17} = \dfrac{3 \cdot 12}{8 \cdot 17}$

• Multiply the numerators. Multiply the denominators.

$= \dfrac{3 \cdot \overset{1}{\cancel{2}} \cdot \overset{1}{\cancel{2}} \cdot 3}{2 \cdot \underset{1}{\cancel{2}} \cdot \underset{1}{\cancel{2}} \cdot 17}$

• Write the prime factorization of each factor. Divide by the common factors.

$= \dfrac{9}{34}$

• Multiply the numbers remaining in the numerator. Multiply the numbers remaining in the denominator.

PROBLEM 3   Multiply: $-\dfrac{7}{12} \cdot \dfrac{9}{14}$

■ **Solution**   See page S1.

The **reciprocal** of a fraction is the fraction with the numerator and denominator interchanged. For instance, the reciprocal of $\frac{2}{3}$ is $\frac{3}{2}$, and the reciprocal of $-\frac{5}{4}$ is $-\frac{4}{5}$. To divide fractions, multiply the dividend by the reciprocal of the divisor.

EXAMPLE 4   Divide: $\dfrac{3}{10} \div \left(-\dfrac{18}{25}\right)$

Solution $\dfrac{3}{10} \div \left(-\dfrac{18}{25}\right) = -\left(\dfrac{3}{10} \div \dfrac{18}{25}\right)$

• The signs are different. The quotient is negative.

$= -\left(\dfrac{3}{10} \cdot \dfrac{25}{18}\right)$

• Change division to multiplication. Invert the divisor.

$= -\left(\dfrac{3 \cdot 25}{10 \cdot 18}\right)$

• Multiply the numerators. Multiply the denominators.

$= -\left(\dfrac{\overset{1}{\cancel{3}} \cdot \overset{1}{\cancel{5}} \cdot 5}{2 \cdot \underset{1}{\cancel{5}} \cdot 2 \cdot \underset{1}{\cancel{3}} \cdot 3}\right)$

$= -\dfrac{5}{12}$

PROBLEM 4   Divide: $-\dfrac{3}{8} \div \left(-\dfrac{5}{12}\right)$

■ **Solution**   See page S1.

Take Note

The method for dividing fractions is sometimes stated "To divide fractions, invert the divisor and multiply." Inverting the divisor means writing its reciprocal.

To multiply decimals, multiply as in the multiplication of whole numbers. Write the decimal point in the product so that the number of decimal places in the product equals the sum of the decimal places in the factors.

EXAMPLE 5 Multiply: $(-6.89)(0.00035)$

Solution

$$\begin{array}{r} 6.89 \\ \times\, 0.00035 \\ \hline 3445 \\ 2067 \\ \hline 0.0024115 \end{array}$$

2 decimal places
5 decimal places

7 decimal places

• **Multiply the absolute values.**

$(-6.89)(0.00035) = -0.0024115$

• **The signs are different. The product is negative.**

PROBLEM 5 Multiply: $(-5.44)(3.8)$

Solution See page S2.

To divide decimals, move the decimal point in the divisor to make it a whole number. Move the decimal point in the dividend the same number of places to the right. Place the decimal point in the quotient directly over the decimal point in the dividend. Then divide as in the division of whole numbers.

EXAMPLE 6 Divide: $1.32 \div 0.27$. Round to the nearest tenth.

Solution $0.27.\overline{)1.32.}$

• **Move the decimal point two places to the right in the divisor and in the dividend. Place the decimal point in the quotient.**

$$\begin{array}{r} 4.88 \approx 4.9 \\ 27\overline{)132.00} \\ -108 \\ \hline 24\ 0 \\ -21\ 6 \\ \hline 2\ 40 \\ -2\ 16 \\ \hline 24 \end{array}$$

• **The symbol $\approx$ is used to indicate that the quotient is an approximate value that has been rounded off.**

PROBLEM 6 Divide $-0.394 \div 1.7$. Round to the nearest hundredth.

Solution See page S2.

Take Note

Moving the decimal point in the numerator and denominator is the same as multiplying the numerator and the denominator by the same number. For the problem at the right, we have

$$1.32 \div 0.27 = \frac{1.32}{0.27}$$
$$= \frac{1.32}{0.27} \cdot \frac{100}{100}$$
$$= \frac{132}{27}$$

OBJECTIVE **3** **Add and subtract rational numbers**

The sign rules for adding integers apply to addition of rational numbers.

To add or subtract rational numbers written as fractions, first rewrite the fractions as equivalent fractions with a common denominator. The common denominator is the **least common multiple (LCM)** of the denominators. The LCM of the denominators is also called the **lowest common denominator (LCD)**.

EXAMPLE 7 Add: $-\dfrac{5}{6} + \dfrac{3}{10}$

Solution Prime factorization of 6 and 10:

$6 = 2 \cdot 3 \qquad 10 = 2 \cdot 5$

$\text{LCM} = 2 \cdot 3 \cdot 5 = 30$

• **Find the LCM of the denominators 6 and 10.**

Take Note

You can find the LCM by multiplying the denominators and then dividing by the greatest *common factor* of the two denominators. In the case of 6 and 10, $6 \cdot 10 = 60$. Now divide by 2, the greatest common factor of 6 and 10.

$$60 \div 2 = 30$$

Alternatively, you can use as the common denominator the product of the denominators, which in this case is 60. Write each fraction with a denominator of 60. Add the fractions. Then simplify the sum.

$$-\frac{5}{6} + \frac{3}{10} = -\frac{50}{60} + \frac{18}{60}$$
$$= \frac{-50 + 18}{60}$$
$$= \frac{-32}{60}$$
$$= -\frac{8}{15}$$

$$-\frac{5}{6} + \frac{3}{10} = -\frac{25}{30} + \frac{9}{30}$$

- Rewrite the fractions as equivalent fractions, using the LCM of the denominators as the common denominator.

$$= \frac{-25 + 9}{30}$$
$$= \frac{-16}{30}$$
$$= -\frac{8}{15}$$

- Add the numerators, and place the sum over the common denominator.

- Write the answer in simplest form.

PROBLEM 7   Subtract: $\dfrac{5}{9} - \dfrac{11}{12}$

■ **Solution**   See page S2.

EXAMPLE 8   Simplify: $-\dfrac{3}{4} + \dfrac{1}{6} - \dfrac{5}{8}$

Solution $-\dfrac{3}{4} + \dfrac{1}{6} - \dfrac{5}{8} = -\dfrac{18}{24} + \dfrac{4}{24} - \dfrac{15}{24}$

- The LCM of 4, 6, and 8 is 24.

$$= \frac{-18}{24} + \frac{4}{24} + \frac{-15}{24}$$
$$= \frac{-18 + 4 + (-15)}{24}$$
$$= \frac{-29}{24}$$
$$= -\frac{29}{24}$$

PROBLEM 8   Simplify: $-\dfrac{7}{8} - \dfrac{5}{6} + \dfrac{1}{2}$

■ **Solution**   See page S2.

To add or subtract decimals, write the numbers so that the decimal points are in a vertical line. Then proceed as in the addition or subtraction of integers. Write the decimal point in the answer directly below the decimal points in the problem.

EXAMPLE 9   Add: $14.02 + 137.6 + 9.852$

Solution
```
   14.02
  137.6
+   9.852
─────────
  161.472
```
- Write the decimals so that the decimal points are in a vertical line.

- Write the decimal point in the sum directly below the decimal points in the problem.

PROBLEM 9   Add: $3.097 + 4.9 + 3.09$

■ **Solution**   See page S2.

EXAMPLE 10 Add: $-114.039 + 84.76$

Solution

$$\begin{array}{r} 114.039 \\ -\ 84.76 \\ \hline 29.279 \end{array}$$

$-114.039 + 84.76$
$= -29.279$

• The signs are different. Subtract the absolute value of the number with the smaller absolute value from the absolute value of the number with the larger absolute value.

• Attach the sign of the number with the larger absolute value.

PROBLEM 10 Subtract: $16.127 - 67.91$

Solution See page S2.

OBJECTIVE **4**   **Convert among percents, fractions, and decimals**

"A population growth rate of 3%," "a manufacturer's discount of 25%," and "an 8% increase in pay" are typical examples of the many ways in which percent is used in applied problems. **Percent** means "parts of 100." Thus 27% means 27 parts of 100.

In applied problems involving a percent, it is usually necessary either to rewrite the percent as a fraction or a decimal, or to rewrite a fraction or a decimal as a percent.

To write 27% as a fraction, remove the percent sign and multiply by $\frac{1}{100}$.

$$27\% = 27\left(\frac{1}{100}\right) = \frac{27}{100}$$

To write a percent as a decimal, remove the percent sign and multiply by 0.01.

To write 33% as a decimal, remove the percent sign and multiply by 0.01.

$$33\% \quad = \quad 33(0.01) \quad = \quad 0.33$$

Move the decimal point two places to the left. Then remove the percent sign.

Write 100% as a decimal.

$$100\% = 100(0.01) = 1$$

EXAMPLE 11 Write 130% as a fraction and as a decimal.

Solution $130\% = 130\left(\frac{1}{100}\right) = \frac{130}{100} = 1\frac{3}{10}$

• To write a percent as a fraction, remove the percent sign and multiply by $\frac{1}{100}$.

$130\% = 130(0.01) = 1.30$

• To write a percent as a decimal, remove the percent sign and multiply by 0.01.

PROBLEM 11   Write 125% as a fraction and as a decimal.

Solution   See page S2.

EXAMPLE 12   Write $33\frac{1}{3}\%$ as a fraction.

Solution $33\frac{1}{3}\% = 33\frac{1}{3}\left(\frac{1}{100}\right) = \frac{100}{3}\left(\frac{1}{100}\right)$

$= \frac{1}{3}$

• Write the mixed number $33\frac{1}{3}$ as the improper fraction $\frac{100}{3}$.

PROBLEM 12   Write $16\frac{2}{3}\%$ as a fraction.

Solution   See page S2.

EXAMPLE 13   Write 0.25% as a decimal.

Solution $0.25\% = 0.25(0.01) = 0.0025$

• Remove the percent sign and multiply by 0.01.

PROBLEM 13   Write 6.08% as a decimal.

Solution   See page S2.

A fraction or decimal can be written as a percent by multiplying by 100%. Recall that 100% = 1, and multiplying a number by 1 does not change the number.

To write $\frac{5}{8}$ as a percent, multiply by 100%.

$\frac{5}{8} = \frac{5}{8}(100\%) = \frac{500}{8}\% = 62.5\%$ or $62\frac{1}{2}\%$

To write 0.82 as a percent, multiply by 100%.

$0.82 \qquad = \qquad 0.82(100\%) \qquad = \qquad 82\%$

Move the decimal point two places to the right. Then write the percent sign.

EXAMPLE 14   Write as a percent.   **A.** 0.027   **B.** 1.34

Solution   **A.** $0.027 = 0.027(100\%) = 2.7\%$

• To write a decimal as a percent, multiply by 100%.

B. $1.34 = 1.34(100\%) = 134\%$

PROBLEM 14   Write as a percent.   **A.** 0.043   **B.** 2.57

Solution   See page S2.

EXAMPLE 15   Write $\frac{5}{6}$ as a percent. Round to the nearest tenth of a percent.

Solution $\frac{5}{6} = \frac{5}{6}(100\%) = \frac{500}{6}\% \approx 83.3\%$

• To write a fraction as a percent, multiply by 100%.

PROBLEM 15   Write $\frac{5}{9}$ as a percent. Round to the nearest tenth of a percent.

Solution   See page S2.

EXAMPLE 16 Write $\frac{7}{16}$ as a percent. Write the remainder in fractional form.

Solution $\frac{7}{16} = \frac{7}{16}(100\%) = \frac{700}{16}\% = 43\frac{3}{4}\%$ • **Multiply the fraction by 100%.**

PROBLEM 16 Write $\frac{9}{16}$ as a percent. Write the remainder in fractional form.

Solution See page S2.

1.3 Concept Review

Determine whether the statement is always true, sometimes true, or never true.

1. To multiply two fractions, you must first rewrite the fractions as equivalent fractions with a common denominator.

2. The number $\frac{\pi}{3}$ is an example of a rational number.

3. A rational number can be written as a terminating decimal.

4. The number 2.585585558... is an example of a repeating decimal.

5. An irrational number is a real number.

6. 37%, 0.37, and $\frac{37}{100}$ are three numbers that have the same value.

7. To write a decimal as a percent, multiply the decimal by $\frac{1}{100}$.

8. If a, b, c, and d are natural numbers, then $\frac{a}{b} + \frac{c}{d} = \frac{a + c}{b + d}$.

9. -12 is an example of a number that is both an integer and a rational number.

10. $\frac{7}{9}$ is an example of a number that is both a rational number and an irrational number.

1.3 Exercises

1 Write rational numbers as decimals

1. To write $\frac{2}{3}$ as a decimal, divide ___?___ by ___?___. The quotient is 0.6666..., which is a ___?___ decimal.

2. A number such as 0.74744744474444..., whose decimal representation neither ends nor repeats, is an example of an ___?___ number.

Write as a decimal. Place a bar over the repeating digits of a repeating decimal.

3. $\frac{1}{3}$ **4.** $\frac{2}{3}$ **5.** $\frac{1}{4}$ **6.** $\frac{3}{4}$ **7.** $\frac{2}{5}$

8. $\frac{4}{5}$ **9.** $\frac{1}{6}$ **10.** $\frac{5}{6}$ **11.** $\frac{1}{8}$ **12.** $\frac{7}{8}$

13. $\frac{2}{9}$ **14.** $\frac{8}{9}$ **15.** $\frac{5}{11}$ **16.** $\frac{10}{11}$ **17.** $\frac{7}{12}$

18. $\frac{11}{12}$ **19.** $\frac{4}{15}$ **20.** $\frac{8}{15}$ **21.** $\frac{7}{16}$ **22.** $\frac{15}{16}$

23. $\frac{6}{25}$ **24.** $\frac{14}{25}$ **25.** $\frac{9}{40}$ **26.** $\frac{21}{40}$ **27.** $\frac{15}{22}$

28. $\frac{19}{22}$ **29.** $\frac{11}{24}$ **30.** $\frac{19}{24}$ **31.** $\frac{5}{33}$ **32.** $\frac{25}{33}$

33. To write $\frac{a}{b}$ as a decimal, we divide a by b (b is not zero). After finding the quotient to ten decimal places, we still have a nonzero remainder and no repeating pattern of digits. Can you conclude that $\frac{a}{b}$ is an irrational number?

34. Is $\frac{\sqrt{2}}{2}$ a rational or an irrational number?

2   Multiply and divide rational numbers

35. The product of 1.762 and −8.4 will have ___?___ decimal places.

36. The reciprocal of $\frac{4}{9}$ is ___?___. To find the quotient $-\frac{2}{3} \div \frac{4}{9}$, find the product $-\frac{2}{3} \cdot$ ___?___. The quotient $-\frac{2}{3} \div \frac{4}{9}$ is ___?___.

Simplify.

37. $\frac{1}{2}\left(-\frac{3}{4}\right)$ **38.** $-\frac{2}{9}\left(-\frac{3}{14}\right)$ **39.** $\left(-\frac{3}{8}\right)\left(-\frac{4}{15}\right)$

40. $\dfrac{5}{8}\left(-\dfrac{7}{12}\right)\dfrac{16}{25}$

41. $\left(\dfrac{1}{2}\right)\left(-\dfrac{3}{4}\right)\left(-\dfrac{5}{8}\right)$

42. $\left(\dfrac{5}{12}\right)\left(-\dfrac{8}{15}\right)\left(-\dfrac{1}{3}\right)$

43. $\dfrac{3}{8} \div \dfrac{1}{4}$

44. $\dfrac{5}{6} \div \left(-\dfrac{3}{4}\right)$

45. $-\dfrac{5}{12} \div \dfrac{15}{32}$

46. $\dfrac{1}{8} \div \left(-\dfrac{5}{12}\right)$

47. $-\dfrac{4}{9} \div \left(-\dfrac{2}{3}\right)$

48. $-\dfrac{6}{11} \div \dfrac{4}{9}$

49. $(1.2)(3.47)$

50. $(-0.8)(6.2)$

51. $(-1.89)(-2.3)$

52. $(6.9)(-4.2)$

53. $(1.06)(-3.8)$

54. $(-2.7)(-3.5)$

55. $(1.2)(-0.5)(3.7)$

56. $(-2.4)(6.1)(0.9)$

57. $(-0.8)(3.006)(-5.1)$

Complete Exercises 58 and 59 without actually finding the products and quotients.

58. State whether each product or quotient is positive or negative.

a. $\left(-\dfrac{11}{12}\right)\left(-\dfrac{5}{4}\right)\left(-\dfrac{1}{2}\right)$ **b.** $-1.572 \div -8.4$

59. State whether each product or quotient is greater than one or less than one.

a. $\dfrac{11}{13} \cdot \dfrac{50}{51}$ **b.** $8.713 \div 7.2$

Simplify. Round to the nearest hundredth.

60. $-24.7 \div 0.09$

61. $-1.27 \div (-1.7)$

62. $9.07 \div (-3.5)$

63. $-354.2086 \div 0.1719$

64. $-2658.3109 \div (-0.0473)$

65. $(-3.92) \div (-45.008)$

3 **Add and subtract rational numbers**

66. The least common multiple of the denominators of the fractions $\dfrac{5}{8}, -\dfrac{1}{6}$, and $\dfrac{2}{9}$ is ____?____.

67. Write the fraction $\dfrac{3}{14}$ as an equivalent fraction with the denominator 28:

$\dfrac{3}{14} = \dfrac{?}{28}$.

Simplify.

68. $\dfrac{3}{8} + \dfrac{5}{8}$

69. $-\dfrac{1}{4} + \dfrac{3}{4}$

70. $\dfrac{7}{8} - \dfrac{3}{8}$

71. $-\dfrac{5}{6} - \dfrac{1}{6}$

72. $-\dfrac{5}{12} - \dfrac{3}{8}$ **73.** $-\dfrac{5}{6} - \dfrac{5}{9}$ **74.** $-\dfrac{6}{13} + \dfrac{17}{26}$ **75.** $-\dfrac{7}{12} + \dfrac{5}{8}$

76. $-\dfrac{5}{8} - \left(-\dfrac{11}{12}\right)$ **77.** $\dfrac{1}{3} + \dfrac{5}{6} - \dfrac{2}{9}$ **78.** $\dfrac{1}{2} - \dfrac{2}{3} + \dfrac{1}{6}$ **79.** $-\dfrac{3}{8} - \dfrac{5}{12} - \dfrac{3}{16}$

80. $-\dfrac{5}{16} + \dfrac{3}{4} - \dfrac{7}{8}$ **81.** $\dfrac{1}{2} - \dfrac{3}{8} - \left(-\dfrac{1}{4}\right)$ **82.** $\dfrac{3}{4} - \left(-\dfrac{7}{12}\right) - \dfrac{7}{8}$ **83.** $\dfrac{1}{3} - \dfrac{1}{4} - \dfrac{1}{5}$

84. $\dfrac{2}{3} - \dfrac{1}{2} + \dfrac{5}{6}$ **85.** $\dfrac{5}{16} + \dfrac{1}{8} - \dfrac{1}{2}$ **86.** $\dfrac{5}{8} - \left(-\dfrac{5}{12}\right) + \dfrac{1}{3}$ **87.** $\dfrac{1}{8} - \dfrac{11}{12} + \dfrac{1}{2}$

88. $-\dfrac{7}{9} + \dfrac{14}{15} + \dfrac{8}{21}$ **89.** $1.09 + 6.2$ **90.** $-32.1 - 6.7$ **91.** $5.13 - 8.179$

92. $-13.092 + 6.9$ **93.** $2.54 - 3.6$ **94.** $5.43 + 7.925$ **95.** $-16.92 - 6.925$

96. $-3.87 + 8.546$ **97.** $6.9027 - 17.692$

98. $2.09 - 6.72 - 5.4$ **99.** $16.4 + 3.09 - 7.93$

100. $-18.39 + 4.9 - 23.7$ **101.** $19 - (-3.72) - 82.75$

102. $-3.07 - (-2.97) - 17.4$ **103.** $-3.09 - 4.6 - 27.3$

104. $317.09 - 46.902 + 583.0714$ **105.** $71.0235 - 86.0974 + 254.309$

Complete Exercises 106 and 107 without actually finding the sums and differences.

106. State whether each sum or difference is positive or negative.

    a. $\dfrac{1}{5} - \dfrac{1}{2}$ **b.** $-21.765 + 15.1$ **c.** $0.837 + (-0.24)$ **d.** $-\dfrac{3}{4} + \dfrac{9}{10}$

107. Estimate each sum to the nearest integer.

    a. $\dfrac{7}{8} + \dfrac{4}{5}$ **b.** $\dfrac{1}{3} + \left(-\dfrac{1}{2}\right)$ **c.** $-0.125 + 1.25$ **d.** $-1.3 + 0.2$

4 Convert among percents, fractions, and decimals

108. **a.** Explain how to convert a fraction to a percent.
b. Explain how to convert a percent to a fraction.

109. **a.** Explain how to convert a decimal to a percent.
b. Explain how to convert a percent to a decimal.

110. Explain why multiplying a number by 100% does not change the value of the number.

111. To write 80% as a fraction, remove the percent sign and multiply by
___?___ : $80\% = 80 \cdot$ ___?___ $=$ ___?___.

112. To write 68% as a decimal, remove the percent sign and multiply by
___?___ : $68\% = 68 \cdot$ ___?___ $=$ ___?___.

113. To write $\frac{3}{10}$ as a percent, multiply by ___?___ : $\frac{3}{10} = \frac{3}{10} \cdot$ ___?___ $=$
___?___.

114. To write 1.25 as a percent, multiply by ___?___ : $1.25 = 1.25 \cdot$ ___?___ $=$
___?___.

Write as a fraction and as a decimal.

115. 75% **116.** 40% **117.** 50% **118.** 10%

119. 64% **120.** 88% **121.** 175% **122.** 160%

123. 19% **124.** 87% **125.** 5% **126.** 2%

127. 450% **128.** 380% **129.** 8% **130.** 4%

Write as a fraction.

131. $11\frac{1}{9}\%$ **132.** $37\frac{1}{2}\%$ **133.** $31\frac{1}{4}\%$ **134.** $66\frac{2}{3}\%$

135. $\frac{1}{2}\%$ **136.** $5\frac{3}{4}\%$ **137.** $6\frac{1}{4}\%$ **138.** $83\frac{1}{3}\%$

Write as a decimal.

139. 7.3% **140.** 9.1% **141.** 15.8% **142.** 0.3%

143. 9.15% **144.** 121.2% **145.** 18.23% **146.** 0.15%

Write as a percent.

147. 0.15 **148.** 0.37 **149.** 0.05 **150.** 0.02

151. 0.175   **152.** 0.125   **153.** 1.15   **154.** 2.142

155. 0.008   **156.** 0.004   **157.** 0.065   **158.** 0.083

Write as a percent. Round to the nearest tenth of a percent.

159. $\dfrac{27}{50}$ **160.** $\dfrac{83}{100}$ **161.** $\dfrac{1}{3}$ **162.** $\dfrac{3}{8}$

163. $\dfrac{4}{9}$ **164.** $\dfrac{9}{20}$ **165.** $2\dfrac{1}{2}$ **166.** $1\dfrac{2}{7}$

Write as a percent. Write the remainder in fractional form.

167. $\dfrac{3}{8}$ **168.** $\dfrac{3}{16}$ **169.** $\dfrac{5}{14}$ **170.** $\dfrac{4}{7}$

171. $1\dfrac{1}{4}$ **172.** $2\dfrac{5}{8}$ **173.** $1\dfrac{5}{9}$ **174.** $1\dfrac{13}{16}$

Complete Exercises 175 and 176 without actually finding the percents.

175. Does $\dfrac{4}{3}$ represent a number greater than 100% or less than 100%?

176. Does 0.055 represent a number greater than 1% or less than 1%?

Employment The graph at the right shows the responses to a survey that asked respondents, "How did you find your most recent job?" Use the graph for Exercises 177 to 179.

177. What fraction of the respondents found their most recent jobs on the Internet?

178. What fraction of the respondents found their most recent jobs through a referral?

179. Did more or less than one-quarter of the respondents find their most recent jobs through a newspaper ad?

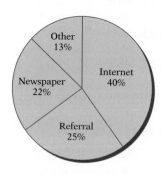

How Did You Find
Your Most Recent Job?

1.3   Applying Concepts

Classify each of the following numbers as a natural number, an integer, a positive integer, a negative integer, a rational number, an irrational number, or a real number. List all that apply.

180. −1   **181.** 28

182. $-\dfrac{9}{34}$

183. -7.707

184. $5.2\overline{6}$

185. $0.171771777\ldots$

Solve.

186. Find the average of $\dfrac{5}{8}$ and $\dfrac{3}{4}$.

187. 🌐 **The Postal Service** Postage for first-class mail is $.39 for the first ounce or fraction of an ounce and $.24 for each additional ounce or fraction of an ounce. Find the cost of mailing, by first-class mail, a letter that weighs $4\dfrac{1}{2}$ oz.

🌐 **Government** The table at the right shows the surplus or deficit, in billions of dollars, for the federal budget for selected years from 1945 through 2000. A negative sign ($-$) indicates a deficit. Use this table for Exercises 188 to 193. (*Source:* U.S. Office of Management and Budget)

Year	Federal Budget Surplus or Deficit (in billions of dollars)
1945	−47.553
1950	−3.119
1955	−2.993
1960	0.301
1965	−1.411
1970	−2.842
1975	−53.242
1980	−73.835
1985	−212.334
1990	−221.194
1995	−163.899
1996	−107.450
1997	−21.940
1998	69.246
1999	79.263
2000	117.305

188. In which year listed was the deficit greatest?

189. Find the difference between the deficits in the years 1980 and 1985.

190. Calculate the difference between the surplus in 1960 and the deficit in 1955.

191. How many times greater was the deficit in 1985 than in 1975? Round to the nearest whole number.

192. What was the average deficit per quarter, in millions of dollars, for the year 1970?

193. Find the average surplus or deficit for the years 1995 through 2000. Round to the nearest million.

194. Use a calculator to determine the decimal representations of $\dfrac{17}{99}$, $\dfrac{45}{99}$, and $\dfrac{73}{99}$. Make a conjecture as to the decimal representation of $\dfrac{83}{99}$. Does your conjecture work for $\dfrac{33}{99}$? What about $\dfrac{1}{99}$?

195. If the same positive integer is added to both the numerator and the denominator of $\dfrac{2}{5}$, is the new fraction less than, equal to, or greater than $\dfrac{2}{5}$?

$\dfrac{2}{3}$		
	$\dfrac{1}{6}$	$\dfrac{5}{6}$
		$-\dfrac{1}{3}$

196. A magic square is one in which the numbers in every row, column, and diagonal sum to the same number. Complete the magic square at the right.

197. Let x represent the price of a car. If the sales tax is 6% of the price, express the total of the price of the car and the sales tax in terms of x.

198. Let x represent the price of a suit. If the suit is on sale at a discount rate of 30%, express the price of the suit after the discount in terms of x.

199. The price of a pen was 60¢. During a storewide sale, the price was reduced to a different whole number of cents, and the entire stock was sold for $54.59. Find the price of the pen during the sale.

200. Find three natural numbers a, b, and c such that $\frac{1}{a} + \frac{1}{b} + \frac{1}{c}$ is a natural number.

201. If a and b are rational numbers and $a < b$, is it always possible to find a rational number c such that $a < c < b$? If not, explain why. If so, show how to find one.

202. In your own words, define **a.** a rational number, **b.** an irrational number, and **c.** a real number.

203. Explain why you "invert and multiply" when dividing a fraction by a fraction.

204. Explain why you need a common denominator when adding two fractions and why you don't need a common denominator when multiplying two fractions.

1.4 Exponents and the Order of Operations Agreement

OBJECTIVE 1 Exponential expressions

Repeated multiplication of the same factor can be written using an exponent.

$$2 \cdot 2 \cdot 2 \cdot 2 \cdot 2 = 2^5 \leftarrow \text{exponent} \qquad a \cdot a \cdot a \cdot a = a^4 \leftarrow \text{exponent}$$

$$\underset{\text{base}}{\uparrow} \qquad\qquad\qquad\qquad \underset{\text{base}}{\uparrow}$$

The **exponent** indicates how many times the factor, called the **base**, occurs in the multiplication. The multiplication $2 \cdot 2 \cdot 2 \cdot 2 \cdot 2$ is in **factored form**. The exponential expression 2^5 is in **exponential form.**

2^1 is read "the first power of two" or just "two." ————→ Usually the exponent 1 is not written.

2^2 is read "the second power of two" or "two squared."

2^3 is read "the third power of two" or "two cubed."

2^4 is read "the fourth power of two."

2^5 is read "the fifth power of two."

a^5 is read "the fifth power of a."

There is a geometric interpretation of the first three natural-number powers.

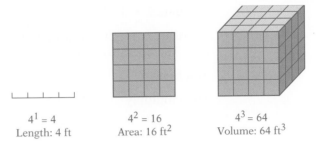

$4^1 = 4$
Length: 4 ft

$4^2 = 16$
Area: 16 ft^2

$4^3 = 64$
Volume: 64 ft^3

To evaluate an exponential expression, write each factor as many times as indicated by the exponent. Then multiply.

$$3^5 = 3 \cdot 3 \cdot 3 \cdot 3 \cdot 3 = 243$$

$$2^3 \cdot 3^2 = (2 \cdot 2 \cdot 2) \cdot (3 \cdot 3) = 8 \cdot 9 = 72$$

Take Note

The −4 is squared only when the negative sign is *inside* the parentheses. In $(-4)^2$, we are squaring −4; in -4^2, we are finding the opposite of 4^2.

EXAMPLE 1 Evaluate $(-4)^2$ and -4^2.

Solution $(-4)^2 = (-4)(-4) = 16$

$-4^2 = -(4 \cdot 4) = -16$

PROBLEM 1 Evaluate $(-5)^3$ and -5^3.

Solution See page S2.

Take Note

The product of an even number of negative factors is positive. The product of an odd number of negative factors is negative.

EXAMPLE 2 Evaluate $(-2)^4$ and $(-2)^5$.

Solution

$(-2)^4 = (-2)(-2)(-2)(-2)$
$\qquad = 4(-2)(-2)$
$\qquad = -8(-2)$
$\qquad = 16$

$(-2)^5 = (-2)(-2)(-2)(-2)(-2)$
$\qquad = 4(-2)(-2)(-2)$
$\qquad = -8(-2)(-2)$
$\qquad = 16(-2)$
$\qquad = -32$

PROBLEM 2 Evaluate $(-3)^3$ and $(-3)^4$.

Solution See page S2.

EXAMPLE 3 Evaluate $(-3)^2 \cdot 2^3$ and $\left(-\frac{2}{3}\right)^3$.

Solution $(-3)^2 \cdot 2^3 = (-3)(-3) \cdot (2)(2)(2) = 9 \cdot 8 = 72$

$$\left(-\frac{2}{3}\right)^3 = \left(-\frac{2}{3}\right)\left(-\frac{2}{3}\right)\left(-\frac{2}{3}\right) = -\frac{2 \cdot 2 \cdot 2}{3 \cdot 3 \cdot 3} = -\frac{8}{27}$$

PROBLEM 3 Evaluate $(3^3)(-2)^3$ and $\left(-\frac{2}{5}\right)^2$.

Solution See page S2.

OBJECTIVE **2**   ## The Order of Operations Agreement

Evaluate $2 + 3 \cdot 5$.

There are two arithmetic operations, addition and multiplication, in this problem. The operations could be performed in different orders.

Add first. $\underbrace{2 + 3} \cdot 5$ Multiply first. $2 + \underbrace{3 \cdot 5}$

Then multiply. $\underbrace{5 \quad \cdot 5}$ Then add. $2 + \underbrace{15}$

                            25   17

In order to prevent there being more than one answer to the same problem, an Order of Operations Agreement has been established.

The Order of Operations Agreement

Step 1 Perform operations inside grouping symbols. **Grouping symbols** include parentheses ( ), brackets [ ], absolute value symbols ||, and the fraction bar.

Step 2 Simplify exponential expressions.

Step 3 Do multiplication and division as they occur from left to right.

Step 4 Do addition and subtraction as they occur from left to right.

EXAMPLE 4   Simplify: $12 - 24(8 - 5) \div 2^2$

Solution $12 - 24(8 - 5) \div 2^2$
$= 12 - 24(3) \div 2^2$ • Perform operations inside grouping symbols.
$= 12 - 24(3) \div 4$ • Simplify exponential expressions.
$= 12 - 72 \div 4$ • Do multiplication and division as they occur
$= 12 - 18$ from left to right.
$= -6$ • Do addition and subtraction as they occur
                                  from left to right.

PROBLEM 4   Simplify: $36 \div (8 - 5)^2 - (-3)^2 \cdot 2$

Solution   See page S2.

One or more of the steps shown in Example 4 may not be needed to simplify an expression. In that case, proceed to the next step in the Order of Operations Agreement.

EXAMPLE 5 Simplify: $\dfrac{4+8}{2+1} - |3 - 1| + 2$

Solution $\dfrac{4+8}{2+1} - |3 - 1| + 2$

$= \dfrac{12}{3} - |2| + 2$ • Perform operations inside grouping symbols (above and below the fraction bar and inside the absolute value symbols).

$= \dfrac{12}{3} - 2 + 2$ • Find the absolute value of 2.

$= 4 - 2 + 2$ • Do multiplication and division as they occur from left to right.

$= 2 + 2$ • Do addition and subtraction as they occur from left to right.

$= 4$

PROBLEM 5 Simplify: $27 \div 3^2 + (-3)^2 \cdot 4$

Solution See page S2.

When an expression has grouping symbols inside grouping symbols, first perform the operations inside the *inner* grouping symbols by following Steps 2, 3, and 4 of the Order of Operations Agreement. Then perform the operations inside the *outer* grouping symbols by following Steps 2, 3, and 4 in sequence.

EXAMPLE 6 Simplify: $6 \div [4 - (6 - 8)] + 2^2$

Solution $6 \div [4 - (6 - 8)] + 2^2$
$= 6 \div [4 - (-2)] + 2^2$ • Perform operations inside inner grouping symbols.

$= 6 \div 6 + 2^2$ • Perform operations inside outer grouping symbols.

$= 6 \div 6 + 4$ • Simplify exponential expressions.
$= 1 + 4$ • Do multiplication and division.
$= 5$ • Do addition and subtraction.

PROBLEM 6 Simplify: $4 - 3[4 - 2(6 - 3)] \div 2$

Solution See page S2.

1.4 Concept Review

Determine whether the statement is always true, sometimes true, or never true.

1. $(-5)^2$, -5^2, and $-(5)^2$ all represent the same number.

2. By the Order of Operations Agreement, addition is performed before division.

3. In the expression 3^8, 8 is the base.

4. The expression 9^4 is in exponential form.

5. To evaluate the expression $6 + 7 \cdot 10$ means to determine what one number it is equal to.

6. When using the Order of Operations Agreement, we consider the absolute value symbol a grouping symbol.

7. Using the Order of Operations Agreement, it is possible to get more than one correct answer to a problem.

8. The Order of Operations Agreement is used for natural numbers, integers, rational numbers, and real numbers.

9. The expression $(2^3)^2$ equals $2^{(3^2)}$.

10. Suppose a and b are positive integers. Then $a^b = b^a$.

1.4 Exercises

1 Exponential expressions

1. In the expression $(-5)^2$, -5 is called the ___?___ and 2 is called the ___?___. To evaluate $(-5)^2$, find the product $(\underline{\quad?\quad})(\underline{\quad?\quad}) = \underline{\quad?\quad}$.

2. The exponential expression 4^3 is read "the ___?___ power of ___?___" or "four ___?___." To evaluate 4^3, find the product $(\underline{\quad?\quad})(\underline{\quad?\quad})(\underline{\quad?\quad}) = \underline{\quad?\quad}$.

Evaluate.

3. 6^2

4. 7^4

5. -7^2

6. -4^3

7. $(-3)^2$

8. $(-2)^3$

9. $(-3)^4$

10. $(-5)^3$

11. $\left(\dfrac{1}{2}\right)^2$

12. $\left(-\dfrac{3}{4}\right)^3$

13. $(0.3)^2$

14. $(1.5)^3$

15. $\left(\dfrac{2}{3}\right)^2 \cdot 3^3$

16. $\left(-\dfrac{1}{2}\right)^3 \cdot 8$

17. $(0.3)^3 \cdot 2^3$

18. $(0.5)^2 \cdot 3^3$

19. $(-3) \cdot 2^2$

20. $(-5) \cdot 3^4$

21. $(-2) \cdot (-2)^3$

22. $(-2) \cdot (-2)^2$

23. $2^3 \cdot 3^3 \cdot (-4)$

24. $(-3)^3 \cdot 5^2 \cdot 10$

25. $(-7) \cdot 4^2 \cdot 3^2$

26. $(-2) \cdot 2^3 \cdot (-3)^2$

27. $\left(\dfrac{2}{3}\right)^2 \cdot \dfrac{1}{4} \cdot 3^3$

28. $\left(\dfrac{3}{4}\right)^2 \cdot (-4) \cdot 2^3$

29. $8^2 \cdot (-3)^5 \cdot 5$

Complete Exercises 30 and 31 without actually finding the products.

30. Is the fifth power of negative eighteen positive or negative?

31. Is the product $-(3^2)(-5^3)$ positive or negative?

2 The Order of Operations Agreement

32. Why do we need an Order of Operations Agreement?

33. Describe each step in the Order of Operations Agreement.

34. Simplify: $2(3^3)$
$2(3^3) = 2(\underline{\quad ? \quad})$ • **Simplify exponential expressions.**
$= \underline{\quad ? \quad}$ • **Do multiplication and division.**

35. Simplify: $3 - 5(6 - 8)^2$
$3 - 5(6 - 8)^2 = 3 - 5(\underline{\quad ? \quad})^2$ • **Perform operations inside grouping symbols.**
$= 3 - 5(\underline{\quad ? \quad})$ • **Simplify exponential expressions.**
$= 3 - \underline{\quad ? \quad}$ • **Do multiplication and division.**
$= \underline{\quad ? \quad}$ • **Do addition and subtraction.**

Simplify by using the Order of Operations Agreement.

36. $4 - 8 \div 2$

37. $2^2 \cdot 3 - 3$

38. $2(3 - 4) - (-3)^2$

39. $16 - 32 \div 2^3$

40. $24 - 18 \div 3 + 2$

41. $8 - (-3)^2 - (-2)$

42. $16 + 15 \div (-5) - 2$

43. $14 - 2^2 - |4 - 7|$

44. $3 - 2[8 - (3 - 2)]$

45. $-2^2 + 4[16 \div (3 - 5)]$

46. $6 + \dfrac{16 - 4}{2^2 + 2} - 2$

47. $24 \div \dfrac{3^2}{8 - 5} - (-5)$

48. $96 \div 2[12 + (6 - 2)] - 3^3$

49. $4 \cdot [16 - (7 - 1)] \div 10$

50. $16 \div 2 - 4^2 - (-3)^2$

51. $18 \div |9 - 2^3| + (-3)$

52. $16 - 3(8 - 3)^2 \div 5$

53. $4(-8) \div [2(7 - 3)^2]$

54. $\dfrac{(-10) + (-2)}{6^2 - 30} \div |2 - 4|$

55. $16 - 4 \cdot \dfrac{3^3 - 7}{2^3 + 2} - (-2)^2$

56. $0.3(1.7 - 4.8) + (1.2)^2$

57. $(1.65 - 1.05)^2 \div 0.4 + 0.8$

58. $\dfrac{3}{8} \div \left|\dfrac{5}{6} + \dfrac{2}{3}\right|$

59. $\left(\dfrac{3}{4}\right)^2 - \left(\dfrac{1}{2}\right)^3 \div \dfrac{3}{5}$

60. Which expression is equivalent to $9 - 2^2(1 - 5)$?
a. $7^2(-4)$ **b.** $5(-4)$ **c.** $9 - 4(-4)$ **d.** $9 + 4(-4)$

61. Which expression is equivalent to $15 + 15 \div 3 - 4^2$?
a. $30 \div 3 - 16$ **b.** $15 + 5 - 16$ **c.** $15 + 5 + 16$ **d.** $15 + 15 \div (-1)^2$

1.4 Applying Concepts

62. Using the Order of Operations Agreement, describe how to simplify Exercise 52.

Place the correct symbol, $<$ or $>$, between the two numbers.

63. $(0.9)^3 \quad 1^5$

64. $(-3)^3 \quad (-2)^5$

65. $(-1.1)^2 \quad (0.9)^2$

Simplify.

66. $1^2 + 2^2 + 3^2 + 4^2$

67. $1^3 + 2^3 + 3^3 + 4^3$

68. $(-1)^3 + (-2)^3 + (-3)^3 + (-4)^3$

69. $(-2)^2 + (-4)^2 + (-6)^2 + (-8)^2$

Solve.

70. Find a rational number, r, that satisfies the condition.
  a. $r^2 < r$ **b.** $r^2 = r$ **c.** $r^2 > r$

71. **Computers** A computer can do 6,000,000 additions in 1 s. To the nearest second, how many seconds will it take the computer to do 10^8 additions?

72. The sum of two natural numbers is 41. Each of the two numbers is the square of a natural number. Find the two numbers.

Determine the ones digit when the expression is evaluated.

73. 34^{202}

74. 23^{502}

75. 27^{622}

76. Prepare a report on the Kelvin scale. Include in your report an explanation of how to convert between the Kelvin scale and the Celsius scale.

1.5 Concepts from Geometry

OBJECTIVE 1   Measures of angles

The word *geometry* comes from the Greek words for "earth" (*geo*) and "measure." The original purpose of geometry was to measure land. Today, geometry is used in many disciplines, such as physics, biology, geology, architecture, art, and astronomy.

Here are some basic geometric concepts.

A **plane** is a flat surface such as a table top that extends indefinitely. Figures that lie entirely in a plane are called **plane figures.**

Plane

Space extends in all directions. Objects in space, such as a baseball, house, or a tree, are called **solids.**

A **line** extends indefinitely in two directions in a plane. A line has no width.

A **ray** starts at a point and extends indefinitely in one direction. By placing a point on the ray at the right, we can name the ray *AB*.

A **line segment** is part of a line and has two endpoints. The line segment *AB* is designated by its two endpoints.

Lines in a plane can be parallel or intersect. **Parallel lines** never meet. The distance between parallel lines in a plane is always the same. We write $p \parallel q$ to indicate line p is parallel to line q. **Intersecting lines** cross at a point in the plane.

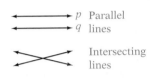

An **angle** is formed when two rays start from the same point. Rays *AB* and *AC* start from the same point *A*. The point at which the rays meet is called the **vertex** of the angle. The symbol $\angle$ is read "angle" and is used to name an angle. We can refer to the angle at the right as $\angle A$, $\angle BAC$, or $\angle x$.

Point of Interest

The Babylonians chose 360° for the measure of one full rotation, probably because they knew there were 365 days in a year and the closest number to 365 with many divisors was 360.

An angle can be measured in **degrees.** The symbol for degree is °. A ray rotated 1 revolution about its beginning point creates an angle of 360°.

The measure of an angle is symbolized by $m\angle$. For instance, $m\angle C = 40°$. Read this as "the measure of angle C is 40°."

$\frac{1}{4}$ of a revolution is $\frac{1}{4}$ of 360°, or 90°. A 90° angle is called a **right angle.** The symbol $\llcorner$ is used to represent a right angle. **Perpendicular lines** are intersecting lines that form right angles. We write $p \perp q$ to indicate line p is perpendicular to line q.

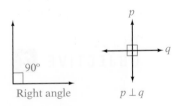

Complementary angles are two angles whose sum is 90°.

$$m\angle A + m\angle B = 35° + 55° = 90°$$

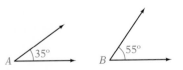

$\angle A$ and $\angle B$ are complementary angles.

$\frac{1}{2}$ of a revolution is $\frac{1}{2}$ of 360°, or 180°. A 180° angle is called a **straight angle.**

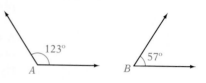

180°

Straight angle

Supplementary angles are two angles whose sum is 180°.

$$m\angle A + m\angle B = 123° + 57° = 180°$$

$\angle A$ and $\angle B$ are supplementary angles.

123°

A

57°

B

EXAMPLE 1   Find the complement of 39°.

Solution   To find the complement of 39°, subtract 39° from 90°.

$$90° - 39° = 51°$$

51° is the complement of 39°.

PROBLEM 1   Find the complement of 87°.

Solution   See page S3.

EXAMPLE 2   Find the supplement of 122°.

Solution   To find the supplement of 122°, subtract 122° from 180°.

$$180° - 122° = 58°$$

58° is the complement of 122°.

PROBLEM 2   Find the supplement of 87°.

Solution   See page S3.

EXAMPLE 3   For the figure at the right, find $m\angle AOB$.

Solution $m\angle AOB$ is the difference between $m\angle AOC$ and $m\angle BOC$.

$$m\angle AOB = 95° - 62° = 33°$$

$$m\angle AOB = 33°$$

A   B

95°

62°

O   C

PROBLEM 3   For the figure at the right, find $m\angle x$.

Solution   See page S3.

x

95°

34°

OBJECTIVE **2**   **Perimeter problems**

Perimeter is the distance around a plane figure. Perimeter is used in buying fencing for a yard, wood for the frame of a painting, and rain gutters around a house. The perimeter of a plane figure is the sum of the lengths of the sides of the figure. Formulas for four common geometric figures are given below.

A **triangle** is a three-sided plane figure.

Perimeter = side 1 + side 2 + side 3

C

A   B

An **isosceles triangle** has two sides of the same length. An **equilateral triangle** has all three sides the same length.

A **parallelogram** is a four-sided plane figure with opposite sides parallel.

Parallelogram

A **rectangle** is a parallelogram that has four right angles.

Width

Length

$$\text{Perimeter} = 2 \cdot \textbf{length} + 2 \cdot \textbf{width}$$

A **square** is a rectangle with four equal sides.

$$\text{Perimeter} = 4 \cdot \textbf{side}$$

Side

A **circle** is a plane figure in which all points are the same distance from point O, the **center of the circle.** The **diameter** of a circle is a line segment across the circle passing through the center. AB is a diameter of the circle at the right. The **radius** of a circle is a line segment from the center of the circle to a point on the circle. OC is a radius of the circle at the right. The perimeter of a circle is called its **circumference.**

$$\textbf{Diameter} = 2 \cdot \textbf{radius} \qquad \text{or} \qquad \textbf{Radius} = \frac{1}{2} \cdot \textbf{diameter}$$

$$\textbf{Circumference} = 2 \cdot \pi \cdot \textbf{radius} \qquad \text{or} \qquad \textbf{Circumference} = \pi \cdot \textbf{diameter},$$

where $\pi \approx 3.14$ or $\frac{22}{7}$.

The diameter of a circle is 25 cm. Find the radius of the circle.

$$\text{Radius} = \frac{1}{2} \cdot \text{diameter}$$
$$= \frac{1}{2} \cdot 25 = 12.5$$

The radius is 12.5 cm.

EXAMPLE 4   Find the perimeter of a rectangle with a width of 6 ft and a length of 18 feet.

Solution   Perimeter $= 2 \cdot \text{length} + 2 \cdot \text{width}$
$= 2 \cdot 18 \text{ ft} + 2 \cdot 6 \text{ ft}$
$= 36 \text{ ft} + 12 \text{ ft} = 48 \text{ ft}$

PROBLEM 4   Find the perimeter of a square that has a side of length 4.2 m.

Solution   See page S3.

EXAMPLE 5 Find the circumference of a circle with a radius of 23 cm. Use 3.14 for π.

Solution Circumference = $2 \cdot \pi \cdot$ radius

$\approx 2 \cdot 3.14 \cdot 23$ cm

$= 144.44$ cm

PROBLEM 5 Find the circumference of a circle with a diameter of 5 in. Use 3.14 for π.

Solution See page S3.

EXAMPLE 6 A chain-link fence costs \$4.37 per foot. How much will it cost to fence a rectangular playground that is 108 ft wide and 195 ft long?

Strategy To find the cost of the fence:

▶ Find the perimeter of the playground.

▶ Multiply the perimeter by the per-foot cost of the fencing.

Solution Perimeter = $2 \cdot$ length + $2 \cdot$ width

$= 2 \cdot 195$ ft + $2 \cdot 108$ ft

$= 390$ ft + 216 ft = 606 ft

Cost = $606 \times \$4.37 = \$2648.22$

The cost is \$2648.22.

PROBLEM 6 A metal strip is being installed around a circular table that has a diameter of 36 in. If the per-foot cost of the metal strip is \$3.21, find the cost for the metal strip. Use 3.14 for π. Round to the nearest cent.

Solution See page S3.

OBJECTIVE ❸ **Area problems**

Area is a measure of the amount of surface in a region. Area is used to describe the size of a rug, a farm, a house, or a national park.

Area is measured in square units.

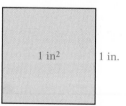

A square that is 1 in. on each side has an area of 1 square inch, which is written 1 in².

A square that is 1 cm on each side has an area of 1 square centimeter, which is written 1 cm².

Areas of common geometric figures are given by the following formulas.

Rectangle

Area = **length · width**

$= 3$ cm $\cdot 2$ cm

$= 6$ cm²

Square

$$\text{Area} = \text{side} \cdot \text{side}$$
$$= 2 \text{ cm} \cdot 2 \text{ cm}$$
$$= 4 \text{ cm}^2$$

Parallelogram

The **base of a parallelogram** is one of the parallel sides. The **height of a parallelogram** is the distance between the base and the opposite parallel side. It is perpendicular to the base.

$$\text{Area} = \text{base} \cdot \text{height}$$
$$= 5 \text{ ft} \cdot 4 \text{ ft}$$
$$= 20 \text{ ft}^2$$

Circle

$$\text{Area} = \pi(\text{radius})^2$$
$$\approx 3.14(4 \text{ in.})^2 = 50.24 \text{ in}^2$$

Triangle

For the triangle at the right, the **base of the triangle** is AB; the **height of the triangle** is CD. Note that the height is perpendicular to the base.

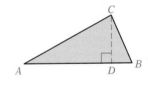

$$\text{Area} = \frac{1}{2} \cdot \text{base} \cdot \text{height}$$

$$= \frac{1}{2} \cdot 5 \text{ in.} \cdot 4 \text{ in.} = 10 \text{ in}^2$$

Take Note

The height of a triangle is always perpendicular to the base. Sometimes it is necessary to extend the base so that a perpendicular line segment can be drawn. The extension is *not* part of the base.

EXAMPLE 7   Find the area of a rectangle whose length is 8 in. and whose width is 6 in.

Solution   Area = length × width
$$= 8 \text{ in.} \times 6 \text{ in.} = 48 \text{ in}^2$$

PROBLEM 7   Find the area of a triangle whose base is 5 ft and whose height is 3 ft.

Solution   See page S3.

EXAMPLE 8   Find the area of a circle whose diameter is 5 cm. Use 3.14 for π.

Solution   Radius $= \frac{1}{2} \cdot$ diameter

$$= \frac{1}{2} \cdot 5 \text{ cm} = 2.5 \text{ cm}$$

Area $= \pi \cdot (\text{radius})^2$
$$\approx 3.14(2.5 \text{ cm})^2 = 19.625 \text{ cm}^2$$

PROBLEM 8   Find the area of a circle whose radius is 6 in. Use 3.14 for π.

Solution   See page S3.

EXAMPLE 9   Find the area of the parallelogram shown at the right.

Solution   Area $=$ base $\cdot$ height
$$= 12 \text{ ft} \times 7 \text{ ft} = 84 \text{ ft}^2$$

PROBLEM 9   Find the area of the parallelogram shown at the right.

Solution   See page S3.

EXAMPLE 10   To conserve water during a drought, a city's water department is offering homeowners a rebate on their water bill of $1.27 per square foot of lawn that is removed from a yard and replaced with drought-resistant plants. What rebate would a homeowner receive who replaced a rectangular lawn area that is 15 ft wide and 25 ft long?

Strategy   To find the amount of the rebate:

▶ Find the area of the replaced lawn.

▶ Multiply the area by the per-square-foot rebate.

Solution   Area $=$ length $\times$ width
$$= 25 \text{ ft} \times 15 \text{ ft} = 375 \text{ ft}^2$$

Rebate $= 375 \times \$1.27 = \$476.25$

The rebate is $476.25.

PROBLEM 10   An interior designer is choosing between two hallway rugs. A nylon rug costs $1.25 per square foot, and a wool rug costs $1.93 per square foot. If the dimensions of the carpet are to be 4 ft by 15 ft, how much more expensive than the nylon rug will the wool rug be?

Solution   See page S3.

1.5   Concept Review

Determine whether the statement is always true, sometimes true, or never true.

1. A ray is designated by its two endpoints.

2. Perpendicular lines form four 90° angles.

3. The sum of the measures of two straight angles is 360°.

4. Every square is a parallelogram.

5. Perimeter is measured in square units.

6. A parallelogram has a base and a height.

1.5   Exercises

1   Measures of angles

1. If $\angle A$ and $\angle B$ are complementary angles, then $m\angle A + m\angle B =$ ___?___.

2. If $\angle C$ and $\angle D$ are supplementary angles, then $m\angle C + m\angle D =$ ___?___.

3. If $\angle E$ is a right angle, then $m\angle E =$ ___?___.

4. If $\angle F$ is a straight angle, then $m\angle F =$ ___?___.

5. When the time is 3 o'clock on an analog clock, is the measure of the smaller angle between the hands of the clock more than or less than 120°?

6. In one hour, the hour hand on an analog clock travels through how many degrees?

7. Find the complement of a 62° angle.

8. Find the complement of a 13° angle.

9. Find the supplement of a 48° angle.

10. Find the supplement of a 106° angle.

11. Find the complement of a 7° angle.

12. Find the complement of a 76° angle.

13. Find the supplement of an 89° angle.

14. Find the supplement of a 21° angle.

15. Angle *AOB* is a straight angle. Find $m\angle AOC$.

16. Angle *AOB* is a straight angle. Find $m\angle COB$.

17. Find $m\angle x$.

18. Find $m\angle x$.

19. Find $m\angle AOB$.

20. Find $m\angle AOB$.

21. Find $m\angle AOC$.

22. Find $m\angle AOC$.

23. Find $m\angle A$.

24. Find $m\angle A$.

2   Perimeter problems

25. A plane figure that has three sides is called a ___?___.

26. The name of a parallelogram in which all angles are the same measure is a ___?___.

27. Find the perimeter of a triangle with sides 2.51 cm, 4.08 cm, and 3.12 cm.

28. Find the perimeter of a triangle with sides 4 ft 5 in., 5 ft 3 in., and 6 ft 11 in.

29. Find the perimeter of a rectangle whose length is 4 ft 8 in. and whose width is 2 ft 5 in.

30. Find the perimeter of a rectangle whose dimensions are 5 m by 8 m.

31. Find the perimeter of a square whose side is 13 in.

32. Find the perimeter of a square whose side is 34 cm.

33. Find the circumference of a circle whose radius is 21 cm. Use 3.14 for π.

34. Find the circumference of a circle whose radius is 3.4 m. Use 3.14 for π.

35. Find the circumference of a circle whose diameter is 1.2 m. Use 3.14 for π.

36. Find the circumference of a circle whose diameter is 15 in. Use 3.14 for π.

37. Art The wood framing for an art canvas costs $4.81 per foot. How much would the wood framing cost for a rectangular picture that measures 3 ft by 5 ft?

38. Ceramics A decorative mosaic tile is being installed on the border of a square wall behind a stove. If one side of the square measures 5 ft and the cost of installing the mosaic tile is $4.86 per foot, find the cost to install the decorative border.

39. Sewing To prevent fraying, a binding is attached to the outside of a circular rug whose radius is 3 ft. If the binding costs $1.05 per foot, find the cost of the binding. Use 3.14 for π.

40. Landscaping A drip irrigation system is installed around a circular flower garden that is 4 ft in diameter. If the irrigation system costs $2.46 per foot, find the cost to place the irrigation system around the flower garden. Use 3.14 for π.

41. In the pattern at the right, the length of one side of a square is 1 unit. If the pattern were to be continued, what would the perimeter of the eighth figure in the pattern be?

42. Which has the greater perimeter, a square whose side is 1 ft or a rectangle that has a length of 2 in. and a width of 1 in.?

3   Area problems

43. The formula for the area of a rectangle is Area = length · ___?___.

44. The formula for the area of a parallelogram is Area = base · ___?___.

45. Find the area of a rectangle that measures 4 ft by 8 ft.

46. Find the area of a rectangle that measures 3.4 cm by 5.6 cm.

47. Find the area of a parallelogram whose height is 14 cm and whose base is 27 cm.

48. Find the area of a parallelogram whose height is 7 ft and whose base is 18 ft.

49. Find the area of a circle whose radius is 4 in. Use 3.14 for π.

50. Find the area of a circle whose radius is 8.2 m. Use 3.14 for π.

51. Find the area of a square whose side measures 4.1 m.

52. Find the area of a square whose side measures 5 yd.

53. Find the area of a triangle whose height is 7 cm and whose base is 15 cm.

54. Find the area of a triangle whose height is 8 in. and whose base is 13 in.

55. Find the area of a circle whose diameter is 17 in. Use 3.14 for π.

56. Find the area of a circle whose diameter is 3.6 m. Use 3.14 for π.

57. Landscaping A landscape architect recommends 0.1 gallon of water per day for each square foot of lawn. How many gallons of water should be used per day on a rectangular lawn area that is 33 ft by 42 ft?

58. Interior Design One side of a square room measures 18 ft. How many square yards of carpet are necessary to carpet the room? *Hint*: $1 \text{ yd}^2 = 9 \text{ ft}^2$.

59. Carpentry A circular, inlaid-wood design for a dining table cost $35 per square foot to build. If the radius of the design is 15 in., find the cost to build the design. Use 3.14 for π. Round to the nearest dollar. *Hint*: $144 \text{ in}^2 = 1 \text{ ft}^2$.

60. Interior Design A circular stained glass window cost $48 per square foot to build. If the diameter of the window is 4 ft, find the cost to build the window. Round to the nearest dollar.

61. Construction The cost of plastering the walls of a rectangular room that is 18 ft long, 14 ft wide, and 8 ft high is $2.56 per square foot. If 125 ft² is not plastered because of doors and windows, find the cost to plaster the room.

62. Interior Design A room is 12 ft long, 9 ft wide, and 9 ft high. Two adjacent walls of the rooms are going to be wallpapered using wallpaper that costs $15.25 per square yard. What is the cost to wallpaper the two walls? *Hint*: $1 \text{ yd}^2 = 9 \text{ ft}^2$.

63. If both the length and the width of a rectangle are doubled, how many times larger is the area of the resulting rectangle?

64. A rectangle has a perimeter of 20 units. What dimensions will result in a rectangle with the greatest possible area? Consider only whole-number dimensions.

1.5   Applying Concepts

65. Find the perimeter and area of the figure. Use 3.14 for π.

66. Find the perimeter and area of the figure.

67. Find the outside perimeter and area of the shaded portion of the figure.

68. Find the area of the shaded portion of the figure.

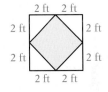

69. A trapezoid is a four-sided plane figure with two parallel sides. The area of a trapezoid is given by Area $= \frac{1}{2} \cdot$ height(base 1 + base 2). See the figure at the right.

    a. Find the area of a trapezoid for which base 1 is 5 in., base 2 is 8 in., and the height is 6 in.

    b. Find the area of the trapezoid shown at the right.

70. Draw parallelogram *ABCD* or one similar to it and then cut it out. Cut along the dotted line to form the shaded triangle. Slide the triangle so that the slanted side corresponds to the slanted side of the parallelogram as shown. Explain how this demonstrates that the area of a parallelogram is the product of the base and the height.

Focus on Problem Solving

Inductive Reasoning   Suppose you take 9 credit hours each semester. The total number of credit hours you have taken at the end of each semester can be described in a list of numbers.

$$9, 18, 27, 36, 45, 54, 63, \ldots$$

The list of numbers that indicates the total credit hours is an ordered list of numbers, called a **sequence.** Each number in a sequence is called a **term** of the sequence. The list is ordered because the position of a number in the list indicates the semester in which that number of credit hours has been taken. For example, the 7th term of the sequence is 63, and a total of 63 credit hours have been taken after the 7th semester.

Assuming the pattern is continued, find the next three numbers in the pattern

$$-6, -10, -14, -18, \ldots$$

This list of numbers is a sequence. The first step in solving this problem is to observe the pattern in the list of numbers. In this case, each number in the list is 4 less than the previous number. The next three numbers are $-22, -26, -30$.

This process of discovering the pattern in a list of numbers is inductive reasoning. **Inductive reasoning** involves making generalizations from specific examples; in other words, we reach a conclusion by making observations about particular facts or cases.

Try the following exercises. Each exercise requires inductive reasoning.

Name the next two terms in the sequence.

1. 1, 3, 5, 7, 1, 3, 5, 7, 1, …   **2.** 1, 4, 2, 5, 3, 6, 4, …

3. 1, 2, 4, 7, 11, 16, …   **4.** A, B, C, G, H, I, M, …

Draw the next shape in the sequence.

5.

6. |• ||• ||•• • |||•• • |||•• • •

Solve.

7. Convert $\frac{1}{11}, \frac{2}{11}, \frac{3}{11}, \frac{4}{11},$ and $\frac{5}{11}$ to decimals. Then use the pattern you observe to convert $\frac{6}{11}, \frac{7}{11},$ and $\frac{9}{11}$ to decimals.

8. Convert $\frac{1}{33}, \frac{2}{33}, \frac{4}{33}, \frac{5}{33},$ and $\frac{7}{33}$ to decimals. Then use the pattern you observe to convert $\frac{8}{33}, \frac{13}{33},$ and $\frac{19}{33}$ to decimals.

Projects & Group Activities

Calculators Does your calculator use the Order of Operations Agreement? To find out, try this problem:

$$2 + 4 \cdot 7$$

If your answer is 30, then the calculator uses the Order of Operations Agreement. If your answer is 42, it does not use that agreement.

Even if your calculator does not use the Order of Operations Agreement, you can still correctly evaluate numerical expressions. The parentheses keys, $\boxed{(}$ and $\boxed{)}$, are used for this purpose.

Remember that $2 + 4 \cdot 7$ means $2 + (4 \cdot 7)$ because the multiplication must be completed before the addition. To evaluate this expression, enter the following:

Enter: 2 $\boxed{+}$ $\boxed{(}$ 4 $\boxed{\times}$ 7 $\boxed{)}$ $\boxed{=}$

Display: 2   2 $\boxed{(}$ 4   4   7   28   30

When using your calculator to evaluate numerical expressions, insert parentheses around multiplications or divisions. This has the effect of forcing the calculator to do the operations in the order you want rather than in the order the calculator wants.

Evaluate.

   1. $3 \cdot (15 - 2 \cdot 3) - 36 \div 3$ **2.** $4 \cdot 2^2 - (12 + 24 \div 6) - 5$

   3. $16 \div 4 \cdot 3 + (3 \cdot 4 - 5) + 2$ **4.** $15 \cdot 3 \div 9 + (2 \cdot 6 - 3) + 4$

Using your calculator to simplify numerical expressions sometimes requires use of the $\boxed{+/-}$ key or, on some calculators, the negative key, which is frequently shown as $\boxed{(-)}$. These keys change the sign of the number currently in the display. To enter -4:

- For those calculators with $\boxed{+/-}$, press 4 and then $\boxed{+/-}$.
- For those calculators with $\boxed{(-)}$, press $\boxed{(-)}$ and then 4.

Here are the keystrokes for evaluating the expression $3(-4) - (-5)$.

      Calculators with $\boxed{+/-}$ key: 3 $\boxed{\times}$ 4 $\boxed{+/-}$ $\boxed{-}$ 5 $\boxed{+/-}$ $\boxed{=}$

      Calculators with $\boxed{(-)}$ key: 3 $\boxed{\times}$ $\boxed{(-)}$ 4 $\boxed{-}$ $\boxed{(-)}$ 5 $\boxed{=}$

This example illustrates that calculators make a distinction between negative and minus. To perform the operation $3 - (-3)$, you cannot enter 3 $\boxed{-}$ $\boxed{-}$ 3. This would result in 0, which is not the correct answer. You must enter

        3 $\boxed{-}$ 3 $\boxed{+/-}$ $\boxed{=}$ or   3 $\boxed{-}$ $\boxed{(-)}$ 3 $\boxed{=}$

Use a calculator to evaluate each of the following expressions.

   5. $-16 \div 2$ **6.** $3(-8)$ **7.** $47 - (-9)$

   8. $-50 - (-14)$ **9.** $4 - (-3)^2$ **10.** $-8 + (-6)^2 - 7$

Chapter 1 Summary

Key Words	*Examples*
A **set** is a collection of objects. The objects in the set are called the **elements** of the set. The **roster method** of writing sets encloses a list of the elements in braces. [1.1.1, p. 2]*	The set of even natural numbers less than 10 is written $A = \{2, 4, 6, 8\}$. The elements in this set are the numbers 2, 4, 6, and 8.
The set of **natural numbers** is $\{1, 2, 3, 4, 5, 6, 7, \ldots\}$. The set of **integers** is $\{\ldots, -4, -3, -2, -1, 0, 1, 2, 3, 4, \ldots\}$. [1.1.1, pp. 2–3]	
A number a **is less than** another number b, written $a < b$, if a is to the left of b on the number line. A number a **is greater than** another number b, written $a > b$, if a is to the right of b on the number line. The symbol $\leq$ means **is less than or equal to.** The symbol $\geq$ means **is greater than or equal to.** [1.1.1, pp. 3–4]	$-9 < 7$ $4 > -5$
Two numbers that are the same distance from zero on the number line but on opposite sides of zero are **opposite numbers,** or **opposites.** The opposite of a number is also called its **additive inverse.** [1.1.2, p. 4]	5 and -5 are opposites.
The **absolute value** of a number is its distance from zero on the number line. The absolute value of a number is positive or zero. [1.1.2, p. 5]	$\lvert-12\rvert = 12$ $-\lvert7\rvert = -7$
A **rational number** is a number that can be written in the form $\frac{a}{b}$, where a and b are integers and $b \neq 0$. A rational number written in this form is commonly called a **fraction.** [1.3.1, p. 24]	$\frac{3}{8}, \frac{-9}{11}$, and $\frac{4}{1}$ are rational numbers.
An **irrational number** is a number that has a decimal representation that never terminates or repeats. [1.3.1, p. 25]	$\pi, \sqrt{2}$, and $2.17117111711117\ldots$ are irrational numbers.
The rational numbers and the irrational numbers taken together are called the **real numbers.** [1.3.1, p. 25]	$\frac{3}{8}, \frac{-9}{11}, \frac{4}{1}, \pi, \sqrt{2}$, and $2.17117111711117\ldots$ are real numbers.
Percent means "parts of 100." [1.3.4, p. 29]	63% means 63 of 100 equal parts.
An expression of the form a^n is in **exponential form,** where a is the **base** and n is the **exponent.** [1.4.1, p. 38]	6^3 is an exponential expression in which 6 is the base and 3 is the exponent.

*The numbers in brackets refer to the objective where the Key Word or Essential Rule or Procedure is first introduced. For example, the reference [1.1.1] stands for Chapter 1, Section 1, Objective 1. This notation will be used in all Chapter Summaries throughout the text.

A **plane** is a flat surface that extends indefinitely. A **line** extends indefinitely in two directions in a plane. A **ray** starts at a point and extends indefinitely in one direction. A **line segment** is part of a line and has two endpoints. [1.5.1, pp. 44–45]

Lines in a plane can be parallel or intersect. **Parallel lines** never meet. The distance between parallel lines in a plane is always the same. **Intersecting lines** cross at a point in the plane. [1.5.1, p. 45]

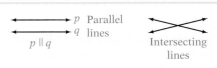

An **angle** is formed when two rays start from the same point. The point at which the rays meet is called the **vertex** of the angle. An angle can be measured in **degrees.** The measure of an angle is symbolized by $m\angle$. [1.5.1, p. 45]

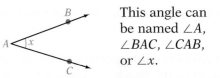

This angle can be named $\angle A$, $\angle BAC$, $\angle CAB$, or $\angle x$.

A **right angle** has a measure of 90°. **Perpendicular lines** are intersecting lines that form right angles. **Complementary angles** are two angles whose sum is 90°. A **straight angle** has a measure of 180°. **Supplementary angles** are two angles whose sum is 180°. [1.5.1, pp. 45–46]

$m\angle A + m\angle B = 90°$

$\angle A$ and $\angle B$ are complementary angles.

$m\angle C + m\angle D = 180°$

$\angle C$ and $\angle D$ are supplementary angles.

A **circle** is a plane figure in which all points are the same distance from point O, the **center** of the circle. The **diameter** of a circle is a line segment across the circle passing through the center. The **radius** of a circle is a line segment from the center of the circle to a point on the circle. The perimeter of a circle is called its **circumference**. [1.5.2, p. 47]

Essential Rules and Procedures

To add two integers with the same sign, add the absolute values of the numbers. Then attach the sign of the addends. [1.2.1, p. 11]

$9 + 3 = 12$
$-9 + (-3) = -12$

To add two integers with different signs, find the absolute value of each number. Then subtract the smaller of these absolute values from the larger one. Attach the sign of the number with the greater absolute value.   [1.2.1, p. 11]

$9 + (-3) = 6$
$-9 + 3 = -6$

To subtract one integer from another, add the opposite of the second integer to the first integer. [1.2.2, pp. 11–12]	$6 - 11 = 6 + (-11) = -5$ $-2 - (-8) = -2 + 8 = 6$
To multiply two integers with the same sign, multiply the absolute values of the numbers. The product is positive. [1.2.3, p. 13]	$3(5) = 15$ $(-3)(-5) = 15$
To multiply two integers with different signs, multiply the absolute values of the numbers. The product is negative. [1.2.3, p. 13]	$-3(5) = -15$ $3(-5) = -15$
To divide two integers with the same sign, divide the absolute values of the numbers. The quotient is positive. [1.2.4, p. 14]	$14 \div 2 = 7$ $-14 \div (-2) = 7$
To divide two integers with different signs, divide the absolute values of the numbers. The quotient is negative. [1.2.4, p. 14]	$14 \div (-2) = -7$ $-14 \div 2 = -7$

Zero and One in Division   [1.2.4, p. 14]

$\dfrac{0}{a} = 0, a \neq 0$ $\qquad\qquad\qquad\qquad\qquad\qquad\qquad$ $\dfrac{0}{3} = 0$

Division by zero is undefined. $\qquad\qquad\qquad\qquad$ $\dfrac{9}{0}$ is undefined.

$\dfrac{a}{a} = 1, a \neq 0$ $\qquad\qquad\qquad\qquad\qquad\qquad\qquad$ $\dfrac{-2}{-2} = 1$

$\dfrac{a}{1} = a$ $\qquad\qquad\qquad\qquad\qquad\qquad\qquad\qquad$ $\dfrac{-6}{1} = -6$

To convert a percent to a decimal, remove the percent sign and multiply by 0.01. [1.3.4, p. 29]	$85\% = 85(0.01) = 0.85$
To convert a percent to a fraction, remove the percent sign and multiply by $\dfrac{1}{100}$. [1.3.4, p. 29]	$25\% = 25 \cdot \dfrac{1}{100} = \dfrac{25}{100} = \dfrac{1}{4}$
To convert a decimal or a fraction to a percent, multiply by 100%. [1.3.4, p. 30]	$0.5 = 0.5(100\%) = 50\%$ $\dfrac{3}{8} = \dfrac{3}{8} \cdot 100\% = \dfrac{300}{8}\% = 37.5\%$

Order of Operations Agreement   [1.4.2, p. 40]

$16 \div (-2)^3 + (7 - 12)$

Step 1 Perform operations inside grouping symbols.
Step 2 Simplify exponential expressions.
Step 3 Do multiplication and division as they occur from left to right.
Step 4 Do addition and subtraction as they occur from left to right.

$\begin{aligned} &= 16 \div (-2)^3 + (-5) \\ &= 16 \div (-8) + (-5) \\ &= -2 + (-5) \\ &= -7 \end{aligned}$

Diameter $= 2 \cdot$ radius $\qquad$ **Radius** $= \dfrac{1}{2} \cdot$ diameter
[1.5.2, p. 47]

Find the diameter of a circle whose radius is 10 in.

$\begin{aligned} \text{Diameter} &= 2 \cdot \text{radius} \\ &= 2(10 \text{ in.}) = 20 \text{ in.} \end{aligned}$

Perimeter is the distance around a plane figure. [1.5.2, pp. 46–47]

Triangle:	Perimeter = side 1 + side 2 + side 3
Rectangle:	Perimeter = 2 · length + 2 · width
Square:	Perimeter = 4 · side
Circle:	Circumference = 2 · π · radius
	Circumference = π · diameter

Find the perimeter of a rectangle whose width is 12 m and whose length is 15 m.

Perimeter = 2 · 15 m + 2 · 12 m = 54 m

Find the circumference of a circle whose radius is 3 in. Use 3.14 for π.

Circumference = 2 · π · 3 in. ≈ 18.84 in.

Area is a measure of the amount of surface in a region. [1.5.3, pp. 48–49]

Triangle:	Area = $\frac{1}{2}$ · base · height
Rectangle:	Area = length · width
Square:	Area = side · side
Parallelogram:	Area = base · height
Circle:	Area = π(radius)^2

Find the area of a triangle whose base is 13 m and whose height is 11 m.

Area = $\frac{1}{2}$ · 13 m · 11 m = 71.5 m^2

Find the area of a circle whose radius is 9 cm.

Area = π · (9 cm)^2 ≈ 254.34 cm^2

Chapter 1 Review Exercises

1. Use the roster method to write the set of natural numbers less than 7.

2. Write $\frac{5}{8}$ as a percent.

3. Evaluate: $-|-4|$

4. Subtract: $16 - (-30) - 42$

5. Find the area of a triangle whose base is 4 cm and whose height is 9 cm.

6. Write $\frac{7}{9}$ as a decimal. Place a bar over the repeating digits of the decimal.

7. Simplify: $(6.02)(-0.89)$

8. Simplify: $\dfrac{-10 + 2}{2 + (-4)} \div 2 + 6$

9. Find the opposite of -4.

10. Subtract: $16 - 30$

11. Write 0.672 as a percent.

12. Write $79\frac{1}{2}\%$ as a fraction.

13. Divide: $-72 \div 8$

14. Write $\frac{17}{20}$ as a decimal.

15. Divide: $\dfrac{5}{12} \div \left(-\dfrac{5}{6}\right)$

16. Simplify: $3^2 - 4 + 20 \div 5$

17. Find $m\angle AOB$ for the figure at the right.

18. Add: $-22 + 14 + (-8)$

19. Multiply: $(-5)(-6)(3)$

20. Subtract: $6.039 - 12.92$

21. Given $A = \{-5, -3, 0\}$, which elements of set A are less than or equal to -3?

22. Write 7% as a decimal.

23. Evaluate: $\dfrac{3}{4} \cdot (4)^2$

24. Place the correct symbol, $<$ or $>$, between the two numbers.

$$-2 \qquad -40$$

25. Add: $13 + (-16)$

26. Find the complement of a 56° angle.

27. Add: $-\dfrac{2}{5} + \dfrac{7}{15}$

28. Evaluate: $(-3^3) \cdot 2^2$

29. Write $2\dfrac{7}{9}$ as a percent. Round to the nearest tenth of a percent.

30. Write 240% as a decimal.

31. Find the supplement of a 28° angle.

32. Divide: $96 \div (-12)$

33. Find the area of a circle whose diameter is 6 m. Use 3.14 for π.

34. Simplify: $2^3 \div 4 - 2(2 - 7)$

35. Evaluate: $|-3|$

36. Write $2\dfrac{8}{9}$ as a percent. Write the remainder in fractional form.

37. Given $C = \{-12, -8, -1, 7\}$, find

    a. the opposite of each element of set C.
    b. the absolute value of each element of set C.

38. Write $\dfrac{7}{11}$ as a decimal. Place a bar over the repeating digits of the decimal.

39. Divide: $0.2654 \div (-0.023)$
Round to the nearest tenth.

40. Simplify: $(7 - 2)^2 - 5 - 3 \cdot 4$

41. Add: $-12 + 8 + (-4)$

42. Add: $-\dfrac{5}{8} + \dfrac{1}{6}$

43. Given $D = \{-24, -17, -9, 0, 4\}$, which elements of set D are greater than -19?

44. Write 0.002 as a percent.

45. Evaluate: $-4^2 \cdot \left(\dfrac{1}{2}\right)^2$

46. Add: $-1.329 + 4.89$

47. Evaluate: $-|17|$

48. Subtract: $-5 - 22 - (-13) - 19 - (-6)$

49. Multiply: $\left(\dfrac{1}{3}\right)\left(-\dfrac{4}{5}\right)\left(\dfrac{3}{8}\right)$

50. Place the correct symbol, $<$ or $>$, between the two numbers.

$$-43 \quad -34$$

51. Find the perimeter of a rectangle whose length is 12 in. and whose width is 10 in.

52. Evaluate $(-2)^3 \cdot 4^2$.

53. Write 0.075 as a percent.

54. Write $\dfrac{19}{35}$ as a percent. Write the remainder in fractional form.

55. Add: $14 + (-18) + 6 + (-20)$

56. Multiply: $-4(-8)(12)(0)$

57. Simplify: $2^3 - 7 + 16 \div (-3 + 5)$

58. Simplify: $\dfrac{3}{4} + \dfrac{1}{2} - \dfrac{3}{8}$

59. Divide: $-128 \div (-8)$

60. Place the correct symbol, $<$ or $>$, between the two numbers.

$$-57 \quad 28$$

61. Evaluate: $\left(-\dfrac{1}{3}\right)^3 \cdot 9^2$

62. Add: $-7 + (-3) + (-12) + 16$

63. Multiply: $5(-2)(10)(-3)$

64. Use the roster method to write the set of negative integers greater than -4.

65. **Landscaping** A landscape company is proposing to replace a rectangular flower bed that measures 8 ft by 12 ft with sod that costs \$2.51 per square foot. Find the cost to replace the flower bed with the sod.

66. **Temperature** Find the temperature after a rise of 14°C from −6°C.

67. **Temperature** The daily low temperatures, in degrees Celsius, for a three-day period were recorded as follows: −8°, 7°, −5°. Find the average low temperature for the three-day period.

68. **Temperature** Use the table to find the difference between the record high temperature and the record low temperature for January in Bismarck, North Dakota.

Bismarck, North Dakota

	Jan	Feb	Mar	Apr	May	Jun	Jul	Aug	Sep	Oct	Nov	Dec
Record High	62°F (1981)	69°F (1992)	80°F (1967)	93°F (1992)	96°F (1980)	107°F (1988)	109°F (1973)	107°F (1973)	105°F (1959)	95°F (1963)	75°F (1978)	65°F (1979)
Record Low	−44°F (1950)	−43°F (1994)	−28°F (1995)	−12°F (1975)	15°F (1967)	30°F (1969)	35°F (1971)	33°F (1988)	11°F (1974)	−10°F (1991)	−30°F (1985)	−40°F (1983)

Source: www.weather.com

69. Temperature Find the temperature after a rise of 7°C from −13°C.

70. Temperature The temperature on the surface of the planet Venus is 480°C. The temperature on the surface of the planet Pluto is −234°C. Find the difference between the surface temperatures on Venus and Pluto.

Chapter 1 Test

▶ View the Chapter Test Videos for fully worked-out solutions to any exercise.

1. Write 55% as a fraction.

2. Given $B = \{-8, -6, -4, -2\}$, which elements of set B are less than −5?

3. Find $m\angle x$ for the figure at the right.

4. Write $\dfrac{3}{20}$ as a decimal.

5. Multiply: $\dfrac{3}{4}\left(-\dfrac{2}{21}\right)$

6. Divide: $-75 \div 5$

7. Evaluate: $\left(-\dfrac{2}{3}\right)^3 \cdot 3^2$

8. Add: $-7 + (-3) + 12$

9. Use the roster method to write the set of positive integers less than or equal to 6.

10. Write 1.59 as a percent.

11. Evaluate: $|-29|$

12. Place the correct symbol, < or >, between the two numbers.

$$-47 \quad -68$$

13. Subtract: $-\dfrac{4}{9} - \dfrac{5}{6}$

14. Find the area of a parallelogram whose base is 10 cm and whose height is 9 cm.

15. Simplify: $8 + \dfrac{12 - 4}{3^2 - 1} - 6$

16. Divide: $-\dfrac{5}{8} \div \left(-\dfrac{3}{4}\right)$

17. Write $\dfrac{3}{13}$ as a percent. Round to the nearest tenth of a percent.

18. Write 6.2% as a decimal.

19. Subtract: $13 - (-5) - 4$

20. Write $\dfrac{13}{30}$ as a decimal. Place a bar over the repeating digits of the decimal.

21. Multiply: $(-0.9)(2.7)$

22. Find the complement of a 28° angle.

23. Evaluate: $2^2 \cdot (-4)^2 \cdot 10$

24. Evaluate: $-|-34|$

25. Find the circumference of a circle whose diameter is 27 in. Use 3.14 for π.

26. Given $A = \{-17, -6, 5, 9\}$, find

    a. the opposite of each element of set A.
    b. the absolute value of each element of set A.

27. Write $\frac{16}{23}$ as a percent. Write the remainder in fractional form.

28. Add: $-18.354 + 6.97$

29. Multiply: $-4(8)(-5)$

30. Simplify: $9(-4) \div [2(8 - 5)^2]$

31. **Temperature** Find the temperature after a rise of 12°C from −8°C.

32. **Temperature** Use the table to find the average of the record low temperatures in Fairbanks, Alaska, for the first four months of the year.

Fairbanks, Alaska

	Jan	Feb	Mar	Apr	May	Jun	Jul	Aug	Sep	Oct	Nov	Dec
Record High	50°F (1981)	47°F (1987)	56°F (1994)	74°F (1960)	89°F (1960)	96°F (1969)	94°F (1975)	93°F (1994)	84°F (1957)	65°F (1969)	49°F (1997)	44°F (1985)
Record Low	−61°F (1969)	−58°F (1993)	−49°F (1956)	−24°F (1986)	−1°F (1964)	30°F (1950)	35°F (1959)	27°F (1987)	3°F (1992)	−27°F (1975)	−46°F (1990)	−62°F (1961)

Source: www.weather.com

33. **Recreation** The recreation department for a city is enclosing a rectangular playground that measures 150 ft by 200 ft with new fencing that costs $6.52 per foot. Find the cost of the new fencing.

2 Variable Expressions

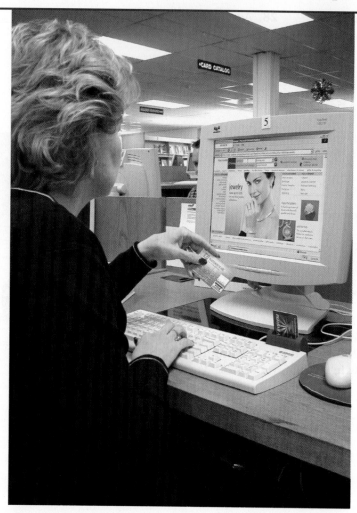

With the rise of online catalogs and Internet stores, shoppers are turning to their computers to make purchases. A recent survey by Consumer Internet Barometer found that approximately 25 percent of people who had purchased a product online were extremely satisfied with their experience. In **Exercise 114 on page 95,** you are asked to use variables to express the number of people who were extremely satisfied with their online purchase in terms of the number of online buyers. This is called a variable expression.

Online Study Center DVD SSM

Need help? For online student resources, such as section quizzes, visit the Online Study Center at www.cengage.com/math/aufmann.

Prep Test

1. Subtract: $-12 - (-15)$

2. Divide: $-36 \div (-9)$

3. Add: $-\dfrac{3}{4} + \dfrac{5}{6}$

4. What is the reciprocal of $-\dfrac{9}{4}$?

5. Divide: $\left(-\dfrac{3}{4}\right) \div \left(-\dfrac{5}{2}\right)$

6. Evaluate: -2^4

7. Evaluate: $\left(\dfrac{2}{3}\right)^3$

8. Evaluate: $3 \cdot 4^2$

9. Evaluate: $7 - 2 \cdot 3$

10. Evaluate: $5 - 7(3 - 2^2)$

2.1 Evaluating Variable Expressions

OBJECTIVE 1

Evaluate variable expressions

Point of Interest

Historical manuscripts indicate that mathematics is at least 4000 years old. Yet it was only 400 years ago that mathematicians started using variables to stand for numbers. The idea that a letter can stand for some number was a critical turning point in mathematics.

Often we discuss a quantity without knowing its exact value, such as the price of gold next month, the cost of a new automobile next year, or the tuition for next semester. In algebra, a letter of the alphabet is used to stand for a quantity that is unknown or one that can change, or *vary*. The letter is called a **variable.** An expression that contains one or more variables is called a **variable expression.**

A variable expression is shown at the right. The expression can be rewritten by writing subtraction as the addition of the opposite.

$$3x^2 - 5y + 2xy - x - 7$$

$$3x^2 + (-5y) + 2xy + (-x) + (-7)$$

Note that the expression has five addends. The **terms** of a variable expression are the addends of the expression. The expression has five terms.

5 terms

$$\underbrace{\overbrace{3x^2 \quad - 5y \quad + 2xy \quad - x}^{\text{Variable terms}} \quad \overbrace{- 7}^{\text{Constant term}}}$$

The terms $3x^2$, $-5y$, $2xy$, and $-x$ are **variable terms.**

The term -7 is a **constant term,** or simply a **constant.**

Each variable term is composed of a **numerical coefficient** and a **variable part** (the variable or variables and their exponents).

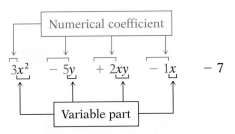

When the numerical coefficient is 1 or -1, the 1 is usually not written ($x = 1x$ and $-x = -1x$).

EXAMPLE 1	Name the variable terms of the expression $2a^2 - 5a + 7$.
Solution	$2a^2, -5a$

PROBLEM 1	Name the constant term of the expression $6n^2 + 3n - 4$.
Solution	See page S3.

Variable expressions occur naturally in science. In a physics lab, a student may discover that a weight of 1 pound will stretch a spring $\frac{1}{2}$ inch. A weight of 2 pounds will stretch the spring 1 inch. By experimenting, the student can discover that the distance the spring will stretch is found by multiplying the weight, in pounds, by $\frac{1}{2}$. By letting W represent the number of pounds attached to the spring, we can represent the distance, in inches, that the spring stretches by the variable expression $\frac{1}{2}W$.

With a weight of W pounds, the spring will stretch $\frac{1}{2} \cdot W = \frac{1}{2}W$ inches.

With a weight of 10 pounds, the spring will stretch $\frac{1}{2} \cdot 10 = 5$ inches.

With a weight of 3 pounds, the spring will stretch $\frac{1}{2} \cdot 3 = 1\frac{1}{2}$ inches.

Replacing the variable or variables in a variable expression with numbers and then simplifying the resulting numerical expression is called **evaluating the variable expression.**

EXAMPLE 2	Evaluate $ab - b^2$ when $a = 2$ and $b = -3$.	
Solution	$ab - b^2$	
	$2(-3) - (-3)^2$	• **Replace each variable in the expression with the number it represents.**
	$= 2(-3) - 9$	• **Use the Order of Operations Agreement to simplify the resulting numerical expression.**
	$= -6 - 9$	
	$= -15$	

PROBLEM 2	Evaluate $2xy + y^2$ when $x = -4$ and $y = 2$.
Solution	See page S3.

EXAMPLE 3	Evaluate $\dfrac{a^2 - b^2}{a - b}$ when $a = 3$ and $b = -4$.	
Solution	$\dfrac{a^2 - b^2}{a - b}$	
	$\dfrac{(3)^2 - (-4)^2}{3 - (-4)}$	• **Replace each variable in the expression with the number it represents.**
	$= \dfrac{9 - 16}{3 - (-4)}$	• **Use the Order of Operations Agreement to simplify the resulting numerical expression.**

$$= \frac{-7}{7}$$

$$= -1$$

PROBLEM 3   Evaluate $\dfrac{a^2 + b^2}{a + b}$ when $a = 5$ and $b = -3$.

Solution   See page S3.

EXAMPLE 4   Evaluate $x^2 - 3(x - y) - z^2$ when $x = 2$, $y = -1$, and $z = 3$.

Solution $x^2 - 3(x - y) - z^2$

$(2)^2 - 3[2 - (-1)] - (3)^2$ • **Replace each variable in the expression with the number it represents.**

$= (2)^2 - 3(3) - (3)^2$ • **Use the Order of Operations Agreement to simplify the resulting numerical expression.**

$= 4 - 3(3) - 9$

$= 4 - 9 - 9$

$= -5 - 9$

$= -14$

PROBLEM 4   Evaluate $x^3 - 2(x + y) + z^2$ when $x = 2$, $y = -4$, and $z = -3$.

Solution   See page S3.

EXAMPLE 5   The diameter of the base of a right circular cylinder is 5 cm. The height of the cylinder is 8.5 cm. Find the volume of the cylinder. Round to the nearest tenth.

8.5 cm

5 cm

Take Note

For your reference, geometric formulas are printed at the back of this textbook.

Solution $V = \pi r^2 h$ • **Use the formula for the volume of a right circular cylinder.**

$V = \pi (2.5)^2 (8.5)$ • $r = \dfrac{1}{2}d = \dfrac{1}{2}(5) = 2.5$

$V = \pi (6.25)(8.5)$ • **Use the π key on your calculator to enter the value of π.**

$V \approx 166.9$

The volume is approximately 166.9 cm³.

PROBLEM 5   The diameter of the base of a right circular cone is 9 cm. The height of the cone is 9.5 cm. Find the volume of the cone. Round to the nearest tenth.

9.5 cm

9 cm

Solution   See page S3.

A graphing calculator can be used to evaluate variable expressions. When the value of each variable is stored in the calculator's memory and a variable expression is then entered on the calculator, the calculator evaluates that variable expression for the values of the variables stored in its memory. See the Appendix for a description of keystroking procedures.

2.1   Concept Review

Determine whether the statement is always true, sometimes true, or never true.

1. The expression $3x^2$ is a variable expression.

2. In the expression $8y^3 - 4y$, the terms are $8y^3$ and $4y$.

3. For the expression x^5, the value of x is 1.

4. For the expression $6a + 7b$, 7 is a constant term.

5. The Order of Operations Agreement is used in evaluating a variable expression.

6. The result of evaluating a variable expression is a single number.

2.1   Exercises

1   Evaluate variable expressions

1. To identify the terms of the variable expression $3x^2 - 4x - 7$, first write subtraction as addition of the opposite: $3x^2 + (\underline{\ ?\ }) + (\underline{\ ?\ })$. The terms of $3x^2 - 4x - 7$ are $\underline{\ ?\ }$, $\underline{\ ?\ }$, and $\underline{\ ?\ }$.

2. Evaluate $mn^2 - m$ when $m = -2$ and $n = 5$.

$mn^2 - m = (-2)(5)^2 - (-2)$ • Replace m with $\underline{\ ?\ }$ and n with $\underline{\ ?\ }$.

$\quad = (-2)(\underline{\ ?\ }) - (-2)$ • Simplify the exponential expression.

$\quad = \underline{\ ?\ } - (-2)$ • Multiply.

$\quad = -50 + \underline{\ ?\ }$ • Write subtraction as addition of the opposite.

$\quad = \underline{\ ?\ }$.   • Add.

Name the terms of the variable expression. Then underline the constant term.

3. $2x^2 + 5x - 8$

4. $-3n^2 - 4n + 7$

5. $6 - a^4$

Name the variable terms of the expression. Then underline the variable part of each term.

6. $9b^2 - 4ab + a^2$

7. $7x^2y + 6xy^2 + 10$

8. $5 - 8n - 3n^2$

Name the coefficients of the variable terms.

9. $x^2 - 9x + 2$

10. $12a^2 - 8ab - b^2$

11. $n^3 - 4n^2 - n + 9$

12. What is the meaning of the phrase "evaluate a variable expression"?

13. What is the difference between the meaning of "the value of the variable" and the meaning of "the value of the variable expression"?

Evaluate the variable expression when $a = 2$, $b = 3$, and $c = -4$.

14. $3a + 2b$

15. $a - 2c$

16. $-a^2$

17. $2c^2$

18. $-3a + 4b$

19. $3b - 3c$

20. $b^2 - 3$

21. $-3c + 4$

22. $16 \div (2c)$

23. $6b \div (-a)$

24. $bc \div (2a)$

25. $-2ab \div c$

26. $a^2 - b^2$

27. $b^2 - c^2$

28. $(a + b)^2$

29. $a^2 + b^2$

30. $2a - (c + a)^2$

31. $(b - a)^2 + 4c$

32. $b^2 - \dfrac{ac}{8}$

33. $\dfrac{5ab}{6} - 3cb$

34. $(b - 2a)^2 + bc$

Evaluate the variable expression when $a = -2$, $b = 4$, $c = -1$, and $d = 3$.

35. $\dfrac{b + c}{d}$

36. $\dfrac{d - b}{c}$

37. $\dfrac{2d + b}{-a}$

38. $\dfrac{b + 2d}{b}$

39. $\dfrac{b - d}{c - a}$

40. $\dfrac{2c - d}{-ad}$

41. $(b + d)^2 - 4a$

42. $(d - a)^2 - 3c$

43. $(d - a)^2 \div 5$

44. $(b - c)^2 \div 5$

45. $b^2 - 2b + 4$

46. $a^2 - 5a - 6$

47. $\dfrac{bd}{a} \div c$

48. $\dfrac{2ac}{b} \div (-c)$

49. $2(b + c) - 2a$

50. $3(b - a) - bc$

51. $\dfrac{b - 2a}{bc^2 - d}$

52. $\dfrac{b^2 - a}{ad + 3c}$

53. $\frac{1}{3}d^2 - \frac{3}{8}b^2$

54. $\frac{5}{8}a^4 - c^2$

55. $\frac{-4bc}{2a - b}$

56. $\frac{abc}{b - d}$

57. $a^3 - 3a^2 + a$

58. $d^3 - 3d - 9$

59. $-\frac{3}{4}b + \frac{1}{2}(ac + bd)$

60. $-\frac{2}{3}d - \frac{1}{5}(bd - ac)$

61. $(b - a)^2 - (d - c)^2$

62. $(b + c)^2 + (a + d)^2$

63. $4ac + (2a)^2$

64. $3dc - (4c)^2$

Evaluate the variable expression when $a = 2.7$, $b = -1.6$, and $c = -0.8$.

65. $c^2 - ab$

66. $(a + b)^2 - c$

67. $\frac{b^3}{c} - 4a$

Complete Exercises 68 and 69 without a calculator.

68. If $\frac{b + c}{abc}$ is evaluated when $a = -25$, $b = 67$, and $c = -82$, will the result be positive or negative?

69. A sphere has a radius of 2 cm.
   a. Can the exact volume of the sphere be V cm³, where V is a whole number?
   b. Can the exact volume of the sphere be V cm², where V is an irrational number?

Solve. Round to the nearest tenth.

70. **Geometry** Find the volume of a sphere that has a radius of 8.5 cm.

71. **Geometry** Find the volume of a right circular cylinder that has a radius of 1.25 in. and a height of 5.25 in.

72. **Geometry** The radius of the base of a right circular cylinder is 3.75 ft. The height of the cylinder is 9.5 ft. Find the surface area of the cylinder.

73. **Geometry** The length of one base of a trapezoid is 17.5 cm, and the length of the other base is 10.25 cm. The height is 6.75 cm. What is the area of the trapezoid?

74. **Geometry** A right circular cone has a height of 2.75 in. The diameter of the base is 1 in. Find the volume of the cone.

75. **Geometry** A right circular cylinder has a height of 12.6 m. The diameter of the base is 7 m. Find the volume of the cylinder.

76. The value of z is the value of $a^2 - 2a$ when $a = -3$. Find the value of z^2.

77. The value of a is the value of $3x^2 - 4x - 5$ when $x = -2$. Find the value of $3a - 4$.

78. The value of c is the value of $a^2 + b^2$ when $a = 2$ and $b = -2$. Find the value of $c^2 - 4$.

79. The value of d is the value of $3w^2 - 2v$ when $w = -1$ and $v = 3$. Find the value of $d^2 - 4d$.

2.1   Applying Concepts

Evaluate the variable expression when $a = -2$ and $b = -3$.

80. $|2a + 3b|$

81. $|-4ab|$

82. $|5a - b|$

Evaluate the variable expression when $a = \frac{2}{3}$ and $b = -\frac{3}{2}$.

83. $\frac{1}{3}a^5b^6$

84. $\dfrac{(2ab)^3}{2a^3b^3}$

85. $|5ab - 8a^2b^2|$

Evaluate the following expressions for $x = 2$, $y = 3$, and $z = -2$.

86. $3^x - x^3$

87. $2^y - y^2$

88. z^y

89. z^x

90. $x^x - y^y$

91. $y^{(x^2)}$

92. For each of the following, determine the first natural number x, greater than 2, for which the second expression is larger than the first. On the basis of your answers, make a conjecture that appears to be true about the expressions x^n and n^x, where $n = 3, 4, 5, 6, 7, \ldots$ and x is a natural number greater than 2.

   a. x^3, 3^x

   b. x^4, 4^x

   c. x^5, 5^x

   d. x^6, 6^x

2.2 Simplifying Variable Expressions

OBJECTIVE 1   **The Properties of the Real Numbers**

The Properties of the Real Numbers describe the way operations on numbers can be performed. Here are some of the Properties of the Real Numbers and an example of each.

The Commutative Property of Addition

If a and b are real numbers, then $a + b = b + a$.

Two terms can be added in either order; the sum is the same.

$$4 + 3 = 7 \quad \text{and} \quad 3 + 4 = 7$$

The Commutative Property of Multiplication

If a and b are real numbers, then $a \cdot b = b \cdot a$.

Two factors can be multiplied in either order; the product is the same.

$$(5)(-2) = -10 \quad \text{and} \quad (-2)(5) = -10$$

The Associative Property of Addition

If a, b, and c are real numbers, then $(a + b) + c = a + (b + c)$.

When three or more terms are added, the terms can be grouped (with parentheses, for example) in any order; the sum is the same.

$$2 + (3 + 4) = 2 + 7 = 9 \quad \text{and} \quad (2 + 3) + 4 = 5 + 4 = 9$$

The Associative Property of Multiplication

If a, b, and c are real numbers, then $(a \cdot b) \cdot c = a \cdot (b \cdot c)$.

When three or more factors are multiplied, the factors can be grouped in any order; the product is the same.

$$(2 \cdot 3) \cdot 4 = 6 \cdot 4 = 24 \quad \text{and} \quad 2 \cdot (3 \cdot 4) = 2 \cdot 12 = 24$$

The Addition Property of Zero

If a is a real number, then $a + 0 = 0 + a = a$.

The sum of a term and zero is the term.

$$4 + 0 = 4 \qquad 0 + 4 = 4$$

The Multiplication Property of Zero

If a is a real number, then $a \cdot 0 = 0 \cdot a = 0$.

The product of a term and zero is zero.

$$(5)(0) = 0 \qquad (0)(5) = 0$$

The Multiplication Property of One

If a is a real number, then $a \cdot 1 = 1 \cdot a = a$.

The product of a term and 1 is the term.

$$6 \cdot 1 = 6 \qquad 1 \cdot 6 = 6$$

The Inverse Property of Addition

If a is a real number, then $a + (-a) = (-a) + a = 0$.

The sum of a number and its opposite is zero.
The opposite of a number is called its **additive inverse.**

$$8 + (-8) = 0 \qquad (-8) + 8 = 0$$

The Inverse Property of Multiplication

If a is a real number, and $a \neq 0$, then $a \cdot \dfrac{1}{a} = \dfrac{1}{a} \cdot a = 1$.

The product of a number and its reciprocal is 1.
$\dfrac{1}{a}$ is the **reciprocal** of a. $\dfrac{1}{a}$ is also called the **multiplicative inverse** of a.

$$7 \cdot \dfrac{1}{7} = 1 \qquad \dfrac{1}{7} \cdot 7 = 1$$

The Distributive Property

If a, b, and c are real numbers, then $a(b + c) = ab + ac$ or $(b + c)a = ba + ca$.

By the Distributive Property, the term outside the parentheses is multiplied by each term inside the parentheses.

$$2(3 + 4) = 2 \cdot 3 + 2 \cdot 4 \qquad (4 + 5)2 = 4 \cdot 2 + 5 \cdot 2$$
$$2 \cdot 7 = 6 + 8 \qquad\qquad 9 \cdot 2 = 8 + 10$$
$$14 = 14 \qquad\qquad\qquad 18 = 18$$

EXAMPLE 1   Complete the statement by using the Commutative Property of Multiplication.

$(6)(5) = (?)(6)$

Solution $(6)(5) = (5)(6)$ • **The Commutative Property of Multiplication states that $a \cdot b = b \cdot a$.**

PROBLEM 1   Complete the statement by using the Inverse Property of Addition.

$7 + ? = 0$

Solution   See page S4.

EXAMPLE 2   Identify the property that justifies the statement.

$2(8 + 5) = 16 + 10$

Solution   The Distributive Property   • **The Distributive Property states that $a(b + c) = ab + ac$.**

PROBLEM 2   Identify the property that justifies the statement.

$5 + (13 + 7) = (5 + 13) + 7$

Solution   See page S4.

OBJECTIVE 2   **Simplify variable expressions using the Properties of Addition**

Like terms of a variable expression are terms with the same variable part. (Because $x^2 = x \cdot x$, x^2 and x are not like terms.)

Constant terms are like terms. 4 and 9 are like terms.

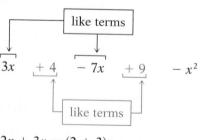

To **combine like terms,** use the Distributive Property $ba + ca = (b + c)a$ to add the coefficients.

$$2x + 3x = (2 + 3)x$$
$$= 5x$$

EXAMPLE 3   Simplify.   **A.** $-2y + 3y$ **B.** $5x - 11x$

Solution   **A.** $-2y + 3y$
$= (-2 + 3)y$ • **Use the Distributive Property $ba + ca = (b + c)a$.**

$$= 1y$$ • Add the coefficients.
$$= y$$ • Use the Multiplication Property of One.

B. $5x - 11x$
$$= [5 + (-11)]x$$ • Use the Distributive Property
$$ba + ca = (b + c)a.$$

$$= -6x$$ • Add the coefficients.

PROBLEM 3 Simplify. **A.** $9x + 6x$ **B.** $-4y - 7y$

Solution See page S4.

In simplifying more complicated expressions, use the Properties of Addition.

The Commutative Property of Addition can be used when adding two like terms. The terms can be added in either order. The sum is the same.

$$2x + (-4x) = -4x + 2x$$
$$[2 + (-4)]x = (-4 + 2)x$$
$$-2x = -2x$$

The Associative Property of Addition is used when adding three or more terms. The terms can be grouped in any order. The sum is the same.

$$3x + 5x + 9x = (3x + 5x) + 9x = 3x + (5x + 9x)$$
$$8x + 9x = 3x + 14x$$
$$17x = 17x$$

By the Addition Property of Zero, the sum of a term and zero is the term.

$$5x + 0 = 0 + 5x = 5x$$

By the Inverse Property of Addition, the sum of a term and its additive inverse is zero.

$$7x + (-7x) = -7x + 7x = 0$$

EXAMPLE 4 Simplify. **A.** $8x + 3y - 8x$ **B.** $4x^2 + 5x - 6x^2 - 2x$

Solution **A.** $8x + 3y - 8x$
$$= 3y + 8x - 8x$$ • Use the Commutative Property of Addition to rearrange the terms.
$$= 3y + (8x - 8x)$$ • Use the Associative Property of Addition to group like terms.
$$= 3y + 0$$ • Use the Inverse Property of Addition.
$$= 3y$$ • Use the Addition Property of Zero.

B. $4x^2 + 5x - 6x^2 - 2x$
$$= 4x^2 - 6x^2 + 5x - 2x$$ • Use the Commutative Property of Addition to rearrange the terms.
$$= (4x^2 - 6x^2) + (5x - 2x)$$ • Use the Associative Property of Addition to group like terms.
$$= -2x^2 + 3x$$ • Combine like terms.

> **PROBLEM 4**   Simplify.   **A.** $3a - 2b + 5a$ **B.** $x^2 - 7 + 9x^2 - 14$
>
> ■ **Solution**   See page S4.

OBJECTIVE **3**   ## Simplify variable expressions using the Properties of Multiplication

The Properties of Multiplication are used in simplifying variable expressions.

The Associative Property is used when multiplying three or more factors.

$$2(3x) = (2 \cdot 3)x = 6x$$

The Commutative Property can be used to change the order in which factors are multiplied.

$$(3x) \cdot 2 = 2 \cdot (3x) = 6x$$

By the Multiplication Property of One, the product of a term and 1 is the term.

$$(8x)(1) = (1)(8x) = 8x$$

By the Inverse Property of Multiplication, the product of a term and its reciprocal is 1.

$$5x \cdot \frac{1}{5x} = \frac{1}{5x} \cdot 5x = 1, \, x \neq 0$$

> **EXAMPLE 5**   Simplify.   **A.** $2(-x)$ **B.** $\frac{3}{2}\left(\frac{2x}{3}\right)$ **C.** $(16x)2$
>
> **Solution**   **A.** $2(-x) = 2(-1 \cdot x)$ • $-x = -1x = -1 \cdot x$
> $= [2 \cdot (-1)]x$ • Use the Associative Property of Multiplication to group factors.
> $= -2x$ • Multiply.
>
> **B.** $\frac{3}{2}\left(\frac{2x}{3}\right) = \frac{3}{2}\left(\frac{2}{3}x\right)$ • Note that $\frac{2x}{3} = \frac{2}{3} \cdot \frac{x}{1} = \frac{2}{3}x$.
> $= \left(\frac{3}{2} \cdot \frac{2}{3}\right)x$ • Use the Associative Property of Multiplication to group factors.
> $= 1x$ • Use the Inverse Property of Multiplication.
> $= x$ • Use the Multiplication Property of One.
>
> **C.** $(16x)2 = 2(16x)$ • Use the Commutative Property of Multiplication to rearrange factors.
> $= (2 \cdot 16)x$ • Use the Associative Property of Multiplication to group factors.
> $= 32x$ • Multiply.
>
> **PROBLEM 5**   Simplify.   **A.** $-7(-2a)$ **B.** $-\frac{5}{6}(-30y^2)$ **C.** $(-5x)(-2)$
>
> ■ **Solution**   See page S4.

OBJECTIVE **4**   ## Simplify variable expressions using the Distributive Property

The Distributive Property is used to remove parentheses from a variable expression.

$$3(2x - 5)$$
$$= 3(2x) - 3(5)$$
$$= 6x - 15$$

An extension of the Distributive Property is used when an expression contains more than two terms.

$$4(x^2 + 6x - 1)$$
$$= 4(x^2) + 4(6x) - 4(1)$$
$$= 4x^2 + 24x - 4$$

EXAMPLE 6   Simplify.   **A.** $-3(5 + x)$ **B.** $-(2x - 4)$

C. $(2y - 6)2$ **D.** $5(3x + 7y - z)$

Solution   **A.** $-3(5 + x)$
$$= -3(5) + (-3)x$$ • Use the Distributive Property.
$$= -15 - 3x$$ • Multiply.

B. $-(2x - 4)$
$$=\quad (2x - 4)$$ • Just as $-x = -1x$,
$-(2x - 4) = \quad (2x - 4)$.
$$= -1(2x) - (-1)(4)$$ • Use the Distributive Property.
$$= -2x + 4$$ • *Note:* When a negative sign immediately precedes the parentheses, remove the parentheses and change the sign of each term inside the parentheses.

C. $(2y - 6)2$
$$= (2y)(2) - (6)(2)$$ • Use the Distributive Property
$$= 4y - 12$$ $(b + c)a = ba + ca$.

D. $5(3x + 7y - z)$
$$= 5(3x) + 5(7y) - 5(z)$$ • Use the Distributive Property.
$$= 15x + 35y - 5z$$

PROBLEM 6   Simplify.   **A.** $7(4 + 2y)$ **B.** $-(5x - 12)$

C. $(3a - 1)5$ **D.** $-3(6a^2 - 8a + 9)$

Solution   See page S4.

OBJECTIVE **5**   **Simplify general variable expressions**

When simplifying variable expressions, use the Distributive Property to remove parentheses and brackets used as grouping symbols.

EXAMPLE 7   Simplify: $4(x - y) - 2(-3x + 6y)$

Solution $4(x - y) - 2(-3x + 6y)$
$$= 4x - 4y + 6x - 12y$$ • Use the Distributive Property to remove parentheses.
$$= 10x - 16y$$ • Combine like terms.

PROBLEM 7   Simplify: $7(x - 2y) - 3(-x - 2y)$

Solution   See page S4.

EXAMPLE 8   Simplify: $2x - 3[2x - 3(x + 7)]$

Solution $2x - 3[2x - 3(x + 7)]$
$= 2x - 3[2x - 3x - 21]$ • Use the Distributive Property to remove the inner grouping symbols.

$= 2x - 3[-x - 21]$ • Combine like terms inside the grouping symbols.

$= 2x + 3x + 63$ • Use the Distributive Property to remove the brackets.

$= 5x + 63$ • Combine like terms.

PROBLEM 8   Simplify: $3y - 2[x - 4(2 - 3y)]$

Solution   See page S4.

2.2 Concept Review

Determine whether the statement is always true, sometimes true, or never true.

1. The Associative Property of Addition states that two terms can be added in either order and the sum will be the same.

2. When three numbers are multiplied, the numbers can be grouped in any order and the product will be the same.

3. The Multiplication Property of One states that multiplying a number by one does not change the number.

4. The sum of a number and its additive inverse is zero.

5. The product of a number and its multiplicative inverse is one.

6. The terms x and x^2 are like terms because both have a coefficient of 1.

7. $3(x + 4) = 3x + 4$ is an example of the correct application of the Distributive Property.

8. To add like terms, add the coefficients; the variable part remains unchanged.

2.2 Exercises

1 The Properties of the Real Numbers

1. The fact that two terms can be added in either order is called the __?__ Property of Addition.

2. The fact that three or more factors can be multiplied by grouping them in any order is called the __?__ Property of Multiplication.

3. The Inverse Property of Multiplication tells us that the product of a number and its __?__ is one.

4. The Inverse Property of Addition tells us that the sum of a number and its __?__ is zero.

Use the given property to complete the statement.

5. The Commutative Property of Multiplication
$2 \cdot 5 = 5 \cdot ?$

6. The Commutative Property of Addition
$9 + 17 = ? + 9$

7. The Associative Property of Multiplication
$(4 \cdot 5) \cdot 6 = 4 \cdot (? \cdot 6)$

8. The Associative Property of Addition
$(4 + 5) + 6 = ? + (5 + 6)$

9. The Distributive Property
$2(4 + 3) = 8 + ?$

10. The Addition Property of Zero
$? + 0 = -7$

11. The Inverse Property of Addition
$8 + ? = 0$

12. The Inverse Property of Multiplication
$\dfrac{1}{-5}(-5) = ?$

13. The Multiplication Property of One
$? \cdot 1 = -4$

14. The Multiplication Property of Zero
$12 \cdot ? = 0$

Identify the property that justifies the statement.

15. $-7 + 7 = 0$

16. $(-8)\left(-\dfrac{1}{8}\right) = 1$

17. $23 + 19 = 19 + 23$

18. $-21 + 0 = -21$

19. $2 + (6 + 14) = (2 + 6) + 14$

20. $(-3 + 9)8 = -24 + 72$

21. $3 \cdot 5 = 5 \cdot 3$

22. $-32(0) = 0$

23. $(4 \cdot 3) \cdot 5 = 4 \cdot (3 \cdot 5)$

24. $\dfrac{1}{4}(1) = \dfrac{1}{4}$

2 Simplify variable expressions using the Properties of Addition

25. What are *like terms*? Give an example of two like terms. Give an example of two terms that are not like terms.

26. Explain the meaning of the phrase "simplify a variable expression."

27. Which of the following are like terms?
$3x, 3x^2, 5x, 5xy$

28. Which of the following are like terms?
$-7a, -7b, -4a, -7a^2$

29. Simplify $5a - 8a$ by combining like terms.

$5a - 8a = 5a + \underline{\ ?\ }$ • **Write subtraction as addition of the opposite.**

$\qquad = [5 + (-8)]a$ • **Use the __?__ Property $ba + ca = (b + c)a$.**

$\qquad = \underline{\ ?\ }\ a$ • **Add the coefficients.**

30. Simplify $6xy - 6x + 7xy$ by combining like terms.

$6xy - 6x + 7xy = 6xy + 7xy - 6x$ • **Use the __?__ Property of Addition to rearrange the terms.**

$\qquad = (6 + 7)(\underline{\ ?\ }) - 6x$ • **Use the Distributive Property $ba + ca = (b + c)a$.**

$\qquad = \underline{\ ?\ } - 6x$ • **Add the coefficients.**

Simplify.

31. $6x + 8x$

32. $12x + 13x$

33. $9a - 4a$

34. $12a - 3a$

35. $4y - 10y$

36. $8y - 6y$

37. $-3b - 7$

38. $-12y - 3$

39. $-12a + 17a$

40. $-3a + 12a$

41. $5ab - 7ab$

42. $9ab - 3ab$

43. $-12xy + 17xy$

44. $-15xy + 3xy$

45. $-3ab + 3ab$

46. $-7ab + 7ab$

47. $-\dfrac{1}{2}x - \dfrac{1}{3}x$

48. $-\dfrac{2}{5}y + \dfrac{3}{10}y$

49. $\dfrac{3}{8}x^2 - \dfrac{5}{12}x^2$

50. $\dfrac{2}{3}y^2 - \dfrac{4}{9}y^2$

51. $3x + 5x + 3x$

52. $8x + 5x + 7x$

53. $5a - 3a + 5a$

54. $10a - 17a + 3a$

55. $-5x^2 - 12x^2 + 3x^2$

56. $-y^2 - 8y^2 + 7y^2$

57. $7x - 8x + 3y$

58. $8y - 10x + 8x$

59. $7x - 3y + 10x$

60. $8y + 8x - 8y$

61. $3a - 7b - 5a + b$

62. $-5b + 7a - 7b + 12a$

63. $3x - 8y - 10x + 4x$

64. $3y - 12x - 7y + 2y$

65. $x^2 - 7x - 5x^2 + 5x$

66. $3x^2 + 5x - 10x^2 - 10x$

67. State whether the given number will be positive, negative, or zero after the variable expression $15a^2 - 12a + 7 - 21a^2 + 29a - 7$ is simplified.
a. the coefficient of a^2 **b.** the coefficient of a **c.** the constant term

68. Which expressions are equivalent to $-10x - 10y - 10y - 10x$?
a. 0 **b.** $-20y$ **c.** $-20x$ **d.** $-20x - 20y$ **e.** $-20y - 20x$

3 **Simplify variable expressions using the Properties of Multiplication**

69. Simplify: $4(-12x)$

$4(-12x) = [4(-12)]x$ • **Use the __?__ Property of Multiplication to group factors.**

$\qquad = \underline{\ ?\ }$ • **Multiply.**

70. Simplify: $\left(\dfrac{1}{2}a^2\right)\left(-\dfrac{3}{2}\right)$

$\left(\dfrac{1}{2}a^2\right)\left(-\dfrac{3}{2}\right) = \left(\underline{}\right)\left(\dfrac{1}{2}a^2\right)$ • Use the **Commutative Property of Multiplication** to rearrange factors.

$= \left(-\dfrac{3}{2}\cdot\underline{}\right)a^2$ • Use the **Associative Property of Multiplication** to group factors.

$= \underline{}\,a^2$ • **Multiply.**

Simplify.

71. $4(3x)$

72. $12(5x)$

73. $-3(7a)$

74. $-2(5a)$

75. $-2(-3y)$

76. $-5(-6y)$

77. $(4x)2$

78. $(6x)12$

79. $(3a)(-2)$

80. $(7a)(-4)$

81. $(-3b)(-4)$

82. $(-12b)(-9)$

83. $-5(3x^2)$

84. $-8(7x^2)$

85. $\dfrac{1}{3}(3x^2)$

86. $\dfrac{1}{5}(5a)$

87. $\dfrac{1}{8}(8x)$

88. $-\dfrac{1}{4}(-4a)$

89. $-\dfrac{1}{7}(-7n)$

90. $\left(\dfrac{3x}{4}\right)\left(\dfrac{4}{3}\right)$

91. $\dfrac{12x}{5}\left(\dfrac{5}{12}\right)$

92. $(-6y)\left(-\dfrac{1}{6}\right)$

93. $(-10n)\left(-\dfrac{1}{10}\right)$

94. $\dfrac{1}{3}(9x)$

95. $\dfrac{1}{7}(14x)$

96. $-\dfrac{1}{5}(10x)$

97. $-\dfrac{1}{8}(16x)$

98. $-\dfrac{2}{3}(12a^2)$

99. $-\dfrac{5}{8}(24a^2)$

100. $-\dfrac{1}{2}(-16y)$

101. $-\dfrac{3}{4}(-8y)$

102. $(16y)\left(\dfrac{1}{4}\right)$

103. $(33y)\left(\dfrac{1}{11}\right)$

104. $(-6x)\left(\dfrac{1}{3}\right)$

105. $(-10x)\left(\dfrac{1}{5}\right)$

106. $(-8a)\left(-\dfrac{3}{4}\right)$

107. After $\dfrac{2}{7}x^2$ is multiplied by a proper fraction, is the coefficient of x^2 greater than one or less than one?

108. After $-152m$ is multiplied by a whole number, is the coefficient of m greater than zero or less than zero?

4 Simplify variable expressions using the Distributive Property

109. Simplify: $-8(3x - 2)$

$-8(3x - 2) = (-8)(3x) - (-8)(2)$ • Use the $\underline{}$ Property.

$= \underline{}\,x + \underline{}$ • **Multiply.**

110. Simplify: $(7a - 3)(-2)$

$(7a - 3)(-2) = (7a)(\underline{\ ?\ }) - 3(\underline{\ ?\ })$ • **Use the Distributive Property.**
$\qquad\qquad = \underline{\ ?\ } + \underline{\ ?\ }$ • **Multiply.**

Simplify.

111. $-(x + 2)$

112. $-(x + 7)$

113. $2(4x - 3)$

114. $5(2x - 7)$

115. $-2(a + 7)$

116. $-5(a + 16)$

117. $-3(2y - 8)$

118. $-5(3y - 7)$

119. $(5 - 3b)7$

120. $(10 - 7b)2$

121. $-3(3 - 5x)$

122. $-5(7 - 10x)$

123. $3(5x^2 + 2x)$

124. $6(3x^2 + 2x)$

125. $-2(-y + 9)$

126. $-5(-2x + 7)$

127. $(-3x - 6)5$

128. $(-2x + 7)7$

129. $2(-3x^2 - 14)$

130. $5(-6x^2 - 3)$

131. $-3(2y^2 - 7)$

132. $-8(3y^2 - 12)$

133. $-(6a^2 - 7b^2)$

134. $3(x^2 + 2x - 6)$

135. $4(x^2 - 3x + 5)$

136. $-2(y^2 - 2y + 4)$

137. $-3(y^2 - 3y - 7)$

138. $2(-a^2 - 2a + 3)$

139. $4(-3a^2 - 5a + 7)$

140. $-5(-2x^2 - 3x + 7)$

141. $-3(-4x^2 + 3x - 4)$

142. $3(2x^2 + xy - 3y^2)$

143. $5(2x^2 - 4xy - y^2)$

144. $-(3a^2 + 5a - 4)$

145. $-(8b^2 - 6b + 9)$

146. After the expression $17x - 31$ is multiplied by a negative integer, is the constant term positive or negative?

147. The expression $5x - 8xy + 7y$ is multiplied by a positive integer. How many variable terms does the resulting expression have?

5 Simplify general variable expressions

148. When simplifying $4(3a - 7) + 2(a - 3)$, the first step is to use the Distributive Property to remove parentheses:
$4(3a - 7) + 2(a - 3) = (\underline{\ ?\ })a - \underline{\ ?\ } + (\underline{\ ?\ })a - \underline{\ ?\ }$

149. When simplifying $12m - (m - 3)$, the first step is to remove the parentheses and change the sign of each term inside the parentheses:
$12m - \underline{\ ?\ } + \underline{\ ?\ }$

Simplify.

150. $4x - 2(3x + 8)$

151. $6a - (5a + 7)$

152. $9 - 3(4y + 6)$

153. $10 - (11x - 3)$

154. $5n - (7 - 2n)$

155. $8 - (12 + 4y)$

156. $3(x + 2) - 5(x - 7)$

157. $2(x - 4) - 4(x + 2)$

158. $12(y - 2) + 3(7 - 3y)$

159. $6(2y - 7) - 3(3 - 2y)$

160. $3(a - b) - 4(a + b)$

161. $2(a + 2b) - (a - 3b)$

162. $4[x - 2(x - 3)]$

163. $2[x + 2(x + 7)]$

164. $-2[3x + 2(4 - x)]$

165. $-5[2x + 3(5 - x)]$

166. $-3[2x - (x + 7)]$

167. $-2[3x - (5x - 2)]$

168. $2x - 3[x - 2(4 - x)]$

169. $-7x + 3[x - 7(3 - 2x)]$

170. $-5x - 2[2x - 4(x + 7)] - 6$

171. $4a - 2[2b - (b - 2a)] + 3b$

172. $2x + 3(x - 2y) + 5(3x - 7y)$

173. $5y - 2(y - 3x) + 2(7x - y)$

174. Which expression is equivalent to $12 - 7(y - 9)$?
  a. $5(y - 9)$ **b.** $12 - 7y - 63$
  c. $12 - 7y + 63$ **d.** $12 - 7y - 9$

175. Which expression is equivalent to $7[3b + 5(b - 6)]$?
  a. $7[3b + 5b - 6)]$ **b.** $7[3b + 5b - 30)]$
  c. $7[3b + 5b + 6)]$ **d.** $7[8b - 6]$

2.2   Applying Concepts

Simplify.

176. $C - 0.7C$

177. $\dfrac{1}{3}(3x + y) - \dfrac{2}{3}(6x - y)$

178. $-\dfrac{1}{4}[2x + 2(y - 6y)]$

Complete.

179. A number that has no reciprocal is _____ .

180. A number that is its own reciprocal is _____ .

181. The additive inverse of $a - b$ is _____.

182. Determine whether the statement is true or false. If the statement is false, give an example that illustrates that it is false.
  a. Division is a commutative operation.
  b. Division is an associative operation.
  c. Subtraction is an associative operation.
  d. Subtraction is a commutative operation.
  e. Addition is a commutative operation.

183. Define an operation $\otimes$ as $a \otimes b = (a \cdot b) - (a + b)$.
  For example, $7 \otimes 5 = (7 \cdot 5) - (7 + 5) = 35 - 12 = 23$.
  a. Is $\otimes$ a commutative operation? Support your answer.
  b. Is $\otimes$ an associative operation? Support your answer.

184. Give examples of two operations that occur in everyday experience and are not commutative (for example, putting on socks and then shoes).

185. In your own words, explain the Distributive Property.

2.3 Translating Verbal Expressions into Variable Expressions

OBJECTIVE **1**   ## Translate a verbal expression into a variable expression

One of the major skills required in applied mathematics is the ability to translate a verbal expression into a variable expression. This requires recognizing the verbal phrases that translate into mathematical operations. Here is a partial list of the phrases used to indicate the different mathematical operations.

Addition	added to	6 added to y	$y + 6$
	more than	8 more than x	$x + 8$
	the sum of	the sum of x and z	$x + z$
	increased by	t increased by 9	$t + 9$
	the total of	the total of 5 and y	$5 + y$
	plus	b plus 17	$b + 17$
Subtraction	minus	x minus 2	$x - 2$
	less than	7 less than t	$t - 7$
	less	7 less t	$7 - t$
	subtracted from	5 subtracted from d	$d - 5$
	decreased by	m decreased by 3	$m - 3$
	the difference between	the difference between y and 4	$y - 4$
Multiplication	times	10 times t	$10t$
	of	one-half of x	$\frac{1}{2}x$
	the product of	the product of y and z	yz
	multiplied by	y multiplied by 11	$11y$
	twice	twice n	$2n$
Division	divided by	x divided by 12	$\dfrac{x}{12}$
	the quotient of	the quotient of y and z	$\dfrac{y}{z}$
	the ratio of	the ratio of t to 9	$\dfrac{t}{9}$
Power	the square of	the square of x	x^2
	the cube of	the cube of a	a^3

Translating a phrase that contains the word *sum, difference, product,* or *quotient* can sometimes cause a problem. In the examples at the right, note where the operation symbol is placed.

the *sum* of x *and* y $\qquad x + y$

the *difference* between x *and* y $\qquad x - y$

the *product* of x *and* y $\qquad x \cdot y$

the *quotient* of x *and* y $\qquad \dfrac{x}{y}$

EXAMPLE 1 Translate into a variable expression.

     A. the total of five times b and c

     B. the quotient of eight less than n and fourteen

     C. thirteen more than the sum of seven and the square of x

Solution **A.** the <u>total</u> of five <u>times</u> b and c • Identify words that indicate mathematical operations.

$\qquad 5b + c$ • Use the operations to write the variable expression.

     B. the <u>quotient</u> of eight <u>less than</u> n and fourteen   • Identify words that indicate mathematical operations.

$\qquad \dfrac{n - 8}{14}$ • Use the operations to write the variable expression.

     C. thirteen <u>more than</u> the <u>sum</u> of seven and the <u>square</u> of x

$\qquad (7 + x^2) + 13$

PROBLEM 1 Translate into a variable expression.

     A. eighteen less than the cube of x

     B. y decreased by the sum of z and nine

     C. the difference between the square of q and the sum of r and t

Solution See page S4.

In most applications that involve translating phrases into variable expressions, the variable to be used is not given. To translate these phrases, a variable must be assigned to an unknown quantity before the variable expression can be written.

Take Note

The expression $n(6 + n^3)$ must have parentheses. If we write $n \cdot 6 + n^3$, then by the Order of Operations Agreement, only the 6 is multiplied by n, but we want n to be multiplied by the *total* of 6 and n^3.

EXAMPLE 2 Translate "a number multiplied by the total of six and the cube of the number" into a variable expression.

Solution the unknown number: n • Assign a variable to one of the unknown quantities.

the cube of the number: n^3 the total of six and the cube of the number: $6 + n^3$ • Use the assigned variable to write an expression for any other unknown quantity.

$n(6 + n^3)$ • Use the assigned variable to write the variable expression.

PROBLEM 2 Translate "a number added to the product of five and the square of the number" into a variable expression.

Solution See page S4.

EXAMPLE 3 Translate "the quotient of twice a number and the difference between the number and twenty" into a variable expression.

Solution the unknown number: n
twice the number: $2n$
the difference between the number and twenty: $n - 20$

$$\frac{2n}{n - 20}$$

PROBLEM 3 Translate "the product of three and the sum of seven and twice a number" into a variable expression.

Solution See page S4.

OBJECTIVE 2 **Translate a verbal expression into a variable expression and then simplify the resulting expression**

After translating a verbal expression into a variable expression, simplify the variable expression by using the Properties of the Real Numbers.

EXAMPLE 4 Translate and simplify "the total of four times an unknown number and twice the difference between the number and eight."

Solution the unknown number: n

     • Assign a variable to one of the unknown quantities.

four times the unknown number: $4n$
twice the difference between the number and eight: $2(n - 8)$

     • Use the assigned variable to write an expression for any other unknown quantity.

$4n + 2(n - 8)$

     • Use the assigned variable to write the variable expression.

$= 4n + 2n - 16$
$= 6n - 16$

     • Simplify the variable expression.

PROBLEM 4 Translate and simplify "a number minus the difference between twice the number and seventeen."

Solution See page S4.

EXAMPLE 5 Translate and simplify "the difference between five-eighths of a number and two-thirds of the same number."

Solution the unknown number: n

     • Assign a variable to one of the unknown quantities.

five-eighths of the number: $\frac{5}{8}n$

     • Use the assigned variable to write an expression for any other unknown quantity.

two-thirds of the number: $\frac{2}{3}n$

$$\frac{5}{8}n - \frac{2}{3}n$$

$$= \frac{15}{24}n - \frac{16}{24}n$$

$$= -\frac{1}{24}n$$

- **Use the assigned variable to write the variable expression.**
- **Simplify the variable expression.**

PROBLEM 5   Translate and simplify "the sum of three-fourths of a number and one-fifth of the same number."

■ **Solution**   See page S4.

OBJECTIVE 3

Translate application problems

Many of the applications of mathematics require that you identify an unknown quantity, assign a variable to that quantity, and then attempt to express another unknown quantity in terms of that variable.

Suppose we know that the sum of two numbers is 10 and that one of the two numbers is 4. We can find the other number by subtracting 4 from 10.

one number: 4
other number: $10 - 4 = 6$
The two numbers are 4 and 6.

Now suppose we know that the sum of two numbers is 10, we don't know either number, and we want to express *both* numbers in terms of the *same* variable.

Let one number be x. Again, we can find the other number by subtracting x from 10.

one number: x
other number: $10 - x$
The two numbers are x and $10 - x$.

Note that the sum of x and $10 - x$ is 10. $x + (10 - x) = x + 10 - x = 10$

EXAMPLE 6   The length of a swimming pool is 20 ft longer than the width. Express the length of the pool in terms of the width.

Solution   the width of the pool: W

the length is 20 more than the width: $W + 20$

- **Assign a variable to the width of the pool.**
- **Express the length of the pool in terms of W.**

Take Note

Any variable can be used. For example, if the width is y, then the length is $y + 20$.

PROBLEM 6   An older computer takes twice as long to process a set of data as does a newer model. Express the amount of time it takes the older computer to process the data in terms of the amount of time it takes the newer model.

■ **Solution**   See page S4.

EXAMPLE 7   An investor divided $5000 between two accounts, one a mutual fund and the other a money market fund. Use one variable to express the amounts invested in each account.

Solution   the amount invested in the mutual fund: x

the amount invested in the money market fund: $5000 - x$

- **Assign a variable to the amount invested in one account.**
- **Express the amount invested in the other account in terms of x.**

Take Note

It is also correct to assign the variable to the amount in the money market fund. Then the amount in the mutual fund is $5000 - x$.

> **PROBLEM 7**   A guitar string 6 ft long was cut into two pieces. Use one variable to express the lengths of the two pieces.
>
> ■ **Solution**   See page S4.

2.3   Concept Review

Determine whether the statement is always true, sometimes true, or never true.

1. "Five less than n" can be translated as "$5 - n$."

2. A variable expression contains an equals sign.

3. If the sum of two numbers is 12 and one of the two numbers is x, then the other number can be expressed as $x - 12$.

4. The words *total* and *times* both indicate multiplication.

5. The words *quotient* and *ratio* both indicate division.

6. The expressions $7y - 8$ and $(7y) - 8$ are equivalent.

7. The phrase "five times the sum of x and y" and the phrase "the sum of five times x and y" yield the same variable expression.

2.3   Exercises

1   Translate a verbal expression into a variable expression

For each phrase, identify the words that indicate mathematical operations.

1. the sum of seven and three times m

2. twelve less than the quotient of x and negative two

3. the total of ten and fifteen divided by a number

4. twenty subtracted from the product of eight and the cube of a number

Translate into a variable expression.

5. d less than nineteen

6. the sum of six and c

7. r decreased by twelve

8. w increased by fifty-five

9. a multiplied by twenty-eight

10. y added to sixteen

11. five times the difference between n and seven

12. thirty less than the square of b

13. y less the product of three and y

14. the sum of four-fifths of m and eighteen

15. the product of negative six and b

16. nine increased by the quotient of t and five

17. four divided by the difference between p and six

18. the product of seven and the total of r and eight

19. the quotient of nine less than x and twice x

20. the product of a and the sum of a and thirteen

21. twenty-one less than the product of s and negative four

22. fourteen more than one-half of the square of z

23. the ratio of eight more than d to d

24. the total of nine times the cube of m and the square of m

25. three-eighths of the sum of t and fifteen

26. s decreased by the quotient of s and two

27. w increased by the quotient of seven and w

28. the difference between the square of c and the total of c and fourteen

29. d increased by the difference between sixteen times d and three

30. the product of eight and the total of b and five

31. a number divided by nineteen

32. thirteen less a number

33. forty more than a number

34. three-sevenths of a number

35. the square of the difference between a number and ninety

36. the quotient of twice a number and five

37. the sum of four-ninths of a number and twenty

38. eight subtracted from the product of fifteen and a number

39. the product of a number and ten more than the number

40. six less than the total of a number and the cube of the number

41. fourteen added to the product of seven and a number

42. the quotient of three and the total of four and a number

43. the quotient of twelve and the sum of a number and two

44. eleven plus one-half of a number

45. the ratio of two and the sum of a number and one

46. a number multiplied by the difference between twice the number and nine

47. the difference between sixty and the quotient of a number and fifty

48. the product of nine less than a number and the number

49. the sum of the square of a number and three times the number

50. the quotient of seven more than twice a number and the number

51. the sum of three more than a number and the cube of the number

52. a number decreased by the difference between the cube of the number and ten

53. a number decreased by one-fourth of the square of the number

54. four less than the product of seven and the square of a number

55. a number decreased by the quotient of seven and the number

56. eighty decreased by the product of thirteen and a number

57. the cube of a number decreased by the product of twelve and the number

58. the quotient of five and the sum of a number and nineteen

59. Which of the following phrases translate(s) into the variable expression $25n^2 - 9$?
   a. the difference between nine and the product of twenty-five and the square of a number
   b. nine subtracted from the square of twenty-five and a number
   c. nine less than the product of twenty-five and the square of a number

60. Which of the following phrases translate(s) into the variable expression $32 - \frac{a}{7}$?
   a. the difference between thirty-two and the quotient of a number and seven
   b. thirty-two decreased by the quotient of a number and seven
   c. thirty-two minus the ratio of a number to seven

2 **Translate a verbal expression into a variable expression and then simplify the resulting expression**

61. The phrase "the total of one-half of a number and three-fourths of the number" can be translated as (__?__)n + (__?__)n. This expression simplifies to ___?___.

62. The phrase "the difference between twelve times a number and fifteen times the number" can be translated as (__?__)n − (__?__)n. This expression simplifies to ___?___.

Translate into a variable expression. Then simplify the expression.

63. a number increased by the total of the number and ten

64. a number added to the product of five and the number

65. a number decreased by the difference between nine and the number

66. eight more than the sum of a number and eleven

67. the difference between one-fifth of a number and three-eighths of the number

68. a number minus the sum of the number and fourteen

69. four more than the total of a number and nine

70. the sum of one-eighth of a number and one-twelfth of the number

71. twice the sum of three times a number and forty

72. the sum of a number divided by two and the number

73. seven times the product of five and a number

74. sixteen multiplied by one-fourth of a number

75. the total of seventeen times a number and twice the number

76. the difference between nine times a number and twice the number

77. a number plus the product of the number and twelve

78. nineteen more than the difference between a number and five

79. three times the sum of the square of a number and four

80. a number subtracted from the product of the number and seven

81. three-fourths of the sum of sixteen times a number and four

82. the difference between fourteen times a number and the product of the number and seven

83. sixteen decreased by the sum of a number and nine

84. eleven subtracted from the difference between eight and a number

85. five more than the quotient of four times a number and two

86. twenty minus the sum of four-ninths of a number and three

87. six times the total of a number and eight

88. four times the sum of a number and twenty

89. seven minus the sum of a number and two

90. three less than the sum of a number and ten

91. one-third of the sum of a number and six times the number

92. twice the quotient of four times a number and eight

93. the total of eight increased by the cube of a number and twice the cube of the number

94. the sum of five more than the square of a number and twice the square of the number

95. twelve more than a number added to the difference between the number and six

96. a number plus four added to the difference between three and twice the number

97. the sum of a number and nine added to the difference between the number and twenty

98. seven increased by a number added to twice the difference between the number and two

99. fourteen plus the product of three less than a number and ten

100. a number plus the product of the number minus five and seven

3   Translate application problems

101. The sum of two numbers is 25. To express both numbers in terms of the same variable, let x be one number. Then the other number is ___?___.

102. The length of a rectangle is five times the width. To express the length and the width in terms of the same variable, let W be the width. Then the length is ___?___.

103. The width of a rectangle is one-half the length. To express the length and the width in terms of the same variable, let L be the length. Then the width is ___?___.

104. An electrician's bill is $75 for materials and $50 an hour for labor. To express the total amount of the bill in terms of the number of hours of labor, let h be the number of hours of labor. Then the cost of the labor is ___?___, so the total amount for the materials and labor is ___?___.

Write a variable expression.

105. The sum of two numbers is 18. Express the two numbers in terms of the same variable.

106. The sum of two numbers is 20. Express the two numbers in terms of the same variable.

107. **Genetics** The human genome contains 11,000 more genes than the roundworm genome. Express the number of genes in the human genome in terms of the number of genes in the roundworm genome. (*Source:* Celera, USA TODAY research)

108. **Noise Level** The noise level of an ambulance siren is 10 decibels louder than that of a car horn. Express the noise level of an ambulance siren in terms of the noise level of a car horn. (*Source:* League for the Hard of Hearing)

109. **Space Exploration** A survey in *USA Today* reported that almost three-fourths of Americans think that money should be spent on exploration of Mars. Express the number of Americans who think that money should be spent on exploration of Mars in terms of the total number of Americans.

110. **Biology** According to the American Podiatric Medical Association, the bones in your foot account for one-fourth of all bones in your body. Express the number of bones in your foot in terms of the number of bones in your body.

111. **Sports** In football, the number of points awarded for a touchdown is three times the number of points awarded for a safety. Express the number of points awarded for a touchdown in terms of the number of points awarded for a safety.

112. **Cost of Living** A cost-of-living calculator at **homefair.com** shows that a person living in Manhattan would need twice the salary of a person living in Miami. Express the salary needed to live in Manhattan in terms of the salary needed to live in Miami.

113. **Astronomy** The diameter of Saturn's moon Rhea is 253 miles more than the diameter of Saturn's moon Dione. Express the diameter of Rhea in terms of the diameter of Dione. (*Source:* NASA)

114. **Online Sales** A recent survey conducted by Consumer Internet Barometer found that approximately 25% of those people who purchased a product online were extremely satisfied with their experience. Express the number of people who were extremely satisfied with their online purchases in terms of the number of people surveyed.

115. **Agriculture** In a recent year, Alabama produced one-half the number of pounds of pecans that Texas produced in the same year. Express the amount of pecans produced in Alabama in terms of the amount produced in Texas. (*Source:* National Agricultural Statistics Service)

116. **Taxes** According to the Internal Revenue Service, it takes about one-fifth the time to fill out Schedule B (interest and dividends) than it does to complete Schedule A (itemized deductions). Express the amount of time it takes to fill out Schedule B in terms of the time it takes to fill out Schedule A.

117. **Demography** According to the U.S. Bureau of the Census, the world population in the year 2050 is expected to be twice the world population in 1980. Express the expected world population in 2050 in terms of the world population in 1980.

118. **Geometry** The length of a rectangle is 5 m more than twice the width. Express the length of the rectangle in terms of the width.

119. **Geometry** In a triangle, the measure of the smallest angle is 10 degrees less than one-half the measure of the largest angle. Express the measure of the smallest angle in terms of the measure of the largest angle.

120. **Sports** A halyard 12 ft long is cut into two pieces. Use the same variable to express the lengths of the two pieces.

121. **Coins** A coin bank contains thirty-five coins in nickels and dimes. Use the same variable to express the number of nickels and the number of dimes in the coin bank.

122. **Travel** Two cars are traveling in opposite directions and at different rates. Two hours later the cars are 200 mi apart. Express the distance traveled by the faster car in terms of the distance traveled by the slower car.

123. **Wages** An employee is paid $720 per week plus $27 for each hour of overtime worked. Express the employee's weekly pay in terms of the number of hours of overtime worked.

124. **Billing** An auto repair bill is $138 for parts and $45 for each hour of labor. Express the amount of the repair bill in terms of the number of hours of labor.

125. **Consumerism** The cost of a cellular phone service is $19.95 per month plus $.08 per minute for phone calls. Express the monthly cost of the phone service in terms of the number of minutes of phone calls.

2.3 Applying Concepts

126. **Chemistry** The chemical formula for glucose (sugar) is $C_6H_{12}O_6$. This formula means that there are twelve hydrogen atoms, six carbon atoms, and six oxygen atoms in each molecule of glucose. If x represents the number of atoms of oxygen in a pound of sugar, express the number of hydrogen atoms in the pound of sugar in terms of x.

127. **Metalwork** A wire whose length is given as x inches is bent into a square. Express the length of a side of the square in terms of x.

128. **Pulleys** A block-and-tackle system is designed so that pulling one end of a rope five feet will move a weight on the other end a distance of three feet. If x represents the distance the rope is pulled, express the distance the weight moves in terms of x.

129. Translate the expressions $5x + 8$ and $5(x + 8)$ into phrases.

130. In your own words, explain how variables are used.

131. Explain the similarities and differences between the expressions "the difference between x and 5" and "5 less than x."

Focus on Problem Solving

From Concrete to Abstract   In your study of algebra, you will find that the problems are less concrete than those you studied in arithmetic. Problems that are concrete provide information pertaining to a specific instance. Algebra is more abstract. Abstract problems are theoretical; they are stated without reference to a specific instance. Let's look at an example of an abstract problem.

How many minutes are there in h hours?

A strategy that can be used to solve this problem is to begin by substituting a number for the variable.

How many minutes are there in 5 hours?

You know that there are 60 minutes in 1 hour. To find the number of minutes in 5 hours, multiply 5 by 60.

$$60 \cdot 5 = 300 \qquad \text{There are 300 minutes in 5 hours.}$$

Use the same procedure to find the number of minutes in h hours: multiply h by 60.

$$60 \cdot h = 60h \qquad \text{There are } 60h \text{ minutes in } h \text{ hours.}$$

This problem might be taken a step further:

If you walk one mile in x minutes, how far can you walk in h hours?

Consider the same problem using numbers in place of the variables.

If you walk one mile in 20 minutes, how far can you walk in 3 hours?

To solve this problem, you need to calculate the number of minutes in 3 hours (multiply 3 by 60), and divide the result by the number of minutes it takes to walk one mile (20 minutes).

$$\frac{60 \cdot 3}{20} = \frac{180}{20} = 9 \qquad \text{If you walk one mile in 20 minutes, you can walk 9 miles in 3 hours.}$$

Use the same procedure to solve the related abstract problem. Calculate the number of minutes in h hours (multiply h by 60), and divide the result by the number of minutes it takes to walk one mile (x minutes).

$$\frac{60 \cdot h}{x} = \frac{60h}{x} \qquad \text{If you walk one mile in } x \text{ minutes, you can walk } \frac{60h}{x} \text{ miles in } h \text{ hours.}$$

At the heart of the study of algebra is the use of variables. It is the variables in the problems above that make them abstract. But it is variables that allow us to generalize situations and state rules about mathematics.

Try each of the following problems.

1. How many hours are there in d days?

2. You earn d dollars an hour. What are your wages for working h hours?

3. If p is the price of one share of stock, how many shares can you purchase with d dollars?

4. A company pays a television station d dollars to air a commercial lasting s seconds. What is the cost per second?

5. After every v videotape rentals, you are entitled to one free rental. You have rented t tapes, where $t < v$. How many more do you need to rent before you are entitled to a free rental?

6. Your car gets g miles per gallon. How many gallons of gasoline does your car consume traveling t miles?

7. If you drink j ounces of juice each day, how many days will q quarts of the juice last?

8. A TV station has m minutes of commercials each hour. How many ads lasting s seconds each can be sold for each hour of programming?

9. A factory worker can assemble p products in m minutes. How many products can the factory worker assemble in h hours?

10. If one candy bar costs n nickels, how many candy bars can be purchased with q quarters?

Projects & Group Activities

Investigation into Operations with Even and Odd Integers

An **even integer** is an integer that is divisible by 2. For example, 6, −12, and 480 are even integers. An **odd integer** is an integer that is not evenly divisible by 2. For example, 3, −25, and 971 are odd integers.

Complete each statement with the word *even* or *odd*.

1. If k is an odd integer, then $k + 1$ is an _____ integer.

2. If k is an odd integer, then $k - 2$ is an _____ integer.

3. If n is an integer, then $2n$ is an _____ integer.

4. If m and n are even integers, then $m - n$ is an _____ integer.

5. If m and n are even integers, then mn is an _____ integer.

6. If m and n are odd integers, then $m + n$ is an _____ integer.

7. If m and n are odd integers, then $m - n$ is an _____ integer.

8. If m and n are odd integers, then mn is an _____ integer.

9. If m is an even integer and n is an odd integer, then $m - n$ is an _____ integer.

10. If m is an even integer and n is an odd integer, then $m + n$ is an _____ integer.

Chapter 2 Summary

Key Words

Key Words	Examples
A **variable** is a letter that is used to stand for a quantity that is unknown or that can change. A **variable expression** is an expression that contains one or more variables. [2.1.1, p. 67]	$5x - 4y + 7z$ is a variable expression. It contains the variables x, y, and z.
The **terms of a variable expression** are the addends of the expression. Each term is a **variable term** or a **constant term.** [2.1.1, p. 67]	The expression $4a^2 - 6b^3 + 7$ has three terms: $4a^2$, $-6b^3$, and 7. Of these, $4a^2$ and $-6b^3$ are variable terms. 7 is a constant term.
A variable term is composed of a **numerical coefficient** and a **variable part.** [2.1.1, p. 67]	For the expression $8p^4r$, 8 is the coefficient and p^4r is the variable part.
Replacing the variables in a variable expression with numbers and then simplifying the numerical expression is called **evaluating the variable expression.** [2.1.1, p. 68]	To evaluate $a^2 - 2b$ when $a = -3$ and $b = -5$, simplify the expression $(-3)^2 - 2(-5)$.
Like terms of a variable expression are the terms with the same variable part. [2.2.2, p. 76]	For the expression $2st - 3t + 9s - 11st$, the terms $2st$ and $-11st$ are like terms.
The **additive inverse** of a number is the opposite of the number [2.2.1, p. 75]	The additive inverse of 8 is -8. The additive inverse of -15 is 15.
The **multiplicative inverse** of a number is the reciprocal of the number. [2.2.1, p. 75]	The multiplicative inverse of $\frac{3}{8}$ is $\frac{8}{3}$.

Essential Rules and Procedures

Essential Rules and Procedures	Examples
The Commutative Property of Addition If a and b are real numbers, then $a + b = b + a$. [2.2.1, p. 74]	$5 + 2 = 7$ and $2 + 5 = 7$
The Commutative Property of Multiplication If a and b are real numbers, then $ab = ba$. [2.2.1, p. 74]	$6(-3) = -18$ and $-3(6) = -18$
The Associative Property of Addition If a, b, and c are real numbers, then $(a + b) + c = a + (b + c)$. [2.2.1, p. 74]	$-1 + (4 + 7) = -1 + 11 = 10$ $(-1 + 4) + 7 = 3 + 7 = 10$
The Associative Property of Multiplication If a, b, and c are real numbers, then $(ab)c = a(bc)$. [2.2.1, p. 74]	$(-2 \cdot 5) \cdot 3 = -10 \cdot 3 = -30$ $-2 \cdot (5 \cdot 3) = -2 \cdot 15 = -30$

The Addition Property of Zero
If a is a real number, then $a + 0 = 0 + a = a$.   [2.2.1, p. 74] $9 + 0 = 9$ $0 + 9 = 9$

The Multiplication Property of Zero
If a is a real number, then $a \cdot 0 = 0 \cdot a = 0$.   [2.2.1, p. 75] $-8(0) = 0$ $0(-8) = 0$

The Multiplication Property of One
If a is a real number, then $1 \cdot a = a \cdot 1 = a$.   [2.2.1, p. 75] $7 \cdot 1 = 7$ $1 \cdot 7 = 7$

The Inverse Property of Addition
If a is a real number, then $a + (-a) = (-a) + a = 0$. $4 + (-4) = 0$ $-4 + 4 = 0$
[2.2.1, p. 75]

The Inverse Property of Multiplication
If a is a real number and $a \neq 0$, then $a \cdot \dfrac{1}{a} = \dfrac{1}{a} \cdot a = 1$. $6 \cdot \dfrac{1}{6} = 1$ $\dfrac{1}{6} \cdot 6 = 1$
[2.2.1, p. 75]

The Distributive Property
If a, b, and c are real numbers, then $a(b + c) = ab + ac$. $5(2 + 3) = 5 \cdot 2 + 5 \cdot 3$
[2.2.1, p. 75] $= 10 + 15$
          $= 25$

Chapter 2 Review Exercises

1. Simplify: $-7y^2 + 6y^2 - (-2y^2)$

2. Simplify: $(12x)\left(\dfrac{1}{4}\right)$

3. Simplify: $\dfrac{2}{3}(-15a)$

4. Simplify: $-2(2x - 4)$

5. Simplify: $5(2x + 4) - 3(x - 6)$

6. Evaluate $a^2 - 3b$ when $a = 2$ and $b = -4$.

7. Complete the statement by using the Inverse Property of Addition.
$-9 + \, ? = 0$

8. Simplify: $-4(-9y)$

9. Simplify: $-2(-3y + 9)$

10. Simplify: $3[2x - 3(x - 2y)] + 3y$

11. Simplify: $-4(2x^2 - 3y^2)$

12. Simplify: $3x - 5x + 7x$

13. Evaluate $b^2 - 3ab$ when $a = 3$ and $b = -2$.

14. Simplify: $\dfrac{1}{5}(10x)$

15. Simplify: $5(3 - 7b)$

16. Simplify: $2x + 3[4 - (3x - 7)]$

17. Identify the property that justifies the statement.
$-4(3) = 3(-4)$

18. Simplify: $3(8 - 2x)$

19. Simplify: $-2x^2 - (-3x^2) + 4x^2$

20. Simplify: $-3x - 2(2x - 7)$

21. Simplify: $-3(3y^2 - 3y - 7)$

22. Simplify: $-2[x - 2(x - y)] + 5y$

23. Evaluate $\dfrac{-2ab}{2b - a}$ when $a = -4$ and $b = 6$.

24. Simplify: $(-3)(-12y)$

25. Simplify: $4(3x - 2) - 7(x + 5)$

26. Simplify: $(16x)\left(\dfrac{1}{8}\right)$

27. Simplify: $-3(2x^2 - 7y^2)$

28. Evaluate $3(a - c) - 2ab$ when $a = 2$, $b = 3$, and $c = -4$.

29. Simplify: $2x - 3(x - 2)$

30. Simplify: $2a - (-3b) - 7a - 5b$

31. Simplify: $-5(2x^2 - 3x + 6)$

32. Simplify: $3x - 7y - 12x$

33. Simplify: $\dfrac{1}{2}(12a)$

34. Simplify: $2x + 3[x - 2(4 - 2x)]$

35. Simplify: $3x + (-12y) - 5x - (-7y)$

36. Simplify: $\left(-\dfrac{5}{6}\right)(-36b)$

37. Complete the statement by using the Distributive Property.
$(6 + 3)7 = 42 + ?$

38. Simplify: $4x^2 + 9x - 6x^2 - 5x$

39. Simplify: $-\dfrac{3}{8}(16x^2)$

40. Simplify: $-3[2x - (7x - 9)]$

41. Simplify: $-(8a^2 - 3b^2)$

42. Identify the property that justifies the statement. $-32(0) = 0$

43. Translate "b decreased by the product of seven and b" into a variable expression.

44. Translate "the sum of a number and twice the square of the number" into a variable expression.

45. Translate "three less than the quotient of six and a number" into a variable expression.

46. Translate "ten divided by the difference between y and two" into a variable expression.

47. Translate and simplify "eight times the quotient of twice a number and sixteen."

48. Translate and simplify "the product of four and the sum of two and five times a number."

49. **Geometry** The length of the base of a triangle is 15 in. more than the height of the triangle. Express the length of the base of the triangle in terms of the height of the triangle.

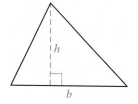

50. **Mixtures** A coffee merchant made 20 lb of a blend of coffee using only mocha java beans and espresso beans. Use the same variable to express the amounts of mocha java beans and espresso beans in the coffee blend.

Chapter 2 Test

View the Chapter Test Videos for fully worked-out solutions to any exercise.

1. Simplify: $(9y)4$

2. Simplify: $7x + 5y - 3x - 8y$

3. Simplify: $8n - (6 - 2n)$

4. Evaluate $3ab - (2a)^2$ when $a = -2$ and $b = -3$.

5. Identify the property that justifies the statement.
$$\frac{3}{8}(1) = \frac{3}{8}$$

6. Simplify: $-4(-x + 10)$

7. Simplify: $\frac{2}{3}x^2 - \frac{7}{12}x^2$

8. Simplify: $(-10x)\left(-\frac{2}{5}\right)$

9. Simplify: $(-4y^2 + 8)6$

10. Complete the statement by using the Inverse Property of Addition.
$$-19 + \text{?} = 0$$

11. Evaluate $\dfrac{-3ab}{2a + b}$ when $a = -1$ and $b = 4$.

12. Simplify: $5(x + y) - 8(x - y)$

13. Simplify: $6b - 9b + 4b$

14. Simplify: $13(6a)$

15. Simplify: $3(x^2 - 5x + 4)$

16. Evaluate $4(b - a) + bc$ when $a = 2$, $b = -3$, and $c = 4$.

17. Simplify: $6x - 3(y - 7x) + 2(5x - y)$

18. Translate "the quotient of eight more than n and seventeen" into a variable expression.

19. Translate "the difference between the sum of a and b and the square of b" into a variable expression.

20. Translate "the sum of the square of a number and the product of the number and eleven" into a variable expression.

21. Translate and simplify "twenty times the sum of a number and nine."

22. Translate and simplify "two more than a number added to the difference between the number and three."

23. Translate and simplify "a number minus the product of one-fourth and twice the number."

24. **Astronomy** The distance from Neptune to the sun is thirty times the distance from Earth to the sun. Express the distance from Neptune to the sun in terms of the distance from Earth to the sun.

25. **Carpentry** A nine-foot board is cut into two pieces of different lengths. Use the same variable to express the lengths of the two pieces.

Cumulative Review Exercises

1. Add: $-4 + 7 + (-10)$

2. Subtract: $-16 - (-25) - 4$

3. Multiply: $(-2)(3)(-4)$

4. Divide: $(-60) \div 12$

5. Write $1\frac{1}{4}$ as a decimal.

6. Write 60% as a fraction and as a decimal.

7. Use the roster method to write the set of negative integers greater than or equal to -4.

8. Write $\frac{2}{25}$ as a percent.

9. Subtract: $\frac{7}{12} - \frac{11}{16} - \left(-\frac{1}{3}\right)$

10. Divide: $\frac{5}{12} \div \left(\frac{3}{2}\right)$

11. Multiply: $\left(-\frac{9}{16}\right)\left(\frac{8}{27}\right)\left(-\frac{3}{2}\right)$

12. Simplify: $-3^2 \cdot \left(-\frac{2}{3}\right)^3$

13. Simplify: $-2^5 \div (3 - 5)^2 - (-3)$

14. Simplify: $\left(-\frac{3}{4}\right)^2 - \left(\frac{3}{8} - \frac{11}{12}\right)$

15. Evaluate $a - 3b^2$ when $a = 4$ and $b = -2$.

16. Simplify: $-2x^2 - (-3x^2) + 4x^2$

17. Simplify: $8a - 12b - 9a$

18. Simplify: $\dfrac{1}{3}(9a)$

19. Simplify: $\left(-\dfrac{5}{8}\right)(-32b)$

20. Simplify: $5(4 - 2x)$

21. Simplify: $-3(-2y + 7)$

22. Simplify: $-2(3x^2 - 4y^2)$

23. Simplify: $-4(2y^2 - 5y - 8)$

24. Simplify: $-4x - 3(2x - 5)$

25. Simplify: $3(4x - 1) - 7(x + 2)$

26. Simplify: $3x + 2[x - 4(2 - x)]$

27. Simplify: $3[4x - 2(x - 4y)] + 5y$

28. Translate "the difference between six and the product of a number and twelve" into a variable expression.

29. Translate and simplify "the total of five and the difference between a number and seven."

30. Internet Connections The speed of a Digital Subscriber Line (DSL) Internet connection is ten times faster than that of a dial-up connection. Express the speed of the DSL connection in terms of the speed of the dial-up connection.

3 Solving Equations and Inequalities

DVD SSM

Online Study Center

Need help? For online student resources, such as section quizzes, visit the Online Study Center at www.cengage.com/math/aufmann.

In what year will these children enter high school? When will these children be eligible to collect Social Security or to retire? How many others will retire that same year? Demographers ask these questions when studying population groups to make projections for the future. These projections are used by organizations such as college administrators and managers of retirement communities. The **Focus on Problem Solving on pages 155–156** provides an example of how demography can be used to plan as far as 50 years into the future.

Prep Test

1. Subtract: $8 - 12$

2. Multiply: $-\dfrac{3}{4}\left(-\dfrac{4}{3}\right)$

3. Multiply: $-\dfrac{5}{8}(16)$

4. Write 90% as a decimal.

5. Write 0.75 as a percent.

6. Evaluate $3x^2 - 4x - 1$ when $x = -4$.

7. Simplify: $3x - 5 + 7x$

8. Simplify: $8x - 9 - 8x$

9. Simplify: $6x - 3(6 - x)$

3.1 Introduction to Equations

OBJECTIVE 1

Determine whether a given number is a solution of an equation

Point of Interest

One of the most famous equations ever stated is E = mc². *This equation, stated by Albert Einstein, shows that there is a relationship between mass* m *and energy* E.

An **equation** expresses the equality of two mathematical expressions. The expressions can be either numerical or variable expressions.

$$\left.\begin{array}{l} 9 + 3 = 12 \\ 3x - 2 = 10 \\ y^2 + 4 = 2y - 1 \\ z = 2 \end{array}\right\} \text{Equations}$$

The equation at the right is true if the variable is replaced by 5.

$$x + 8 = 13$$
$$5 + 8 = 13 \qquad \text{A true equation}$$

The equation $x + 8 = 13$ is false if the variable is replaced by 7.

$$7 + 8 = 13 \qquad \text{A false equation}$$

A **solution** of an equation is a number that, when substituted for the variable, results in a true equation. 5 is a solution of the equation $x + 8 = 13$. 7 is not a solution of the equation $x + 8 = 13$.

EXAMPLE 1 Is -3 a solution of the equation $4x + 16 = x^2 - 5$?

Solution

$$4x + 16 = x^2 - 5$$

$4(-3) + 16$	$(-3)^2 - 5$
$-12 + 16$	$9 - 5$

$$4 = 4$$

Yes, -3 is a solution of the equation $4x + 16 = x^2 - 5$.

• Replace the variable by the given number, -3.

• Evaluate the numerical expressions using the Order of Operations Agreement.

• Compare the results. If the results are equal, the given number is a solution. If the results are not equal, the given number is not a solution.

PROBLEM 1   Is $\dfrac{1}{4}$ a solution of $5 - 4x = 8x + 2$?

Solution   See page S5.

EXAMPLE 2   Is -4 a solution of $4 + 5x = x^2 - 2x$?

Solution

$$4 + 5x = x^2 - 2x$$

$4 + 5(-4)$	$(-4)^2 - 2(-4)$
$4 + (-20)$	$16 - (-8)$

$$-16 \neq 24$$

No, -4 is not a solution
of the equation
$4 + 5x = x^2 - 2x$.

- **Replace the variable by the given number, -4.**
- **Evaluate the numerical expressions using the Order of Operations Agreement.**
- **Compare the results. If the results are equal, the given number is a solution. If the results are not equal, the given number is not a solution.**

PROBLEM 2   Is 5 a solution of $10x - x^2 = 3x - 10$?

Solution   See page S5.

OBJECTIVE 2

Solve equations of the form $x + a = b$

To **solve an equation** means to find a solution of the equation. The simplest equation to solve is an equation of the form **variable = constant,** because the constant is the solution.

If $x = 5$, then 5 is the solution of the equation because $5 = 5$ is a true equation.

The solution of the equation shown at the right is 7.

$$x + 2 = 9 \qquad 7 + 2 = 9$$

Note that if 4 is added to each side of the equation, the solution is still 7.

$$x + 2 + 4 = 9 + 4$$
$$x + 6 = 13 \qquad 7 + 6 = 13$$

If -5 is added to each side of the equation, the solution is still 7.

$$x + 2 + (-5) = 9 + (-5)$$
$$x - 3 = 4 \qquad 7 - 3 = 4$$

This illustrates the Addition Property of Equations.

Take Note

Think of an equation as a balance scale. If the weights added to each side of the equation are not the same, the pans no longer balance.

Addition Property of Equations

The same number or variable term can be added to each side of an equation without changing the solution of the equation.

This property is used in solving equations. Note the effect of adding, to each side of the equation $x + 2 = 9$, the opposite of the constant term 2. After each side of the equation is simplified, the equation is in the form variable = constant. The solution is the constant.

$$x + 2 = 9$$
$$x + 2 + (-2) = 9 + (-2)$$
$$x + 0 = 7$$
$$x = 7$$

$$\boxed{\text{variable}} = \boxed{\text{constant}}$$

The solution is 7.

In solving an equation, the goal is to rewrite the given equation in the form *variable* = *constant*. The Addition Property of Equations can be used to rewrite an equation in this form. The Addition Property of Equations is used to remove a term from one side of an equation by adding the opposite of that term to each side of the equation.

EXAMPLE 3 Solve and check: $y - 6 = 9$

Solution

$y - 6 = 9$

$y - 6 + 6 = 9 + 6$

$y + 0 = 15$

$y = 15$

- The goal is to rewrite the equation in the form *variable* = *constant*.
- Add **6** to each side of the equation (the Addition Property of Equations).
- Simplify using the Inverse Property of Addition.
- Simplify using the Addition Property of Zero. Now the equation is in the form *variable* = *constant*.

Check

$$\frac{y - 6 = 9}{15 - 6 \mid 9}$$

$9 = 9$

- This is a true equation. The solution checks.

The solution is 15.

- Write the solution.

PROBLEM 3 Solve and check: $x - \dfrac{1}{3} = -\dfrac{3}{4}$

Solution See page S5.

Because subtraction is defined in terms of addition, the Addition Property of Equations makes it possible to subtract the same number from each side of an equation without changing the solution of the equation.

Solve: $y + \dfrac{1}{2} = \dfrac{5}{4}$

The goal is to rewrite the equation in the form *variable* = *constant*.

$$y + \frac{1}{2} = \frac{5}{4}$$

Add the opposite of the constant term $\frac{1}{2}$ to each side of the equation. This is equivalent to subtracting $\frac{1}{2}$ from each side of the equation.

$$y + \frac{1}{2} - \frac{1}{2} = \frac{5}{4} - \frac{1}{2}$$

$$y + 0 = \frac{5}{4} - \frac{2}{4}$$

$$y = \frac{3}{4}$$

The solution $\frac{3}{4}$ checks.

The solution is $\dfrac{3}{4}$.

EXAMPLE 4   Solve: $\dfrac{1}{2} = x + \dfrac{2}{3}$

Solution $\dfrac{1}{2} = x + \dfrac{2}{3}$

$\dfrac{1}{2} - \dfrac{2}{3} = x + \dfrac{2}{3} - \dfrac{2}{3}$ • Subtract $\dfrac{2}{3}$ from each side of the equation.

$-\dfrac{1}{6} = x$ • Simplify each side of the equation.

The solution is $-\dfrac{1}{6}$.

PROBLEM 4   Solve: $-8 = 5 + x$

Solution   See page S5.

Note from the solution to Example 4 that an equation can be rewritten in the form *constant = variable*. Whether the equation is written in the form *variable = constant* or in the form *constant = variable*, the solution is the constant.

OBJECTIVE **3**   **Solve equations of the form $ax = b$**

The solution of the equation shown at the right is 3.
$$2x = 6 \qquad\qquad 2 \cdot 3 = 6$$

Note that if each side of the equation is multiplied by 5, the solution is still 3.
$$5 \cdot 2x = 5 \cdot 6$$
$$10x = 30 \qquad\qquad 10 \cdot 3 = 30$$

If each side is multiplied by -4, the solution is still 3.
$$(-4) \cdot 2x = (-4) \cdot 6$$
$$-8x = -24 \qquad\qquad -8 \cdot 3 = -24$$

This illustrates the Multiplication Property of Equations.

Multiplication Property of Equations

Each side of an equation can be multiplied by the same nonzero number without changing the solution of the equation.

This property is used in solving equations. Note the effect of multiplying each side of the equation $2x = 6$ by the reciprocal of the coefficient 2. After each side of the equation is simplified, the equation is in the form variable = constant. The solution is the constant.

$$2x = 6$$
$$\dfrac{1}{2} \cdot 2x = \dfrac{1}{2} \cdot 6$$
$$1x = 3$$
$$x = 3$$

variable = constant

The solution is 3.

In solving an equation, the goal is to rewrite the given equation in the form variable = constant. The Multiplication Property of Equations can be used to rewrite an equation in this form. The Multiplication Property of Equations is used to remove a coefficient from a variable term in an equation by multiply-ing each side of the equation by the reciprocal of the coefficient.

EXAMPLE 5   Solve: $\dfrac{3x}{4} = -9$

Solution

$$\frac{3x}{4} = -9$$

$$\frac{4}{3} \cdot \frac{3}{4}x = \frac{4}{3}(-9)$$

$$1x = -12$$

$$x = -12$$

The solution is -12.

- $\frac{3x}{4} = \frac{3}{4}x$

- **Multiply each side of the equation by the reciprocal of the coefficient $\frac{3}{4}$ (the Multiplication Property of Equations).**
- **Simplify using the Inverse Property of Multiplication.**
- **Simplify using the Multiplication Property of One. Now the equation is in the form *variable = constant.***

- **Write the solution.**

PROBLEM 5   Solve: $-\dfrac{2x}{5} = 6$

Solution   See page S5.

Because division is defined in terms of multiplication, the Multiplication Property of Equations makes it possible to divide each side of an equation by the same number without changing the solution of the equation.

Solve: $8x = 16$

The goal is to rewrite the equation in the form *variable = constant*.

$$8x = 16$$

Multiply each side of the equation by the reciprocal of 8. This is equivalent to dividing each side by 8.

$$\frac{8x}{8} = \frac{16}{8}$$

$$x = 2$$

The solution 2 checks.

The solution is 2.

When using the Multiplication Property of Equations to solve an equation, multiply each side of the equation by the reciprocal of the coefficient when the coefficient is a fraction. Divide each side of the equation by the coefficient when the coefficient is an integer or a decimal.

EXAMPLE 6   Solve and check: $4x = 6$

Solution

$$4x = 6$$

$$\frac{4x}{4} = \frac{6}{4}$$

$$x = \frac{3}{2}$$

- **Divide each side of the equation by 4, the coefficient of x.**

- **Simplify each side of the equation.**

Check
$$\frac{4x = 6}{4\left(\dfrac{3}{2}\right)\ \bigg|\ 6}$$
$$6 = 6$$
• **This is a true equation. The solution checks.**

The solution is $\dfrac{3}{2}$.

PROBLEM 6   Solve and check: $6x = 10$

Solution   See page S5.

Before using one of the Properties of Equations, check to see whether one or both sides of the equation can be simplified. In Example 7, like terms appear on the left side of the equation. The first step in solving this equation is to combine the like terms so that there is only one variable term on the left side of the equation.

EXAMPLE 7   Solve: $5x - 9x = 12$

Solution
$$5x - 9x = 12$$
$$-4x = 12$$ • **Combine like terms.**
$$\frac{-4x}{-4} = \frac{12}{-4}$$ • **Divide each side of the equation by -4.**
$$x = -3$$

The solution is -3.

PROBLEM 7   Solve: $4x - 8x = 16$

Solution   See page S5.

OBJECTIVE [4]   ## Application problems: uniform motion

Any object that travels at a constant speed in a straight line is said to be in *uniform motion*. **Uniform motion** means that the speed and direction of an object do not change. For instance, a car traveling at a constant speed of 45 mph on a straight road is in uniform motion.

> **Take Note**
>
> A car traveling in a *circle* at a constant speed of 45 mph is *not* in uniform motion because the direction of the car is always changing.

The solution of a uniform motion problem is based on the equation $d = rt$, where d is the distance traveled, r is the rate of travel, and t is the time spent traveling. Suppose a car travels at 50 mph for 3 h. Because the rate (50 mph) and the time (3 h) are known, we can find the distance traveled by solving the equation $d = rt$ for d.

$$d = rt$$
$$d = 50(3) \qquad • \ r = 50, t = 3$$
$$d = 150$$

The car travels a distance of 150 mi.

A jogger runs 3 mi in 45 min. What is the rate of the jogger in miles per hour?

Because the answer must be in miles per *hour* and the time is given in *minutes*, convert 45 min to hours.

$$45 \text{ min} = \frac{3}{4} \text{ h}$$

To find the rate of the jogger, solve the equation $d = rt$ for r using $d = 3$ and $t = \frac{3}{4}$.

$$d = rt$$
$$3 = r\left(\frac{3}{4}\right)$$
$$3 = \frac{3}{4}r$$
$$\left(\frac{4}{3}\right)3 = \left(\frac{4}{3}\right)\frac{3}{4}r$$
$$4 = r$$

The rate of the jogger is 4 mph.

If two objects are moving in opposite directions, then the rate at which the distance between them is increasing is the sum of the speeds of the two objects. For instance, in the diagram at the right, two cars start from the same point and travel in opposite directions. The distance between them is changing at the rate of 70 mph.

Similarly, if two objects are moving toward each other, the distance between them is decreasing at a rate that is equal to the sum of the speeds. The rate at which the two planes at the right are approaching one another is 800 mph.

EXAMPLE 8   Two cars start from the same point and move in opposite directions. The car moving west is traveling 45 mph, and the car moving east is traveling 60 mph. In how many hours will the cars be 210 mi apart?

Strategy   The distance is 210 mi. Therefore, $d = 210$. The cars are moving in opposite directions, so the rate at which the distance between them is changing is the sum of the rates of the two cars. The rate is 45 mph + 60 mph = 105 mph. Therefore, $r = 105$. To find the time, solve the equation $d = rt$ for t.

Solution
$$d = rt$$
$$210 = 105t \quad \bullet\ d = 210, r = 105$$
$$\frac{210}{105} = \frac{105t}{105}$$
$$2 = t$$

In 2 h, the cars will be 210 mi apart.

PROBLEM 8 Two cyclists start at the same time at opposite ends of an 80-mile course. One cyclist is traveling 18 mph, and the second cyclist is traveling 14 mph. How long after they begin will they meet?

Solution See page S5.

If a motorboat is on a river that is flowing at a rate of 4 mph, the boat will float down the river at a speed of 4 mph even though the motor is not on. Now suppose the motor is turned on and the power adjusted so that the boat will travel at 10 mph without the aid of the current. Then, if the boat is moving *with* the current, its effective speed is the speed of the boat using power plus the speed of the current: 10 mph + 4 mph = 14 mph. However, if the boat is moving in the opposite direction of the current, the current slows the boat down, and the effective speed of the boat is the speed of the boat using power minus the speed of the current: 10 mph − 4 mph = 6 mph.

There are other situations in which these concepts may be applied.

Take Note

"ft/s" is an abbreviation for "feet per second."

EXAMPLE 9 An airline passenger is walking between two airline terminals and decides to get on a moving sidewalk that is 150 ft long. If the passenger walks at a rate of 7 ft/s and the moving sidewalk moves at a rate of 9 ft/s, how long, in seconds, will it take the passenger to walk from one end of the moving sidewalk to the other?

Strategy The distance is 150 ft. Therefore, $d = 150$. The passenger is traveling at 7 ft/s and the moving sidewalk is traveling at 9 ft/s. The rate of the passenger is the sum of the two rates, or 16 ft/s. Therefore, $r = 16$. To find the time, solve the equation $d = rt$ for t.

Solution
$$d = rt$$
$$150 = 16t \qquad \bullet \; \boldsymbol{d = 150, r = 16}$$
$$\frac{150}{16} = \frac{16t}{16}$$
$$9.375 = t$$

It will take the passenger 9.375 s to travel the length of the moving sidewalk.

PROBLEM 9 A plane that can normally travel at 250 mph in calm air is flying into a headwind of 25 mph. How far can the plane fly in 3 h?

Solution See page S5.

OBJECTIVE [5]   **Applications of percent**

The solution of a problem that involves a percent requires solving the basic percent equation.

> **The Basic Percent Equation**
>
> $$\text{Percent} \cdot \text{base} = \text{amount}$$
> $$P \quad\cdot\quad B \quad = \quad A$$

To translate a problem involving a percent into an equation, remember that the word *of* translates into "multiply" and the word *is* translates into "=." The base usually follows the word *of*.

20% of what number is 30?

Given: $P = 20\% = 0.20$
          $A = 30$
Unknown: Base

$$PB = A$$
$$(0.20)B = 30$$
$$\frac{0.20B}{0.20} = \frac{30}{0.20}$$
$$B = 150$$

The number is 150.

What percent of 40 is 30?

Given: $B = 40$
          $A = 30$
Unknown: Percent

$$PB = A$$
$$P(40) = 30$$
$$40P = 30$$
$$\frac{40P}{40} = \frac{30}{40}$$

We must write the fraction as a percent in order to answer the question.

$$P = \frac{3}{4}$$
$$P = 75\%$$

30 is 75% of 40.

Find 25% of 200.

Given: $P = 25\% = 0.25$
          $B = 200$
Unknown: Amount

$$PB = A$$
$$0.25(200) = A$$
$$50 = A$$

25% of 200 is 50.

In most cases, we write a percent as a decimal before solving the basic percent equation. However, some percents are more easily written as a fraction. For example,

$$33\frac{1}{3}\% = \frac{1}{3} \qquad 66\frac{2}{3}\% = \frac{2}{3} \qquad 16\frac{2}{3}\% = \frac{1}{6} \qquad 83\frac{1}{3}\% = \frac{5}{6}$$

EXAMPLE 10   12 is $33\frac{1}{3}$% of what number?

Solution

$PB = A$ • $33\frac{1}{3}\% = \frac{1}{3}$

$\frac{1}{3}B = 12$

$3 \cdot \frac{1}{3}B = 3 \cdot 12$

$B = 36$

The number is 36.

PROBLEM 10   27 is what percent of 60?

Solution   See page S6.

EXAMPLE 11   During a recent year, nearly 1.2 million dogs or litters were registered with the American Kennel Club. The most popular breed was the Labrador retriever, with 172,841 registered. What percent of the registrations were Labrador retrievers? Round to the nearest tenth of a percent. (*Source:* American Kennel Club)

Strategy   To find the percent, solve the basic percent equation using $B = 1.2$ million $= 1,200,000$ and $A = 172,841$. The percent is unknown.

Solution

$PB = A$

$P(1,200,000) = 172,841$

$\dfrac{P(1,200,000)}{1,200,000} = \dfrac{172,841}{1,200,000}$

$P \approx 0.144$

$P \approx 14.4\%$

Approximately 14.4% of the registrations were Labrador retrievers.

PROBLEM 11   A student correctly answered 72 of the 80 questions on an exam. What percent of the questions were answered correctly?

Solution   See page S6.

EXAMPLE 12   According to the Centers for Disease Control and Prevention, 30.8% of the adult population of Kentucky smokes. How many adults in Kentucky smoke? Use a figure of 3,000,000 for the number of adults in Kentucky.

Strategy   To find the number of adults who smoke, solve the basic percent equation using $B = 3,000,000$ and $P = 30.8\% = 0.308$. The amount is unknown.

Solution

$PB = A$

$0.308(3,000,000) = A$

$924,000 = A$

Approximately 924,000 adults in Kentucky smoke.

Point of Interest

As noted at the right, 172,841 of the dogs or litters registered were Labrador retrievers. Listed below are the next most popular breeds and their registrations.
Golden retrievers: 66,300
German shepherds: 57,660
Dachshunds: 54,773
Beagles: 52,026

PROBLEM 12 The price of a digital camcorder is $895. A 6% sales tax is added to the price. How much is the sales tax?

Solution See page S6.

The simple interest that an investment earns is given by the equation

$$I = Prt$$

where I is the simple interest, P is the principal, or amount invested, r is the simple interest rate, and t is the time.

A $1500 investment has an annual simple interest rate of 7%. Find the simple interest earned on the investment after 18 months.

The time is given in months, but the interest rate is an annual rate. Therefore, we must convert 18 months to years.

18 months $= 1.5$ years

To find the interest earned, solve the equation $I = Prt$ for I using $P = 1500$, $r = 0.07$, and $t = 1.5$.

$I = Prt$
$I = 1500(0.07)(1.5)$
$I = 157.5$

The interest earned is $157.50.

EXAMPLE 13 In April, Marshall Wardell was charged $8.72 in interest on an unpaid credit card balance of $545. Find the annual interest rate for this credit card.

Strategy The interest is $8.72. Therefore, $I = 8.72$. The unpaid balance is $545. This is the principal on which interest is calculated. Therefore, $P = 545$. The time is 1 month. Because the *annual* interest rate must be found and the time is given as 1 month, write 1 month as $\dfrac{1}{12}$ year. Therefore, $t = \dfrac{1}{12}$. To find the interest rate, solve the equation $I = Prt$ for r.

Solution

$$I = Prt$$

$$8.72 = 545r\left(\frac{1}{12}\right)$$ • $I = 8.72, P = 545, t = \dfrac{1}{12}$

$$8.72 = \frac{545}{12}r$$

$$\frac{12}{545}(8.72) = \frac{12}{545}\left(\frac{545}{12}r\right)$$

$$0.192 = r$$

The annual interest rate is 19.2%.

PROBLEM 13   Clarissa Adams purchased a $1000 municipal bond that earns an annual simple interest rate of 6.4%. How much must she deposit into a bank account that earns 8% annual simple interest so that the interest earned from each account after one year is the same?

Solution   See page S6.

The amount of a substance in a solution can be given as a percent of the total solution. For instance, if a certain fruit juice drink is advertised as containing 27% cranberry juice, then 27% of the contents of the bottle must be cranberry juice.

Solving problems involving mixtures is based on the percent mixture equation

$$Q = Ar$$

where Q is the quantity of a substance in the solution, A is the amount of the solution, and r is the percent concentration of the substance.

The formula for a perfume requires that the concentration of jasmine be 1.2% of the total amount of perfume. How many ounces of jasmine are in a 2-ounce bottle of this perfume?

The amount of perfume is 2 oz. Therefore, $A = 2$. The percent concentration is 1.2%, so $r = 0.012$. To find the number of ounces of jasmine, solve the equation $Q = Ar$ for Q.

$Q = Ar$
$Q = 2(0.012)$
$Q = 0.024$

The bottle contains 0.024 oz of jasmine.

EXAMPLE 14   To make a certain color of blue, 4 oz of cyan must be contained in 1 gal of paint. What is the percent concentration of cyan in the paint?

Strategy   The amount of cyan is given in ounces and the amount of paint is given in gallons; we must convert ounces to gallons or gallons to ounces. For this problem, we will convert gallons to ounces: 1 gal = 128 oz.

Solution   To find the percent concentration of cyan, solve the equation $Q = Ar$ for r using $Q = 4$ and $A = 128$.

$Q = Ar$
$4 = 128r$
$\dfrac{4}{128} = \dfrac{128r}{128}$
$0.03125 = r$

The percent concentration of cyan is 3.125%.

PROBLEM 14   The concentration of sugar in Choco-Pops cereal is 25%. If a bowl of this cereal contains 2 oz of sugar, how many ounces of cereal are in the bowl?

Solution   See page S6.

3.1 Concept Review

Determine whether the statement is always true, sometimes true, or never true.

1. Both sides of an equation can be multiplied by the same number without changing the solution of the equation.

2. Both sides of an equation can be divided by the same number without changing the solution of the equation.

3. For an equation of the form $ax = b$, $a \neq 0$, multiplying both sides of the equation by the reciprocal of a will result in an equation of the form $x = constant$.

4. Use the Multiplication Property of Equations to remove a term from one side of an equation.

5. Adding a negative 3 to each side of an equation yields the same result as subtracting 3 from each side of the equation.

6. In the basic percent equation, the amount follows the word *of*.

7. An equation contains an equals sign.

3.1 Exercises

1 Determine whether a given number is a solution of an equation

1. Complete the sentence using the word *expression* or the word *equation*.
   a. $8x = 4x + 10$ is an ___?___.   **b.** $8x - 4x + 10$ is an ___?___.

2. Determine whether -3 is a solution of the equation $9 - 5x = -3 - 9x$.

$9 - 5x$	$= -3 - 9x$	
$9 - 5(-3)$	$-3 - 9(-3)$	• Replace the variable by the given number, ___?___.
$9 + $ ___?___	$-3 + $ ___?___	• Evaluate the numerical expressions.
___?___	___?___	• Compare the results.

   The results are ___?___; therefore, -3 is a solution of the equation $9 - 5x = -3 - 9x$.

3. Is 4 a solution of
   $2x = 8$?

4. Is 3 a solution of
   $y + 4 = 7$?

5. Is -1 a solution of
   $2b - 1 = 3$?

6. Is -2 a solution of
   $3a - 4 = 10$?

7. Is 1 a solution of
   $4 - 2m = 3$?

8. Is 2 a solution of
   $7 - 3n = 2$?

9. Is 5 a solution of
   $2x + 5 = 3x$?

10. Is 4 a solution of
    $3y - 4 = 2y$?

11. Is 0 a solution of
    $4a + 5 = 3a + 5$?

12. Is 0 a solution of
$4 - 3b = 4 - 5b$?

13. Is -2 a solution of
$4 - 2n = n + 10$?

14. Is -3 a solution of
$5 - m = 2 - 2m$?

15. Is 3 a solution of
$z^2 + 1 = 4 + 3z$?

16. Is 2 a solution of
$2x^2 - 1 = 4x - 1$?

17. Is -1 a solution of
$y^2 - 1 = 4y + 3$?

18. Is -2 a solution of
$m^2 - 4 = m + 3$?

19. Is 4 a solution of
$x(x + 1) = x^2 + 5$?

20. Is 3 a solution of
$2a(a - 1) = 3a + 3$?

21. Is $-\frac{1}{4}$ a solution of
$8t + 1 = -1$?

22. Is $\frac{1}{2}$ a solution of
$4y + 1 = 3$?

23. Is $\frac{2}{5}$ a solution of
$5m + 1 = 10m - 3$?

24. Is $\frac{3}{4}$ a solution of
$8x - 1 = 12x + 3$?

25. Is 2.1 a solution of
$x^2 - 4x = x + 1.89$?

26. Is 1.5 a solution of
$c^2 - 3c = 4c - 8.25$?

2 Solve equations of the form $x + a = b$

27. How is the Addition Property of Equations used to solve an equation?

28. Explain why the goal in solving an equation is to write the equation in the form *variable* = *constant*.

29. To solve the equation $p - 30 = 57$, use the Addition Property of Equations to add ____?____ to each side of the equation. The solution is ____?____.

30. To solve the equation $18 + n = 25$, ____?____ 18 from each side of the equation. The solution is ____?____.

31. Without solving the equation $x + \frac{13}{15} = -\frac{21}{43}$, determine whether x is less than or greater than $-\frac{21}{43}$. Explain your answer.

32. Without solving the equation $x - \frac{11}{16} = \frac{19}{24}$, determine whether x is less than or greater than $\frac{19}{24}$. Explain your answer.

Solve and check.

33. $x + 5 = 7$

34. $y + 3 = 9$

35. $b - 4 = 11$

36. $z - 6 = 10$

37. $2 + a = 8$

38. $5 + x = 12$

39. $m + 9 = 3$

40. $t + 12 = 10$

41. $n - 5 = -2$

42. $x - 6 = -5$

43. $b + 7 = 7$

44. $y - 5 = -5$

45. $a - 3 = -5$

46. $x - 6 = -3$

47. $z + 9 = 2$

48. $n + 11 = 1$

49. $10 + m = 3$

50. $8 + x = 5$

51. $9 + x = -3$

52. $10 + y = -4$

53. $b - 5 = -3$

54. $t - 6 = -4$

55. $2 = x + 7$

56. $-8 = n + 1$

57. $4 = m - 11$

58. $-6 = y - 5$

59. $12 = 3 + w$

60. $-9 = 5 + x$

61. $4 = -10 + b$

62. $-7 = -2 + x$

63. $m + \dfrac{2}{3} = -\dfrac{1}{3}$

64. $c + \dfrac{3}{4} = -\dfrac{1}{4}$

65. $x - \dfrac{1}{2} = \dfrac{1}{2}$

66. $x - \dfrac{2}{5} = \dfrac{3}{5}$

67. $\dfrac{5}{8} + y = \dfrac{1}{8}$

68. $\dfrac{4}{9} + a = -\dfrac{2}{9}$

69. $m + \dfrac{1}{2} = -\dfrac{1}{4}$

70. $b + \dfrac{1}{6} = -\dfrac{1}{3}$

71. $x + \dfrac{2}{3} = \dfrac{3}{4}$

72. $n + \dfrac{2}{5} = \dfrac{2}{3}$

73. $-\dfrac{5}{6} = x - \dfrac{1}{4}$

74. $-\dfrac{1}{4} = c - \dfrac{2}{3}$

75. $-\dfrac{1}{21} = m + \dfrac{2}{3}$

76. $\dfrac{5}{9} = b - \dfrac{1}{3}$

77. $\dfrac{5}{12} = n + \dfrac{3}{4}$

78. $d + 1.3619 = 2.0148$

79. $w + 2.932 = 4.801$

80. $-0.813 + x = -1.096$

81. $-1.926 + t = -1.042$

3 Solve equations of the form $ax = b$

82. How is the Multiplication Property of Equations used to solve an equation?

83. Why, when the Multiplication Property of Equations is used, must the number that multiplies each side of the equation not be zero?

84. To solve the equation $\frac{2}{3}w = -18$, use the Multiplication Property of Equations to multiply each side of the equation by ___?___. The solution is ___?___.

85. To solve the equation $56 = 8n$, ___?___ each side of the equation by 8. The solution is ___?___.

86. Without solving the equation $-\frac{15}{41}x = -\frac{23}{25}$, determine whether x is less than or greater than zero. Explain your answer.

87. Without solving the equation $\frac{5}{28}x = -\frac{3}{44}$, determine whether x is less than or greater than zero. Explain your answer.

Solve and check.

88. $5x = 15$

89. $4y = 28$

90. $3b = -12$

91. $2a = -14$

92. $-3x = 6$

93. $-5m = 20$

94. $-3x = -27$

95. $-6n = -30$

96. $20 = 4c$ **97.** $18 = 2t$ **98.** $-32 = 8w$ **99.** $-56 = 7x$

100. $8d = 0$ **101.** $-5x = 0$ **102.** $36 = 9z$ **103.** $35 = -5x$

104. $-64 = 8a$ **105.** $-32 = -4y$ **106.** $-42 = 6t$ **107.** $-12m = -144$

108. $\dfrac{x}{3} = 2$ **109.** $\dfrac{x}{4} = 3$ **110.** $-\dfrac{y}{2} = 5$ **111.** $-\dfrac{b}{3} = 6$

112. $\dfrac{n}{7} = -4$ **113.** $\dfrac{t}{6} = -3$ **114.** $\dfrac{2}{5}x = 12$ **115.** $-\dfrac{4}{3}c = -8$

116. $\dfrac{5}{6}y = -20$ **117.** $-\dfrac{2}{3}d = 8$ **118.** $-\dfrac{3}{5}m = 12$ **119.** $-\dfrac{3}{4}x = -24$

120. $\dfrac{2n}{3} = 2$ **121.** $\dfrac{5x}{6} = -10$ **122.** $\dfrac{-3z}{8} = 9$ **123.** $\dfrac{-4x}{5} = -12$

124. $-6 = -\dfrac{2}{3}y$ **125.** $-15 = -\dfrac{3}{5}x$ **126.** $\dfrac{2}{9} = \dfrac{2}{3}y$ **127.** $-\dfrac{6}{7} = -\dfrac{3}{4}b$

128. $-\dfrac{2}{5}m = -\dfrac{6}{7}$ **129.** $5x + 2x = 14$ **130.** $3n + 2n = 20$ **131.** $7d - 4d = 9$

132. $10y - 3y = 21$ **133.** $2x - 5x = 9$ **134.** $\dfrac{x}{1.4} = 3.2$ **135.** $\dfrac{z}{2.9} = -7.8$

136. $3.4a = 7.004$ **137.** $2.3m = 2.415$ **138.** $-3.7x = 7.77$ **139.** $-1.6m = 5.44$

140. In the equation $15x = y$, y is a positive integer. Is the value of x a negative number?

141. In the equation $-6x = y$, y is a negative integer. Is the value of x a negative number?

142. In the equation $-\dfrac{1}{4}x = y$, y is a positive integer. Is the value of x a negative number?

4   Application problems: uniform motion

143. In the formula $d = rt$, d represents ___?___, r represents ___?___, and t represents ___?___.

144. A car that travels 10 mi in 30 min is traveling at a rate of ___?___ miles per hour.

145. Maria and Nathan start hiking at the same time. Maria hikes at 3 mph and Nathan hikes at 2.5 mph. After t hours, Maria has hiked ___?___ miles and Nathan has hiked ___?___ miles.

146. A plane flies at a rate of 325 mph in calm air. The wind is blowing at 30 mph. Flying with the wind, the plane travels ___?___ mph. Flying against the wind, the plane travels ___?___ mph.

147. Joe and John live 2 mi apart. They leave their houses at the same time and walk toward each other until they meet. Joe walks faster than John does.
   a. Is the distance walked by Joe less than, equal to, or greater than the distance walked by John?
   b. Is the time spent walking by Joe less than, equal to, or greater than the time spent walking by John?
   c. What is the total distance traveled by both Joe and John?

148. Morgan and Emma ride their bikes from Morgan's house to the store. Morgan begins biking 5 min before Emma begins. Emma bikes faster than Morgan and catches up with her just as they reach the store.
   a. Is the distance biked by Emma less than, equal to, or greater than the distance biked by Morgan?
   b. Is the time spent biking by Emma less than, equal to, or greater than the time spent biking by Morgan?

149. A train travels at 45 mph for 3 h and then increases its speed to 55 mph for 2 more hours. How far does the train travel in the 5-hour period?

150. As part of a training program for the Boston Marathon, a runner wants to build endurance by running at a rate of 9 mph for 20 min. How far will the runner travel in that time period?

151. It takes a hospital dietician 40 min to drive from home to the hospital, a distance of 20 mi. What is the dietician's average rate of speed?

152. Marcella leaves home at 9:00 A.M. and drives to school, arriving at 9:45 A.M. If the distance between home and school is 27 mi, what is Marcella's average rate of speed?

153. The Ride for Health Bicycle Club has chosen a 36-mile course for this Saturday's ride. If the riders plan on averaging 12 mph while they are riding and they have a 1-hour lunch break planned, how long will it take them to complete the trip?

154. Palmer's average running speed is 3 kilometers per hour faster than his walking speed. If Palmer can run around a 30-kilometer course in 2 h, how many hours would it take for Palmer to walk the same course?

155. A shopping mall has a moving sidewalk that takes shoppers from the shopping area to the parking garage, a distance of 250 ft. If your normal walking rate is 5 ft/s and the moving sidewalk is traveling at 3 ft/s, how many seconds would it take you to walk on the moving sidewalk from the parking garage to the shopping area?

156. K&B River Tours offers a river trip that takes passengers from the K&B dock to a small island that is 24 mi away. The passengers spend 1 h at the island and then return to the K&B dock. If the speed of the boat is 10 mph in calm water and the rate of the current is 2 mph, how long does the trip last?

157. Two joggers start at the same time from opposite ends of an 8-mile jogging trail and begin running toward each other. One jogger is running at a rate of 5 mph, and the other jogger is running at a rate of 7 mph. How long, in minutes, after they start will the two joggers meet?

158. Two cyclists start from the same point at the same time and move in opposite directions. One cyclist is traveling at 8 mph, and the other cyclist is traveling at 9 mph. After 30 min, how far apart are the two cyclists?

159. Petra, who can paddle her canoe at a rate of 10 mph in calm water, is paddling her canoe on a river whose current is 2 mph. How long will it take her to travel 4 mi upstream against the current?

160. At 8:00 A.M., a train leaves a station and travels at a rate of 45 mph. At 9:00 A.M., a second train leaves the same station on the same track and travels in the direction of the first train at a speed of 60 mph. At 10:00 A.M., how far apart are the two trains?

5 Applications of percent

161. Employee A had an annual salary of $52,000, Employee B had an annual salary of $58,000, and Employee C had an annual salary of $56,000 before each employee was given a 5% raise. Which of the three employees now has the highest annual salary? Explain how you arrived at your answer.

162. Each of three employees earned an annual salary of $65,000 before Employee A was given a 3% raise, Employee B was given a 6% raise, and Employee C was given a 4.5% raise. Which of the three employees now has the highest annual salary? Explain how you arrived at your answer.

Solve.

163. 12 is what percent of 50?

164. What percent of 125 is 50?

165. Find 18% of 40.

166. What is 25% of 60?

167. 12% of what is 48?

168. 45% of what is 9?

169. What is $33\frac{1}{3}\%$ of 27?

170. Find $16\frac{2}{3}\%$ of 30.

171. What percent of 12 is 3?

172. 10 is what percent of 15?

173. 60% of what is 3?

174. 75% of what is 6?

175. 12 is what percent of 6?

176. 20 is what percent of 16?

177. $5\frac{1}{4}$% of what is 21?

178. $37\frac{1}{2}$% of what is 15?

179. Find 15.4% of 50.

180. What is 18.5% of 46?

181. 1 is 0.5% of what?

182. 3 is 1.5% of what?

183. $\frac{3}{4}$% of what is 3?

184. $\frac{1}{2}$% of what is 3?

185. Find 125% of 16.

186. What is 250% of 12?

187. 16.4 is what percent of 20.4? Round to the nearest percent.

188. Find 18.3% of 625. Round to the nearest tenth.

189. Without solving an equation, determine whether 40% of 80 is less than, equal to, or greater than 80% of 40.

190. Without solving an equation, determine whether $\frac{1}{4}$% of 80 is less than, equal to, or greater than 25% of 80.

Complete Exercises 191 to 193 by replacing the question marks with the correct number from the problem situation or with the word *unknown*.

191. Problem Situation: It rained on 24 of the 30 days of June. What percent of the days in June were rainy days?
Using the formula $PB = A$, $P = $ ___?___ , $B = $ ___?___ , and $A = $ ___?___ .

192. Problem Situation: $7000 invested in a simple interest account earns $420 of interest in 2 years. What is the annual simple interest rate?
Using the formula $I = Prt$, $I = $ ___?___ , $P = $ ___?___ , $r = $ ___?___ , and $t = $ ___?___ .

193. Problem Situation: The label on a 32-ounce bottle of lemonade states that it contains 10% real lemon juice. How many ounces of real lemon juice are in the bottle?
Using the formula $Q = Ar$, $Q = $ ___?___ , $A = $ ___?___ , and $r = $ ___?___ .

194. a. Convert 30 months to years.   **b.** Convert 3 months to years.
c. Convert 9 months to years.   **d.** Convert 15 months to years.

195. **Stadiums** The Arthur Ashe Tennis Stadium in New York has a seating capacity of 22,500 people. Of these seats, 1.11% are wheelchair-accessible seats. How many seats in the stadium are reserved for wheelchair accessibility? Round to the nearest whole number.

196. **Education** The graph at the right shows the sources of revenue in a recent year for public schools in the United States. The total revenue was $419.8 billion dollars. How many billion dollars more did public schools receive from the state than from the federal government? Round to the nearest billion dollars. (*Source*: Census Bureau)

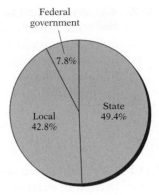

Sources of Revenue for Public Schools

197. **Natural Resources** On average, a person uses 13.2 gal of water per day for showering. This is 17.8% of the total amount of water used per person per day in the average single-family home. Find the total amount of water used per person per day in the average single-family home. Round to the nearest whole number. (*Source:* American Water Works Association)

198. **Business** During a recent year, 276 billion product coupons were issued by manufacturers. Shoppers redeemed 4.8 billion of these coupons. What percent of the coupons issued were redeemed by customers? Round to the nearest tenth of a percent. (*Source:* NCH NuWorld Consumer Behavior Study, America Coupon Council)

199. **Travel** According to the annual Summer Vacation Survey conducted by Myvesta, a nonprofit consumer education organization, the average summer vacation costs $2252. If $1850 of this amount is charged on a credit card, what percent of the vacation cost is charged? Round to the nearest tenth of a percent.

200. **The Internet** A recent survey by Internetworldstats.com found that there were 973 million people worldwide who had access to the Internet. What percent of the world's population had access to the Internet? Use a figure of 6.4 billion people for the world population. Round to the nearest tenth of a percent.

201. **The Internet** The graph at the right shows the responses to a Yahoo! survey that asked people how many hours per week they typically spend online. How many people were surveyed?

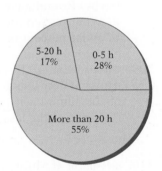

Hours per Week Spent Online

202. **Food Industry** Of the 63,800 pizzerias in the United States, 2750 are in New York. What percent of the pizzerias in the United States are in New York? Round to the nearest tenth of a percent. (*Source*: USA TODAY, February 22, 2005)

203. **Safety** Recently, the National Safety Council collected data on the leading causes of accidental death. The findings revealed that for people age 20, 30 died from a fall, 47 from fire, 200 from drowning, and 1950 from motor vehicle accidents. What percent of the accidental deaths were not attributed to motor vehicle accidents? Round to the nearest percent.

204. **Health** According to *Health* magazine, the average American has increased his or her daily consumption of calories from 18 years ago by 11.6%. If the average daily consumption was 1970 calories 18 years ago, what is the average daily consumption today? Round to the nearest whole number.

205. **Energy** The Energy Information Administration reports that if every U.S. household switched 4 h of lighting per day from incandescent bulbs to compact fluorescent bulbs, we would save 31.7 billion kilowatt-hours of electricity a year, or 33% of the total electricity used for home lighting. What is the total electricity used for home lighting in this country? Round to the nearest tenth of a billion.

206. **The Federal Government** To override a presidential veto, at least $66\frac{2}{3}\%$ of the Senate must vote to override the veto. There are 100 senators in the Senate. What is the minimum number of votes needed to override a veto?

207. **Advertising** Suppose that 125 million people saw a particular 30-second commercial for a soft drink during Super Bowl XL and that the cost for the commercial was approximately $2.5 million.
  a. If the soft drink manufacturer makes a profit of $.08 on each can sold, what percent of the people watching the commercial would have to buy one can of the soft drink for the company to recover the cost of the commercial?
  b. What percent of the people watching the commercial would have to purchase one six-pack of the soft drink for the company to recover the cost of the commercial? Round to the nearest tenth of a percent.

208. **Recreation** The graph at the right shows participation in All-American Soap Box Derbies. (*Source*: All-American Soap Box Derby) Round answers to the nearest tenth of a percent.
  a. What percent of the participants in 2000 were male?
  b. What percent of the participants in 2004 were female?

Participation in Soap Box Derbies

209. **Consumerism** A 16-horsepower lawn tractor with automatic transmission sells for $1579.99. This is 11% more than the price of the same lawn tractor with a standard transmission. What is the price of the less expensive model? Round to the nearest cent.

210. **Investment** If Miranda Perry invests $2500 in an account that earns an 8% annual simple interest rate, how much interest will Miranda have earned after 9 months?

211. **Investment** Kachina Caron invests $1200 in a simple interest account and earns $72 in 8 months. What is the annual simple interest rate?

212. **Investment** How much money must Andrea invest for two years in an account that earns an annual simple interest rate of 8% if she wants to earn $300 from the investment?

213. **Investment** Sal Boxer divided a gift of $3000 into two different accounts. He placed $1000 in one account that earned an annual simple interest rate of 7.5%. The remaining money was placed in an account that earned an annual simple interest rate of 8.25%. How much interest did Sal earn from the two accounts after one year?

214. Investment If Americo invests $2500 at an 8% annual simple interest rate and Octavia invests $3000 at a 7% annual simple interest rate, which of the two will earn the greater amount of interest in one year?

215. Investment Makana invested $900 in an account that earned an annual simple interest rate that was 1% higher than the rate her friend Marlys earned on her investment. If Marlys earned $51 after one year from an investment of $850, how much did Makana earn after one year?

216. Investment A $2000 investment at an annual simple interest rate of 6% earned as much interest after one year as another investment in an account that earned 8% annual simple interest. How much was invested at 8%?

217. Investment An investor places $1000 in an account that earns 9% annual simple interest and $1000 in an account that earns 6% annual simple interest. If each investment is left in the account for the same period of time, is the interest rate on the combined investment less than 6%, between 6% and 9%, or greater than 9%?

218. Mixture Problem The concentration of platinum in a necklace is 15%. The necklace weighs 12 g. Find the amount of platinum in the necklace.

219. Mixture Problem A 250-milliliter solution of a fabric dye contains 5 ml of hydrogen peroxide. What is the percent concentration of the hydrogen peroxide?

220. Mixture Problem A carpet is made of a blend of wool and other fibers. If the concentration of wool in the carpet is 75% and the carpet weighs 175 lb, how much wool is in the carpet?

221. Mixture Problem Apple Dan's 32-ounce apple-flavored fruit drink contains 8 oz of apple juice. Forty ounces of a generic brand of apple-flavored fruit drink contains 9 oz of apple juice. Which of the two brands has the greater concentration of apple juice?

222. Mixture Problem Bakers use simple syrup in many of their recipes. Simple syrup is made by combining 500 g of sugar with 500 g of water and mixing it well until the sugar dissolves. What is the percent concentration of sugar in simple syrup?

223. Mixture Problem A pharmacist has 50 g of a topical cream that contains 75% glycerin. How many grams of the cream are not glycerin?

224. Mixture Problem A chemist has 100 ml of a solution that is 9% acetic acid. If the chemist adds 50 ml of pure water to this solution, what is the percent concentration of the resulting mixture?

225. Mixture Problem A 500-gram salt and water solution contains 50 g of salt. This mixture is left in the open air and 100 g of water evaporates from the solution. What is the percent concentration of salt in the remaining solution?

3.1 Applying Concepts

Solve.

226. $\dfrac{2m + m}{5} = -9$

227. $\dfrac{3y - 8y}{7} = 15$

228. $\dfrac{1}{\dfrac{1}{x}} = 5$

229. $\dfrac{1}{\dfrac{1}{x}} + 8 = -19$

230. $\dfrac{4}{\dfrac{3}{b}} = 8$

231. $\dfrac{5}{\dfrac{7}{a}} - \dfrac{3}{\dfrac{7}{a}} = 6$

232. Solve for x: $x \div 28 = 1481$ remainder 25

233. **Geometry** Find the value of x in the diagram shown at the right.

234. **Consumerism** Your bill for dinner, including a 7.25% sales tax, was $92.74. You want to leave a 15% tip on the cost of the dinner before the sales tax. Find the amount of the tip to the nearest dollar.

235. **Consumerism** The total cost for a dinner was $97.52. This included a 15% tip calculated on the cost of the dinner after a 6% sales tax. Find the cost of dinner before the tip and tax.

236. **Business** A retailer decides to increase the original price of each item in the store by 10%. After the price increase, the retailer notices a significant drop in sales and so decides to reduce the current price of each item in the store by 10%. Are the prices back to the original prices? If not, are the prices lower or higher than the original prices?

237. If a quantity increases by 100%, how many times its original value is the new value?

238. Make up an equation of the form $x + a = b$ that has 2 as a solution.

239. Make up an equation of the form $ax = b$ that has -2 as a solution.

240. **Monthly Mortgage Payments** Suppose you have a $100,000 30-year mortgage. What is the difference between the monthly payment if the interest rate on your loan is 7.75% and the monthly payment if the interest rate is 7.25%? (*Hint:* You will need to discuss the question with an agent at a bank that provides mortgage services, discuss the question with a real estate agent, or find and use the formula for determining the monthly payment on a mortgage.)

241. The following problem does not contain enough information: "How many hours does it take to fly from Los Angeles to New York?" What additional information do we need in order to answer the question?

3.2   General Equations

OBJECTIVE **1**   **Solve equations of the form $ax + b = c$**

In solving an equation of the form $ax + b = c$, the goal is to rewrite the equation in the form *variable = constant*. This requires applying both the Addition and the Multiplication Properties of Equations.

Solve: $\dfrac{2}{5}x - 3 = -7$

$$\dfrac{2}{5}x - 3 = -7$$

Add 3 to each side of the equation.

$$\dfrac{2}{5}x - 3 + 3 = -7 + 3$$

Simplify.

$$\dfrac{2}{5}x = -4$$

Multiply each side of the equation by the reciprocal of the coefficient $\dfrac{2}{5}$.

$$\dfrac{5}{2} \cdot \dfrac{2}{5}x = \dfrac{5}{2}(-4)$$

Simplify. Now the equation is in the form *variable = constant*.

$$x = -10$$

Check $\dfrac{2}{5}x - 3 = -7$

$$\begin{array}{c|c} \dfrac{2}{5}(-10) - 3 & -7 \\ -4 - 3 & -7 \\ -7 = -7 & \end{array}$$

Write the solution.   The solution is -10.

EXAMPLE 1   Solve: $3x - 7 = -5$

Solution

$3x - 7 = -5$

$3x - 7 + 7 = -5 + 7$ • **Add 7** to each side of the equation.

$3x = 2$ • **Simplify.**

$\dfrac{3x}{3} = \dfrac{2}{3}$ • **Divide each side of the equation by 3.**

$x = \dfrac{2}{3}$ • **Simplify.** Now the equation is in the form *variable = constant*.

The solution is $\dfrac{2}{3}$.   • **Write the solution.**

PROBLEM 1   Solve: $5x + 7 = 10$

Solution   See page S6.

EXAMPLE 2   Solve: $5 = 9 - 2x$

Solution

$$5 = 9 - 2x$$

$$5 - 9 = 9 - 9 - 2x$$ • Subtract 9 **from each side of the equation.**

$$-4 = -2x$$ • **Simplify.**

$$\frac{-4}{-2} = \frac{-2x}{-2}$$ • **Divide each side of the equation by** -2.

$$2 = x$$ • **Simplify.**

The solution is 2.   • **Write the solution.**

PROBLEM 2   Solve: $11 = 11 + 3x$

Solution   See page S6.

Note in Example 4 in the Introduction to Equations section that the original equation, $\frac{1}{2} = x + \frac{2}{3}$, contained fractions with denominators of 2 and 3. The least common multiple of 2 and 3 is 6. The least common multiple has the property that both 2 and 3 will divide evenly into it. Therefore, if both sides of the equation are multiplied by 6, both of the denominators will divide evenly into 6. The result is an equation that does not contain any fractions. Multiplying an equation that contains fractions by the LCM of the denominators is called **clearing denominators.** It is an alternative method of solving an equation that contains fractions.

Solve: $\dfrac{1}{2} = x + \dfrac{2}{3}$

$$\frac{1}{2} = x + \frac{2}{3}$$

Multiply both sides of the equation by 6, the LCM of the denominators.

$$6\left(\frac{1}{2}\right) = 6\left(x + \frac{2}{3}\right)$$

Simplify each side of the equation. Use the Distributive Property on the right side of the equation.

$$3 = 6(x) + 6\left(\frac{2}{3}\right)$$

Note that multiplying both sides of the equation by the LCM of the denominators eliminated the fractions.

$$3 = 6x + 4$$

Solve the resulting equation.

$$3 - 4 = 6x + 4 - 4$$
$$-1 = 6x$$
$$\frac{-1}{6} = \frac{6x}{6}$$
$$-\frac{1}{6} = x$$

The solution is $-\dfrac{1}{6}$.

EXAMPLE 3 Solve: $\dfrac{2}{3} + \dfrac{1}{4}x = -\dfrac{1}{3}$

Solution

$$\dfrac{2}{3} + \dfrac{1}{4}x = -\dfrac{1}{3}$$

$$12\left(\dfrac{2}{3} + \dfrac{1}{4}x\right) = 12\left(-\dfrac{1}{3}\right)$$

$$12\left(\dfrac{2}{3}\right) + 12\left(\dfrac{1}{4}x\right) = -4$$

$$8 + 3x = -4$$
$$8 - 8 + 3x = -4 - 8$$
$$3x = -12$$
$$\dfrac{3x}{3} = \dfrac{-12}{3}$$
$$x = -4$$

• The equation contains fractions. Find the LCM of the denominators.
• The LCM of 3 and 4 is 12. Multiply each side of the equation by 12.
• Use the Distributive Property to multiply the left side of the equation by 12.
• The equation now contains no fractions.

The solution is −4.

PROBLEM 3 Solve: $\dfrac{5}{2} - \dfrac{2}{3}x = \dfrac{1}{2}$

Solution See page S6.

OBJECTIVE 2 Solve equations of the form *ax* + *b* = *cx* + *d*

In solving an equation of the form $ax + b = cx + d$, the goal is to rewrite the equation in the form *variable* = *constant*. Begin by rewriting the equation so that there is only one variable term in the equation. Then rewrite the equation so that there is only one constant term.

Solve: $4x - 5 = 6x + 11$

	$4x - 5 = 6x + 11$
Subtract $6x$ from each side of the equation.	$4x - 6x - 5 = 6x - 6x + 11$
Simplify. Now there is only one variable term in the equation.	$-2x - 5 = 11$
Add 5 to each side of the equation.	$-2x - 5 + 5 = 11 + 5$
Simplify. Now there is only one constant term in the equation.	$-2x = 16$
Divide each side of the equation by -2.	$\dfrac{-2x}{-2} = \dfrac{16}{-2}$
Simplify. Now the equation is in the form *variable* = *constant*.	$x = -8$

Check $4x - 5 = 6x + 11$

$4(-8) - 5$	$6(-8) + 11$
$-32 - 5$	$-48 + 11$
$-37 = -37$	

Write the solution.   The solution is -8.

EXAMPLE 4   Solve: $4x - 3 = 8x - 7$

Solution $4x - 3 = 8x - 7$

$4x - 8x - 3 = 8x - 8x - 7$ • Subtract 8x from each side of the
                                    equation.

$-4x - 3 = -7$ • Simplify. Now there is only one
                          variable term in the equation.

$-4x - 3 + 3 = -7 + 3$ • Add 3 to each side of the equation.
$-4x = -4$ • Simplify. Now there is only one
                        constant term in the equation.

$\dfrac{-4x}{-4} = \dfrac{-4}{-4}$ • Divide each side of the equation by
                                           −4.

$x = 1$ • Simplify. Now the equation is in the
                     form *variable* = *constant*.

The solution is 1.   • Write the solution.

PROBLEM 4   Solve: $5x + 4 = 6 + 10x$

Solution   See page S7.

> ## Take Note
>
> As shown below, we could have rewritten the equation in the form *constant* = *variable* by subtracting 4x from each side, adding 7 to each side, and then dividing each side by 4.
>
> $4x - 3 = 8x - 7$
>
> $-3 = 4x - 7$
>
> $4 = 4x$
>
> $1 = x$
>
> The solution is 1.

OBJECTIVE **3**   **Solve equations containing parentheses**

When an equation contains parentheses, one of the steps in solving the equation requires the use of the Distributive Property. The Distributive Property is used to remove parentheses from a variable expression. $a(b + c) = ab + ac$

Solve: $4 + 5(2x - 3) = 3(4x - 1)$

	$4 + 5(2x - 3) = 3(4x - 1)$
Use the Distributive Property to remove parentheses.	$4 + 10x - 15 = 12x - 3$
Simplify.	$10x - 11 = 12x - 3$
Subtract $12x$ from each side of the equation.	$10x - 12x - 11 = 12x - 12x - 3$
Simplify. Now there is only one variable term in the equation.	$-2x - 11 = -3$
Add 11 to each side of the equation.	$-2x - 11 + 11 = -3 + 11$

Simplify. Now there is only one constant term in the equation.

$$-2x = 8$$

Divide each side of the equation by -2.

$$\frac{-2x}{-2} = \frac{8}{-2}$$

Simplify. Now the equation is in the form *variable = constant*.

$$x = -4$$

Check $\overline{\quad 4 + 5(2x - 3) = 3(4x - 1) \quad}$

$$
\begin{array}{c|c}
4 + 5[2(-4) - 3] & 3[4(-4) - 1] \\
4 + 5(-8 - 3) & 3(-16 - 1) \\
4 + 5(-11) & 3(-17) \\
4 - 55 & -51 \\
-51 = & -51
\end{array}
$$

Write the solution.   The solution is -4.

∎

In Chapter 2, we discussed the use of a graphing calculator to evaluate variable expressions. The same procedure can be used to check the solution of an equation. Consider the example above. After we divide both sides of the equation by -2, the solution appears to be -4. To check this solution, store the value of x, -4, in the calculator. Evaluate the expression on the left side of the original equation: $4 + 5(2x - 3)$. The result is -51. Now evaluate the expression on the right side of the original equation: $3(4x - 1)$. The result is -51. Because the results are equal, the solution -4 checks. See the Appendix for a description of keystroking procedures.

EXAMPLE 5   Solve: $3x - 4(2 - x) = 3(x - 2) - 4$

Solution $3x - 4(2 - x) = 3(x - 2) - 4$
$3x - 8 + 4x = 3x - 6 - 4$ • Use the Distributive Property to remove parentheses.

$7x - 8 = 3x - 10$ • Simplify.
$7x - 3x - 8 = 3x - 3x - 10$ • Subtract $3x$ from each side of the equation.
$4x - 8 = -10$
$4x - 8 + 8 = -10 + 8$ • Add 8 to each side of the equation.
$4x = -2$
$\dfrac{4x}{4} = \dfrac{-2}{4}$ • Divide each side of the equation by 4.

$x = -\dfrac{1}{2}$ • The equation is in the form *variable = constant*.

The solution is $-\dfrac{1}{2}$.

PROBLEM 5   Solve: $5x - 4(3 - 2x) = 2(3x - 2) + 6$

Solution   See page S7.

EXAMPLE 6   Solve: $3[2 - 4(2x - 1)] = 4x - 10$

Solution $3[2 - 4(2x - 1)] = 4x - 10$
$3[2 - 8x + 4] = 4x - 10$ • Use the Distributive Property to remove the parentheses.

$3[6 - 8x] = 4x - 10$ • Simplify inside the brackets.
$18 - 24x = 4x - 10$ • Use the Distributive Property to remove the brackets.

$18 - 24x - 4x = 4x - 4x - 10$ • Subtract $4x$ from each side of the equation.
$18 - 28x = -10$

$18 - 18 - 28x = -10 - 18$ • Subtract 18 from each side of the equation.
$-28x = -28$

$\dfrac{-28x}{-28} = \dfrac{-28}{-28}$ • Divide each side of the equation by -28.

$x = 1$

The solution is 1.

PROBLEM 6   Solve: $-2[3x - 5(2x - 3)] = 3x - 8$

Solution   See page S7.

OBJECTIVE **4**   **Application problems**

EXAMPLE 7   A company uses the equation $V = C - 6000t$ to determine the depreciated value V, after t years, of a milling machine that originally cost C dollars. If a milling machine originally cost $50,000, in how many years will the depreciated value of the machine be $38,000?

Strategy   To find the number of years, replace C with 50,000 and V with 38,000 in the given equation, and solve for t.

Solution
$$V = C - 6000t$$
$$38,000 = 50,000 - 6000t$$
$$38,000 - 50,000 = 50,000 - 50,000 - 6000t$$
$$-12,000 = -6000t$$
$$\frac{-12,000}{-6000} = \frac{-6000t}{-6000}$$
$$2 = t$$

The depreciated value of the machine will be $38,000 in 2 years.

PROBLEM 7   The value V of an investment of $7500 at an annual simple interest rate of 6% is given by the equation $V = 450t + 7500$, where t is the amount of time, in years, that the money is invested. In how many years will the value of a $7500 investment be $10,200?

Solution   See page S7.

A lever system is shown below. It consists of a lever, or bar; a fulcrum; and two forces, F_1 and F_2. The distance d represents the length of the lever, x represents the distance from F_1 to the fulcrum, and $d - x$ represents the distance from F_2 to the fulcrum.

Take Note

This system balances because

$F_1x = F_2(d - x)$
$60(6) = 90(10 - 6)$
$60(6) = 90(4)$
$360 = 360$

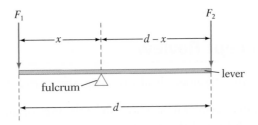

A principle of physics states that when the lever system balances,

$$F_1x = F_2(d - x)$$

EXAMPLE 8   A lever is 10 ft long. A force of 100 lb is applied to one end of the lever, and a force of 400 lb is applied to the other end. When the system balances, how far is the fulcrum from the 100-pound force?

Strategy   Draw a diagram of the situation.

The lever is 10 ft long, so $d = 10$. One force is 100 lb, so $F_1 = 100$. The other force is 400 lb, so $F_2 = 400$. To find the distance of the fulcrum from the 100-pound force, replace the variables F_1, F_2, and d in the lever-system equation with the given values, and solve for x.

Solution

$$F_1x = F_2(d - x)$$
$$100x = 400(10 - x)$$
$$100x = 4000 - 400x$$
$$100x + 400x = 4000 - 400x + 400x$$
$$500x = 4000$$
$$\frac{500x}{500} = \frac{4000}{500}$$
$$x = 8$$

The fulcrum is 8 ft from the 100-pound force.

> **PROBLEM 8** A lever is 14 ft long. At a distance of 6 ft from the fulcrum, a force of 40 lb is applied. How large a force must be applied to the other end of the lever so that the system will balance?
>
> ■ **Solution**   See page S7.

3.2   Concept Review

Determine whether the statement is always true, sometimes true, or never true.

1. The same variable term can be added to both sides of an equation without changing the solution of the equation.

2. The same variable term can be subtracted from both sides of an equation without changing the solution of the equation.

3. An equation of the form $ax + b = c$ cannot be solved if a is a negative number.

4. The solution of the equation $\frac{x}{3} = 0$ is 0.

5. The solution of the equation $\frac{x}{0} = 3$ is 0.

6. In solving an equation of the form $ax + b = cx + d$, the goal is to rewrite the equation in the form *variable = constant*.

7. In solving an equation of the form $ax + b = cx + d$, subtracting cx from each side of the equation results in an equation with only one variable term in it.

3.2   Exercises

1   **Solve equations of the form $ax + b = c$**

1. The first step in solving the equation $5 + 8x = 29$ is to subtract ___?___ from each side of the equation. The second step is to divide each side of the equation by ___?___.

2. To clear denominators from the equation $\frac{x}{9} + 2 = \frac{1}{6}$, multiply each side of the equation by ___?___, the least common multiple of the denominators 9 and 6.

Complete Exercises 3 and 4 without actually finding the solutions.

3. Is the solution of the equation $15x + 73 = -347$ positive or negative?

4. Is the solution of the equation $17 = 25 - 40a$ positive or negative?

Solve and check.

5. $3x + 1 = 10$

6. $4y + 3 = 11$

7. $2a - 5 = 7$

8. $5m - 6 = 9$

9. $5 = 4x + 9$

10. $2 = 5b + 12$

11. $13 = 9 + 4z$

12. $7 - c = 9$

13. $2 - x = 11$

14. $4 - 3w = -2$

15. $5 - 6x = -13$

16. $8 - 3t = 2$

17. $-5d + 3 = -12$

18. $-8x - 3 = -19$

19. $-7n - 4 = -25$

20. $-12x + 30 = -6$

21. $-13 = -11y + 9$

22. $2 = 7 - 5a$

23. $3 = 11 - 4n$

24. $-35 = -6b + 1$

25. $-8x + 3 = -29$

26. $-3m - 21 = 0$

27. $7x - 3 = 3$

28. $8y + 3 = 7$

29. $6a + 5 = 9$

30. $3m + 4 = 11$

31. $11 = 15 + 4n$

32. $4 = 2 - 3c$

33. $9 - 4x = 6$

34. $7 - 8z = 0$

35. $1 - 3x = 0$

36. $6y - 5 = -7$

37. $8b - 3 = -9$

38. $5 - 6m = 2$

39. $7 - 9a = 4$

40. $9 = -12c + 5$

41. $10 = -18x + 7$

42. $2y + \dfrac{1}{3} = \dfrac{7}{3}$

43. $3x - \dfrac{5}{6} = \dfrac{13}{6}$

44. $5y + \dfrac{3}{7} = \dfrac{3}{7}$

45. $9x + \dfrac{4}{5} = \dfrac{4}{5}$

46. $4 = 7 - 2w$

47. $7 = 9 - 5a$

48. $-6y + 5 = 13$

49. $-4x + 3 = 9$

50. $\dfrac{1}{2}a - 3 = 1$

51. $\dfrac{1}{3}m - 1 = 5$

52. $\dfrac{2}{5}y + 4 = 6$

53. $\dfrac{3}{4}n + 7 = 13$

54. $-\dfrac{2}{3}x + 1 = 7$

55. $-\dfrac{3}{8}b + 4 = 10$

56. $\dfrac{x}{4} - 6 = 1$

57. $\dfrac{y}{5} - 2 = 3$

58. $\dfrac{2x}{3} - 1 = 5$

59. $\dfrac{3c}{7} - 1 = 8$

60. $4 - \dfrac{3}{4}z = -2$

61. $3 - \dfrac{4}{5}w = -9$

62. $5 + \dfrac{2}{3}y = 3$

63. $17 + \dfrac{5}{8}x = 7$

64. $17 = 7 - \dfrac{5}{6}t$

65. $\dfrac{2}{3} = y - \dfrac{1}{2}$

66. $\dfrac{3}{4} = \dfrac{1}{12}x + 2$

67. $\dfrac{3}{8} = \dfrac{5}{12} - \dfrac{1}{3}b$

68. $\dfrac{2}{3} = \dfrac{3}{4} - \dfrac{1}{2}y$

69. $7 = \dfrac{2x}{5} + 4$

70. $5 - \dfrac{4c}{7} = 8$

71. $7 - \dfrac{5}{9}y = 9$

72. $6a + 3 + 2a = 11$

73. $5y + 9 + 2y = 23$

74. $7x - 4 - 2x = 6$

75. $11z - 3 - 7z = 9$

76. $2x - 6x + 1 = 9$

77. $b - 8b + 1 = -6$

78. $-1 = 5m + 7 - m$

79. $8 = 4n - 6 + 3n$

80. $0.15y + 0.025 = -0.074$

81. $1.2x - 3.44 = 1.3$

82. $3.5 = 3.5 + 0.076x$

83. $-6.5 = 4.3y - 3.06$

Solve.

84. If $2x - 3 = 7$, evaluate $3x + 4$.

85. If $3x + 5 = -4$, evaluate $2x - 5$.

86. If $4 - 5x = -1$, evaluate $x^2 - 3x + 1$.

87. If $2 - 3x = 11$, evaluate $x^2 + 2x - 3$.

2 Solve equations of the form $ax + b = cx + d$

88. To solve the equation $7x - 4 = 2x + 6$, we subtract $2x$ from each side of the equation and add 4 to each side of the equation. The resulting equation is ___?___ = ___?___. The solution of the equation is ___?___.

89. To solve $\frac{1}{6}x - 7 = \frac{3}{4}x$, begin by clearing denominators:

$(\underline{\;?\;})\left(\frac{1}{6}x - 7\right) = (\underline{\;?\;})\left(\frac{3}{4}x\right)$
• Multiply each side of the equation by the LCM of the denominators, 6 and 4.

$12\left(\frac{1}{6}x\right) - (12)(7) = 9x$
• Use the ___?___ Property on the left side of the equation. Simplify the right side.

$\underline{\;?\;}x - \underline{\;?\;} = 9x$
• Simplify.

$2x - \underline{\;?\;} - 84 = 9x - \underline{\;?\;}$
• Subtract $2x$ from each side of the equation.

$-84 = \underline{\;?\;}x$
• Simplify.

$-\dfrac{84}{7} = \dfrac{7x}{7}$
• ___?___ each side of the equation by ___?___.

$\underline{\;?\;} = x$
• Simplify.

Complete Exercises 90 and 91 without actually finding the solutions.

90. Describe the step that will allow you to rewrite the equation $2x - 3 = 7x + 12$ so that it has one variable term with a positive coefficient.

91. If you rewrite the equation $8 - y = y + 6$ so that it has one variable term on the left side of the equation, what will be the coefficient of the variable?

Solve and check.

92. $8x + 5 = 4x + 13$

93. $6y + 2 = y + 17$

94. $7m + 4 = 6m + 7$

95. $11n + 3 = 10n + 11$

96. $5x - 4 = 2x + 5$

97. $9a - 10 = 3a + 2$

98. $12y - 4 = 9y - 7$

99. $13b - 1 = 4b - 19$

100. $15x - 2 = 4x - 13$

101. $7a - 5 = 2a - 20$

102. $3x + 1 = 11 - 2x$

103. $n - 2 = 6 - 3n$

104. $2x - 3 = -11 - 2x$

105. $4y - 2 = -16 - 3y$

106. $2b + 3 = 5b + 12$

107. $m + 4 = 3m + 8$

108. $4x - 7 = 5x + 1$

109. $6d - 2 = 7d + 5$

110. $4y - 8 = y - 8$

111. $5a + 7 = 2a + 7$

112. $6 - 5x = 8 - 3x$

113. $10 - 4n = 16 - n$

114. $2x - 4 = 6x$

115. $2b - 10 = 7b$

116. $8m = 3m + 20$

117. $9y = 5y + 16$

118. $-x - 4 = -3x - 16$

119. $8 - 4x = 18 - 5x$

120. $6 - 10a = 8 - 9a$

121. $5 - 7m = 2 - 6m$

122. $8b + 5 = 5b + 7$

123. $6y - 1 = 2y + 2$

124. $7x - 8 = x - 3$

125. $10x - 3 = 3x - 1$

126. $5n + 3 = 2n + 1$

127. $8a - 2 = 4a - 5$

128. $\dfrac{1}{5}d = \dfrac{1}{2}d + 3$

129. $\dfrac{3}{4}x = \dfrac{1}{12}x + 2$

130. $\dfrac{2}{3}a = \dfrac{1}{5}a + 7$

131. $\dfrac{4}{5}c - 7 = \dfrac{1}{10}c$

132. $\dfrac{1}{2}y = 10 - \dfrac{1}{3}y$

133. $\dfrac{2}{3}b = 2 - \dfrac{5}{6}b$

134. $8.7y = 3.9y + 9.6$

135. $4.5x - 5.4 = 2.7x$

136. $5.6x = 7.2x - 6.4$

Solve.

137. If $5x = 3x - 8$, evaluate $4x + 2$.

138. If $7x + 3 = 5x - 7$, evaluate $3x - 2$.

139. If $2 - 6a = 5 - 3a$, evaluate $4a^2 - 2a + 1$.

140. If $1 - 5c = 4 - 4c$, evaluate $3c^2 - 4c + 2$.

3 Solve equations containing parentheses

141. Use the Distributive Property to remove the parentheses from the equation $4x + 3(x + 6) = 74$: $4x + \underline{\ \ ?\ \ } + \underline{\ \ ?\ \ } = 74$.

142. Use the Distributive Property to remove the parentheses from the equation $9x - 5(4 - x) = 2(x + 2)$:
$9x - \underline{\ \ ?\ \ } + \underline{\ \ ?\ \ } = \underline{\ \ ?\ \ } + \underline{\ \ ?\ \ }$.

143. In each of the following equations, y is the same positive integer. For which equations will x have the same solution?
a. $5 - 2(x - 1) = y$ **b.** $3(x - 1) = y$
c. $5 - 2x + 2 = y$ **d.** $5 - 2x + 1 = y$

144. In solving the equation $9 - (8 - x) = 5x - 1$, how many times will you use the Distributive Property to remove parentheses?

Solve and check.

145. $5x + 2(x + 1) = 23$

146. $6y + 2(2y + 3) = 16$

147. $9n - 3(2n - 1) = 15$

148. $12x - 2(4x - 6) = 28$

149. $7a - (3a - 4) = 12$

150. $9m - 4(2m - 3) = 11$

151. $5(3 - 2y) + 4y = 3$

152. $4(1 - 3x) + 7x = 9$

153. $10x + 1 = 2(3x + 5) - 1$

154. $5y - 3 = 7 + 4(y - 2)$

155. $4 - 3a = 7 - 2(2a + 5)$

156. $9 - 5x = 12 - (6x + 7)$

157. $3y - 7 = 5(2y - 3) + 4$

158. $2a - 5 = 4(3a + 1) - 2$

159. $5 - (9 - 6x) = 2x - 2$

160. $7 - (5 - 8x) = 4x + 3$

161. $3[2 - 4(y - 1)] = 3(2y + 8)$

162. $5[2 - (2x - 4)] = 2(5 - 3x)$

163. $3a + 2[2 + 3(a - 1)] = 2(3a + 4)$

164. $5 + 3[1 + 2(2x - 3)] = 6(x + 5)$

165. $-2[4 - (3b + 2)] = 5 - 2(3b + 6)$

166. $-4[x - 2(2x - 3)] + 1 = 2x - 3$

167. $0.3x - 2(1.6x) - 8 = 3(1.9x - 4.1)$

168. $0.56 - 0.4(2.1y + 3) = 0.2(2y + 6.1)$

Solve.

169. If $4 - 3a = 7 - 2(2a + 5)$, evaluate $a^2 + 7a$.

170. If $9 - 5x = 12 - (6x + 7)$, evaluate $x^2 - 3x - 2$.

171. If $2z - 5 = 3(4z + 5)$, evaluate $\dfrac{z^2}{z - 2}$.

172. If $3n - 7 = 5(2n + 7)$, evaluate $\dfrac{n^2}{2n - 6}$.

4 Application problems

Physics Black ice is an ice covering on roads that is especially difficult to see and therefore extremely dangerous for motorists. The distance that a car traveling 30 mph will slide after its brakes are applied is related to the outside temperature by the formula $C = \frac{1}{4}D - 45$, where C is the Celsius temperature and D is the distance in feet that the car will slide.

173. Determine the distance a car will slide on black ice when the outside temperature is $-3°C$.

174. Determine the distance a car will slide on black ice when the outside temperature is $-11°C$.

Physics The pressure at a certain depth in the ocean can be approximated by the equation $P = \frac{1}{2}D + 15$, where P is the pressure in pounds per square inch and D is the depth in feet.

175. Find the depth of a diver when the pressure on the diver is 35 lb/in².

176. Find the depth of a diver when the pressure on the diver is 45 lb/in².

Physics The distance s, in feet, that an object will fall in t seconds is given by $s = 16t^2 + vt$, where v is the initial downward velocity of the object in feet per second.

177. Find the initial velocity of an object that falls 80 ft in 2 s.

178. Find the initial velocity of an object that falls 144 ft in 3 s.

Forensic Science Forensic scientists have determined that the equation $H = 2.9L + 78.1$ can be used to approximate the height H, in centimeters, of an adult on the basis of the length L, in centimeters, of its humerus (the bone extending from the shoulder to the elbow).

Humerus

179. Use this formula to approximate the height of an adult whose humerus measures 36 cm.

180. According to this formula, what is the length of the humerus of an adult whose height is 168 cm?

Business The fare, F, to be charged a customer by a taxi company is calculated using the formula $F = 1.50 + 0.95(m - 1)$, where m is the number of miles traveled.

181. A customer is charged $6.25. How many miles was the passenger driven?

182. A passenger is charged $9.10. Find the number of miles the customer was driven.

Employment A person's accurate typing speed can be approximated by the equation $S = \frac{W - 5e}{10}$, where S is the accurate typing speed in words per minute, W is the number of words typed in ten minutes, and e is the number of errors made.

183. After taking a 10-minute typing test, a job candidate was told that he had an accurate speed of 35 words per minute. He had typed a total of 390 words. How many errors did he make?

184. A job applicant took a 10-minute typing test and was told that she had an accurate speed of 37 words per minute. If she had typed a total of 400 words, how many errors did she make?

Business A telephone company estimates that the number N of phone calls made per day between two cities of populations P_1 and P_2 that are d miles apart is given by the equation $N = \frac{2.51P_1P_2}{d^2}$.

185. Estimate the population P_2, given that P_1 is 48,000, the number of phone calls is 1,100,000, and the distance between the cities is 75 mi. Round to the nearest thousand.

186. Estimate the population P_1, given that P_2 is 125,000, the number of phone calls is 2,500,000, and the distance between the cities is 50 mi. Round to the nearest thousand.

Business To determine the break-even point, or the number of units that must be sold so that no profit or loss occurs, an economist uses the equation $Px = Cx + F$, where P is the selling price per unit, x is the number of units sold, C is the cost to make each unit, and F is the fixed cost.

187. An economist has determined that the selling price per unit for a television is $250. The cost to make one television is $165, and the fixed cost is $29,750. Find the break-even point.

188. A manufacturing engineer determines that the cost per unit for a compact disc is $3.35 and that the fixed cost is $6180. The selling price for the compact disc is $8.50. Find the break-even point.

Lever Systems Use the lever-system equation $F_1x = F_2(d - x)$.

189. In the lever-system equation $F_1x = F_2(d - x)$, what does x represent? What does d represent? What does $d - x$ represent?

190. Two children sit on a seesaw that is 12 ft long. One child weighs 85 lb, and the other child weighs 65 lb. If x is the distance of the 65-pound child from the fulcrum when the seesaw balances, state the value of each of the other variables in the lever-system formula $F_1x = F_2(d - x)$:
$F_1 = \underline{\ \ ?\ \ }$, $F_2 = \underline{\ \ ?\ \ }$, and $d = \underline{\ \ ?\ \ }$.

For Exercises 191 to 193, use the following information: Two people sit on a seesaw that is 8 ft long. The seesaw balances when the fulcrum is 3 ft from one of the people.

191. How far is the fulcrum from the other person?

192. Which person is heavier, the person who is 3 ft from the fulcrum or the other person?

193. If the two people switch places, will the seesaw still balance?

194. Suppose an 80-pound child is sitting at one end of a 7-foot seesaw, and a 60-pound child is sitting at the other end. The 80-pound child is 3 ft from the fulcrum. Use the lever-system equation to explain why the seesaw balances.

195. Two children are sitting 8 ft apart on a seesaw. One child weighs 60 lb and the second child weighs 50 lb. The fulcrum is 3.5 ft from the child weighing 60 lb. Is the seesaw balanced?

50 lb 3.5 ft 60 lb
8 ft

196. An adult and a child are on a seesaw that is 14 ft long. The adult weighs 175 lb and the child weighs 70 lb. How many feet from the child must the fulcrum be placed so that the seesaw balances?

197. A lever 10 ft long is used to balance a 100-pound rock. The fulcrum is placed 2 ft from the rock. What force must be applied to the other end of the lever to balance the rock?

F_2 100 lb 2 ft

198. A 50-pound weight is applied to the left end of a seesaw that is 10 ft long. The fulcrum is 4 ft from the 50-pound weight. A weight of 30 lb is applied to the right end of the seesaw. Is the 30-pound weight adequate to balance the seesaw?

199. In preparation for a stunt, two acrobats are standing on a plank that is 18 ft long. One acrobat weighs 128 lb, and the second acrobat weighs 160 lb. How far from the 128-pound acrobat must the fulcrum be placed so that the acrobats are balanced on the plank?

200. A screwdriver 9 in. long is used as a lever to open a can of paint. The tip of the screwdriver is placed under the lip of the lid with the fulcrum 0.15 in. from the lip. A force of 30 lb is applied to the other end of the screwdriver. Find the force on the lip of the lid.

3.2 Applying Concepts

Solve. If the equation has no solution, write "No solution."

201. $3(2x - 1) - (6x - 4) = -9$

202. $\dfrac{1}{5}(25 - 10b) + 4 = \dfrac{1}{3}(9b - 15) - 6$

203. $3[4(w + 2) - (w + 1)] = 5(2 + w)$

204. $\dfrac{2(5x - 6) - 3(x - 4)}{7} = x + 2$

205. Solve for x: $32{,}166 \div x = 518$ remainder 50

206. One-half of a certain number equals two-thirds of the same number. Find the number.

207. Write an equation of the form $ax + b = cx + d$ that has 4 as a solution.

208. Does the sentence "Solve $3x - 4(x - 1)$" make sense? Why or why not?

209. The equation $x = x + 1$ has no solution, whereas the solution of the equation $2x + 1 = 1$ is zero. Is there a difference between no solution and a solution of zero? Explain your answer.

3.3 Inequalities

OBJECTIVE **1** ## Solve inequalities using the Addition Property of Inequalities

An expression that contains the symbol $>$, $<$, $\geq$, or $\leq$ is called an **inequality**. An inequality expresses the relative order of two mathematical expressions. The expressions can be either numerical or variable expressions.

$$\left. \begin{array}{l} 4 > 2 \\ 3x \leq 7 \\ x^2 - 2x > y + 4 \end{array} \right\} \text{Inequalities}$$

The **solution set of an inequality** is a set of numbers, each element of which, when substituted for the variable, results in a true inequality. The solution set of an inequality can be graphed on the number line.

The graph of the solution set of $x > 1$ is shown at the right. The solution set is the real numbers greater than 1. The parenthesis on the graph indicates that 1 is not included in the solution set.

The graph of the solution set of $x \geq 1$ is shown at the right. The bracket at 1 indicates that 1 is included in the solution set.

The graph of the solution set of $x < -1$ is shown at the right. The numbers less than -1 are to the left of -1 on the number line.

EXAMPLE 1 Graph: $x < 3$

Solution

• The solution set is the numbers less than 3.

PROBLEM 1 Graph: $x > -2$

Solution See page S7.

The inequality at the right is true if the variable is replaced by 7, 9.3, or $\frac{15}{2}$.

$$x + 3 > 8$$

$$\left. \begin{array}{l} 7 + 3 > 8 \\ 9.3 + 3 > 8 \\ \dfrac{15}{2} + 3 > 8 \end{array} \right\} \text{True inequalities}$$

The inequality $x + 3 > 8$ is false if the variable is replaced by 4, 1.5, or $-\frac{1}{2}$.

$$\left. \begin{array}{l} 4 + 3 > 8 \\ 1.5 + 3 > 8 \\ -\dfrac{1}{2} + 3 > 8 \end{array} \right\} \text{False inequalities}$$

There are many values of the variable x that will make the inequality $x + 3 > 8$ true. The solution set of $x + 3 > 8$ is any number greater than 5.

The graph of the solution set of $x + 3 > 8$ is shown at the right.

In solving an inequality, the goal is to rewrite the given inequality in the form *variable* > *constant* or *variable* < *constant*. The Addition Property of Inequalities is used to rewrite an inequality in this form.

Addition Property of Inequalities

The same number can be added to each side of an inequality without changing the solution set of the inequality.

$$\text{If } a > b, \text{ then } a + c > b + c.$$
$$\text{If } a < b, \text{ then } a + c < b + c.$$

The Addition Property of Inequalities also holds true for an inequality containing the symbol $\geq$ or $\leq$.

The Addition Property of Inequalities is used when, in order to rewrite an inequality in the form *variable* > *constant* or *variable* < *constant*, a term must be removed from one side of the inequality. Add the opposite of the term to each side of the inequality.

Because subtraction is defined in terms of addition, the Addition Property of Inequalities makes it possible to subtract the same number from each side of an inequality without changing the solution set of the inequality.

Solve: $x + 4 < 5$

$$x + 4 < 5$$

Subtract 4 from each side of the inequality.

$$x + 4 - 4 < 5 - 4$$

Simplify.

$$x < 1$$

The graph of the solution set of $x + 4 < 5$ is shown at the right.

Solve: $5x - 6 \leq 4x - 4$

$$5x - 6 \leq 4x - 4$$

Subtract $4x$ from each side of the inequality.

$$5x - 4x - 6 \leq 4x - 4x - 4$$

Simplify.

$$x - 6 \leq -4$$

Add 6 to each side of the inequality.

$$x - 6 + 6 \leq -4 + 6$$

Simplify.

$$x \leq 2$$

EXAMPLE 2 Solve and graph the solution set of $x + 5 > 3$.

Solution

$x + 5 > 3$
$x + 5 - 5 > 3 - 5$ • Subtract 5 from each side of the inequality.
$x > -2$

$-5\ -4\ -3\ -2\ -1\ \ 0\ \ 1\ \ 2\ \ 3\ \ 4\ \ 5$

PROBLEM 2 Solve and graph the solution set of $x + 2 < -2$.

Solution See page S7.

EXAMPLE 3 Solve: $7x - 14 \le 6x - 16$

Solution

$7x - 14 \le 6x - 16$
$7x - 6x - 14 \le 6x - 6x - 16$ • Subtract $6x$ from each side of the inequality.
$x - 14 \le -16$
$x - 14 + 14 \le -16 + 14$ • Add 14 to each side of the inequality.
$x \le -2$

PROBLEM 3 Solve: $5x + 3 > 4x + 5$

Solution See page S7.

OBJECTIVE **2** **Solve inequalities using the Multiplication Property of Inequalities**

In solving an inequality, the goal is to rewrite the given inequality in the form *variable* $>$ *constant* or *variable* $<$ *constant*. The Multiplication Property of Inequalities is used when, in order to rewrite an inequality in this form, a coefficient must be removed from one side of the inequality.

> **Take Note**
>
> $c > 0$ means c is a positive number.
>
> The inequality symbols are not changed.

Multiplication Property of Inequalities — Rule 1

Each side of an inequality can be multiplied by the same positive number without changing the solution set of the inequality.

If $a > b$ and $c > 0$, then $ac > bc$.   If $a < b$ and $c > 0$, then $ac < bc$.

$5 > 4$ • A true inequality
$5(2) > 4(2)$ • Multiply by *positive* 2.
$10 > 8$ • A true inequality

> **Take Note**
>
> $c < 0$ means c is a negative number.
>
> The inequality symbol is reversed in each case.

Multiplication Property of Inequalities — Rule 2

If each side of an inequality is multiplied by the same negative number and the inequality symbol is reversed, then the solution set of the inequality is not changed.

If $a > b$ and $c < 0$, then $ac < bc$.   If $a < b$ and $c < 0$, then $ac > bc$.

$$6 < 9$$ • **A true inequality**

$$6(-3) > 9(-3)$$ • **Multiply by *negative* 3 and reverse the inequality symbol.**

$$-18 > -27$$ • **A true inequality**

The Multiplication Property of Inequalities also holds true for an inequality containing the symbol $\geq$ or $\leq$.

Solve: $-\dfrac{3}{2}x \leq 6$

Multiply each side of the inequality by the reciprocal of the coefficient $-\dfrac{3}{2}$. Because $-\dfrac{2}{3}$ is a negative number, the inequality symbol must be reversed.

$$-\dfrac{3}{2}x \leq 6$$

$$-\dfrac{2}{3}\left(-\dfrac{3}{2}x\right) \geq -\dfrac{2}{3}(6)$$

Simplify.

The graph of the solution set of $-\dfrac{3}{2}x \leq 6$ is shown at the right.

$$x \geq -4$$

Recall that division is defined in terms of multiplication. Therefore, the Multiplication Property of Inequalities allows each side of an inequality to be divided by the same number. When each side of an inequality is divided by a positive number, the inequality symbol remains the same. When each side of an inequality is divided by a negative number, the inequality symbol must be reversed.

Take Note

Any time an inequality is multiplied or divided by a negative number, the inequality symbol must be reversed. Compare these two examples:

$2x < -4$ Divide each side by
$\dfrac{2x}{2} < \dfrac{-4}{2}$ *positive* 2. The
   inequality symbol
$x < -2$ is *not* reversed.

$-2x < 4$ Divide each side by
$\dfrac{-2x}{-2} > \dfrac{4}{-2}$ *negative* 2. The
   inequality symbol
$x > -2$ *is* reversed.

Solve: $-5x > 8$

Divide each side of the inequality by -5. Because -5 is a negative number, the inequality symbol must be reversed.

Simplify.

$$-5x > 8$$

$$\dfrac{-5x}{-5} < \dfrac{8}{-5}$$

$$x < -\dfrac{8}{5}$$

EXAMPLE 4 Solve and graph the solution set of $7x < -14$.

Solution
$$7x < -14$$
$$\dfrac{7x}{7} < \dfrac{-14}{7}$$ • **Divide each side of the inequality by 7. Because 7 is a *positive* number, do not change the inequality symbol.**
$$x < -2$$

PROBLEM 4 Solve and graph the solution set of $3x < 9$.

Solution See page S7.

EXAMPLE 5   Solve: $-\dfrac{5}{8}x \leq \dfrac{5}{12}$

Solution $-\dfrac{5}{8}x \leq \dfrac{5}{12}$

$-\dfrac{8}{5}\left(-\dfrac{5}{8}x\right) \geq -\dfrac{8}{5}\left(\dfrac{5}{12}\right)$ • Multiply each side of the inequality by the reciprocal of $-\dfrac{5}{8}$. $-\dfrac{8}{5}$ is a negative number. Reverse the inequality symbol.

$x \geq -\dfrac{2}{3}$

PROBLEM 5   Solve: $-\dfrac{3}{4}x \geq 18$

Solution   See page S7.

OBJECTIVE 3   Solve general inequalities

In solving an inequality, it is often necessary to apply both the Addition and the Multiplication Properties of Inequalities.

<table>
<tr><td colspan="2">Solve: $3x - 2 < 5x + 4$</td></tr>
<tr><td>Subtract $5x$ from each side of the inequality. Simplify.</td><td>$3x - 2 < 5x + 4$
$3x - 5x - 2 < 5x - 5x + 4$
$-2x - 2 < 4$</td></tr>
<tr><td>Add 2 to each side of the inequality. Simplify.</td><td>$-2x - 2 + 2 < 4 + 2$
$-2x < 6$</td></tr>
<tr><td>Divide each side of the inequality by -2. Because -2 is a negative number, the inequality symbol must be reversed. Simplify.</td><td>$\dfrac{-2x}{-2} > \dfrac{6}{-2}$
$x > -3$</td></tr>
</table>

> ### Take Note
>
> Solving these inequalities is similar to solving the equations in Section 3.2 *except* that when you multiply or divide the inequality by a negative number, you must reverse the inequality symbol.

EXAMPLE 6   Solve: $7x - 3 \leq 3x + 17$

Solution $7x - 3 \leq 3x + 17$
$7x - 3x - 3 \leq 3x - 3x + 17$ • Subtract $3x$ from each side of the inequality.
$4x - 3 \leq 17$
$4x - 3 + 3 \leq 17 + 3$ • Add 3 to each side of the inequality.
$4x \leq 20$
$\dfrac{4x}{4} \leq \dfrac{20}{4}$ • Divide each side of the inequality by 4.
$x \leq 5$

PROBLEM 6   Solve: $5 - 4x > 9 - 8x$

Solution   See page S8.

When an inequality contains parentheses, one of the steps in solving the inequality requires the use of the Distributive Property.

Solve: $-2(x - 7) > 3 - 4(2x - 3)$

$$-2(x - 7) > 3 - 4(2x - 3)$$

Use the Distributive Property to remove parentheses. Simplify.

$$-2x + 14 > 3 - 8x + 12$$
$$-2x + 14 > 15 - 8x$$

Add $8x$ to each side of the inequality. Simplify.

$$-2x + 8x + 14 > 15 - 8x + 8x$$
$$6x + 14 > 15$$

Subtract 14 from each side of the inequality. Simplify.

$$6x + 14 - 14 > 15 - 14$$
$$6x > 1$$

Divide each side of the inequality by 6.

$$\frac{6x}{6} > \frac{1}{6}$$

Simplify.

$$x > \frac{1}{6}$$

EXAMPLE 7   Solve: $3(3 - 2x) \geq -5x - 2(3 - x)$

Solution

$$3(3 - 2x) \geq -5x - 2(3 - x)$$
$$9 - 6x \geq -5x - 6 + 2x$$ • **Use the Distributive Property.**
$$9 - 6x \geq -3x - 6$$
$$9 - 6x + 3x \geq -3x + 3x - 6$$ • **Add $3x$ to each side of the inequality.**
$$9 - 3x \geq -6$$
$$9 - 9 - 3x \geq -6 - 9$$ • **Subtract 9 from each side of the inequality.**
$$-3x \geq -15$$
$$\frac{-3x}{-3} \leq \frac{-15}{-3}$$ • **Divide each side of the inequality by -3. Reverse the inequality symbol.**
$$x \leq 5$$

PROBLEM 7   Solve: $8 - 4(3x + 5) \leq 6(x - 8)$

Solution   See page S8.

3.3   Concept Review

Determine whether the statement is always true, sometimes true, or never true.

1. The same variable term can be added to both sides of an inequality without changing the solution set of the inequality.

2. The same variable term can be subtracted from both sides of an inequality without changing the solution set of the inequality.

3. Both sides of an inequality can be multiplied by the same number without changing the solution set of the inequality.

4. Both sides of an inequality can be divided by the same number without changing the solution set of the inequality.

5. Suppose $a > 0$ and $b < 0$. Then $ab > 0$.

6. Suppose $a < 0$. Then $a^2 > 0$.

7. Suppose $a > 0$ and $b < 0$. Then $a^2 > b$.

8. Suppose $a > b$. Then $-a > -b$.

9. Suppose $a < b$. Then $ac < bc$.

10. Suppose $a \neq 0$, $b \neq 0$, and $a > b$. Then $\frac{1}{a} > \frac{1}{b}$.

3.3 Exercises

1 Solve inequalities using the Addition Property of Inequalities

Complete Exercises 1 and 2 by replacing the question mark in the first statement with "includes" or "does not include." Replace the question mark in the second statement with the correct inequality symbol: $>$, $<$, $\geq$, or $\leq$.

1. The graph of the solution set shown at the right ___?___ the number -2. In the graph of the solution set of the inequality, x ___?___ -2.

2. The graph of the solution set shown at the right ___?___ the number -3. In the graph of the solution set of the inequality, x ___?___ -3.

Graph.

3. $x > 2$

4. $x \geq -1$

5. $x \leq 0$

6. $x < 4$

7. Which numbers are solutions of the inequality $x + 7 \leq -3$?
   a. -17 **b.** 8 **c.** -10 **d.** 0

8. Which numbers are solutions of the inequality $x - 5 < -6$?
   a. 1 **b.** -1 **c.** 12 **d.** -5

Solve and graph the solution set.

9. $x + 1 < 3$

10. $y + 2 < 2$

11. $x - 5 > -2$

12. $x - 3 > -2$

13. $n + 4 \geq 7$

14. $x + 5 \geq 3$

15. $x - 6 \leq -10$

16. $y - 8 \leq -11$

17. $5 + x \geq 4$

18. $-2 + n \geq 0$

For Exercises 19 to 22, state whether the solution set of an inequality in the given form contains only negative numbers, only positive numbers, or both negative and positive numbers.

19. $x + n < a$, where n and a are both positive and $n > a$

20. $x + n > a$, where n and a are both positive and $n < a$

21. $x - n > -a$, where n and a are both positive and $n > a$

22. $x - n > -a$, where n and a are both positive and $n < a$

Solve.

23. $y - 3 \geq -12$

24. $x + 8 \geq -14$

25. $3x - 5 < 2x + 7$

26. $5x + 4 < 4x - 10$

27. $8x - 7 \geq 7x - 2$

28. $3n - 9 \geq 2n - 8$

29. $2x + 4 < x - 7$

30. $9x + 7 < 8x - 7$

31. $4x - 8 \leq 2 + 3x$

32. $5b - 9 < 3 + 4b$

33. $6x + 4 \geq 5x - 2$

34. $7x - 3 \geq 6x - 2$

35. $2x - 12 > x - 10$

36. $3x + 9 > 2x + 7$

37. $d + \dfrac{1}{2} < \dfrac{1}{3}$

38. $x - \dfrac{3}{8} < \dfrac{5}{6}$

39. $x + \dfrac{5}{8} \geq -\dfrac{2}{3}$

40. $y + \dfrac{5}{12} \geq -\dfrac{3}{4}$

41. $2x - \dfrac{1}{2} < x + \dfrac{3}{4}$

42. $6x - \dfrac{1}{3} \leq 5x - \dfrac{1}{2}$

43. $3x + \dfrac{5}{8} > 2x + \dfrac{5}{6}$

44. $4b - \dfrac{7}{12} \geq 3b - \dfrac{9}{16}$

45. $x + 5.8 \leq 4.6$

46. $n - 3.82 \leq 3.95$

47. $x - 0.23 \leq 0.47$

48. $3.8x < 2.8x - 3.8$

49. $1.2x < 0.2x - 7.3$

2   Solve inequalities using the Multiplication Property of Inequalities

50. Which numbers are solutions of the inequality $5x > 15$?
   a. 6   **b.** −4   **c.** 3   **d.** 5

51. Which numbers are solutions of the inequality $-4x \leq 12$?
   a. 0   **b.** 3   **c.** −3   **d.** −4

Complete Exercises 52 and 53 by replacing the question mark with "remains the same" or "is reversed."

52. The inequality $x + 4 > -8$ can be solved by subtracting 4 from each side of the inequality. The inequality symbol _____?_____.

53. The inequality $-4x > 8$ can be solved by dividing each side of the inequality by -4. The inequality symbol _____?_____.

Solve and graph the solution set.

54. $3x < 12$

55. $8x \le -24$

56. $5y \ge 15$

57. $24x > -48$

58. $16x \le 16$

59. $3x > 0$

60. $-8x > 8$

61. $-2n \le -8$

62. $-6b > 24$

63. $-4x < 8$

Solve.

64. $-5y \ge 20$

65. $3x < 5$

66. $7x > 2$

67. $-8x \le -40$

68. $-6x \le -40$

69. $10x > -25$

70. $-3x \ge \dfrac{6}{7}$

71. $-5x \ge \dfrac{10}{3}$

72. $\dfrac{5}{6}n < 15$

73. $\dfrac{2}{3}x < -12$

74. $\dfrac{5}{6}x < -20$

75. $-\dfrac{3}{8}x < 6$

76. $\dfrac{3}{4}x < 12$

77. $\dfrac{2}{3}y \ge 4$

78. $\dfrac{5}{8}x \ge 10$

79. $-\dfrac{2}{3}x \le 4$

80. $-\dfrac{3}{7}x \le 6$

81. $-\dfrac{2}{11}b \ge -6$

82. $-\dfrac{4}{7}x \ge -12$

83. $\dfrac{2}{3}n < \dfrac{1}{2}$

84. $\dfrac{3}{5}x > \dfrac{7}{10}$

85. $-\dfrac{2}{3}x \ge \dfrac{4}{7}$

86. $-\dfrac{3}{8}x \ge \dfrac{9}{14}$

87. $-\dfrac{3}{4}y \ge -\dfrac{5}{8}$

88. $-\dfrac{8}{9}x \ge -\dfrac{16}{27}$

89. $\dfrac{2}{3}x \le \dfrac{9}{14}$

90. $\dfrac{7}{12}x \le \dfrac{9}{14}$

91. $-\dfrac{3}{5}y < \dfrac{9}{10}$

92. $-\dfrac{5}{12}y < \dfrac{1}{6}$

93. $-0.27x < 0.135$

94. $-0.63x < 4.41$

95. $8.4y \ge -6.72$

96. $3.7y \ge -1.48$

97. $1.5x \leq 6.30$

98. $2.3x \leq 5.29$

99. $-3.9x \geq -19.5$

100. $0.035x < -0.0735$

101. $0.07x < -0.378$

102. $-11.7x \leq 4.68$

Complete Exercises 103 and 104 without actually solving the inequalities or using a calcualtor.

103. A number n is a solution of the inequality $-0.8157n < 7.304$. Which of the following must be true?
a. n is positive.   **b.** n is negative.   **c.** n is 0.
d. n can be positive, negative, or 0.

104. A number n is a solution of the inequality $-917n \geq -10,512$. Which of the following must be true?
a. n is positive.   **b.** n is negative.   **c.** n is 0.
d. n can be positive, negative, or 0.

3   Solve general inequalities

105. In your own words, state the Addition Property of Inequalities and the Multiplication Property of Inequalities.

106. What differentiates solving linear equations from solving linear inequalities?

107. Solve: $9 - 5x \geq -2x$

$$9 - 5x \geq -2x$$
$$9 - 5x + \underline{\quad ? \quad} \geq -2x + \underline{\quad ? \quad}$$
$$9 - \underline{\quad ? \quad} \geq \underline{\quad ? \quad}$$
$$9 - 9 - 3x \geq 0 - 9$$

$$\underline{\quad ? \quad} \geq \underline{\quad ? \quad}$$
$$\frac{-3x}{?} \quad ? \quad \frac{-9}{?}$$
$$x \leq \underline{\quad ? \quad}$$

- Add 2x to each side of the inequality.
- Simplify.
- Subtract ___?___ from each side of the inequality.
- Simplify.
- Divide each side of the inequality by -3. Reverse the inequality symbol.
- Simplify.

108. The first step of solving the inequality $8(3x - 1) < 11x + 5$ is to use the ___?___ Property to ___?___.

Solve.

109. $4x - 8 < 2x$

110. $7x - 4 < 3x$

111. $2x - 8 > 4x$

112. $3y + 2 > 7y$

113. $8 - 3x \leq 5x$

114. $10 - 3x \leq 7x$

115. $3x + 2 \geq 5x - 8$

116. $2n - 9 \geq 5n + 4$

117. $5x - 2 < 3x - 2$

118. $8x - 9 > 3x - 9$

119. $0.1(180 + x) > x$

120. $x > 0.2(50 + x)$

121. $0.15x + 55 > 0.10x + 80$

122. $-3.6b + 16 < 2.8b + 25.6$

123. $2(3x - 1) > 3x + 4$

124. $5(2x + 7) > -4x - 7$

125. $3(2x - 5) \geq 8x - 5$

126. $5x - 8 \geq 7x - 9$

127. $2(2y - 5) \le 3(5 - 2y)$

128. $2(5x - 8) \le 7(x - 3)$

129. $5(2 - x) > 3(2x - 5)$

130. $4(3d - 1) > 3(2 - 5d)$

131. $5(x - 2) > 9x - 3(2x - 4)$

132. $3x - 2(3x - 5) > 4(2x - 1)$

133. $4 - 3(3 - n) \le 3(2 - 5n)$

134. $15 - 5(3 - 2x) \le 4(x - 3)$

135. $2x - 3(x - 4) \ge 4 - 2(x - 7)$

136. $4 + 2(3 - 2y) \le 4(3y - 5) - 6y$

137. $\frac{1}{2}(9x - 10) \le -\frac{1}{3}(12 - 6x)$

138. $\frac{1}{4}(8 - 12d) < \frac{2}{5}(10d + 15)$

139. $\frac{2}{3}(9t - 15) + 4 < 6 + \frac{3}{4}(4 - 12t)$

140. $\frac{3}{8}(16 - 8c) - 9 \ge \frac{3}{5}(10c - 15) + 7$

141. $3[4(n - 2) - (1 - n)] > 5(n - 4)$

142. $2(m + 7) \le 4[3(m - 2) - 5(1 + m)]$

143. What number is a solution of $3x - 4 \ge 5$ but not a solution of $3x - 4 > 5$?

144. What number is a solution of $8 - 2(x + 6) \le 4$ but not a solution of $8 - 2(x + 6) < 4$?

145. Which inequalities are equivalent to the inequality $-7x - 2 > -4x + 1$?
a. $-3 > -11x$ **b.** $3x > 3$ **c.** $-3 > 3x$ **d.** $3x < -3$

146. Which inequalities are equivalent to the inequality $10 - 7(x - 4) \ge 3$?
a. $-7x + 38 \ge 3$ **b.** $3x - 12 \ge 3$ **c.** $35 \ge 7x$ **d.** $-18 - 7x \ge 3$

3.3 Applying Concepts

Use the roster method to list the set of positive integers that are solutions of the inequality.

147. $7 - 2b \le 15 - 5b$

148. $13 - 8a \ge 2 - 6a$

149. $2(2c - 3) < 5(6 - c)$

150. $-6(2 - d) \ge 4(4d - 9)$

Use the roster method to list the set of integers that are common to the solution sets of the two inequalities.

151. $5x - 12 \le x + 8$
$3x - 4 \ge 2 + x$

152. $6x - 5 > 9x - 2$
$5x - 6 < 8x + 9$

153. $4(x - 2) \le 3x + 5$
$7(x - 3) \ge 5x - 1$

154. $3(x + 2) < 2(x + 4)$
$4(x + 5) > 3(x + 6)$

Graph.

155. $|x| < 3$

156. $|x| < 4$

157. $|x| > 2$

158. $|x| > 1$

Focus on Problem Solving

Analyzing Data

WEB

Demography is the statistical study of human populations. Many groups are interested in the size of certain segments of the population and projections of population growth. For example, public school administrators want estimates of the number of school-age children who will be living in their district 10 years from now.

The U.S. government provides estimates of the future population of the United States. You can find these projections at the Census Bureau website at **www.census.gov.** The table below contains data from this website.

	Age	Under 5	5-17	18-24	25-34	35-44	45-54	55-64	65 and older
2010	Male	10,272	26,639	15,388	19,286	19,449	21,706	16,973	16,966
	Female	9,827	25,363	14,774	19,565	19,993	22,455	18,457	22,749
2050	Male	13,748	35,227	18,734	25,034	24,550	22,340	21,127	36,289
	Female	13,165	33,608	18,069	25,425	25,039	23,106	22,517	45,710

Population Projections of the United States, by Age and Sex (in thousands)

For the following exercises, round all percents to the nearest hundredth of a percent.

1. Which of the age groups listed are of interest to public school officials?

2. Which age group is of interest to retirement home administrators?

3. Which age groups are of concern to accountants determining future benefits to be paid out by the Social Security Administration?

4. Which age group is of interest to manufacturers of disposable diapers?

5. Which age groups are of primary concern to college and university admissions officers?

6. In which age groups do males outnumber females? In which do females outnumber males?

7. What percent of the projected population aged 65 and older in the year 2010 is female? Does this percent decrease for the projected population in 2050? If so, by how much?

8. Find the difference between the percent of the population that will be under 18 in 2010 and the percent that will be under 18 in 2050.

9. Assume that the work force consists of people aged 25 to 64. Find the decrease in the percent of the population represented by that age group from 2010 to 2050.

10. Find the increase in the percent of the population represented by those aged 65 and older from 2010 to 2050.

11. Why are the sizes of the current work force and the population aged 65 and older of concern to the Social Security Administration?

12. Describe any patterns you see in the table.

13. Calculate a statistic based on the data in the table and explain why it would be of interest to an institution (such as a school system) or a manufacturer of consumer goods (such as a baby food manufacturer).

Projects & Group Activities

The Consumer Price Index

WEB

The consumer price index (CPI) is a percent that is written without the percent sign. For instance, a CPI of 160.1 means 160.1%. This number means that an item that cost $100 between 1982 and 1984 (the base years) would cost $160.10 today. Determining the cost is an application of the basic percent equation.

$$PB = A$$

(CPI)(cost in base year) = cost today

$$1.601(100) = 160.1 \qquad \bullet \ \mathbf{160.1\% = 1.601}$$

The table below gives the CPI for various products in October 2005. If you have Internet access, you can obtain current data for the items below plus other items not on this list by visiting the website of the Bureau of Labor Statistics at **www.bls.gov.**

Product	CPI
All items	199.2
Food and beverages	192.5
Housing	198.4
Clothes	122.7
Transportation	184.0
Medical Care	326.2
Energy	204.3
Education: Tuition	454.7

1. Of the items listed, are there any items that cost more than twice as much in 2005 as they cost during the base years? If so, which ones?

2. Of the items listed, are there any items that cost more than one-and-one-half times as much in 2005 as they cost during the base years, but less than twice as much as they cost during the base years? If so, which ones?

3. If the average cost for tuition for one semester at a public college was $4000 in the base years, what was the average cost for tuition for one semester at a public college in 2005?

4. If a new car cost $30,000 in 2005, what would a comparable new car have cost during the base years? Use the transportation category.

5. If rent for an urban apartment in 2005 was $3000, what was the rent for the same apartment during the base years?

6. The CPI for all items in the summer of 1970 was 39.0. What salary in 2005 would have had the same purchasing power as a salary of $10,000 in 1970?

Chapter 3 Summary

Key Words

An **equation** expresses the equality of two mathematical expressions. [3.1.1, p. 106]	$5(3x - 2) = 4x + 7$ is an equation.
A **solution of an equation** is a number that, when substituted for the variable, results in a true equation. [3.1.1, p. 106]	1 is the solution of the equation $6x - 4 = 2$ because $6(1) - 4 = 2$ is a true equation.
To **solve** an equation means to find a solution of the equation. The goal is to rewrite the equation in the form **variable = constant,** because the constant is the solution. [3.1.2, p. 107]	The equation $x = -9$ is in the form *variable = constant*. The constant, -9, is the solution of the equation.
An **inequality** is an expression that contains the symbol $<, >, \leq$, or $\geq$. [3.3.1, p. 144]	$8x - 1 \geq 5x + 23$ is an inequality.
The **solution set of an inequality** is a set of numbers, each element of which, when substituted for the variable, results in a true inequality. [3.3.1, p. 144]	The solution set of $8x - 1 \geq 5x + 23$ is $x \geq 8$ because every number greater than or equal to 8, when substituted for the variable, results in a true inequality.

Essential Rules and Procedures

The Addition Property of Equations
The same number or variable term can be added to each side of an equation without changing the solution of the equation. [3.1.2, p. 107]

$$x + 12 = -19$$
$$x + 12 - 12 = -19 - 12$$
$$x = -31$$

The Multiplication Property of Equations
Each side of an equation can be multiplied by the same non-zero number without changing the solution of the equation. [3.1.3, p. 109]

$$-6x = 24$$
$$\frac{-6x}{-6} = \frac{24}{-6}$$
$$x = -4$$

To solve an equation of the form $ax + b = c$ or an equation of the form $ax + b = cx + d$, use both the Addition and the Multiplication Properties of Equations. [3.2.1 and 3.2.2, pp. 129, 131]

$$7x - 4 = 3x + 16$$
$$7x - 3x - 4 = 3x - 3x + 16$$
$$4x - 4 = 16$$
$$4x - 4 + 4 = 16 + 4$$
$$4x = 20$$
$$\frac{4x}{4} = \frac{20}{4}$$
$$x = 5$$

To solve an equation containing parentheses, use the Distributive Property to remove parentheses. [3.2.3, p. 132]

$$3(2x - 1) = 15$$
$$6x - 3 = 15$$
$$6x - 3 + 3 = 15 + 3$$
$$6x = 18$$
$$\frac{6x}{6} = \frac{18}{6}$$
$$x = 3$$

The Addition Property of Inequalities
The same number or variable term can be added to each side of an inequality without changing the solution set of the inequality.

If $a > b$, then $a + c > b + c$.
If $a < b$, then $a + c < b + c$. [3.3.1, p. 145]

$$x - 9 \le 14$$
$$x - 9 + 9 \le 14 + 9$$
$$x \le 23$$

The Multiplication Property of Inequalities

Rule 1 Each side of an inequality can be multiplied by the same **positive number** without changing the solution set of the inequality.
If $a > b$ and $c > 0$, then $ac > bc$.
If $a < b$ and $c > 0$, then $ac < bc$.

$$7x < -21$$
$$\frac{7x}{7} < \frac{-21}{7}$$
$$x < -3$$

Rule 2 If each side of an inequality is multiplied by the same **negative number** and the inequality symbol is reversed, then the solution set of the inequality is not changed.
If $a > b$ and $c < 0$, then $ac < bc$.
If $a < b$ and $c < 0$, then $ac > bc$. [3.3.2, p. 146]

$$-7x \ge 21$$
$$\frac{-7x}{-7} \le \frac{21}{-7}$$
$$x \le -3$$

The Basic Percent Equation
Percent · base = amount
$$P \cdot B = A$$
[3.1.5, p. 114]

40% of what number is 16?
$$PB = A$$
$$0.40B = 16$$
$$\frac{0.40B}{0.40} = \frac{16}{0.40}$$
$$B = 40$$

The number is 40.

Uniform Motion Equation

Distance = rate · time

$$d = rt$$

[3.1.4, p. 111]

A car travels 200 mi in 4 h. Find the rate of speed.

$$d = rt$$
$$200 = r \cdot 4$$
$$50 = r$$

The rate of speed is 50 mph.

Simple Interest Equation

Simple interest = principal · simple interest rate · time

$$I = prt$$

[3.1.5, p. 116]

A $5000 investment earns an annual simple interest rate of 4%. Find the interest earned in 6 months.

$$I = prt$$
$$I = 5000(0.04)(0.5)$$
$$I = 100$$

The interest earned is $100.

Percent Mixture Equation

Quantity of a substance in a solution
= amount of the solution · percent concentration
of the substance

$$Q = Ar$$

[3.1.5, p. 117]

An 8-ounce bottle of cough syrup is 2% alcohol. Find the amount of alcohol in the cough syrup.

$$Q = Ar$$
$$Q = 8(0.02)$$
$$Q = 0.16$$

The syrup contains 0.16 oz alcohol.

Lever-System Equation

$F_1 x = F_2(d - x)$, where F_1 and F_2 are two forces, d is the length of the lever, x is the distance from F_1 to the fulcrum, and $d - x$ is the distance from F_2 to the fulcrum   [3.2.4, p. 135]

A 30-pound child is sitting at one end of an 8-foot seesaw, 5 ft from the fulcrum. A 50-pound child is sitting at the other end. The seesaw balances.

$$F_1 x = F_2(d - x)$$
$$30(5) = 50(8 - 5)$$
$$30(5) = 50(3)$$
$$150 = 150$$

Chapter 3 Review Exercises

1. Is 3 a solution of $5x - 2 = 4x + 5$?

2. Solve: $x - 4 = 16$

3. Solve: $8x = -56$

4. Solve: $5x - 6 = 29$

5. Solve: $5x + 3 = 10x - 17$

6. Solve: $3(5x + 2) + 2 = 10x + 5[x - (3x - 1)]$

7. What is 81% of 500?

8. 18 is 72% of what number?

9. 27 is what percent of 40?

10. Graph: $x \leq -2$

11. Solve and graph the solution set of $x - 3 > -1$.

12. Solve and graph the solution set of $3x > -12$.

13. Solve: $3x + 4 \geq -8$

14. Solve: $7x - 2(x + 3) \geq x + 10$

15. Is 2 a solution of $x^2 + 4x + 1 = 3x + 7$?

16. Solve: $4.6 = 2.1 + x$

17. Solve: $\dfrac{x}{7} = -7$

18. Solve: $14 + 6x = 17$

19. Solve: $12y - 1 = 3y + 2$

20. Solve: $x + 5(3x - 20) = 10(x - 4)$

21. What is $66\dfrac{2}{3}\%$ of 24?

22. 60 is 48% of what number?

23. 0.5 is what percent of 3?

24. Solve and graph the solution set of $2 + x < -2$.

25. Solve and graph the solution set of $5x \leq -10$.

26. Solve: $6x + 3(2x - 1) = -27$

27. Solve: $a - \dfrac{1}{6} = \dfrac{2}{3}$

28. Solve: $\dfrac{3}{5}a = 12$

29. Solve: $32 = 9x - 4 - 3x$

30. Solve: $-4[x + 3(x - 5)] = 3(8x + 20)$

31. Solve: $4x - 12 < x + 24$

32. What is $\dfrac{1}{2}\%$ of 3000?

33. Solve: $3x + 7 + 4x = 42$

34. Solve: $5x - 6 > 19$

35. 8 is what percent of 200?

36. Solve: $6x - 9 < 4x + 3(x + 3)$

37. Solve: $5 - 4(x + 9) > 11(12x - 9)$

38. **Geometry** Find the measure of the third angle of a triangle if the first angle is 20° and the second angle is 50°. Use the equation $A + B + C = 180°$, where A, B, and C are the measures of the angles of a triangle.

39. **Lever Systems** A lever is 12 ft long. At a distance of 2 ft from the fulcrum, a force of 120 lb is applied. How large a force must be applied to the other end of the lever so that the system will balance? Use the lever-system equation $F_1 x = F_2(d - x)$.

40. **Geometry** Use the equation $P = 2L + 2W$, where P is the perimeter of a rectangle, L is its length, and W is its width, to find the width of a rectangle that has a perimeter of 49 ft and a length of 18.5 ft.

41. **Discounts** Find the discount on a 26-inch, 21-speed dual-index grip-shifting bicycle if the sale price is $128 and the regular price is $159.99. Use the equation $S = R - D$, where S is the sale price, R is the regular price, and D is the discount.

42. **Conservation** In Central America and Mexico, 1184 plants and animals are at risk of extinction. This represents approximately 10.7% of all the species at risk of extinction on Earth. Approximately how many plants and animals are at risk of extinction on Earth? (*Source:* World Conservation Union)

Mexico

Honduras

Belize

Guatemala

El Salvador

Nicaragua

Costa Rica

Panama

43. Physics The pressure at a certain depth in the ocean can be approximated by the equation $P = 15 + \frac{1}{2}D$, where P is the pressure in pounds per square inch and D is the depth in feet. Use this equation to find the depth when the pressure is 55 lb/in².

44. Lever Systems A lever is 8 ft long. A force of 25 lb is applied to one end of the lever, and a force of 15 lb is applied to the other end. Find the location of the fulcrum when the system balances. Use the lever-system equation $F_1x = F_2(d - x)$.

45. Geometry Find the length of a rectangle when the perimeter is 84 ft and the width is 18 ft. Use the equation $P = 2L + 2W$, where P is the perimeter of a rectangle, L is the length, and W is the width.

46. Uniform Motion Problem A motorboat that can travel 15 mph in calm water is traveling with the current of a river that is moving at 5 mph. How long will it take the motorboat to travel 30 mi?

47. Investments Cathy Serano would like to earn $125 per year from two investments. She has found one investment that will pay her $75 per year. How much must she invest in an account that earns an annual simple interest rate of 8% to reach her goal?

48. Mixture Problem A 150-milliliter acid solution contains 9 ml of hydrochloric acid. What is the percent concentration of hydrochloric acid?

Chapter 3 Test

 View the Chapter Test Videos for fully worked-out solutions to any exercise.

1. Solve: $\frac{3}{4}x = -9$

2. Solve: $6 - 5x = 5x + 11$

3. Solve: $3x - 5 = -14$

4. Is -2 a solution of $x^2 - 3x = 2x - 6$?

5. Solve: $x + \frac{1}{2} = \frac{5}{8}$

6. Solve: $5x - 2(4x - 3) = 6x + 9$

7. Solve: $7 - 4x = -13$

8. Solve: $11 - 4x = 2x + 8$

9. Solve: $x - 3 = -8$

10. Solve: $3x - 2 = 5x + 8$

11. Solve: $-\frac{3}{8}x = 5$

12. Solve: $6x - 3(2 - 3x) = 4(2x - 7)$

13. Solve: $6 - 2(5x - 8) = 3x - 4$

14. Solve: $9 - 3(2x - 5) = 12 + 5x$

15. Solve: $3(2x - 5) = 8x - 9$

16. 20 is what percent of 16?

17. 30% of what is 12?

18. Graph: $x > -2$

19. Solve and graph the solution set of $-2 + x \leq -3$.

20. Solve and graph the solution set of $\frac{3}{8}x > -\frac{3}{4}$.

21. Solve: $x + \frac{1}{3} > \frac{5}{6}$

22. Solve: $3(x - 7) \geq 5x - 12$

23. Solve: $-\frac{3}{8}x \leq 6$

24. Solve: $4x - 2(3 - 5x) \leq 6x + 10$

25. Solve: $3(2x - 5) \geq 8x - 9$

26. Solve: $15 - 3(5x - 7) < 2(7 - 2x)$

27. Solve: $-6x + 16 = -2x$

28. 20 is $83\frac{1}{3}\%$ of what number?

29. Solve and graph the solution set of $\frac{2}{3}x \geq 2$.

30. Is 5 a solution of $x^2 + 2x + 1 = (x + 1)^2$?

31. Space Travel A person's weight on the moon is $16\frac{2}{3}\%$ of the person's weight on Earth. If an astronaut weighs 180 lb on Earth, how much would the astronaut weigh on the moon?

32. Chemistry A chemist mixes 100 g of water at 80°C with 50 g of water at 20°C. Use the equation $m_1 \cdot (T_1 - T) = m_2 \cdot (T - T_2)$ to find the final temperature of the water after mixing. In this equation, m_1 is the quantity of water at the hotter temperature, T_1 is the temperature of the hotter water, m_2 is the quantity of water at the cooler temperature, T_2 is the temperature of the cooler water, and T is the final temperature of the water after mixing.

33. Manufacturing A financial manager has determined that the cost per unit for a calculator is $15 and that the fixed costs per month are $2000. Find the number of calculators produced during a month in which the total cost was $5000. Use the equation $T = U \cdot N + F$, where T is the total cost, U is the cost per unit, N is the number of units produced, and F is the fixed cost.

34. Uniform Motion Problem Two hikers start at the same time from opposite ends of a 15-mile course. One hiker is walking at a rate of 3.5 mph, and the second hiker is walking at a rate of 4 mph. How long after they begin will they meet?

35. Investments Victor Jameson has invested $750 in a simple interest account that has an annual interest rate of 6.2%. How much must he invest in a second account that earns 5% simple interest so that the interest earned on the second account is the same as that earned on the first account?

36. Mixture Problem An 8-ounce glass of chocolate milk contains 2 oz of chocolate syrup. Find the percent concentration of chocolate syrup in the chocolate milk.

Cumulative Review Exercises

1. Subtract: $-6 - (-20) - 8$

2. Multiply: $(-2)(-6)(-4)$

3. Subtract: $-\dfrac{5}{6} - \left(-\dfrac{7}{16}\right)$

4. Divide: $-2\dfrac{1}{3} \div 1\dfrac{1}{6}$

5. Simplify: $-4^2 \cdot \left(-\dfrac{3}{2}\right)^3$

6. Simplify: $25 - 3 \cdot \dfrac{(5-2)^2}{2^3+1} - (-2)$

7. Evaluate $3(a - c) - 2ab$ when $a = 2$, $b = 3$, and $c = -4$.

8. Simplify: $3x - 8x + (-12x)$

9. Simplify: $2a - (-3b) - 7a - 5b$

10. Simplify: $(16x)\left(\dfrac{1}{8}\right)$

11. Simplify: $-4(-9y)$

12. Simplify: $-2(-x^2 - 3x + 2)$

13. Simplify: $-2(x - 3) + 2(4 - x)$

14. Simplify: $-3[2x - 4(x - 3)] + 2$

15. Use the roster method to write the set of negative integers greater than -8.

16. Write $\dfrac{7}{8}$ as a percent. Write the remainder in fractional form.

17. Write 342% as a decimal.

18. Write $62\dfrac{1}{2}\%$ as a fraction.

19. Is -3 a solution of $x^2 + 6x + 9 = x + 3$?

20. Solve: $x - 4 = -9$

21. Solve: $\dfrac{3}{5}x = -15$

22. Solve: $13 - 9x = -14$

23. Solve: $5x - 8 = 12x + 13$

24. Solve: $8x - 3(4x - 5) = -2x - 11$

25. Solve: $-\dfrac{3}{4}x > \dfrac{2}{3}$

26. Solve: $5x - 4 \geq 4x + 8$

27. Solve: $3x + 17 < 5x - 1$

28. Translate "the difference between eight and the quotient of a number and twelve" into a variable expression.

29. Translate and simplify "the sum of a number and two more than the number."

30. **Dollar Bills** A club treasurer has some five-dollar bills and some ten-dollar bills. The treasurer has a total of 35 bills. Use one variable to express the number of each denomination of bill.

31. Fishing A fishing wire 3 ft long is cut into two pieces, one shorter than the other. Express the length of the shorter piece in terms of the length of the longer piece.

32. Taxes A computer programmer receives a weekly wage of $650, and $110.50 is deducted for income tax. Find the percent of the computer programmer's salary deducted for income tax.

33. Foot Racing The world record time for a 1-mile race can be approximated by the equation $t = 17.08 - 0.0067y$, where t is the time in minutes and y is the year of the race. Use this equation to predict the year in which the first "4-minute mile" was run. (The actual year was 1954.) Round to the nearest whole number.

34. Chemistry A chemist mixes 300 g of water at 75°C with 100 g of water at 15°C. Use the equation $m_1 \cdot (T_1 - T) = m_2 \cdot (T - T_2)$ to find the final temperature of the water. In this equation, m_1 is the quantity of water at the hotter temperature, T_1 is the temperature of the hotter water, m_2 is the quantity of water at the cooler temperature, T_2 is the temperature of the cooler water, and T is the final temperature of the water after mixing.

35. Lever Systems A lever is 25 ft long. At a distance of 12 ft from the fulcrum, a force of 26 lb is applied. How large a force must be applied to the other end of the lever so that the system will balance? Use the lever system equation $F_1 x = F_2(d - x)$.

4 Solving Equations and Inequalities: Applications

Online Study Center

Need help? For online student resources, such as section quizzes, visit the Online Study Center at www.cengage.com/math/aufmann.

How do TV stations know which of their programs receive the best ratings? Most stations use data from Nielsen Media Research, which surveys television viewers to determine the number of people watching particular TV shows. The larger the audience, the greater the number of points the show receives. Programs with the highest ratings can demand higher fees from companies who pay to have their commercials aired during the show. The **Projects & Group Activities on pages 235 and 236** describe the meaning of Nielsen rating points and their relationship to market share.

Prep Test

1. Simplify: $R - 0.35R$

2. Simplify: $0.08x + 0.05(400 - x)$

3. Simplify: $n + (n + 2) + (n + 4)$

4. Translate into a variable expression: "The difference between five and twice a number."

5. Write 0.4 as a percent.

6. Solve: $25x + 10(9 - x) = 120$

7. Solve: $36 = 48 - 48r$

8. Solve: $4(2x - 5) < 12$

9. A snack mixture weighs 20 oz and contains nuts and pretzels. Let n represent the number of ounces of nuts in the mixture. Express the number of ounces of pretzels in the mixture in terms of n.

4.1 Translating Sentences into Equations

OBJECTIVE 1

Translate a sentence into an equation and solve

An equation states that two mathematical expressions are equal. Therefore, to translate a sentence into an equation requires recognizing the words or phrases that mean "equals." Some of these phrases that mean "equals" are *is*, *is equal to*, *amounts to*, and *represents*.

Once the sentence is translated into an equation, the equation can be solved by rewriting the equation in the form *variable = constant*.

EXAMPLE 1 Translate "two times the sum of a number and eight equals the sum of four times the number and six" into an equation and solve.

Solution   the unknown number: n • **Assign a variable to the unknown quantity.**

two times the sum of a number and eight	equals	the sum of four times the number and six

• **Find two verbal expressions for the same value.**

$$2(n + 8) = 4n + 6$$

• **Write a mathematical expression for each verbal expression. Write the equals sign.**
• **Solve the equation.**

$$2n + 16 = 4n + 6$$
$$2n - 4n + 16 = 4n - 4n + 6$$
$$-2n + 16 = 6$$
$$-2n + 16 - 16 = 6 - 16$$
$$-2n = -10$$
$$\frac{-2n}{-2} = \frac{-10}{-2}$$
$$n = 5$$

The number is 5.

PROBLEM 1   Translate "nine less than twice a number is five times the sum of the number and twelve" into an equation and solve.

Solution   See page S8.

OBJECTIVE **2**   Application problems

EXAMPLE 2   The temperature of the sun on the Kelvin scale is 6500 K. This is 4740° less than the temperature on the Fahrenheit scale. Find the Fahrenheit temperature.

Strategy   To find the Fahrenheit temperature, write and solve an equation using F to represent the Fahrenheit temperature.

Solution

6500	is	4740° less than the Fahrenheit temperature

$$6500 = F - 4740$$
$$6500 + 4740 = F - 4740 + 4740$$
$$11,240 = F$$

The temperature of the sun is 11,240°F.

PROBLEM 2   A molecule of octane gas has eight carbon atoms. This represents twice the number of carbon atoms in a butane gas molecule. Find the number of carbon atoms in a butane gas molecule.

Solution   See page S8.

EXAMPLE 3 A board 10 ft long is cut into two pieces. Three times the length of the shorter piece is twice the length of the longer piece. Find the length of each piece.

Strategy Draw a diagram. To find the length of each piece, write and solve an equation using x to represent the length of the shorter piece and $10 - x$ to represent the length of the longer piece.

Take Note

We could also let x represent the length of the longer piece and let $10 - x$ represent the length of the shorter piece. Then our equation would be

$$3(10 - x) = 2x$$

Show that this equation results in the same solutions.

Solution

three times the length of the shorter piece	is	twice the length of the longer piece

$$3x = 2(10 - x)$$
$$3x = 20 - 2x$$
$$3x + 2x = 20 - 2x + 2x$$
$$5x = 20$$
$$\frac{5x}{5} = \frac{20}{5}$$
$$x = 4$$

$$10 - x = 10 - 4 = 6$$

• **The length of the shorter piece is 4 ft.**

• **Substitute the value of x into the variable expression for the longer piece and evaluate.**

The length of the shorter piece is 4 ft. The length of the longer piece is 6 ft.

PROBLEM 3 A company manufactures 160 bicycles per day. Four times the number of 3-speed bicycles made each day equals 30 less than the number of 10-speed bicycles made each day. Find the number of 10-speed bicycles manufactured each day.

■ **Solution** See page S8.

4.1   Concept Review

Determine whether the statement is always true, sometimes true, or never true.

1. When two expressions represent the same value, we say that the expressions are equal to each other.

2. Both "four less than a number" and "the difference between four and a number" are translated as "$4 - n$."

3. When translating a sentence into an equation, we can use any variable to represent an unknown number.

4. When translating a sentence into an equation, translate the word *is* as "=."

5. If a rope 19 inches long is cut into two pieces and one of the pieces has length x inches, then the length of the other piece can be expressed as $(x - 19)$ inches.

6. In addition to a number, the answer to an application problem must have a unit, such as meters, dollars, minutes, or miles per hour.

4.1 Exercises

1 Translate a sentence into an equation and solve

1. When we translate a sentence into an equation, the word *is* translates into the ____?____ sign.

2. The sum of two numbers is twelve. If n represents one of the numbers, then the other number is represented by ____?____.

Translate into an equation and solve.

3. The difference between a number and fifteen is seven. Find the number.

4. The sum of five and a number is three. Find the number.

5. The product of seven and a number is negative twenty-one. Find the number.

6. The quotient of a number and four is two. Find the number.

7. Four less than three times a number is five. Find the number.

8. The difference between five and twice a number is one. Find the number.

9. Four times the sum of twice a number and three is twelve. Find the number.

10. Twenty-one is three times the difference between four times a number and five. Find the number.

11. Twelve is six times the difference between a number and three. Find the number.

12. The difference between six times a number and four times the number is negative fourteen. Find the number.

13. Twenty-two is two less than six times a number. Find the number.

14. Negative fifteen is three more than twice a number. Find the number.

15. Seven more than four times a number is three more than two times the number. Find the number.

16. The difference between three times a number and four is five times the number. Find the number.

17. Eight less than five times a number is four more than eight times the number. Find the number.

18. The sum of a number and six is four less than six times the number. Find the number.

19. Twice the difference between a number and twenty-five is three times the number. Find the number.

20. Four times a number is three times the difference between thirty-five and the number. Find the number.

21. The sum of two numbers is twenty. Three times the smaller is equal to two times the larger. Find the two numbers.

22. The sum of two numbers is fifteen. One less than three times the smaller is equal to the larger. Find the two numbers.

23. The sum of two numbers is eighteen. The total of three times the smaller and twice the larger is forty-four. Find the two numbers.

24. The sum of two numbers is two. The difference between eight and twice the smaller number is two less than four times the larger. Find the two numbers.

25. The sum of two numbers is fourteen. One number is ten more than the other number. Write two different equations that can be used to find the numbers by first writing an equation in which n represents "the larger number" and then writing an equation in which n represents "the smaller number."

26. The sum of two numbers is seven. Twice one number is four less than the other number. Which of the following equations does *not* represent this situation?
  a. $2n = 7 - n - 4$ **b.** $2(7 - x) = x - 4$
  c. $2x + 4 = 7 - x$ **d.** $2n - 4 = 7 - n$

2   Application problems

27. The number of calories in a cup of low-fat milk is two-thirds the number of calories in a cup of whole milk. In this situation, let n represent the number of calories in a cup of ___?___ milk, and let $\frac{2}{3}n$ represent the number of calories in a cup of ___?___ milk.

28. A cup of low-fat milk has 100 calories. Use the information in Exercise 27 to write an equation that can be used to find the number of calories in a cup of whole milk: _____?_____ = _____?_____ .

Write an equation and solve.

29. **Depreciation** As a result of depreciation, the value of a car is now $9600. This is three-fifths of its original value. Find the original value of the car.

30. **Structures** The length of the Royal Gorge Bridge in Colorado is 320 m. This is one-fourth the length of the Golden Gate Bridge. Find the length of the Golden Gate Bridge.

The Golden Gate Bridge

31. **Nutrition** One slice of cheese pizza contains 290 calories. A medium-size orange has one-fifth that number of calories. How many calories are in a medium-size orange?

32. **History** John D. Rockefeller died in 1937. At the time of his death, Rockefeller had accumulated a wealth of $1,400 million, which was equal to one-sixty-fifth of the gross national product of the United States at that time. What was the U.S. gross national product in 1937? (*Source: The Wealthy 100: A Ranking of the Richest Americans, Past and Present*)

33. **Agriculture** A soil supplement that weighs 18 lb contains iron, potassium, and a mulch. There is fifteen times as much mulch as iron and twice as much potassium as iron. Find the amount of mulch in the soil supplement.

34. **Commissions** A real estate agent sold two homes and received commissions totaling $6000. The agent's commission on one home was one and one-half times the commission on the second home. Find the agent's commission on each home.

John D. Rockefeller

35. **Safety** Loudness, or the intensity of sound, is measured in decibels. The sound level of a television is about 70 decibels, which is considered a safe hearing level. A food blender runs at 20 decibels higher than a TV, and a jet engine's decibel reading is 40 less than twice that of a blender. At this level, exposure can cause hearing loss. Find the intensity of the sound of a jet engine.

36. **Education** A university employs a total of 600 teaching assistants and research assistants. There are three times as many teaching assistants as research assistants. Find the number of research assistants employed by the university.

37. **Consumerism** The purchase price of a new big-screen TV, including finance charges, was $3276. A down payment of $450 was made. The remainder was paid in 24 equal monthly installments. Find the monthly payment.

Point of Interest

The low-frequency pulses or whistles made by blue whales have been measured at up to 188 decibels, making them the loudest sounds produced by a living organism.

38. Consumerism The purchase price of a new computer system, including finance charges, was $6350. A down payment of $350 was made. The remainder was paid in 24 equal monthly installments. Find the monthly payment.

39. Geometry Greek architects considered a rectangle whose length was approximately 1.6 times its width to be the most visually appealing. Find the length and width of a rectangle constructed in this manner if the sum of the length and width is 130 ft.

40. Geography Greenland, the largest island in the world, is 21 times larger than Iceland. The combined area of Greenland and Iceland is 880,000 mi². Find the area of Greenland.

41. Consumerism The cost to replace a water pump in a sports car was $600. This included $375 for the water pump and $45 per hour for labor. How many hours of labor were required to replace the water pump?

42. Utilities The cost of electricity in a certain city is $.08 for each of the first 300 kWh (kilowatt-hours) and $.13 for each kWh over 300 kWh. Find the number of kilowatt-hours used by a family that receives a $51.95 electric bill.

43. Consumerism The fee charged by a ticketing agency for a concert is $5.50 plus $37.50 for each ticket purchased. If your total charge for tickets is $343, how many tickets are you purchasing?

44. Carpentry A carpenter is building a wood door frame. The height of the frame is 1 ft less than three times the width. What is the width of the largest door frame that can be constructed from a board 19 ft long? (*Hint:* A door frame consists of only three sides; there is no frame below a door.)

45. Construction The length of a rectangular cement patio is 3 ft less than three times the width. The sum of the length and width of the patio is 21 ft. Find the length of the patio.

46. Carpentry A 20-foot board is cut into two pieces. Twice the length of the shorter piece is 4 ft more than the length of the longer piece. Find the length of the shorter piece.

47. Labor Unions A union charges monthly dues of $4.00 plus $.15 for each hour worked during the month. A union member's dues for March were $29.20. How many hours did the union member work during the month of March?

48. Business The cellular phone service for a business executive is $35 per month plus $.40 per minute of phone use. In a month when the executive's cellular phone bill was $99.80, how many minutes did the executive use the phone?

49. Business A technical information hotline charges a customer $9.00 plus $.50 per minute to answer questions about software. How many minutes did a customer who received a bill for $14.50 use this service?

50. Metalwork A wire 12 ft long is cut into two pieces. Each piece is bent into the shape of a square. The perimeter of the larger square is twice the perimeter of the smaller square. Find the perimeter of the larger square.

4.1 Applying Concepts

51. The amount of liquid in a container triples every minute. The container becomes completely filled at 3:40 P.M. What fractional part of the container is filled at 3:39 P.M.?

52. Travel A cyclist traveling at a constant speed completes $\frac{3}{5}$ of a trip in $1\frac{1}{2}$ h. In how many additional hours will the cyclist complete the entire trip?

53. Postage The rate for first-class mail is $.39 for the first ounce and $.24 for each additional ounce or fraction of an ounce. If the cost to mail a package first class is $3.27, how much does the package weigh?

54. Wages Four employees are paid at four consecutive levels on a wage scale. The difference between any two consecutive levels is $320 per month. The average of the four employees' monthly wages is $3880. What is the monthly wage of the highest-paid employee?

55. Coins A coin bank contains nickels, dimes, and quarters. There are 14 nickels in the bank, $\frac{1}{6}$ of the coins are dimes, and $\frac{3}{5}$ of the coins are quarters. How many coins are in the coin bank?

56. Business During one day at an office, one-half of the amount of money in the petty cash drawer was used in the morning, and one-third of the remaining money was used in the afternoon, leaving $5 in the petty cash drawer at the end of the day. How much money was in the petty cash drawer at the start of the day?

57. A formula is an equation that relates variables in a known way. Find two examples of formulas that are used in your college major. Explain what each of the variables represents.

4.2 Integer, Coin, and Stamp Problems

OBJECTIVE 1 **Consecutive integer problems**

Recall that the integers are the numbers ..., $-4, -3, -2, -1, 0, 1, 2, 3, 4, ...$.

An **even integer** is an integer that is divisible by 2. Examples of even integers are -8, 0, and 22.

An **odd integer** is an integer that is not divisible by 2. Examples of odd integers are -17, 1, and 39.

Consecutive integers are integers that follow one another in order. Examples of consecutive integers are shown at the right. (Assume the variable n represents an integer.)	11, 12, 13 $-8, -7, -6$ $n, n + 1, n + 2$
Examples of **consecutive even integers** are shown at the right. (Assume the variable n represents an even integer.)	24, 26, 28 $-10, -8, -6$ $n, n + 2, n + 4$
Examples of **consecutive odd integers** are shown at the right. (Assume the variable n represents an odd integer.)	19, 21, 23, $-1, 1, 3$ $n, n + 2, n + 4$

Solve: The sum of three consecutive odd integers is 51. Find the integers.

> **STRATEGY** **for solving a consecutive integer problem**
>
> ▶ Let a variable represent one of the integers. Express each of the other integers in terms of that variable. Remember that consecutive integers differ by 1. Consecutive even or consecutive odd integers differ by 2.

First odd integer: n
Second odd integer: $n + 2$
Third odd integer: $n + 4$

▶ Determine the relationship among the integers.

The sum of the three odd integers is 51.

$$n + (n + 2) + (n + 4) = 51$$
$$3n + 6 = 51$$
$$3n = 45$$
$$n = 15$$

$n + 2 = 15 + 2 = 17$ • Substitute the value of *n* into the variable expressions
$n + 4 = 15 + 4 = 19$ for the second and third integers.

The three consecutive odd integers are 15, 17, and 19.

> **EXAMPLE 1**   Find three consecutive even integers such that three times the second integer is six more than the sum of the first and third integers.
>
> **Strategy**   ▶ First even integer: n
> Second even integer: $n + 2$
> Third even integer: $n + 4$
> ▶ Three times the second integer equals six more than the sum of the first and third integers.
>
> **Solution**
> $$3(n + 2) = n + (n + 4) + 6$$
> $$3n + 6 = 2n + 10$$
> $$n + 6 = 10$$
> $$n = 4$$ • The first even integer is 4.
>
> $$n + 2 = 4 + 2 = 6$$
> $$n + 4 = 4 + 4 = 8$$ • Substitute the value of *n* into the variable expressions for the second and third integers.
>
> The three consecutive even integers are 4, 6, and 8.

PROBLEM 1   Find three consecutive integers whose sum is -12.

Solution   See page S8.

OBJECTIVE 2

3 • 25 = 75 cents

d • 10 = 10d cents

Coin and stamp problems

In solving problems that deal with coins or stamps of different values, it is necessary to represent the values of the coins or stamps in the same unit of money. Frequently, the unit of money is cents.

The value of 3 quarters in cents is $3 \cdot 25$ or 75 cents.
The value of 4 nickels in cents is $4 \cdot 5$ or 20 cents.
The value of d dimes in cents is $d \cdot 10$ or $10d$ cents.

Solve: A coin bank contains $1.20 in dimes and quarters. In all, there are nine coins in the bank. Find the number of quarters in the bank.

STRATEGY   **for solving a coin problem**

▶ For each denomination of coin, write a numerical or variable expression for the number of coins, the value of the coin in cents, and the total value of the coins in cents. The results can be recorded in a table.

The total number of coins is 9.

Number of quarters: x
Number of dimes: $9 - x$

Take Note

Use the information given in the problem to fill in the number and value columns of the table. Fill in the total value column by multiplying the two expressions you wrote in each row.

Coin	Number of coins	·	Value of coin in cents	=	Total value in cents
Quarter	x	·	25	=	$25x$
Dime	$9 - x$	·	10	=	$10(9 - x)$

▶ Determine the relationship between the total values of the different coins. Use the fact that the sum of the total values of the different denominations of coins is equal to the total value of all the coins.

The sum of the total values of the different denominations of coins is equal to the total value of all the coins (120 cents).

$$25x + 10(9 - x) = 120$$
$$25x + 90 - 10x = 120$$
$$15x + 90 = 120$$
$$15x = 30$$
$$x = 2$$

• **The total value of the quarters plus the total value of the dimes equals the amount of money in the bank.**

There are 2 quarters in the bank.

EXAMPLE 2   A collection of stamps consists of 3¢ stamps and 8¢ stamps. The number of 8¢ stamps is five more than three times the number of 3¢ stamps. The total value of all the stamps is $1.75. Find the number of each type of stamp in the collection.

Strategy   ▶ Number of 3¢ stamps: x
Number of 8¢ stamps: $3x + 5$

Stamp	Number	Value	Total value
3¢	x	3	$3x$
8¢	$3x + 5$	8	$8(3x + 5)$

▶ The sum of the total values of the different types of stamps equals the total value of all the stamps (175 cents).

Solution $3x + 8(3x + 5) = 175$
$3x + 24x + 40 = 175$
$27x + 40 = 175$
$27x = 135$
$x = 5$

• **The total value of the 3¢ stamps plus the total value of the 8¢ stamps equals the total value of all the stamps.**

$3x + 5 = 3(5) + 5$
$= 15 + 5 = 20$

• **Find the number of 8¢ stamps.**

There are five 3¢ stamps and twenty 8¢ stamps in the collection.

PROBLEM 2   A coin bank contains nickels, dimes, and quarters. There are five times as many nickels as dimes and six more quarters than dimes. The total value of all the coins is $6.30. Find the number of each kind of coin in the bank.

Solution   See page S8.

4.2 Concept Review

Determine whether the statement is always true, sometimes true, or never true.

1. An even integer is a multiple of 2.

2. When $10d$ is used to represent the value of d dimes, 10 is written as the coefficient of d because it is the number of cents in one dime.

3. Given the consecutive odd integers -5 and -3, the next consecutive odd integer is -1.

4. If the first of three consecutive odd integers is n, then the second and third consecutive odd integers are represented as $n + 1$ and $n + 3$.

5. You have a total of 20 coins in nickels and dimes. If n represents the number of nickels you have, then $n - 20$ represents the number of dimes you have.

6. You have a total of seven coins in dimes and quarters. The total value of the coins is $1.15. If d represents the number of dimes you have, then $10d + 25(7 - d) = 1.15$.

4.2 Exercises

1 Consecutive integer problems

1. Integers that follow one another in order are called ___?___ integers.

2. Two consecutive integers differ by ___?___. Two consecutive even integers differ by ___?___. Two consecutive odd integers differ by ___?___.

3. ✎ Explain how to represent three consecutive integers using only one variable.

4. ✎ Explain why both consecutive even integers and consecutive odd integers are represented algebraically as $n, n + 2, n + 4, \ldots$.

5. The sum of three consecutive integers is 54. Find the integers.

6. The sum of three consecutive integers is 75. Find the integers.

7. The sum of three consecutive even integers is 84. Find the integers.

8. The sum of three consecutive even integers is 48. Find the integers.

9. The sum of three consecutive odd integers is 57. Find the integers.

10. The sum of three consecutive odd integers is 81. Find the integers.

11. Find two consecutive even integers such that five times the first integer is equal to four times the second integer.

12. Find two consecutive even integers such that six times the first integer equals three times the second integer.

13. Nine times the first of two consecutive odd integers equals seven times the second. Find the integers.

14. Five times the first of two consecutive odd integers is three times the second. Find the integers.

15. Find three consecutive integers whose sum is negative twenty-four.

16. Find three consecutive even integers whose sum is negative twelve.

17. Three times the smallest of three consecutive even integers is two more than twice the largest. Find the integers.

18. Twice the smallest of three consecutive odd integers is five more than the largest. Find the integers.

19. Find three consecutive odd integers such that three times the middle integer is six more than the sum of the first and third integers.

20. Find three consecutive odd integers such that four times the middle integer is equal to two less than the sum of the first and third integers.

21. Which of the following could *not* be used to represent three consecutive even integers?
 a. $n + 2, n + 4, n + 6$ b. $n, n + 4, n + 6$
 c. $n + 1, n + 3, n + 5$ d. $n - 2, n, n + 2$

22. If n is an odd integer, which expression represents the third consecutive odd integer after n?
 a. $n + 6$ b. $n + 4$ c. $n + 3$ d. $n + 2$

2 Coin and stamp problems

23. Explain how to represent the total value of x nickels using the equation

 Number of coins · Value of the coin in cents = Total value in cents

24. Suppose a coin purse contains only dimes and quarters. In the context of this situation, explain the meaning of the statement "The sum of the total values of the different denominations of coins is equal to the total value of all the coins."

25. A bank contains 32 coins in nickels and dimes. Let n represent the number of nickels. Complete the following table.

Coin	Number of coins	.	Value of the coin in cents	=	Total value of the coins in cents
Nickel	n	.	?	=	?
Dime	?	.	?	=	?

26. The total value of the 32 coins in Exercise 25 is $2.70. The total value of the coins in cents is ___?___. Use this information and the information in the table in Exercise 25 to write an equation that can be solved to find the number of nickels in the bank: ___?___ + ___?___ = ___?___.

27. **a.** How many pennies are in d dollars?
   b. How many nickels are in d dollars?
   c. How many quarters are in d dollars?

28. **a.** How many cents are n 39¢ stamps worth?
   b. How many dollars are n 39¢ stamps worth?

29. A bank contains 27 coins in dimes and quarters. The coins have a total value of $4.95. Find the number of dimes and quarters in the bank.

30. A coin purse contains 18 coins in nickels and dimes. The coins have a total value of $1.15. Find the number of nickels and dimes in the coin purse.

31. A business executive bought 40 stamps for $14.40. The purchase included 39¢ stamps and 24¢ stamps. How many of each type of stamp were bought?

32. A postal clerk sold some 34¢ stamps and some 23¢ stamps. Altogether, 15 stamps were sold for a total cost of $4.44. How many of each type of stamp were sold?

33. A drawer contains 29¢ stamps and 3¢ stamps. The number of 29¢ stamps is four less than three times the number of 3¢ stamps. The total value of all the stamps is $1.54. How many 29¢ stamps are in the drawer?

34. The total value of the dimes and quarters in a bank is $6.05. There are six more quarters than dimes. Find the number of each type of coin in the bank.

35. A child's piggy bank contains 44 coins in quarters and dimes. The coins have a total value of $8.60. Find the number of quarters in the bank.

36. A coin bank contains nickels and dimes. The number of dimes is 10 less than twice the number of nickels. The total value of all the coins is $2.75. Find the number of each type of coin in the bank.

37. A total of 26 bills are in a cash box. Some of the bills are one-dollar bills, and the rest are five-dollar bills. The total amount of cash in the box is $50. Find the number of each type of bill in the cash box.

38. A bank teller cashed a check for $200 using twenty-dollar bills and ten-dollar bills. In all, 12 bills were handed to the customer. Find the number of twenty-dollar bills and the number of ten-dollar bills.

39. A coin bank contains pennies, nickels, and dimes. There are six times as many nickels as pennies and four times as many dimes as pennies. The total amount of money in the bank is $7.81. Find the number of pennies in the bank.

40. A coin bank contains pennies, nickels, and quarters. There are seven times as many nickels as pennies and three times as many quarters as pennies. The total amount of money in the bank is $5.55. Find the number of pennies in the bank.

41. A collection of stamps consists of 22¢ stamps and 40¢ stamps. The number of 22¢ stamps is three more than four times the number of 40¢ stamps. The total value of the stamps is $8.34. Find the number of 22¢ stamps in the collection.

42. A collection of stamps consists of 2¢ stamps, 8¢ stamps, and 14¢ stamps. The number of 2¢ stamps is five more than twice the number of 8¢ stamps. The number of 14¢ stamps is three times the number of 8¢ stamps. The total value of the stamps is $2.26. Find the number of each type of stamp in the collection.

43. A collection of stamps consists of 3¢ stamps, 7¢ stamps, and 12¢ stamps. The number of 3¢ stamps is five less than the number of 7¢ stamps. The number of 12¢ stamps is one-half the number of 7¢ stamps. The total value of all the stamps is $2.73. Find the number of each type of stamp in the collection.

44. A collection of stamps consists of 2¢ stamps, 5¢ stamps, and 7¢ stamps. There are nine more 2¢ stamps than 5¢ stamps and twice as many 7¢ stamps as 5¢ stamps. The total value of the stamps is $1.44. Find the number of each type of stamp in the collection.

45. A collection of stamps consists of 6¢ stamps, 8¢ stamps, and 15¢ stamps. The number of 6¢ stamps is three times the number of 8¢ stamps. There are six more 15¢ stamps than there are 6¢ stamps. The total value of all the stamps is $5.16. Find the number of each type of stamp.

46. A child's piggy bank contains nickels, dimes, and quarters. There are twice as many nickels as dimes and four more quarters than nickels. The total value of all the coins is $9.40. Find the number of each type of coin.

4.2   Applying Concepts

47. Find four consecutive even integers whose sum is -36.

48. Find four consecutive odd integers whose sum is -48.

49. A coin bank contains only dimes and quarters. The number of quarters in the bank is two less than twice the number of dimes. There are 34 coins in the bank. How much money is in the bank?

50. A postal clerk sold twenty stamps to a customer. The number of 39¢ stamps purchased was two more than twice the number of 24¢ stamps purchased. If the customer bought only 39¢ stamps and 24¢ stamps, how much money did the clerk collect from the customer?

51. Find three consecutive odd integers such that the sum of the first and third integers is twice the second integer.

52. Find four consecutive integers such that the sum of the first and fourth integers equals the sum of the second and third integers.

 Geometry Problems

OBJECTIVE **1**   **Perimeter problems**

Recall that the **perimeter** of a plane geometric figure is a measure of the distance around the figure. Perimeter is used, for example, in buying fencing for a lawn and in determining how much baseboard is needed for a room.

The perimeter of a triangle is the sum of the lengths of the three sides. Therefore, if a, b, and c represent the lengths of the sides of a triangle, the perimeter, P, of the triangle is given by $P = a + b + c$.

$P = a + b + c$

Two special types of triangles are shown below. An **isosceles triangle** has two sides of equal length. The three sides of an **equilateral triangle** are of equal length.

Isosceles triangle
$AC = BC$
$\angle A = \angle B$

Equilateral triangle
$AB = AC = BC$
$\angle A = \angle B = \angle C$

Point
of Interest

Leonardo da Vinci painted the Mona Lisa on a rectangular canvas whose height was approximately 1.6 times its width. Rectangles with these proportions, called **golden rectangles,** *were used extensively in Renaissance art.*

The perimeter of a rectangle is the sum of the lengths of the four sides. Let L represent the length and W represent the width of a rectangle. Then the perimeter, P, of the rectangle is given by $P = L + W + L + W$. Combine like terms and the formula is $P = 2L + 2W$.

$P = 2L + 2W$

A square is a rectangle in which each side has the same length. Let s represent the length of each side of a square. Then the perimeter, P, of the square is given by $P = s + s + s + s$. Combine like terms and the formula is $P = 4s$.

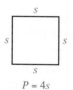

$P = 4s$

Formulas for Perimeters of Geometric Figures

Perimeter of a triangle: $P = a + b + c$
Perimeter of a rectangle: $P = 2L + 2W$
Perimeter of a square: $P = 4s$

The perimeter of a rectangle is 26 ft. The length of the rectangle is 1 ft more than twice the width. Find the width and length of the rectangle.

Strategy

Let a variable represent the width.   Width: W
Represent the length in terms of that variable.   Length: $2W + 1$
Use the formula for the perimeter of a
rectangle.

2W + 1

W

Solution

$$P = 2L + 2W$$

$P = 26$. Substitute $2W + 1$ for L. $26 = 2(2W + 1) + 2W$

Use the Distributive Property.	$26 = 4W + 2 + 2W$
Combine like terms.	$26 = 6W + 2$
Subtract 2 from each side of the equation.	$24 = 6W$
Divide each side of the equation by 6.	$4 = W$
Find the length of the rectangle by substituting 4 for W in $2W + 1$.	$L = 2W + 1$ $= 2(4) + 1 = 8 + 1 = 9$

The width is 4 ft. The length is 9 ft.

EXAMPLE 1   The perimeter of an isosceles triangle is 25 ft. The length of the third side is 2 ft less than the length of one of the equal sides. Find the measures of the three sides of the triangle.

Strategy ▶ Each equal side: x
The third side: $x - 2$
▶ Use the equation for the perimeter of a triangle.

Solution $P = a + b + c$

$25 = x + x + (x - 2)$
$25 = 3x - 2$
$27 = 3x$
$9 = x$

$x - 2 = 9 - 2 = 7$ • Substitute the value of *x* into the variable expression for the length of the third side.

Each of the equal sides measures 9 ft.
The third side measures 7 ft.

PROBLEM 1   A carpenter is designing a square patio with a perimeter of 52 ft. What is the length of each side?

Solution   See page S9.

OBJECTIVE **2**   **Problems involving angles formed by intersecting lines**

Recall that a unit used to measure angles is the **degree.** The symbol for degree is °. $\angle$ is the symbol for angle.

One complete revolution is 360°. It is likely that the Babylonians chose 360° for a circle because they knew that there are 365 days in one year, and 360 is the closest number to 365 that is divisible by many numbers.

A 90° angle is called a **right angle.** The symbol ⌐ represents a right angle. Angle C ($\angle C$) is a right angle.

A 180° angle is called a **straight angle.** The angle at the right is a straight angle.

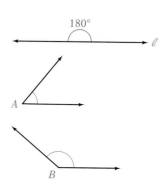

An **acute angle** is an angle whose measure is between 0° and 90°. $\angle A$ at the right is an acute angle.

An **obtuse angle** is an angle whose measure is between 90° and 180°. $\angle B$ at the right is an obtuse angle.

Given the diagram at the left, find x.

Strategy   The sum of the measures of the three angles is 360°. To find x, write an equation and solve for x.

Solution $3x + 4x + 5x = 360°$
$12x = 360°$
$x = 30°$

The measure of x is 30°.

Complementary angles are two angles whose measures have the sum 90°.

$\angle D + \angle E = 70° + 20° = 90°$

$\angle D$ and $\angle E$ are complementary angles.

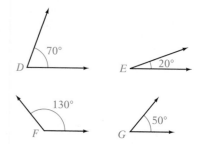

Supplementary angles are two angles whose measures have the sum 180°.

$\angle F + \angle G = 130° + 50° = 180°$

$\angle F$ and $\angle G$ are supplementary angles.

EXAMPLE 2   Find the complement of a 39° angle.

Strategy   To find the complement, let x represent the complement of a 39° angle. Use the fact that complementary angles are two angles whose sum is 90° to write an equation. Solve for x.

Solution $39° + x = 90°$

$x = 51°$ • **Subtract 39 from each side of the equation.**

The complement of a 39° angle is a 51° angle.

PROBLEM 2   Find the supplement of a 107° angle.

Solution   See page S9.

Parallel lines never meet. The distance between them is always the same. The symbol ‖ means "is parallel to." In the figure at the right, $\ell_1 \| \ell_2$.

Perpendicular lines are intersecting lines that form right angles. The symbol ⊥ means "is perpendicular to." In the figure at the right, $p \perp q$.

Four angles are formed by the intersection of two lines. If the two lines are perpendicular, then each of the four angles is a right angle. If the two lines are not perpendicular, then two of the angles formed are acute angles and two of the angles formed are obtuse angles. The two acute angles are always opposite each other, and the two obtuse angles are always opposite each other.

In the figure at the right, $\angle w$ and $\angle y$ are acute angles, and $\angle x$ and $\angle z$ are obtuse angles.

Two angles that are on opposite sides of the intersection of two lines are called **vertical angles.** Vertical angles have the same measure. $\angle w$ and $\angle y$ are vertical angles. $\angle x$ and $\angle z$ are vertical angles.

Vertical angles have the same measure.

$$\angle w = \angle y$$
$$\angle x = \angle z$$

Two angles that share a common side are called **adjacent angles.** For the figure shown above, $\angle x$ and $\angle y$ are adjacent angles, as are $\angle y$ and $\angle z$, $\angle z$ and $\angle w$, and $\angle w$ and $\angle x$. Adjacent angles of intersecting lines are supplementary angles.

Adjacent angles of intersecting lines are supplementary angles.

$$\angle x + \angle y = 180°$$
$$\angle y + \angle z = 180°$$
$$\angle z + \angle w = 180°$$
$$\angle w + \angle x = 180°$$

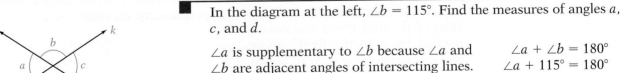

In the diagram at the left, $\angle b = 115°$. Find the measures of angles a, c, and d.

$\angle a$ is supplementary to $\angle b$ because $\angle a$ and $\angle b$ are adjacent angles of intersecting lines.

$$\angle a + \angle b = 180°$$
$$\angle a + 115° = 180°$$
$$\angle a = 65°$$

$\angle c = \angle a$ because $\angle c$ and $\angle a$ are vertical angles.

$$\angle c = 65°$$

$\angle d = \angle b$ because $\angle d$ and $\angle b$ are vertical angles.

$$\angle d = 115°$$

EXAMPLE 3 Find x.

Strategy The angles labeled are adjacent angles of intersecting lines and are therefore supplementary angles. To find x, write an equation and solve for x.

Solution
$$x + (x + 70°) = 180°$$
$$2x + 70° = 180°$$
$$2x = 110°$$
$$x = 55°$$

PROBLEM 3 Find x.

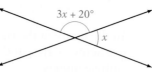

■ **Solution** See page S9.

A line that intersects two other lines at different points is called a **transversal.** If the lines cut by a transversal t are parallel lines and the transversal is not perpendicular to the parallel lines, all four acute angles have the same measure and all four obtuse angles have the same measure. In the figure at the right,

$$\angle b = \angle d = \angle x = \angle z$$
$$\angle a = \angle c = \angle w = \angle y$$

Alternate interior angles are two non-adjacent angles that are on opposite sides of the transversal and between the lines. In the figure above, $\angle c$ and $\angle w$ are alternate interior angles, and $\angle d$ and $\angle x$ are alternate interior angles. Alternate interior angles have the same measure.

Alternate interior angles have the same measure.
$$\angle c = \angle w$$
$$\angle d = \angle x$$

Alternate exterior angles are two non-adjacent angles that are on opposite sides of the transversal and outside the parallel lines. In the figure above, $\angle a$ and $\angle y$ are alternate exterior angles, and $\angle b$ and $\angle z$ are alternate exterior angles. Alternate exterior angles have the same measure.

Alternate exterior angles have the same measure.
$$\angle a = \angle y$$
$$\angle b = \angle z$$

Corresponding angles are two angles that are on the same side of the transversal and are both acute angles or are both obtuse angles. In the figure at the left, the following pairs of angles are corresponding angles: $\angle a$ and $\angle w$, $\angle d$ and $\angle z$, $\angle b$ and $\angle x$, and $\angle c$ and $\angle y$. Corresponding angles have the same measure.

Corresponding angles have the same measure.

$$\angle a = \angle w$$
$$\angle d = \angle z$$
$$\angle b = \angle x$$
$$\angle c = \angle y$$

In the diagram at the left, $\ell_1 \| \ell_2$ and $\angle f = 58°$. Find the measures of $\angle a$, $\angle c$, and $\angle d$.

$\angle a$ and $\angle f$ are corresponding angles. $\angle a = \angle f = 58°$

$\angle c$ and $\angle f$ are alternate interior angles. $\angle c = \angle f = 58°$

$\angle d$ is supplementary to $\angle a$.

$$\angle d + \angle a = 180°$$
$$\angle d + 58° = 180°$$
$$\angle d = 122°$$

EXAMPLE 4   Given $\ell_1 \| \ell_2$, find x.

Strategy $3x = y$ because corresponding angles have the same measure. $y + (x + 40°) = 180°$ because adjacent angles of intersecting lines are supplementary angles.

Substitute $3x$ for y and solve for x.

Solution
$$y + (x + 40°) = 180°$$
$$3x + (x + 40°) = 180°$$
$$4x + 40° = 180°$$
$$4x = 140°$$
$$x = 35°$$

PROBLEM 4   Given $\ell_1 \| \ell_2$, find x.

Solution   See page S9.

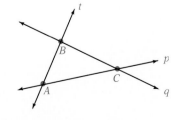

OBJECTIVE 3   **Problems involving the angles of a triangle**

If the lines cut by a transversal are not parallel lines, the three lines will intersect at three points. In the figure at the right, the transversal t intersects lines p and q. The three lines intersect at points A, B, and C. The geometric figure formed by line segments AB, BC, and AC is a **triangle**.

The angles within the region enclosed by the triangle are called **interior angles.** In the figure at the right, angles a, b, and c are interior angles. The sum of the measures of the interior angles is 180°.

$$\angle a + \angle b + \angle c = 180°$$

The Sum of the Measures of the Interior Angles of a Triangle

The sum of the measures of the interior angles of a triangle is 180°.

An angle adjacent to an interior angle is an **exterior angle.** In the figure at the right, angles m and n are exterior angles for angle a. The sum of the measures of an interior and an exterior angle is 180°.

$$\angle a + \angle m = 180°$$
$$\angle a + \angle n = 180°$$

Given that $\angle c = 40°$ and $\angle e = 60°$, find the measure of $\angle d$.

$\angle a$ and $\angle e$ are vertical angles.

$$\angle a = \angle e = 60°$$

The sum of the interior angles is 180°.

$$\angle c + \angle a + \angle b = 180°$$
$$40° + 60° + \angle b = 180°$$
$$100° + \angle b = 180°$$
$$\angle b = 80°$$

$\angle b$ and $\angle d$ are supplementary angles.

$$\angle b + \angle d = 180°$$
$$80° + \angle d = 180°$$
$$\angle d = 100°$$

EXAMPLE 5   Given that $\angle a = 45°$ and $\angle x = 100°$, find the measures of angles b, c, and y.

Strategy ▶ To find the measure of ∠b, use the fact that ∠b and ∠x are supplementary angles.
▶ To find the measure of ∠c, use the fact that the sum of the measures of the interior angles of a triangle is 180°.
▶ To find the measure of ∠y, use the fact that ∠c and ∠y are vertical angles.

Solution $\angle b + \angle x = 180°$
$\angle b + 100° = 180°$
$\angle b = 80°$

$\angle a + \angle b + \angle c = 180°$
$45° + 80° + \angle c = 180°$
$125° + \angle c = 180°$
$\angle c = 55°$

$\angle y = \angle c = 55°$

PROBLEM 5   Given that $\angle y = 55°$, find the measures of angles a, b, and d.

Solution   See page S9.

EXAMPLE 6   Two angles of a triangle measure 43° and 86°. Find the measure of the third angle.

Strategy   To find the measure of the third angle, use the fact that the sum of the measures of the interior angles of a triangle is 180°. Write an equation using x to represent the measure of the third angle. Solve the equation for x.

Solution $x + 43° + 86° = 180°$
$x + 129° = 180°$
$x = 51°$

The measure of the third angle is 51°.

PROBLEM 6   One angle of a triangle is a right angle, and one angle measures 27°. Find the measure of the third angle.

Solution   See page S9.

4.3   Concept Review

Determine whether the statement is always true, sometimes true, or never true.

1. The formula for the perimeter of a rectangle is $P = 2L + 2W$, where L represents the length and W represents the width of a rectangle.

2. In the formula for the perimeter of a triangle, $P = a + b + c$, the variables a, b, and c represent the measures of the three angles of a triangle.

3. If two angles of a triangle measure 52° and 73°, then the third angle of the triangle measures 55°.

4. An isosceles triangle has two sides of equal measure and two angles of equal measure.

5. The perimeter of a geometric figure is a measure of the area of the figure.

6. In a right triangle, the sum of the measures of the two acute angles is 90°.

4.3 Exercises

1 Perimeter problems

1. What is the difference between an isosceles triangle and an equilateral triangle?

2. Which of the following units can be used to measure perimeter?
   a. feet
   b. square miles
   c. meters
   d. ounces
   e. cubic inches
   f. centimeters

3. The length of the third side of an isosceles triangle is three units less than twice the length of one of the equal sides. If x is the length of one of the equal sides, an expression for the length of the third side is _____?_____.

4. The width of a rectangle is 25% of the length of the rectangle.
   a. If L is the length of the rectangle, then the width of the rectangle is _____?_____.
   b. Write an expression for the perimeter of the rectangle:
      $2(\underline{\quad?\quad}) + 2(\underline{\quad?\quad})$.
   c. Simplify the expression you wrote for the perimeter of the rectangle: _____?_____.

5. True or false? The formula for the perimeter of a rectangle can be written as $P = 2(L + W)$.

6. The perimeter of an isosceles triangle is 54 ft. Let s be the length of one of the two equal sides. Is it possible for s to be 30 ft?

7. In an isosceles triangle, the third side is 50% of the length of one of the equal sides. Find the length of each side when the perimeter is 125 ft.

8. In an isosceles triangle, the length of one of the equal sides is three times the length of the third side. The perimeter is 21 m. Find the length of each side.

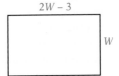

9. The perimeter of a rectangle is 42 m. The length of the rectangle is 3 m less than twice the width. Find the length and width of the rectangle.

10. The width of a rectangle is 25% of the length. The perimeter is 250 cm. Find the length and width of the rectangle.

11. The perimeter of a rectangle is 120 ft. The length of the rectangle is twice the width. Find the length and width of the rectangle.

12. The perimeter of a rectangle is 50 m. The width of the rectangle is 5 m less than the length. Find the length and width of the rectangle.

13. The perimeter of a triangle is 110 cm. One side is twice the second side. The third side is 30 cm more than the second side. Find the length of each side.

14. The perimeter of a triangle is 33 ft. One side of the triangle is 1 ft longer than the second side. The third side is 2 ft longer than the second side. Find the length of each side.

15. The width of the rectangular foundation of a building is 30% of the length. The perimeter of the foundation is 338 ft. Find the length and width of the foundation.

16. The perimeter of a rectangular playground is 440 ft. If the width is 100 ft, what is the length of the playground?

17. A rectangular vegetable garden has a perimeter of 64 ft. The length of the garden is 20 ft. What is the width of the garden?

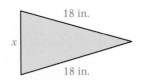

18. Each of two sides of a triangular banner measures 18 in. If the perimeter of the banner is 46 in., what is the length of the third side of the banner?

19. The perimeter of a square picture frame is 48 in. Find the length of each side of the frame.

20. A square rug has a perimeter of 32 ft. Find the length of each side of the rug.

2 Problems involving angles formed by intersecting lines

21. Name the number of degrees in each of the following.
    a. a right angle
    b. a straight angle
    c. one complete revolution
    d. an acute angle
    e. an obtuse angle
    f. complementary angles
    g. supplementary angles

22. Determine whether enough information is given to solve the problem.
    a. Find the sum of the measures of the two acute angles in a right triangle.
    b. Find the measures of the two acute angles in a right triangle.

23. Let x be the complement of a 53° angle. Then $x + 53 = $ ___?___, so $x = $ ___?___. The complement of a 53° angle is a ___?___ angle.

24. Find x.

$x + x + 20 + 2x = $ ___?___   • A straight angle measures 180°.
($ $___?___$)x + 20 = 180$ • Combine like terms.
$4x = $ ___?___   • Subtract 20 from each side of the equation.
$x = $ ___?___   • Divide each side of the equation by 4.

25. Find the complement of a 28° angle.

26. Find the complement of a 46° angle.

27. Find the supplement of a 73° angle.

28. Find the supplement of a 119° angle.

Find the measure of ∠*x*.

29.

30.

31.

Find the measure of ∠*a*.

32.

33.

34.

35.

Find *x*.

36.

37.

38.

39.

40.

41.

Find the measure of ∠x.

42.

43.

Find x.

44.

45.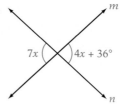

For Exercises 46 to 49, use the following diagram, in which $\ell_1 \| \ell_2$.

46. True or false? ∠a and ∠b have the same measure even if ℓ_1 and ℓ_2 are not parallel.

47. True or false? ∠a and ∠c have the same measure even if ℓ_1 and ℓ_2 are not parallel.

48. True or false? ∠c and ∠d are supplementary only if ℓ_1 and ℓ_2 are parallel.

49. True or false? ∠c and ∠d have the same measure only if t and ℓ_2 are perpendicular.

Given that $\ell_1 \| \ell_2$, find the measures of angles a and b.

50.

51.

52.

53.

Given that $\ell_1 \| \ell_2$, find x.

54.

55.

56.

57.

58. Given that $\angle a = 51°$, find the measure of $\angle b$.

59. Given that $\angle a = 38°$, find the measure of $\angle b$.

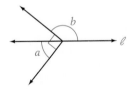

3 Problems involving the angles of a triangle

60. The three angles within the region enclosed by a triangle are called the triangle's ___?___ angles. An angle adjacent to one of these angles is an ___?___ angle of the triangle.

61. Given that $\angle x = 50°$ and $\angle c = 85°$, find the measure of $\angle a$.

$\angle b = \angle x = 50°$

$\angle b + \angle c + \angle a = $ ___?___

__?__ + __?__ + $\angle a = 180°$

__?__ + $\angle a = 180°$

$\angle a = $ __?__

- ___?___ angles have the same measure.
- The sum of the measures of the interior angles of a triangle is 180°.
- Replace $\angle b$ with 50° and $\angle c$ with 85°.
- Add.
- Subtract 135° from each side of the equation.

62. Given that $\angle a = 95°$ and $\angle b = 70°$, find the measures of angles x and y.

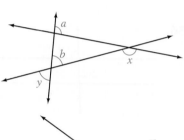

63. Given that $\angle a = 35°$ and $\angle b = 55°$, find the measures of angles x and y.

64. Given that $\angle y = 45°$, find the measures of angles a and b.

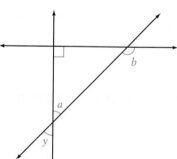

65. Given that $\angle y = 130°$, find the measures of angles a and b.

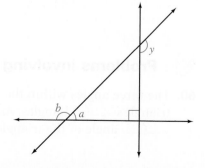

66. Given that $AO \perp OB$, express in terms of x the number of degrees in $\angle BOC$.

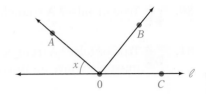

67. Given that $AO \perp OB$, express in terms of x the number of degrees in $\angle AOC$.

68. One angle in a triangle is a right angle, and one angle measures 30°. What is the measure of the third angle?

69. A triangle has a 45° angle and a right angle. Find the measure of the third angle.

70. Two angles of a triangle measure 42° and 103°. Find the measure of the third angle.

71. Two angles of a triangle measure 62° and 45°. Find the measure of the third angle.

72. A triangle has a 13° angle and a 65° angle. What is the measure of the third angle?

73. A triangle has a 105° angle and a 32° angle. What is the measure of the third angle?

74. In an isosceles triangle, one angle is three times the measure of one of the equal angles. Find the measure of each angle.

75. In an isosceles triangle, one angle is 10° less than three times the measure of one of the equal angles. Find the measure of each angle.

76. In an isosceles triangle, one angle is 16° more than twice the measure of one of the equal angles. Find the measure of each angle.

77. In a triangle, one angle is twice the measure of the second angle. The third angle is three times the measure of the second angle. Find the measure of each angle.

78. True or false? A triangle can have two right angles.

79. True or false? If one angle of a triangle is a right angle, then the other two angles of the triangle are complementary.

80. True or false? A triangle has nine exterior angles.

81. True or false? A triangle that has an exterior angle that is a right angle must also have an interior angle that is a right angle.

4.3 Applying Concepts

82. A rectangle and an equilateral triangle have the same perimeter. The length of the rectangle is three times the width. Each side of the triangle is 8 cm. Find the length and width of the rectangle.

83. The length of a rectangle is 1 cm more than twice the width. If the length of the rectangle is decreased by 2 cm and the width is decreased by 1 cm, the perimeter is 20 cm. Find the length and width of the original rectangle.

84. For the figure at the right, find the sum of the measures of angles x, y, and z.

85. For the figure at the right, explain why $\angle a + \angle b = \angle x$. Write a rule that describes the relationship between an exterior angle of a triangle and the opposite interior angles. Use the rule to write an equation involving angles a, c, and z.

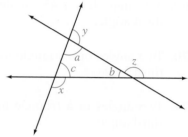

86. The width of a rectangle is $8x$. The perimeter is $48x$. Find the length of the rectangle in terms of the variable x.

87. Write a report stating the arguments of the proponents of changing to the metric system in the United States or a report stating the arguments of those opposed to switching from the U.S. Customary System of measurement to the metric system.

88. Prepare a report on the use of geometric form in architecture.

4.4 Markup and Discount Problems

OBJECTIVE **1** Markup problems

Cost is the price that a business pays for a product. **Selling price** is the price for which a business sells a product to a customer. The difference between selling price and cost is called **markup**. Markup is added to a retailer's cost to cover the expenses of operating a business. Markup is usually expressed as a percent of the retailer's cost. This percent is called the **markup rate.**

The basic markup equations used by a business are

$$\text{Selling price} = \text{Cost} + \text{Markup}$$
$$S \qquad = \quad C \ + \quad M$$

$$\text{Markup} = \text{Markup rate} \cdot \text{Cost}$$
$$M \quad = \qquad r \qquad \cdot \ C$$

By substituting $r \cdot C$ for M in the first equation, we can also write selling price as

$$S = C + M$$
$$S = C + (r \cdot C)$$
$$S = C + rC$$

The equation $S = C + rC$ is the equation used to solve the markup problems in this section.

EXAMPLE 1   The manager of a clothing store buys a suit for \$180 and sells the suit for \$252. Find the markup rate.

Strategy   Given: $C = \$180$
$\qquad\qquad\qquad S = \$252$
Unknown markup rate: r
Use the equation $S = C + rC$.

Solution
$$S = C + rC$$
$$252 = 180 + 180r$$

- **Substitute the values of C and S into the equation.**

$$252 - 180 = 180 - 180 + 180r$$
$$72 = 180r$$
$$\frac{72}{180} = \frac{180r}{180}$$
$$0.4 = r$$

- **Subtract 180 from each side of the equation.**

- **Divide each side of the equation by 180.**
- **The decimal must be changed to a percent.**

The markup rate is 40%.

PROBLEM 1   The cost to the manager of a sporting goods store for a tennis racket is \$120. The selling price of the racket is \$180. Find the markup rate.

Solution   See page S9.

EXAMPLE 2   The manager of a furniture store uses a markup rate of 45% on all items. The selling price of a chair is \$232. Find the cost of the chair.

Strategy   Given: $r = 45\% = 0.45$
$\qquad\qquad\qquad S = \$232$
Unknown cost: C
Use the equation $S = C + rC$.

Solution
$$S = C + rC$$
$$232 = C + 0.45C$$
$$232 = 1.45C \qquad$$ • **C + 0.45C = 1C + 0.45C = (1 + 0.45)C**
$$160 = C$$

The cost of the chair is \$160.

PROBLEM 2   A hardware store employee uses a markup rate of 40% on all items. The selling price of a lawnmower is $266. Find the cost.

Solution   See page S9.

OBJECTIVE 2   ## Discount problems

Discount is the amount by which a retailer reduces the regular price of a product for a promotional sale. Discount is usually expressed as a percent of the regular price. This percent is called the **discount rate** or **markdown rate.**

The basic discount equations used by a business are

$$\begin{array}{ccccc} \text{Sale price} & = & \text{Regular price} & - & \text{Discount} \\ S & = & R & - & D \end{array}$$

$$\begin{array}{ccccc} \text{Discount} & = & \text{Discount rate} & \cdot & \text{Regular price} \\ D & = & r & \cdot & R \end{array}$$

By substituting $r \cdot R$ for D in the first equation, we can also write sale price as

$$S = R - D$$
$$S = R - (r \cdot R)$$
$$S = R - rR$$

The equation $S = R - rR$ is the equation used to solve the discount problems in this section.

EXAMPLE 3   In a garden supply store, the regular price of a 100-foot garden hose is $48. During an "after-summer sale," the hose is being sold for $36. Find the discount rate.

Strategy   Given: $R = \$48$
$S = \$36$
Unknown discount rate: r
Use the equation $S = R - rR$.

Solution
$$S = R - rR$$
$$36 = 48 - 48r$$

• Substitute the values of R and S into the equation.

$$36 - 48 = 48 - 48 - 48r$$
$$-12 = -48r$$
$$\frac{-12}{-48} = \frac{-48r}{-48}$$
$$0.25 = r$$

• Subtract 48 from each side of the equation.

• Divide each side of the equation by -48.
• The decimal must be changed to a percent.

The discount rate is 25%.

PROBLEM 3   A case of motor oil that regularly sells for $39.80 is on sale for $29.85. What is the discount rate?

Solution   See page S9.

EXAMPLE 4 The sale price for a chemical sprayer is $27.30. This price is 35% off the regular price. Find the regular price.

Strategy Given: $S = \$27.30$
$r = 35\% = 0.35$
Unknown regular price: R
Use the equation $S = R - rR$.

Solution $S = R - rR$
$27.30 = R - 0.35R$
$27.30 = 0.65R$ • $R - 0.35R = 1R - 0.35R = (1 - 0.35)R$
$42 = R$

The regular price is $42.00.

PROBLEM 4 The sale price for a telephone is $43.50. This price is 25% off the regular price. Find the regular price.

Solution See page S10.

4.4 Concept Review

Determine whether the statement is always true, sometimes true, or never true.

1. In the markup equation $S = C + rC$, the variable r represents the markup rate.

2. Markup is an amount of money, whereas markup rate is a percent.

3. In the discount equation $S = R - rR$, the variable R represents the discount rate.

4. In the markup equation, S represents sale price, and in the discount equation, S represents selling price.

5. $R - 0.45R = 1R - 0.45R = (1 - 0.45)R = 0.55R$ is an example of the application of the Distributive Property.

4.4 Exercises

1 Markup problems

1. Explain the difference between the cost and the selling price of a product.

2. Explain the difference between markup and markup rate.

Complete Exercises 3 and 4 by replacing the question marks with the correct number from the problem situation or with the word *unknown*.

3. **Problem Situation:** A pair of jeans sells for $40. The store uses a markup rate of 25%. Find the cost of the pair of jeans.
   In the formula $S = C + rC$, $S = $ ___?___, $C = $ ___?___, and $r = $ ___?___.

4. **Problem Situation:** A washing machine that costs $620 is sold for $806. Find the markup rate.
   In the formula $S = C + rC$, $S = $ ___?___, $C = $ ___?___, and $r = $ ___?___.

5. A computer software retailer uses a markup rate of 40%. Find the selling price of a computer game that costs the retailer $40.

6. A car dealer advertises a 5% markup over cost. Find the selling price of a car that costs the dealer $26,000.

7. An electronics store uses a markup rate of 58%. Find the selling price of a camcorder that costs the store owner $358.

8. The cost to a landscape architect for a 25-gallon tree is $65. Find the selling price of the tree if the markup rate used by the architect is 30%.

9. A set of golf clubs costing $360 is sold for $630. Find the markup rate on the set of golf clubs.

10. A jeweler purchases a diamond ring for $7198.50. The selling price is $14,397. Find the markup rate.

11. A freezer costing $360 is sold for $520. Find the markup rate. Round to the nearest tenth of a percent.

12. A grocer purchases a can of fruit juice for $1.96. The selling price of the fruit juice is $2.45. Find the markup rate.

13. A watch costing $98 is sold for $156.80. Find the markup rate on the watch.

14. A sofa costing $320 is sold for $479. Find the markup rate. Round to the nearest tenth of a percent.

15. The selling price of a compact disc player is $168. The markup rate used by the seller is 40%. Find the cost of the compact disc player.

16. A manufacturer of exercise equipment uses a markup rate of 45%. One of the manufacturer's treadmills has a selling price of $580. Find the cost of the treadmill.

17. A markup rate of 40% was used on a basketball with a selling price of $82.60. Find the cost of the basketball.

18. A digitally recorded compact disc has a selling price of $18.90. The markup rate is 40%. Find the cost of the CD.

19. A markup rate of 25% is used on a computer that has a selling price of $2187.50. Find the cost of the computer.

20. The selling price of a portable CD player is $132. The markup rate used by the retailer is 60%. Find the cost to the retailer.

21. True or False? If a store uses a markup rate of 35%, you can find the store's cost for an item by dividing the selling price of the item by $1 + 0.35$, or 1.35.

22. If the markup rate on an item is 100%, what is the relationship between the selling price of the item and the cost of the item?

2 Discount problems

23. Explain the meaning of sale price and discount.

24. Explain the difference between discount and discount rate.

Complete Exercises 25 and 26 by replacing the question marks with the correct number from the problem situation or with the word *unknown*.

25. **Problem Situation:** The regular price of a camera is $375. The camera is on sale for $318.75. Find the discount rate.
In the formula $S = R - rR$, $S = $ ____?____ , $R = $ ____?____ , and $r = $ ____?____ .

26. **Problem Situation:** The sale price of a pair of shoes is $44, which is 20% off the regular price. Find the regular price.
In the formula $S = R + rR$, $S = $ ____?____ , $R = $ ____?____ , and $r = $ ____?____ .

27. A tennis racket that regularly sells for $135 is on sale for 25% off the regular price. Find the sale price.

28. A fax machine that regularly sells for $219.99 is on sale for $33\frac{1}{3}\%$ off the regular price. Find the sale price.

29. A supplier of electrical equipment offers a 5% discount for a purchase that is paid for within 30 days. A transformer regularly sells for $230. Find the discount price of a transformer that is paid for 10 days after the purchase.

30. A clothing wholesaler offers a discount of 10% per shirt when 10 to 20 shirts are purchased and a discount of 15% per shirt when 21 to 50 shirts are purchased. A shirt regularly sells for $27. Find the sale price per shirt when 35 shirts are purchased.

31. A car stereo system that regularly sells for $425 is on sale for $318.75. Find the discount rate.

32. A pair of roller blades that regularly sells for $99.99 is on sale for $79.99. Find the discount rate. Round to the nearest percent.

33. An oak bedroom set with a regular price of $1295 is on sale for $995. Find the discount rate. Round to the nearest tenth of a percent.

34. A stereo set with a regular price of $495 is on sale for $395. Find the markdown rate. Round to the nearest tenth of a percent.

35. A digital camera with a regular price of $325 is on sale for $201.50. Find the markdown rate.

36. A luggage set with a regular price of $178 is on sale for $103.24. Find the discount rate.

37. The sale price of a free-weight home gym is $408, which is 20% off the regular price. Find the regular price.

38. The sale price of a toboggan is $77, which is 30% off the regular price. Find the regular price.

39. A mechanic's tool set is on sale for $180 after a markdown of 40% off the regular price. Find the regular price.

40. The sale price of a modem is $126, which is 30% off the regular price. Find the regular price.

41. A telescope is on sale for $165 after a markdown of 40% off the regular price. Find the regular price.

42. An exercise bike is on sale for $390, having been marked down 25% off the regular price. Find the regular price.

43. True or false? If a store uses a discount rate of 15%, you can find the sale price for an item by multiplying the regular price of the item by $1 - 0.15$, or 0.85.

44. If the discount rate on an item is 50%, which of the following is true?
  a. $S = 2R$ **b.** $R = 2S$ **c.** $S = R$ **d.** $0.50S = R$

4.4 Applying Concepts

45. A pair of shoes that now sells for $63 has been marked up 40%. Find the markup on the pair of shoes.

46. The sale price of a motorcycle helmet is 25% off the regular price. The discount is $70. Find the sale price.

47. A refrigerator selling for $770 has a markup of $220. Find the markup rate.

48. The sale price of a copy machine is $765 after a discount of $135. Find the discount rate.

49. The manager of a camera store uses a markup rate of 30%. Find the cost of a camera selling for $299.

50. The sale price of a television is $180. Find the regular price if the sale price was computed by taking $\frac{1}{3}$ off the regular price followed by an additional 25% discount on the reduced price.

51. A customer buys four tires, three at the regular price and one for 20% off the regular price. The four tires cost $304. What was the regular price of a tire?

52. A lamp, originally priced at under $100, was on sale for 25% off the regular price. When the regular price, a whole number of dollars, was discounted, the discounted price was also a whole number of dollars. Find the largest possible number of dollars in the regular price of the lamp.

53. A used car is on sale for a discount of 20% off the regular price of $8500. An additional 10% discount on the sale price was offered. Is the result a 30% discount? What is the single discount that would give the same sale price?

54. Write a report on series trade discounts. Explain how to convert a series discount to a single-discount equivalent.

4.5 Investment Problems

OBJECTIVE 1   ### Investment problems

Recall that the annual simple interest that an investment earns is given by the equation $I = Pr$, where I is the simple interest, P is the principal, or the amount invested, and r is the simple interest rate.

Point of Interest

You may be familiar with the simple interest formula $I = Prt$. If so, you know that t represents time. In the problems in this section, time is always 1 (one year), so the formula $I = Prt$ simplifies to

$$I = Pr(1)$$
$$I = Pr$$

The annual simple interest rate on a $4500 investment is 8%. Find the annual simple interest earned on the investment.

Given: $P = \$4500$ $I = Pr$
         $r = 8\% = 0.08$ $I = 4500(0.08)$
Unknown interest: I $I = 360$

The annual simple interest earned is $360.

Solve: An investor has a total of $10,000 to deposit in two simple interest accounts. On one account, the annual simple interest rate is 7%. On the second account, the annual simple interest rate is 8%. How much should be invested in each account so that the total annual interest earned is $785?

> **STRATEGY** **for solving a problem involving money deposited in two simple interest accounts**
>
> ▶ For each amount invested, use the equation $Pr = I$. Write a numerical or variable expression for the principal, the interest rate, and the interest earned. The results can be recorded in a table.

The sum of the amounts invested is $10,000.

Amount invested at 7%: x
Amount invested at 8%: $\$10,000 - x$

Take Note

Use the information given in the problem to fill in the principal and interest rate columns of the table. Fill in the interest earned column by multiplying the two expressions you wrote in each row.

	Principal, P	·	Interest rate, r	=	Interest earned, I
Amount at 7%	x	·	0.07	=	$0.07x$
Amount at 8%	$10,000 - x$	·	0.08	=	$0.08(10,000 - x)$

> ▶ Determine how the amounts of interest earned on the individual investments are related. For example, the total interest earned by both accounts may be known, or it may be known that the interest earned on one account is equal to the interest earned on the other account.

The sum of the interest earned by the two investments equals the total annual interest earned ($785).

$$0.07x + 0.08(10{,}000 - x) = 785$$
$$0.07x + 800 - 0.08x = 785$$
$$-0.01x + 800 = 785$$
$$-0.01x = -15$$
$$x = 1500$$

• The interest earned on the 7% account plus the interest earned on the 8% account equals the total annual interest earned.

$$10{,}000 - x = 10{,}000 - 1500 = 8500$$

• Substitute the value of x into the variable expression for the amount invested at 8%.

The amount invested at 7% is $1500.
The amount invested at 8% is $8500.

EXAMPLE 1 An investment counselor invested 75% of a client's money into a 9% annual simple interest money market fund. The remainder was invested in 6% annual simple interest government securities. Find the amount invested in each if the total annual interest earned is $3300.

Strategy ▶ Amount invested: x
Amount invested at 9%: $0.75x$
Amount invested at 6%: $0.25x$

	Principal	·	Rate	=	Interest
Amount at 9%	$0.75x$	·	0.09	=	$0.09(0.75x)$
Amount at 6%	$0.25x$	·	0.06	=	$0.06(0.25x)$

▶ The sum of the interest earned by the two investments equals the total annual interest earned ($3300).

Solution
$$0.09(0.75x) + 0.06(0.25x) = 3300$$
$$0.0675x + 0.015x = 3300$$
$$0.0825x = 3300$$

• The interest earned on the 9% account plus the interest earned on the 6% account equals the total annual interest earned.

$$x = 40{,}000$$

• The amount invested is $40,000.

$$0.75x = 0.75(40{,}000) = 30{,}000$$

• Find the amount invested at 9%.

$$0.25x = 0.25(40{,}000) = 10{,}000$$

• Find the amount invested at 6%.

The amount invested at 9% is $30,000.
The amount invested at 6% is $10,000.

PROBLEM 1 An investment of $2500 is made at an annual simple interest rate of 7%. How much additional money must be invested at 10% so that the total interest earned will be 9% of the total investment?

Solution See page S10.

4.5 Concept Review

Determine whether the statement is always true, sometimes true, or never true.

1. In the simple interest formula $I = Pr$, the variable I represents the simple interest earned.

2. For one year, you have $1000 deposited in an account that pays 5% annual simple interest. You will earn exactly $5 in simple interest on this account.

3. For one year, you have x dollars deposited in an account that pays 7% annual simple interest. You will earn $0.07x$ in simple interest on this account.

4. If you have a total of $8000 deposited in two accounts and you represent the amount you have in the first account as x, then the amount in the second account is represented as $8000 - x$.

5. The amount of interest earned on one account is $0.05x$ and the amount of interest earned on a second account is $0.08(9000 - x)$. If the two accounts earn the same amount of interest, then we can write the equation $0.05x + 0.08(9000 - x)$.

6. If the amount of interest earned on one account is $0.06x$ and the amount of interest earned on a second account is $0.09(4000 - x)$, then the total interest earned on the two accounts can be represented as $0.06x + 0.09(4000 - x)$.

4.5 Exercises

1 Investment problems

1. You invest an amount of money at an annual simple interest rate of 5.2%. You invest a second amount, $1000 more than the first, at an annual simple interest rate of 7.2%. Let x represent the amount invested at 5.2%. Complete the following table.

	Principal, P	$\cdot$	Interest rate, r	$=$	Interest earned, I
Amount at 5.2%	x	$\cdot$	?	$=$	?
Amount at 7.2%	?	$\cdot$	?	$=$	?

2. The total annual interest earned on the investments in Exercise 1 is $320. Use this information and the information in the table in Exercise 1 to write an equation that can be solved to find the amount of money invested at 5.2%: _____?_____ + _____?_____ = _____?_____ .

3. A dentist invested a portion of $15,000 in a 7% annual simple interest account and the remainder in a 6.5% annual simple interest government bond. The two investments earn $1020 in interest annually. How much was invested in each account?

4. A university alumni association invested part of $20,000 in preferred stock that earns 8% annual simple interest, and the remainder in a municipal bond that earns 7% annual simple interest. The amount of interest earned each year is $1520. How much was invested in each account?

5. A professional athlete deposited an amount of money into a high-yield mutual fund that earns 13% annual simple interest. A second deposit, $2500 more than the first, was placed in a certificate of deposit earning 7% annual simple interest. In one year, the total interest earned on both investments was $475. How much money was invested in the mutual fund?

6. Jan Moser made a deposit into a 7% annual simple interest account. She made another deposit, $1500 less than the first, in a certificate of deposit earning 9% annual simple interest. The total interest earned on both investments for one year was $505. How much money was deposited in the certificate of deposit?

7. A team of cancer research specialists received a grant of $300,000 to be used for cancer research. They deposited some of the money in a 10% simple interest account and the remainder in an 8.5% annual simple interest account. How much was deposited in each account if the annual interest is $28,500?

8. Reggie Means invested part of $30,000 in municipal bonds that earn 6.5% annual simple interest and the remainder of the money in 8.5% corporate bonds. How much is invested in each account if the total annual interest earned is $2190?

9. To provide for retirement income, Teresa Puelo purchases a $5000 bond that earns 7.5% annual simple interest. How much money does Teresa have invested in bonds that earn 8% annual simple interest if the total annual interest earned from the two investments is $615?

10. After the sale of some income property, Jeremy Littlefield invested $40,000 in a certificate of deposit that earns 7.25% annual simple interest. How much money does he have invested in certificates that earn an annual simple interest rate of 8.5% if the total annual interest earned from the two investments is $5025?

11. Suki Hiroshi has made an investment of $2500 at an annual simple interest rate of 7%. How much money does she have invested at an annual simple interest rate of 11% if the total interest earned is 9% of the total investment?

12. Mae Jackson has a total of $6000 invested in two simple interest accounts. The annual simple interest rate on one account is 9%. The annual simple interest rate on the second account is 6%. How much is invested in each account if both accounts earn the same amount of interest?

13. A charity deposited a total of $54,000 in two simple interest accounts. The annual simple interest rate on one account is 8%. The annual simple interest rate on the second account is 12%. How much was invested in each account if the total annual interest earned is 9% of the total investment?

14. A sports foundation deposited a total of $24,000 into two simple interest accounts. The annual simple interest rate on one account is 7%. The annual simple interest rate on the second account is 11%. How much is invested in each account if the total annual interest earned is 10% of the total investment?

15. Wayne Miller, an investment banker, invested 55% of the bank's available cash in an account that earns 8.25% annual simple interest. The remainder of the cash was placed in an account that earns 10% annual simple interest. The interest earned in one year was $58,743.75. Find the total amount invested.

16. Mohammad Aran, a financial planner, recommended that 40% of a client's cash account be invested in preferred stock earning 9% annual simple interest. The remainder of the client's cash was placed in Treasury bonds earning 7% annual simple interest. The total annual interest earned from the two investments was $2496. Find the total amount invested.

17. Sarah Ontkean is the manager of a mutual fund. She placed 30% of the fund's available cash in a 6% annual simple interest account, 25% in 8% corporate bonds, and the remainder in a money market fund earning 7.5% annual simple interest. The total annual interest earned from the investments was $35,875. Find the total amount invested.

18. Joseph Abruzzio is the manager of a trust. He invested 30% of a client's cash in government bonds that earn 6.5% annual simple interest, 30% in utility stocks that earn 7% annual simple interest, and the remainder in an account that earns 8% annual simple interest. The total annual interest earned from the investments was $5437.50. Find the total amount invested.

19. The amount of annual interest earned on the x dollars that Beth invested in one simple interest account was $0.03x$, and the amount of annual interest earned on the money that Beth invested in another simple interest account was $0.05(5000 - x)$.

a. What were the interest rates on the two accounts?
b. What was the total amount of money that Beth had invested in the two accounts?

20. Refer to the investments described in Exercise 19. Which of the following could be true about the total amount T of interest earned on Beth's two accounts? There may be more than one correct answer.
a. $T < 150$ b. $T > 150$ c. $T < 250$ d. $T > 250$

4.5 Applying Concepts

21. A sales representative invests in a stock paying 9% dividends. A research consultant invests $5000 more than the sales representative in bonds paying 8% annual simple interest. The research consultant's income from the investment is equal to the sales representative's. Find the amount of the research consultant's investment.

22. A financial manager invested 20% of a client's money in bonds paying 9% annual simple interest, 35% in an 8% simple interest account, and the remainder in 9.5% corporate bonds. Find the amount invested in each if the total annual interest earned is $5325.

23. A plant manager invested $3000 more in stocks than in bonds. The stocks paid 8% annual simple interest, and the bonds paid 9.5% annual simple interest. Both investments yielded the same income. Find the total annual interest received on both investments.

24. A bank offers a customer a 2-year certificate of deposit (CD) that earns 8% compound annual interest. This means that the interest earned each year is added to the principal before the interest for the next year is calculated. Find the value in 2 years of a nurse's investment of $2500 in this CD.

25. A bank offers a customer a 3-year certificate of deposit (CD) that earns 8.5% compound annual interest. This means that the interest earned each year is added to the principal before the interest for the next year is calculated. Find the value in 3 years of an accountant's investment of $3000 in this CD.

26. Write an essay on the topic of annual percentage rates.

27. Financial advisors may predict how much money we should have saved for retirement by the ages of 35, 45, 55, and 65. One such prediction is included in the table at the right.
a. According to the estimates in the table, how much should a couple who have earnings of $75,000 have saved for retirement by age 55?
b. Write an explanation of how interest and interest rates affect the level of savings required at any given age. What effect do inflation rates have on savings?

Minimum Levels of Savings Required for Married Couples to Be Prepared for Retirement Savings Accumulation by Age			
	35	45	55	65
Earnings = $50,000	8,000	23,000	90,000	170,000
Earnings = $75,000	17,000	60,000	170,000	310,000
Earnings = $100,000	34,000	110,000	280,000	480,000
Earnings = $150,000	67,000	210,000	490,000	840,000

4.6 Mixture Problems

OBJECTIVE 1   ## Value mixture problems

A value mixture problem involves combining two ingredients that have different prices into a single blend. For example, a coffee merchant may blend two types of coffee into a single blend, or a candy manufacturer may combine two types of candy to sell as a "variety pack."

The solution of a value mixture problem is based on the equation $V = AC$, where V is the value of an ingredient, A is the amount of the ingredient, and C is the cost per unit of the ingredient.

Find the value of 5 oz of a gold alloy that costs $185 per ounce.

Given: $A = 5$ oz $V = AC$
       $C = \$185$ $V = 5(185)$
Unknown value: V $V = 925$

The value of the 5 oz of gold alloy is $925.

Solve: A coffee merchant wants to make 9 lb of a blend of coffee costing $6 per pound. The blend is made using a $7 grade and a $4 grade of coffee. How many pounds of each of these grades should be used?

> **STRATEGY**   **for solving a mixture problem**
>
> ▶ For each ingredient in the mixture, write a numerical or variable expression for the amount of the ingredient used, the unit cost of the ingredient, and the value of the amount used. For the blend, write a numerical or variable expression for the amount, the unit cost of the blend, and the value of the amount. The results can be recorded in a table.

The sum of the amounts is 9 lb.

Amount of $7 coffee: x

Amount of $4 coffee: $9 - x$

	Amount, A	·	Unit cost, C	=	Value, V
$7 grade	x	·	7	=	$7x$
$4 grade	$9 - x$	·	4	=	$4(9 - x)$
$6 blend	9	·	6	=	$6(9)$

> ▶ Determine how the values of the individual ingredients are related. Use the fact that the sum of the values of these ingredients is equal to the value of the blend.

The sum of the values of the $7 grade and the $4 grade is equal to the value of the $6 blend.

$7x + 4(9 - x) = 6(9)$ • **The value of the $7 grade plus the value of the $4**
$7x + 36 - 4x = 54$ **grade equals the value of the blend.**
$3x + 36 = 54$
$3x = 18$
$x = 6$

$9 - x = 9 - 6 = 3$ • **Substitute the value of x into the variable expression**
                                              for the amount of $4 grade.

The merchant must use 6 lb of the $7 coffee and 3 lb of the $4 coffee.

EXAMPLE 1 How many ounces of a silver alloy that costs $6 per ounce must be mixed with 10 oz of a silver alloy that costs $8 per ounce to make a mixture that costs $6.50 per ounce?

Strategy ▶ Ounces of $6 alloy: x

	Amount	Cost	Value
$6 alloy	x	6	$6x$
$8 alloy	10	8	$8(10)$
$6.50 mixture	$10 + x$	6.50	$6.50(10 + x)$

▶ The sum of the values before mixing equals the value after mixing.

Solution $6x + 8(10) = 6.50(10 + x)$ • **The value of the $6 alloy plus the**
$6x + 80 = 65 + 6.5x$ **value of the $8 alloy equals the**
$-0.5x + 80 = 65$ **value of the mixture.**
$-0.5x = -15$
$x = 30$

30 oz of the $6 silver alloy must be used.

PROBLEM 1 A gardener has 20 lb of a lawn fertilizer that costs $.90 per pound. How many pounds of a fertilizer that costs $.75 per pound should be mixed with this 20 lb of lawn fertilizer to produce a mixture that costs $.85 per pound?

Solution See page S10.

OBJECTIVE 2   Percent mixture problems

Recall that the amount of a substance in a solution can be given as a percent of the total solution. For example, in a 5% saltwater solution, 5% of the total solution is salt. The remaining 95% is water.

The solution of a percent mixture problem is based on the equation $Q = Ar$, where Q is the quantity of a substance in the solution, r is the percent of concentration, and A is the amount of solution.

A 500-milliliter bottle contains a 3% solution of hydrogen peroxide. Find the amount of hydrogen peroxide in the solution.

Given: $A = 500$ $Q = Ar$
        $r = 3\% = 0.03$ $Q = 500(0.03)$
Unknown amount: Q $Q = 15$

The bottle contains 15 ml of hydrogen peroxide.

Solve: How many gallons of 15% salt solution must be mixed with 4 gal of a 20% salt solution to make a 17% salt solution?

> **STRATEGY**   **for solving a percent mixture problem**

> ▶ For each solution, use the equation $Ar = Q$. Write a numerical or variable expression for the amount of solution, the percent of concentration, and the quantity of the substance in the solution. The results can be recorded in a table.

The unknown quantity of 15% solution: x

	Amount of solution, A	·	Percent of concentration, r	=	Quantity of substance, Q
15% solution	x	·	0.15	=	$0.15x$
20% solution	4	·	0.20	=	$0.20(4)$
17% solution	$x + 4$	·	0.17	=	$0.17(x + 4)$

> ▶ Determine how the quantities of the substance in the individual solutions are related. Use the fact that the sum of the quantities of the substances being mixed is equal to the quantity of the substance after mixing.

The sum of the quantities of salt in the 15% solution and in the 20% solution is equal to the quantity of salt in the 17% solution.

$0.15x + 0.20(4) = 0.17(x + 4)$ • **The amount of salt in the 15% solution plus the**
    $0.15x + 0.8 = 0.17x + 0.68$ **amount of salt in the 20% solution equals the**
  $-0.02x + 0.8 = 0.68$ **amount of salt in the 17% solution.**
        $-0.02x = -0.12$
            $x = 6$

6 gal of the 15% solution are required.

> **EXAMPLE 2**   A chemist wishes to make 3 L of a 7% acid solution by mixing a 9% acid solution and a 4% acid solution. How many liters of each solution should the chemist use?

x L of   +   (3 − x) L of   =   3 L of
9% acid   4% acid   7% acid

Strategy   ▶ Liters of 9% solution: x
              Liters of 4% solution: $3 - x$

	Amount	Percent	Quantity
9%	x	0.09	$0.09x$
4%	$3 - x$	0.04	$0.04(3 - x)$
7%	3	0.07	$0.07(3)$

▶ The sum of the quantities before mixing is equal to the quantity after mixing.

Solution $0.09x + 0.04(3 - x) = 0.07(3)$
              $0.09x + 0.12 - 0.04x = 0.21$
              $0.05x + 0.12 = 0.21$
              $0.05x = 0.09$

              $x = 1.8$

              $3 - x = 3 - 1.8 = 1.2$

- **The amount of acid in the 9% solution plus the amount of acid in the 4% solution equals the amount of acid in the 7% solution.**
- **1.8 L of the 9% solution are needed.**
- **Find the amount of the 4% solution needed.**

The chemist needs 1.8 L of the 9% solution and 1.2 L of the 4% solution.

PROBLEM 2   How many quarts of pure orange juice are added to 5 qt of fruit drink that is 10% orange juice to make an orange drink that is 25% orange juice?

Solution   See pages S10.

4.6 Concept Review

Determine whether the statement is always true, sometimes true, or never true.

1. Both value mixture and percent mixture problems involve combining two or more ingredients into a single substance.

2. In the value mixture equation $V = AC$, the variable A represents the quantity of an ingredient.

3. Suppose we are mixing two salt solutions. Then the variable Q in the percent mixture equation $Q = Ar$ represents the amount of salt in a solution.

4. If we combine an alloy that costs $8 an ounce with an alloy that costs $5 an ounce, the cost of the resulting mixture will be greater than $8 an ounce.

5. If we combine a 9% acid solution with a solution that is 4% acid, the resulting solution will be less than 4% acid.

6. If 8 L of a solvent costs $75 per liter, then the value of the 8 L of solvent is $600.

7. If 100 oz of a silver alloy is 25% silver, then the alloy contains 25 oz of silver.

4.6 Exercises

1   Value mixture problems

1. a. The total value of a 7-pound bag of cat food that costs $1.50 per pound is ___?___ .
   b. The cost per pound of a 5-pound bag of sugar that has a total value of $1.80 is ___?___ .

2. To make bread, Maya uses a flour mixture that combines organic whole-wheat flour that costs $1.70 per pound with unbleached flour that costs $.50 per pound. Ten pounds of her mixture costs $1.30 per pound. Let x be the amount of whole-wheat flour in the mixture.
   a. Complete the following table.

	Amount, A	·	Unit cost, C	=	Value V
Whole-wheat flour	x	·	?	=	?
Unbleached flour	?	·	?	=	?
Mixture	?	·	?	=	?

   b. Use the expressions in the last column of the table in part a to write an equation that can be solved to find the number of pounds of whole-wheat flour in Maya's mixture: ___?___ + ___?___ = ___?___ .

3. Explain the meaning of each variable in the equation $V = AC$. Give an example of how this equation is used.

4. Suppose you are mixing peanuts that cost $4 per pound with raisins that cost $2 per pound. In the context of this situation, explain the meaning of the statement "The sum of the values of these ingredients is equal to the value of the blend."

5. At a veterinary clinic, a special high-protein dog food that costs $6.75 per pound is mixed with a vitamin supplement that costs $3.25 per pound. How many pounds of each should be used to make 5 lb of a mixture that costs $4.65 per pound?

6. A wild bird seed mix is made by combining 100 lb of millet seed costing $.60 per pound with sunflower seeds costing $1.10 per pound. How many pounds of sunflower seeds are needed to make a mixture that costs $.70 per pound?

7. Find the cost per pound of a coffee mixture made from 8 lb of coffee that costs $9.20 per pound and 12 lb of coffee that costs $5.50 per pound.

8. How many pounds of chamomile tea that costs $4.20 per pound must be mixed with 12 lb of orange tea that costs $2.25 per pound to make a mixture that costs $3.40 per pound?

9. A goldsmith combined an alloy that costs $4.30 per ounce with an alloy that costs $1.80 per ounce. How many ounces of each were used to make a mixture of 200 oz costing $2.50 per ounce?

10. An herbalist has 30 oz of herbs costing $2 per ounce. How many ounces of herbs costing $1 per ounce should be mixed with these 30 oz of herbs to produce a mixture costing $1.60 per ounce?

11. A health food store has a section in which you can create your own chocolate-covered fruit mixes. You choose 2 lb of the cherries that cost $4.50 per pound. You also choose blueberries that cost $3.75 per pound. How many pounds of blueberries can you add to create a mixture that costs $4.25 per pound?

12. Find the cost per ounce of a mixture of 200 oz of a cologne that costs $7.50 per ounce and 500 oz of a cologne that costs $4.00 per ounce.

13. How many kilograms of hard candy that costs $7.50 per kilogram must be mixed with 24 kg of jelly beans that cost $3.25 per kilogram to make a mixture that costs $4.50 per kilogram?

14. A grocery store offers a cheese sampler that includes a pepper cheddar cheese that costs $16 per kilogram and Pennsylvania Jack that costs $6 per kilogram. How many kilograms of each were used to make a 5-kilogram mixture that costs $9 per kilogram?

15. A snack food is made by mixing 5 lb of popcorn that costs $.80 per pound with caramel that costs $2.40 per pound. How much caramel is needed to make a mixture that costs $1.40 per pound?

16. A lumber company combined oak wood chips that cost $3.10 per pound with pine wood chips that cost $2.50 per pound. How many pounds of each were used to make an 80-pound mixture costing $2.65 per pound?

17. The manager of a farmer's market has 500 lb of grain that costs $1.20 per pound. How many pounds of meal costing $.80 per pound should be mixed with the 500 lb of grain to produce a mixture that costs $1.05 per pound?

18. A caterer made an ice cream punch by combining fruit juice that costs $4.50 per gallon with ice cream that costs $6.50 per gallon. How many gallons of each were used to make 100 gal of punch costing $5 per gallon?

19. The manager of a specialty food store combined almonds that cost $4.50 per pound with walnuts that cost $2.50 per pound. How many pounds of each were used to make a 100-pound mixture that costs $3.24 per pound?

20. Find the cost per pound of a "house blend" of coffee that is made from 12 lb of Central American coffee that costs $8 per pound and 30 lb of South American coffee that costs $4.50 per pound.

21. Find the cost per pound of a sugar-coated breakfast cereal made from 40 lb of sugar that costs $2.00 per pound and 120 lb of corn flakes that cost $1.20 per pound.

22. Find the cost per ounce of a gold alloy made from 25 oz of pure gold that costs $482 per ounce and 40 oz of an alloy that costs $300 per ounce.

23. Find the cost per ounce of a sunscreen made from 100 oz of a lotion that costs $2.50 per ounce and 50 oz of a lotion that costs $4.00 per ounce.

24. How many liters of a blue dye that costs $1.60 per liter must be mixed with 18 L of anil that costs $2.50 per liter to make a mixture that costs $1.90 per liter?

25. A grocer mixes peanuts that cost $3 per pound with almonds that cost $7 per pound. Which of the following could be true about the cost, C, per pound of the mixture? There may be more than one correct answer.
    a. $C = \$10$ b. $C > \$7$ c. $C < \$7$ d. $C < \$3$ e. $C > \$3$ f. $C = \$4$

26. A snack mix is made from 3 pounds of sunflower seeds that cost S dollars per pound and 4 pounds of raisins that cost R dollars per pound. Which expression gives the cost, C, per pound of the mixture?
    a. $7(S + R)$ b. $3S + 4R$ c. $S + R$ d. $\dfrac{3S + 4R}{7}$

2   Percent mixture problems

27. A 250-milliliter bottle contains a solution that is 90% isopropyl alcohol. The amount of isopropyl alcohol in the solution is $250(\underline{\quad ? \quad}) = \underline{\quad ? \quad}$ ml.

28. A juice drink that is 60% real fruit juice is made by mixing some juice that is 20% real fruit juice with 32 oz of a juice that is 75% real fruit juice. Let x be the amount of the 20% real fruit juice that is in the mixture.
    a. Complete the following table.

	Amount A	$\cdot$	Percent of concentration, r	$=$	Quantity Q
75% real fruit juice	?	$\cdot$	?	$=$	?
20% real fruit juice	x	$\cdot$	?	$=$	?
Mixture	?	$\cdot$	?	$=$	?

  b. Use the expressions in the last column of the table in part a to write an equation that can be solved to find the amount of the 20% real fruit juice that is in the mixture: ___?___ + ___?___ = ___?___ .

29. Explain the meaning of each variable in the equation $Q = Ar$. Give an example of how this equation is used.

30. Suppose you are mixing a 5% acid solution with a 10% acid solution. In the context of this situation, explain the meaning of the statement "The sum of the quantities of the substances being mixed is equal to the quantity of the substance after mixing."

31. Forty ounces of a 30% gold alloy are mixed with 60 oz of a 20% gold alloy. Find the percent concentration of the resulting gold alloy.

32. One hundred ounces of juice that is 50% tomato juice are added to 200 oz of a vegetable juice that is 25% tomato juice. What is the percent concentration of tomato juice in the resulting mixture?

33. How many gallons of a 15% acid solution must be mixed with 5 gal of a 20% acid solution to make a 16% acid solution?

34. How many pounds of a chicken feed that is 50% corn must be mixed with 400 lb of a feed that is 80% corn to make a chicken feed that is 75% corn?

35. A rug is made by weaving 20 lb of yarn that is 50% wool with a yarn that is 25% wool. How many pounds of the yarn that is 25% wool must be used if the finished rug is to be 35% wool?

36. Five gallons of a dark green latex paint that is 20% yellow paint are combined with a lighter green latex paint that is 40% yellow paint. How many gallons of the lighter green paint must be used to create a green paint that is 25% yellow paint?

37. How many gallons of a plant food that is 9% nitrogen must be combined with another plant food that is 25% nitrogen to make 10 gal of a plant food that is 15% nitrogen?

38. A chemist wants to make 50 ml of a 16% acid solution by mixing a 13% acid solution and an 18% acid solution. How many milliliters of each solution should the chemist use?

39. Five grams of sugar are added to a 45-gram serving of a breakfast cereal that is 10% sugar. What is the percent concentration of sugar in the resulting mixture?

x ml of 13% acid   + $(50 - x)$ ml of 18% acid   =   50 ml of 16% acid

40. Thirty ounces of pure silver are added to 50 oz of a silver alloy that is 20% silver. What is the percent concentration of the resulting alloy?

41. To make the potpourri mixture sold at a florist shop, 70 oz of a potpourri that is 80% lavender are combined with a potpourri that is 60% lavender. The resulting potpourri is 74% lavender. How much of the potpourri that is 60% lavender is used?

42. The manager of a garden shop mixes grass seed that is 40% rye grass with 40 lb of grass seed that is 60% rye grass to make a mixture that is 56% rye grass. How much of the 40% rye grass is used?

43. A hair dye is made by blending a 7% hydrogen peroxide solution and a 4% hydrogen peroxide solution. How many milliliters of each are used to make a 300-milliliter solution that is 5% hydrogen peroxide?

44. At a cosmetics company, 40 L of pure aloe cream are mixed with 50 L of a moisturizer that is 64% aloe. What is the percent concentration of aloe in the resulting mixture?

45. How many ounces of pure chocolate must be added to 150 oz of chocolate topping that is 50% chocolate to make a topping that is 75% chocolate?

46. How many ounces of pure bran flakes must be added to 50 oz of cereal that is 40% bran flakes to produce a mixture that is 50% bran flakes?

47. A hair stylist combines 12 oz of shampoo that is 20% conditioner with an 8-ounce bottle of pure shampoo. What is the percent concentration of conditioner in the 20-ounce mixture?

48. A clothing manufacturer has some pure silk thread and some thread that is 85% silk. How many kilograms of each must be woven together to make 75 kg of cloth that is 96% silk?

49. How many ounces of dried apricots must be added to 18 oz of a snack mix that contains 20% dried apricots to make a mixture that is 25% dried apricots?

50. A recipe for a rice dish calls for 12 oz of a rice mixture that is 20% wild rice and 8 oz of pure wild rice. What is the percent concentration of wild rice in the 20-ounce mixture?

51. True or false? A 10% salt solution can be combined with some amount of a 20% salt solution to create a 30% salt solution.

52. True or false? When n ounces of 100% acid are mixed with $2n$ ounces of pure water, the resulting mixture is a 50% acid solution.

4.6 Applying Concepts

53. Find the cost per ounce of a mixture of 30 oz of an alloy that costs $4.50 per ounce, 40 oz of an alloy that costs $3.50 per ounce, and 30 oz of an alloy that costs $3.00 per ounce.

54. A grocer combined walnuts that cost $2.60 per pound and cashews that cost $3.50 per pound with 20 lb of peanuts that cost $2.00 per pound. Find the amount of walnuts and the amount of cashews used to make the 50-pound mixture costing $2.72 per pound.

55. How many ounces of water evaporated from 50 oz of a 12% salt solution to produce a 15% salt solution?

56. A chemist mixed pure acid with water to make 10 L of a 30% acid solution. How much pure acid and how much water did the chemist use?

57. How many grams of pure water must be added to 50 g of pure acid to make a solution that is 40% acid?

58. A radiator contains 15 gal of a 20% antifreeze solution. How many gallons must be drained from the radiator and replaced by pure antifreeze so that the radiator will contain 15 gal of a 40% antifreeze solution?

59. Tickets to a performance by the community theater cost $5.50 for adults and $2.75 for children. A total of 120 tickets were sold for $563.75. How many adults and how many children attended the performance?

60. Explain why we look for patterns and relationships in mathematics. Include a discussion of the relationship between value mixture problems and percent mixture problems and how understanding one of these can make it easier to understand the other. Also discuss why understanding how to solve the value mixture problems in this section can be helpful in solving Exercise 59.

4.7 Uniform Motion Problems

OBJECTIVE 1 ## Uniform motion problems

A train that travels constantly in a straight line at 50 mph is in *uniform motion*. Recall that **uniform motion** means the speed of an object does not change.

The solution of a uniform motion problem is based on the equation $d = rt$, where d is the distance traveled, r is the rate of travel, and t is the time spent traveling.

A car travels at 50 mph for 3 h.

$$d = rt$$
$$d = 50(3)$$
$$d = 150$$

The car travels a distance of 150 mi.

Solve: A car leaves a town traveling at 35 mph. Two hours later, a second car leaves the same town, on the same road, traveling at 55 mph. In how many hours after the second car leaves will the second car pass the first car?

> **STRATEGY**   **for solving a uniform motion problem**
>
> ▶ For each object, use the equation $rt = d$. Write a numerical or variable expression for the rate, time, and distance. The results can be recorded in a table.

The first car traveled 2 h longer than the second car.

Unknown time for the second car: t
Time for the first car: $t + 2$

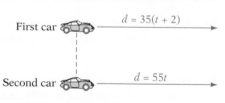

Take Note

Use the information given in the problem to fill in the rate and time columns of the table. Fill in the distance column by multiplying the two expressions you wrote in each row.

	Rate, r	·	Time, t	=	Distance, d
First car	35	·	$t + 2$	=	$35(t + 2)$
Second car	55	·	t	=	$55t$

> ▶ Determine how the distances traveled by the individual objects are related. For example, the total distance traveled by both objects may be known, or it may be known that the two objects traveled the same distance.

The two cars travel the same distance.

$35(t + 2) = 55t$ • **The distance traveled by the first car equals the**
$35t + 70 = 55t$ **distance traveled by the second car.**
$\quad\quad 70 = 20t$
$\quad\quad 3.5 = t$

The second car will pass the first car in 3.5 h.

EXAMPLE 1 Two cars, the first traveling 10 mph faster than the second, start at the same time from the same point and travel in opposite directions. In 3 h, they are 288 mi apart. Find the rate of the second car.

Strategy ▶ Rate of second car: r
Rate of first car: $r + 10$

	Rate	Time	Distance
First car	$r + 10$	3	$3(r + 10)$
Second car	r	3	$3r$

▶ The total distance traveled by the two cars is 288 mi.

Solution

$3(r + 10) + 3r = 288$
$3r + 30 + 3r = 288$
$6r + 30 = 288$
$6r = 258$
$r = 43$

• **The distance traveled by the first car plus the distance traveled by the second car is 288 mi.**

The second car is traveling 43 mph.

PROBLEM 1 Two trains, one traveling at twice the speed of the other, start at the same time from stations that are 306 mi apart and travel toward each other. In 3 h, the trains pass each other. Find the rate of each train.

Solution See page S10.

EXAMPLE 2 A bicycling club rides out into the country at a speed of 16 mph and returns over the same road at 12 mph. How far does the club ride out into the country if it travels a total of 7 h?

Strategy ▶ Time spent riding out: t
Time spent riding back: $7 - t$

	Rate	Time	Distance
Out	16	t	$16t$
Back	12	$7 - t$	$12(7 - t)$

▶ The distance out equals the distance back.

Solution $16t = 12(7 - t)$
$16t = 84 - 12t$
$28t = 84$
$t = 3$ • **The time is 3 h. Find the distance.**

The distance out $= 16t = 16(3) = 48$.

The club rides 48 mi into the country.

PROBLEM 2   On a survey mission, a pilot flew out to a parcel of land and back in 7 h. The rate out was 120 mph. The rate back was 90 mph. How far away was the parcel of land?

Solution   See page S11.

4.7   Concept Review

Determine whether the statement is always true, sometimes true, or never true.

1. The solution of a uniform motion problem is based on the equation $d = rt$, where r is a percent.

2. If you drive at a constant speed of 60 mph for 4 h, you will travel a total distance of 240 mi.

3. It takes a student a total of 5 h to drive to a friend's house and back. If the variable t is used to represent the time it took to drive to the friend's house, then the expression $t - 5$ is used to represent the time spent on the return trip.

4. If the speed of one train is 20 mph slower than that of a second train, then the speeds of the two trains can be represented as r and $20 - r$.

5. A car and a bus both travel from city A to city B. The car leaves city A 1 h later than the bus, but both vehicles arrive in city B at the same time. If t represents the time the car was traveling, then $t + 1$ represents the time the bus was traveling. If t represents the time the bus was traveling, then $t - 1$ represents the time the car was traveling.

6. Two cars travel the same distance. If the distance traveled by the first car is represented by the expression $35t$, and the distance traveled by the second car is represented by the expression $45(t + 1)$, then we can write the equation $35t = 45(t + 1)$.

4.7 Exercises

1 Uniform motion problems

1. Sara and Jessica leave school and go in opposite directions. Sara runs and Jessica walks. The rate at which Sara runs is three times faster than the rate at which Jessica walks. After 5 min, the girls are 3520 ft apart. Let r represent Jessica's rate.
   a. Complete the following table.

	Rate, r	$\cdot$	Time, t	$=$	Distance, d
Sara	?	$\cdot$	?	$=$	?
Jessica	r	$\cdot$	?	$=$	?

   b. Use the expressions in the last column of the table in part a to write an equation that can be solved to find Jessica's rate:
   _____? + _____? = _____?.

2. The solution of the equation from part b of Exercise 1 is 176. This means that Jessica walks at a rate of 176 ___?___ per ___?___. Because Sara's rate is three times Jessica's rate, Sara runs at a rate of ___?___.

For Exercises 3 and 4, state whether the equation you would write to solve the problem would involve (**a**) setting two distances equal to each other, or (**b**) adding two distances together to equal a total distance.

3. **Problem Situation:** Sam hiked up a mountain at a rate of 2.5 mph and returned along the same trail at a rate of 3 mph. His total hiking time was 11 h. How long was the hiking trail?

4. **Problem Situation:** Sam hiked 16 mi. He hiked at one rate for the first 2 h of his hike and then decreased his speed by 0.5 mph for the last 3 h of his hike. What was Sam's speed for the first 2 h?

5. Two planes start from the same point and fly in opposite directions. The first plane is flying 25 mph slower than the second plane. In 2 h, the planes are 470 mi apart. Find the rate of each plane.

470 mi

6. Two cyclists start from the same point and ride in opposite directions. One cyclist rides twice as fast as the other. In 3 h, they are 81 mi apart. Find the rate of each cyclist.

7. One speed skater starts across a frozen lake at an average speed of 8 meters per second. Ten seconds later, a second speed skater starts from the same point and skates in the same direction at an average speed of 10 meters per second. How many seconds after the second skater starts will the second skater overtake the first skater?

8. A long-distance runner started on a course running at an average speed of 6 mph. Half an hour later, a second runner began the same course at an average speed of 7 mph. How long after the second runner starts will the second runner overtake the first runner?

9. Michael Chan leaves a dock in his motorboat and travels at an average speed of 9 mph toward the Isle of Shoals, a small island off the coast of Massachusetts. Two hours later, a tour boat leaves the same dock and travels at an average speed of 18 mph toward the same island. How many hours after the tour boat leaves will Michael's boat be alongside the tour boat?

10. A 555-mile, 5-hour plane trip was flown at two speeds. For the first part of the trip, the average speed was 105 mph. For the remainder of the trip, the average speed was 115 mph. How long did the plane fly at each speed?

11. An executive drove from home at an average speed of 30 mph to an airport where a helicopter was waiting. The executive boarded the helicopter and flew to the corporate offices at an average speed of 60 mph. The entire distance was 150 mi. The entire trip took 3 h. Find the distance from the airport to the corporate offices.

12. A jogger starts from one end of a 15-mile nature trail at 8:00 A.M. One hour later, a cyclist starts from the other end of the trail and rides toward the jogger. If the rate of the jogger is 6 mph and the rate of the cyclist is 9 mph, at what time will the two meet?

13. After a sailboat had been on the water for 3 h, a change in the wind direction reduced the average speed of the boat by 5 mph. The entire distance sailed was 57 mi. The total time spent sailing was 6 h. How far did the sailboat travel in the first 3 h?

14. A car and a bus set out at 3 P.M. from the same point headed in the same direction. The average speed of the car is twice the average speed of the bus. In 2 h, the car is 68 mi ahead of the bus. Find the rate of the car.

15. A passenger train leaves a train depot 2 h after a freight train leaves the same depot. The freight train is traveling 20 mph slower than the passenger train. Find the rate of each train if the passenger train overtakes the freight train in 3 h.

16. A stunt driver was needed at the production site of a Hollywood movie. The average speed of the stunt driver's flight to the site was 150 mph, and the average speed of the return trip was 100 mph. Find the distance of the round trip if the total flying time was 5 h.

17. A ship traveling east at 25 mph is 10 mi from a harbor when another ship leaves the harbor traveling east at 35 mph. How long does it take the second ship to catch up to the first ship?

18. At 10 A.M. a plane leaves Boston, Massachusetts, for Seattle, Washington, a distance of 3000 mi. One hour later a plane leaves Seattle for Boston. Both planes are traveling at a speed of 500 mph. How many hours after the plane leaves Seattle will the planes pass each other?

19. At noon a train leaves Washington, D.C., headed for Charleston, South Carolina, a distance of 500 mi. The train travels at a speed of 60 mph. At 1 P.M. a second train leaves Charleston headed for Washington, D.C., traveling at 50 mph. How long after the train leaves Charleston will the two trains pass each other?

20. A race car driver starts along a 50-mile race course traveling at an average speed of 90 mph. Fifteen minutes later a second driver starts along the same course at an average speed of 120 mph. Will the second car overtake the first car before the drivers reach the end of the course?

21. A bus traveled on a straight road for 2 h at an average speed that was 20 mph faster than its average speed on a winding road. The time spent on the winding road was 3 h. Find the average speed on the winding road if the total trip was 210 mi.

22. A bus traveling at a rate of 60 mph overtakes a car traveling at a rate of 45 mph. If the car had a 1-hour head start, how far from the starting point does the bus overtake the car?

23. A car traveling at 48 mph overtakes a cyclist who, riding at 12 mph, had a 3-hour head start. How far from the starting point does the car overtake the cyclist?

24. A plane left Kennedy Airport Tuesday morning for a 605-mile, 5-hour trip. For the first part of the trip, the average speed was 115 mph. For the remainder of the trip, the average speed was 125 mph. How long did the plane fly at each speed?

4.7 **Applying Concepts**

25. A car and a cyclist start at 10 A.M. from the same point, headed in the same direction. The average speed of the car is 5 mph more than three times the average speed of the cyclist. In 1.5 h, the car is 46.5 mi ahead of the cyclist. Find the rate of the cyclist.

26. A cyclist and a jogger set out at 11 A.M. from the same point, headed in the same direction. The average speed of the cyclist is twice the average speed of the jogger. In 1 h, the cyclist is 7 mi ahead of the jogger. Find the rate of the cyclist.

27. A car and a bus set out at 2 P.M. from the same point, headed in the same direction. The average speed of the car is 30 mph slower than twice the average speed of the bus. In 2 h, the car is 30 mi ahead of the bus. Find the rate of the car.

28. At 10 A.M., two campers left their campsite by canoe and paddled downstream at an average speed of 12 mph. They then turned around and paddled back upstream at an average rate of 4 mph. The total trip took 1 h. At what time did the campers turn around downstream?

29. At 7 A.M., two joggers start from opposite ends of an 8-mile course. One jogger is running at a rate of 4 mph, and the other is running at a rate of 6 mph. At what time will the joggers meet?

30. A truck leaves a depot at 11 A.M. and travels at a speed of 45 mph. At noon, a van leaves the same place and travels the same route at a speed of 65 mph. At what time does the van overtake the truck?

31. A bicyclist rides for 2 h at a speed of 10 mph and then returns at a speed of 20 mph. Find the cyclist's average speed for the trip.

32. A car travels a 1-mile track at an average speed of 30 mph. At what average speed must the car travel the next mile so that the average speed for the 2 mi is 60 mph?

33. Explain why the motion problems in this section are restricted to *uniform* motion.

34. Explain why 60 mph is the same as 88 ft/s.

4.8   Inequalities

OBJECTIVE ▪1▪   Applications of inequalities

Solving application problems requires recognition of the verbal phrases that translate into mathematical symbols. Here is a partial list of the phrases used to indicate each of the four inequality symbols.

< is less than	> is greater than
	     is more than
	     exceeds

≤   is less than or equal to
     maximum
     at most
     or less
	≥ is greater than or equal to
	     minimum
	     at least
	     or more

EXAMPLE 1   A student must have at least 450 points out of 500 points on five tests to receive an A in a course. One student's results on the first four tests were 93, 79, 87, and 94. What scores on the last test will enable this student to receive an A in the course?

Strategy   To find the scores, write and solve an inequality using N to represent the score on the last test.

Solution

| total number of points on the five tests | is greater than or equal to | 450 |

$$93 + 79 + 87 + 94 + N \geq 450$$
$$353 + N \geq 450$$
$$353 - 353 + N \geq 450 - 353$$
$$N \geq 97$$

The student's score on the last test must be equal to or greater than 97.

PROBLEM 1 An appliance dealer will make a profit on the sale of a television set if the cost of the new set is less than 70% of the selling price. What minimum selling price will enable the dealer to make a profit on a television set that costs the dealer $340?

Solution See page S11.

EXAMPLE 2 The base of a triangle is 8 in., and the height is $(3x - 5)$ in. Express as an integer the maximum height of the triangle when the area is less than 112 in².

Strategy To find the maximum height:
▶ Replace the variables in the area formula by the given values and solve for x.
▶ Replace the variable in the expression $3x - 5$ with the value found for x.

Solution

| one-half the base times the height | is less than | 112 in² |

$$\frac{1}{2}(8)(3x - 5) < 112$$
$$4(3x - 5) < 112$$
$$12x - 20 < 112$$
$$12x - 20 + 20 < 112 + 20$$
$$12x < 132$$
$$\frac{12x}{12} < \frac{132}{12}$$
$$x < 11$$

$$3x - 5 = 3(11) - 5 = 28$$

• Substitute the value of x into the variable expression for the height. Note that the height <u>is less than</u> 28 because $x < 11$.

The maximum height of the triangle is 27 in.

PROBLEM 2 Company A rents cars for $9 per day and 10¢ per mile driven. Company B rents cars for $12 per day and 8¢ per mile driven. You want to rent a car for one week. What is the maximum number of miles you can drive a Company A car if it is to cost you less than a Company B car?

Solution See page S11.

4.8   Concept Review

Determine whether the statement is always true, sometimes true, or never true.

1. Both "is greater than" and "is more than" are represented by the inequality symbol $\geq$.

2. A minimum refers to a lower limit, whereas a maximum refers to an upper limit.

3. Given that $x > \frac{32}{6}$, the minimum integer that satisfies the inequality is 6.

4. Given that $x < \frac{25}{4}$, the maximum integer that satisfies the inequality is 7.

5. A rental car costs $15 per day and 20¢ per mile driven. If m represents the number of miles the rental car is driven, then the expression $15 + 0.20m$ represents the cost to rent the car for one week.

6. A patient's physician recommends a maximum cholesterol level of 205 units. The patient's cholesterol level is 199 units and therefore must be lowered 6 units in order to meet the physician's recommended level.

4.8   Exercises

1   Application of inequalities

For Exercises 1 to 4, translate each sentence into an inequality.

1. The maximum value of a number n is 50.

2. A number n is at least 102.

3. 500 is more than 12% of a number n.

4. The sum of a number n and 45% of the number is at most 200.

5. **Integer Problem** Three-fifths of a number is greater than two-thirds. Find the smallest integer that satisfies the inequality.

6. **Sports** To be eligible for a basketball tournament, a basketball team must win at least 60% of its remaining games. If the team has 17 games remaining, how many games must the team win to qualify for the tournament?

7. **Income Taxes** To avoid a tax penalty, at least 90% of a self-employed person's total annual income tax liability must be paid by April 15. What amount of income tax must be paid by April 15 by a person with an annual income tax liability of $3500?

8. **Health** A health official recommends a maximum cholesterol level of 220 units. A patient has a cholesterol level of 275. By how many units must this patient's cholesterol level be reduced to satisfy the recommended maximum level?

9. **Recycling** A service organization will receive a bonus of $200 for collecting more than 1850 lb of aluminum cans during its four collection drives. On the first three drives, the organization collected 505 lb, 493 lb, and 412 lb. How many pounds of cans must the organization collect on the fourth drive to receive the bonus?

10. **Education** A professor scores all tests with a maximum of 100 points. To earn an A in this course, a student must have an average of at least 92 on four tests. One student's grades on the first three tests were 89, 86, and 90. Can this student earn an A grade?

11. **Education** A student must have an average of at least 80 points on five tests to receive a B in a course. The student's grades on the first four tests were 75, 83, 86, and 78. What scores on the last test will enable this student to receive a B in the course?

12. **Compensation** A car sales representative receives a commission that is the greater of $250 or 8% of the selling price of a car. What dollar amounts in the sale price of a car will make the commission offer more attractive than the $250 flat fee?

13. **Compensation** A sales representative for a stereo store has the option of a monthly salary of $2000 or a 35% commission on the selling price of each item sold by the representative. What dollar amounts in sales will make the commission more attractive than the monthly salary?

14. **Integer Problem** Four times the sum of a number and five is less than six times the number. Find the smallest integer that satisfies the inequality.

15. **Compensation** The sales agent for a jewelry company is offered a flat monthly salary of $3200 or a salary of $1000 plus an 11% commission on the selling price of each item sold by the agent. If the agent chooses the $3200 salary, what dollar amount does the agent expect to sell in one month?

16. **Compensation** A baseball player is offered an annual salary of $200,000 or a base salary of $100,000 plus a bonus of $1000 for each hit over 100 hits. How many hits will result in this baseball player earning more than $200,000?

17. **Consumerism** A computer bulletin board service charges a flat fee of $10 per month or $4 per month plus $.10 for each minute the service is used. For how many minutes must a person use this service for the cost to exceed $10?

18. **Business** A site licensing fee for a computer program is $1500. The fee allows a company to use the program at any computer terminal within the company. Alternatively, a company can choose to pay $200 for each computer terminal it has. How many computer terminals must a company have for the site licensing fee to be the more economical plan?

19. **Nutrition** For a product to be labeled orange juice, a state agency requires that at least 80% of the drink be real orange juice. How many ounces of artificial flavors can be added to 32 oz of real orange juice if the drink is to be labeled orange juice?

20. **Nutrition** Grade A hamburger cannot contain more than 20% fat. How much fat can a butcher mix with 300 lb of lean meat to meet the 20% requirement?

21. **Consumerism** A shuttle service taking skiers to a ski area charges $8 per person each way. Four skiers are debating whether to take the shuttle bus or rent a car for $45 plus $.25 per mile. Assuming that the skiers will share the cost of the car and that they want the least expensive method of transportation, how far away is the ski area if they choose to take the shuttle service?

22. **Utilities** A residential water bill is based on a flat fee of $10 plus a charge of $.75 for each 1000 gal of water used. Find the number of gallons of water a family can use and have a monthly water bill that is less than $55.

23. **Consumerism** Company A rents cars for $25 per day and 8¢ per mile driven. Company B rents cars for $15 per day and 14¢ per mile driven. You want to rent a car for one day. Find the maximum number of miles you can drive a Company B car if it is to cost you less than a Company A car.

24. **Geometry** A rectangle is 8 ft wide and $(2x + 7)$ ft long. Express as an integer the maximum length of the rectangle when the perimeter is less than 54 ft.

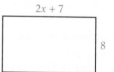

25. An automatic garage door opener costs $325 plus an installation labor charge of $30 per hour, with a minimum of 1 h and a maximum of 3 h of labor. Which of the following are *not* possible amounts for the total cost of the door and installation? There may be more than one answer.
  a. $355   **b.** $450   **c.** $325   **d.** $415   **e.** $350

26. True or false? If a student's test average after four tests is 80, the maximum amount the student can raise his average on the next test is 4 points (assume a test is worth 100 points).

4.8 Applying Concepts

27. Integer Problem Find three positive consecutive odd integers such that three times the sum of the first two integers is less than four times the third integer. (*Hint:* There is more than one solution.)

28. Integer Problem Find three positive consecutive even integers such that four times the sum of the first two integers is less than or equal to five times the third integer. (*Hint:* There is more than one solution.)

29. Aviation A maintenance crew requires between 30 min and 45 min to prepare an aircraft for its next flight. How many aircraft can this crew prepare for flight in a 6-hour period of time?

30. Postage The postage rate for first-class mail is $.39 for the first ounce and $.24 for each additional ounce or fraction of an ounce. Find the largest whole number of ounces a package can weigh if it is to cost you less than $3 to mail the package.

31. Fund Raising Your class decides to publish a calendar to raise money. The initial cost, regardless of the number of calendars printed, is $900. After the initial cost, each calendar costs $1.50 to produce. What is the minimum number of calendars your class must sell at $6 per calendar to make a profit of at least $1200?

32. Debt Carried by Americans During a recent year, the mean (average) household income of Americans under age 35 was $48,297. The mean household income of Americans aged 35 to 50 was $60,427. The graph on the next page shows average amounts of debt carried during the same year by those under 35 and by those aged 35 to 50.
   a. In which categories is the average debt carried by Americans under age 35 greater than the average debt carried by Americans aged 35 to 50?
   b. In which categories is the average debt carried by Americans under age 35 greater than $10,000?
   c. For the categories shown in the graph, what was the total average debt of Americans under age 35? How much greater is this debt than that of Americans aged 35 to 50?
   d. Given the answers to parts a, b, and c, what is the significance of the average incomes of these two age groups?
   e. Write a paragraph describing any other observations you can make from the data.

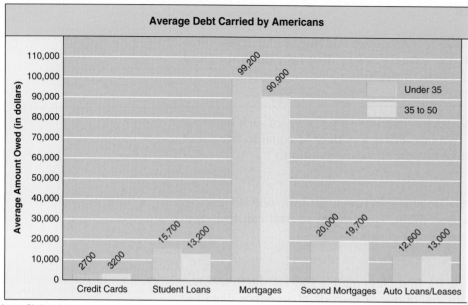

Average Debt Carried by Americans

Source: Claritas, Inc.

Focus on Problem Solving

Diagramming Problems   How do you best remember something? Do you remember best what you hear? The word *aural* means "pertaining to the ear"; people with a strong aural memory remember best those things that they hear. The word *visual* means "pertaining to the sense of sight"; people with a strong visual memory remember best that which they see written down. Some people claim their memory is in their writing hand—they remember something only if they write it down! The method by which you best remember something is probably also the method by which you can best learn something new.

In problem-solving situations, try to capitalize on your strengths. If you tend to understand material better when you hear it spoken, read application problems aloud or have someone else read them to you. If writing helps you to organize ideas, rewrite application problems in your own words.

No matter what your main strength, visualizing a problem can be a valuable aid in problem solving. A drawing, sketch, diagram, or chart can be a useful tool in problem solving, just as calculators and computers are tools. Making a diagram can help you gain an understanding of the relationships inherent in a problem-solving situation. A sketch will help you to organize the given information and devise or discover a method by which the solution can be determined.

A tour bus drives 5 mi south, then 4 mi west, then 3 mi north, and then 4 mi east. How far is the tour bus from the starting point?

Draw a diagram of the given information.

From the diagram, we can see that the solution can be determined by subtracting 3 from 5: $5 - 3 = 2$.

The bus is 2 mi from the starting point.

If you roll two ordinary six-sided dice and multiply the two numbers that appear on top, how many different products are there?

Make a chart of the possible products. In the chart below, repeated products are marked with an asterisk.

$1 \cdot 1 = 1$	$2 \cdot 1 = 2^*$	$3 \cdot 1 = 3^*$	$4 \cdot 1 = 4^*$	$5 \cdot 1 = 5^*$	$6 \cdot 1 = 6^*$
$1 \cdot 2 = 2$	$2 \cdot 2 = 4^*$	$3 \cdot 2 = 6^*$	$4 \cdot 2 = 8^*$	$5 \cdot 2 = 10^*$	$6 \cdot 2 = 12^*$
$1 \cdot 3 = 3$	$2 \cdot 3 = 6^*$	$3 \cdot 3 = 9$	$4 \cdot 3 = 12^*$	$5 \cdot 3 = 15^*$	$6 \cdot 3 = 18^*$
$1 \cdot 4 = 4$	$2 \cdot 4 = 8$	$3 \cdot 4 = 12^*$	$4 \cdot 4 = 16$	$5 \cdot 4 = 20^*$	$6 \cdot 4 = 24^*$
$1 \cdot 5 = 5$	$2 \cdot 5 = 10$	$3 \cdot 5 = 15$	$4 \cdot 5 = 20$	$5 \cdot 5 = 25$	$6 \cdot 2 = 30^*$
$1 \cdot 6 = 6$	$2 \cdot 6 = 12$	$3 \cdot 6 = 18$	$4 \cdot 6 = 24$	$5 \cdot 6 = 30$	$6 \cdot 6 = 36$

By counting the products that are not repeats, we can see that there are 18 different products.

In this chapter, you may have noticed that a drawing accompanies the strategy step of many application problems. We encourage you to draw a diagram when solving the application problems in these sections, as well as in any other situation where it can prove helpful. Doing so will undoubtedly improve your problem-solving skills.

Projects & Group Activities

Nielsen Ratings

WEB

Nielsen Media Research surveys television viewers to determine the numbers of people watching particular shows. There are an estimated 105.5 million U.S. households with televisions. Each **rating point** represents 1% of that number, or 1,055,000 households. For instance, if *60 Minutes* received a rating of 9.6, then 9.6%, or $(0.096)(105,500,000) = 10,128,000$, households watched that program.

A rating point does not mean that 105,500,000 people are watching a program. A rating point refers to the number of TV sets tuned to that program; there may be more than one person watching a television set in the household.

Nielsen Media Research also describes a program's share of the market. **Share** is the percent of television sets in use that are tuned to a program. Suppose that the same week *60 Minutes* received 9.6 rating points, the show received a share of 19%. This means that 19% of all households with a television *turned on* were tuned to *60 Minutes*, whereas only 9.6% of all households *with a television* were tuned to the program.

1. If *60 Minutes* received a Nielsen rating of 10.8 and a share of 19, how many TV households watched the program that week? How many TV households were watching television during that hour? Round to the nearest hundred thousand.

2. Suppose *Desperate Housewives* received a rating of 16.2 and a share of 28. How many TV households watched the program that week? How many TV households were watching television during that hour? Round to the nearest hundred thousand.

3. Suppose *CSI* received a rating of 13.6 during a week in which 34,750,000 people watched the show. Find the average number of people per TV household who watched the program. Round to the nearest tenth.

The cost to advertise during a program is related to its Nielsen rating. The sponsor (the company paying for the advertisement) pays a certain number of dollars for each rating point a show receives.

4. Suppose a television network charges $35,000 per rating point for a 30-second commercial on a daytime talk show. Determine the cost for three 30-second commercials if the Nielsen rating of the show is 11.5.

Nielsen Media Research also tracks the exposure of advertisements. For example, it might be reported that commercials for McDonald's had 500,000,000 household exposures during a week when its advertisement was aired 90 times.

5. Information regarding household exposure of advertisements can be found in *USA Today* each Monday. For a recent week, find the information for the top four advertised products. For each product, calculate the average household exposure for each time the ad was aired.

Nielsen Media Research has a website on the Internet. You can locate the site by using a search engine.

6. Find the top two prime-time television shows for last week. Calculate the number of TV households that watched the programs. Compare the figures with the figures for the top two sports programs for last week.

Chapter 4 Summary

Key Words

Consecutive integers follow one another in order. [4.2.1, p. 174]

The **perimeter** of a geometric figure is a measure of the distance around the figure. [4.3.1, p. 181]

Examples

11, 12, 13 are consecutive integers.
−9, −8, −7 are consecutive integers.

The perimeter of a triangle is the sum of the lengths of the three sides.
The perimeter of a rectangle is the sum of the lengths of the four sides.

An angle is measured in **degrees.** A 90° angle is a **right angle.** A 180° angle is a **straight angle.** One complete revolution is 360°. An **acute angle** is an angle whose measure is between 0° and 90°. An **obtuse angle** is an angle whose measure is between 90° and 180°. An **isosceles triangle** has two sides of equal measure. The three sides of an **equilateral triangle** are of equal measure. **Complementary angles** are two angles whose measures have the sum 90°. **Supplementary angles** are two angles whose measures have the sum 180°.   [4.3.1, 4.3.2, pp. 182–184]

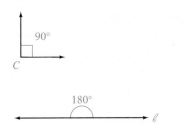

Parallel lines never meet; the distance between them is always the same. **Perpendicular lines** are intersecting lines that form right angles. Two angles that are on opposite sides of the intersection of two lines are **vertical angles;** vertical angles have the same measure. Two angles that share a common side are **adjacent angles;** adjacent angles of intersecting lines are supplementary angles.   [4.3.2, pp. 184–185]

A line that intersects two other lines at two different points is a **transversal.** If the lines cut by a transversal are parallel lines, then pairs of equal angles are formed: **alternate interior angles, alternate exterior angles,** and **corresponding angles.** [4.3.2, pp. 186–187]

$$\angle b = \angle d = \angle x = \angle z$$
$$\angle a = \angle c = \angle w = \angle y$$

Cost is the price that a business pays for a product. **Selling price** is the price for which a business sells a product to a customer. **Markup** is the difference between selling price and cost. **Markup rate** is the markup expressed as a percent of the retailer's cost.   [4.4.1, p. 198]

If a business pays $100 for a product and sells that product for $140, then the cost of the product is $100, the selling price is $140, and the markup is $140 − $100 = $40.

Discount is the amount by which a retailer reduces the regular price of a product. **Discount rate** is the discount expressed as a percent of the regular price.   [4.4.2, p. 200]

The regular price of a product is $100. The product is now on sale for $75. The discount on the product is $100 − $75 = $25.

Essential Rules and Procedures

Consecutive Integers
$n, n + 1, n + 2, \ldots$ [4.2.1, p. 174]

The sum of three consecutive integers is 135.

$$n + (n + 1) + (n + 2) = 135$$

Consecutive Even or Consecutive Odd Integers
$n, n + 2, n + 4, \ldots$ [4.2.1, p. 174]

The sum of three consecutive odd integers is 135.

$$n + (n + 2) + (n + 4) = 135$$

Coin and Stamp Equation

$$\underset{\substack{\text{Number} \\ \text{of coins}}}{} \cdot \underset{\substack{\text{Value of} \\ \text{coin in cents}}}{} = \underset{\substack{\text{Total value} \\ \text{in cents}}}{}$$ [4.2.2, p. 175]

A coin bank contains $1.80 in dimes and quarters. In all, there are twelve coins in the bank. How many dimes are in the bank?

$$10d + 25(12 - d) = 180$$

Formulas for Perimeter
Triangle: $P = a + b + c$
Rectangle: $P = 2L + 2W$
Square: $P = 4s$
[4.3.1, p. 182]

The perimeter of a rectangle is 108 m. The length is 6 m more than three times the width. Find the width of the rectangle.

$$108 = 2(3W + 6) + 2W$$

The perimeter of an isosceles triangle is 34 ft. The length of the third side is 5 ft less than the length of one of the equal sides. Find the length of one of the equal sides.

$$34 = x + x + (x - 5)$$

Sum of the Angles of a Triangle
The sum of the measures of the interior angles of a triangle is 180°.
$$\angle A + \angle B + \angle C = 180°$$
The sum of an interior and corresponding exterior angle is 180°.
[4.3.3, p. 188]

In a right triangle, the measure of one acute angle is 12° more than the measure of the smallest angle. Find the measure of the smallest angle.

$$x + (x + 12) + 90 = 180$$

Basic Markup Equation
$S = C + rC$ [4.4.1, p. 199]

The manager of a department buys a pasta maker machine for $70 and sells the machine for $98. Find the markup rate.

$$98 = 70 + 70r$$

Basic Discount Equation
$S = R - rR$ [4.4.2, p. 200]

The sale price for a leather bomber jacket is $95. This price is 24% off the regular price. Find the regular price.

$$95 = R - 0.24R$$

Annual Simple Interest Equation
$I = Pr$ [4.5.1, p. 206]

You invest a portion of $10,000 in a 7% annual simple interest account and the remainder in a 6% annual simple interest bond. The two investments earn total annual interest of $680. How much is invested in the 7% account?

$$0.07x + 0.06(10,000 - x) = 680$$

Value Mixture Equation
$V = AC$ [4.6.1, p. 212]

An herbalist has 30 oz of herbs costing \$2 per ounce. How many ounces of herbs costing \$1 per ounce should be mixed with the 30 oz to produce a mixture costing \$1.60 per ounce?

$$30(2) + 1x = 1.60(30 + x)$$

Percent Mixture Equation
$Q = Ar$ [4.6.2, p. 213]

Forty ounces of a 30% gold alloy are mixed with 60 oz of a 20% gold alloy. Find the percent concentration of the resulting gold alloy.

$$0.30(40) + 0.20(60) = x(100)$$

Uniform Motion Equation
$d = rt$ [4.7.1, p. 222]

A boat traveled from a harbor to an island at an average speed of 20 mph. The average speed on the return trip was 15 mph. The total trip took 3.5 h. How long did it take to travel to the island?

$$20t = 15(3.5 - t)$$

Chapter 4 Review Exercises

1. Translate "seven less than twice a number is equal to the number" into an equation and solve.

2. Music A piano wire is 35 in. long. A note can be produced by dividing this wire into two parts so that three times the length of the shorter piece is twice the length of the longer piece. Find the length of the shorter piece.

3. Integer Problem The sum of two numbers is twenty-one. Three times the smaller number is two less than twice the larger number. Find the two numbers.

4. Geometry Translate "the sum of twice a number and six equals four times the difference between the number and two" into an equation and solve.

5. Discounts A ceiling fan that regularly sells for \$90 is on sale for \$60. Find the discount rate.

6. Investments A total of \$15,000 is deposited into two simple interest accounts. The annual simple interest rate on one account is 6%. The annual simple interest rate on the second account is 7%. How much should be invested in each account so that the total interest earned is \$970?

7. **Geometry** In an isosceles triangle, the measure of one of the two equal angles is 15° more than the measure of the third angle. Find the measure of each angle.

8. **Uniform Motion Problem** A motorcyclist and a bicyclist set out at 8 A.M. from the same point, headed in the same direction. The speed of the motorcyclist is three times the speed of the bicyclist. In 2 h, the motorcyclist is 60 mi ahead of the bicyclist. Find the rate of the motorcyclist.

9. **Geometry** In an isosceles triangle, the measure of one angle is 25° less than half the measure of one of the equal angles. Find the measure of each angle.

10. **Markup** The manager of a sporting goods store buys packages of cleats for $5.25 each and sells them for $9.45 each. Find the markup rate.

11. **Percent Mixture** A dairy owner mixes 5 gal of cream that is 30% butterfat with 8 gal of milk that is 4% butterfat. Find the percent concentration of butterfat in the resulting mixture.

12. **Geometry** The length of a rectangle is four times the width. The perimeter is 200 ft. Find the length and width of the rectangle.

13. **Business** The manager of an accounting firm is investigating contracts whereby large quantities of material can be photocopied at minimum cost. The contract from the Copy Center offers a fee of $50 per week and $.03 per page. The Prints 4 U Company offers a fee of $27 per week and $.05 per page. What is the minimum number of copies per week that could be ordered from the Copy Center if these copies are to cost less than copies from Prints 4 U?

14. **Discounts** The sale price for a video game is $26.56, which is 17% off the regular price. Find the regular price.

15. **Food Mixtures** The owner of a health food store combined cranberry juice that cost $1.79 per quart with apple juice that cost $1.19 per quart. How many quarts of each were used to make 10 qt of a cranapple juice mixture costing $1.61 per quart?

16. **Discounts** A famous mystery writer is contracted to autograph copies of her new book at a bookstore. As a special promotion that day, the book is selling for $33.74, which is only 30% above the cost of the book. Find the cost of the book.

17. **Integer Problem** The sum of two numbers is thirty-six. The difference between the larger number and eight equals the total of four and three times the smaller number. Find the two numbers.

18. **Investments** An engineering consultant invested $14,000 in an individual retirement account paying 8.15% annual simple interest. How much money does the consultant have deposited in an account paying 12% annual simple interest if the total interest earned is 9.25% of the total investment?

19. **Integer Problem** You have removed all the hearts from a standard deck of playing cards and have arranged them in numerical order. Suppose I pick two consecutive cards and tell you their sum is 15. Name the two cards I picked.

20. **Percent Mixture** A pharmacist has 15 L of an 80% alcohol solution. How many liters of pure water should be added to the alcohol solution to make an alcohol solution that is 75% alcohol?

21. **Test Scores** A student's grades on five sociology exams were 68, 82, 90, 73, and 95. What is the lowest score this student can receive on the sixth exam and still have earned a total of at least 480 points?

22. Translate "the opposite of seven is equal to one-half a number less ten" into an equation and solve.

23. ⬤ **Structures** The Empire State Building is 1472 ft tall. This is 654 ft less than twice the height of the Eiffel Tower. Find the height of the Eiffel Tower.

24. **Geometry** One angle of a triangle is 15° more than the measure of the second angle. The third angle is 15° less than the measure of the second angle. Find the measure of each angle.

25. **Business** The manager of a refreshment stand at a local stadium tallied the receipts for one evening. There was a total of $263 in one-dollar bills and five-dollar bills. In all, there were 155 bills. Find the number of one-dollar bills.

26. **Carpentry** A board 10 ft long is cut into two pieces. Four times the length of the shorter piece is 2 ft less than two times the length of the longer piece. Find the length of the longer piece.

27. **Compensation** An optical engineer's consulting fee was $600. This included $80 for supplies and $65 for each hour of consultation. Find the number of hours of consultation.

28. **Stamps** A stamp collector has 12¢ stamps and 17¢ stamps with a total face value of $15.53. The number of 12¢ stamps is three more than twice the number of 17¢ stamps. How many of each type are in the collection?

29. **Markup** A furniture store uses a markup rate of 60%. The store sells a solid oak curio cabinet for $1074. Find the cost of the curio cabinet.

30. Swimming Pools The largest swimming pool in the world is located in Casablanca, Morocco, and is 480 m long. Two swimmers start at the same time from opposite ends of the pool and swim toward each other. One swimmer's rate is 65 m/min. The other swimmer's rate is 55 m/min. In how many minutes after they begin will they meet?

31. Geometry The perimeter of a triangle is 35 in. The second side is 4 in. longer than the first side. The third side is 1 in. shorter than twice the first side. Find the measure of each side.

32. Integer Problem The sum of three consecutive odd integers is −45. Find the integers.

33. Geometry A rectangle is 15 ft long and $(2x - 4)$ ft wide. Express as an integer the maximum width of the rectangle when the perimeter is less than 52 ft.

34. Geometry Given that $\ell_1 \| \ell_2$, find the measures of angles a and b.

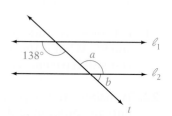

Chapter 4 Test

 View the Chapter Test Videos for fully worked-out solutions to any exercise.

1. Translate "the sum of six times a number and thirteen is five less than the product of three and the number" into an equation and solve.

2. Translate "the difference between three times a number and fifteen is twenty-seven" into an equation and solve.

3. Integer Problem The sum of two numbers is 18. The difference between four times the smaller number and seven is equal to the sum of two times the larger number and five. Find the two numbers.

4. Carpentry A board 18 ft long is cut into two pieces. Two feet less than the product of five and the length of the shorter piece is equal to the difference between three times the length of the longer piece and eight. Find the length of each piece.

5. Markup The manager of a sports shop uses a markup rate of 50%. The selling price for a set of golf clubs is $300. Find the cost of the golf clubs.

6. Discounts A pair of running shoes that regularly sells for $100 is on sale for $80. Find the discount rate.

7. Percent Mixture How many gallons of a 15% acid solution must be mixed with 5 gal of a 20% acid solution to make a 16% acid solution?

8. Geometry The perimeter of a rectangle is 38 m. The length of the rectangle is 1 m less than three times the width. Find the length and width of the rectangle.

9. Integer Problem Find three consecutive odd integers such that three times the first integer is one less than the sum of the second and third integers.

10. Floral Deliveries Florist A charges a $3 delivery fee plus $21 per bouquet delivered. Florist B charges a $15 delivery fee plus $18 per bouquet delivered. An organization wants to send each resident of a small nursing home a bouquet for Valentine's Day. How many residents are in the nursing home if it is more economical for the organization to use Florist B?

11. Investments A total of $7000 is deposited into two simple interest accounts. On one account, the annual simple interest rate is 10%, and on the second account, the annual simple interest rate is 15%. How much should be invested in each account so that the total annual interest earned is $800?

12. Food Mixtures A coffee merchant wants to make 12 lb of a blend of coffee costing $6 per pound. The blend is made using a $7 grade and a $4 grade of coffee. How many pounds of each of these grades should be used?

13. Uniform Motion Two planes start at the same time from the same point and fly in opposite directions. The first plane is flying 100 mph faster than the second plane. In 3 h, the two planes are 1050 mi apart. Find the rate of each plane.

14. Geometry In a triangle, the first angle is 15° more than the second angle. The third angle is three times the second angle. Find the measure of each angle.

15. Coins A coin bank contains 50 coins in nickels and quarters. The total amount of money in the bank is $9.50. Find the number of nickels and the number of quarters in the bank.

16. Investments A club treasurer deposited $2400 in two simple interest accounts. The annual simple interest rate on one account is 6.75%. The annual simple interest rate on the other account is 9.45%. How much should be deposited in each account so that the same interest is earned on each account?

17. Geometry The width of a rectangle is 12 ft. The length is $(3x + 5)$ ft. Express as an integer the minimum length of the rectangle if the area is greater than 276 ft^2.

18. Discounts A file cabinet that normally sells for $99 is on sale for 20% off. Find the sale price.

Cumulative Review Exercises

1. Given $B = \{-12, -6, -3, -1\}$, which elements of set B are less than -4?

2. Simplify: $-2 + (-8) - (-16)$

3. Simplify: $\left(-\dfrac{2}{3}\right)^3\left(-\dfrac{3}{4}\right)^2$

4. Simplify: $\dfrac{5}{6} - \left(\dfrac{2}{3}\right)^2 \div \left(\dfrac{1}{2} - \dfrac{1}{3}\right)$

5. Evaluate $-|-18|$.

6. Evaluate $b^2 - (a - b)^2$ when $a = 4$ and $b = -1$.

7. Simplify: $5x - 3y - (-4x) + 7y$

8. Simplify: $-4(3 - 2x - 5x^3)$

9. Simplify: $-2[x - 3(x - 1) - 5]$

10. Simplify: $-3x^2 - (-5x^2) + 4x^2$

11. Is 2 a solution of $4 - 2x - x^2 = 2 - 4x$?

12. Solve: $9 - x = 12$

13. Solve: $-\dfrac{4}{5}x = 12$

14. Solve: $8 - 5x = -7$

15. Solve: $-6x - 4(3 - 2x) = 4x + 8$

16. Write 40% as a fraction.

17. Solve and graph the solution set of $4x \geq 16$.

18. Solve: $-15x \leq 45$

19. Solve: $2x - 3 > x + 15$

20. Solve: $12 - 4(x - 1) \leq 5(x - 4)$

21. Write 0.025 as a percent.

22. Write $\dfrac{3}{25}$ as a percent.

23. Find $16\dfrac{2}{3}\%$ of 18.

24. 40% of what is 18?

25. Translate "the sum of eight times a number and twelve is equal to the product of four and the number" into an equation and solve.

26. **Construction**   The area of the cement foundation of a house is 2000 ft². This is 200 ft² more than three times the area of the garage. Find the area of the garage.

27. **Repair Bills**   An auto repair bill was $313. This includes $88 for parts and $45 for each hour of labor. Find the number of hours of labor.

28. Libraries A survey of 250 librarians showed that 50 of the libraries had a particular reference book on their shelves. What percent of the libraries had the reference book?

29. Investments A deposit of $4000 is made into an account that earns 11% annual simple interest. How much money is also deposited in an account that pays 14% annual simple interest if the total annual interest earned is 12% of the total investment?

30. Markup The manager of a department store buys a chain necklace for $80 and sells it for $140. Find the markup rate.

31. Metallurgy How many grams of a gold alloy that costs $4 per gram must be mixed with 30 g of a gold alloy that costs $7 per gram to make an alloy costing $5 per gram?

32. Percent Mixture How many ounces of pure water must be added to 70 oz of a 10% salt solution to make a 7% salt solution?

33. Geometry In an isosceles triangle, the third angle is 8° less than twice the measure of one of the equal angles. Find the measure of one of the equal angles.

34. Integer Problem Three times the second of three consecutive even integers is 14 more than the sum of the first and third integers. Find the middle integer.

35. Coins A coin bank contains dimes and quarters. The number of quarters is five less than four times the number of dimes. The total amount in the bank is $6.45. Find the number of dimes in the bank.

CHAPTER

5 Linear Equations and Inequalities

OBJECTIVES

DVD

SSM

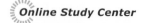
Online Study Center

Need help? For online student resources, such as section quizzes, visit the Online Study Center at www.cengage.com/math/aufmann.

Millions of people live and work in New York City every day, making it one of the busiest places on Earth. The U.S. Bureau of the Census records how many people live in a particular city each year and keeps track of how populations grow and change. By comparing the population over the years, we are able to determine the rate of change in the population and then use that rate to predict populations in the future. Average rate of change, which is discussed in **Section 5.4, Exercise 71 on page 297,** provides projections of the population of the United States for every five years from 2005 to 2030.

Prep Test

1. Simplify: $\dfrac{5 - (-7)}{4 - 8}$

2. Evaluate $\dfrac{a - b}{c - d}$ when $a = 3$, $b = -2$, $c = -3$, and $d = 2$.

3. Simplify: $-3(x - 4)$

4. Solve: $3x + 6 = 0$

5. Solve $4x + 5y = 20$ when $y = 0$.

6. Solve $3x - 7y = 11$ when $x = -1$.

7. Given $y = -4x + 5$, find the value of y when $x = -2$.

8. Simplify: $\dfrac{1}{4}(3x - 16)$

9. Which of the following are solutions of the inequality $-4 < x + 3$?
   a. 0   **b.** -3 **c.** 5   **d.** -7 **e.** -10

5.1 The Rectangular Coordinate System

OBJECTIVE 1 Graph points in a rectangular coordinate system

Before the 15th century, geometry and algebra were considered separate branches of mathematics. That all changed when René Descartes, a French mathematician who lived from 1596 to 1650, founded **analytic geometry.** In this geometry, a *coordinate system* is used to study the relationships between variables.

A **rectangular coordinate system** is formed by two number lines, one horizontal and one vertical, that intersect at the zero point of each line. The point of intersection is called the **origin.** The two axes are called the **coordinate axes,** or simply the **axes.** Generally, the horizontal axis is labeled the **x-axis,** and the vertical axis is labeled the **y-axis.**

The axes determine a **plane,** which can be thought of as a large, flat sheet of paper. The two axes divide the plane into four regions called **quadrants,** which are numbered counterclockwise from I to IV starting at the upper right.

Each point in the plane can be identified by a pair of numbers called an **ordered pair.** The first number of the ordered pair measures a horizontal distance and is called the **abscissa,** or **x-coordinate.** The second number of the pair measures a vertical distance and is called the **ordinate,** or **y-coordinate.** The ordered pair (x, y) associated with a point is also called the **coordinates** of the point.

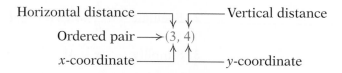

To **graph,** or **plot, a point in the plane,** place a dot at the location given by the ordered pair. For example, to graph the point $(4, 1)$, start at the origin. Move 4 units to the right and then 1 unit up. Draw a dot. To graph $(-3, -2)$, start at the origin. Move 3 units left and then 2 units down. Draw a dot.

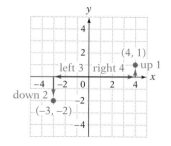

The **graph of an ordered pair** is the dot drawn at the coordinates of the point in the plane. The graphs of the ordered pairs $(4, 1)$ and $(-3, -2)$ are shown at the right.

The graphs of the points whose coordinates are $(2, 3)$ and $(3, 2)$ are shown at the right. Note that they are different points. The order in which the numbers in an ordered pair appear *is* important.

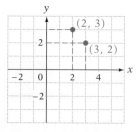

Each point in the plane is associated with an ordered pair, and each ordered pair is associated with a point in the plane. Although only integers are labeled on the coordinate grid, any ordered pair can be graphed by approximating its location. The graphs of the ordered pairs $\left(\frac{3}{2}, -\frac{4}{3}\right)$ and $(-2.4, 3.5)$ are shown at the right.

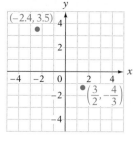

EXAMPLE 1   Graph the ordered pairs $(-2, -3)$, $(3, -2)$, $(1, 3)$, and $(4, 1)$.

Solution

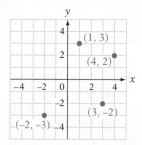

PROBLEM 1 Graph the ordered pairs $(-1, 3)$, $(1, 4)$, $(-4, 0)$, and $(-2, -1)$.

Solution See page S11.

EXAMPLE 2 Find the coordinates of each of the points.

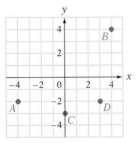

Solution $A(-4, -2)$, $B(4, 4)$, $C(0, -3)$, $D(3, -2)$

PROBLEM 2 Find the coordinates of each of the points.

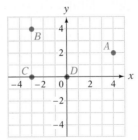

Solution See page S11.

OBJECTIVE **2** **Scatter diagrams**

There are many situations in which the relationship between two variables may be of interest. For example, a college admissions director wants to know the relationship between SAT scores (one variable) and success in college (the second variable). An employer is interested in the relationship between scores on a pre-employment test and ability to perform a job.

A researcher can investigate the relationship between two variables by means of regression analysis, which is a branch of statistics. The study of the relationship between two variables may begin with a **scatter diagram,** which is a graph of some of the known data.

The following table gives the record times for races of different lengths at a junior high track meet. Record times are rounded to the nearest second. Lengths are given in meters.

Length, x	100	200	400	800	1000	1500
Time, y	20	40	100	200	260	420

The scatter diagram for these data is shown at the right. Each ordered pair represents the length of the race and the record time. For example, the ordered pair (400, 100) indicates that the record for the 400 m race is 100 s.

EXAMPLE 3 To test a heart medicine, a doctor measures the heart rate, in beats per minute, of five patients before and after they take the medication. The results are recorded in the following table. Graph the scatter diagram for these data.

Before medicine, x	85	80	85	75	90
After medicine, y	75	70	70	80	80

Strategy   Graph the ordered pairs on a rectangular coordinate system where the horizontal axis represents the heart rate before taking the medication and the vertical axis represents the heart rate after taking the medication.

Solution

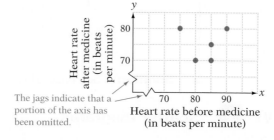

PROBLEM 3   A study by the Federal Aviation Administration showed that narrow, over-the-wing emergency exit rows slow passenger evacuation. The table at the top of the next page shows the space between seats, in inches, and the evacuation time, in seconds, for a group of 35 passengers. The longest evacuation times are recorded in the table. Graph the scatter diagram for these data.

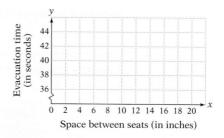

Space between seats, x	6	10	13	15	20
Evacuation time, y	44	43	38	36	37

■ **Solution** See page S11.

OBJECTIVE **3** ## Average rate of change

The table at the left shows the population of the United States for each decade from 1800 to 2000. (*Source:* U.S. Bureau of the Census) These data are graphed in the scatter diagram below.

Population of the United States

Year	Population (in millions)
1800	5
1810	7
1820	10
1830	13
1840	17
1850	23
1860	31
1870	40
1880	50
1890	63
1900	76
1910	92
1920	106
1930	123
1940	132
1950	151
1960	179
1970	203
1980	227
1990	249
2000	281

One way to describe how the population of the United States has changed over time is to calculate the change in population for a given time period. For example, we can find the change in population from 1990 to 2000.

Population in 2000 − population in 1990 = 281 million − 249 million

= 32 million

The amount of change in the population, 32 million, does not describe how rapid the growth in population was. To describe the rate of growth, or the *rate of change*, we must consider the number of years over which that growth took place. To determine how rapidly the population grew from 1990 to 2000, divide the change in population by the number of years during which that change took place.

$$\frac{\text{Change in population}}{\text{Change in years}} = \frac{\text{population in 2000} - \text{population in 1990}}{2000 - 1990}$$

$$= \frac{281 - 249}{2000 - 1990}$$

$$= \frac{32}{10} = 3.2$$

The average rate of change was 3.2 million people per year. This means that *on average*, from 1990 to 2000, the population of the United States increased by 3.2 million people per year.

Consider the two points on the graph that correspond to these years:

$$(1990, 249) \text{ and } (2000, 281)$$

Note that the average rate of change is calculated by dividing the difference between the y values of the two points by the difference between the x values of the two points.

Average Rate of Change

The average rate of change of y with respect to x is $\dfrac{\text{change in } y}{\text{change in } x}$.

To calculate the average rate of change, think

$$\frac{y \text{ value of second point} - y \text{ value of first point}}{x \text{ value of second point} - x \text{ value of first point}}$$

Find the average rate of change per year in the U.S. population from 1980 to 1990.

In 1980, the population was 227 million: $(1980, 227)$
In 1990, the population was 249 million: $(1990, 249)$

$$\text{Average rate of change} = \frac{\text{change in } y}{\text{change in } x}$$

$$= \frac{\text{population in 1990} - \text{population in 1980}}{1990 - 1980}$$

$$= \frac{249 - 227}{1990 - 1980}$$

$$= \frac{22}{10} = 2.2$$

The average rate of change in the population was 2.2 million people per year.

From 1990 to 2000, the average rate of change was 3.2 million people per year, whereas from 1980 to 1990, the average rate of change was 2.2 million people per year. The rate of change in the U.S. population is not constant; it varies for different intervals of time.

EXAMPLE 4 Find the average rate of change per year in the U.S. population from 1800 to 1900.

Solution   In 1800, the population was 5 million: (1800, 5)
In 1900, the population was 76 million: (1900, 76)

$$\begin{aligned}\text{Averate rate} \atop \text{of change} &= \frac{\text{change in } y}{\text{change in } x}\\[4pt]&= \frac{\text{population in 1900} - \text{population in 1800}}{1900 - 1800}\\[4pt]&= \frac{76 - 5}{1900 - 1800}\\[4pt]&= \frac{71}{100} = 0.71\end{aligned}$$

The average rate of change in the population was 0.71 million people per year, or 710,000 people per year.

Note that if both the ordinates and the abscissas are subtracted in the reverse order, the result is the same.

$$\begin{aligned}\text{Average rate} \atop \text{of change} &= \frac{\text{population in 1800} - \text{population in 1900}}{1800 - 1900}\\[4pt]&= \frac{5 - 76}{1800 - 1900} = \frac{-71}{-100} = 0.71\end{aligned}$$

PROBLEM 4 Find the average rate of change per year in the U.S. population from 1900 to 2000.

Solution   See page S11.

The table below shows weights of fetuses during various stages of prenatal development in humans. Use these data for Example 5 and Problem 5.

Number of weeks after conception	21	24	28	30	38
Weight, in pounds	1	2	3	4	7.5

EXAMPLE 5   Find the average rate of change per week in the weight of a fetus from 21 weeks after conception to 30 weeks after conception.

Solution   21 weeks after conception, the weight is 1 lb: (21, 1)
30 weeks after conception, the weight is 4 lb: (30, 4)

$$\begin{aligned}\text{Average rate} \atop \text{of change} &= \frac{\text{change in } y}{\text{change in } x}\\[4pt]&= \frac{\text{weight after 30 weeks} - \text{weight after 21 weeks}}{30 - 21}\\[4pt]&= \frac{4 - 1}{30 - 21} = \frac{3}{9}\\[4pt]&= \frac{1}{3} = 0.\overline{3}\end{aligned}$$

The average rate of change in weight is $0.\overline{3}$ lb per week.

PROBLEM 5   Find the average rate of change per week in the weight of a fetus from 28 weeks after conception to 38 weeks after conception.

   Solution   See page S11.

5.1   Concept Review

Determine whether the statement is always true, sometimes true, or never true.

1. The point (0, 0) on a rectangular coordinate system is at the origin.

2. When a point is plotted in the rectangular coordinate system, the first number in the ordered pair indicates a movement up or down from the origin. The second number in the ordered pair indicates a movement left or right.

3. In an xy-coordinate system, the first number is the y-coordinate and the second number is the x-coordinate.

4. When a point is plotted in the rectangular coordinate system, a negative x value indicates a movement to the left. A negative y value indicates a movement down.

5. Any point plotted in quadrant III has a positive y value.

6. In the figure at the right, point C is the graph of the point whose coordinates are $(-4, -2)$.

7. Any point on the x-axis has y-coordinate 0.

8. Any point on the y-axis has x-coordinate 0.

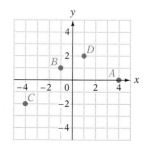

5.1   Exercises

1   **Graph points in a rectangular coordinate system**

Complete Exercises 1 and 2 by replacing each question mark with the word *left, right, up,* or *down.*

1. To graph the point $(5, -4)$, start at the origin and move 5 units ___?___ and 4 units ___?___.

2. To graph the point $(-1, 7)$, start at the origin and move 1 unit ___?___ and 7 units ___?___.

3. Describe the signs of the coordinates of a point in **a.** quadrant I, **b.** quadrant II, **c.** quadrant III, and **d.** quadrant IV.

4. In which quadrant is the point located? **a.** $(2, -4)$ **b.** $(-3, 2)$ **c.** $(-1, -6)$

5. Graph the ordered pairs (−2, 1), (3, −5), (−2, 4), and (0, 3).

6. Graph the ordered pairs (5, −1), (−3, −3), (−1, 0), and (1, −1).

7. Graph the ordered pairs (0, 0), (0, −5), (−3, 0), and (0, 2).

8. Graph the ordered pairs (−4, 5), (−3, 1), (3, −4), and (5, 0).

9. Graph the ordered pairs (−1, 4), (−2, −3), (0, 2), and (4, 0).

10. Graph the ordered pairs (5, 2), (−4, −1), (0, 0), and (0, 3).

11. Find the coordinates of each of the points.

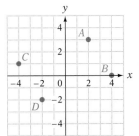

12. Find the coordinates of each of the points.

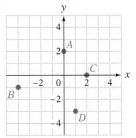

13. Find the coordinates of each of the points.

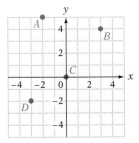

14. Find the coordinates of each of the points.

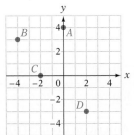

15. a. Name the abscissas of points *A* and *C*.
   b. Name the ordinates of points *B* and *D*.

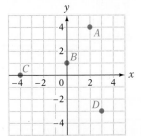

16. a. Name the abscissas of points *A* and *C*.
   b. Name the ordinates of points *B* and *D*.

17. Let a and b be positive numbers such that $a < b$. In which quadrant is each point located?

a. (a, b) **b.** $(-a, b)$ **c.** $(b - a, -b)$ **d.** $(a - b, -b - a)$

18. Let a and b be positive numbers. State whether the two given points lie on the x-axis, the y-axis, a horizontal line other than the x-axis, or a vertical line other than the y-axis.

a. $(-a, b)$ and $(-a, 0)$ **b.** $(a, 0)$ and $(-b, 0)$

2 Scatter diagrams

19. Look at the table of data in Exercise 21. The lowest x value is ___?___ and the highest x value is ___?___. The lowest y value is ___?___ and the highest y value is ___?___. In a scatter diagram of the data, the x-axis must show values from at least ___?___ to ___?___, and the y-axis must show values from at least ___?___ to ___?___.

20. Look at the table of data in Exercise 22. The lowest x value is ___?___ and the highest x value is ___?___. The lowest y value is ___?___ and the highest y value is ___?___. In a scatter diagram of the data, the x-axis must show values from at least ___?___ to ___?___, and the y-axis must show values from at least ___?___ to ___?___.

21. **Fuel Efficiency** The American Council for an Energy-Efficient Economy releases rankings of environmentally friendly and unfriendly cars and trucks sold in the United States. The following table shows the fuel usage, in miles per gallon, in the city and on the highway, for the twelve 2005-model vehicles ranked best for the environment. Graph the scatter diagram for these data.

Fuel usage, in mpg, city, x	30	57	60	47	32	35	28	36	30	28	36	26
Fuel usage in mpg, highway, y	34	56	51	48	41	42	35	44	36	35	31	35

22. **Fuel Efficiency** The American Council for an Energy-Efficient Economy releases rankings of environmentally friendly and unfriendly cars and trucks sold in the United States. The following table shows the fuel usage, in miles per gallon, in the city and on the highway, for the twelve 2005-model vehicles ranked worst for the environment. Graph the scatter diagram for these data.

Fuel usage, in mpg, city, x	9	13	13	12	9	13	14	12	10	13	9	12
Fuel usage in mpg, highway, y	12	17	17	14	13	17	17	16	14	14	15	16

23. **Olympics** The following table shows the weight, in pounds, and the height, in inches, of some of the members of the U.S. Women's Soccer Team that won a gold medal in the 2004 Olympic games. Graph the scatter diagram for these data.

Weight, in pounds, x	150	134	128	134	134	128	148	130	126	134
Height, in inches, y	69	65	67	67	67	68	66	64	64	71

24. **Basketball** The following table shows the weight, in pounds, and the height, in inches, of some of the members of a Seattle Supersonics professional basketball team. Graph the scatter diagram for these data.

Weight, in pounds, x	205	190	210	255	245	260	215	225	245	225
Height, in inches, y	77	76	74	81	80	80	82	74	84	78

25. **Incomes** To determine trends in income levels, economists use inflation-adjusted values. These numbers take into consideration how inflation affects purchase power. The following table shows the median income, rounded to the nearest hundred, for selected years in both actual dollars (before inflation) and 2005 inflation-adjusted dollars. (*Source:* U.S. Census Bureau) Graph the scatter diagram for these data.

Year	Actual Median Income, x	Inflation-adjusted Median Income, y
2000	40,700	46,100
2001	42,000	46,100
2002	42,200	45,100
2003	42,400	44,500
2004	43,300	44,500
2005	44,400	44,400

26. **Sports** A basketball coach wants to determine whether there is a relationship between the number of shots attempted and the number of shots made. The following table shows the performances of six players on the team for one game. Graph the scatter diagram for these data.

Shots attempted, x	13	11	8	5	4	1
Shots made, y	11	7	5	4	3	1

3   Average rate of change

27. Look at the table of values in Exercise 30, in which you are asked to calculate average rates of change for pairs of data points. When finding an average rate of change between two data points in this table, will you put the values that represent time in the numerator or the denominator?

28. Look at the table of values in Exercise 32. Which of the following fractions is the correct one to use to find the average rate of change per month in the length of a fetus from the fourth month of pregnancy to the eighth month of pregnancy?

 a. $\dfrac{4-8}{16-7}$ b. $\dfrac{16-7}{8-4}$ c. $\dfrac{8-4}{16-7}$ d. $\dfrac{7-16}{14-8}$

Population of Colonial America

Year	Population
1610	350
1620	2,300
1630	4,600
1640	26,600
1650	50,400
1660	75,100
1670	111,900
1680	151,500
1690	210,400
1700	250,900
1710	331,700
1720	466,200
1730	629,400
1740	905,600
1750	1,170,800
1760	1,593,600
1770	2,148,100
1780	2,780,400

29. **Temperature** On September 10 in midstate New Hampshire, the temperature at 6 A.M. was 45°F. At 2 P.M. on the same day, the temperature was 77°F. Find the average rate of change in temperature per hour.

30. **Demography** The table at the right shows the population of Colonial America for each decade from 1610 to 1780. (*Source:* infoplease.com) These figures are estimates, because this period was prior to the establishment of the U.S. Census in 1790.
 a. Find the average annual rate of change in the population of the Colonies from 1650 to 1750.
 b. Was the average annual rate of change in the population from 1650 to 1750 greater than or less than the average annual rate of change in the population from 1700 to 1750?
 c. During which decade was the average annual rate of change the least? What was the average annual rate of change during that decade?

31. **Minimum Wage** The following table shows the minimum hourly wage for selected years. (*Source:* Employment Policy Institute, www.epi.org/issueguides/minwage/table4.gif)

Year	1970	1975	1980	1985	1990	1995	2000	2005
Minimum wage	1.60	2.10	3.10	3.35	3.69	4.25	5.15	5.15

 a. What was the average annual rate of change in the minimum wage from 1970 to 1990?
 b. Find the average rate of change in the minimum wage from 1990 to 2005. Is this more or less than the average annual rate of change in the minimum wage from 1970 to 1990?

32. **Child Development** The following table shows average lengths of fetuses for selected stages of prenatal development in humans. (*Source:* Surebaby.com)
 a. What is the average rate of change per month in the length of a fetus from the sixth month of pregnancy to the eighth month of pregnancy?
 b. Find the average rate of change per month in the length of a fetus from the second month of pregnancy to the fourth month of

pregnancy. Is this greater than or less than the average rate of change per month from the sixth month to the eighth month?

Month of pregnancy	2	4	6	8
Length, in inches	1	7	12	16

33. **Demography** The following table shows the projected population of baby boomers for the years 2000, 2031, and 2046. (*Source:* U.S. Census Bureau)
  a. Find the average rate of change per year in the population of the baby boomer generation from 2031 to 2046 (*Note:* A negative average rate of change denotes a decrease.)
  b. Find the average rate of change per year in the population of baby boomers from 2000 to 2046. Round to the nearest hundred thousand.

Year	2000	2031	2046
Population, in millions	79	51	19

34. **Car Prices** The following table shows the mileage on and corresponding value of a used 2004 MINI Cooper, 2-door hatchback one year after it was purchased. (*Source:* www.kbb.com, Dec. 11, 2005)

Mileage	10,000	20,000	30,000	40,000	50,000	60,000
Value, in dollars	18,525	17,850	16,625	15,125	13,975	13,150

  a. What was the per-mile change in the value of the car between 10,000 mi and 60,000 mi? Round to the nearest cent per mile. (*Note:* A negative average rate of change denotes a decrease.)
  b. Write a sentence explaining the meaning of the answer to part a.

35. **Minimum Wage** The following table shows buying power of a worker earning the federal minimum wage for various years. This is not the *actual* minimum wage but the minimum wage adjusted for inflation. For instance, the actual minimum wage in 1970 was $1.60. Spending $1.60 in 1970 was the same as spending $6.95 in 2005. (*Source:* Employment Policy Institute, www.epi.org/issueguides/minwage/table4.gif)

Year	1970	1975	1980	1985	1990	1995	2000	2005
Minimum wage	6.95	6.70	6.94	5.79	5.33	5.40	5.83	5.15

  a. What was the average annual rate of change in the inflation-adjusted minimum wage from 1980 to 2005? (*Note:* A negative average rate of change denotes a decrease.)
  b. Prior to 1990, in which five-year period did the average annual rate of change in the inflation-adjusted minimum wage increase? What was the average annual rate of change during that period?

36. **School Enrollments** The following table shows the projected population of adults 18 to 19 years old for selected years from 2005 to 2030. (*Source:* Proximity, www.proximityone.com/cdtrends.htm)

Year	2005	2010	2015	2020	2025	2030
Population projection, in millions	8.4	8.6	8.1	8.6	9.0	9.4

a. Find the average annual rate of change of the U.S. population of adults 18–19 years old from 2005 to 2030.

b. In which five-year period shown did the average annual rate of change of this population decline? What was the average annual rate of change for that period?

For Exercises 37 and 38, use the following table of data. The table shows the temperature, in degrees Fahrenheit, of a cup of coffee, measured every 10 min over a period of one and one-half hours.

Minutes	0	10	20	30	40	50	60	70	80	90
Temperature, °F	177.3	144.6	122.3	107.0	96.6	89.4	84.6	81.2	78.9	77.4

37. 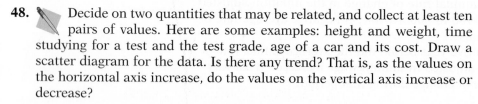 During which 10-minute interval was the average rate of change closest to −1 degree per minute?

38. During which 30-minute interval was the average rate of change closest to −1 degree per minute?

5.1   Applying Concepts

What is the distance from the given point to the horizontal axis?

39. (−5, 1)   **40.** (3, −4)   **41.** (−6, 0)

What is the distance from the given point to the vertical axis?

42. (−2, 4)   **43.** (1, −3)   **44.** (5, 0)

45. Name the coordinates of a point plotted at the origin of the rectangular coordinate system.

46. A computer screen has a coordinate system that is different from the *xy*-coordinate system we have discussed. In one mode, the origin of the coordinate system is the top left point of the screen, as shown at the right. Plot the points whose coordinates are (200, 400), (0, 100), and (100, 300).

47. Write a paragraph explaining how to plot points in a rectangular coordinate system.

48. Decide on two quantities that may be related, and collect at least ten pairs of values. Here are some examples: height and weight, time studying for a test and the test grade, age of a car and its cost. Draw a scatter diagram for the data. Is there any trend? That is, as the values on the horizontal axis increase, do the values on the vertical axis increase or decrease?

49. There is a coordinate system on Earth that consists of *longitude* and *latitude*. Write a report on how location is determined on the surface of Earth.

5.2   Graphs of Straight Lines

OBJECTIVE 1   **Determine solutions of linear equations in two variables**

An equation of the form $y = mx + b$, where m is the coefficient of x and b is a constant, is a **linear equation in two variables.** Examples of linear equations follow.

$$y = 3x + 4 \qquad (m = 3, b = 4)$$
$$y = 2x - 3 \qquad (m = 2, b = -3)$$
$$y = -\frac{2}{3}x + 1 \qquad \left(m = -\frac{2}{3}, b = 1\right)$$
$$y = -2x \qquad (m = -2, b = 0)$$
$$y = x + 2 \qquad (m = 1, b = 2)$$

In a linear equation, the exponent of each variable is 1. The equations $y = 2x^2 - 1$ and $y = \frac{1}{x}$ are not linear equations.

A **solution of a linear equation in two variables** is an ordered pair of numbers (x, y) that makes the equation a true statement.

Take Note

An ordered pair is of the form (x, y). For the ordered pair $(1, -2)$, 1 is the x value and -2 is the y value. Substitute 1 for x and -2 for y.

Is $(1, -2)$ a solution of $y = 3x - 5$?

Replace x with 1. Replace y with -2.

$$\begin{array}{c|c} y = 3x - 5 \\ \hline -2 & 3(1) - 5 \\ & 3 - 5 \end{array}$$

Compare the results. If the results are equal, the given ordered pair is a solution. If the results are not equal, the given ordered pair is not a solution.

$$-2 = -2$$

Yes, $(1, -2)$ is a solution of the equation $y = 3x - 5$.

Besides the ordered pair $(1, -2)$, there are many other ordered-pair solutions of the equation $y = 3x - 5$. For example, the method used above can be used to show that $(2, 1)$, $(-1, -8)$, $\left(\frac{2}{3}, -3\right)$, and $(0, -5)$ are also solutions.

EXAMPLE 1   Is $(-3, 2)$ a solution of $y = 2x + 2$?

Solution

$$\begin{array}{c|c} y = 2x + 2 \\ \hline 2 & 2(-3) + 2 \\ & -6 + 2 \\ & -4 \end{array}$$

• **Replace x with -3 and y with 2.**

$$2 \neq -4$$

No, $(-3, 2)$ is not a solution of $y = 2x + 2$.

PROBLEM 1   Is $(2, -4)$ a solution of $y = -\frac{1}{2}x - 3$?

Solution   See page S12.

In general, a linear equation in two variables has an infinite number of ordered-pair solutions. By choosing any value for x and substituting that value into the linear equation, we can find a corresponding value of y.

Find the ordered-pair solution of $y = 2x - 5$ that corresponds to $x = 1$.

$$y = 2x - 5$$

Substitute 1 for x. $y = 2 \cdot 1 - 5$
Solve for y. $y = 2 - 5$
                          $y = -3$

The ordered-pair solution is $(1, -3)$.

EXAMPLE 2   Find the ordered-pair solution of $y = \frac{2}{3}x - 1$ that corresponds to $x = 3$.

Solution $y = \frac{2}{3}x - 1$

$y = \frac{2}{3}(3) - 1$ • **Substitute 3 for x.**

$y = 2 - 1$ • **Solve for y.**

$y = 1$ • **When x = 3, y = 1.**

The ordered-pair solution is $(3, 1)$.

PROBLEM 2   Find the ordered-pair solution of $y = -\frac{1}{4}x + 1$ that corresponds to $x = 4$.

Solution   See page S12.

OBJECTIVE 2   **Graph equations of the form $y = mx + b$**

The **graph of an equation in two variables** is a drawing of the ordered-pair solutions of the equation. For a linear equation in two variables, the graph is a straight line.

To graph a linear equation, find ordered-pair solutions of the equation. Do this by choosing any value of x and finding the corresponding value of y. Repeat this procedure, choosing different values for x, until you have found the number of solutions desired.

Because the graph of a linear equation in two variables is a straight line, and a straight line is determined by two points, it is necessary to find only two solutions. However, finding at least three points will ensure accuracy.

Graph $y = 2x + 1$.

Choose any values of x, and then find the corresponding values of y. The numbers 0, 2, and -1 were chosen arbitrarily for x. It is convenient to record these solutions in a table.

x	$y = 2x + 1$	y
0	$2(0) + 1$	1
2	$2(2) + 1$	5
-1	$2(-1) + 1$	-1

Graph the ordered-pair solutions $(0, 1)$, $(2, 5)$, and $(-1, -1)$. Draw a line through the ordered-pair solutions.

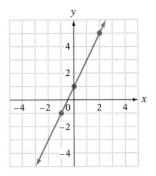

Take Note

If the three points you graph do not lie on a straight line, you have made an arithmetic error in calculating a point or you have plotted a point incorrectly.

Note that the points whose coordinates are $(-2, -3)$ and $(1, 3)$ are on the graph and that these ordered pairs are solutions of the equation $y = 2x + 1$.

Remember that a graph is a drawing of the ordered-pair solutions of an equation. Therefore, every point on the graph is a solution of the equation, and every solution of the equation is a point on the graph.

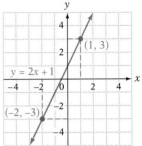

EXAMPLE 3   Graph: $y = 3x - 2$

Solution

x	y
0	-2
2	4
-1	-5

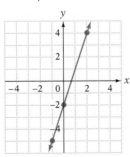

PROBLEM 3   Graph: $y = 3x + 1$

Solution   See page S12.

Graphing utilities create graphs by plotting points and then connecting the points to form a curve. Using a graphing utility, enter the equation $y = 3x - 2$ and verify the graph drawn in Example 3. (Refer to the Appendix for instructions on using a graphing calculator to graph a linear equation.) Trace along the graph and verify that $(0, -2)$, $(2, 4)$, and $(-1, -5)$ are coordinates of points on the graph. Now enter the equation $y = 3x + 1$ given in Problem 3. Verify that the ordered pairs you found for this equation are the coordinates of points on the graph.

When m is a fraction in the equation $y = mx + b$, choose values of x that will simplify the evaluation. For example, to graph $y = \frac{1}{3}x - 1$, we might choose the numbers 0, 3, and −3 for x. Note that these numbers are multiples of the denominator of $\frac{1}{3}$, the coefficient of x.

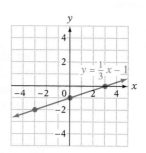

EXAMPLE 4   Graph: $y = \frac{1}{2}x - 1$

Solution

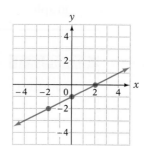

x	y
0	−1
2	0
−2	−2

PROBLEM 4   Graph: $y = \frac{1}{3}x - 3$

Solution   See page S12.

Using a graphing utility, enter the equation $y = \frac{1}{2}x - 1$ and verify the graph drawn in Example 4. Trace along the graph and verify that $(0, -1)$, $(2, 0)$, and $(-2, -2)$ are the coordinates of points on the graph. Follow the same procedure for Problem 4. (See the Appendix for instructions on entering a fractional coefficient of x.)

OBJECTIVE **3**   **Graph equations of the form $Ax + By = C$**

An equation in the form $Ax + By = C$, where A and B are coefficients and C is a constant, is also a linear equation. Examples of these equations are shown below.

$$2x + 3y = 6 \qquad (A = 2, B = 3, C = 6)$$
$$x - 2y = -4 \qquad (A = 1, B = -2, C = -4)$$
$$2x + y = 0 \qquad (A = 2, B = 1, C = 0)$$
$$4x - 5y = 2 \qquad (A = 4, B = -5, C = 2)$$

One method of graphing an equation of the form $Ax + By = C$ involves first solving the equation for y and then following the same procedure used for graphing an equation of the form $y = mx + b$. To solve the equation for y means to rewrite the equation so that y is alone on one side of the equation and the term containing x and the constant are on the other side of the equation. The Addition and Multiplication Properties of Equations are used to rewrite an equation of the form $Ax + By = C$ in the form $y = mx + b$.

Solve the equation $3x + 2y = 4$ for y.

The equation is in the form
$Ax + By = C$.
$$3x + 2y = 4$$

Use the Addition Property of
Equations to subtract the term $3x$
from each side of the equation.
$$3x - 3x + 2y = -3x + 4$$

Simplify. Note that on the right side
of the equation, the term containing
x is first, followed by the constant.
$$2y = -3x + 4$$

Use the Multiplication Property of
Equations to multiply each side of
the equation by the reciprocal of
the coefficient of y. (The coefficient
of y is 2; the reciprocal of 2 is $\frac{1}{2}$.)
$$\frac{1}{2} \cdot 2y = \frac{1}{2}(-3x + 4)$$

Simplify. Use the Distributive
Property on the right side of the
equation.
$$y = \frac{1}{2}(-3x) + \frac{1}{2}(4)$$

The equation is now in the form
$y = mx + b$, with $m = -\frac{3}{2}$ and $b = 2$.
$$y = -\frac{3}{2}x + 2$$

In solving the equation $3x + 2y = 4$ for y, where we multiplied both sides of the equation by $\frac{1}{2}$, we could have divided both sides of the equation by 2, as shown at the right. In simplifying the right side after dividing both sides by 2, be sure to divide *each term* by 2.

$$2y = -3x + 4$$
$$\frac{2y}{2} = \frac{-3x + 4}{2}$$
$$y = \frac{-3x}{2} + \frac{4}{2}$$
$$y = -\frac{3}{2}x + 2$$

Being able to solve an equation of the form $Ax + By = C$ for y is important because most graphing utilities require that an equation be in the form $y = mx + b$ when the equation of the line is entered for graphing.

EXAMPLE 5 Write $3x - 4y = 12$ in the form $y = mx + b$.

Solution

$$3x - 4y = 12$$

$$3x - 3x - 4y = -3x + 12$$ • **Subtract $3x$ from each side of the equation.**

$$-4y = -3x + 12$$ • **Simplify.**

$$\frac{-4y}{-4} = \frac{-3x + 12}{-4}$$ • **Divide each side of the equation by -4.**

$$y = \frac{-3x}{-4} + \frac{12}{-4}$$

$$y = \frac{3}{4}x - 3$$

PROBLEM 5 Write $5x - 2y = 10$ in the form $y = mx + b$.

Solution See page S12.

To graph an equation of the form $Ax + By = C$, we can first solve the equation for y and then follow the same procedure used for graphing an equation of the form $y = mx + b$. An example follows.

Graph: $3x + 4y = 12$

Write the equation in the form $y = mx + b$.

$$3x + 4y = 12$$

$$4y = -3x + 12$$

$$y = -\frac{3}{4}x + 3$$

Find at least three solutions.
Display the ordered pairs in a table.

x	y
0	3
4	0
-4	6

Graph the ordered pairs on a rectangular coordinate system, and draw a straight line through the points.

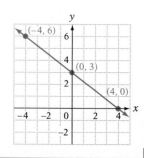

EXAMPLE 6 Graph. **A.** $2x - 5y = 10$ **B.** $x + 2y = 6$

Solution **A.** $2x - 5y = 10$

$$-5y = -2x + 10$$

$$y = \frac{2}{5}x - 2$$

B. $x + 2y = 6$

$$2y = -x + 6$$

$$y = -\frac{1}{2}x + 3$$

$$y = \frac{2}{5}x - 2 \qquad\qquad y = -\frac{1}{2}x + 3$$

x	y
0	-2
5	0
-5	-4

x	y
0	3
-2	4
4	1

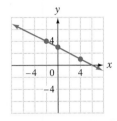

PROBLEM 6   Graph.   **A.** $5x - 2y = 10$ **B.** $x - 3y = 9$

Solution   See page S12.

The graph of the equation $2x + 3y = 6$ is shown at the right. The graph crosses the x-axis at $(3, 0)$. This point is called the **x-intercept.** The graph crosses the y-axis at $(0, 2)$. This point is called the **y-intercept.**

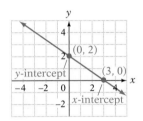

Find the x-intercept and the y-intercept of the graph of the equation $2x + 3y = 6$ algebraically.

To find the x-intercept, let $y = 0$.
(Any point on the x-axis has y-coordinate 0.)

$$2x + 3y = 6$$
$$2x + 3(0) = 6$$
$$2x = 6$$
$$x = 3$$

The x-intercept is $(3, 0)$.

To find the y-intercept, let $x = 0$.
(Any point on the y-axis has x-coordinate 0.)

$$2x + 3y = 6$$
$$2(0) + 3y = 6$$
$$3y = 6$$
$$y = 2$$

The y-intercept is $(0, 2)$.

Take Note

To find the x-intercept, let $y = 0$.
To find the y-intercept, let $x = 0$.

Another method of graphing some equations of the form $Ax + By = C$ is to find the x- and y-intercepts, plot both intercepts, and then draw a line through the two points.

EXAMPLE 7   Find the x- and y-intercepts for $x - 2y = 4$. Graph the line.

Solution x-intercept: $x - 2y = 4$

$$x - 2(0) = 4$$ • **To find the x-intercept, let $y = 0$.**

$$x = 4$$

The x-intercept is $(4, 0)$.

y-intercept: $x - 2y = 4$

$$0 - 2y = 4$$ • **To find the y-intercept, let $x = 0$.**

$$-2y = 4$$

$$y = -2$$

The y-intercept is $(0, -2)$.

• **Graph the ordered pairs (4, 0) and (0, −2). Draw a straight line through the points.**

PROBLEM 7   Find the x- and y-intercepts for $4x - y = 4$. Graph the line.

Solution   See page S12.

The graph of an equation in which one of the variables is missing is either a horizontal line or a vertical line.

The equation $y = 2$ could be written $0 \cdot x + y = 2$. No matter what value of x is chosen, y is always 2. Some solutions to the equation are $(3, 2)$, $(-1, 2)$, $(0, 2)$, and $(-4, 2)$. The graph is shown at the right.

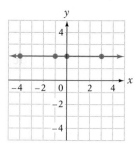

The **graph of $y = b$** is a horizontal line passing through the point whose coordinates are $(0, b)$.

Note that $(0, b)$ is the y-intercept of the graph of $y = b$. An equation of the form $y = b$ does not have an x-intercept.

The equation $x = -2$ could be written $x + 0 \cdot y = -2$. No matter what value of y is chosen, x is always -2. Some solutions to the equation are $(-2, 3)$, $(-2, -2)$, $(-2, 0)$, and $(-2, 2)$. The graph is shown at the right.

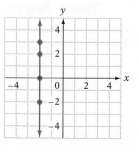

The **graph of $x = a$** is a vertical line passing through the point whose coordinates are $(a, 0)$.

Note that $(a, 0)$ is the x-intercept of the graph of $x = a$. An equation of the form $x = a$ does not have a y-intercept.

EXAMPLE 8   Graph.   **A.** $y = -2$ **B.** $x = 3$

Solution   **A.** The graph of an equation of the form $y = b$ is a horizontal line with y-intercept $(0, b)$.

B. The graph of an equation of the form $x = a$ is a vertical line with x-intercept $(a, 0)$.

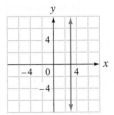

PROBLEM 8   Graph.   **A.** $y = 3$ **B.** $x = -4$

Solution   See page S12.

5.2   Concept Review

Determine whether the statement is always true, sometimes true, or never true.

1. The equation $y = 3x^2 - 6$ is an example of a linear equation in two variables.

2. The value of m in the equation $y = 4x + 9$ is 9.

3. $(3, 5)$ is a solution of the equation $y = x + 2$.

4. The graph of a linear equation in two variables is a straight line.

5. To find the x-intercept of the graph of a linear equation, let $x = 0$.

6. The graph of an equation of the form $y = b$ is a horizontal line.

7. The graph of the equation $x = -4$ has an x-intercept of $(0, -4)$.

8. The graph shown at the right has a y-intercept of $(0, 3)$.

9. The graph of the equation $x = 2$ is a line that goes through every point that has an x-coordinate of 2.

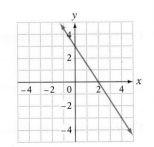

5.2 Exercises

1 Determine solutions of linear equations in two variables

1. To decide whether the ordered pair (1, 7) is a solution of the equation $y = 2x + 5$, substitute 1 for ___?___ and 7 for ___?___ to see whether the ordered pair (1, 7) makes the equation $y = 2x + 5$ a true statement

2. Find the ordered-pair solution of $y = -\dfrac{1}{4}x + 3$ that corresponds to $x = -8$.

$y = -\dfrac{1}{4}x + 3$

$y = -\dfrac{1}{4}(-8) + 3$ • Substitute ___?___ for ___?___.

$y = \underline{\quad ? \quad} + 3$ • Multiply.

$y = \underline{\quad ? \quad}$ • Add.

The ordered-pair solution that corresponds to $x = -8$ is (___?___, ___?___).

For the given linear equation, find the value of m and the value of b.

3. $y = 4x + 1$

4. $y = -3x - 2$

5. $y = \dfrac{5}{6}x + \dfrac{1}{6}$

6. $y = -x$

7. Is (3, 4) a solution of $y = -x + 7$?

8. Is (2, −3) a solution of $y = x + 5$?

9. Is (−1, 2) a solution of $y = \dfrac{1}{2}x - 1$?

10. Is (1, −3) a solution of $y = -2x - 1$?

11. Is (4, 1) a solution of $y = \dfrac{1}{4}x + 1$?

12. Is (−5, 3) a solution of $y = -\dfrac{2}{5}x + 1$?

13. Is (0, 4) a solution of $y = \dfrac{3}{4}x + 4$?

14. Is (−2, 0) a solution of $y = -\dfrac{1}{2}x - 1$?

15. Is (0, 0) a solution of $y = 3x + 2$?

16. Is (0, 0) a solution of $y = -\dfrac{3}{4}x$?

17. Find the ordered-pair solution of $y = 3x - 2$ that corresponds to $x = 3$.

18. Find the ordered-pair solution of $y = 4x + 1$ that corresponds to $x = -1$.

19. Find the ordered-pair solution of $y = \dfrac{2}{3}x - 1$ that corresponds to $x = 6$.

20. Find the ordered-pair solution of $y = \dfrac{3}{4}x - 2$ that corresponds to $x = 4$.

21. Find the ordered-pair solution of $y = -3x + 1$ that corresponds to $x = 0$.

22. Find the ordered-pair solution of $y = \dfrac{2}{5}x - 5$ that corresponds to $x = 0$.

23. Find the ordered-pair solution of $y = \dfrac{2}{5}x + 2$ that corresponds to $x = -5$.

24. Find the ordered-pair solution of $y = -\dfrac{1}{6}x - 2$ that corresponds to $x = 12$.

25. Use the linear equation $y = -3x + 6$.
   a. For what value of x is the ordered pair $(x, 0)$ a solution of the linear equation $y = -3x + 6$?
   b. Suppose (x, a) is a solution of the linear equation $y = -3x + 6$, such that $x > 2$. Is a a positive or a negative number?

26. Let $y = mx + b$ be a linear equation in which $b = -2m$. For what value of x will the ordered pair $(x, 0)$ be a solution of the equation?

2   Graph equations of the form $y = mx + b$

27. Find three points on the graph of $y = 3x - 4$ by finding the y values that correspond to x values of -1, 0, and 1.
   a. When $x = -1$, $y = $ ___?___. A point on the graph is (___?___, ___?___).
   b. When $x = 0$, $y = $ ___?___. A point on the graph is (___?___, ___?___).
   c. When $x = 1$, $y = $ ___?___. A point on the graph is (___?___, ___?___).

28. To find points on the graph of $y = \dfrac{1}{5}x - 8$, it is helpful to choose x values that are divisible by ___?___.

Graph.

29. $y = 2x - 3$

30. $y = -2x + 2$

31. $y = \dfrac{1}{3}x$

32. $y = -3x$

33. $y = \dfrac{2}{3}x - 1$

34. $y = \dfrac{3}{4}x + 2$

35. $y = -\dfrac{1}{4}x + 2$

36. $y = -\dfrac{1}{3}x + 1$

37. $y = -\dfrac{2}{5}x + 1$

38. $y = -\dfrac{1}{2}x + 3$

39. $y = 2x - 4$

40. $y = 3x - 4$

41. $y = -x + 2$

42. $y = -x - 1$

43. $y = -\dfrac{2}{3}x + 1$

44. $y = 5x - 4$

45. $y = -3x + 2$

46. $y = -x + 3$

Graph using a graphing utility.

47. $y = 3x - 4$

48. $y = -2x + 3$

49. $y = 2x - 3$

50. $y = -2x - 3$

51. $y = -\dfrac{2}{3}x$

52. $y = \dfrac{3}{2}x$

53. $y = \dfrac{3}{4}x + 2$

54. $y = -\dfrac{1}{3}x + 2$

55. $y = -\dfrac{3}{2}x - 3$

56. $y = -\dfrac{2}{5}x + 2$

57. $y = \dfrac{1}{4}x - 2$

58. $y = \dfrac{2}{3}x - 4$

3 Graph equations of the form $Ax + By = C$

59. Write the equation $x - 2y = -10$ in the form $y = mx + b$.

$$x - 2y = -10$$
$$x - x - 2y = -x - 10$$ • Subtract ___?___ from each side of the equation.
$$\underline{\quad ? \quad} = -x - 10$$ • Simplify the left side of the equation.
$$\frac{-2y}{-2} = \frac{-x - 10}{-2}$$ • Divide each side of the equation by ___?___.
$$y = \underline{\quad ? \quad} x + \underline{\quad ? \quad}$$ • Simplify.

60. a. The x-intercept of the graph of a linear equation is the point where the graph crosses the ___?___. Its ___?___-coordinate is 0.
b. The y-intercept of the graph of a linear equation is the point where the graph crosses the ___?___. Its ___?___-coordinate is 0.

Complete Exercises 61 and 62 by using the word *horizontal* or *vertical*.

61. The graph of the equation $y = 7$ is a ___?___ line passing through the point whose coordinates are $(0, 7)$.

62. The graph of the equation $x = -10$ is a ___?___ line passing through the point whose coordinates are $(-10, 0)$.

Solve for y. Write the equation in the form $y = mx + b$.

63. $3x + y = 10$

64. $2x + y = 5$

65. $4x - y = 3$

66. $5x - y = 7$

67. $3x + 2y = 6$

68. $2x + 3y = 9$

69. $2x - 5y = 10$

70. $5x - 2y = 4$

71. $2x + 7y = 14$

72. $6x - 5y = 10$

73. $x + 3y = 6$

74. $x - 4y = 12$

Graph.

75. $3x + y = 3$

76. $2x + y = 4$

77. $2x + 3y = 6$

78. $3x + 2y = 4$

79. $x - 2y = 4$

80. $x - 3y = 6$

81. $2x - 3y = 6$

82. $3x - 2y = 8$

83. $y = 4$ 　　　　　**84.** $y = -4$ 　　　　　**85.** $x = -2$ 　　　　　**86.** $x = 3$

Find the x- and y-intercepts.

87. $x - y = 3$ 　　　　**88.** $3x + 4y = 12$ 　　　**89.** $y = 2x - 6$ 　　　**90.** $y = 2x + 10$

91. $x - 5y = 10$ 　　　**92.** $3x + 2y = 12$ 　　　**93.** $y = 3x + 12$ 　　　**94.** $y = 5x + 10$

95. $2x - 3y = 0$ 　　　**96.** $3x + 4y = 0$ 　　　**97.** $y = \dfrac{1}{2}x + 3$ 　　　**98.** $y = \dfrac{2}{3}x - 4$

Graph by using x- and y-intercepts.

99. $5x + 2y = 10$ 　　　　　**100.** $x - 3y = 6$ 　　　　　**101.** $3x - 4y = 12$

102. $2x - 3y = -6$ 　　　　　**103.** $2x + 3y = 6$ 　　　　　**104.** $x + 2y = 4$

105. $2x + 5y = 10$ 　　　　　**106.** $3x + 4y = 12$ 　　　　　**107.** $x - 3y = 6$

108. $3x - y = 6$ 　　　　　**109.** $x - 4y = 8$ 　　　　　**110.** $4x + 3y = 12$

111. $2x + y = 3$ 　　　　　**112.** $3x + y = -5$ 　　　　　**113.** $4x - 3y = 6$

Graph using a graphing utility. Verify that the graph has the correct x- and y-intercepts.

114. $x - 2y = -4$ **115.** $3x + 4y = -12$ **116.** $3x - 2y = -6$

117. $2x - y = 4$ **118.** $3x - 4y = 4$ **119.** $2x - 3y = 9$

120. Suppose A and B are positive and C is negative. Is the y-intercept of the graph of $Ax + By = C$ above or below the x-axis?

121. Suppose A and C are negative and B is positive. Is the x-intercept of the graph of $Ax + By = C$ to the left or to the right of the y-axis?

5.2   Applying Concepts

122. a. Show that the equation $y + 3 = 2(x + 4)$ is a linear equation by writing it in the form $y = mx + b$.
 b. Find the ordered-pair solution that corresponds to $x = -4$.

123. a. Show that the equation $y + 4 = -\frac{1}{2}(x + 2)$ is a linear equation by writing it in the form $y = mx + b$.
 b. Find the ordered-pair solution that corresponds to $x = -2$.

124. For the linear equation $y = 2x - 3$, what is the increase in y that results when x is increased by 1?

125. For the linear equation $y = -x - 4$, what is the decrease in y that results when x is increased by 1?

126. Write the equation of a line that has $(0, 0)$ as both the x-intercept and the y-intercept.

127. Explain **a.** why the y-coordinate of any point on the x-axis is 0 and **b.** why the x-coordinate of any point on the y-axis is 0.

5.3 Slopes of Straight Lines

OBJECTIVE 1   **Find the slope of a straight line**

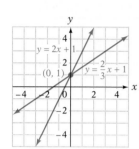

The graphs of $y = \frac{2}{3}x + 1$ and $y = 2x + 1$ are shown at the left. Each graph crosses the y-axis at $(0, 1)$, but the graphs have different slants. The **slope** of a line is a measure of the slant of the line. The symbol for slope is m.

The slope of a line is the ratio of the change in the y-coordinates between any two points on the line to the change in the x-coordinates.

The line containing the points whose coordinates are $(-2, -3)$ and $(6, 1)$ is graphed at the right. The change in y is the difference between the two y-coordinates.

Change in $y = 1 - (-3) = 4$

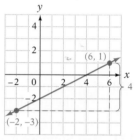

The change in x is the difference between the two x-coordinates.

Change in $x = 6 - (-2) = 8$

Take Note

The change in the y values can be thought of as the *rise* of the line, and the change in the x values can be thought of as the *run*. Then

slope $= m = \dfrac{\text{rise}}{\text{run}}$.

$$m = \frac{\text{rise}}{\text{run}}$$

For the line containing the points whose coordinates are $(-2, -3)$ and $(6, 1)$,

$$\text{Slope} = m = \frac{\text{change in } y}{\text{change in } x} = \frac{4}{8} = \frac{1}{2}$$

The slope of the line can also be described as the ratio of the vertical change (4 units) to the horizontal change (8 units) from the point whose coordinates are $(-2, -3)$ to the point whose coordinates are $(6, 1)$.

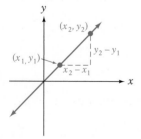

Slope Formula

The slope of a line containing two points P_1 and P_2, whose coordinates are (x_1, y_1) and (x_2, y_2), is given by

$$\text{Slope} = m = \frac{y_2 - y_1}{x_2 - x_1}, \; x_1 \neq x_2$$

In the slope formula, the points P_1 and P_2 are any two points on the line. The slope of a line is constant; therefore, the slope calculated using any two points on the line will be the same.

In Section 1, Objective 3 of this chapter, we calculated the average rate of change in the U.S. population for different intervals of time. In each case, the average rate of change was different. Note that the graph of the population data did not lie on a straight line.

The graph of an equation of the form $y = mx + b$ is a straight line, and the average rate of change is constant. We can calculate the average rate of change between any two points on the line and it will always be the same. For a linear equation, the rate of change is referred to as slope.

Find the slope of the line containing the points whose coordinates are $(-1, 1)$ and $(2, 3)$.

Let $P_1 = (-1, 1)$ and $P_2 = (2, 3)$. Then $x_1 = -1$, $y_1 = 1$, $x_2 = 2$, and $y_2 = 3$.

$$m = \frac{y_2 - y_1}{x_2 - x_1} = \frac{3 - 1}{2 - (-1)} = \frac{2}{3}$$

It does not matter which point is named P_1 and which P_2; the slope of the line will be the same. If the points are reversed, then $P_1 = (2, 3)$ and $P_2 = (-1, 1)$.

$$m = \frac{y_2 - y_1}{x_2 - x_1} = \frac{1 - 3}{-1 - 2} = \frac{-2}{-3} = \frac{2}{3}$$

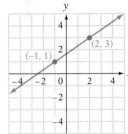

Positive slope

This is the same result. Here the slope is a positive number. A line that slants upward to the right has a **positive slope.**

Take Note

Positive slope means that the value of y increases as the value of x increases.

Find the slope of the line containing the points whose coordinates are $(-3, 4)$ and $(2, -2)$.

Let $P_1 = (-3, 4)$ and $P_2 = (2, -2)$.

$$m = \frac{y_2 - y_1}{x_2 - x_1} = \frac{-2 - 4}{2 - (-3)} = \frac{-6}{5} = -\frac{6}{5}$$

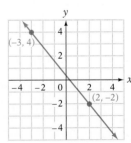

Negative slope

Take Note

Negative slope means that the value of y decreases as the value of x increases. Compare this to positive slope.

Here the slope is a negative number. A line that slants downward to the right has a **negative slope.**

Find the slope of the line containing the points whose coordinates are $(-1, 3)$ and $(4, 3)$.

Let $P_1 = (-1, 3)$ and $P_2 = (4, 3)$.

$$m = \frac{y_2 - y_1}{x_2 - x_1} = \frac{3 - 3}{4 - (-1)} = \frac{0}{5} = 0$$

Zero slope

When $y_1 = y_2$, the graph is a horizontal line. A horizontal line has **zero slope.**

Find the slope of the line containing the points whose coordinates are $(2, -2)$ and $(2, 4)$.

Let $P_1 = (2, -2)$ and $P_2 = (2, 4)$.

$$m = \frac{y_2 - y_1}{x_2 - x_1} = \frac{4 - (-2)}{2 - 2} = \frac{6}{0} \leftarrow \begin{array}{l}\text{Not a real}\\\text{number}\end{array}$$

Undefined slope

When $x_1 = x_2$, the denominator of $\frac{y_2 - y_1}{x_2 - x_1}$ is 0 and the graph is a vertical line. Because division by zero is not defined, the slope of the line is not defined. The slope of a vertical line is **undefined.**

EXAMPLE 1   Find the slope of the line containing the points P_1 and P_2.

A. $P_1(-2, -1)$, $P_2(3, 4)$ **B.** $P_1(-3, 1)$, $P_2(2, -2)$
C. $P_1(-1, 4)$, $P_2(-1, 0)$ **D.** $P_1(-1, 2)$, $P_2(4, 2)$

Solution   **A.** $m = \dfrac{y_2 - y_1}{x_2 - x_1} = \dfrac{4 - (-1)}{3 - (-2)} = \dfrac{5}{5} = 1$

The slope is 1.

B. $m = \dfrac{y_2 - y_1}{x_2 - x_1} = \dfrac{-2 - 1}{2 - (-3)} = \dfrac{-3}{5}$

The slope is $-\dfrac{3}{5}$.

C. $m = \dfrac{y_2 - y_1}{x_2 - x_1} = \dfrac{0 - 4}{-1 - (-1)} = \dfrac{-4}{0}$

The slope is undefined.

D. $m = \dfrac{y_2 - y_1}{x_2 - x_1} = \dfrac{2 - 2}{4 - (-1)} = \dfrac{0}{5} = 0$

The slope is 0.

PROBLEM 1   Find the slope of the line containing the points P_1 and P_2.

A. $P_1(-1, 2), P_2(1, 3)$ **B.** $P_1(1, 2), P_2(4, -5)$

C. $P_1(2, 3), P_2(2, 7)$ **D.** $P_1(1, -3), P_2(-5, -3)$

Solution   See page S12.

Two lines in the rectangular coordinate system that never intersect are called **parallel lines.** The lines l_1 and l_2 graphed at the right are parallel lines. Calculating the slope of each line, we have

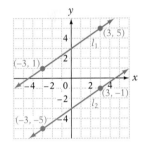

$$\text{Slope of } l_1 = \dfrac{y_2 - y_1}{x_2 - x_1} = \dfrac{5 - 1}{3 - (-3)} = \dfrac{4}{6} = \dfrac{2}{3}$$

$$\text{Slope of } l_2 = \dfrac{y_2 - y_1}{x_2 - x_1} = \dfrac{-1 - (-5)}{3 - (-3)} = \dfrac{4}{6} = \dfrac{2}{3}$$

Note that these parallel lines have the same slope. This is true of all parallel lines.

Take Note

We must distinguish between vertical and nonvertical lines in the description of parallel lines at the right because vertical lines in the rectangular coordinate system are parallel, but their slopes are undefined.

Parallel Lines

Two nonvertical lines in the rectangular coordinate system are parallel if and only if they have the same slope. Any two vertical lines in the rectangular coordinate system are parallel lines.

EXAMPLE 2   Is the line containing the points $(-2, 1)$ and $(-5, -1)$ parallel to the line that contains the points $(1, 0)$ and $(4, 2)$?

Solution   Find the slope of the line through $(-2, 1)$ and $(-5, -1)$.

$$\dfrac{y_2 - y_1}{x_2 - x_1} = \dfrac{-1 - 1}{-5 - (-2)} = \dfrac{-2}{-3} = \dfrac{2}{3}$$

Find the slope of the line through $(1, 0)$ and $(4, 2)$.

$$\dfrac{y_2 - y_1}{x_2 - x_1} = \dfrac{2 - 0}{4 - 1} = \dfrac{2}{3}$$

The slopes are equal.
The lines are parallel.

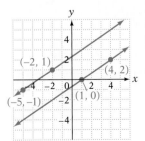

> **PROBLEM 2**   Is the line containing the points $(-2, -3)$ and $(7, 1)$ parallel to the line that contains the points $(1, 4)$ and $(-5, 6)$?
>
> **Solution**   See page S12.

There are many applications of the concept of slope. Here is one example.

 When Florence Griffith-Joyner set the world record for the 100-meter dash, her rate of speed was approximately 9.5 m/s. The graph at the right shows the distance she ran during her record-setting run. From the graph, note that after 4 s she had traveled 38 m and that after 6 s she had traveled 57 m. The slope of the line between these two points is

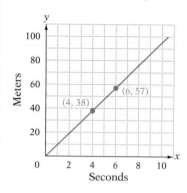

$$m = \frac{57 - 38}{6 - 4} = \frac{19}{2} = 9.5$$

Note that the slope of the line is the same as the rate at which she was running, 9.5 m/s. The average speed of an object is related to slope.

EXAMPLE 3   The graph at the right shows the height of a plane above an airport during its 30-minute descent from cruising altitude to landing. Find the slope of the line. Write a sentence that explains the meaning of the slope.

Solution $m = \dfrac{y_2 - y_1}{x_2 - x_1}$

$$= \frac{5000 - 20{,}000}{25 - 10} = \frac{-15{,}000}{15} = -1000$$

A slope of -1000 means that the height of the plane is *decreasing* at the rate of 1000 ft per minute.

PROBLEM 3   The graph at the right shows the decline in the value of a used car over a five-year period. Find the slope of the line. Write a sentence that states the meaning of the slope.

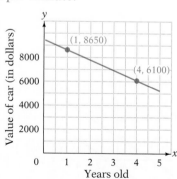

Solution   See page S13.

OBJECTIVE **2** **Graph a line using the slope and y-intercept**

Recall that we can find the y-intercept of a linear equation by letting $x = 0$.
To find the y-intercept of $y = 3x + 4$, let $x = 0$.

$$y = 3x + 4$$
$$y = 3(0) + 4$$
$$y = 4$$

The y-intercept is (0, 4).

The constant term of $y = 3x + 4$ is the y-coordinate of the y-intercept.

In general, for any equation of the form $y = mx + b$, the y-intercept is $(0, b)$.

The graph of the equation $y = \frac{2}{3}x + 1$ is shown at

the right. The points whose coordinates are
$(-3, -1)$ and $(3, 3)$ are on the graph. The slope of
the line is

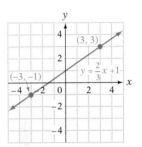

$$m = \frac{3 - (-1)}{3 - (-3)} = \frac{4}{6} = \frac{2}{3}$$

Note that the slope of the line has the same value as
the coefficient of x.

Slope-Intercept Form of a Straight Line

For any equation of the form **$y = mx + b$,** the slope of the line is m, the
coefficient of x. The y-intercept is **$(0, b)$**. The equation

$$y = mx + b$$

is called the **slope-intercept form of a straight line.**

The slope of the graph of $y = -\frac{3}{4}x + 1$ is $-\frac{3}{4}$. The y-intercept is (0, 1).

$$y = \boxed{m}\, x + \boxed{b}$$
$$y = \boxed{-\frac{3}{4}}\, x + \boxed{1}$$

Slope $= m = -\dfrac{3}{4}$ ———↑   ↑—y-intercept $= (0, b) = (0, 1)$

Find the slope and y-intercept of the graph of $y = \frac{5}{2}x - 6$.

Slope $= m = \dfrac{5}{2}$ $b = -6$

The slope is $\dfrac{5}{2}$.   The y-intercept is $(0, -6)$.

When the equation of a straight line is in the form $y = mx + b$, the graph can be
drawn using the slope and y-intercept. First locate the y-intercept. Use the slope
to find a second point on the line. Then draw a line through the two points.

Graph $y = 2x - 3$ by using the slope and y-intercept.

y-intercept $= (0, b) = (0, -3)$

$$m = 2 = \frac{2}{1} = \frac{\text{change in } y}{\text{change in } x}$$

Beginning at the y-intercept, move right 1 unit (change in x) and then up 2 units (change in y).

$(1, -1)$ are the coordinates of a second point on the graph.

Draw a line through $(0, -3)$ and $(1, -1)$.

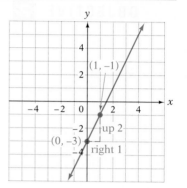

Using a graphing utility, enter the equation $y = 2x - 3$ and verify the graph shown above. Trace along the graph and verify that $(0, -3)$ is the y-intercept and that the point whose coordinates are $(1, -1)$ is on the graph.

EXAMPLE 4   Graph $y = -\frac{2}{3}x + 1$ by using the slope and y-intercept.

Solution y-intercept $= (0, b) = (0, 1)$

$$m = -\frac{2}{3} = \frac{-2}{3}$$

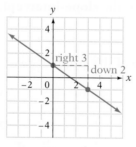

- A slope of $\frac{-2}{3}$ means to move right 3 units and then down 2 units.

PROBLEM 4   Graph $y = -\frac{1}{4}x - 1$ by using the slope and y-intercept.

Solution   See page S13.

EXAMPLE 5   Graph $2x - 3y = 6$ by using the slope and y-intercept.

Solution $2x - 3y = 6$

$$-3y = -2x + 6$$ • Solve the equation for y.

$$y = \frac{2}{3}x - 2$$

y-intercept $= (0, -2)$

$$m = \frac{2}{3}$$

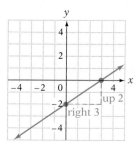

PROBLEM 5   Graph $x - 2y = 4$ by using the slope and y-intercept.

Solution   See page S13.

5.3   Concept Review

Determine whether the statement is always true, sometimes true, or never true.

1. In the equation $y = mx + b$, m is the symbol for slope.

2. The formula for slope is $m = \dfrac{y_2 - y_1}{x_2 - x_1}$.

3. A vertical line has zero slope, and the slope of a horizontal line is undefined.

4. Any two points on a line can be used to find the slope of the line.

5. Shown at the right is the graph of a line with negative slope.

6. The y-intercept of the graph of the equation $y = -2x + 5$ is $(5, 0)$.

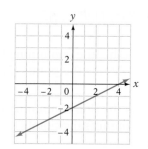

5.3   Exercises

1   Find the slope of a straight line

1.   Explain how to find the slope of a line when you know two points on the line.

2.   What is the difference between a line that has zero slope and a line whose slope is undefined?

3. Identify each x value and each y value to insert in the slope formula $m = \dfrac{y_2 - y_1}{x_2 - x_1}$ to find the slope of the line containing $P_1(1, -4)$ and $P_2(3, 2)$.

$y_2 = $ ___?___; $y_1 = $ ___?___; $x_2 = $ ___?___; $x_1 = $ ___?___

4. The slope of the line containing $P_1(-4, 3)$ and $P_2(1, -3)$ is $m = \dfrac{-3 - ?}{1 - (?)}$ = ___?___. Does this line slant downward to the right or upward to the right?

Find the slope of the line containing the points P_1 and P_2.

5. $P_1(4, 2)$, $P_2(3, 4)$

6. $P_1(2, 1)$, $P_2(3, 4)$

7. $P_1(-1, 3)$, $P_2(2, 4)$

8. $P_1(-2, 1)$, $P_2(2, 2)$

9. $P_1(2, 4)$, $P_2(4, -1)$

10. $P_1(1, 3)$, $P_2(5, -3)$

11. $P_1(-2, 3)$, $P_2(2, 1)$

12. $P_1(5, -2)$, $P_2(1, 0)$

13. $P_1(8, -3)$, $P_2(4, 1)$

14. $P_1(0, 3)$, $P_2(2, -1)$

15. $P_1(3, -4)$, $P_2(3, 5)$

16. $P_1(-1, 2)$, $P_2(-1, 3)$

17. $P_1(4, -2)$, $P_2(3, -2)$

18. $P_1(5, 1)$, $P_2(-2, 1)$

19. $P_1(0, -1)$, $P_2(3, -2)$

20. $P_1(3, 0)$, $P_2(2, -1)$

21. $P_1(-2, 3)$, $P_2(1, 3)$

22. $P_1(4, -1)$, $P_2(-3, -1)$

23. $P_1(-2, 4)$, $P_2(-1, -1)$

24. $P_1(6, -4)$, $P_2(4, -2)$

25. $P_1(-2, -3)$, $P_2(-2, 1)$

26. $P_1(5, 1)$, $P_2(5, -2)$

27. $P_1(-1, 5)$, $P_2(5, 1)$

28. $P_1(-1, 5)$, $P_2(7, 1)$

29. Is the line containing the points $(-4, 2)$ and $(1, 6)$ parallel to the line that contains the points $(2, -4)$ and $(7, 0)$?

30. Is the line containing the points $(-5, 0)$ and $(0, 2)$ parallel to the line that contains the points $(5, 1)$ and $(0, -1)$?

31. Is the line containing the points $(-2, -3)$ and $(7, 1)$ parallel to the line that contains the points $(6, -5)$ and $(4, 1)$?

32. Is the line containing the points $(4, -3)$ and $(2, 5)$ parallel to the line that contains the points $(-2, -3)$ and $(-4, 1)$?

33. **Postal Service** The graph at the right shows the work accomplished by an electronic mail sorter. Find the slope of the line. Write a sentence that explains the meaning of the slope.

34. Health The graph at the right shows the relationship between distance walked and calories burned. Find the slope of the line. Write a sentence that explains the meaning of the slope.

35. Fuel Consumption The graph at the right shows how the amount of gasoline in the tank of a car decreases as the car is driven at a constant speed of 60 mph. Find the slope of the line. Write a sentence that states the meaning of the slope.

36. Computer Science The graph at the right shows the relationship between time and the number of kilobytes of a file remaining to be downloaded. Find the slope of the line. Write a sentence that states the meaning of the slope.

37. Let l be a line passing through points (a, b) and (c, d).
  a. Describe any relationship(s) that must exist between the numbers a, b, c, and d in order for the slope of l to be undefined.
  b. Describe any relationship(s) that must exist between the numbers a, b, c, and d in order for the slope of l to be 0.

  c. Suppose a, b, c, and d are all positive with $a > c$ and $d > b$. Does l slant upward to the right or downward to the right?

38. Line l passes through the point $(-2, 4)$ and is parallel to the line that passes through the points $(-4, 1)$ and $(0, 3)$.
  a. Which quadrants does line l pass through?
  b. Are there any points (a, b) on the line l for which both a and b are negative?

2 Graph a line using the slope and *y*-intercept

39. The slope of the line with equation $y = 5x - 3$ is ____?____, and its *y*-intercept is ____?____.

40. Why is an equation of the form $y = mx + b$ said to be in slope-intercept form?

Graph by using the slope and y-intercept.

41. $y = 3x + 1$

42. $y = -2x - 1$

43. $y = \dfrac{2}{5}x - 2$

44. $y = \dfrac{3}{4}x + 1$

45. $2x + y = 3$

46. $3x - y = 1$

47. $x - 2y = 4$

48. $x + 3y = 6$

49. $y = \dfrac{2}{3}x$

50. $y = \dfrac{1}{2}x$

51. $y = -x + 1$

52. $y = -x - 3$

53. $3x - 4y = 12$

54. $5x - 2y = 10$

55. $y = -4x + 2$

56. $y = 5x - 2$

57. $4x - 5y = 20$

58. $x - 3y = 6$

59. Suppose A, B, and C are all positive numbers. Does the y-intercept of the graph of $Ax + By = C$ lie above or below the x-axis? Does the graph slant upward to the right or downward to the right?

60. Suppose A is a negative number, and B and C are positive numbers. Does the y-intercept of the graph of $Ax + By = C$ lie above or below the x-axis? Does the graph slant upward to the right or downward to the right?

5.3 Applying Concepts

61. What effect does increasing the coefficient of x have on the graph of $y = mx + b$, $m > 0$?

62. What effect does decreasing the coefficient of x have on the graph of $y = mx + b$, $m > 0$?

63. What effect does increasing the constant term have on the graph of $y = mx + b$?

64. What effect does decreasing the constant term have on the graph of $y = mx + b$?

65. Match each equation with its graph.

i. $y = -2x + 4$

ii. $y = 2x - 4$

iii. $y = 2$

iv. $2x + 4y = 0$

v. $y = \dfrac{1}{2}x + 4$

vi. $y = -\dfrac{1}{4}x - 2$

A.

B.

C.

D.

E.

F.

66. Which of the graphs shows a constant rate of change?

a.

b.

c.

d.

67. Do the graphs of all straight lines have a y-intercept? If not, give an example of one that does not.

68. If two lines have the same slope and the same y-intercept, must the graphs of the lines be the same? If not, give an example.

69. What does the highway sign shown at the right have to do with slope?

5.4 Equations of Straight Lines

OBJECTIVE 1   **Find the equation of a line using the equation $y = mx + b$**

When the slope of a line and a point on the line are known, the equation of the line can be written using the slope-intercept form, $y = mx + b$. In the first example shown below, the known point is the y-intercept. In the second example, the known point is a point other than the y-intercept.

Find the equation of the line that has slope 3 and y-intercept $(0, 2)$.

$$y = mx + b$$

The given slope, 3, is m. Replace m with 3.

$$y = 3x + b$$

The given point, $(0, 2)$, is the y-intercept. Replace b with 2.

$$y = 3x + 2$$

The equation of the line that has slope 3 and y-intercept $(0, 2)$ is $y = 3x + 2$.

Find the equation of the line that has slope $\frac{1}{2}$ and contains the point whose coordinates are $(-2, 4)$.

$$y = mx + b$$

The given slope, $\frac{1}{2}$, is m. Replace m with $\frac{1}{2}$.

$$y = \frac{1}{2}x + b$$

The given point, $(-2, 4)$, is a solution of the equation of the line. Replace x and y in the equation with the coordinates of the point.

$$4 = \frac{1}{2}(-2) + b$$

Solve for b, the y-intercept.

$$4 = -1 + b$$
$$5 = b$$

Write the equation of the line by replacing m and b in the equation by their values.

$$y = mx + b$$
$$y = \frac{1}{2}x + 5$$

The equation of the line that has slope $\frac{1}{2}$ and contains the point whose coordinates are $(-2, 4)$ is $y = \frac{1}{2}x + 5$.

Take Note

Every ordered pair is of the form (x, y). For the point $(-2, 4)$, -2 is the x value and 4 is the y value. Substitute -2 for x and 4 for y.

EXAMPLE 1   Find the equation of the line that contains the point whose coordinates are $(3, -3)$ and has slope $\frac{2}{3}$.

Solution $y = mx + b$

$y = \dfrac{2}{3}x + b$ • **Replace _m_ with the given slope.**

$-3 = \dfrac{2}{3}(3) + b$ • **Replace _x_ and _y_ in the equation with the coordinates of the given point.**

$-3 = 2 + b$ • **Solve for _b_.**

$-5 = b$

$y = \dfrac{2}{3}x - 5$ • **Write the equation of the line by replacing _m_ and _b_ in _y = mx + b_ by their values.**

PROBLEM 1   Find the equation of the line that contains the point whose coordinates are $(4, -2)$ and has slope $\dfrac{3}{2}$.

Solution   See page S13.

OBJECTIVE 2   **Find the equation of a line using the point-slope formula**

An alternative method for finding the equation of a line, given the slope and the coordinates of a point on the line, involves use of the point-slope formula. The point-slope formula is derived from the formula for slope.

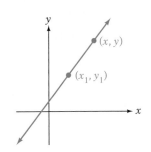

Let (x_1, y_1) be the coordinates of the given point on the line, and let (x, y) be the coordinates of any other point on the line. Use the formula for slope.

$$\dfrac{y - y_1}{x - x_1} = m$$

Multiply both sides of the equation by $(x - x_1)$.

$$\dfrac{y - y_1}{x - x_1}(x - x_1) = m(x - x_1)$$

Simplify.

$$y - y_1 = m(x - x_1)$$

Point-Slope Formula

The equation of the line that has slope m and contains the point whose coordinates are (x_1, y_1) can be found by the point-slope formula:

$$\boldsymbol{y - y_1 = m(x - x_1)}$$

EXAMPLE 2   Use the point-slope formula to find the equation of a line that passes through the point whose coordinates are $(-2, -1)$ and has slope $\dfrac{3}{2}$.

Solution $(x_1, y_1) = (-2, -1)$ • **Let (x_1, y_1) be the given point.**

$m = \dfrac{3}{2}$ • **_m_ is the given slope.**

$$y - y_1 = m(x - x_1)$$

• This is the point-slope formula.

$$y - (-1) = \frac{3}{2}[x - (-2)]$$

• Substitute -2 for x_1, -1 for y_1, and $\frac{3}{2}$ for m.

$$y + 1 = \frac{3}{2}(x + 2)$$

• Rewrite the equation in the form $y = mx + b$.

$$y + 1 = \frac{3}{2}x + 3$$

$$y = \frac{3}{2}x + 2$$

PROBLEM 2   Use the point-slope formula to find the equation of a line that passes through the point whose coordinates are (5, 4) and has slope $\frac{2}{5}$.

■   **Solution**   See page S13.

OBJECTIVE 3   **Find the equation of a line given two points**

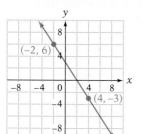

The line that passes through the points whose coordinates are $(-2, 6)$ and $(4, -3)$ is shown at the left. We can find the equation of this line as follows.

Use the slope formula with $(x_1, y_1) = (-2, 6)$ and $(x_2, y_2) = (4, -3)$ to find the slope of the line between the two points.

$$m = \frac{y_2 - y_1}{x_2 - x_1} = \frac{-3 - 6}{4 - (-2)} = \frac{-9}{6} = -\frac{3}{2}$$

The slope of the line is $-\frac{3}{2}$.

Now use the point-slope formula with $m = -\frac{3}{2}$ and $(x_1, y_1) = (-2, 6)$.

$$y - y_1 = m(x - x_1)$$

• Use the point-slope formula.

$$y - 6 = -\frac{3}{2}[x - (-2)]$$

• $m = -\frac{3}{2}$; $(x_1, y_1) = (-2, 6)$

$$y - 6 = -\frac{3}{2}(x + 2)$$

$$y - 6 = -\frac{3}{2}x - 3$$

• Use the Distributive Property.

$$y = -\frac{3}{2}x + 3$$

• Write in slope-intercept form.

Check: You can check that this is the correct equation by substituting $(-2, 6)$ and $(4, -3)$ into the equation, as shown on the next page.

Take Note

We could have used $(4, -3)$ for (x_1, y_1) instead of $(-2, 6)$. The result would have been the same.

$$y - y_1 = m(x - x_1)$$

$$y - (-3) = -\frac{3}{2}(x - 4)$$

$$y + 3 = -\frac{3}{2}x + 6$$

$$y = -\frac{3}{2}x + 3$$

$$y = -\frac{3}{2}x + 3$$

6	$-\frac{3}{2}(-2) + 3$	• $(x, y) = (-2, 6)$
6	$3 + 3$	
$6 = 6$	$\checkmark$	

$$y = -\frac{3}{2}x + 3$$

-3	$-\frac{3}{2}(4) + 3$	• $(x, y) = (4, -3)$
-3	$-6 + 3$	
$-3 = -3$	$\checkmark$	

The equation of the line is $y = -\frac{3}{2}x + 3$.

EXAMPLE 3   Find the equation of the line that passes through the points whose coordinates are $(-4, -5)$ and $(8, 4)$.

Solution   Find the slope of the line between the two points.

$$m = \frac{y_2 - y_1}{x_2 - x_1} = \frac{4 - (-5)}{8 - (-4)} = \frac{9}{12} = \frac{3}{4} \qquad \text{• Let } (x_1, y_1) = (-4, -5) \text{ and } (x_2, y_2) = (8, 4).$$

$$y - y_1 = m(x - x_1) \qquad \text{• Use the point-slope formula.}$$

$$y - (-5) = \frac{3}{4}[x - (-4)] \qquad \text{• } m = \frac{3}{4}; (x_1, y_1) = (-4, -5)$$

$$y + 5 = \frac{3}{4}(x + 4)$$

$$y + 5 = \frac{3}{4}x + 3 \qquad \text{• Use the Distributive Property.}$$

$$y = \frac{3}{4}x - 2 \qquad \text{• Write in slope-intercept form.}$$

The equation of the line is $y = \frac{3}{4}x - 2$.

PROBLEM 3   Find the equation of the line that passes through the points whose coordinates are $(-3, -9)$ and $(1, -1)$.

Solution   See page S13.

If the two given points lie on a horizontal line, the procedure above can be used to find the equation of the line. However, it is quicker to just remember that the equation of a horizontal line is $y = b$, where b is the y-intercept of the graph of the line. This is the y-coordinate of each of the two given points.

Find the equation of the line that passes through the points whose coordinates are $(-4, -2)$ and $(2, -2)$.

The y-coordinates of the two points are the same. The points lie on a horizontal line. The equation of the line is $y = b$, where b is the y-intercept of the graph of the line. The equation of the line is $y = -2$.

If the two given points lie on a vertical line, the procedure above cannot be used to find the equation of the line. In this case, remember that the equation of a vertical line is $x = a$, where a is the x-intercept of the graph of the line. This is the x-coordinate of each of the two given points.

Find the equation of the line that passes through the points whose coordinates are (3, 4) and (3, −5).

The x-coordinates of the two points are the same. The points lie on a vertical line. The equation of the line is $x = a$, where a is the x-intercept of the graph of the line. The equation of the line is $x = 3$.

5.4 Concept Review

Determine whether the statement is always true, sometimes true, or never true.

1. The graph of the equation $y = 5x + 7$ has slope 5 and y-intercept (0, 7).

2. If the equation of a line has y-intercept (0, 4), then 4 can be substituted for b in the equation $y = mx + b$.

3. Suppose the equation of a line contains the point (−3, 1). Then when y is −3, x is 1.

4. The point-slope formula is $y - y_1 = mx - x_1$.

5. The point-slope formula can be used to find the equation of a line with zero slope.

6. If it is stated that the y-intercept is 2, then the y-intercept is the point (2, 0).

5.4 Exercises

1 **Find the equation of a line using the equation $y = mx + b$**

1. In the equation of the line that has slope 3 and y-intercept (0, 1), $m = $ ____?____ and $b = $ ____?____. The equation is $y = $ ____?____.

2. To find the equation of the line that contains the point whose coordinates are $(-4, 1)$ and has slope $\frac{3}{2}$, first use the given point and slope to find the y-intercept of the line:

$$y = mx + b$$ • **Write the slope-intercept form of the equation of a line.**

$$1 = \frac{3}{2}(-4) + b$$ • **Substitute** ____?____ **for y,** ____?____ **for m, and** ____?____ **for x.**

$$1 = \underline{\quad ? \quad} + b$$ • **Solve for b.**

$$\underline{\quad ? \quad} = b$$

The y-intercept of the line through $(-4, 1)$ that has slope $\frac{3}{2}$ is $(0, \underline{\quad ? \quad})$.

Use the slope-intercept form.

3. Find the equation of the line that contains the point whose coordinates are $(0, 2)$ and has slope 2.

4. Find the equation of the line that contains the point whose coordinates are $(0, -1)$ and has slope -2.

5. Find the equation of the line that contains the point whose coordinates are $(-1, 2)$ and has slope -3.

6. Find the equation of the line that contains the point whose coordinates are $(2, -3)$ and has slope 3.

7. Find the equation of the line that contains the point whose coordinates are $(3, 1)$ and has slope $\frac{1}{3}$.

8. Find the equation of the line that contains the point whose coordinates are $(-2, 3)$ and has slope $\frac{1}{2}$.

9. Find the equation of the line that contains the point whose coordinates are $(4, -2)$ and has slope $\frac{3}{4}$.

10. Find the equation of the line that contains the point whose coordinates are $(2, 3)$ and has slope $-\frac{1}{2}$.

11. Find the equation of the line that contains the point whose coordinates are $(5, -3)$ and has slope $-\frac{3}{5}$.

12. Find the equation of the line that contains the point whose coordinates are $(5, -1)$ and has slope $\frac{1}{5}$.

13. Find the equation of the line that contains the point whose coordinates are $(2, 3)$ and has slope $\frac{1}{4}$.

14. Find the equation of the line that contains the point whose coordinates are $(-1, 2)$ and has slope $-\frac{1}{2}$.

15. Find the equation of the line that contains the point whose coordinates are $(-3, -5)$ and has slope $-\frac{2}{3}$.

16. Find the equation of the line that contains the point whose coordinates are $(-4, 0)$ and has slope $\frac{5}{2}$.

2   **Find the equation of a line using the point-slope formula**

17. When is the point-slope formula used?

18. Explain the meaning of each variable in the point-slope formula.

Use the point-slope formula.

19. Find the equation of the line that passes through the point whose coordinates are $(1, -1)$ and has slope 2.

20. Find the equation of the line that passes through the point whose coordinates are $(2, 3)$ and has slope -1.

21. Find the equation of the line that passes through the point whose coordinates are $(-2, 1)$ and has slope -2.

22. Find the equation of the line that passes through the point whose coordinates are $(-1, -3)$ and has slope -3.

23. Find the equation of the line that passes through the point whose coordinates are $(0, 0)$ and has slope $\frac{2}{3}$.

24. Find the equation of the line that passes through the point whose coordinates are $(0, 0)$ and has slope $-\frac{1}{5}$.

25. Find the equation of the line that passes through the point whose coordinates are $(2, 3)$ and has slope $\frac{1}{2}$.

26. Find the equation of the line that passes through the point whose coordinates are $(3, -1)$ and has slope $\frac{2}{3}$.

27. Find the equation of the line that passes through the point whose coordinates are $(-4, 1)$ and has slope $-\frac{3}{4}$.

28. Find the equation of the line that passes through the point whose coordinates are $(-5, 0)$ and has slope $-\frac{1}{5}$.

29. Find the equation of the line that passes through the point whose coordinates are $(-2, 1)$ and has slope $\frac{3}{4}$.

30. Find the equation of the line that passes through the point whose coordinates are $(3, -2)$ and has slope $\frac{1}{6}$.

31. Find the equation of the line that passes through the point whose coordinates are $(-3, -5)$ and has slope $-\frac{4}{3}$.

32. Find the equation of the line that passes through the point whose coordinates are $(3, -1)$ and has slope $\frac{3}{5}$.

33. **a.** Use the point-slope formula to find the equation of the line with slope m and y-intercept $(0, b)$.
b. Does your answer to part a simplify to the slope-intercept form of a straight line with slope m and y-intercept $(0, b)$?

34. **a.** Use the point-slope formula to find the equation of the line that goes through the point $(5, 3)$ and has slope 0.
b. Does your answer to part a simplify to the equation of a horizontal line through $(0, b)$?

3   Find the equation of a line given two points

Find the equation of the line through the given points.

35. $(-2, -2)$ and $(1, 7)$ **36.** $(1, 5)$ and $(3, 9)$ **37.** $(-5, 1)$ and $(2, -6)$ **38.** $(-3, 9)$ and $(1, 1)$

39. $(5, -1)$ and $(-5, 11)$ **40.** $(-6, 12)$ and $(-4, 9)$ **41.** $(-10, -3)$ and $(5, -9)$ **42.** $(-6, -13)$ and $(6, -1)$

43. $(1, 5)$ and $(-6, 5)$ **44.** $(-3, -4)$ and $(5, -4)$ **45.** $(5, -1)$ and $(5, -7)$ **46.** $(-3, 6)$ and $(-3, 0)$

47. $(-20, -8)$ and $(5, 12)$ **48.** $(-6, 19)$ and $(2, 7)$ **49.** $(0, -2)$ and $(-6, 1)$ **50.** $(15, -9)$ and $(-20, 5)$

51. $(6, -11)$ and $(-3, 1)$ **52.** $(14, -1)$ and $(-7, -7)$ **53.** $(3, 6)$ and $(0, -3)$ **54.** $(5, 9)$ and $(-5, 3)$

55. $(-1, -3)$ and $(2, 6)$ **56.** $(-3, 6)$ and $(4, -8)$ **57.** $(3, -5)$ and $(3, 1)$ **58.** $(2, -1)$ and $(5, -1)$

59. Is it possible to find the equation of one line through three given points? Explain.

60. If $y = 2x - 3$ and (x_1, y_1) and (x_2, y_2) are the coordinates of two points on the graph of the line, what is the value of $\dfrac{y_2 - y_1}{x_2 - x_1}$?

5.4 **Applying Concepts**

Is there a linear equation that contains all the given ordered pairs? If there is, find the equation.

61. (5, 1), (4, 2), (0, 6)

62. (−2, −4), (0, −3), (4, −1)

63. (−1, −5), (2, 4), (0, 2)

64. (3, −1), (12, −4), (−6, 2)

The given ordered pairs are solutions of the same linear equation. Find n.

65. (0, 1), (4, 9), (3, n)

66. (2, 2), (−1, 5), (3, n)

67. (2, −2), (−2, −4), (4, n)

68. (1, −2), (−2, 4), (4, n)

Temperature The relationship between Celsius and Fahrenheit temperature can be given by a linear equation. Water freezes at 0°C or at 32°F. Water boils at 100°C or at 212°F.

69. Write a linear equation expressing Fahrenheit temperature in terms of Celsius temperature.

70. Graph the equation found in Exercise 69.

When researchers analyze data given in a table or in a scatter diagram, they may try to find the equation of a line that approximates the data. There are various methods that can be used to find this line. One of these is to choose two data points and find the equation of the line using those points.

71. **Population** The table at the right shows the projected population of the United States in millions. (*Source:* www.npg.org/popfacts.htm)
   a. Find the equation of the line between (2005, 295.9) and (2025, 353.1).

   b. Using the equation from part a, find the projected population of the United States in 2015.
   c. Find the absolute value of the difference between the answer to part b and the projected population for 2015 given in the table. This number is called the **absolute error.**

Year	Population (in millions)
2005	295.9
2010	310.6
2015	325.4
2020	339.6
2025	353.1
2030	366.0

72. **Salaries** The table at the right shows the median weekly salary of a union member for various years. (*Source:* www.bls.gov)
   a. Find the equation of the line between (2000, 696) and (2004, 781).

   b. What was the average annual rate of change in the median weekly salary for a union employee between 2000 and 2004?
   c. If the trend shown by the equation in part a were to continue, what would be the median weekly salary of a union worker in 2012?

Year	Weekly Salary (in dollars)
2000	696
2001	718
2002	740
2003	760
2004	781

5.5 Functions

OBJECTIVE 1   ## Introduction to functions

The definition of *set* given in the chapter "Prealgebra Review" stated that a set is a collection of objects. Recall that the objects in a set are called the elements of the set. The elements in a set can be anything.

The set of planets in our solar system is

{Mercury, Venus, Earth, Mars, Jupiter, Saturn, Uranus, Neptune, Pluto}

The set of colors in a rainbow is

{red, orange, yellow, green, blue, indigo, violet}

The objects in a set can be ordered pairs. When the elements in a set are ordered pairs, the set is called a relation. A **relation** is any set of ordered pairs.

The set {(1, 1), (2, 4), (3, 9), (4, 16), (5, 25)} is a relation. There are five elements in the set. The elements are the ordered pairs (1, 1), (2, 4), (3, 9), (4, 16), and (5, 25).

The following table shows the number of hours that each of eight students spent in the math lab during the week of the math midterm exam and the score that each of these students received on the math midterm.

Hours	2	3	4	4	5	6	6	7
Score	60	70	70	80	85	85	95	90

This information can be written as the relation

{(2, 60), (3, 70), (4, 70), (4, 80), (5, 85), (6, 85), (6, 95), (7, 90)}

where the first coordinate of each ordered pair is the hours spent in the math lab and the second coordinate is the score on the midterm exam.

The **domain** of a relation is the set of first coordinates of the ordered pairs. The **range** is the set of second coordinates of the ordered pairs. For the relation above,

Domain = {2, 3, 4, 5, 6, 7}   Range = {60, 70, 80, 85, 90, 95}

The **graph of a relation** is the graph of the ordered pairs that belong to the relation. The graph of the relation given above is shown at the left. The horizontal axis represents the domain (the hours spent in the math lab) and the vertical axis represents the range (the exam score).

A **function** is a special type of relation in which no two ordered pairs have the same first coordinate and different second coordinates. The relation above is not a function because the ordered pairs (4, 70) and (4, 80) have the same first coordinate and different second coordinates. The ordered pairs (6, 85) and (6, 95) also have the same first coordinate and different second coordinates.

The table at the right describes a grading scale that defines a relationship between a test score and a letter grade. Some of the ordered pairs in this relation are (38, F), (73, C), and (94, A).

Score	Letter Grade
90–100	A
80–89	B
70–79	C
60–69	D
0–59	F

This relation defines a function because no two ordered pairs can have the *same* first coordinate and *different* second coordinates. For instance, it is not possible to have an average of 73 paired with any grade other than C. Both (73, C) and (73, A) cannot be ordered pairs belonging to the function, or two students with the same score would receive different grades. Note that (81, B) and (88, B) are ordered pairs of this function. Ordered pairs of a function may have the same *second* coordinate paired with different *first* coordinates.

The domain of this function is $\{0, 1, 2, 3, \ldots, 98, 99, 100\}$.

The range of this function is $\{A, B, C, D, F\}$.

EXAMPLE 1   Find the domain and range of the relation $\{(-5, 1), (-3, 3), (-1, 5)\}$. Is the relation a function?

Solution   The domain is $\{-5, -3, -1\}$.
- **The domain of the relation is the set of the first components of the ordered pairs.**

The range is $\{1, 3, 5\}$.
- **The range of the relation is the set of the second components of the ordered pairs.**

No two ordered pairs have the same first coordinate. The relation is a function.

PROBLEM 1   Find the domain and range of the relation $\{(1, 0), (1, 1), (1, 2), (1, 3), (1, 4)\}$. Is the relation a function?

Solution   See page S13.

Although a function can be described in terms of ordered pairs or in a table, functions are often described by an equation. The letter f is commonly used to represent a function, but any letter can be used.

The "square" function assigns to each real number its square. The square function is described by the equation

$$f(x) = x^2 \qquad \text{read } f(x) \text{ as "}f \text{ of } x\text{" or "the value of } f \text{ at } x.\text{"}$$

$f(x)$ is the symbol for the number that is paired with x. In terms of ordered pairs, this is written $(x, f(x))$. $f(x)$ is the **value of the function** at x because it is the result of evaluating the variable expression. For example, $f(4)$ means to replace x by 4 and then simplify the resulting numerical expression. This process is called **evaluating the function.**

The notation $f(4)$ is used to indicate the number that is paired with 4. To evaluate $f(x) = x^2$ at 4, replace x with 4 and simplify.

$$f(x) = x^2$$
$$f(4) = 4^2$$
$$f(4) = 16$$

The square function squares a number, and when 4 is squared, the result is 16. For the square function, the number 4 is paired with 16. In other words, when x is 4, $f(x)$ is 16. The ordered pair $(4, 16)$ is an element of the function.

It is important to remember that $f(x)$ does not mean f times x. The letter f stands for the function, and $f(x)$ is the number that is paired with x.

EXAMPLE 2   Evaluate $f(x) = 2x - 4$ at $x = 3$. Write an ordered pair that is an element of the function.

Solution $f(x) = 2x - 4$
$f(3) = 2(3) - 4$ • $f(3)$ **is the number that is paired with 3.**
$f(3) = 6 - 4$ **Replace** x **by 3 and evaluate.**
$f(3) = 2$

The ordered pair (3, 2) is an element of the function.

PROBLEM 2   Evaluate $f(x) = -5x + 1$ at $x = 2$. Write an ordered pair that is an element of the function.

Solution   See page S13.

When a function is described by an equation and the domain is specified, the range of the function can be found by evaluating the function at each point of the domain.

EXAMPLE 3   Find the range of the function given by the equation $f(x) = -3x + 2$ if the domain is $\{-4, -2, 0, 2, 4\}$. Write five ordered pairs that belong to the function.

Solution $f(x) = -3x + 2$
$f(-4) = -3(-4) + 2 = 12 + 2 = 14$ • **Replace** x **by each**
$f(-2) = -3(-2) + 2 = 6 + 2 = 8$ **member of the**
$f(0) = -3(0) + 2 = 0 + 2 = 2$ **domain.**
$f(2) = -3(2) + 2 = -6 + 2 = -4$
$f(4) = -3(4) + 2 = -12 + 2 = -10$

The range is $\{-10, -4, 2, 8, 14\}$.

The ordered pairs (−4, 14), (−2, 8), (0, 2), (2, −4), and (4, −10) belong to the function.

PROBLEM 3   Find the range of the function given by the equation $f(x) = 4x - 3$ if the domain is $\{-5, -3, -1, 1\}$. Write four ordered pairs that belong to the function.

Solution   See page S13.

OBJECTIVE 2   Graphs of linear functions

The solutions of the equation

$$y = 7x - 3$$

are ordered pairs (x, y). For example, the ordered pairs (−1, −10), (0, −3), and (1, 4) are solutions of the equation. Therefore, this equation defines a relation.

It is not possible to substitute one value of x into the equation $y = 7x - 3$ and get two different values of y. For example, the number 1 in the domain cannot be paired with any number other than 4 in the range. (*Remember:* A function cannot have ordered pairs in which the same first coordinate is paired with different second coordinates.) Therefore, the equation defines a function.

The equation $y = 7x - 3$ is an equation of the form $y = mx + b$. In general, any equation of the form $y = mx + b$ is a function.

In the equation $y = 7x - 3$, the variable y is called the **dependent variable** because its value *depends* on the value of x. The variable x is called the **independent variable.** We choose a value for x and substitute that value into the equation to determine the value of y. We say that y is a function of x.

When an equation defines y as a function of x, functional notation is frequently used to emphasize that the relation is a function. In this case, it is common to use the notation $f(x)$. Therefore, we can write the equation

$$y = 7x - 3$$

in functional notation as

$$f(x) = 7x - 3$$

> **Take Note**
>
> When y is a function of x, y and $f(x)$ are interchangeable.

The **graph of a function** is a graph of the ordered pairs (x, y) of the function. Because the graph of the equation $y = mx + b$ is a straight line, a function of the form $f(x) = mx + b$ is a **linear function.**

Graph: $f(x) = \dfrac{2}{3}x - 1$

Think of the function as the equation $y = \dfrac{2}{3}x - 1$.

This is the equation of a straight line.

The y-intercept is $(0, -1)$. The slope is $\dfrac{2}{3}$.

Graph the point $(0, -1)$. From the y-intercept, go right 3 units and then up 2 units. Graph the point $(3, 1)$.

Draw a line through the two points.

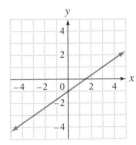

EXAMPLE 4   Graph: $f(x) = \dfrac{3}{4}x + 2$

Solution $f(x) = \dfrac{3}{4}x + 2$

$$y = \dfrac{3}{4}x + 2$$

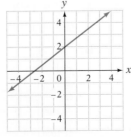

- **Think of the function as the equation $y = \dfrac{3}{4}x + 2$.**

- **The graph is a straight line with y-intercept $(0, 2)$ and slope $\dfrac{3}{4}$.**

PROBLEM 4   Graph: $f(x) = -\dfrac{1}{2}x - 3$

Solution   See page S14.

Graphing utilities are used to graph functions. Using a graphing utility, enter the equation $y = \frac{3}{4}x + 2$ and verify the graph drawn in Example 4.

Trace along the graph and verify that $(-4, -1)$, $(0, 2)$, and $(4, 5)$ are coordinates of points on the graph. Now enter the equation given in Problem 4 and verify the graph you drew.

There are a variety of applications of linear functions. For example, suppose an installer of marble kitchen countertops charges $250 plus $180 per foot of countertop. The equation that describes the total cost, C (in dollars), for having x feet of countertop installed is $C = 180x + 250$. In this situation, C is a function of x; the total cost depends on how many feet of countertop are installed. Therefore, we could rewrite the equation

$$C = 180x + 250$$

as the function

$$f(x) = 180x + 250$$

To graph this equation, we first choose a reasonable domain—for example, values of x between 0 and 25. It would not be reasonable to have $x \le 0$, because no one would order the installation of 0 ft of countertop, and any amount less than 0 would be a negative amount of countertop. The upper limit of 25 is chosen because most kitchens have less than 25 ft of countertop.

Choosing $x = 5$, 10, and 20 results in the ordered pairs $(5, 1150)$, $(10, 2050)$, and $(20, 3850)$. Graph these points and draw a line through them. The graph is shown at the left.

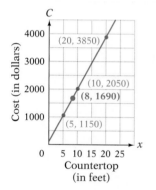

The point whose coordinates are $(8, 1690)$ is on the graph. This ordered pair can be interpreted to mean that 8 ft of countertop costs $1690 to install.

EXAMPLE 5 The value, V, of an investment of $2500 at an annual simple interest rate of 6% is given by the equation $V = 150t + 2500$, where t is the amount of time, in years, that the money is invested.

A. Write the equation in functional notation.

B. Graph the equation for values of t between 0 and 10.

C. The point whose coordinates are $(5, 3250)$ is on the graph. Write a sentence that explains the meaning of this ordered pair.

Solution   **A.** $V = 150t + 2500$

$f(t) = 150t + 2500$

• The value V of the investment depends on the amount of time t it is invested. The value V is a function of the time t.

B.

• Some ordered pairs of the function are $(2, 2800)$, $(4, 3100)$, and $(6, 3400)$.

C. The ordered pair (5, 3250) means that in 5 years the value of the investment will be $3250.

PROBLEM 5 A car is traveling at a uniform speed of 40 mph. The distance, d (in miles), the car travels in t hours is given by the equation $d = 40t$.

A. Write the equation in functional notation.

B. Use the coordinate axes at the right to graph this equation for values of t between 0 and 5.

C. The point whose coordinates are (3, 120) is on the graph. Write a sentence that explains the meaning of this ordered pair.

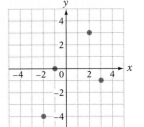

■ **Solution** See page S14.

5.5   Concept Review

Determine whether the statement is always true, sometimes true, or never true.

1. The graph shown at the right is the graph of a function.

2. For the relation graphed at the right, the domain is $\{-2, -1, 2, 3\}$.

3. The graph of the function $f(x) = -\frac{2}{3}x + 5$ has a positive slope.

4. The graphs of $y = \frac{1}{4}x - 6$ and $f(x) = \frac{1}{4}x - 6$ are identical.

5. The value of the function $\{(-3, 3), (-2, 2), (-1, 1), (0, 0)\}$ at -2 is 2.

6. A function can be represented in a table, by an equation, by a graph, or in a chart.

7. The graph of a function of the form $f(x) = mx + b$ is a straight line.

8. The equation $y = 7x - 1$ defines a function.

5.5   Exercises

1   Introduction to functions

1. A relation is a set of _____?_____. The set of first coordinates of the ordered pairs is called the _____?_____ of the relation. The set of second coordinates is called the _____?_____ of the relation.

2. **a.** The symbol $f(x)$ is read "f ___?___ x" or "the value of f ___?___ x." It is a symbol for the number that the function f pairs with ___?___.
   b. The symbol $f(3)$ is a symbol for the number that the function f pairs with ___?___.
   c. If $f(x) = 4x - 1$, then $f(3) = 4(\underline{}) - 1 = \underline{}$. This means that $(\underline{}, \underline{})$ is an ordered pair of the function f.

For Exercises 3 and 4 use the following sets. Set A is the set of all dates of the year ([January 1, January 2, January 3, . . .]). Set B is the set of all the people in the world.

3. A relation has domain A and range B. Each ordered pair in the relation is in the form (date, person born on that date). Is this relation a function?

4. A relation has domain B and range A. Each ordered pair in the relation is in the form (person, birth date of that person). Is this relation a function?

5. **Aviation** The table at the right shows the percent of on-time arrivals and on-time departures for selected U.S. airports. (*Source:* Federal Aviation Authority) Write a relation where the first coordinate is the percent of on-time arrivals and the second coordinate percent of on-time departures. Is the relation a function?

6. **Health** The table at the right shows the United States Department of Agriculture limit on saturated fat intake, in grams. Write a relation where the first coordinate is a person's daily Calorie intake and the second coordinate is the limit on saturated fat intake. Is the relation a function?

7. **Jogging** The table at the right shows the number of Calories a 150-pound person burns while running at various speeds, in miles per hour. Write a relation where the first coordinate is the speed of the runner and the second coordinate is the number Calories burned. Is the relation a function?

8. **Health** The table at the right shows the birth rate of various countries, in births per thousand, and life expectancy, in years. (*Source:* www.cia.gov) Write a relation where the first coordinate is the birth rate and the second coordinate is the life expectancy. Is the relation a function?

Percent On-time

Arrivals	Departures
87.7	91.0
71.4	84.0
79.1	84.5
90.1	91.6
82.5	94.3
68.4	74.5
82.5	80.2

Daily Calories	Saturated Fat (in grams)
1600	18
2000	20
2200	24
2500	25
2800	31

Speed (in mph)	Calories
4	411
5	514
6	618
7	720
8	823

Country	Birth Rate	Life Expectancy
Belgium	10.48	78.6
Brazil	16.8	71.7
Martinique	14.14	79.0
Mexico	21.0	75.2
Sweden	10.36	80.4
United States	14.14	77.7

9. ● Physics The speeds of a car in miles per hour and the distances, in feet, needed to stop at those speeds are recorded in the table at the right. (*Source:* AAA Foundation for Traffic Safety) Write a relation in which the first coordinate is the speed in miles per hour and the second coordinate is the distance needed to stop. Is the relation a function?

Speed (in miles per hour)	Distance Needed to Stop (in feet)
55	273
65	355
75	447
85	549

10. ● Biology The following table shows the length of the humerus (the long bone from the shoulder to the elbow), in centimeters, and the total wingspan, in centimeters, of several pterosaurs, which are extinct flying reptiles of the order Pterosauria. Write a relation in which the first coordinate is the length of the humerus and the second coordinate is the wingspan. Is the relation a function?

Length of humerus, in centimeters	24	32	22	15	4.4	17	15
Wingspan, in centimeters	600	750	430	300	68	370	310

Find the domain and range of the relation. State whether or not the relation is a function.

11. $\{(0, 0), (2, 0), (4, 0), (6, 0)\}$

12. $\{(-2, 2), (0, 2), (1, 2), (2, 2)\}$

13. $\{(2, 2), (2, 4), (2, 6), (2, 8)\}$

14. $\{(-4, 4), (-2, 2), (0, 0), (-2, -2)\}$

15. $\{(0, 0), (1, 1), (2, 2), (3, 3)\}$

16. $\{(0, 5), (1, 4), (2, 3), (3, 2), (4, 1), (5, 0)\}$

17. $\{(-2, -3), (2, 3), (-1, 2), (1, 2), (-3, 4), (3, 4)\}$

18. $\{(-1, 0), (0, -1), (1, 0), (2, 3), (3, 5)\}$

Evaluate the function at the given value of x. Write an ordered pair that is an element of the function.

19. $f(x) = 4x; x = 10$

20. $f(x) = 8x; x = 11$

21. $f(x) = x - 5; x = -6$

22. $f(x) = x + 7; x = -9$

23. $f(x) = 3x^2; x = -2$

24. $f(x) = x^2 - 1; x = -8$

25. $f(x) = 5x + 1; x = \dfrac{1}{2}$

26. $f(x) = 2x - 6; x = \dfrac{3}{4}$

27. $f(x) = \dfrac{2}{5}x + 4; x = -5$

28. $f(x) = \dfrac{3}{2}x - 5; x = 2$

29. $f(x) = 2x^2; x = -4$

30. $f(x) = 4x^2 + 2; x = -3$

Find the range of the function defined by the given equation. Write five ordered pairs that belong to the function.

31. $f(x) = 3x - 4$; domain $= \{-5, -3, -1, 1, 3\}$

32. $f(x) = 2x + 5$; domain $= \{-10, -5, 0, 5, 10\}$

33. $f(x) = \dfrac{1}{2}x + 3$; domain $= \{-4, -2, 0, 2, 4\}$

34. $f(x) = \dfrac{3}{4}x - 1$; domain $= \{-8, -4, 0, 4, 8\}$

35. $f(x) = x^2 + 6$; domain $= \{-3, -1, 0, 1, 3\}$

36. $f(x) = 3x^2 + 6$; domain $= \{-2, -1, 0, 1, 2\}$

2 Graphs of linear functions

37. In the linear equation $y = 5x - 9$, the independent variable is ___?___ and the dependent variable is ___?___. To write this equation in function notation, replace y with the symbol ___?___.

38. To graph the function $f(x) = \frac{1}{2}x + 4$, replace $f(x)$ with ___?___. This is the equation of a line with y-intercept ___?___ and slope ___?___.

Graph.

39. $f(x) = 5x$

40. $f(x) = -4x$

41. $f(x) = x + 2$

42. $f(x) = x - 3$

43. $f(x) = 6x - 1$

44. $f(x) = 3x + 4$

45. $f(x) = -2x + 3$

46. $f(x) = -5x - 2$

47. $f(x) = \frac{1}{3}x - 4$

48. $f(x) = \frac{3}{5}x + 1$

49. $f(x) = 4$

50. $f(x) = -3$

Graph using a graphing utility.

51. $f(x) = 2x - 1$

52. $f(x) = -3x - 1$

53. $f(x) = -\frac{1}{2}x + 1$

54. $f(x) = \dfrac{2}{3}x + 4$

55. $f(x) = \dfrac{3}{4}x + 1$

56. $f(x) = -\dfrac{1}{2}x - 2$

57. $f(x) = -\dfrac{4}{3}x + 5$

58. $f(x) = \dfrac{5}{2}x$

59. $f(x) = -1$

60. Let $f(x) = 7x + 10$. If m and n are positive numbers such that $m > n$, is $f(m) - f(n)$ positive or negative?

61. Can the equation of a vertical line be written in function notation?

62. **Depreciation** Depreciation is the declining value of an asset. For instance, a company purchases a truck for $20,000. The truck is an asset worth $20,000. In 5 years, however, the value of the truck will have declined, and it may be worth only $4000. An equation that represents this decline is $V = 20,000 - 3200x$, where V is the value, in dollars, of the truck after x years.
  a. Write the equation in functional notation.
  b. Use the coordinate axes at the right to graph the equation for values of x between 0 and 5.
  c. The point (4, 7200) is on the graph. Write a sentence that explains the meaning of this ordered pair.

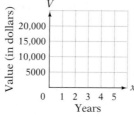

63. **Depreciation** A company uses the equation $V = 30,000 - 5000x$ to estimate the depreciated value, in dollars, of a computer. (See Exercise 62.)
  a. Write the equation in functional notation.
  b. Use the coordinate axes at the right to graph the equation for values of x between 0 and 5.
  c. The point (1, 25,000) is on the graph. Write a sentence that explains the meaning of this ordered pair.

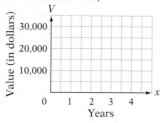

64. **Business** An architect charges a fee of $500 plus $2.65 per square foot to design a house. The equation that represents the architect's fee is given by $F = 2.65s + 500$, where F is the fee, in dollars, and s is the number of square feet in the house.
  a. Write the equation in functional notation.
  b. Use the coordinate axes at the right to graph the equation for values of s between 0 and 5000.
  c. The point (3500, 9775) is on the graph. Write a sentence that explains the meaning of this ordered pair.

65. **Business** A rental car company charges a "drop-off" fee of $50 to return a car to a location different than that from which it was rented. In addition, it charges a fee of $.18 per mile the car is driven. An equation that represents the total cost to rent a car from this company is $C = 0.18m + 50$, where C is the total cost, in dollars, and m is the number of miles the car is driven.

a. Write the equation in functional notation.

b. Use the coordinate axes at the right to graph the equation for values of m between 0 and 1000.

c. The point (500, 140) is on the graph. Write a sentence that explains the meaning of this ordered pair.

5.5 Applying Concepts

66. **a.** A function f consists of the ordered pairs $\{(-4, -6), (-2, -2), (0, 2), (2, 6), (4, 10)\}$. Find $f(2)$.

b. A function f consists of the ordered pairs $\{(0, 9), (1, 8), (2, 7), (3, 6), (4, 5)\}$. Find $f(1)$.

67. **Health** The average annual number of cigarettes smoked by an American adult for the years 1991 through 2000 is shown in the table at the right. (*Source:* USDA Economic Research Service Agricultural Outlook)

a. Do these data represent a function? Why or why not?

b. If the data represent a function, do they represent a linear function? Why or why not?

c. If the data represent a function, is the year a function of the number of cigarettes smoked, or is the number of cigarettes smoked a function of the year?

d. If you had to predict the average annual number of cigarettes smoked in 2001 on the basis of the information in the table, would you predict that it would be more or less than 2000? Explain your answer.

Year	Average Annual Number of Cigarettes Smoked
1991	2727
1992	2647
1993	2543
1994	2524
1995	2505
1996	2482
1997	2423
1998	2320
1999	2136
2000	2103

68. **Height-Time Graphs** A child's height is a function of the child's age. The graph of this function is not linear, because children go through growth spurts as they develop. However, for the graph to be reasonable, the function must be an increasing function (that is, as the age increases, the height increases), because children do not get shorter as they grow older. Match each function described below with a reasonable graph of the function.

a. The height of a plane above the ground during take-off depends on how long it has been since the plane left the gate.

b. The height of a football above the ground is related to the number of seconds that have passed since it was punted.

c. A basketball player is dribbling a basketball. The basketball's distance from the floor is related to the number of seconds that have passed since the player began dribbling the ball.

d. Two children are seated together on a roller coaster. The height of the children above the ground depends on how long they have been on the ride.

69.   Investigating a relationship between two variables is an important task in the application of mathematics. For example, botanists study the relationship between the number of bushels of wheat yielded per acre and the amount of watering per acre. Environmental scientists study the relationship between the incidence of skin cancer and the amount of ozone in the atmosphere. Business analysts study the relationship between the price of a product and the number of products that are sold at that price. Describe a relationship that is important to your major field of study.

70.   Functions are a part of our everyday lives. For example, the cost to mail a package via first-class mail is a function of the weight of the package. The tuition paid by a part-time student is a function of the number of credit hours the student registers for. Provide other examples of functions.

5.6 Graphing Linear Inequalities

OBJECTIVE **1**   **Graph inequalities in two variables**

Point of Interest

Linear inequalities play an important role in applied mathematics. They are used in a branch of mathematics called linear programming, which was developed during World War II to solve problems in supplying the Air Force with the machine parts necessary to keep planes flying. Today its applications have been broadened to many other disciplines.

The graph of the linear equation $y = x - 2$ separates a plane into three sets:

the set of points on the line

the set of points above the line

the set of points below the line

The point whose coordinates are $(3, 1)$ is a solution of $y = x - 2$.

$$\frac{y = x - 2}{1 \mid 3 - 2}$$
$$1 = 1$$

The point whose coordinates are $(3, 3)$ is a solution of $y > x - 2$.

$$\frac{y > x - 2}{3 \mid 3 - 2}$$
$$3 > 1$$

Any point above the line is a solution of $y > x - 2$.

The point whose coordinates are $(3, -1)$ is a solution of $y < x - 2$.

$$\frac{y < x - 2}{-1 \mid 3 - 2}$$
$$-1 < 1$$

Any point below the line is a solution of $y < x - 2$.

The solution set of $y = x - 2$ is all points on the line. The solution set of $y > x - 2$ is all points above the line. The solution set of $y < x - 2$ is all points below the line. The solution set of an inequality in two variables is a **half-plane.**

The following illustrates the procedure for graphing a linear inequality.

Graph the solution set of $2x + 3y \leq 6$.

Solve the inequality for y.

$$2x + 3y \leq 6$$
$$2x - 2x + 3y \leq -2x + 6$$
$$3y \leq -2x + 6$$
$$\frac{3y}{3} \leq \frac{-2x + 6}{3}$$
$$y \leq -\frac{2}{3}x + 2$$

Change the inequality to an equality and graph the line. If the inequality is $\geq$ or $\leq$, the line is in the solution set and is shown by a **solid line.** If the inequality is $>$ or $<$, the line is not a part of the solution set and is shown by a **dashed line.**

$$y = -\frac{2}{3}x + 2$$

If the inequality is in the form $y > mx + b$ or $y \geq mx + b$, shade the **upper half-plane.** If the inequality is in the form $y < mx + b$ or $y \leq mx + b$, shade the **lower half-plane.**

The equation $y \leq -\frac{2}{3}x + 2$ is in the form $y \leq mx + b$. Draw a solid line and shade the lower half-plane.

The inequality $2x + 3y \leq 6$ can also be graphed as shown below.

Graph the solution set of $2x + 3y \leq 6$.

Change the inequality to an equality.

$$2x + 3y = 6$$

Find the x- and y-intercepts of the equation. To find the x-intercept, let $y = 0$.

$$2x + 3(0) = 6$$
$$2x = 6$$
$$x = 3$$

The x-intercept is $(3, 0)$.

To find the y-intercept, let $x = 0$.

$$2(0) + 3y = 6$$
$$3y = 6$$
$$y = 2$$

The y-intercept is $(0, 2)$.

Graph the ordered pairs $(3, 0)$ and $(0, 2)$. Draw a solid line through the points because the inequality is $\leq$.

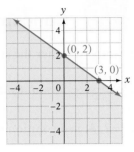

The point $(0, 0)$ can be used to determine which region to shade. If $(0, 0)$ is a solution of the inequality, then shade the region that includes the point $(0, 0)$.

If $(0, 0)$ is not a solution of the inequality, then shade the region that does not include the point $(0, 0)$. For this example, $(0, 0)$ is a solution of the inequality. The region that contains the point $(0, 0)$ is shaded.

$$2x + 3y \leq 6$$
$$2(0) + 3(0) \leq 6$$
$$0 \leq 6 \quad \text{True}$$

If the line passes through the point $(0, 0)$, another point must be used to determine which region to shade. For example, use the point $(1, 0)$.

Take Note

Any ordered pair is of the form (x, y). For the point $(0, 0)$, substitute 0 for x and 0 for y in the inequality.

It is important to note that every point in the shaded region is a solution of the inequality and that every solution of the inequality is a point in the shaded region. No point outside of the shaded region is a solution of the inequality.

EXAMPLE 1   Graph the solution set of $3x + y > -2$.

Solution

$$3x + y > -2$$
$$3x - 3x + y > -3x - 2 \qquad \text{• Solve the inequality for } y.$$
$$y > -3x - 2$$

• Graph $y = -3x - 2$ as a dashed line. Shade the upper half-plane.

PROBLEM 1   Graph the solution set of $x - 3y < 2$.

Solution   See page S14.

EXAMPLE 2   Graph the solution set of $y > 3$.

Solution

• The inequality is solved for y. Graph $y = 3$ as a dashed line. Shade the upper half-plane.

PROBLEM 2   Graph the solution set of $x < 3$.

Solution   See page S14.

5.6 Concept Review

Determine whether the statement is always true, sometimes true, or never true.

1. $y \geq \frac{1}{2}x - 5$ is an example of a linear equation in two variables.

2. $(-2, 4)$ is a solution of $y > x + 2$.

3. $(3, 0)$ is a solution of $y \leq x - 1$.

4. Every point above the line $y = x - 3$ is a solution of $y < x - 3$.

5. $(0, 0)$ is not a solution of $y > x + 4$. Therefore, the point $(0, 0)$ should not be in the shaded region that indicates the solution set of the inequality.

6. In the graph of an inequality in two variables, any point in the shaded region is a solution of the inequality, and any point not in the shaded region is not a solution of the inequality.

5.6 Exercises

1 Graph inequalities in two variables

1. In the graph of a linear inequality, what does a solid line represent? What does a dashed line represent?

2. In the graph of a linear inequality, what does the shaded portion of the graph represent?

Graph the solution set.

3. $y > 2x + 3$

4. $y > 3x - 9$

5. $y > \frac{3}{2}x - 4$

6. $y > -\frac{5}{4}x + 1$

7. $y \leq -\frac{3}{4}x - 1$

8. $y \leq -\frac{5}{2}x - 4$

9. $y \leq -\frac{6}{5}x - 2$

10. $y < \frac{4}{5}x + 3$

11. $x + y > 4$ **12.** $x - y > -3$ **13.** $2x + y \geq 4$ **14.** $3x + y \geq 6$

15. $y \leq -2$ **16.** $y > 3$ **17.** $2x + 2y \leq -4$ **18.** $-4x + 3y < -12$

19. If $(0, 0)$ is a point on the graph of the linear inequality $Ax + By > C$, where C is not zero, is C positive or negative?

20. If $Ax + By < C$, where C is a negative number, is $(0, 0)$ a point on the graph of this linear inequality?

5.6   Applying Concepts

Write the inequality given its graph.

21.

22.

23.

24.

Graph the solution set.

25. $y - 5 < 4(x - 2)$

26. $y + 3 < 6(x + 1)$

27. $3x - 2(y + 1) \leq y - (5 - x)$

28. $2x - 3(y + 1) \geq y - (7 - x)$

29. Does an inequality in two variables define a relation? Why or why not? Does an inequality in two variables define a function? Why or why not?

Focus on Problem Solving

Counterexamples   Some of the exercises in this text ask you to determine whether a statement is true or false. For instance, the statement "Every real number has a reciprocal" is false because 0 is a real number and 0 does not have a reciprocal.

Finding an example, such as "0 has no reciprocal," to show that a statement is not always true is called finding a counterexample. A *counterexample* is an example that shows that a statement is not always true.

Consider the statement "The product of two numbers is greater than either factor." A counterexample to this statement is the factors $\frac{2}{3}$ and $\frac{3}{4}$. The product of these numbers is $\frac{1}{2}$, and $\frac{1}{2}$ is smaller than $\frac{2}{3}$ or $\frac{3}{4}$. There are many other counterexamples to the given statement.

Here are some counterexamples to the statement "The square of a number is always larger than the number."

$$\left(\frac{1}{2}\right)^2 = \frac{1}{4} \quad \text{but} \quad \frac{1}{4} < \frac{1}{2} \qquad 1^2 = 1 \quad \text{but} \quad 1 = 1$$

For each of the next five statements, find at least one counterexample to show that the statement, or conjecture, is false.

1. The product of two integers is always a positive number.

2. The sum of two prime numbers is never a prime number.

3. For all real numbers, $|x + y| = |x| + |y|$.

4. If x and y are nonzero real numbers and $x > y$, then $x^2 > y^2$.

5. The quotient of any two nonzero real numbers is less than either one of the numbers.

When a problem is posed, it may not be known whether the statement is true or false. For instance, Christian Goldbach (1690–1764) stated that every even integer greater than 2 can be written as the sum of two prime numbers. No one has been able to find a counterexample to this statement, but neither has anyone been able to prove that it is always true.

In the next five exercises, answer true if the statement is always true. If there is an instance when the statement is false, give a counterexample.

6. The reciprocal of a positive number is always smaller than the number.

7. If $x < 0$, then $|x| = -x$.

8. For any two real numbers x and y, $x + y > x - y$.

9. For any positive integer n, $n^2 + n + 17$ is a prime number.

10. The list of numbers 1, 11, 111, 1111, 11111, … contains infinitely many composite numbers. (*Hint:* A number is divisible by 3 if the sum of the digits of the number is divisible by 3.)

Projects & Group Activities

Graphing Linear Equations with a Graphing Utility

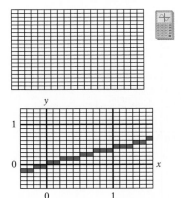

A computer or graphing calculator screen is divided into *pixels*. There are approximately 6000 to 790,000 pixels available on the screen (depending on the computer or calculator). The greater the number of pixels, the smoother a graph will appear. A portion of a screen is shown at the left. Each little rectangle represents one pixel.

The graphing utilities that are used by computers or calculators to graph an equation do basically what we have shown in the text: They choose values of x and, for each, calculate the corresponding value of y. The pixel corresponding to the ordered pair is then turned on. The graph is jagged because pixels are much larger than the dots we draw on paper.

The graph of $y = 0.45x$ is shown at the left as the calculator drew it (jagged).

The x- and y-axes have been chosen so that each pixel represents $\frac{1}{10}$ of a unit.

Consider the region of the graph where $x = 1$, 1.1, and 1.2.

The corresponding values of y are 0.45, 0.495, and 0.54. Because the y-axis is in tenths, the numbers 0.45, 0.495, and 0.54 are rounded to the nearest tenth before plotting. Rounding 0.45, 0.495, and 0.54 to the nearest tenth results in 0.5 for each number. Thus the ordered pairs (1, 0.45), (1.1, 0.495), and (1.2, 0.54) are graphed as (1, 0.5), (1.1, 0.5), and (1.2, 0.5). These points appear as three illuminated horizontal pixels. The graph of the line appears horizontal. However, if you use the TRACE feature of the calculator (see the Appendix), the actual y-coordinate for each value of x is displayed.

Here are the keystrokes to graph $y = \frac{2}{3}x + 1$. First the equation is entered. Then the domain (Xmin to Xmax) and the range (Ymin to Ymax) are entered. This is called the **viewing window.**

By changing the keystrokes 2 $\boxed{\text{X, T, }\Theta\text{, }n}$ $\boxed{\div}$ 3 $\boxed{+}$ 1, you can graph different equations.

1. $y = 2x + 1$ For $2x$, you may enter $2 \times x$ or just $2x$. The times sign $\times$ is not necessary on many graphing calculators.

2. $y = -\frac{1}{2}x - 2$ Use the $\boxed{(-)}$ key to enter a negative sign.

3. $3x + 2y = 6$ Solve for y. Then enter the equation.

4. $4x + 3y = 75$ You must adjust the viewing window.
Suggestion: Xmin = −25, Xmax = 25, Xscl = 5, Ymin = −35, Ymax = 35, Yscl = 5. See the Appendix for assistance.

Chapter 5 Summary

Key Words

A **rectangular coordinate system** is formed by two number lines, one horizontal and one vertical, that intersect at the zero point of each line. The number lines that make up a rectangular coordinate system are called the **coordinate axes,** or simply the **axes.** The **origin** is the point of intersection of the two coordinate axes. Generally, the horizontal axis is labeled the **x-axis**, and the vertical axis is labeled the **y-axis.** A rectangular coordinate system divides the plane determined by the axes into four regions called **quadrants.**   [5.1.1, pp. 247]

Examples

The coordinate axes determine a **plane.** Every point in the plane can be identified by an **ordered pair** (x, y). The first number in an ordered pair is called the **x-coordinate** or the **abscissa.** The second number is called the **y-coordinate** or the **ordinate.** The **coordinates** of a point are the numbers in the ordered pair associated with the point.   [5.1.1, pp. 248]

The ordered pair $(4, -9)$ has x-coordinate 4 and y-coordinate −9.

An equation of the form $y = mx + b$, where m is the coefficient of x and b is a constant, is a **linear equation in two variables.** A **solution of a linear equation in two variables** is an ordered pair (x, y) that makes the equation a true statement. [5.2.1, p. 261]

$y = 2x + 3$ is an example of a linear equation in two variables. The ordered pair $(1, 5)$ is a solution of this equation because when 1 is substituted for x and 5 is substituted for y, the result is a true equation.

The point at which a graph crosses the x-axis is called the **x-intercept.** At the x-intercept, the y-coordinate is 0. The point at which a graph crosses the y-axis is called the **y-intercept.** At the y-intercept, the x-coordinate is 0.   [5.2.3, p. 267]

An equation of the form $Ax + By = C$ is also a **linear equation in two variables.**   [5.2.3, p. 264]

$5x - 2y = 10$ is an example of an equation in $Ax + By = C$ form.

The **graph of $y = b$** is a horizontal line with y-intercept $(0, b)$. The **graph of $x = a$** is a vertical line with x-intercept $(a, 0)$. [5.2.3, p. 268]

The graph of $y = -3$ is a horizontal line with y-intercept $(0, -3)$. The graph of $x = 2$ is a vertical line with x-intercept $(2, 0)$.

The **slope** of a line is a measure of the slant of the line. The symbol for slope is m. A line that slants upward to the right has a **positive slope.** A line that slants downward to the right has a **negative slope.** A horizontal line has **zero slope.** The slope of a vertical line is **undefined.**   [5.3.1, pp. 276–278]

For the graph of $y = 4x - 3$, $m = 4$; the slope is positive.

For the graph of $y = -6x + 1$, $m = -6$; the slope is negative.

For the graph of $y = -7$, $m = 0$; the slope is 0.

For the graph of $x = 8$, the slope is undefined.

Two lines in the rectangular coordinate system that never intersect are **parallel lines.** Parallel lines have the same slope. [5.3.1, p. 279]

The lines $y = -2x + 1$ and $y = -2x - 3$ have the same slope and different y-intercepts. The lines are parallel.

A **relation** is any set of ordered pairs. The **domain** of a relation is the set of first coordinates of the ordered pairs. The **range** is the set of second coordinates of the ordered pairs.   [5.5.1, p. 298]

For the relation $\{(-2, -5), (0, -3), (4, -1)\}$, the domain is $\{-2, 0, 4\}$ and the range is $\{-5, -3, -1\}$.

A **function** is a relation in which no two ordered pairs have the same first coordinate and different second coordinates. [5.5.1, p. 298]

$\{(-2, -5), (0, -3), (4, -1)\}$ is a function. $\{(-2, -5), (-2, -3), (4, -1)\}$ is not a function because two ordered pairs have the same x-coordinate, -2, and different y-coordinates.

A function of the form $f(x) = mx + b$ is a **linear function.** Its graph is a straight line.   [5.5.2, p. 301]

$f(x) = -3x + 8$ is an example of a linear function.

The solution set of a linear inequality in two variables is a **half-plane.**   [5.6.1, p. 310]

The solution set of $y > x - 2$ is all points above the line $y = x - 2$. The solution set of $y < x - 2$ is all points below the line $y = x - 2$.

Essential Rules and Procedures

Average Rate of Change

The average rate of change of y with respect to x is $\dfrac{\text{change in } y}{\text{change in } x}$. [5.1.3, p. 252]

The average U.S. household income in 1980 was \$41,910, whereas in 2000 it was \$57,045. (*Source:* U.S. Census Bureau; adjusted for inflation and given in 2000 dollars)

$$\frac{57{,}045 - 41{,}910}{2000 - 1980} = 756.75$$

The average annual rate of change in household income from 1980 to 2000 was \$756.75.

To find the x-intercept, let $y = 0$.
To find the y-intercept, let $x = 0$.   [5.2.3, p. 267]

To find the x-intercept of $4x - 3y = 12$, let $y = 0$. To find the y-intercept, let $x = 0$.

$$
\begin{aligned}
4x - 3y &= 12 \\
4x - 3(0) &= 12 \\
4x - 0 &= 12 \\
4x &= 12 \\
x &= 3
\end{aligned}
\qquad
\begin{aligned}
4x - 3y &= 12 \\
4(0) - 3y &= 12 \\
0 - 3y &= 12 \\
-3y &= 12 \\
y &= -4
\end{aligned}
$$

The x-intercept is $(3, 0)$.   The y-intercept is $(0, -4)$.

Slope of a Linear Equation

$$\text{Slope} = m = \frac{y_2 - y_1}{x_2 - x_1}, \; x_2 \neq x_1 \quad [5.3.1, \text{ p. } 276]$$

To find the slope of the line between the points $(2, -3)$ and $(-1, 6)$, let $P_1 = (2, -3)$ and $P_2 = (-1, 6)$. Then $(x_1, y_1) = (2, -3)$ and $(x_2, y_2) = (-1, 6)$.

$$m = \frac{y_2 - y_1}{x_2 - x_1} = \frac{6 - (-3)}{-1 - 2} = \frac{9}{-3} = -3$$

Slope-Intercept Form of a Linear Equation

$y = mx + b$ [5.3.2, p. 281]

For the equation $y = -4x + 7$, the slope $= m = -4$ and the y-intercept $= (0, b) = (0, 7)$.

Point-Slope Formula

$y - y_1 = m(x - x_1)$ [5.4.2, p. 289]

To find the equation of the line that contains the point $(6, -1)$ and has slope 2, let $(x_1, y_1) = (6, -1)$ and $m = 2$.

$$
\begin{aligned}
y - y_1 &= m(x - x_1) \\
y - (-1) &= 2(x - 6) \\
y + 1 &= 2x - 12 \\
y &= 2x - 13
\end{aligned}
$$

Chapter 5 Review Exercises

1. Find the ordered-pair solution of $y = -\frac{2}{3}x + 2$ that corresponds to $x = 3$.

2. Find the equation of the line that contains the point whose coordinates are $(0, -1)$ and has slope 3.

3. Graph: $x = -3$

4. Graph the ordered pairs $(-3, 1)$ and $(0, 2)$.

5. Evaluate $f(x) = 3x^2 + 4$ at $x = -5$.

6. Find the slope of the line that contains the points whose coordinates are $(3, -4)$ and $(1, -4)$.

7. Graph: $y = 3x + 1$

8. Graph: $3x - 2y = 6$

9. Find the equation of the line that contains the point whose coordinates are $(-1, 2)$ and has slope $-\frac{2}{3}$.

10. Find the x- and y-intercepts for $6x - 4y = 12$.

11. Graph the line that has slope $\frac{1}{2}$ and y-intercept $(0, -1)$.

12. Graph: $f(x) = -\frac{2}{3}x + 4$

13. Find the equation of the line that contains the point whose coordinates are $(-3, 1)$ and has slope $\frac{2}{3}$.

14. Find the slope of the line that contains the points whose coordinates are $(2, -3)$ and $(4, 1)$.

15. Evaluate $f(x) = \frac{3}{5}x + 2$ at $x = -10$.

16. Find the domain and range of the relation $\{(-20, -10), (-10, -5), (0, 0), (10, 5)\}$. Is the relation a function?

17. Graph: $y = -\frac{3}{4}x + 3$

18. Graph the line that has slope 2 and y-intercept $(0, -2)$.

19. Graph the ordered pairs $(-2, -3)$ and $(2, 4)$.

20. Graph: $f(x) = 5x + 1$

21. Find the x- and y-intercepts for $2x - 3y = 12$.

22. Find the equation of the line that contains the point whose coordinates are $(-1, 0)$ and has slope 2.

23. Graph: $y = 3$

24. Graph the solution set of $3x + 2y \leq 12$.

25. Is the line containing the points $(-2, 1)$ and $(3, 5)$ parallel to the line that contains the points $(4, -5)$ and $(9, -1)$?

26. Find the equation of the line through the points whose coordinates are $(4, 14)$ and $(-8, -1)$.

27. Graph the line that has slope -1 and y-intercept $(0, 2)$.

28. Graph: $2x - 3y = 6$

29. Find the ordered-pair solution of $y = 2x - 1$ that corresponds to $x = -2$.

30. Find the equation of the line that contains the point $(0, 2)$ and has slope -3.

31. Graph: $f(x) = 2x$

32. Evaluate $f(x) = 3x - 5$ at $x = \dfrac{5}{3}$.

33. Find the equation of the line through the points whose coordinates are $(-6, 0)$ and $(3, -3)$.

34. Find the equation of the line that contains the point whose coordinates are $(2, -1)$ and has slope $\dfrac{1}{2}$.

35. Is $(-10, 0)$ a solution of $y = \dfrac{1}{5}x + 2$?

36. Find the ordered-pair solution of $y = 4x - 9$ that corresponds to $x = 2$.

37. Find the x- and y-intercepts for $4x - 3y = 0$.

38. Find the equation of the line that contains the point whose coordinates are $(-2, 3)$ and has zero slope.

39. Graph the solution set of $6x - y > 6$.

40. Graph the line that has slope -3 and y-intercept $(0, 1)$.

41. Find the equation of the line that contains the point whose coordinates are $(0, -4)$ and has slope 3.

42. Graph: $x + 2y = -4$

43. Find the domain and range of the relation $\{(-10, -5), (-5, 0), (5, 0), (-10, 0)\}$. Is the relation a function?

44. Find the range of the function given by the equation $f(x) = 3x + 7$ if the domain is $\{-20, -10, 0, 10, 20\}$.

45. Find the range of the function given by the equation $f(x) = \frac{1}{3}x + 4$ if the domain is $\{-6, -3, 0, 3, 6\}$.

46. **Life Expectancy** The table below shows the average number of years women and men were predicted to live beyond age 65 in 1950, 1960, 1970, 1980, 1990, and 2000. (*Source:* 2000 Social Security Trustees Report) Figures are rounded to the nearest whole number. Graph the scatter diagram for these data.

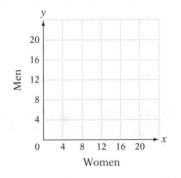

Women, x	15	16	17	18	19	19
Men, y	13	13	13	14	15	16

47. **Airline Industry** The major airlines routinely overbook flights, but generally passengers voluntarily give up their seats when offered free airline tickets as compensation. The table below gives the number of passengers who voluntarily gave up their seats and the number who involuntarily gave up their seats during a five-year period. Numbers are rounded to the nearest ten thousand. (*Source:* USA TODAY analysis of Department of Transportation data) Graph the scatter diagram for these data.

Number of volunteers, in ten thousands, x	60	77	79	90	102
Number involuntarily bumped, in ten thousands, y	4	5	5	6	5

48. **Automobile Tires** The following table shows the tread depth, in millimeters, of a tire and the number of miles, in thousands, that have been driven on that tire.

Miles driven	25	35	40	20	45
Tread depth	4.8	3.5	2.1	5.5	1.0

Write a relation in which the first coordinate is the number of miles driven and the second coordinate is the tread depth. Is the relation a function?

49. **Building Contractors** A contractor uses the equation $C = 70s + 40{,}000$ to estimate the cost of building a new house. In this equation, C is the total cost, in dollars, and s is the number of square feet in the home.
a. Write the equation in functional notation.
b. Use the coordinate axes at the right to graph the equation for values of s between 0 and 5000.
c. The point (1500, 145,000) is on the graph. Write a sentence that explains the meaning of this ordered pair.

50. **Hourly Wages** The average hourly wage of a U.S. worker in 1996 was $11.90. In 2005, the average hourly wage was $16.00. (*Source:* Federal Reserve Bank of St. Louis) Find the average annual rate of change in the average hourly wage from 1996 to 2005. Round to the nearest cent.

Chapter 5 Test

▶ View the Chapter Test Videos for fully worked-out solutions to any exercise.

1. Find the equation of the line that contains the point whose coordinates are $(9, -3)$ and has slope $-\frac{1}{3}$.

2. Find the slope of the line that contains the points whose coordinates are $(9, 8)$ and $(-2, 1)$.

3. Find the x- and y-intercepts for $3x - 2y = 24$.

4. Find the ordered-pair solution of $y = -\frac{4}{3}x - 1$ that corresponds to $x = 9$.

5. Graph: $5x + 3y = 15$

6. Graph: $y = \frac{1}{4}x + 3$

7. Evaluate $f(x) = 4x + 7$ at $x = \frac{3}{4}$.

8. Is $(6, 3)$ a solution of $y = \frac{2}{3}x + 1$?

9. Graph the line that has slope $-\dfrac{2}{3}$ and y-intercept $(0, 4)$.

10. Graph the solution set of $2x - y \geq 2$.

11. Graph the ordered pairs $(3, -2)$ and $(0, 4)$.

12. Graph the line that has slope 2 and y-intercept $(0, -4)$.

13. Find the equation of the line through the points whose coordinates are $(-5, 5)$ and $(10, 14)$.

14. Find the equation of the line that contains the point whose coordinates are $(0, 7)$ and has slope $-\dfrac{2}{5}$.

15. Find the equation of the line that contains the point whose coordinates are $(2, 1)$ and has slope 4.

16. Evaluate $f(x) = 4x^2 - 3$ at $x = -2$.

17. Graph: $y = -2x - 1$

18. Graph the solution set of $y > 2$.

19. Graph: $x = 4$

20. Graph the line that has slope $\dfrac{1}{2}$ and y-intercept $(0, -3)$.

21. Graph: $f(x) = -\dfrac{2}{3}x + 2$

22. Graph: $f(x) = -5x$

23. Evaluate $f(x) = -3x + 7$ at $x = -6$.

24. Find the range of the function given by the equation $f(x) = -3x + 5$ if the domain is $\{-7, -2, 0, 4, 9\}$.

25. Is the line containing the points $(-3, -2)$ and $(6, 0)$ parallel to the line that contains the points $(6, -4)$ and $(3, 2)$?

26. 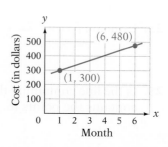 **Drivers** Drivers over age 70 number about 18 million today, up from about 13 million ten years ago. (*Source:* National Highway Traffic Safety Administration) Find the average annual rate of change in the number of drivers over age 70 for the past decade.

27. Fire Science The distance, in miles, a house is from a fire station and the amount, in thousands of dollars, of fire damage that house sustained in a fire are given in the following table. Graph the scatter diagram for these data.

Distance (in miles), x	3.5	4.0	5.5	6.0
Damage (in thousands of dollars), y	25	30	40	35

28. Manufacturing A company that manufactures toasters has fixed costs of $1000 each month. The manufacturing cost per toaster is $8. An equation that represents the total cost to manufacture the toasters is $C = 8t + 1000$, where C is the total cost, in dollars, and t is the number of toasters manufactured each month.

a. Write the equation in functional notation.

b. Use the coordinate axes at the right to graph the equation for values of t between 0 and 500.

c. The point (340, 3720) is on the graph. Write a sentence that explains the meaning of this ordered pair.

29. Test Scores The data in the following table show a reading test grade and the final exam grade in a history class.

Reading test grade	8.5	9.4	10.1	11.4	12.0
History exam	64	68	76	87	92

Write a relation in which the first coordinate is the reading test grade and the second coordinate is the score on the history final exam. Is the relation a function?

30. Lumber The graph at the right shows the cost, in dollars, per 1000 board feet of lumber over a six-month period. Find the slope of the line. Write a sentence that states the meaning of the slope.

Cumulative Review Exercises

1. Simplify: $12 - 18 \div 3 \cdot (-2)^2$

2. Evaluate $\dfrac{a - b}{a^2 - c}$ when $a = -2$, $b = 3$, and $c = -4$.

3. Simplify: $4(2 - 3x) - 5(x - 4)$

4. Solve: $2x - \dfrac{2}{3} = \dfrac{7}{3}$

5. Solve: $3x - 2[x - 3(2 - 3x)] = x - 6$

6. Write $6\frac{2}{3}\%$ as a fraction.

7. Use the roster method to write the set of natural numbers less than 9.

8. Given $D = \{-23, -18, -4, 0, 5\}$, which elements of set D are greater than -16?

9. Solve: $8a - 3 \geq 5a - 6$

10. Solve $4x - 5y = 15$ for y.

11. Find the ordered-pair solution of $y = 3x - 1$ that corresponds to $x = -2$.

12. Find the slope of the line that contains the points whose coordinates are $(2, 3)$ and $(-2, 3)$.

13. Find the x- and y-intercepts for $5x + 2y = 20$.

14. Find the equation of the line that contains the point whose coordinates are $(3, 2)$ and has slope -1.

15. Graph: $y = \dfrac{1}{2}x + 2$

16. Graph: $3x + y = 2$

17. Graph: $f(x) = -4x - 1$

18. Graph the solution set of $x - y \leq 5$.

19. Find the domain and range of the relation $\{(0, 4), (1, 3), (2, 2), (3, 1), (4, 0)\}$. Is the relation a function?

20. Evaluate $f(x) = -4x + 9$ at $x = 5$.

21. Find the range of the function given by the equation $f(x) = -\frac{5}{3}x + 3$ if the domain is $\{-9, -6, -3, 0, 3, 6\}$.

22. Integer Problem The sum of two numbers is 24. Twice the smaller number is three less than the larger number. Find the two numbers.

23. Lever Systems A lever is 8 ft long. A force of 80 lb is applied to one end of the lever, and a force of 560 lb is applied to the other end. Where is the fulcrum located when the system balances? The lever-system equation is $F_1x = F_2(d - x)$.

24. Geometry The perimeter of a triangle is 49 ft. The length of the first side is twice the length of the third side, and the length of the second side is 5 ft more than the length of the third side. Find the length of the first side.

25. Discount A suit that regularly sells for $89 is on sale for 30% off the regular price. Find the sale price.

6

Systems of Linear Equations

OBJECTIVES

6.1
  1 Solve systems of linear equations by graphing

6.2
  1 Solve systems of linear equations by the substitution method

6.3
  1 Solve systems of linear equations by the addition method

6.4
  1 Rate-of-wind and water-current problems
  2 Application problems

DVD   SSM

Online Study Center

Need help? For online student resources, such as section quizzes, visit the Online Study Center at www.cengage.com/math/aufmann.

Have you ever noticed that your flight in one direction seems longer than your flight in the other direction? Recall from Section 3.1 that if a boat is traveling with the current, the effective speed of the boat is increased. When the boat is traveling against the current, the current slows the boat down. The same is true for airplanes and the wind. If the plane is flying against a headwind, the wind will slow the plane down. **In Exercises 6, 10, 11, and 13 on page 354,** you will use systems of equations to determine the rates of planes in calm air and rates of the wind.

Prep Test

1. Solve $3x - 4y = 24$ for y.

2. Solve: $50 + 0.07x = 0.05(x + 1400)$

3. Simplify: $-3(2x - 7y) + 3(2x + 4y)$

4. Simplify: $4x + 2(3x - 5)$

5. Is $(-4, 2)$ a solution of $3x - 5y = -22$?

6. Find the x- and y-intercepts of $3x - 4y = 12$.

7. Are the graphs of $y = -3x + 6$ and $y = -3x - 4$ parallel?

8. Graph: $y = \dfrac{5}{4}x - 2$

9. One hiker starts along a trail walking at a speed of 3 mph. One-half hour later, another hiker starts on the same trail walking at a speed of 4 mph. How long after the second hiker starts will the two hikers be side by side?

Solving Systems of Linear Equations by Graphing

6.1

OBJECTIVE 1 Solve systems of linear equations by graphing

Equations considered together are called a **system of equations.** A system of equations is shown at the right.

$$2x + y = 3$$
$$x + y = 1$$

A solution of a system of linear equations can be found by graphing the lines of the system on the same coordinate axes. Three examples of **systems of linear equations in two variables** are shown on the next page, along with the graphs of the equations of each system.

The systems of equations at the right are *systems of linear equations* because the graph of each of the equations in the system is a line. Also, each equation has two variables. In future math courses, you will study equations that contain more than two variables.

System I

$$x - 2y = -8$$
$$2x + 5y = 11$$

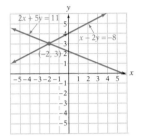

System II

$$4x + 2y = 6$$
$$y = -2x + 3$$

System III

$$4x + 6y = 12$$
$$6x + 9y = -9$$

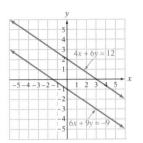

For System I, the two lines intersect at a single point whose coordinates are $(-2, 3)$. Because this point lies on both lines, it is a solution of each equation of the system of equations. We can check this by replacing x by -2 and y by 3 in each equation. The check is shown below.

$x - 2y = -8$		$2x + 5y = 11$	
$-2 - 2(3)$	-8	$2(-2) + 5(3)$	11
$-2 - 6$	-8	$-4 + 15$	11
	$-8 = -8$ ✓		$11 = 11$ ✓

• Replace x by -2 and y by 3.

A **solution of a system of equations in two variables** is an ordered pair that is a solution of each equation of the system. The ordered pair $(-2, 3)$ is a solution of System I.

Is $(-1, 4)$ a solution of the following system of equations?

$$7x + 3y = 5$$
$$3x - 2y = 12$$

$7x + 3y = 5$		$3x - 2y = 12$	
$7(-1) + 3(4)$	5	$3(-1) - 2(4)$	12
$-7 + 12$	5	$-3 - 8$	12
	$5 = 5$ ✓		$-11 \neq 12$ Does not check.

• Replace x by -1 and y by 4.

Using the system of equations above and the graph at the right, note that the graph of the ordered pair $(-1, 4)$ lies on the graph of $7x + 3y = 5$ but *not on both lines*. The ordered pair $(-1, 4)$ is *not* a solution of the system of equations. The ordered pair $(2, -3)$, however, does lie on both lines and therefore is a solution of the system of equations.

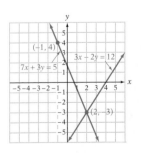

EXAMPLE 1   Is $(1, -3)$ a solution of the system $3x + 2y = -3$
$x - 3y = 6$?

Solution

$3x + 2y = -3$	
$3 \cdot 1 + 2(-3)$	-3
$3 + (-6)$	-3
$-3 = -3$	

$x - 3y = 6$	
$1 - 3(-3)$	6
$1 - (-9)$	6
$10 \neq 6$	

No, $(1, -3)$ is not a solution of the system of equations.

PROBLEM 1   Is $(-1, -2)$ a solution of the system $2x - 5y = 8$
$-x + 3y = -5$?

Solution   See page S14.

Take Note

The fact that there are an infinite number of ordered pairs that are solutions of the system of equations at the right does not mean that *every* ordered pair is a solution. For instance, $(0, 3)$, $(-2, 7)$, and $(2, -1)$ are solutions. However, $(3, 1)$, $(-1, 4)$, and $(1, 6)$ are not solutions. You should verify these statements.

System II from the preceding page and the graph of the equations of that system are shown again at the right. Note that the graph of $y = -2x + 3$ lies directly on top of the graph of $4x + 2y = 6$. Thus the two lines intersect at an infinite number of points. Because the graphs intersect at an infinite number of points, there are an infinite number of solutions of this system of equations. Since each equation represents the same set of points, the solutions of the system of equations can be stated by using the ordered pairs of either one of the equations. Therefore, we can say "The solutions are the ordered pairs that satisfy $4x + 2y = 6$," or we can say "The solutions are the ordered pairs that satisfy $y = -2x + 3$."

$4x + 2y = 6$
$y = -2x + 3$

System III from the previous page and the graph of the equations of that system are shown again at the right. Note that in this case the graphs of the lines are parallel and do not intersect. Since the graphs do not intersect, there is no point that is on both lines. Therefore, the system of equations has no solution.

$4x + 6y = 12$
$6x + 9y = -9$

For a system of linear equations in two variables, the graphs can intersect at one point, the graphs can intersect at infinitely many points (the graphs are the same line), or the lines can be parallel and never intersect. Such systems are called **independent, dependent,** and **inconsistent,** respectively.

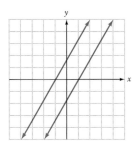

Independent   **Dependent**   **Inconsistent**

One solution   Infinitely many solutions   No solutions

Solving a system of equations means finding the ordered-pair solutions of the system. One way to do this is to draw the graphs of the equations in the system and determine where the graphs intersect.

Solve by graphing: $2x + 3y = 6$
$ 2x + y = -2$

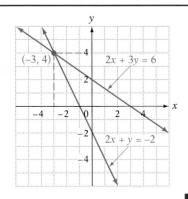

Graph each line.

The graphs of the equations intersect at one point.

The system of equations is independent.

Find the point of intersection.

The solution is $(-3, 4)$.

The INTERSECT feature on a graphing calculator can be used to find the solution of the system of equations given above. However, if this feature is used to estimate the solution, the estimated solution might be $(-3.03, 4.05)$ or some other ordered pair that contains decimals. When these values are rounded to the nearest integer, the ordered pair becomes $(-3, 4)$, which is the solution of the system. This solution can be verified by replacing x by -3 and y by 4 in the system of equations.

Solve by graphing: $2x - y = 1$
$ 6x - 3y = 12$

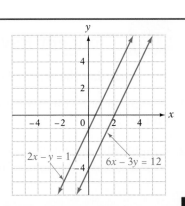

Graph each line.

The lines are parallel and therefore do not intersect.

The system of equations is inconsistent and has no solution.

■

Solve by graphing: $2x + 3y = 6$
$6x + 9y = 18$

Graph each line.

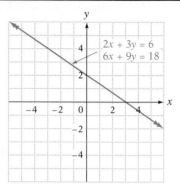

The two equations represent the same line. The system of equations is dependent and, therefore, has an infinite number of solutions.

The solutions are the ordered pairs that are solutions of the equation $2x + 3y = 6$.

By choosing values for x, substituting these values into the equation $2x + 3y = 6$, and finding the corresponding values for y, we can find some specific ordered-pair solutions. For example, $(3, 0)$, $(0, 2)$, and $(6, -2)$ are solutions of this system of equations.

■

EXAMPLE 2 Solve by graphing.   **A.** $x - 2y = 2$ **B.** $4x - 2y = 6$
$x + y = 5$ $y = 2x - 3$

Solution **A.**

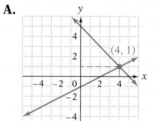

The solution is $(4, 1)$.

B.

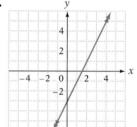

The system of equations is dependent. The solutions are the ordered pairs that satisfy the equation $y = 2x - 3$.

PROBLEM 2 Solve by graphing. **A.** $x + 3y = 3$ **B.** $y = 3x - 1$
$-x + y = 5$ $6x - 2y = -6$

Solution See page S14.

6.1 Concept Review

Determine whether the statement is always true, sometimes true, or never true.

1. A solution of a system of linear equations in two variables is an ordered pair (x, y).

2. Graphically, the solution of an independent system of linear equations in two variables is the point of intersection of the graphs of the two equations.

3. Suppose an ordered pair is a solution of one equation in a system of linear equations and not of the other equation. Then the system has no solution.

4. A system of linear equations has either one solution, represented graphically by two lines intersecting at exactly one point, or no solutions, represented graphically by two parallel lines.

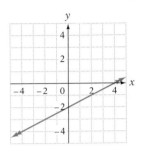

5. The system of two linear equations graphed at the right has no solution.

6. An independent system of equations has no solution.

6.1   Exercises

1   Solve systems of linear equations by graphing

1. What is a system of equations?

2. How can you determine whether an ordered pair is a solution of a system of equations in two variables?

3. Is (2, 3) a solution of the system $3x + 4y = 18$
$2x - y = 1$?

4. Is (2, −1) a solution of the system $x - 2y = 4$
$2x + y = 3$?

5. Is (1, −2) a solution of the system
$3x - y = 5$
$2x + 5y = -8$?

6. Is (−1, −1) a solution of the system
$x - 4y = 3$
$3x + y = 2$?

7. Is (4, 3) a solution of the system $5x - 2y = 14$
$x + y = 8$?

8. Is (2, 5) a solution of the system $3x + 2y = 16$
$2x - 3y = 4$?

9. Is (−1, 3) a solution of the system $4x - y = -5$
$2x + 5y = 13$?

10. Is (4, −1) a solution of the system
$x - 4y = 9$
$2x - 3y = 11$?

11. Is (0, 0) a solution of the system $4x + 3y = 0$
$2x - y = 1$?

12. Is (2, 0) a solution of the system $3x - y = 6$
$x + 3y = 2$?

13. Is (2, −3) a solution of the system
$y = 2x - 7$
$3x - y = 9$?

14. Is (−1, −2) a solution of the system
$3x - 4y = 5$
$y = x - 1$?

15. Is (5, 2) a solution of the system $y = 2x - 8$
$y = 3x - 13$?

16. Is (−4, 3) a solution of the system
$y = 2x + 11$
$y = 5x - 19$?

17. Explain how to solve a system of two equations in two variables by graphing.

18. An independent system of equations has ___?___ solution(s), an inconsistent system of equations has ___?___ solution(s), and a dependent system of equations has ___?___ solution(s).

For Exercises 19 to 24, state whether the system of equations is independent, inconsistent, or dependent.

19.

20.

21.

22.

23.

24.

For Exercises 25 to 30, use the graph of the equations in the system to determine the solution of the system of equations.

25.

26.

27.

28.

29.

30.

Solve by graphing.

31. $x - y = 3$
$x + y = 5$

32. $2x - y = 4$
$x + y = 5$

33. $x + 2y = 6$
$x - y = 3$

34. $3x - y = 3$
$2x + y = 2$

35. $3x - 2y = 6$
$y = 3$

36. $\qquad x = 2$
$3x + 2y = 4$

37. $x = 3$
$y = -2$

38. $x + 1 = 0$
$y - 3 = 0$

39. $\qquad y = 2x - 6$
$x + y = 0$

40. $5x - 2y = 11$
$y = 2x - 5$

41. $\quad 2x + y = -2$
$6x + 3y = 6$

42. $\quad x + y = 5$
$3x + 3y = 6$

43. $4x - 2y = 4$
$y = 2x - 2$

44. $2x + 6y = 6$
$y = -\dfrac{1}{3}x + 1$

45. $\quad x - y = 5$
$2x - y = 6$

46. $5x - 2y = 10$
$3x + 2y = 6$

47. $3x + 4y = 0$
$2x - 5y = 0$

48. $2x - 3y = 0$
$y = -\dfrac{1}{3}x$

49. $\quad x - 3y = 3$
$2x - 6y = 12$

50. $4x + 6y = 12$
$6x + 9y = 18$

51. $3x + 2y = -4$
$x = 2y + 4$

52. $5x + 2y = -14$
$3x - 4y = 2$

53. $\quad 4x - y = 5$
$3x - 2y = 5$

54. $2x - 3y = 9$
$4x + 3y = -9$

 Solve by graphing. Then use a graphing utility to verify your solution.

55. $5x - 2y = 10$
$3x + 2y = 6$

56. $\quad x - y = 5$
$2x + y = 4$

57. $2x - 5y = 4$
$x - y = -1$

58. $\quad x - 2y = -5$
$3x + 4y = -15$

59. $2x + 3y = 6$
$y = -\dfrac{2}{3}x + 1$

60. $2x - 5y = 10$
$y = \dfrac{2}{5}x - 2$

In Exercises 61 and 62, A, B, C, and D are nonzero real numbers.

61. Is the following system of equations independent, inconsistent, or dependent?
$y = Ax + B$
$y = Ax + C, B \neq C$

62. Is the following system of equations independent, inconsistent, or dependent?
$x = C$
$y = D$

6.1   Applying Concepts

Write a system of equations given the graph.

63.

64.

65.

66.

67. Determine whether the statement is always true, sometimes true, or never true.
   a. Two parallel lines have the same slope.
   b. Two different lines with the same y-intercept are parallel.
   c. Two different lines with the same slope are parallel.

68. Write three different systems of equations: **a.** one that has $(-3, 5)$ as its only solution, **b.** one for which there is no solution, and **c.** one that is a dependent system of equations.

69. Explain how you can determine from the graph of a system of two equations in two variables whether it is an independent system of equations. Explain how you can determine whether it is an inconsistent system of equations.

Solving Systems of Linear Equations by the Substitution Method

6.2

OBJECTIVE 1

Solve systems of linear equations by the substitution method

A graphical solution of a system of equations is based on approximating the coordinates of a point of intersection. However, the point $\left(\frac{1}{4}, \frac{1}{2}\right)$ would be difficult to read from a graph. An algebraic method called the **substitution method** can be used to find an exact solution of a system of equations. To use the substitution method, we must write one of the equations of the system in terms of x or in terms of y.

Solve by substitution: $2x + 5y = -11$ (1)
$y = 3x - 9$ (2)

Equation (2) states that $y = 3x - 9$.

Substitute $3x - 9$ for y in equation (1).

$$2x + 5(3x - 9) = -11$$

Solve for x.

$$2x + 15x - 45 = -11$$
$$17x - 45 = -11$$
$$17x = 34$$
$$x = 2$$

Note that $x = 2$. Now we must find y.

Substitute the value of x into equation (2) and solve for y. (2)

$$y = 3x - 9$$
$$y = 3 \cdot 2 - 9$$
$$y = 6 - 9$$
$$y = -3$$

The solution is $(2, -3)$.

The graph of the system of equations given above is shown at the right. Note that the lines intersect at the point whose coordinates are $(2, -3)$, which is the algebraic solution we determined by the substitution method.

Solve by substitution: $5x + y = 4$ (1)
$2x - 3y = 5$ (2)

Equation (1) is the easier equation to solve for one variable in terms of the other.

Solve equation (1) for y.

$$5x + y = 4$$
$$y = -5x + 4$$

Substitute $-5x + 4$ for y in equation (2). Solve for x.

$$2x - 3y = 5$$
$$2x - 3(-5x + 4) = 5$$
$$2x + 15x - 12 = 5$$
$$17x - 12 = 5$$
$$17x = 17$$
$$x = 1$$

> **Take Note**
>
> You can *always* check the solution to an independent system of equations. Use the skill you developed in Objective 6.1.1 to check that the ordered pair is a solution of each equation in the system.

Substitute the value of x in equation (1) and solve for y.

$$(1) \qquad 5x + y = 4$$
$$5(1) + y = 4$$
$$5 + y = 4$$
$$y = -1$$

The solution is $(1, -1)$.

Solve by substitution: $\quad y = 3x - 1 \quad (1)$
$$y = -2x - 6 \quad (2)$$

Substitute $-2x - 6$ for y in equation (1).

Solve for x.

$$y = 3x - 1$$
$$-2x - 6 = 3x - 1$$
$$-5x - 6 = -1$$
$$-5x = 5$$
$$x = -1$$

Substitute the value of x into either equation and solve for y. Equation (1) is used here.

$$y = 3x - 1$$
$$y = 3(-1) - 1$$
$$y = -3 - 1$$
$$y = -4$$

The solution is $(-1, -4)$.

EXAMPLE 1   Solve by substitution: $3x + 4y = -2 \quad (1)$
$$-x + 2y = 4 \quad (2)$$

Solution

$$-x + 2y = 4$$
$$-x = -2y + 4$$
$$x = 2y - 4$$

• Solve equation (2) for x.

$$3x + 4y = -2$$
$$3(2y - 4) + 4y = -2$$
$$6y - 12 + 4y = -2$$
$$10y - 12 = -2$$
$$10y = 10$$
$$y = 1$$

• Substitute $2y - 4$ for x in equation (1).
• Solve for y.

$$-x + 2y = 4$$
$$-x + 2(1) = 4$$
$$-x + 2 = 4$$
$$-x = 2$$
$$x = -2$$

• Substitute the value of y into equation (2).
• Solve for x.

The solution is $(-2, 1)$.

PROBLEM 1   Solve by substitution: $7x - y = 4$
$3x + 2y = 9$

■ **Solution**   See page S14.

Take Note

Solve equation (1) for y. The resulting equation is $y = -2x + \frac{5}{2}$. Thus both lines have the same slope, -2, but different y-intercepts. The lines are parallel.

EXAMPLE 2   Solve by substitution: $4x + 2y = 5$ (1)
$y = -2x + 1$ (2)

Solution $4x + 2y = 5$ • **Substitute $-2x + 1$ for y in equation (1).**
$4x + 2(-2x + 1) = 5$
$4x - 4x + 2 = 5$
$2 = 5$

$2 = 5$ is not a true equation. The system of equations is inconsistent. The system does not have a solution.

PROBLEM 2   Solve by substitution: $3x - y = 4$
$y = 3x + 2$

■ **Solution**   See page S14.

Take Note

Solve equation (1) for y. The resulting equation is $y = 3x - 2$, which is the same as equation (2).

EXAMPLE 3   Solve by substitution: $6x - 2y = 4$ (1)
$y = 3x - 2$ (2)

Solution $6x - 2y = 4$ • **Substitute $3x - 2$ for y in equation (1).**
$6x - 2(3x - 2) = 4$
$6x - 6x + 4 = 4$
$4 = 4$

$4 = 4$ is a true equation. The system of equations is dependent. The solutions are the ordered pairs that satisfy the equation $y = 3x - 2$.

PROBLEM 3   Solve by substitution: $y = -2x + 1$
$6x + 3y = 3$

■ **Solution**   See page S14.

Note from Examples 2 and 3 above: If, when you are solving a system of equations, the variable is eliminated and the result is a false equation, such as $2 = 5$, the system is inconsistent and does not have a solution. If the result is a true equation, such as $4 = 4$, the system is dependent and has an infinite number of solutions.

6.2 Concept Review

Determine whether the statement is always true, sometimes true, or never true.

1. If one of the equations in a system of two linear equations is $y = x + 2$, then $x + 2$ can be substituted for y in the other equation in the system.

2. If a system of equations contains the equations $y = 2x + 1$ and $x + y = 5$, then $x + 2x + 1 = 5$.

3. If the equation $x = 4$ results from solving a system of equations by the substitution method, then the solution of the system of equations is 4.

4. If the true equation $6 = 6$ results from solving a system of equations by the substitution method, then the system of equations has an infinite number of solutions.

5. If the false equation $0 = 7$ results from solving a system of equations by the substitution method, then the system of equations is independent.

6. The ordered pair $(0, 0)$ is a solution of a system of linear equations.

6.2 Exercises

1 Solve systems of linear equations by the substitution method

1. Use this system of equations: (1) $y = 3x - 5$
                                                      (2) $x = 2$
To solve the system by substitution, substitute ____?____ for x in equation (1): $y = 3(2) - 5 = $ ___?___.
The solution of the system of equations is (___?___, ___?___).

2. Use this system of equations: (1) $y = x + 4$
                                                      (2) $3x + y = 12$
To solve the system by substitution, substitute ____?____ for y in equation (2): $3x + x + 4 = 12$.
Solving the equation $3x + x + 4 = 12$ for x gives $x = $ ___?___.
To find y, substitute this value of x into equation (1): $y = $ ___?___ $+ 4 = $ ___?___.
The solution of the system of equations is (___?___, ___?___).

Solve by substitution.

3. $2x + 3y = 7$
   $x = 2$

4. $y = 3$
   $3x - 2y = 6$

5. $y = x - 3$
   $x + y = 5$

6. $y = x + 2$
   $x + y = 6$

7. $x = y - 2$
   $x + 3y = 2$

8. $x = y + 1$
   $x + 2y = 7$

9. $2x + 3y = 9$
   $y = x - 2$

10. $3x + 2y = 11$
   $y = x + 3$

11. $3x - y = 2$
   $y = 2x - 1$

12. $2x - y = -5$
   $y = x + 4$

13. $x = 2y - 3$
   $2x - 3y = -5$

14. $x = 3y - 1$
   $3x + 4y = 10$

15. $y = 4 - 3x$
   $3x + y = 5$

16. $y = 2 - 3x$
   $6x + 2y = 7$

17. $x = 3y + 3$
   $2x - 6y = 12$

18. $x = 2 - y$
$3x + 3y = 6$

19. $3x + 5y = -6$
$x = 5y + 3$

20. $y = 2x + 3$
$4x - 3y = 1$

21. $x = 4y - 3$
$2x - 3y = 0$

22. $x = 2y$
$-2x + 4y = 6$

23. $y = 2x - 9$
$3x - y = 2$

24. $y = x + 4$
$2x - y = 6$

25. $3x + 4y = 7$
$x = 3 - 2y$

26. $3x - 5y = 1$
$y = 4x - 2$

27. $2x - y = 4$
$3x + 2y = 6$

28. $x + y = 12$
$3x - 2y = 6$

29. $4x - 3y = 5$
$x + 2y = 4$

30. $3x - 5y = 2$
$2x - y = 4$

31. $7x - y = 4$
$5x + 2y = 1$

32. $x - 7y = 4$
$-3x + 2y = 6$

33. $4x - 3y = -1$
$y = 2x - 3$

34. $3x - 7y = 28$
$x = 3 - 4y$

35. $7x + y = 14$
$2x - 5y = -33$

36. $3x + y = 4$
$4x - 3y = 1$

37. $x - 4y = 9$
$2x - 3y = 11$

38. $3x - y = 6$
$x + 3y = 2$

39. $4x - y = -5$
$2x + 5y = 13$

40. $3x - y = 5$
$2x + 5y = -8$

41. $3x + 4y = 18$
$2x - y = 1$

42. $4x + 3y = 0$
$2x - y = 0$

43. $5x + 2y = 0$
$x - 3y = 0$

44. $6x - 3y = 6$
$2x - y = 2$

45. $3x + y = 4$
$9x + 3y = 12$

46. $x - 5y = 6$
$2x - 7y = 9$

47. $x + 7y = -5$
$2x - 3y = 5$

48. $y = 2x + 11$
$y = 5x - 1$

49. $y = 2x - 8$
$y = 3x - 13$

50. $y = -4x + 2$
$y = -3x - 1$

51. $x = 3y + 7$
$x = 2y - 1$

52. $x = 4y - 2$
$x = 6y + 8$

53. $x = 3 - 2y$
$x = 5y - 10$

54. $y = 2x - 7$
$y = 4x + 5$

55. $3x - y = 11$
$2x + 5y = -4$

56. $-x + 6y = 8$
$2x + 5y = 1$

In Exercises 57 and 58, A, B, C, and D are nonzero real numbers.

57. Is the following system of equations independent, inconsistent, or dependent?

$x + y = A$
$\quad x = A - y$

58. Is the following system of equations independent, inconsistent, or dependent?

$x + y = B$
$\quad y = C - x, C \neq B$

6.2 Applying Concepts

Rewrite each equation so that the coefficients are integers. Then solve the system of equations.

59. $0.1x - 0.6y = -0.4$
$-0.7x + 0.2y = 0.5$

60. $0.8x - 0.1y = 0.3$
$0.5x - 0.2y = -0.5$

61. $0.4x + 0.5y = 0.2$
$0.3x - 0.1y = 1.1$

62. $-0.1x + 0.3y = 1.1$
$0.4x - 0.1y = -2.2$

63. $1.2x + 0.1y = 1.9$
$0.1x + 0.3y = 2.2$

64. $1.25x - 0.01y = 1.5$
$0.24x - 0.02y = -1.52$

For what value of k does the system of equations have no solution?

65. $2x - 3y = 7$
$kx - 3y = 4$

66. $8x - 4y = 1$
$2x - ky = 3$

67. $\quad x = 4y + 4$
$kx - 8y = 4$

68. The following was offered as a solution to the system of equations shown at the right.

$$2x + 5y = 10 \qquad \bullet \text{ Equation (2)}$$

$$2x + 5\left(\frac{1}{2}x + 2\right) = 10 \qquad \bullet \text{ Substitute } \frac{1}{2}x + 2 \text{ for } y.$$

$$2x + \frac{5}{2}x + 10 = 10 \qquad \bullet \text{ Solve for } x.$$

$$\frac{9}{2}x = 0$$

$$x = 0$$

(1) $\quad y = \dfrac{1}{2}x + 2$

(2) $\quad 2x + 5y = 10$

At this point the student stated that because $x = 0$, the system of equations has no solution. If this assertion is correct, is the system of equations independent, dependent, or inconsistent? If the assertion is not correct, what is the correct solution?

69. When you solve a system of equations by the substitution method, how do you determine whether the system of equations is dependent? How do you determine whether the system of equations is inconsistent?

<table>
<tr><td>6.3</td><td></td></tr>
</table>

Solving Systems of Linear Equations by the Addition Method

OBJECTIVE **1**   **Solve systems of linear equations by the addition method**

Another algebraic method for solving a system of equations is called the **addition method.** It is based on the Addition Property of Equations.

In the system of equations at the right, note the effect of adding equation (2) to equation (1). Because $2y$ and $-2y$ are opposites, adding the equations results in an equation with only one variable.

$$
\begin{array}{ll}
(1) & 3x + 2y = 4 \\
(2) & 4x - 2y = 10 \\
& 7x + 0y = 14 \\
& 7x = 14
\end{array}
$$

The solution of the resulting equation is the first coordinate of the ordered-pair solution of the system.

$$
\begin{array}{l}
7x = 14 \\
x = 2
\end{array}
$$

The second coordinate is found by substituting the value of x into equation (1) or (2) and then solving for y. Equation (1) is used here.

$$
\begin{array}{ll}
(1) & 3x + 2y = 4 \\
& 3 \cdot 2 + 2y = 4 \\
& 6 + 2y = 4 \\
& 2y = -2 \\
& y = -1
\end{array}
$$

The solution is $(2, -1)$.

Sometimes adding the two equations does not eliminate one of the variables. In this case, use the Multiplication Property of Equations to rewrite one or both of the equations so that when the equations are added, one of the variables is eliminated.

To do this, first choose which variable to eliminate. The coefficients of that variable must be opposites. Multiply each equation by a constant that will produce coefficients that are opposites.

Solve by the addition method:
$$
\begin{array}{ll}
3x + 2y = 7 & (1) \\
5x - 4y = 19 & (2)
\end{array}
$$

To eliminate y, multiply each side of equation (1) by 2.

$$
\begin{array}{l}
2(3x + 2y) = 2 \cdot 7 \\
5x - 4y = 19
\end{array}
$$

Now the coefficients of the y terms are opposites.

$$
\begin{array}{l}
6x + 4y = 14 \\
5x - 4y = 19
\end{array}
$$

Add the equations.
Solve for x.

$$
\begin{array}{l}
11x + 0y = 33 \\
11x = 33 \\
x = 3
\end{array}
$$

Substitute the value of x into one of the equations and solve for y. Equation (2) is used here.

$$
\begin{array}{ll}
(2) & 5x - 4y = 19 \\
& 5 \cdot 3 - 4y = 19 \\
& 15 - 4y = 19 \\
& -4y = 4 \\
& y = -1
\end{array}
$$

The solution is $(3, -1)$.

Solve by the addition method: $5x + 6y = 3$ (1)
$2x - 5y = 16$ (2)

To eliminate x, multiply each side of equation (1) by 2 and each side of equation (2) by -5. Note how the constants are selected. The negative sign is used so that the coefficients will be opposites.

$$2 \diagdown (5x + 6y) = 2 \cdot 3$$
$$-5 \diagup (2x - 5y) = -5 \cdot 16$$

Now the coefficients of the x terms are opposites.

$$10x + 12y = 6$$
$$-10x + 25y = -80$$

Add the equations.
Solve for y.

$$0x + 37y = -74$$
$$37y = -74$$
$$y = -2$$

Substitute the value of y into one of the equations and solve for x. Equation (1) is used here.

(1) $5x + 6y = 3$
$5x + 6(-2) = 3$
$5x - 12 = 3$
$5x = 15$
$x = 3$

The solution is $(3, -2)$.

Solve by the addition method: $5x = 2y - 7$ (1)
$3x + 4y = 1$ (2)

Write equation (1) in the form $Ax + By = C$.

$$5x - 2y = -7$$
$$3x + 4y = 1$$

Eliminate y. Multiply each side of equation (1) by 2.

$$2(5x - 2y) = 2(-7)$$
$$3x + 4y = 1$$

Now the coefficients of the y terms are opposites.

$$10x - 4y = -14$$
$$3x + 4y = 1$$

Add the equations.
Solve for x.

$$13x + 0y = -13$$
$$13x = -13$$
$$x = -1$$

Substitute the value of x into one of the equations and solve for y. Equation (1) is used here.

$$5x = 2y - 7$$
$$5(-1) = 2y - 7$$
$$-5 = 2y - 7$$
$$2 = 2y$$
$$1 = y$$

The solution is $(-1, 1)$.

Solve by the addition method: $2x + y = 2$ (1)
$4x + 2y = -5$ (2)

To eliminate y, multiply each side of equation (1) by -2.

$$-4x - 2y = -4$$
$$4x + 2y = -5$$

Add the equations.

This is not a true equation.

$$0x + 0y = -9$$
$$0 = -9$$

The system of equations is inconsistent. The system does not have a solution.

The graphs of the two equations in the preceding system of equations are shown at the left. Note that the graphs are parallel and therefore do not intersect. Thus the system of equations has no solution.

EXAMPLE 1   Solve by the addition method: $2x + 4y = 7$ (1)
$5x - 3y = -2$ (2)

Solution

$5(2x + 4y) = 5 \cdot 7$
$-2(5x - 3y) = -2 \cdot (-2)$

$10x + 20y = 35$
$-10x + 6y = 4$
$26y = 39$

$y = \dfrac{39}{26} = \dfrac{3}{2}$

$2x + 4\left(\dfrac{3}{2}\right) = 7$

$2x + 6 = 7$
$2x = 1$
$x = \dfrac{1}{2}$

- **Eliminate *x*. Multiply each side of equation (1) by 5 and each side of equation (2) by −2.**

- **Add the equations.**

- **Solve for *y*.**

- **Substitute the value of *y* in equation (1).**

- **Solve for *x*.**

The solution is $\left(\dfrac{1}{2}, \dfrac{3}{2}\right)$.

PROBLEM 1   Solve by the addition method: $x - 2y = 1$
$2x + 4y = 0$

Solution   See page S15.

EXAMPLE 2   Solve by the addition method: $6x + 9y = 15$ (1)
$4x + 6y = 10$ (2)

Solution

$4(6x + 9y) = 4 \cdot 15$
$-6(4x + 6y) = -6 \cdot 10$

$24x + 36y = 60$
$-24x - 36y = -60$
$0 = 0$

- **Eliminate *x*. Multiply each side of equation (1) by 4 and each side of equation (2) by −6.**

- **Add the equations.**

$0 = 0$ is a true equation. The system of equations is dependent. The solutions are ordered pairs that satisfy the equation $6x + 9y = 15$.

PROBLEM 2   Solve by the addition method: $2x - 3y = 4$
$-4x + 6y = -8$

Solution   See page S15.

6.3   Concept Review

Determine whether the statement is always true, sometimes true, or never true.

1. When using the addition method of solving a system of linear equations, if you multiply one side of an equation by a number, then you must multiply the other side of the equation by the same number.

2. When a system of linear equations is being solved by the addition method, in order for one of the variables to be eliminated, the coefficients of one of the variables must be opposites.

3. If the two equations in a system of equations have the same slope and different y-intercepts, then the system of equations has an infinite number of solutions.

4. You are using the addition method to solve the system of equations shown at the right. The first step you will perform is to add the two equations.
$$3x + 2y = 6$$
$$2x + 3y = -6$$

5. If the equation $y = -2$ results from solving a system of equations by the addition method, then the solution of the system of equations is -2.

6. If the true equation $-3 = -3$ results from solving a system of equations by the addition method, then the system of equations is dependent.

6.3   Exercises

1   **Solve systems of linear equations by the addition method**

1. Use this system of equations: (1) $-3x - y = 5$
   (2) $x - 4y = 7$
   a. To eliminate x from the system of equations by using the addition method, multiply each side of equation (2) by ___?___.
   b. To eliminate y from the system of equations by using the addition method, multiply each side of equation (1) by ___?___.

2. Use this system of equations: (1) $2x - 3y = 3$
   (2) $x + 6y = 9$

a. To eliminate x from the system of equations by using the addition method, multiply each side of equation (____?____) by (____?____).
b. To eliminate y from the system of equations by using the addition method, multiply each side of equation (____?____) by (____?____).

Solve by the addition method.

3. $x + y = 4$
$x - y = 6$

4. $2x + y = 3$
$x - y = 3$

5. $x + y = 4$
$2x + y = 5$

6. $x - 3y = 2$
$x + 2y = -3$

7. $2x - y = 1$
$x + 3y = 4$

8. $x - 2y = 4$
$3x + 4y = 2$

9. $4x - 5y = 22$
$x + 2y = -1$

10. $3x - y = 11$
$2x + 5y = 13$

11. $2x - y = 1$
$4x - 2y = 2$

12. $x + 3y = 2$
$3x + 9y = 6$

13. $4x + 3y = 15$
$2x - 5y = 1$

14. $3x - 7y = 13$
$6x + 5y = 7$

15. $2x - 3y = 5$
$4x - 6y = 3$

16. $2x + 4y = 3$
$3x + 6y = 8$

17. $5x - 2y = -1$
$x + y = 4$

18. $4x - 3y = 1$
$8x + 5y = 13$

19. $5x + 7y = 10$
$3x - 14y = 6$

20. $7x + 10y = 13$
$4x + 5y = 6$

21. $3x - 2y = 0$
$6x + 5y = 0$

22. $5x + 2y = 0$
$3x + 5y = 0$

23. $2x - 3y = 16$
$3x + 4y = 7$

24. $3x + 4y = 10$
$4x + 3y = 11$

25. $x + 3y = 4$
$2x + 5y = 1$

26. $-2x + 7y = 9$
$3x + 2y = -1$

27. $7x - 2y = 13$
$5x + 3y = 27$

28. $3x + 5y = -11$
$2x - 7y = 3$

29. $8x - 3y = 11$
$6x - 5y = 11$

30. $4x - 8y = 36$
$3x - 6y = 27$

31. $5x + 15y = 20$
$2x + 6y = 8$

32. $2x - 3y = 4$
$-x + 4y = 3$

33. $3x = 2y + 7$
$5x - 2y = 13$

34. $2y = 4 - 9x$
$9x - y = 25$

35. $2x + 9y = 5$
$5x = 6 - 3y$

36. $3x - 4 = y + 18$
$4x + 5y = -21$

37. $2x + 3y = 7 - 2x$
$7x + 2y = 9$

38. $5x - 3y = 3y + 4$
$4x + 3y = 11$

39. $3x + y = 1$
$5x + y = 2$

40. $2x - y = 1$
$2x - 5y = -1$

41. $4x + 3y = 3$
$x + 3y = 1$

42. $2x - 5y = 4$
$x + 5y = 1$

43. $3x - 4y = 1$
$4x + 3y = 1$

44. $2x - 7y = -17$
$3x + 5y = 17$

45. $y = 2x - 3$
$4x + 4y = -1$

46. $4x - 2y = 5$
$2x + 3y = 4$

6.3 Applying Concepts

Solve.

47. $x - 0.2y = 0.2$
$0.2x + 0.5y = 2.2$

48. $0.5x - 1.2y = 0.3$
$0.2x + y = 1.6$

49. $1.25x - 1.5y = -1.75$
$2.5x - 1.75y = -1$

50. The point of intersection of the graphs of the equations $Ax + 2y = 2$ and $2x + By = 10$ is $(2, -2)$. Find A and B.

51. The point of intersection of the graphs of the equations $Ax - 4y = 9$ and $4x + By = -1$ is $(-1, -3)$. Find A and B.

52. Given that the graphs of the equations $2x - y = 6$, $3x - 4y = 4$, and $Ax - 2y = 0$ all intersect at the same point, find A.

53. Given that the graphs of the equations $3x - 2y = -2$, $2x - y = 0$, and $Ax + y = 8$ all intersect at the same point, find A.

54. For what value of k is the system of equations dependent?

a. $2x + 3y = 7$
$4x + 6y = k$

b. $y = \dfrac{2}{3}x - 3$
$y = kx - 3$

c. $x = ky - 1$
$y = 2x + 2$

55. For what values of k is the system of equations independent?

a. $x + y = 7$
$kx + y = 3$

b. $x + 2y = 4$
$kx + 3y = 2$

c. $2x + ky = 1$
$x + 2y = 2$

56. Describe in your own words the process of solving a system of equations by the addition method.

6.4 Application Problems in Two Variables

OBJECTIVE 1   Rate-of-wind and water-current problems

Solving motion problems that involve an object moving with or against a wind or current normally requires two variables. One variable represents the speed of the moving object in calm air or still water, and a second variable represents the rate of the wind or current.

A plane flying with the wind will travel a greater distance per hour than it would travel without the wind. The resulting rate of the plane is represented by the sum of the plane's speed and the rate of the wind.

A plane traveling against the wind, on the other hand, will travel a shorter distance per hour than it would travel without the wind. The resulting rate of the plane is represented by the difference between the plane's speed and the rate of the wind.

The same principle is used to describe the rate of a boat traveling with or against a water current.

Solve: Flying with the wind, a small plane can fly 750 mi in 3 h. Against the wind, the plane can fly the same distance in 5 h. Find the rate of the plane in calm air and the rate of the wind.

STRATEGY   **for solving rate-of-wind and water-current problems**

▶ Choose one variable to represent the rate of the object in calm conditions and a second variable to represent the rate of the wind or current. Use these variables to express the rate of the object with and against the wind or current. Then use these expressions for the rate, as well as the time traveled with and against the wind or current and the fact that $rt = d$, to write expressions for the distance traveled by the object. The results can be recorded in a table.

Rate of plane in calm air: p
Rate of wind: w

With wind: 750 mi in 3 h

Against wind: 750 mi in 5 h

	Rate	·	Time	=	Distance
With the wind	$p + w$	·	3	=	$3(p + w)$
Against the wind	$p - w$	·	5	=	$5(p - w)$

▶ Determine how the expressions for distance are related.

The distance traveled with the wind is 750 mi. $3(p + w) = 750$
The distance traveled against the wind is 750 mi. $5(p - w) = 750$

Solve the system of equations.

$3(p + w) = 750$ $\dfrac{3(p + w)}{3} = \dfrac{750}{3}$ $p + w = 250$

$5(p - w) = 750$ $\dfrac{5(p - w)}{5} = \dfrac{750}{5}$ $p - w = 150$

$ 2p = 400$
$ p = 200$

Substitute the value of p in the equation $p + w = 250$. $p + w = 250$
Solve for w. $200 + w = 250$
$ w = 50$

The rate of the plane in calm air is 200 mph.
The rate of the wind is 50 mph.

EXAMPLE 1 A 600-mile trip from one city to another takes 4 h when a plane is flying with the wind. The return trip against the wind takes 5 h. Find the rate of the plane in still air and the rate of the wind.

Strategy

With wind: 600 mi in 4 h

Against wind: 600 mi in 5 h

▶ Rate of the plane in still air: p
Rate of the wind: w

	Rate	Time	Distance
With wind	$p + w$	4	$4(p + w)$
Against wind	$p - w$	5	$5(p - w)$

▶ The distance traveled with the wind is 600 mi.
The distance traveled against the wind is 600 mi.

Solution $4(p + w) = 600$ (1)
$5(p - w) = 600$ (2)

$$\frac{4(p + w)}{4} = \frac{600}{4}$$ • Simplify equation (1) by dividing each side of the equation by 4.

$$\frac{5(p - w)}{5} = \frac{600}{5}$$ • Simplify equation (2) by dividing each side of the equation by 5.

$p + w = 150$
$p - w = 120$

$2p = 270$ • Add the two equations.
$p = 135$ • Solve for p, the rate of the plane in still air.
$p + w = 150$ • Substitute the value of p into one of the
$135 + w = 150$ equations.
$w = 15$ • Solve for w, the rate of the wind.

The rate of the plane in still air is 135 mph.
The rate of the wind is 15 mph.

PROBLEM 1 A canoeist paddling with the current can travel 24 mi in 3 h. Against the current, it takes 4 h to travel the same distance. Find the rate of the current and the rate of the canoeist in calm water.

Solution See page S15.

OBJECTIVE 2 Application problems

The application problems in this section are varieties of those problems solved earlier in the text. Each of the strategies for the problems in this section will result in a system of equations.

Point of Interest

The Babylonians had a method for solving a system of equations. Here is an adaptation of a problem from an ancient Babylonian text (around 1500 B.C.). "There are two silver blocks. The sum of $\frac{1}{7}$ of the first block and $\frac{1}{11}$ of the second block is one sheqel (a weight). The first block diminished by $\frac{1}{7}$ of its weight equals the second diminished by $\frac{1}{11}$ of its weight. What are the weights of the two blocks?"

Solve: A jeweler purchased 5 oz of a gold alloy and 20 oz of a silver alloy for a total cost of $700. The next day, at the same prices per ounce, the jeweler purchased 4 oz of the gold alloy and 30 oz of the silver alloy for a total cost of $630. Find the cost per ounce of the silver alloy.

STRATEGY **for solving an application problem in two variables**

▶ Choose one variable to represent one of the unknown quantities and a second variable to represent the other unknown quantity. Write numerical or variable expressions for all the remaining quantities. These results can be recorded in two tables, one for each of the conditions.

Cost per ounce of gold: g Cost per ounce of silver: s

First day

	Amount	·	Unit cost	=	Value
Gold	5	·	g	=	$5g$
Silver	20	·	s	=	$20s$

Second day

	Amount	·	Unit cost	=	Value
Gold	4	·	g	=	$4g$
Silver	30	·	s	=	$30s$

▶ Determine a system of equations. The strategies presented in the chapter "Solving Equations and Inequalities: Applications" can be used to determine the relationships between the expressions in the tables. Each table will give one equation of the system.

The total value of the purchase on the first day was $700. The total value of the purchase on the second day was $630.

$$5g + 20s = 700$$
$$4g + 30s = 630$$

Solve the system of equations.

$$\begin{array}{l} 5g + 20s = 700 \\ 4g + 30s = 630 \end{array} \longrightarrow \begin{array}{l} 4(5g + 20s) = 4 \cdot 700 \\ -5(4g + 30s) = -5 \cdot 630 \end{array} \longrightarrow \begin{array}{l} 20g + 80s = 2800 \\ -20g - 150s = -3150 \\ \hline \qquad\quad -70s = -350 \\ \qquad\qquad\quad s = 5 \end{array}$$

The cost per ounce of the silver alloy was $5.

EXAMPLE 2   A store owner purchased 20 incandescent light bulbs and 30 fluorescent bulbs for a total cost of $40. A second purchase, at the same prices, included 30 incandescent bulbs and 10 fluorescent bulbs for a total cost of $25. Find the cost of an incandescent bulb and of a fluorescent bulb.

Strategy   ▶ Cost of an incandescent bulb: I
Cost of a fluorescent bulb: F

First
purchase

	Amount	Unit cost	Value
Incandescent	20	I	$20I$
Fluorescent	30	F	$30F$

Second
purchase

	Amount	Unit cost	Value
Incandescent	30	I	$30I$
Fluorescent	10	F	$10F$

▶ The total of the first purchase was $40.
The total of the second purchase was $25.

Solution

$$20I + 30F = 40 \quad (1)$$
$$30I + 10F = 25 \quad (2)$$

$$20I + 30F = 40$$
$$(-3)(30I + 10F) = (-3)(25)$$

• Eliminate *F*. Multiply each side of equation (2) by −3.

$$20I + 30F = 40$$
$$-90I - 30F = -75$$
$$-70I = -35$$
$$I = 0.5$$

• Add the two equations.
• Solve for *I*, the cost of an incandescent bulb.

$$20I + 30F = 40$$
$$20(0.5) + 30F = 40$$
$$10 + 30F = 40$$
$$30F = 30$$
$$F = 1$$

• Substitute the value of *I* into one of the equations.
• Solve for *F*.

The cost of an incandescent bulb was $.50.
The cost of a fluorescent bulb was $1.00.

PROBLEM 2   Two coin banks contain only dimes and quarters. In the first bank, the total value of the coins is $3.90. In the second bank, there are twice as many dimes as in the first bank and one-half the number of quarters. The total value of the coins in the second bank is $3.30. Find the number of dimes and the number of quarters in the first bank.

Solution   See page S15.

6.4   Concept Review

Determine whether the statement is always true, sometimes true, or never true.

1. A plane flying with the wind is traveling faster than it would be traveling without the wind.

2. The uniform motion equation $r = dt$ is used to solve rate-of-wind and water-current problems.

3. If b represents the rate of a boat in calm water and c represents the rate of the water current, then $b + c$ represents the rate of the boat while it is traveling against the current.

4. Both sides of an equation can be divided by the same number without changing the solution of the equation.

5. If, in a system of equations, p represents the rate of a plane in calm air and w represents the rate of the wind, and the solution of the system is $p = 100$, this means that the rate of the wind is 100.

6. The system of equations at the right represents the following problem:

$$2(p + w) = 600$$
$$3(p - w) = 600$$

A plane flying with the wind flew 600 mi in 2 h. Flying against the wind, the plane could fly the same distance in 3 h. Find the rate of the plane in calm air.

6.4 Exercises

1 Rate-of-wind and water-current problems

1. A boat travels down a river for 2 h (traveling with the current), then turns around and takes 3 h to return (traveling against the current). Let b be the rate of the boat, in miles per hour, in calm water, and let c be the rate of the current, in miles per hour. Complete the following table by replacing the question marks.

	Rate, r	·	Time, t	=	Distance, d
With current	?	·	?	=	?
Against current	?	·	?	=	?

2. Suppose the distance traveled down the river by the boat in Exercise 1 is 36 mi. Use the expressions in the last column of the table in Exercise 1 to write a system of equations that can be solved to find the rate of the boat in calm water and the rate of the current.

3. Traveling with the wind, a plane flies m miles in h hours. Traveling against the wind, the plane flies n miles in h hours. Is m less than, equal to, or greater than n?

4. Traveling against the current, it takes a boat h hours to go m miles. Traveling with the current, the boat takes k hours to go m miles. Is k less than, equal to, or greater than h?

5. A whale swimming against an ocean current traveled 60 mi in 2 h. Swimming in the opposite direction, with the current, the whale was able to travel the same distance in 1.5 h. Find the speed of the whale in calm water and the rate of the ocean current.

6. A plane flying with the jet stream flew from Los Angeles to Chicago, a distance of 2250 mi, in 5 h. Flying against the jet stream, the plane could fly only 1750 mi in the same amount of time. Find the rate of the plane in calm air and the rate of the wind.

7. A rowing team rowing with the current traveled 40 km in 2 h. Rowing against the current, the team could travel only 16 km in 2 h. Find the team's rowing rate in calm water and the rate of the current.

With the current
$2(x + y) = 40$

Against the current
$2(x - y) = 16$

8. Rowing with the current, a canoeist paddled 14 mi in 2 h. Against the current, the canoeist could paddle only 10 mi in the same amount of time. Find the rate of the canoeist in calm water and the rate of the current.

9. A motorboat traveling with the current went 35 mi in 3.5 h. Traveling against the current, the boat went 12 mi in 3 h. Find the rate of the boat in calm water and the rate of the current.

10. A small plane, flying into a headwind, flew 270 mi in 3 h. Flying with the wind, the plane traveled 260 mi in 2 h. Find the rate of the plane in calm air and the rate of the wind.

11. A private Learjet 31A transporting passengers was flying with a tailwind and traveled 1120 mi in 2 h. Flying against the wind on the return trip, the jet was able to travel only 980 mi in 2 h. Find the speed of the jet in calm air and the rate of the wind.

12. A rowing team rowing with the current traveled 18 mi in 2 h. Against the current, the team rowed a distance of 8 mi in the same amount of time. Find the rate of the rowing team in calm water and the rate of the current.

13. A seaplane flying with the wind flew from an ocean port to a lake, a distance of 240 mi, in 2 h. Flying against the wind, it made the trip from the lake to the ocean port in 3 h. Find the rate of the plane in calm air and the rate of the wind.

14. The bird capable of the fastest flying speed is the swift. A swift flying with the wind to a favorite feeding spot traveled 26 mi in 0.2 h. On the return trip, against the wind, the swift was able to travel only 16 mi in the same amount of time. Find the rate of the swift in calm air and the rate of the wind.

15. A Boeing Apache Longbow military helicopter traveling directly into a strong headwind was able to travel 450 mi in 2.5 h. The return trip, now with a tailwind, took 1 h 40 min. Find the speed of the helicopter in calm air and the rate of the wind.

16. With the wind, a quarterback passes a football 140 ft in 2 s. Against the wind, the same pass would have traveled 80 ft in 2 s. Find the rate of the pass and the rate of the wind.

2   Application problems

17. You purchased theater tickets for 4 adults and 2 children. For the same performance, your neighbor purchased tickets for 2 adults and 3 children. Let A be the cost per adult's ticket and C be the cost per child's ticket. Complete the following tables by replacing the question marks.

Your purchase	Amount	·	Unit cost	=	Value
Adult's ticket	?	·	?	=	?
Child's ticket	?	·	?	=	?

Neighbor's purchase	Amount	·	Unit cost	=	Value
Adult's ticket	?	·	?	=	?
Child's ticket	?	·	?	=	?

18. See Exercise 17. Suppose your tickets cost $320 and your neighbor's tickets cost $240. Use the expressions in the last column of the tables in Exercise 17 to write a system of equations that can be solved to find the cost per adult's ticket and the cost per child's ticket.

19. A merchant mixes 4 lb of cinnamon tea with 1 lb of spice tea to create a mixture that costs $2 per pound. When the merchant mixes 1 lb of the cinnamon tea with 4 lb of the spice tea, the mixture costs $3 per pound. Is the cost per pound of the cinnamon tea less than, equal to, or greater than the cost per pound of the spice tea?

20. The total value of nickels and dimes in a bank is $2. If the nickels were dimes and the dimes were nickels, the total value would be $3. Is the number of nickels in the bank less than, equal to, or greater than the number of dimes in the bank?

21. **Business** The manager of a computer software store received two shipments of software. The cost of the first shipment, which contained 12 identical word processing programs and 10 identical spreadsheet programs, was $6190. The second shipment, at the same prices, contained 5 copies of the word processing program and 8 copies of the spreadsheet program. The cost of the second shipment was $3825. Find the cost for one copy of the word processing program.

22. **Business** The manager of a discount clothing store received two shipments of fall clothing. The cost of the first shipment, which contained 10 identical sweaters and 20 identical jackets, was $800. The second shipment, at the same prices, contained 5 of the same sweaters and 15 of the same jackets. The cost of the second shipment was $550. Find the cost of one jacket.

23. **Business** A baker purchased 12 lb of wheat flour and 15 lb of rye flour for a total cost of $18.30. A second purchase, at the same prices, included 15 lb of wheat flour and 10 lb of rye flour. The cost of the second purchase was $16.75. Find the cost per pound of the wheat and rye flours.

24. **Consumerism** A computer online service charges one hourly rate for regular use but a higher hourly rate for designated "premium" areas. One customer was charged $14 after spending 2 h in premium areas and 9 regular hours. Another customer spent 3 h in premium areas and 6 regular hours and was charged $13.50. What is the service charge per hour for regular and premium services?

25. **Wages** Shelly Egan works as a stocker at a grocery store during her summer vacation. She gets paid a standard hourly rate for her day hours but a higher hourly rate for any hours she works during the night shift. One week she worked 17 daylight hours and 8 nighttime hours and earned $191. The next week she earned $219 for a total of 12 daytime and 15 nighttime hours. What is the rate she is being paid for daytime hours and what is the rate for nighttime hours?

26. **Consumerism** For using a computerized financial news network for 50 min during prime time and 70 min during non-prime time, a customer was charged $10.75. A second customer was charged $13.35 for using the network for 60 min of prime time and 90 min of non-prime time. Find the cost per minute for using the financial news network during prime time.

27. **Sports** A basketball team scored 87 points in two-point baskets and three-point baskets. If the two-point baskets had been three-point baskets and the three-point baskets had been two-point baskets, the team would have scored 93 points. Find how many two-point baskets and how many three-point baskets the team scored.

28. **Consumerism** The employees of a hardware store ordered lunch from a local delicatessen. The lunch consisted of 4 turkey sandwiches and 7 orders of french fries, for a total cost of $23.30. The next day, the employees ordered 5 turkey sandwiches and 5 orders of french fries totaling $25.75. What does the delicatessen charge for a turkey sandwich? What is the charge for an order of french fries?

$5n + 25q$

29. **Coin Problems** Two coin banks contain only nickels and quarters. The total value of the coins in the first bank is $2.90. In the second bank, there are two more quarters than in the first bank and twice as many nickels. The total value of the coins in the second bank is $3.80. Find the number of nickels and the number of quarters in the first bank.

$5(2n) + 25(q + 2)$

30. **Coin Problems** Two coin banks contain only nickels and dimes. The total value of the coins in the first bank is $3. In the second bank, there are 4 more nickels than in the first bank and one-half as many dimes. The total value of the coins in the second bank is $2. Find the number of nickels and the number of dimes in the first bank.

31. **Coin Problems** The total value of the dimes and quarters in a coin bank is $3.30. If the quarters were dimes and the dimes were quarters, the total value of the coins would be $3. Find the number of dimes and the number of quarters in the bank.

32. **Coin Problems** The total value of the nickels and dimes in a coin bank is $3. If the nickels were dimes and the dimes were nickels, the total value of the coins would be $3.75. Find the number of nickels and the number of dimes in the bank.

6.4 Applying Concepts

33. **Geometry** Two angles are supplementary. The larger angle is 15° more than twice the measure of the smaller angle. Find the measures of the two angles. (Supplementary angles are two angles whose sum is 180°.)

34. **Geometry** Two angles are complementary. The larger angle is four times the measure of the smaller angle. Find the measure of the two angles. (Complementary angles are two angles whose sum is 90°.)

35. **Investments** An investment club placed a portion of its funds in a 9% annual simple interest account and the remainder in an 8% annual simple interest account. The amount of interest earned for one year was $860. If the amounts placed in each account had been reversed, the interest earned would have been $840. How much was invested in each account?

36. **Investments** An investor has $5000 to invest in two accounts. The first account earns 8% annual simple interest, and the second account earns 10% annual simple interest. How much money should be invested in each account so that the annual interest earned is $600?

37. **Coin Problems** The value of the nickels and dimes in a coin bank is $.25. If the number of nickels and the number of dimes were doubled, the value of the coins would be $.50. How many nickels and how many dimes are in the bank?

38. **Coin Problems** A coin bank contains nickels and dimes, but there are no more than 27 coins. The value of the coins is $2.10. How many different combinations of nickels and/or dimes could be in the bank?

Focus on Problem Solving

Using a Table and Searching for a Pattern

Consider the numbers 10, 12, and 28 and the sum of the proper factors (the natural-number factors less than the number) of those numbers.

$$10: 1 + 2 + 5 = 8 \quad 12: 1 + 2 + 3 + 4 + 6 = 16$$
$$28: 1 + 2 + 4 + 7 + 14 = 28$$

10 is called a *deficient number* because the sum of its proper factors is less than the number ($8 < 10$). 12 is called an *abundant number* because the sum of its proper factors is greater than the number ($16 > 12$), and 28 is called a *perfect number* because the sum of its proper divisors equals the number ($28 = 28$).

Our goal for this "Focus on Problem Solving" is to try to find a method that will determine whether a number is deficient, abundant, or perfect without having to first find all the factors and then add them up. We will use a table and search for a pattern.

Before we begin, recall that a prime number is a number greater than 1 whose only factors are itself and 1 and that each natural number greater than 1 has a unique prime factorization. For instance, the prime factorization of 36 is given by $36 = 2^2 \cdot 3^2$. Note that the proper factors of 36 (1, 2, 3, 4, 6, 9, 12, 18) can be represented in terms of the same prime numbers.

$$1 = 2^0, \quad 2 = 2^1, \quad 3 = 3^1, \quad 4 = 2^2, \quad 6 = 2 \cdot 3, \quad 9 = 3^2, \quad 12 = 2^2 \cdot 3,$$
$$18 = 2 \cdot 3^2$$

Now let us consider a trial problem of determining whether 432 is deficient, abundant, or perfect.

Take Note

This table contains the factor $432 = 2^4 \cdot 3^3$, which is not a proper factor.

We write the prime factorization of 432 as $2^4 \cdot 3^3$ and place the factors of 432 in a table as shown at the right. This table contains *all* the factors of 432 represented in terms of the prime-number factors. The sum of each column is shown at the bottom.

	1	$1 \cdot 3$	$1 \cdot 3^2$	$1 \cdot 3^3$
	2	$2 \cdot 3$	$2 \cdot 3^2$	$2 \cdot 3^3$
	2^2	$2^2 \cdot 3$	$2^2 \cdot 3^2$	$2^2 \cdot 3^3$
	2^3	$2^3 \cdot 3$	$2^3 \cdot 3^2$	$2^3 \cdot 3^3$
	2^4	$2^4 \cdot 3$	$2^4 \cdot 3^2$	$2^4 \cdot 3^3$
Sum	31	$31 \cdot 3$	$31 \cdot 3^2$	$31 \cdot 3^3$

Here is the calculation of the sum for the column headed by $1 \cdot 3$.

$$1 \cdot 3 + 2 \cdot 3 + 2^2 \cdot 3 + 2^3 \cdot 3 + 2^4 \cdot 3 = (1 + 2 + 2^2 + 2^3 + 2^4)3 = 31(3)$$

For the column headed by $1 \cdot 3^2$ there is a similar situation.

$$1 \cdot 3^2 + 2 \cdot 3^2 + 2^2 \cdot 3^2 + 2^3 \cdot 3^2 + 2^4 \cdot 3^2 = (1 + 2 + 2^2 + 2^3 + 2^4)3^2 = 31(3^2)$$

The sum of *all* the factors (including 432) is the sum of the last row.

$$\text{Sum of all factors} = 31 + 31 \cdot 3 + 31 \cdot 3^2 + 31 \cdot 3^3 = 31(1 + 3 + 3^2 + 3^3)$$
$$= 31(40) = 1240$$

To find the sum of the *proper* factors, we must subtract 432 from 1240; we get 808 (see "Take Note" on the preceding page). Thus 432 is abundant.

We now look for some pattern for the sum of all the factors. Note that

Sum of left $1 + 2 + 2^2 + 2^3 + 2^4 = $ ⌐ ⌐ $ = 1 + 3 + 3^2 + 3^3$ Sum of
  column   top row

$$31(40) = 1240$$

This suggests that the sum of the proper factors can be found by finding the sum of all the prime-power factors for each prime, multiplying those numbers, and then subtracting the original number. Although we have not proved this for all cases, it is a true statement.

For instance, to find the sum of the proper factors of 3240, first find the prime factorization:

$$3240 = 2^3 \cdot 3^4 \cdot 5$$

Now find the following sums:

$$1 + 2 + 2^2 + 2^3 = 15 \qquad 1 + 3 + 3^2 + 3^3 + 3^4 = 121 \qquad 1 + 5 = 6$$

The sum of the proper factors $= (15)(121)6 - 3240 = 7650$. 3240 is abundant.

Determine whether the number is deficient, abundant, or perfect.

1. 200   **2.** 3125   **3.** 8128   **4.** 10,000
5. Is a prime number deficient, abundant, or perfect?

Projects & Group Activities

Solving a System of Equations with a Graphing Calculator

A graphing calculator can be used to approximate the solution of a system of equations in two variables. Graph each equation of the system of equations, and then approximate the coordinates of the point of intersection. The process by which you approximate the solution depends on the make and model of calculator you have. In all cases, however, you must first solve each equation in the system of equations for y.

Solve: $2x - 5y = 9$
         $4x + 3y = 2$

Solve each equation for y.

$2x - 5y = 9$ $4x + 3y = 2$
$-5y = -2x + 9$ $3y = -4x + 2$
$y = \dfrac{2}{5}x - \dfrac{9}{5}$ $y = -\dfrac{4}{3}x + \dfrac{2}{3}$

The graphing calculator screens on the next page are taken from a TI-83 Plus. Similar screens would appear if a different graphing calculator were used.

For the TI-83, TI-83 Plus, and TI-84 Plus, press $\boxed{\text{Y=}}$. Enter one equation as Y1 and the other as Y2. The result should be similar to the screen at the right.

Press $\boxed{\text{GRAPH}}$. The graphs of the two equations should appear on the screen. If the point of intersection is not on the screen, adjust the viewing window by pressing the $\boxed{\text{WINDOW}}$ key.

Press $\boxed{\text{2nd}}$ CALC 5 $\boxed{\text{ENTER}}$ $\boxed{\text{ENTER}}$ $\boxed{\text{ENTER}}$. After a few seconds, the point of intersection will appear at the bottom of the screen as X = 1.4230769, Y = −1.230769.

Solve by using a graphing calculator.

1. $4x - 5y = 48$
$5x + 7y = 7$

2. $3x + 2y = 11$
$7x - 6y = 13$

3. $x = 3y + 2$
$y = 4x - 2$

4. $x = 2y - 5$
$x = 3y + 2$

Chapter 6 Summary

Key Words

Equations considered together are called a **system of equations.** [6.1.1, p. 328]

A **solution of a system of equations in two variables** is an ordered pair that is a solution of each equation of the system. [6.1.1, p. 329]

Examples

An example of a system of equations is

$$4x + y = 6$$
$$3x + 2y = 7$$

The solution of the system of equations shown above is the ordered pair (1, 2) because it is a solution of each equation in the system.

An **independent system of equations** has one solution. The graphs of the equations in an independent system of linear equations intersect at one point.   [6.1.1, pp. 330–331]

An **inconsistent system of equations** has no solution. The graphs of the equations in an inconsistent system of linear equations are parallel lines. If, when you are solving a system of equations algebraically, the variable is eliminated and the result is a false equation, such as $-3 = 8$, the system is inconsistent.   [6.1.1/6.2.1/6.3.1, pp. 330–331, 339, 344–345]

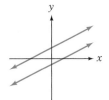

A **dependent system of equations** has an infinite number of solutions. The graphs of the equations in a dependent system of linear equations represent the same line. If, when you are solving a system of equations algebraically, the variable is eliminated and the result is a true equation, such as $1 = 1$, the system is dependent.   [6.1.1/6.2.1/6.3.1, pp. 330–331, 339, 345]

Essential Rules and Procedures

To solve a system of linear equations in two variables by graphing, graph each equation on the same coordinate system. If the lines graphed intersect at one point, the point of intersection is the ordered pair that is a solution of the system. If the lines graphed are parallel, the system is inconsistent. If the lines represent the same line, the system is dependent. [6.1.1, pp. 328–331]

Solve by graphing: $x + 2y = 4$
$$2x + y = -1$$

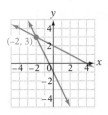

The solution is $(-2, 3)$.

To solve a system of linear equations by the substitution method, one variable must be written in terms of the other variable. [6.2.1, p. 337]

Solve by substitution: $2x - y = 5$ (1)
$$3x + y = 5 \quad (2)$$

$3x + y = 5$
$y = -3x + 5$ • **Solve equation (2) for y.**

$2x - y = 5$
$2x - (-3x + 5) = 5$ • **Substitute for y in equation (1).**
$2x + 3x - 5 = 5$
$5x = 10$
$x = 2$

$y = -3x + 5$ • **Substitute the**
$y = -3(2) + 5$ **value of x to**
$y = -1$ **find y.**

The solution is $(2, -1)$.

To solve a system of linear equations by the addition method, use the Multiplication Property of Equations to rewrite one or both of the equations so that the coefficients of one variable are opposites. Then add the two equations and solve for the variables.   [6.3.1, p. 343]

Solve by the addition method:

$3x + y = 4$ (1)
$x + y = 6$ (2)

$3x + y = 4$
$-x - y = -6$ • Multiply both sides of equation (2) by -1.

$2x = -2$ • Add the two equations.
$x = -1$ • Solve for x.

• Substitute the value of x to find y.

$x + y = 6$
$-1 + y = 6$
$y = 7$

The solution is $(-1, 7)$.

Chapter 6 Review Exercises

1. Solve by substitution: $4x + 7y = 3$
$x = y - 2$

2. Solve by graphing: $3x + y = 3$
$x = 2$

3. Solve by the addition method: $3x + 8y = -1$
$x - 2y = -5$

4. Solve by substitution: $8x - y = 2$
$y = 5x + 1$

5. Solve by graphing: $x + y = 2$
$x - y = 0$

6. Solve by the addition method: $4x - y = 9$
$2x + 3y = -13$

7. Solve by substitution: $-2x + y = -4$
$x = y + 1$

8. Solve by the addition method:
$8x - y = 25$
$32x - 4y = 100$

9. Solve by the addition method: $5x - 15y = 30$
$2x + 6y = 0$

10. Solve by graphing: $3x - y = 6$
$y = -3$

11. Solve by the addition method: $7x - 2y = 0$
$2x + y = -11$

12. Solve by substitution: $x - 5y = 4$
$y = x - 4$

13. Is $(-1, -3)$ a solution of the system
$5x + 4y = -17$
$2x - y = 1$?

14. Solve by the addition method:
$6x + 4y = -3$
$12x - 10y = -15$

15. Solve by the addition method: $5x + 2y = -9$
$12x - 7y = 2$

16. Solve by graphing: $x - 3y = 12$
$y = x - 6$

17. Solve by the addition method:
$5x + 7y = 21$
$20x + 28y = 63$

18. Solve by substitution: $9x + 12y = -1$
$x - 4y = -1$

19. Solve by graphing: $4x - 2y = 8$
$\qquad\qquad\qquad\qquad y = 2x - 4$

20. Solve by the addition method:
$\qquad\qquad\qquad 3x + y = -2$
$\qquad\qquad\qquad -9x - 3y = 6$

21. Solve by the addition method: $11x - 2y = 4$
$\qquad\qquad\qquad\qquad\qquad\qquad\qquad 25x - 4y = 2$

22. Solve by substitution: $4x + 3y = 12$
$\qquad\qquad\qquad\qquad\qquad y = -\dfrac{4}{3}x + 4$

23. Solve by graphing: $\qquad y = -\dfrac{1}{4}x + 3$
$\qquad\qquad\qquad\qquad\qquad\quad 2x - y = 6$

24. Solve by the addition method: $\qquad 2x - y = 5$
$\qquad\qquad\qquad\qquad\qquad\qquad\qquad 10x - 5y = 20$

25. Solve by substitution: $6x + 5y = -2$
$\qquad\qquad\qquad\qquad\qquad y = 2x - 2$

26. Is $(-2, 0)$ a solution of the system
$\qquad -x + 9y = 2$
$\qquad 6x - 4y = 12$?

27. Solve by the addition method: $6x - 18y = 7$
$\qquad\qquad\qquad\qquad\qquad\qquad\quad 9x + 24y = 2$

28. Solve by substitution: $12x - 9y = 18$
$\qquad\qquad\qquad\qquad\qquad y = \dfrac{4}{3}x - 3$

29. Solve by substitution: $\quad 9x - y = -3$
$\qquad\qquad\qquad\qquad\qquad 18x - y = 0$

30. Solve by graphing: $x + 2y = 3$
$\qquad\qquad\qquad\qquad\qquad y = -\dfrac{1}{2}x + 1$

31. Solve by the addition method: $7x - 9y = 9$
$\qquad\qquad\qquad\qquad\qquad\qquad\quad 3x - y = 1$

32. Solve by substitution: $7x + 3y = -16$
$\qquad\qquad\qquad\qquad\qquad x - 2y = 5$

33. Solve by substitution: $5x - 3y = 6$
$\qquad\qquad\qquad\qquad\qquad x - y = 2$

34. Solve by the addition method: $\quad 6x + y = 12$
$\qquad\qquad\qquad\qquad\qquad\qquad\quad 9x + 2y = 18$

35. Solve by the addition method: $5x + 12y = 4$
$\qquad\qquad\qquad\qquad\qquad\qquad\quad x + 6y = 8$

36. Solve by substitution: $6x - y = 0$
$\qquad\qquad\qquad\qquad\qquad 7x - y = 1$

37. Uniform Motion Flying with the wind, a plane can travel 800 mi in 4 h. Against the wind, the plane requires 5 h to fly the same distance. Find the rate of the plane in calm air and the rate of the wind.

38. Recreation Admission to a movie theater is $7 for adults and $5 for children. If the receipts from 200 tickets were $1120, how many adult tickets and how many children's tickets were sold?

39. Uniform Motion A canoeist traveling with the current traveled the 30 mi between two riverside campsites in 3 h. The return trip took 5 h. Find the rate of the canoeist in still water and the rate of the current.

40. Postage A small wood carving company mailed 190 advertisements, some requiring 33¢ in postage and others requiring 55¢ in postage. If the total cost for the mailings was $75.90, how many mailings that required 33¢ were sent?

41. Uniform Motion A boat traveling with the current went 48 km in 3 h. Against the current, the boat traveled 24 km in 2 h. Find the rate of the boat in calm water and the rate of the current.

42. Purchases A music shop sells some compact discs for $15 and some for $10. A customer spent $120 on 10 compact discs. How many at each price did the customer purchase?

43. Uniform Motion With a tailwind, a flight crew flew 420 km in 3 h. Flying against the tailwind, the crew flew 440 km in 4 h. Find the rate of the plane in calm air and the rate of the wind.

44. Uniform Motion A paddle boat can travel 4 mi downstream in 1 h. Paddling upstream, against the current, the paddle boat travels 2 mi in 1 h. Find the rate of the boat in calm water and the rate of the current.

45. Farming A silo contains a mixture of lentils and corn. If 50 bushels of lentils were added to this mixture, there would be twice as many bushels of lentils as bushels of corn. If 150 bushels of corn were added to the original mixture, there would be the same amount of corn as lentils. How many bushels of each are in the silo?

46. Uniform Motion Flying with the wind, a small plane flew 360 mi in 3 h. Against the wind, the plane took 4 h to fly the same distance. Find the rate of the plane in calm air and the rate of the wind.

47. Coins A coin purse contains 80¢ in nickels and dimes. If there are 12 coins in all, how many dimes are in the coin purse?

48. Uniform Motion A pilot flying with the wind flew 2100 mi from one city to another in 6 h. The return trip against the wind took 7 h. Find the rate of the plane in calm air and the rate of the wind.

49. Investments An investor buys 1500 shares of stock, some costing $6 per share and the rest costing $25 per share. If the total cost of the stock is $12,800, how many shares of each did the investor buy?

50. Uniform Motion Rowing with the current, a sculling team went 24 mi in 2 h. Rowing against the current, the team went 18 mi in 3 h. Find the rate of the sculling team in calm water and the rate of the current.

Chapter 6 Test

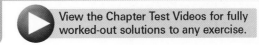

View the Chapter Test Videos for fully worked-out solutions to any exercise.

1. Solve by substitution: $4x - y = 11$
$$y = 2x - 5$$

2. Solve by the addition method: $4x + 3y = 11$
$$5x - 3y = 7$$

3. Is $(-2, 3)$ a solution of the system
$2x + 5y = 11$
$x + 3y = 7$?

4. Solve by substitution: $x = 2y + 3$
$$3x - 2y = 5$$

5. Solve by the addition method: $2x - 5y = 6$
$$4x + 3y = -1$$

6. Solve by graphing: $3x + 2y = 6$
$$5x + 2y = 2$$

7. Solve by substitution: $4x + 2y = 3$
$$y = -2x + 1$$

8. Solve by substitution: $3x + 5y = 1$
$$2x - y = 5$$

9. Solve by the addition method: $7x + 3y = 11$
$$2x - 5y = 9$$

10. Solve by substitution: $3x - 5y = 13$
$$x + 3y = 1$$

11. Solve by the addition method: $5x + 6y = -7$
$$3x + 4y = -5$$

12. Is $(2, 1)$ a solution of the system $3x - 2y = 8$
$$4x + 5y = 3?$$

13. Solve by substitution: $3x - y = 5$
$$y = 2x - 3$$

14. Solve by the addition method: $3x + 2y = 2$
$$5x - 2y = 14$$

15. Solve by graphing: $3x + 2y = 6$
$$3x - 2y = 6$$

16. Solve by substitution: $x = 3y + 1$
$$2x + 5y = 13$$

17. Solve by the addition method: $5x + 4y = 7$
$$3x - 2y = 13$$

18. Solve by graphing: $3x + 6y = 2$
$$y = -\frac{1}{2}x + \frac{1}{3}$$

19. Solve by substitution: $4x - 3y = 1$
$$2x + y = 3$$

20. Solve by the addition method: $5x - 3y = 29$
$$4x + 7y = -5$$

21. Solve by substitution: $3x - 5y = -23$
$$x + 2y = -4$$

22. Solve by the addition method: $9x - 2y = 17$
$$5x + 3y = -7$$

23. **Uniform Motion** With the wind, a plane flies 240 mi in 2 h. Against the wind, the plane requires 3 h to fly the same distance. Find the rate of the plane in calm air and the rate of the wind.

24. **Uniform Motion** With the current, a motorboat can travel 48 mi in 3 h. Against the current, the boat requires 4 h to travel the same distance. Find the rate of the boat in calm water and the rate of the current.

25. **Coins** Two coin banks contain only dimes and nickels. In the first bank, the total value of the coins is $5.50. In the second bank, there are one-half as many dimes as in the first bank and 10 fewer nickels. The total value of the coins in the second bank is $3. Find the number of dimes and the number of nickels in the first bank.

Cumulative Review Exercises

1. Given $A = \{-8, -4, 0\}$, which elements of set A are less than or equal to -4?

2. Use the roster method to write the set of positive integers less than or equal to 10.

3. Simplify: $12 - 2(7 - 5)^2 \div 4$

4. Simplify: $2[5a - 3(2 - 5a) - 8]$

5. Evaluate $\dfrac{a^2 - b^2}{2a}$ when $a = 4$ and $b = -2$.

6. Solve: $-\dfrac{3}{4}x = \dfrac{9}{8}$

7. Solve: $4 - 3(2 - 3x) = 7x - 9$

8. Solve: $3[2 - 4(x + 1)] = 6x - 2$

9. Solve: $-7x - 5 > 4x + 50$

10. Solve: $5 + 2(x + 1) \le 13$

11. What percent of 50 is 12?

12. Find the x- and y-intercepts of $3x - 6y = 12$.

13. Find the slope of the line that contains the points whose coordinates are $(2, -3)$ and $(-3, 4)$.

14. Find the equation of the line that contains the point whose coordinates are $(-2, 3)$ and has slope $-\dfrac{3}{2}$.

15. Graph: $3x - 2y = 6$

16. Graph: $y = -\dfrac{1}{3}x + 3$

17. Graph the solution set of $y > -3x + 4$.

18. Graph: $f(x) = \dfrac{3}{4}x + 2$

19. Find the domain and range of the relation $\{(-5, 5), (0, 5), (1, 5), (5, 5)\}$. Is the relation a function?

20. Evaluate $f(x) = -2x - 5$ at $x = -4$.

21. Is $(2, 0)$ a solution of the system $5x - 3y = 10$
$4x + 7y = 8$?

22. Solve by substitution: $2x - 3y = -7$
$x + 4y = 2$

23. Solve by graphing: $2x + 3y = 6$
$3x + y = 2$

24. Solve by the addition method: $5x - 2y = 8$
$4x + 3y = 11$

25. Find the range of the function given by the equation $f(x) = 5x - 2$ if the domain is $\{-4, -2, 0, 2, 4\}$.

26. Manufacturing A business manager has determined that the cost per unit for a camera is $90 and that the fixed costs per month are $3500. Find the number of cameras produced during a month in which the total cost was $21,500. Use the equation $T = U \cdot N + F$, where T is the total cost, U is the cost per unit, N is the number of units produced, and F is the fixed cost.

27. Investments A total of $8750 is invested in two simple interest accounts. On one account, the annual simple interest rate is 9.6%. On the second account, the annual simple interest rate is 7.2%. How much should be invested in each account so that both accounts earn the same amount of interest?

28. Uniform Motion Flying with the wind, a plane can fly 570 mi in 3 h. Flying against the wind, it takes the same amount of time to fly 390 mi. Find the rate of the plane in calm air and the rate of the wind.

29. Uniform Motion With the current, a motorboat can travel 24 mi in 2 h. Against the current, the boat requires 3 h to travel the same distance. Find the rate of the boat in calm water.

30. Coins Two coin banks contain only dimes and nickels. In the first bank, the total value of the coins is $5.25. In the second bank, there are one-half as many dimes as in the first bank and 15 fewer nickels. The total value of the coins in the second bank is $2.50. Find the number of dimes in the first bank.

7 Polynomials

As we learned in the chapter "Linear Equations and Inequalities," the population of the United States grows from year to year. This has resulted in a drastic decrease in woodlands and farmland and an increase in land used for housing developments and shopping centers. It has led demographers (people who study the characteristics of human populations, such as their size, growth, density, and distribution) to ask questions about population and land allocation. The **Projects & Group Activities on page 409** ask you to determine the answers to questions concerning land allocation.

Online Study Center

 DVD   SSM

Need help? For online student resources, such as section quizzes, visit the Online Study Center at www.cengage.com/math/aufmann.

Prep Test

1. Subtract: $-2 - (-3)$

2. Multiply: $-3(6)$

3. Simplify: $-\dfrac{24}{-36}$

4. Evaluate $3n^4$ when $n = -2$.

5. If $\dfrac{a}{b}$ is a fraction in simplest form, what number is not a possible value of b?

6. Are $2x^2$ and $2x$ like terms?

7. Simplify: $3x^2 - 4x + 1 + 2x^2 - 5x - 7$

8. Simplify: $-4y + 4y$

9. Simplify: $-3(2x - 8)$

10. Simplify: $3xy - 4y - 2(5xy - 7y)$

7.1 Addition and Subtraction of Polynomials

OBJECTIVE 1   Add polynomials

A **monomial** is a number, a variable, or a product of numbers and variables. For instance,

7	b	$\dfrac{2}{3}a$	$12xy^2$
A number	A variable	A product of a number and a variable	A product of a number and variables

The expression $3\sqrt{x}$ is not a monomial because $\sqrt{x}$ cannot be written as a product of variables. The expression $\dfrac{2x}{y^2}$ is not a monomial because it is a *quotient* of variables.

A **polynomial** is a variable expression in which the terms are monomials.

A polynomial of *one* term is a **monomial.** $-7x^2$ is a monomial.

A polynomial of *two* terms is a **binomial.** $4x + 2$ is a binomial.

A polynomial of *three* terms is a **trinomial.** $7x^2 + 5x - 7$ is a trinomial.

The terms of a polynomial in one variable are usually arranged so that the exponents of the variable decrease from left to right. This is called **descending order.**

$$4x^3 - 3x^2 + 6x - 1$$
$$5y^4 - 2y^3 + y^2 - 7y + 8$$

The **degree of a polynomial in one variable** is the value of the largest exponent on the variable. The degree of $4x^3 - 3x^2 + 6x - 1$ is 3. The degree of $5y^4 - 2y^3 + y^2 - 7y + 8$ is 4. The degree of a nonzero constant is zero. For instance, the degree of 7 is zero. The number zero has no degree.

Polynomials can be added, using either a vertical or a horizontal format, by combining like terms.

EXAMPLE 1   Add: $(2x^2 + x - 1) + (3x^3 + 4x^2 - 5)$
Use a vertical format.

Solution

$$\begin{array}{r} 2x^2 + x - 1 \\ 3x^3 + 4x^2 \quad - 5 \\ \hline 3x^3 + 6x^2 + x - 6 \end{array}$$

• Arrange the terms of each polynomial in descending order with like terms in the same column.
• Combine the terms in each column.

PROBLEM 1   Add: $(2x^2 + 4x - 3) + (5x^2 - 6x)$
Use a vertical format.

Solution   See page S15.

EXAMPLE 2   Add: $(3x^3 - 7x + 2) + (7x^2 + 2x - 7)$
Use a horizontal format.

Solution $(3x^3 - 7x + 2) + (7x^2 + 2x - 7)$
$= 3x^3 + 7x^2 + (-7x + 2x) + (2 - 7)$

$= 3x^3 + 7x^2 - 5x - 5$

• Use the Commutative and Associative Properties of Addition to rearrange and group like terms.
• Combine like terms, and write the polynomial in descending order.

PROBLEM 2   Add: $(-4x^2 - 3xy + 2y^2) + (3x^2 - 4y^2)$
Use a horizontal format.

Solution   See page S16.

OBJECTIVE **2**   **Subtract polynomials**

The **opposite** of the polynomial $x^2 - 2x + 3$ is $-(x^2 - 2x + 3)$.

To simplify the opposite of a polynomial, remove the parentheses and change the sign of every term inside the parentheses.

$$-(x^2 - 2x + 3) = -x^2 + 2x - 3$$

Take Note

The **opposite of a polynomial** is the polynomial with the sign of every term changed.

Polynomials can be subtracted using either a vertical or a horizontal format. To subtract, add the opposite of the second polynomial to the first.

EXAMPLE 3 Subtract: $(-3x^2 - 7) - (-8x^2 + 3x - 4)$
Use a vertical format.

Solution The opposite of $-8x^2 + 3x - 4$ is $8x^2 - 3x + 4$.

$$
\begin{array}{r}
-3x^2 \qquad - 7 \\
\underline{8x^2 - 3x + 4} \\
5x^2 - 3x - 3
\end{array}
$$

• **Write the terms of each polynomial in descending order with like terms in the same column.**

• **Combine the terms in each column.**

PROBLEM 3 Subtract: $(8y^2 - 4xy + x^2) - (2y^2 - xy + 5x^2)$
Use a vertical format.

Solution See page S16.

EXAMPLE 4 Subtract: $(5x^2 - 3x + 4) - (-3x^3 - 2x + 8)$
Use a horizontal format.

Solution
$$
\begin{aligned}
&(5x^2 - 3x + 4) - (-3x^3 - 2x + 8) \\
&= (5x^2 - 3x + 4) + (3x^3 + 2x - 8) \\
&= 3x^3 + 5x^2 + (-3x + 2x) + (4 - 8) \\
&= 3x^3 + 5x^2 - x - 4
\end{aligned}
$$

• **Rewrite subtraction as addition of the opposite.**

• **Combine like terms. Write the polynomial in descending order.**

PROBLEM 4 Subtract: $(-3a^2 - 4a + 2) - (5a^3 + 2a - 6)$
Use a horizontal format.

Solution See page S16.

  Concept Review

Determine whether the statement is always true, sometimes true, or never true.

1. The terms of a polynomial are monomials.

2. The polynomial $5x^3 + 4x^6 + 3x + 2$ is written in descending order.

3. The degree of the polynomial $7x^2 - 8x + 1$ is 3.

4. Like terms have the same coefficient and the same variable part.

5. The opposite of the polynomial $ax^3 - bx^2 + cx + d$ is $-ax^3 + bx^2 - cx - d$.

6. Subtraction is addition of the opposite.

7.1 Exercises

1 Add polynomials

State whether the polynomial is a monomial, a binomial, or a trinomial.

1. $8x^4 - 6x^2$

2. $4a^2b^2 + 9ab + 10$

3. $7x^3y^4$

State whether or not the expression is a monomial.

4. $3\sqrt{x}$

5. $\dfrac{4}{x}$

6. x^2y^2

State whether or not the expression is a polynomial.

7. $\dfrac{1}{5}x^3 + \dfrac{1}{2}x$

8. $\dfrac{1}{5x^2} + \dfrac{1}{2x}$

9. $x + \sqrt{5}$

10. In your own words, explain the terms *monomial, binomial, trinomial,* and *polynomial.* Give an example of each.

11. To use a vertical format to add polynomials, arrange the terms of each polynomial in ___?___ order with ___?___ terms in the same column.

12. Use a horizontal format to add $(-4y^3 + 3xy + x^3) + (2y^3 - 8xy)$.

$(-4y^3 + 3xy + x^3) + (2y^3 - 8xy)$

$= (-4y^3 + \underline{\ \ ?\ \ }) + (3xy + \underline{\ \ ?\ \ }) + x^3$

$= \underline{\ \ ?\ \ }$

- Use the Commutative and Associative Properties of Addition to rearrange and group like terms.
- Combine like terms and write the terms of the polynomial in descending order.

Add. Use a vertical format.

13. $(x^2 + 7x) + (-3x^2 - 4x)$

14. $(3y^2 - 2y) + (5y^2 + 6y)$

15. $(y^2 + 4y) + (-4y - 8)$

16. $(3x^2 + 9x) + (6x - 24)$

17. $(2x^2 + 6x + 12) + (3x^2 + x + 8)$

18. $(x^2 + x + 5) + (3x^2 - 10x + 4)$

19. $(x^3 - 7x + 4) + (2x^2 + x - 10)$

20. $(3y^3 + y^2 + 1) + (-4y^3 - 6y - 3)$

21. $(2a^3 - 7a + 1) + (-3a^2 - 4a + 1)$

22. $(5r^3 - 6r^2 + 3r) + (r^2 - 2r - 3)$

Add. Use a horizontal format.

23. $(4x^2 + 2x) + (x^2 + 6x)$

24. $(-3y^2 + y) + (4y^2 + 6y)$

25. $(4x^2 - 5xy) + (3x^2 + 6xy - 4y^2)$

26. $(2x^2 - 4y^2) + (6x^2 - 2xy + 4y^2)$

27. $(2a^2 - 7a + 10) + (a^2 + 4a + 7)$

28. $(-6x^2 + 7x + 3) + (3x^2 + x + 3)$

29. $(5x^3 + 7x - 7) + (10x^2 - 8x + 3)$

30. $(3y^3 + 4y + 9) + (2y^2 + 4y - 21)$

31. $(2r^2 - 5r + 7) + (3r^3 - 6r)$

32. $(3y^3 + 4y + 14) + (-4y^2 + 21)$

33. $(3x^2 + 7x + 10) + (-2x^3 + 3x + 1)$

34. $(7x^3 + 4x - 1) + (2x^2 - 6x + 2)$

For Exercises 35 and 36, use these three polynomials in which a, b, c, and d are all positive numbers.

$$P = ax^3 + bx^2 - cx + d$$

$$Q = -ax^3 - bx^2 + cx - d$$

$$R = -ax^3 + bx^2 + cx + d$$

35. Which sum will be a polynomial of degree 3, $P + Q$, $Q + R$, or $P + R$?

36. Which sum will be zero, $P + Q$, $Q + R$, or $P + R$?

2 Subtract polynomials

37. The opposite of $7x^2 + 5x - 3$ is $-(7x^2 + 5x - 3) = $ ___?___ .

38. $(5x^2 + 7x - 2) - (4x^2 - 6x + 3) = (5x^2 + 7x - 2) + ($ ___?___ $)$

Subtract. Use a vertical format.

39. $(x^2 - 6x) - (x^2 - 10x)$

40. $(y^2 + 4y) - (y^2 + 10y)$

41. $(2y^2 - 4y) - (-y^2 + 2)$

42. $(-3a^2 - 2a) - (4a^2 - 4)$

43. $(x^2 - 2x + 1) - (x^2 + 5x + 8)$

44. $(3x^2 + 2x - 2) - (5x^2 - 5x + 6)$

45. $(4x^3 + 5x + 2) - (-3x^2 + 2x + 1)$

46. $(5y^2 - y + 2) - (-2y^3 + 3y - 3)$

47. $(2y^3 + 6y - 2) - (y^3 + y^2 + 4)$

48. $(-2x^2 - x + 4) - (-x^3 + 3x - 2)$

Subtract. Use a horizontal format.

49. $(y^2 - 10xy) - (2y^2 + 3xy)$

50. $(x^2 - 3xy) - (-2x^2 + xy)$

51. $(3x^2 + x - 3) - (x^2 + 4x - 2)$

52. $(5y^2 - 2y + 1) - (-3y^2 - y - 2)$

53. $(-2x^3 + x - 1) - (-x^2 + x - 3)$

54. $(2x^2 + 5x - 3) - (3x^3 + 2x - 5)$

55. $(4a^3 - 2a + 1) - (a^3 - 2a + 3)$

56. $(b^2 - 8b + 7) - (4b^3 - 7b - 8)$

57. $(4y^3 - y - 1) - (2y^2 - 3y + 3)$

58. $(3x^2 - 2x - 3) - (2x^3 - 2x^2 + 4)$

For Exercises 59 and 60, P and Q are polynomials such that $P = ax^2 - bx + c$ and $Q = -dx^2 - ex + f$, where a, b, c, d, e, and f are all positive numbers.

59. If $a > d$, $b > e$, and $c > f$, state the sign of the coefficient of each term of $P - Q$.
  a. the x^2 term   **b.** the x term   **c.** the constant term

60. If $a < d$, $b > e$, and $c < f$, state the sign of the coefficient of each term of $Q - P$.
  a. the x^2 term   **b.** the x term   **c.** the constant term

7.1   Applying Concepts

Simplify.

61. $\left(\dfrac{2}{3}a^2 + \dfrac{1}{2}a - \dfrac{3}{4}\right) - \left(\dfrac{5}{3}a^2 + \dfrac{1}{2}a + \dfrac{1}{4}\right)$

62. $\left(\dfrac{3}{5}x^2 + \dfrac{1}{6}x - \dfrac{5}{8}\right) + \left(\dfrac{2}{5}x^2 + \dfrac{5}{6}x - \dfrac{3}{8}\right)$

Solve.

63. What polynomial must be added to $3x^2 - 4x - 2$ so that the sum is $-x^2 + 2x + 1$?

64. What polynomial must be added to $-2x^3 + 4x - 7$ so that the sum is $x^2 - x - 1$?

65. What polynomial must be subtracted from $6x^2 - 4x - 2$ so that the difference is $2x^2 + 2x - 5$?

66. What polynomial must be subtracted from $2x^3 - x^2 + 4x - 2$ so that the difference is $x^3 + 2x - 8$?

67. Is it possible to subtract two polynomials, each of degree 3, and have the difference be a polynomial of degree 2? If so, give an example. If not, explain why not.

68. Is it possible to add two polynomials, each of degree 3, and have the sum be a polynomial of degree 2? If so, give an example. If not, explain why not.

7.2 **Multiplication of Monomials**

OBJECTIVE 1   **Multiply monomials**

Recall that in the exponential expression x^5, x is the base and 5 is the exponent. The exponent indicates the number of times the base occurs as a factor.

The product of exponential expressions with the *same* base can be simplified by writing each expression in factored form and writing the result with an exponent.

$$x^3 \cdot x^2 = \overbrace{(x \cdot x \cdot x)}^{3 \text{ factors}} \cdot \overbrace{(x \cdot x)}^{2 \text{ factors}}$$
$$\underbrace{\qquad\qquad\qquad}_{5 \text{ factors}}$$
$$= x \cdot x \cdot x \cdot x \cdot x$$
$$= x^5$$

Adding the exponents results in the same product.

$$x^3 \cdot x^2 = x^{3+2} = x^5$$

Rule for Multiplying Exponential Expressions

If m and n are integers, then $x^m \cdot x^n = x^{m+n}$.

For example, in the expression $a^2 \cdot a^6 \cdot a$, the bases are the same. The expression can be simplified by adding the exponents. Recall that $a = a^1$.

$$a^2 \cdot a^6 \cdot a = a^{2+6+1} = a^9$$

Take Note

The Rule for Multiplying Exponential Expressions requires that the bases be the same. The expression $x^3 y^2$ cannot be simplified.

EXAMPLE 1   Multiply: $(2xy)(3x^2y)$

Solution $(2xy)(3x^2y)$
$= (2 \cdot 3)(x \cdot x^2)(y \cdot y)$
- **Use the Commutative and Associative Properties of Multiplication to rearrange and group factors.**

$= 6x^{1+2}y^{1+1}$
- **Multiply variables with the same base by adding the exponents.**

$= 6x^3y^2$

PROBLEM 1   Multiply: $(3x^2)(6x^3)$

Solution   See page S16.

EXAMPLE 2   Multiply: $(2x^2y)(-5xy^4)$

Solution $(2x^2y)(-5xy^4)$
$= [2(-5)](x^2 \cdot x)(y \cdot y^4)$
- **Use the Properties of Multiplication to rearrange and group factors.**

$= -10x^3y^5$
- **Multiply variables with the same base by adding the exponents.**

PROBLEM 2   Multiply: $(-3xy^2)(-4x^2y^3)$

Solution   See page S16.

A power of a monomial can be simplified by rewriting the expression in factored form and then using the Rule for Multiplying Exponential Expressions.

$$(x^2)^3 = x^2 \cdot x^2 \cdot x^2$$
$$= x^{2+2+2}$$
$$= x^6$$

$$(x^4y^3)^2 = (x^4y^3)(x^4y^3)$$
$$= x^4 \cdot y^3 \cdot x^4 \cdot y^3$$
$$= (x^4 \cdot x^4)(y^3 \cdot y^3)$$
$$= x^{4+4}y^{3+3}$$
$$= x^8y^6$$

Note that multiplying each exponent inside the parentheses by the exponent outside the parentheses gives the same result.

$$(x^2)^3 = x^{2\cdot3} = x^6 \qquad (x^4y^3)^2 = x^{4\cdot2}y^{3\cdot2} = x^8y^6$$

Rule for Simplifying Powers of Exponential Expressions

If m and n are integers, then $(x^m)^n = x^{mn}$.

Simplify: $(x^5)^2$

Multiply the exponents.

$$(x^5)^2 = x^{5\cdot2} = x^{10}$$

Rule for Simplifying Powers of Products

If m, n, and p are integers, then $(x^my^n)^p = x^{mp}y^{np}$.

Simplify: $(c^5d^3)^6$

Multiply each exponent inside the parentheses by the exponent outside the parentheses.

$$(c^5d^3)^6 = c^{5\cdot6}d^{3\cdot6}$$
$$= c^{30}d^{18}$$

Simplify: $(3a^2b)^3$

Multiply each exponent inside the parentheses by the exponent outside the parentheses.

$$(3a^2b)^3 = 3^{1\cdot3}a^{2\cdot3}b^{1\cdot3}$$
$$= 3^3a^6b^3$$
$$= 27a^6b^3$$

EXAMPLE 3   Simplify: $(-2x)(-3xy^2)^3$

Solution
$$(-2x)(-3xy^2)^3$$
$$= (-2x)(-3)^3x^3y^6$$
$$= (-2x)(-27)x^3y^6$$
$$= [-2(-27)](x \cdot x^3)y^6$$
$$= 54x^4y^6$$

- Multiply each exponent in $-3xy^2$ by the exponent outside the parentheses.
- Simplify $(-3)^3$.
- Use the Properties of Multiplication to rearrange and group factors.
- Multiply variable expressions with the same base by adding the exponents.

> **PROBLEM 3** Simplify: $(3x)(2x^2y)^3$
>
> **Solution** See page S16.

7.2 Concept Review

Determine whether the statement is always true, sometimes true, or never true.

1. In the expression $(6x)^4$, x is the base and 4 is the exponent.

2. To multiply $x^m \cdot x^n$, multiply the exponents.

3. The expression "a power of a monomial" means the monomial is the base of an exponential expression.

4. $x^6 \cdot x \cdot x^8 = x^{14}$

5. $(4x^3y^5)^2 = 4x^6y^{10}$

6. $a^2 \cdot b^7 = ab^9$

7.2 Exercises

1 Multiply monomials

1. Explain how to multiply two exponential expressions with the same base. Provide an example.

2. Use the Rule for Multiplying Exponential Expressions to multiply:
$(x^7)(x^2) = x^{\underline{?}+\underline{?}} = \underline{\quad?\quad}$.

3. Multiply: $(5a^6b)(2a^5b^3)$

$(5a^6b)(2a^5b^3)$

$= (5 \cdot \underline{\quad?\quad})(a^6 \cdot \underline{\quad?\quad})(b \cdot \underline{\quad?\quad})$ · Use the Commutative and Associative Properties of Multiplication to rearrange and group factors.

$= (\underline{\quad?\quad})(a^{\underline{?}+\underline{?}})(b^{\underline{?}+\underline{?}})$ · Multiply variables with the same base by $\underline{\quad?\quad}$ the exponents.

$= 10a^{\underline{?}}b^{\underline{?}}$ · Simplify.

4. State whether the expression can be simplified using the Rule for Multiplying Exponential Expressions.
a. $x^4 + x^5$ b. x^4x^5 c. x^4y^4 d. $x^4 + x^4$

Multiply.

5. $(x)(2x)$ **6.** $(-3y)(y)$ **7.** $(3x)(4x)$

8. $(7y^3)(7y^2)$ **9.** $(-2a^3)(-3a^4)$ **10.** $(5a^6)(-2a^5)$

11. $(x^2y)(xy^4)$ **12.** $(x^2y^4)(xy^7)$ **13.** $(-2x^4)(5x^5y)$

14. $(-3a^3)(2a^2b^4)$ **15.** $(x^2y^4)(x^5y^4)$ **16.** $(a^2b^4)(ab^3)$

17. $(2xy)(-3x^2y^4)$ **18.** $(-3a^2b)(-2ab^3)$ **19.** $(x^2yz)(x^2y^4)$

20. $(-ab^2c)(a^2b^5)$ **21.** $(a^2b^3)(ab^2c^4)$ **22.** $(x^2y^3z)(x^3y^4)$

23. $(-a^2b^2)(a^3b^6)$ **24.** $(xy^4)(-xy^3)$ **25.** $(-6a^3)(a^2b)$

26. $(2a^2b^3)(-4ab^2)$ **27.** $(-5y^4z)(-8y^6z^5)$ **28.** $(3x^2y)(-4xy^2)$

29. $(10ab^2)(-2ab)$ **30.** $(x^2y)(yz)(xyz)$ **31.** $(xy^2z)(x^2y)(z^2y^2)$

32. $(-2x^2y^3)(3xy)(-5x^3y^4)$ **33.** $(4a^2b)(-3a^3b^4)(a^5b^2)$ **34.** $(3ab^2)(-2abc)(4ac^2)$

2   Simplify powers of monomials

35.   Explain how to simplify a power of an exponential expression. Provide an example.

State whether the expression is the product of two exponential expressions or a power of an exponential expression.

36. a. $b^4 \cdot b^8$ **b.** $(b^4)^8$ **37. a.** $(2z)^2$ **b.** $2z \cdot z$

38. a. $(3a^4)^5$ **b.** $(3a^4)(5a)$ **39. a.** $x(-xy^4)$ **b.** $(-xy)^4$

40. a. Use the Rule for Simplifying Powers of Exponential Expressions to simplify:
$(x^4)^7 = x^{(\,?\,)(\,?\,)} = \underline{\quad?\quad}$

b. Use the Rule for Simplifying Powers of Products to simplify:
$(x^4y^2)^6 = x^{(\,?\,)(\,?\,)}y^{(\,?\,)(\,?\,)} = \underline{\quad?\quad}$

41.   State whether or not the expression can be simplified using the Rule for Simplifying Powers of Products.
a. $(xy)^3$ **b.** $(x + y)^3$ **c.** $(a^3 + b^4)^2$ **d.** $(a^3b^4)^2$

42.   **a.** True or false? $a^2b^5 = ab^{10}$
b. True or false? $a^2b^5 = ab^7$
c. True or false? $(a^2b^5)^2 = a^4b^{25}$
d. True or false? $(a^2 + b^5)^2 = a^4 + b^{10}$

Simplify.

43. $(2^2)^3$　　　　　　**44.** $(3^2)^2$　　　　　　　　**45.** $(-2)^2$　　　　　　　**46.** $(-3)^3$

47. $(-2^2)^3$　　　　　**48.** $(-2^3)^3$　　　　　　　**49.** $(x^3)^3$　　　　　　　**50.** $(y^4)^2$

51. $(x^7)^2$　　　　　　**52.** $(y^5)^3$　　　　　　　　**53.** $(-x^2)^2$　　　　　　**54.** $(-x^2)^3$

55. $(2x)^2$　　　　　　**56.** $(3y)^3$　　　　　　　　**57.** $(-2x^2)^3$　　　　　**58.** $(-3y^3)^2$

59. $(x^2y^3)^2$　　　　　**60.** $(x^3y^4)^5$　　　　　　　**61.** $(3x^2y)^2$　　　　　　**62.** $(-2ab^3)^4$

63. $(a^2)(3a^2)^3$　　　　　　　　**64.** $(b^2)(2a^3)^4$　　　　　　　**65.** $(-2x)(2x^3)^2$

66. $(2y)(-3y^4)^3$　　　　　　　**67.** $(x^2y)(x^2y)^3$　　　　　　　**68.** $(a^3b)(ab)^3$

69. $(ab^2)^2(ab)^2$　　　　　　　**70.** $(x^2y)^2(x^3y)^3$　　　　　　**71.** $(-2x)(-2x^3y)^3$

72. $(-3y)(-4x^2y^3)^3$　　　　　**73.** $(-2x)(-3xy^2)^2$　　　　　　**74.** $(-3y)(-2x^2y)^3$

75. $(ab^2)(-2a^2b)^3$　　　　　　**76.** $(a^2b^2)(-3ab^4)^2$　　　　　**77.** $(-2a^3)(3a^2b)^3$

78. $(-3b^2)(2ab^2)^3$　　　　　　**79.** $(-3ab)^2(-2ab)^3$　　　　　**80.** $(-3a^2b)^3(-3ab)^3$

7.2 Applying Concepts

Simplify.

81. $(6x)(2x^2) + (4x^2)(5x)$　　　　　　　　　**82.** $(2a^7)(7a^2) - (6a^3)(5a^6)$

83. $(3a^2b^2)(2ab) - (9ab^2)(a^2b)$　　　　　　**84.** $(3x^2y^2)^2 - (2xy)^4$

85. $(5xy^3)(3x^4y^2) - (2x^3y)(x^2y^4)$　　　　　**86.** $a^2(ab^2)^3 - a^3(ab^3)^2$

87. $4a^2(2ab)^3 - 5b^2(a^5b)$　　　　　　　　**88.** $9x^3(3x^2y)^2 - x(x^3y)^2$

89. $-2xy(x^2y)^3 - 3x^5(xy^2)^2$　　　　　　　**90.** $5a^2b(ab^2)^2 + b^3(2a^2b)^2$

91. $a^n \cdot a^n$　　　　　**92.** $(a^n)^2$　　　　　　　**93.** $(a^2)^n$　　　　　　**94.** $a^2 \cdot a^n$

For Exercises 95–98, answer true or false. If the answer is false, correct the right side of the equation.

95. $(-a)^5 = -a^5$　　　　　　　　　　　**96.** $(-b)^8 = b^8$

97. $(x^2)^5 = x^{2+5} = x^7$　　　　　　　　**98.** $x^3 + x^3 = 2x^{3+3} = 2x^6$

99. Evaluate $(2^3)^2$ and $2^{(3^2)}$. Are the results the same? If not, which expression has the larger value?

100. What is the Order of Operations for the expression x^{m^n}?

101. If n is a positive integer and $x^n = y^n$, when is $x = y$?

102. **Geometry** The length of a rectangle is $4ab$. The width is $2ab$. Find the perimeter of the rectangle in terms of ab.

4ab

2ab

103. The distance a rock will fall in t seconds is $16t^2$ ft (neglecting air resistance). Find other examples of quantities that can be expressed in terms of an exponential expression, and explain where the expression is used.

7.3 Multiplication of Polynomials

OBJECTIVE 1 **Multiply a polynomial by a monomial**

To multiply a polynomial by a monomial, use the Distributive Property and the Rule for Multiplying Exponential Expressions.

Simplify: $-2x(x^2 - 4x - 3)$

$-2x(x^2 - 4x - 3)$
$= -2x(x^2) - (-2x)(4x) - (-2x)(3)$ • Use the Distributive Property.
$= -2x^3 + 8x^2 + 6x$ • Use the Rule for Multiplying
     Exponential Expressions.

EXAMPLE 1 Multiply.   **A.** $(5x + 4)(-2x)$ **B.** $x^3(2x^2 - 3x + 2)$

Solution   **A.** $(5x + 4)(-2x)$
     $= 5x(-2x) + 4(-2x)$ • Use the Distributive Property.
     $= -10x^2 - 8x$ • Use the Rule for Multiplying
          Exponential Expressions.

     B. $x^3(2x^2 - 3x + 2)$
     $= 2x^5 - 3x^4 + 2x^3$

PROBLEM 1 Multiply.   **A.** $(-2y + 3)(-4y)$ **B.** $-a^2(3a^2 + 2a - 7)$

Solution See page S16.

OBJECTIVE 2 **Multiply two polynomials**

Multiplication of two polynomials requires the repeated application of the Distributive Property.

$$(y - 2)(y^2 + 3y + 1) = (y - 2)(y^2) + (y - 2)(3y) + (y - 2)(1)$$
$$= y^3 - 2y^2 + 3y^2 - 6y + y - 2$$
$$= y^3 + y^2 - 5y - 2$$

A convenient method of multiplying two polynomials is to use a vertical format similar to that used for multiplication of whole numbers.

$$\begin{array}{r} y^2 + 3y + 1 \\ y - 2 \\ \hline -2y^2 - 6y - 2 \\ y^3 + 3y^2 + \ y \\ \hline y^3 + \ y^2 - 5y - 2 \end{array}$$

Multiply each term in the trinomial by -2.
Multiply each term in the trinomial by y.
Like terms must be in the same column.
Add the terms in each column.

EXAMPLE 2   Multiply: $(2b^3 - b + 1)(2b + 3)$

Solution

$$\begin{array}{r} 2b^3 - \ b + 1 \\ 2b + 3 \\ \hline 6b^3 \qquad - 3b + 3 \\ 4b^4 \qquad - 2b^2 + 2b \\ \hline 4b^4 + 6b^3 - 2b^2 - \ b + 3 \end{array}$$

• Multiply $2b^3 - b + 1$ by 3.
• Multiply $2b^3 - b + 1$ by $2b$. Arrange the terms in descending order.
• Add the terms in each column.

PROBLEM 2   Multiply: $(2y^3 + 2y^2 - 3)(3y - 1)$

Solution   See page S16.

EXAMPLE 3   Multiply: $(4a^3 - 5a - 2)(3a - 2)$

Solution

$$\begin{array}{r} 4a^3 - \ 5a - 2 \\ 3a - 2 \\ \hline -8a^3 \qquad + 10a + 4 \\ 12a^4 \qquad - 15a^2 - \ 6a \\ \hline 12a^4 - 8a^3 - 15a^2 + \ 4a + 4 \end{array}$$

• Multiply $4a^3 - 5a - 2$ by -2.
• Multiply $4a^3 - 5a - 2$ by $3a$.
• Add the terms in each column.

PROBLEM 3   Multiply: $(3x^3 - 2x^2 + x - 3)(2x + 5)$

Solution   See page S16.

OBJECTIVE 3   **Multiply two binomials**

It is often necessary to find the product of two binomials. The product can be found using a method called **FOIL**, which is based on the Distributive Property. The letters of FOIL stand for **F**irst, **O**uter, **I**nner, and **L**ast.

Take Note

FOIL is not really a different way of multiplying. It is based on the Distributive Property.

$(2x + 3)(x + 5)$
$= 2x(x + 5) + 3(x + 5)$
  $\ \ $ F $\quad$ O $\qquad$ I $\quad$ L
$= 2x^2 + 10x + 3x + 15$
$= 2x^2 + 13x + 15$

Multiply: $(2x + 3)(x + 5)$

Multiply the First terms.	$(2x + 3)(x + 5)$	$2x \cdot x = 2x^2$
Multiply the Outer terms.	$(2x + 3)(x + 5)$	$2x \cdot 5 = 10x$
Multiply the Inner terms.	$(2x + 3)(x + 5)$	$3 \cdot x \ = 3x$
Multiply the Last terms.	$(2x + 3)(x + 5)$	$3 \cdot 5 \ = 15$

$$\qquad\qquad\qquad\qquad\quad \textbf{F} \quad\ \ \textbf{O} \quad\ \textbf{I} \quad \textbf{L}$$

Add the products. $(2x + 3)(x + 5)$ $= 2x^2 + 10x + 3x + 15$
Combine like terms. $= 2x^2 + 13x + 15$

EXAMPLE 4 Multiply: $(4x - 3)(3x - 2)$

Solution $(4x - 3)(3x - 2)$

$= 4x(3x) + 4x(-2) + (-3)(3x) + (-3)(-2)$ • Use the FOIL
$= 12x^2 - 8x - 9x + 6$ method.
$= 12x^2 - 17x + 6$ • Combine like
                                                terms.

PROBLEM 4 Multiply: $(4y - 5)(3y - 3)$

Solution See page S16.

EXAMPLE 5 Multiply: $(3x - 2y)(x + 4y)$

Solution $(3x - 2y)(x + 4y)$

$= 3x(x) + 3x(4y) + (-2y)(x) + (-2y)(4y)$ • Use the FOIL
$= 3x^2 + 12xy - 2xy - 8y^2$ method.
$= 3x^2 + 10xy - 8y^2$ • Combine like
                                                terms.

PROBLEM 5 Multiply: $(3a + 2b)(3a - 5b)$

Solution See page S16.

OBJECTIVE **4**   **Multiply binomials that have special products**

The expression $(a + b)(a - b)$ is the product of the **sum and difference of two terms.** The first binomial in the expression is a sum; the second is a difference. The two terms are a and b. The first term in each binomial is a. The second term in each binomial is b.

The expression $(a + b)^2$ is the **square of a binomial.** The first term in the binomial is a. The second term in the binomial is b.

Using FOIL, it is possible to find a pattern for the product of the sum and difference of two terms and for the square of a binomial.

The Sum and Difference of Two Terms

$$(a + b)(a - b) = a^2 - ab + ab - b^2$$
$$= a^2 - b^2$$

Square of first term ⎯⎯⎯⎯⎯⎯⎯⎯⎯⎯⎯⎯⎯⎯⎯⎯⎯

Square of second term ⎯⎯⎯⎯⎯⎯⎯⎯⎯⎯⎯⎯⎯⎯⎯

The Square of a Binomial

$$(a + b)^2 = (a + b)(a + b) = a^2 + ab + ab + b^2$$
$$= a^2 + 2ab + b^2$$

Square of first term

Twice the product of the two terms

Square of last term

$$(a - b)^2 = (a - b)(a - b) = a^2 - ab - ab + b^2$$
$$= a^2 - 2ab + b^2$$

Square of first term

Twice the product of the two terms

Square of last term

EXAMPLE 6   Multiply: $(2x + 3)(2x - 3)$

Solution $(2x + 3)(2x - 3)$ • $(2x + 3)(2x - 3)$ is the product of the sum and difference of two terms.

$= (2x)^2 - 3^2$ • Square the first term. Square the second term.
$= 4x^2 - 9$ • Simplify.

PROBLEM 6   Multiply: $(2a + 5c)(2a - 5c)$

Solution   See page S16.

EXAMPLE 7   Multiply: $(4c + 5d)^2$

Solution $(4c + 5d)^2$ • $(4c + 5d)^2$ is the square of a binomial.

$= (4c)^2 + 2(4c)(5d) + (5d)^2$ • Square the first term. Find twice the product of the two terms. Square the second term.

$= 16c^2 + 40cd + 25d^2$ • Simplify.

PROBLEM 7   Multiply: $(3x + 2y)^2$

Solution   See page S16.

EXAMPLE 8   Multiply: $(3x - 2)^2$

Solution $(3x - 2)^2$ • $(3x - 2)^2$ is the square of a binomial.

$= (3x)^2 + 2(3x)(-2) + (-2)^2$ • Square the first term. Find twice the product of the two terms. Square the last term.

$= 9x^2 - 12x + 4$ • Simplify.

PROBLEM 8   Multiply: $(6x - y)^2$

Solution   See page S16.

OBJECTIVE 5   Application problems

EXAMPLE 9   The radius of a circle is $(x - 4)$ ft. Find the area of the circle in terms of the variable x. Leave the answer in terms of π.

Strategy   To find the area, replace the variable r in the formula $A = \pi r^2$ with the given value, and solve for A.

Solution

$A = \pi r^2$
$A = \pi(x - 4)^2$ • **This is the square of a binomial.**
$A = \pi(x^2 - 8x + 16)$
$A = \pi x^2 - 8\pi x + 16\pi$

The area is $(\pi x^2 - 8\pi x + 16\pi)$ ft^2.

PROBLEM 9   The length of a rectangle is $(x + 7)$ m. The width is $(x - 4)$ m. Find the area of the rectangle in terms of the variable x.

Solution   See page S16.

EXAMPLE 10   The length of a side of a square is $(3x + 5)$ in. Find the area of the square in terms of the variable x.

Strategy   To find the area of the square, replace the variable s in the formula $A = s^2$ with the given value and simplify.

Solution

$A = s^2$
$A = (3x + 5)^2$ • **This is the square of a binomial.**
$A = 9x^2 + 30x + 25$

The area is $(9x^2 + 30x + 25)$ in^2.

PROBLEM 10   The base of a triangle is $(x + 3)$ cm and the height is $(4x - 6)$ cm. Find the area of the triangle in terms of the variable x.

Solution   See page S16.

7.3   Concept Review

Determine whether the statement is always true, sometimes true, or never true.

1. To multiply a monomial times a polynomial, use the Distributive Property to multiply each term of the polynomial by the monomial.

2. To multiply two polynomials, multiply each term of one polynomial by the other polynomial.

3. A binomial is a polynomial of degree 2.

4. $(x + 7)(x - 7)$ is the product of the sum and difference of the same two terms.

5. To square a binomial means to multiply it times itself.

6. The square of a binomial is a trinomial.

7. The FOIL method is used to multiply two polynomials.

8. Using the FOIL method, the terms $3x$ and 5 are the "First" terms in $(3x + 5)(2x + 7)$

7.3 Exercises

1 Multiply a polynomial by a monomial

1. Multiply: $-3y(y + 7)$
$-3y(y + 7) = \underline{\ ?\ }(y) + (\underline{\ ?\ })(7)$

$= \underline{\ ?\ } - \underline{\ ?\ }$

- Use the _?_ Property to multiply each term of $(y + 7)$ by _?_.
- In the first term, the bases are the same. Add the exponents.

2. Multiply: $5x^3(x^2 + 2x - 10)$
$5x^3(x^2 + 2x - 10)$
$= (\underline{\ ?\ })(x^2) + (\underline{\ ?\ })(2x) - (\underline{\ ?\ })(10)$

$= 5x^{\underline{?}} + 10x^{\underline{?}} - 50x^{\underline{?}}$

- Use the Distributive Property to multiply each term of _?_ by $5x^3$.
- Use the Rule for Multiplying Exponential Expressions.

Multiply.

3. $x(x - 2)$

4. $y(3 - y)$

5. $-x(x + 7)$

6. $-y(7 - y)$

7. $3a^2(a - 2)$

8. $4b^2(b + 8)$

9. $-5x^2(x^2 - x)$

10. $-6y^2(y + 2y^2)$

11. $-x^3(3x^2 - 7)$

12. $-y^4(2y^2 - y^6)$

13. $2x(6x^2 - 3x)$

14. $3y(4y - y^2)$

15. $(2x - 4)3x$

16. $(2x + 1)2x$

17. $-xy(x^2 - y^2)$

18. $-x^2y(2xy - y^2)$

19. $x(2x^3 - 3x + 2)$

20. $y(-3y^2 - 2y + 6)$

21. $-a(-2a^2 - 3a - 2)$

22. $-b(5b^2 + 7b - 35)$

23. $x^2(3x^4 - 3x^2 - 2)$

24. $y^3(-4y^3 - 6y + 7)$

25. $2y^2(-3y^2 - 6y + 7)$

26. $4x^2(3x^2 - 2x + 6)$

27. $(a^2 + 3a - 4)(-2a)$

28. $(b^3 - 2b + 2)(-5b)$

29. $-3y^2(-2y^2 + y - 2)$

30. $-5x^2(3x^2 - 3x - 7)$

31. $xy(x^2 - 3xy + y^2)$

32. $ab(2a^2 - 4ab - 6b^2)$

2   Multiply two polynomials

33. Which expression(s) are equivalent to $4x - x(3x - 1)$?

    a. $4x - 3x^2 - x$ **b.** $-3x^2 + 5x$ **c.** $4x - 3x^2 + x$
    d. $9x^2 - 3x$ **e.** $3x(3x - 1)$

34. Which expression(s) are equivalent to $b^3(b^3 - b^2)$?

    a. $b^9 - b^6$ **b.** $b^{27} - b^8$ **c.** b^3
    d. $b^6 - b^5$ **e.** b

Multiply.

35. $(x^2 + 3x + 2)(x + 1)$

36. $(x^2 - 2x + 7)(x - 2)$

37. $(a - 3)(a^2 - 3a + 4)$

38. $(2x - 3)(x^2 - 3x + 5)$

39. $(-2b^2 - 3b + 4)(b - 5)$

40. $(-a^2 + 3a - 2)(2a - 1)$

41. $(3x - 5)(-2x^2 + 7x - 2)$

42. $(2a - 1)(-a^2 - 2a + 3)$

43. $(x^3 - 3x + 2)(x - 4)$

44. $(y^3 + 4y^2 - 8)(2y - 1)$

45. $(3y - 8)(5y^2 + 8y - 2)$

46. $(4y - 3)(3y^2 + 3y - 5)$

47. $(5a^3 - 15a + 2)(a - 4)$

48. $(3b^3 - 5b^2 + 7)(6b - 1)$

49. $(y + 2)(y^3 + 2y^2 - 3y + 1)$

50. $(2a - 3)(2a^3 - 3a^2 + 2a - 1)$

For Exercises 51 and 52, use this product: $(ax^3 + bx + c)(dx + e)$, where a, b, c, d, and e are nonzero real numbers.

51.   **a.** What is the degree of the simplified product?
      b. At most, how many terms will the simplified product have?

52. Does the simplified product have an x^2 term? If so, what is its coefficient?

3 Multiply two binomials

53. For the product $(4x - 3)(x + 5)$:
The **First** terms are ___?___ and ___?___.
The **Outer** terms are ___?___ and ___?___.
The **Inner** terms are ___?___ and ___?___.
The **Last** terms are ___?___ and ___?___.

For the product of the binomials, name **a.** the first terms, **b.** the outer terms, **c.** the inner terms, and **d.** the last terms.

54. $(y - 8)(2y + 3)$ **55.** $(3d + 4)(d - 1)$

56. Use the FOIL method to multiply $(x + 2)(8x - 3)$.
The product of the **First** terms is $x \cdot 8x =$ ___?___.
The product of the **Outer** terms is $x \cdot (-3) =$ ___?___.
The product of the **Inner** terms is $2 \cdot 8x =$ ___?___.
The product of the **Last** terms is $2 \cdot (-3) =$ ___?___.
The sum of these four products is ___?___.

Multiply.

57. $(x + 1)(x + 3)$ **58.** $(y + 2)(y + 5)$ **59.** $(a - 3)(a + 4)$

60. $(b - 6)(b + 3)$ **61.** $(y + 3)(y - 8)$ **62.** $(x + 10)(x - 5)$

63. $(y - 7)(y - 3)$ **64.** $(a - 8)(a - 9)$ **65.** $(2x + 1)(x + 7)$

66. $(y + 2)(5y + 1)$ **67.** $(3x - 1)(x + 4)$ **68.** $(7x - 2)(x + 4)$

69. $(4x - 3)(x - 7)$ **70.** $(2x - 3)(4x - 7)$ **71.** $(3y - 8)(y + 2)$

72. $(5y - 9)(y + 5)$ **73.** $(3x + 7)(3x + 11)$ **74.** $(5a + 6)(6a + 5)$

75. $(7a - 16)(3a - 5)$ **76.** $(5a - 12)(3a - 7)$ **77.** $(3b + 13)(5b - 6)$

78. $(x + y)(2x + y)$ **79.** $(2a + b)(a + 3b)$ **80.** $(3x - 4y)(x - 2y)$

81. $(2a - b)(3a + 2b)$ **82.** $(5a - 3b)(2a + 4b)$ **83.** $(2x + y)(x - 2y)$

84. $(3x - 7y)(3x + 5y)$ **85.** $(2x + 3y)(5x + 7y)$ **86.** $(5x + 3y)(7x + 2y)$

87. $(3a - 2b)(2a - 7b)$ **88.** $(5a - b)(7a - b)$ **89.** $(a - 9b)(2a + 7b)$

90. $(2a + 5b)(7a - 2b)$ **91.** $(10a - 3b)(10a - 7b)$ **92.** $(12a - 5b)(3a - 4b)$

93. $(5x + 12y)(3x + 4y)$ **94.** $(11x + 2y)(3x + 7y)$ **95.** $(2x - 15y)(7x + 4y)$

96. $(5x + 2y)(2x - 5y)$ **97.** $(8x - 3y)(7x - 5y)$ **98.** $(2x - 9y)(8x - 3y)$

99. 🗣 Suppose a and b are positive numbers such that $a > b$. Will the coefficient of the x term of the product $(ax - b)(x + 1)$ be positive or negative?

100. 🗣 If the constant terms of two binomials are both negative, is the constant term of the product of the two binomials also negative?

4 **Multiply binomials that have special products**

101. The product $(a + b)(a - b) = a^2 - b^2$, so $(5x + 1)(5x - 1) = (\underline{\quad ? \quad})^2 - (\underline{\quad ? \quad})^2 = \underline{\quad ? \quad} - \underline{\quad ? \quad}$.

102. The product $(a + b)^2 = a^2 + 2ab + b^2$, so
$(3x + 7)^2 = (\underline{\quad ? \quad})^2 + 2(\underline{\quad ? \quad})(\underline{\quad ? \quad}) + (\underline{\quad ? \quad})^2$
$= \underline{\quad ? \quad} + \underline{\quad ? \quad} + \underline{\quad ? \quad}$.

Multiply.

103. $(y - 5)(y + 5)$

104. $(y + 6)(y - 6)$

105. $(2x + 3)(2x - 3)$

106. $(4x - 7)(4x + 7)$

107. $(x + 1)^2$

108. $(y - 3)^2$

109. $(3a - 5)^2$

110. $(6x - 5)^2$

111. $(3x - 7)(3x + 7)$

112. $(9x - 2)(9x + 2)$

113. $(2a + b)^2$

114. $(x + 3y)^2$

115. $(x - 2y)^2$

116. $(2x - 3y)^2$

117. $(4 - 3y)(4 + 3y)$

118. $(4x - 9y)(4x + 9y)$

119. $(5x + 2y)^2$

120. $(2a - 9b)^2$

For Exercises 121 to 124, state whether the coefficient of the x term of the product is positive, negative, or zero.

121. 🗣 $(ax + b)(ax - b)$, where $a > 0$ and $b > 0$

122. 🗣 $(ax + b)(ax + b)$, where $a > 0$ and $b < 0$

123. 🗣 $(ax + b)^2$, where $a > 0$ and $b > 0$

124. 🗣 $(ax + b)^2$, where $a < 0$ and $b < 0$

5 **Application problems**

125. The length of a rectangle is $(2x + 5)$ ft and the width of the rectangle is $(2x - 5)$ ft. The expression that represents the area of the rectangle is $(\underline{\quad ? \quad})(\underline{\quad ? \quad}) = \underline{\quad ? \quad}$.

126. The length of the side of a square is $(3a - 1)$. The expression that represents the area of the square is $(\underline{\quad ? \quad})^2 = \underline{\quad ? \quad}$.

Geometry Problems

127. The length of a rectangle is $5x$ ft. The width is $(2x - 7)$ ft. Find the area of the rectangle in terms of the variable x.

128. The width of a rectangle is $(x - 6)$ m. The length is $(2x + 3)$ m. Find the area of the rectangle in terms of the variable x.

129. The width of a rectangle is $(3x + 1)$ in. The length of the rectangle is twice the width. Find the area of the rectangle in terms of the variable x.

130. The width of a rectangle is $(4x - 3)$ cm. The length of the rectangle is twice the width. Find the area of the rectangle in terms of the variable x.

131. The length of a side of a square is $(2x + 1)$ km. Find the area of the square in terms of the variable x.

132. The length of a side of a square is $(2x - 3)$ yd. Find the area of the square in terms of the variable x.

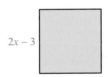

133. The base of a triangle is $4x$ m and the height is $(2x + 5)$ m. Find the area of the triangle in terms of the variable x.

134. The base of a triangle is $(2x + 6)$ in. and the height is $(x - 8)$ in. Find the area of the triangle in terms of the variable x.

135. The radius of a circle is $(x + 4)$ cm. Find the area of the circle in terms of the variable x. Leave the answer in terms of π.

136. The radius of a circle is $(x - 3)$ ft. Find the area of the circle in terms of the variable x. Leave the answer in terms of π.

137. **Sports** A softball diamond has dimensions 45 ft by 45 ft. A base path border x feet wide lies on both the first-base side and the third-base side of the diamond. Express the total area of the softball diamond and the base path in terms of the variable x.

138. **Sports** An athletic field has dimensions 30 yd by 100 yd. An end zone that is w yards wide borders each end of the field. Express the total area of the field and the end zones in terms of the variable w.

7.3 Applying Concepts

Simplify.

139. $(a + b)^2 - (a - b)^2$

140. $(x + 3y)^2 + (x + 3y)(x - 3y)$

141. $(3a^2 - 4a + 2)^2$

142. $(x + 4)^3$

143. $3x^2(2x^3 + 4x - 1) - 6x^3(x^2 - 2)$

144. $(3b + 2)(b - 6) + (4 + 2b)(3 - b)$

145. $x^n(x^n + 1)$

146. $(x^n + 1)(x^n - 1)$

147. $(x^n + 1)(x^n + 1)$

148. $(x^n - 1)^2$

149. $(x + 1)(x - 1)$

150. $(x + 1)(-x^2 + x - 1)$

151. $(x + 1)(x^3 - x^2 + x - 1)$

152. $(x + 1)(-x^4 + x^3 - x^2 + x - 1)$

Use the pattern of the answers to Exercises 149 to 152 to write the product.

153. $(x + 1)(x^5 - x^4 + x^3 - x^2 + x - 1)$

154. $(x + 1)(-x^6 + x^5 - x^4 + x^3 - x^2 + x - 1)$

Solve.

155. Find $(4n^3)^2$ if $2n - 3 = 4n - 7$.

156. What polynomial has quotient $x^2 + 2x - 1$ when divided by $x + 3$?

157. What polynomial has quotient $3x - 4$ when divided by $4x + 5$?

158. Subtract $4x^2 - x - 5$ from the product of $x^2 + x + 3$ and $x - 4$.

159. Add $x^2 + 2x - 3$ to the product of $2x - 5$ and $3x + 1$.

160. If a polynomial of degree 3 is multiplied by a polynomial of degree 2, what is the degree of the resulting polynomial?

161. Is it possible to multiply a polynomial of degree 2 by a polynomial of degree 2 and have the product be a polynomial of degree 3? If so, give an example. If not, explain why not.

7.4 Integer Exponents and Scientific Notation

OBJECTIVE **1** ### Integer exponents

The quotient of two exponential expressions with the *same* base can be simplified by writing each expression in factored form, dividing by the common factors, and then writing the result with an exponent.

$$\frac{x^5}{x^2} = \frac{\overset{1}{\cancel{x}} \cdot \overset{1}{\cancel{x}} \cdot x \cdot x \cdot x}{\underset{1}{\cancel{x}} \cdot \underset{1}{\cancel{x}}} = x^3$$

Note that subtracting the exponents results in the same quotient.

$$\frac{x^5}{x^2} = x^{5-2} = x^3$$

To divide two monomials with the same base, subtract the exponents of the like bases.

Simplify: $\dfrac{a^7}{a^3}$

The bases are the same. Subtract the exponent in the denominator from the exponent in the numerator.

$$\frac{a^7}{a^3} = a^{7-3} = a^4$$

Simplify: $\dfrac{r^8 s^6}{r^7 s}$

Subtract the exponents of the like bases.

$$\frac{r^8 s^6}{r^7 s} = r^{8-7} s^{6-1} = r s^5$$

Recall that for any number a, $a \neq 0$, $\dfrac{a}{a} = 1$. This property is true for exponential expressions as well. For example, for $x \neq 0$, $\dfrac{x^4}{x^4} = 1$.

This expression also can be simplified using the rule for dividing exponential expressions with the same base.

$$\frac{x^4}{x^4} = x^{4-4} = x^0$$

Because $\dfrac{x^4}{x^4} = 1$ and $\dfrac{x^4}{x^4} = x^{4-4} = x^0$, the following definition of zero as an exponent is used.

Zero as an Exponent

If $x \neq 0$, then $x^0 = 1$. The expression 0^0 is not defined.

Simplify: $(12a^3)^0$, $a \neq 0$

Any nonzero expression to the zero power is 1. $\qquad (12a^3)^0 = 1$

Simplify: $-(xy^4)^0$, $x \neq 0$, $y \neq 0$

Any nonzero expression to the zero power is 1. Because the negative sign is outside the parentheses, the answer is -1. $\qquad -(xy^4)^0 = -(1) = -1$

The meaning of a negative exponent can be developed by examining the quotient $\dfrac{x^4}{x^6}$.

The expression can be simplified by writing the numerator and denominator in factored form, dividing by the common factors, and then writing the result with an exponent.

$$\frac{x^4}{x^6} = \frac{\cancel{x} \cdot \cancel{x} \cdot \cancel{x} \cdot \cancel{x}}{\cancel{x} \cdot \cancel{x} \cdot \cancel{x} \cdot \cancel{x} \cdot x \cdot x} = \frac{1}{x^2}$$

Now simplify the same expression by subtracting the exponents of the like bases.

$$\frac{x^4}{x^6} = x^{4-6} = x^{-2}$$

Because $\dfrac{x^4}{x^6} = \dfrac{1}{x^2}$ and $\dfrac{x^4}{x^6} = x^{-2}$, the expressions $\dfrac{1}{x^2}$ and x^{-2} must be equal. The following definition of a negative exponent is used.

Definition of Negative Exponents

If n is a positive integer and $x \neq 0$, then $x^{-n} = \dfrac{1}{x^n}$ and $\dfrac{1}{x^{-n}} = x^n$.

Evaluate 2^{-4}.

Write the expression with a positive exponent. Then simplify. $\qquad 2^{-4} = \dfrac{1}{2^4} = \dfrac{1}{16}$

Now that negative exponents have been defined, the Rule for Dividing Exponential Expressions can be stated.

Rule for Dividing Exponential Expressions

If m and n are integers and $x \neq 0$, then $\dfrac{x^m}{x^n} = x^{m-n}$.

EXAMPLE 1 Write $\dfrac{3^{-3}}{3^2}$ with a positive exponent. Then evaluate.

Solution

$\dfrac{3^{-3}}{3^2} = 3^{-3-2}$ • 3^{-3} and 3^2 have the same base. Subtract the exponents.

$= 3^{-5}$

$= \dfrac{1}{3^5}$ • Use the Definition of Negative Exponents to write the expression with a positive exponent.

$= \dfrac{1}{243}$ • Evaluate.

PROBLEM 1 Write $\dfrac{2^{-2}}{2^3}$ with a positive exponent. Then evaluate.

Solution See page S16.

The rules for simplifying exponential expressions and powers of exponential expressions are true for all integers. These rules are restated here.

Rules for Exponents

If m, n, and p are integers, then

$$x^m \cdot x^n = x^{m+n} \qquad (x^m)^n = x^{mn} \qquad (x^m y^n)^p = x^{mp} y^{np}$$

$$\dfrac{x^m}{x^n} = x^{m-n}, x \neq 0 \qquad x^{-n} = \dfrac{1}{x^n}, x \neq 0 \qquad x^0 = 1, x \neq 0$$

An exponential expression is in simplest form when it is written with only positive exponents.

Simplify: $a^{-7}b^3$

Rewrite a^{-7} with a positive exponent. $\qquad a^{-7}b^3 = \dfrac{b^3}{a^7}$

EXAMPLE 2 Simplify: $\dfrac{x^{-4}y^6}{xy^2}$

Solution

$\dfrac{x^{-4}y^6}{xy^2} = x^{-4-1}y^{6-2}$ • Divide variables with the same base by subtracting the exponents.

$= x^{-5}y^4$

$= \dfrac{y^4}{x^5}$ • Write the expression with only positive exponents.

PROBLEM 2 Simplify: $\dfrac{b^8}{a^{-5}b^6}$

Solution See page S16.

Simplify: $6d^{-4}, d \neq 0$

$6d^{-4} = 6 \cdot \dfrac{1}{d^4} = \dfrac{6}{d^4}$ • Use the Definition of Negative Exponents to rewrite the expression with a positive exponent.

Take Note

In the example at the bottom of this page, the exponent on d is -4 (negative 4). The d^{-4} is written in the denominator as d^4. The exponent on 6 is 1 (positive 1). The 6 remains in the numerator.

Note that we indicated $d \neq 0$. This is necessary because division by zero is not defined. In this textbook, we will assume that values of the variables are chosen so that division by zero does not occur.

EXAMPLE 3   Simplify: **A.** $\dfrac{-35a^6b^{-2}}{25a^{-2}b^5}$ **B.** $(-2x)(3x^{-2})^{-3}$

Solution   **A.** $\dfrac{-35a^6b^{-2}}{25a^{-2}b^5} = -\dfrac{35a^6b^{-2}}{25a^{-2}b^5}$

- A negative sign is placed in front of a fraction.

$$= -\dfrac{\overset{1}{\cancel{5}} \cdot 7a^{6-(-2)}b^{-2-5}}{\underset{1}{\cancel{5}} \cdot 5}$$

- Factor the coefficients. Divide by the common factors. Divide variables with the same base by subtracting the exponents.

$$= -\dfrac{7a^8b^{-7}}{5}$$

$$= -\dfrac{7a^8}{5b^7}$$

- Write the expression with only positive exponents.

B. $(-2x)(3x^{-2})^{-3} = (-2x)(3^{-3}x^6)$

- Use the Rule for Simplifying Powers of Products.

$$= \dfrac{-2x \cdot x^6}{3^3}$$

- Write the expression with positive exponents.

$$= -\dfrac{2x^7}{27}$$

- Use the Rule for Multiplying Exponential Expressions, and simplify the numerical exponential expression.

PROBLEM 3   Simplify: **A.** $\dfrac{12x^{-8}y^4}{-16xy^{-3}}$ **B.** $(-3ab)(2a^3b^{-2})^{-3}$

Solution   See page S17.

OBJECTIVE 2   Scientific notation

Very large and very small numbers are encountered in the fields of science and engineering. For example, the charge of an electron is 0.000000000000000000160 coulomb. These numbers can be written more easily in scientific notation. In **scientific notation,** a number is expressed as a product of two factors, one a number between 1 and 10 and the other a power of 10.

To change a number written in decimal notation to scientific notation, write it in the form $a \times 10^n$, where a is a number between 1 and 10 and n is an integer.

For numbers greater than 10, move the decimal point to the right of the first digit. The exponent n is positive and equal to the number of places the decimal point has been moved.

$$240{,}000 = 2.4 \times 10^5$$

$$93{,}000{,}000 = 9.3 \times 10^7$$

For numbers less than 1, move the decimal point to the right of the first nonzero digit. The exponent n is negative. The absolute value of the exponent is equal to the number of places the decimal point has been moved.

$$0.00030 = 3.0 \times 10^{-4}$$

$$0.0000832 = 8.32 \times 10^{-5}$$

Look at the last example above: $0.0000832 = 8.32 \times 10^{-5}$. Using the Definition of Negative Exponents,

$$10^{-5} = \dfrac{1}{10^5} = \dfrac{1}{100{,}000} = 0.00001$$

Because $10^{-5} = 0.00001$, we can write

$$8.32 \times 10^{-5} = 8.32 \times 0.00001 = 0.0000832$$

which is the number we started with. We have not changed the value of the number; we have just written it in another form.

EXAMPLE 4 Write the number in scientific notation.
  A. 824,300,000,000   **B.** 0.000000961

Solution **A.** $824,300,000,000 = 8.243 \times 10^{11}$ • Move the decimal point 11 places to the left. The exponent on 10 is 11.

  B. $0.000000961 = 9.61 \times 10^{-7}$ • Move the decimal point 7 places to the right. The exponent on 10 is −7.

PROBLEM 4 Write the number in scientific notation.
  A. 57,000,000,000   **B.** 0.000000017

Solution See page S17.

Changing a number written in scientific notation to decimal notation also requires moving the decimal point.

When the exponent on 10 is positive, move the decimal point to the right the same number of places as the exponent.

$$3.45 \times 10^9 = 3,450,000,000$$
$$2.3 \times 10^8 = 230,000,000$$

When the exponent on 10 is negative, move the decimal point to the left the same number of places as the absolute value of the exponent.

$$8.1 \times 10^{-3} = 0.0081$$
$$6.34 \times 10^{-6} = 0.00000634$$

EXAMPLE 5 Write the number in decimal notation.
  A. 7.329×10^6 **B.** 6.8×10^{-10}

Solution **A.** $7.329 \times 10^6 = 7,329,000$ • The exponent on 10 is positive. Move the decimal point 6 places to the right.

  B. $6.8 \times 10^{-10} = 0.00000000068$ • The exponent on 10 is negative. Move the decimal point 10 places to the left.

PROBLEM 5 Write the number in decimal notation.
  A. 5×10^{12} **B.** 4.0162×10^{-9}

Solution See page S17.

The rules for multiplying and dividing with numbers in scientific notation are the same as those for calculating with algebraic expressions. The power of 10 corresponds to the variable, and the number between 1 and 10 corresponds to the coefficient of the variable.

	Algebraic Expression	**Scientific Notation**
Multiplication	$(4x^{-3})(2x^5) = 8x^2$	$(4 \times 10^{-3})(2 \times 10^5) = 8 \times 10^2$
Division	$\dfrac{6x^5}{3x^{-2}} = 2x^{5-(-2)} = 2x^7$	$\dfrac{6 \times 10^5}{3 \times 10^{-2}} = 2 \times 10^{5-(-2)} = 2 \times 10^7$

EXAMPLE 6   Multiply or divide.

A. $(3.0 \times 10^5)(1.1 \times 10^{-8})$ **B.** $\dfrac{7.2 \times 10^{13}}{2.4 \times 10^{-3}}$

Solution   **A.** $(3.0 \times 10^5)(1.1 \times 10^{-8}) = 3.3 \times 10^{-3}$ • Multiply 3.0 and 1.1. Add the exponents on 10.

B. $\dfrac{7.2 \times 10^{13}}{2.4 \times 10^{-3}} = 3 \times 10^{16}$ • Divide 7.2 by 2.4. Subtract the exponents on 10.

PROBLEM 6   Multiply or divide.

A. $(2.4 \times 10^{-9})(1.6 \times 10^3)$ **B.** $\dfrac{5.4 \times 10^{-2}}{1.8 \times 10^{-4}}$

Solution   See page S17.

7.4   Concept Review

Determine whether the statement is always true, sometimes true, or never true.

1. The expression $\dfrac{x^5}{y^3}$ can be simplified by subtracting the exponents.

2. The rules of exponents can be applied to expressions that contain an exponent of zero or contain negative exponents.

3. The expression 3^{-2} represents the reciprocal of 3^2.

4. $5x^0 = 0$

5. The expression 4^{-3} represents a negative number.

6. To be in simplest form, an exponential expression cannot contain any negative exponents.

7. $2x^{-5} = \dfrac{1}{2x^5}$

8. $x^4y^{-6} = \dfrac{1}{x^4y^6}$

7.4 Exercises

1 Integer exponents

Write with a positive or zero exponent. Then evaluate.

1. 5^{-2}

2. 3^{-3}

3. $\dfrac{1}{8^{-2}}$

4. $\dfrac{1}{12^{-1}}$

5. $\dfrac{3^{-2}}{3}$

6. $\dfrac{5^{-3}}{5}$

7. $\dfrac{2^3}{2^3}$

8. $\dfrac{3^{-2}}{3^{-2}}$

9. Explain how to rewrite a variable that has a negative exponent as an expression with a positive exponent.

10. As long as x is not zero, x^0 is defined to be equal to ___?___. Using this definition, $3^0 =$ ___?___, $(7x^3)^0 =$ ___?___, and $-2x^0 =$ ___?___.

11. Simplify: $\dfrac{8x^{10}}{2x^3}$

$\dfrac{8x^{10}}{2x^3} = ($___?___$)x^{?\ -\ ?}$ • Divide the coefficients by the common factor 2. Divide the variable parts by subtracting the exponents.

$=$ ___?___   • Simplify.

12. Simplify: $\dfrac{a^3b^7}{a^5b}$

$\dfrac{a^3b^7}{a^5b} = a^{?\ -\ ?}b^{?\ -\ ?}$ • Divide variables with the same base by subtracting the exponents.

$= a^{?}b^{?}$ • Simplify.

$= \dfrac{b^6}{?}$ • Write the expression with only positive exponents.

Simplify.

13. $\dfrac{y^7}{y^3}$

14. $\dfrac{z^9}{z^2}$

15. $\dfrac{a^8}{a^5}$

16. $\dfrac{c^{12}}{c^5}$

17. $\dfrac{p^5}{p}$

18. $\dfrac{w^9}{w}$

19. $\dfrac{4x^8}{2x^5}$

20. $\dfrac{12z^7}{4z^3}$

21. $\dfrac{22k^5}{11k^4}$

22. $\dfrac{14m^{11}}{7m^{10}}$

23. $\dfrac{m^9n^7}{m^4n^5}$

24. $\dfrac{y^5z^6}{yz^3}$

25. $\dfrac{6r^4}{4r^2}$

26. $\dfrac{8x^9}{12x^6}$

27. $\dfrac{-16a^7}{24a^6}$

28. $\dfrac{-18b^5}{27b^4}$

29. x^{-2}

30. y^{-10}

31. $\dfrac{1}{a^{-6}}$

32. $\dfrac{1}{b^{-4}}$

33. $4x^{-7}$

34. $-6y^{-1}$

35. $\dfrac{5}{b^{-8}}$

36. $\dfrac{-3}{v^{-3}}$

37. $\dfrac{1}{3x^{-2}}$

38. $\dfrac{2}{5c^{-6}}$

39. $(ab^5)^0$

40. $(32x^3y^4)^0$

41. $\dfrac{y^3}{y^8}$

42. $\dfrac{z^4}{z^6}$

43. $\dfrac{a^5}{a^{11}}$

44. $\dfrac{m}{m^7}$

45. $\dfrac{4x^2}{12x^5}$

46. $\dfrac{6y^8}{8y^9}$

47. $\dfrac{-12x}{-18x^6}$

48. $\dfrac{-24c^2}{-36c^{11}}$

49. $\dfrac{x^6y^5}{x^8y}$

50. $\dfrac{a^3b^2}{a^2b^3}$

51. $\dfrac{2m^6n^2}{5m^9n^{10}}$

52. $\dfrac{5r^3t^7}{6r^5t^7}$

53. $\dfrac{pq^3}{p^4q^4}$

54. $\dfrac{a^4b^5}{a^5b^6}$

55. $\dfrac{3x^4y^5}{6x^4y^8}$

56. $\dfrac{14a^3b^6}{21a^5b^6}$

57. $\dfrac{14x^4y^6z^2}{16x^3y^9z}$

58. $\dfrac{24a^2b^7c^9}{36a^7b^5c}$

59. $\dfrac{15mn^9p^3}{30m^4n^9p}$

60. $\dfrac{25x^4y^7z^2}{20x^5y^9z^{11}}$

61. $(-2xy^{-2})^3$

62. $(-3x^{-1}y^2)^2$

63. $(3x^{-1}y^{-2})^2$

64. $(5xy^{-3})^{-2}$

65. $(2x^{-1})(x^{-3})$

66. $(-2x^{-5})x^7$

67. $(-5a^2)(a^{-5})^2$

68. $(2a^{-3})(a^7b^{-1})^3$

69. $(-2ab^{-2})(4a^{-2}b)^{-2}$

70. $(3ab^{-2})(2a^{-1}b)^{-3}$

71. $(-5x^{-2}y)(-2x^{-2}y^2)$

72. $\dfrac{a^{-3}b^{-4}}{a^2b^2}$

73. $\dfrac{3x^{-2}y^2}{6xy^2}$

74. $\dfrac{2x^{-2}y}{8xy}$

75. $\dfrac{3x^{-2}y}{xy}$

76. $\dfrac{2x^{-1}y^4}{x^2y^3}$

77. $\dfrac{2x^{-1}y^{-4}}{4xy^2}$

78. $\dfrac{12a^2b^3}{-27a^2b^2}$

79. $\dfrac{-16xy^4}{96x^4y^4}$

80. $\dfrac{-8x^2y^4}{44y^2z^5}$

81. True or false?

    a. $\dfrac{a^{4n}}{a^n} = a^4$ b. $\dfrac{1}{a^{m-n}} = a^{n-m}$

82. True or false?

    a. $a^{-n}a^n = 1$ b. $\dfrac{a^n}{b^m} = \left(\dfrac{a}{b}\right)^{n-m}$

2   Scientific notation

83. Why might a number be written in scientific notation instead of decimal notation?

84. A number is written in scientific notation if it is written as the product of a number between ___?___ and ___?___ and a power of ___?___.

85. To write the number 354,000,000 in scientific notation, move the decimal point ___?___ places to the ___?___. The exponent on 10 is ___?___.

86. To write the number 0.0000000086 in scientific notation, move the decimal point ___?___ places to the ___?___. The exponent on 10 is ___?___.

Determine whether the number is written in scientific notation. If not, explain why not.

87. 39.4×10^3 88. 0.8×10^{-6} 89. $7.1 \times 10^{2.4}$ 90. 5.8×10^{-132}

Write the number in scientific notation.

91. 2,370,000   92. 75,000   93. 0.00045   94. 0.000076

95. 309,000   96. 819,000,000   97. 0.000000601   98. 0.00000000096

Write the number in decimal notation.

99. 7.1×10^5 100. 2.3×10^7 101. 4.3×10^{-5} 102. 9.21×10^{-7}

103. 6.71×10^8 104. 5.75×10^9 105. 7.13×10^{-6} 106. 3.54×10^{-8}

107. Astronomy Astrophysicists estimate that the radius of the Milky Way galaxy is 1,000,000,000,000,000,000,000 m. Write this number in scientific notation.

108. Geology The mass of Earth is 5,980,000,000,000,000,000,000,000 kg. Write this number in scientific notation.

109. Physics Carbon nanotubes are cylinders of carbon atoms that have remarkable properties, especially for their strength. Some nanotubes with a diameter of 0.0000000004 m have been created. Write this number in scientific notation.

110. Biology The weight of a single *E. coli* bacterium is 0.000000000000665 g. Write this number in scientific notation.

111. Archeology The weight of the Great Pyramid of Cheops is estimated to be 12,000,000,000 lb. Write this number in scientific notation.

112. Biophysics Biologists and physicists are working together to measure the mass of a virus. Currently, a virus with a mass of 0.00000000000000000039 g can be measured. Write this number in scientific notation.

113. Food Science The frequency (oscillations per second) of a microwave generated by a microwave oven is approximately 2,450,000,000 hertz. (1 hertz is one oscillation in one second.) Write this number in scientific notation.

Great Pyramid of Cheops

114. Astronomy One light-year is the distance traveled by light in one year. One light-year is 5,880,000,000,000 mi. Write this number in scientific notation.

Multiply or divide.

115. $(1.9 \times 10^{12})(3.5 \times 10^{7})$

116. $(4.2 \times 10^{7})(1.8 \times 10^{-5})$

117. $(2.3 \times 10^{-8})(1.4 \times 10^{-6})$

118. $(3 \times 10^{-20})(2.4 \times 10^{9})$

119. $\dfrac{6.12 \times 10^{14}}{1.7 \times 10^{9}}$

120. $\dfrac{6 \times 10^{-8}}{2.5 \times 10^{-2}}$

121. $\dfrac{5.58 \times 10^{-7}}{3.1 \times 10^{11}}$

122. $\dfrac{9.03 \times 10^{6}}{4.3 \times 10^{-5}}$

123. $a \times 10^{n}$ and $a \times 10^{-m}$ are numbers written in scientific notation, where n and m are positive integers such that $n < m$. Is $(a \times 10^{n})(a \times 10^{-m})$ greater than or less than 1?

124. $a \times 10^{-n}$ and $a \times 10^{-m}$ are numbers written in scientific notation, where n and m are positive integers such that $n > m$. Is $\dfrac{a \times 10^{-m}}{a \times 10^{-n}}$ greater than or less than 1?

7.4 Applying Concepts

Evaluate.

125. $8^{-2} + 2^{-5}$

126. $9^{-2} + 3^{-3}$

127. Evaluate 2^x and 2^{-x} when $x = -2, -1, 0, 1,$ and 2.

128. Evaluate 3^x and 3^{-x} when $x = -2, -1, 0, 1,$ and 2.

Write in decimal notation.

129. 2^{-4}

130. 25^{-2}

Simplify.

131. $\left(\dfrac{9x^2y^4}{3xy^2}\right) - \left(\dfrac{12x^5y^6}{6x^4y^4}\right)$

132. $\left(\dfrac{6x^2 + 9x}{3x}\right) + \left(\dfrac{8xy^2 + 4y^2}{4y^2}\right)$

133. $\left(\dfrac{6x^4yz^3}{2x^2y^3}\right)\left(\dfrac{2x^2z^3}{4y^2z}\right) \div \left(\dfrac{6x^2y^3}{x^4y^2z}\right)$

134. $\left(\dfrac{5x^2yz^3}{3x^4yz^3}\right) \div \left(\dfrac{10x^2y^5z^4}{2y^3z}\right) \div \left(\dfrac{5y^4z^2}{x^2y^6z}\right)$

Complete.

135. If $m = n$ and $a \neq 0$, then $\dfrac{a^m}{a^n} = $ _____ .

136. If $m = n + 1$ and $a \neq 0$, then $\dfrac{a^m}{a^n} = $ _____ .

Solve.

137. $(-4.8)^x = 1$

138. $-6.3^x = -1$

Determine whether each equation is true or false. If the equation is false, change the right side of the equation to make a true equation.

139. $(2a)^{-3} = \dfrac{2}{a^3}$

140. $((a^{-1})^{-1})^{-1} = \dfrac{1}{a}$

141. $(2 + 3)^{-1} = 2^{-1} + 3^{-1}$

142. If $x \neq \dfrac{1}{3}$, then $(3x - 1)^0 = (1 - 3x)^0$.

143. Why is the condition $x \neq \dfrac{1}{3}$ given in Exercise 142?

144. If x is a nonzero real number, is x^{-2} always positive, always negative, or positive or negative depending on whether x is positive or negative? Explain your answer.

145. If x is a nonzero real number, is x^{-3} always positive, always negative, or positive or negative depending on whether x is positive or negative? Explain your answer.

7.5 Division of Polynomials

OBJECTIVE 1   Divide a polynomial by a monomial

Note that $\dfrac{8+4}{2}$ can be simplified by first adding the terms in the numerator and then dividing the result. It can also be simplified by first dividing each term in the numerator by the denominator and then adding the result.

$$\frac{8+4}{2} = \frac{12}{2} = 6$$

$$\frac{8+4}{2} = \frac{8}{2} + \frac{4}{2} = 4 + 2 = 6$$

To divide a polynomial by a monomial, divide each term in the numerator by the denominator, and write the sum of the quotients.

$$\frac{a+b}{c} = \frac{a}{c} + \frac{b}{c}$$

Divide: $\dfrac{6x^2 + 4x}{2x}$

Divide each term of the polynomial $6x^2 + 4x$ by the monomial $2x$. Simplify.

$$\frac{6x^2 + 4x}{2x} = \frac{6x^2}{2x} + \frac{4x}{2}$$

$$= 3x + 2$$

EXAMPLE 1   Divide: $\dfrac{6x^3 - 3x^2 + 9x}{3x}$

Solution

$$\frac{6x^3 - 3x^2 + 9x}{3x} = \frac{6x^3}{3x} - \frac{3x^2}{3x} + \frac{9x}{3x}$$

$$= 2x^2 - x + 3$$

- Divide each term of the polynomial by the monomial $3x$.
- Simplify each expression.

PROBLEM 1   Divide: $\dfrac{4x^3y + 8x^2y^2 - 4xy^3}{2xy}$

Solution   See page S17.

EXAMPLE 2   Divide: $\dfrac{12x^2y - 6xy + 4x^2}{2xy}$

Solution

$$\frac{12x^2y - 6xy + 4x^2}{2xy}$$

$$= \frac{12x^2y}{2xy} - \frac{6xy}{2xy} + \frac{4x^2}{2xy}$$

- Divide each term of the polynomial by the monomial $2xy$.

$$= 6x - 3 + \frac{2x}{y}$$

- Simplify each expression.

PROBLEM 2   Divide: $\dfrac{24x^2y^2 - 18xy + 6y}{6xy}$

Solution   See page S17.

OBJECTIVE 2   Divide polynomials

To divide polynomials, use a method similar to that used for division of whole numbers. The same equation used to check division of whole numbers is used to check polynomial division.

$$\textbf{(Quotient} \times \textbf{Divisor)} + \textbf{Remainder} = \textbf{Dividend}$$

For example, for the division at the left,

$$\textbf{(Quotient} \times \textbf{Divisor)} + \textbf{Remainder} = \textbf{Dividend}$$
$$(3 \times 5) \qquad + \quad 2 \quad = \quad 17$$

$$\begin{array}{r} 3 \\ 5\overline{)17} \\ -15 \\ \hline 2 \end{array}$$

Divide: $(x^2 - 5x + 8) \div (x - 3)$

Step 1

$$x - 3\overline{)x^2 - 5x + 8}$$ with quotient x

$$\underline{x^2 - 3x}$$
$$-2x + 8$$

Think: $x\overline{)x^2} = \dfrac{x^2}{x} = x$

Multiply: $x(x - 3) = x^2 - 3x$

Subtract: $(x^2 - 5x) - (x^2 - 3x) = -2x$

Bring down $+ 8$.

Step 2

$$x - 3\overline{)x^2 - 5x + 8}$$ with quotient $x - 2$
$$\underline{x^2 - 3x}$$
$$-2x + 8$$
$$\underline{-2x + 6}$$
$$2$$

Think: $x\overline{)-2x} = \dfrac{-2x}{x} = -2$

Multiply: $-2(x - 3) = -2x + 6$

Subtract: $(-2x + 8) - (-2x + 6) = 2$

The remainder is 2.

Check:

Quotient $\times$ Divisor $+$ Remainder $=$ Dividend

$(x - 2)(x - 3) + 2 = x^2 - 3x - 2x + 6 + 2 = x^2 - 5x + 8$

$(x^2 - 5x + 8) \div (x - 3) = x - 2 + \dfrac{2}{x - 3}$

If a term is missing in the dividend, insert the term with zero as its coefficient. This helps keep like terms in the same column. This is illustrated in Example 3.

EXAMPLE 3   Divide: $(6x + 2x^3 + 26) \div (x + 2)$

Solution

$$x + 2\overline{)2x^3 + 0x^2 + 6x + 26}$$ with quotient $2x^2 - 4x + 14$
$$\underline{2x^3 + 4x^2}$$
$$-4x^2 + 6x$$
$$\underline{-4x^2 - 8x}$$
$$14x + 26$$
$$\underline{14x + 28}$$
$$-2$$

• Arrange the terms in descending order. There is no term of x^2 in $2x^3 + 6x + 26$. Insert $0x^2$ for the missing term so that like terms will be in columns.

$(6x + 2x^3 + 26) \div (x + 2) = 2x^2 - 4x + 14 - \dfrac{2}{x + 2}$

> **PROBLEM 3** Divide: $(x^3 - 2x - 4) \div (x - 2)$
>
> **Solution** See page S17.

7.5 Concept Review

Determine whether the statement is always true, sometimes true, or never true.

1. For $c \neq 0$, $\dfrac{a - b}{c} = \dfrac{a}{c} - \dfrac{b}{c}$.

2. For $x \neq 0$, $\dfrac{9x^2 + 6x}{3x} = 3x + 6x$.

3. Given $(6x^2 + x - 6) \div (3x + 2) = 2x - 1 - \dfrac{4}{3x + 2}$, then

$(3x + 2)(2x - 1) - \dfrac{4}{3x + 2} = 6x^2 + x - 6$.

7.5 Exercises

1 Divide a polynomial by a monomial

1. Replace each question mark to make a true statement.

$$\frac{18y^5 + 3y}{3y} = \frac{18y^5}{?} + \frac{3y}{?}$$

$$= \underline{\quad ? \quad} + \underline{\quad ? \quad}$$

2. Replace each question mark to make a true statement.

$$\frac{12x^3 - 8x^2}{4x^2} = \frac{12x^3}{?} - \frac{8x^2}{?}$$

$$= \underline{\quad ? \quad} - \underline{\quad ? \quad}$$

Divide.

3. $\dfrac{2x + 2}{2}$

4. $\dfrac{5y + 5}{5}$

5. $\dfrac{10a - 25}{5}$

6. $\dfrac{16b - 40}{8}$

7. $\dfrac{3a^2 + 2a}{a}$

8. $\dfrac{6y^2 + 4y}{y}$

9. $\dfrac{4b^3 - 3b}{b}$ **10.** $\dfrac{12x^2 - 7x}{x}$ **11.** $\dfrac{3x^2 - 6x}{3x}$

12. $\dfrac{10y^2 - 6y}{2y}$ **13.** $\dfrac{5x^2 - 10x}{-5x}$ **14.** $\dfrac{3y^2 - 27y}{-3y}$

15. $\dfrac{x^3 + 3x^2 - 5x}{x}$ **16.** $\dfrac{a^3 - 5a^2 + 7a}{a}$ **17.** $\dfrac{x^6 - 3x^4 - x^2}{x^2}$

18. $\dfrac{a^8 - 5a^5 - 3a^3}{a^2}$ **19.** $\dfrac{5x^2y^2 + 10xy}{5xy}$ **20.** $\dfrac{8x^2y^2 - 24xy}{8xy}$

21. $\dfrac{9y^6 - 15y^3}{-3y^3}$ **22.** $\dfrac{4x^4 - 6x^2}{-2x^2}$ **23.** $\dfrac{3x^2 - 2x + 1}{x}$

24. $\dfrac{8y^2 + 2y - 3}{y}$ **25.** $\dfrac{-3x^2 + 7x - 6}{x}$ **26.** $\dfrac{2y^2 - 6y + 9}{y}$

27. $\dfrac{16a^2b - 20ab + 24ab^2}{4ab}$ **28.** $\dfrac{22a^2b + 11ab - 33ab^2}{11ab}$ **29.** $\dfrac{9x^2y + 6xy - 3xy^2}{xy}$

30. Every division equation has a related multiplication equation. For instance, $\dfrac{16}{2} = 8$ means that $16 = 8 \cdot 2$. What is the related multiplication equation for $\dfrac{15x^2 + 12x}{3x} = 5x + 4$?

31. How can multiplication be used to check that $\dfrac{8x^3 - 12x^2 - 4x}{4x} = 2x^2 - 3x - 1$?

2 Divide polynomials

32. Let P and Q be polynomials. To find the quotient $P \div Q$ using long division, place ___?___ inside the long-division symbol and ___?___ outside the long-division symbol.

33. Use this long division:

$$\begin{array}{r} 3x \\ x-2\overline{)3x^2 - 4x + 7} \\ \underline{3x^2 - 6x} \\ 2x + 7 \end{array}$$

a. The term $3x$ in the quotient came from dividing ___?___ by ___?___.
b. The polynomial $3x^2 - 6x$ came from finding the product of ___?___ and ___?___.
c. The term $2x$ in the last line came from subtracting ___?___ - (___?___).
d. Finish the division. The quotient is ___?___. The remainder is ___?___.

Divide.

34. $(b^2 - 14b + 49) \div (b - 7)$ **35.** $(x^2 - x - 6) \div (x - 3)$ **36.** $(y^2 + 2y - 35) \div (y + 7)$

37. $(2x^2 + 5x + 2) \div (x + 2)$ **38.** $(2y^2 - 13y + 21) \div (y - 3)$ **39.** $(4x^2 - 16) \div (2x + 4)$

40. $(2y^2 + 7) \div (y - 3)$ **41.** $(x^2 + 1) \div (x - 1)$ **42.** $(x^2 + 4) \div (x + 2)$

43. $(6x^2 - 7x) \div (3x - 2)$ **44.** $(6y^2 + 2y) \div (2y + 4)$ **45.** $(5x^2 + 7x) \div (x - 1)$

46. $(6x^2 - 5) \div (x + 2)$ **47.** $(a^2 + 5a + 10) \div (a + 2)$ **48.** $(b^2 - 8b - 9) \div (b - 3)$

49. $(2y^2 - 9y + 8) \div (2y + 3)$ **50.** $(3x^2 + 5x - 4) \div (x - 4)$ **51.** $(8x + 3 + 4x^2) \div (2x - 1)$

52. $(10 + 21y + 10y^2) \div (2y + 3)$ **53.** $(15a^2 - 8a - 8) \div (3a + 2)$ **54.** $(12a^2 - 25a - 7) \div (3a - 7)$

55. $(5 - 23x + 12x^2) \div (4x - 1)$ **56.** $(24 + 6a^2 + 25a) \div (3a - 1)$

57. $(x^3 + 3x^2 + 5x + 3) \div (x + 1)$ **58.** $(x^3 - 6x^2 + 7x - 2) \div (x - 1)$

59. $(x^4 - x^2 - 6) \div (x^2 + 2)$ **60.** $(x^4 + 3x^2 - 10) \div (x^2 - 2)$

61. True or false? When a sixth-degree polynomial is divided by a third-degree polynomial, the quotient is a second-degree polynomial.

62. True or false? When a polynomial of degree $3n$ is divided by a polynomial of degree n, the degree of the quotient polynomial is $2n$.

7.5 Applying Concepts

In Exercises 63 and 64, replace the question marks with expressions to make a true statement.

63. If $\dfrac{x^2 - x - 6}{x - 3} = x + 2$, then $x^2 - x - 6 = (?)(?)$.

64. If $\dfrac{x^2 + 2x - 3}{x - 2} = x + 4 + \dfrac{5}{x - 2}$, then $x^2 + 2x - 3 = (?)(?) + ?$.

Solve.

65. The product of a monomial and $4b$ is $12a^2b$. Find the monomial.

66. The product of a monomial and $6x$ is $24xy^2$. Find the monomial.

67. The quotient of a polynomial and $2x + 1$ is $2x - 4 + \dfrac{7}{2x + 1}$. Find the polynomial.

68. The quotient of a polynomial and $x - 3$ is $x^2 - x + 8 + \dfrac{22}{x - 3}$. Find the polynomial.

Focus on Problem Solving

Dimensional Analysis In solving application problems, it may be useful to include units in order to organize the problem so that the answer is in the proper units. Using units to organize and check the correctness of an application is called **dimensional analysis.** We use the operations of multiplying units and dividing units in applying dimensional analysis to application problems.

The Rule for Multiplying Exponential Expressions states that we multiply two expressions with the same base by adding the exponents.

$$x^4 \cdot x^6 = x^{4+6} = x^{10}$$

In calculations that involve quantities, the units are operated on algebraically.

A rectangle measures 3 m by 5 m. Find the area of the rectangle.

$$A = LW = (5 \text{ m})(3 \text{ m}) = (5 \cdot 3)(\text{m} \cdot \text{m}) = 15 \text{ m}^2$$

The area of the rectangle is 15 m² (square meters).

A box measures 10 cm by 5 cm by 3 cm. Find the volume of the box.

$$V = LWH = (10 \text{ cm})(5 \text{ cm})(3 \text{ cm}) = (10 \cdot 5 \cdot 3)(\text{cm} \cdot \text{cm} \cdot \text{cm}) = 150 \text{ cm}^3$$

The volume of the box is 150 cm³ (cubic centimeters).

Find the area of a square whose side measures $(3x + 5)$ in.

$$A = s^2 = [(3x + 5) \text{ in.}]^2 = (3x + 5)^2 \text{ in}^2 = (9x^2 + 30x + 25) \text{ in}^2$$

The area of the square is $(9x^2 + 30x + 25)$ in² (square inches).

Dimensional analysis is used in the conversion of units.

The following example converts the unit miles to feet. The equivalent measures 1 mi and 5280 ft are used to form the following rates, which are called conversion factors: $\frac{1 \text{ mi}}{5280 \text{ ft}}$ and $\frac{5280 \text{ ft}}{1 \text{ mi}}$. Because 1 mi = 5280 ft, both of the conversion factors $\frac{1 \text{ mi}}{5280 \text{ ft}}$ and $\frac{5280 \text{ ft}}{1 \text{ mi}}$ are equal to 1.

1 mi
5280 ft

To convert 3 mi to feet, multiply 3 mi by the conversion factor $\frac{5280 \text{ ft}}{1 \text{ mi}}$.

3 mi
15,840 ft

$$3 \text{ mi} = 3 \text{ mi} \cdot 1 = \frac{3 \text{ mi}}{1} \cdot \frac{5280 \text{ ft}}{1 \text{ mi}} = \frac{3 \text{ mi} \cdot 5280 \text{ ft}}{1 \text{ mi}} = 3 \cdot 5280 \text{ ft} = 15{,}840 \text{ ft}$$

There are two important points in the above illustration. First, you can think of dividing the numerator and denominator by the common unit "mile" just as you would divide the numerator and denominator of a fraction by a common factor. Second, the conversion factor $\frac{5280 \text{ ft}}{1 \text{ mi}}$ is equal to 1, and multiplying an expression by 1 does not change the value of the expression.

In the application problem that follows, the units are kept in the problem while the problem is worked.

In 2005, a horse named Afleet Alex won the Preakness, covering the 1.1875-mile course in 1.92 min. Find Afleet Alex's speed in miles per hour. Round to the nearest tenth.

Strategy   To find the average speed, use the formula $r = \frac{d}{t}$, where r is the speed, d is the distance, and t is the time. Use the conversion factor $\frac{60 \text{ min}}{1 \text{ h}}$.

Solution $r = \dfrac{d}{t} = \dfrac{1.1875 \text{ mi}}{1.92 \text{ min}} = \dfrac{1.1875 \text{ mi}}{1.92 \text{ min}} \cdot \dfrac{60 \text{ min}}{1 \text{ h}}$

$$= \dfrac{71.25 \text{ mi}}{1.92 \text{ h}} \approx 37.1 \text{ mph}$$

Afleet Alex's average speed was 37.1 mph.

Try each of the following problems. Round to the nearest tenth or to the nearest cent.

1. Convert 88 ft/s to miles per hour.

2. Convert 8 m/s to kilometers per hour (1 km = 1000 m).

3. A carpet is to be placed in a meeting hall that is 36 ft wide and 80 ft long. At $21.50 per square yard, how much will it cost to carpet the meeting hall?

4. A carpet is to be placed in a room that is 20 ft wide and 30 ft long. At $22.25 per square yard, how much will it cost to carpet the area?

5. Find the number of gallons of water in a fish tank that is 36 in. long and 24 in. wide and is filled to a depth of 16 in. (1 gal = 231 in^3).

6. Find the number of gallons of water in a fish tank that is 24 in. long and 18 in. wide and is filled to a depth of 12 in. (1 gal = 231 in^3).

7. A $\frac{1}{4}$-acre commercial lot is on sale for $2.15 per square foot. Find the sale price of the commercial lot (1 acre = 43,560 ft^2).

8. A 0.75-acre industrial parcel was sold for $98,010. Find the parcel's price per square foot (1 acre = 43,560 ft^2).

9. A new driveway will require 800 ft^3 of concrete. Concrete is ordered by the cubic yard. How much concrete should be ordered?

10. In 2005, Catherine Ndereba won her fourth Boston Marathon. She ran the 26-mile course in 2.42 h. Find Catherine Ndereba's speed in feet per second. Round to the nearest tenth.

11. The Marianas Trench in the Pacific Ocean is the deepest part of the ocean. Its depth is 6.85 mi. The speed of sound under water is 4700 ft/s. Find the time it takes sound to travel from the surface to the bottom of the Marianas Trench and back.

Projects & Group Activities

Population and Land Allocation*

Texas

Rhode Island

One of the Projects & Group Activities in the chapter "Linear Equations and Inequalities" involved population projections. You were asked to make predictions about the population of the United States and of the world. In this project, you are asked to determine hypothetical land allocation for the world's population today. Use the figure 6×10^9 for the current world population and the figure 2.9×10^8 for the current U.S. population. One square mile is approximately 2.8×10^7 ft^2.

1. If every person in the world moved to Texas and each person were given an equal amount of land, how many square feet of land would each person have? The area of Texas is 2.619×10^5 mi^2.

2. If every person in the United States moved to Rhode Island and each person were given an equal amount of land, how many square feet of land would each person have? The area of Rhode Island is 1.0×10^3 mi^2. Round to the nearest whole number.

*Source: www.infoplease.com

3. Suppose every person in the world were given a plot of land the size of a two-car garage (22 ft × 22 ft).
   a. How many people would fit in a square mile? Round to the nearest hundred.
   b. How many square miles would be required to accommodate the entire world population? Round to the nearest hundred.

4. If the total land area of Earth were divided equally, how many acres of land would each person be allocated? Use a figure of $5.7 \times 10^7 \text{ mi}^2$ for the land area of Earth. One acre is 43,560 ft^2. Round to the nearest tenth.

5. If every person on Earth were given a plot of land the size of a two-car garage, what would be the carrying capacity of Earth? Round to the nearest hundred billion.

Chapter 7 Summary

Key Words

A **monomial** is a number, a variable, or a product of numbers and variables. [7.1.1, p. 369]	5 is a number. y is a variable. $8a^2b^3$ is a product of numbers and variables. 5, y, and $8a^2b^3$ are monomials.
A **polynomial** is a variable expression in which the terms are monomials. [7.1.1, p. 369]	As shown above, 5, y, and $8a^2b^3$ are monomials. Therefore, $5 + y + 8a^2b^3$ is a polynomial.
A polynomial of one term is a **monomial.** [7.1.1, p. 369]	5, y, and $8a^2b^3$ are monomials.
A polynomial of two terms is a **binomial.** [7.1.1, p. 369]	$x + 9$, $y^2 - 3$, and $6a + 7b$ are binomials.
A polynomial of three terms is a **trinomial.** [7.1.1, p. 369]	$x^2 + 2x - 1$ is a trinomial.
The **degree of a polynomial in one variable** is the largest exponent on a variable. [7.1.1, p. 370]	The degree of $8x^3 - 5x^2 + 4x - 12$ is 3.
The **opposite of a polynomial** is the polynomial with the sign of every term changed to its opposite. [7.1.2, p. 370]	The opposite of the polynomial $x^2 - 3x + 4$ is $-x^2 + 3x - 4$.

Examples

Essential Rules and Procedures

Addition of Polynomials
To add polynomials, add the coefficients of the like terms. [7.1.1, p. 370]

$$
\begin{aligned}
(2x^2 &+ 3x - 4) + (3x^3 - 4x^2 + 2x - 5) \\
&= 3x^3 + (2x^2 - 4x^2) + (3x + 2x) \\
&\quad + (-4 - 5) \\
&= 3x^3 - 2x^2 + 5x - 9
\end{aligned}
$$

Subtraction of Polynomials
To subtract polynomials, add the opposite of the second polynomial to the first.   [7.1.2, p. 370]

$$(3y^2 - 8y - 9) - (5y^2 - 10y + 3)$$
$$= (3y^2 - 8y - 9) + (-5y^2 + 10y - 3)$$
$$= (3y^2 - 5y^2) + (-8y + 10y)$$
$$\quad + (-9 - 3)$$
$$= -2y^2 + 2y - 12$$

Rule for Multiplying Exponential Expressions
If m and n are integers, then $x^m \cdot x^n = x^{m+n}$.   [7.2.1, p. 375]

$$b^5 \cdot b^4 = b^{5+4} = b^9$$

Rule for Simplifying Powers of Exponential Expressions
If m and n are integers, then $(x^m)^n = x^{mn}$.   [7.2.2, p. 376]

$$(y^3)^7 = y^{3(7)} = y^{21}$$

Rule for Simplifying Powers of Products
If m, n, and p are integers, then $(x^m y^n)^p = x^{mp} y^{np}$.   [7.2.2, p. 376]

$$(a^6 b^2)^3 = a^{6(3)} b^{2(3)} = a^{18} b^6$$

FOIL Method
To find the product of two binomials, add the products of the **F**irst terms, the **O**uter terms, the **I**nner terms, and the **L**ast terms.   [7.3.3, p. 381]

$$(4x + 3)(2x - 1)$$
$$= (4x)(2x) + (4x)(-1)$$
$$\quad + (3)(2x) + (3)(-1)$$
$$= 8x^2 - 4x + 6x - 3$$
$$= 8x^2 + 2x - 3$$

The Sum and Difference of Two Terms
$(a + b)(a - b) = a^2 - b^2$ [7.3.4, p. 382]

$$(3x + 4)(3x - 4) = (3x)^2 - 4^2$$
$$= 9x^2 - 16$$

The Square of a Binomial
$(a + b)^2 = a^2 + 2ab + b^2$

$$(2x + 5)^2 = (2x)^2 + 2(2x)(5) + 5^2$$
$$= 4x^2 + 20x + 25$$

$(a - b)^2 = a^2 - 2ab + b^2$ [7.3.4, p. 383]

$$(2x - 5)^2 = (2x)^2 - 2(2x)(5) + (-5)^2$$
$$= 4x^2 - 20x + 25$$

Zero as an Exponent
Any nonzero expression to the zero power equals 1.
[7.4.1, p. 391]

$$17^0 = 1 \qquad (5y)^0 = 1, y \neq 0$$

Definition of Negative Exponents
If n is a positive integer and $x \neq 0$, then $x^{-n} = \dfrac{1}{x^n}$ and $\dfrac{1}{x^{-n}} = x^n$.
[7.4.1, p. 392]

$$x^{-6} = \frac{1}{x^6} \quad \text{and} \quad \frac{1}{x^{-6}} = x^6$$

Rule for Dividing Exponential Expressions
If m and n are integers and $x \neq 0$, then $\dfrac{x^m}{x^n} = x^{m-n}$.
[7.4.1, p. 392]

$$\frac{y^8}{y^3} = y^{8-3} = y^5$$

Scientific Notation

To express a number in scientific notation, write it in the form $a \times 10^n$, where a is a number between 1 and 10 and n is an integer. If the number is greater than 10, the exponent on 10 will be positive. If the number is less than 1, the exponent on 10 will be negative.

$367,000,000 = 3.67 \times 10^8$

$0.0000059 = 5.9 \times 10^{-6}$

To change a number written in scientific notation to decimal notation, move the decimal point to the right if the exponent on 10 is positive and to the left if the exponent on 10 is negative. Move the decimal point the same number of places as the absolute value of the exponent on 10.   [7.4.2, pp. 394–395]

$2.418 \times 10^7 = 24,180,000$

$9.06 \times 10^{-5} = 0.0000906$

To divide a polynomial by a monomial, divide each term in the numerator by the denominator and write the sum of the quotients.   [7.5.1, p. 402]

$$\frac{8xy^3 - 4y^2 + 12y}{4y}$$

$$= \frac{8xy^3}{4y} - \frac{4y^2}{4y} + \frac{12y}{4y}$$

$$= 2xy^2 - y + 3$$

To check polynomial division, use the same equation used to check division of whole numbers:

(Quotient × divisor) + remainder = dividend

[7.5.2, p. 403]

$$\begin{array}{r} x - 4 \\ x + 3\overline{)x^2 - x - 10} \\ \underline{x^2 + 3x} \\ -4x - 10 \\ \underline{-4x - 12} \\ 2 \end{array}$$

Check:

$(x - 4)(x + 3) + 2 = x^2 - x - 12 + 2$
$\qquad\qquad\qquad\quad = x^2 - x - 10$

$(x^2 - x - 10) \div (x + 3)$

$$= x - 4 + \frac{2}{x + 3}$$

Chapter 7 Review Exercises

1. Add: $(12y^2 + 17y - 4) + (9y^2 - 13y + 3)$

2. Multiply: $(5xy^2)(-4x^2y^3)$

3. Multiply: $-2x(4x^2 + 7x - 9)$

4. Multiply: $(5a - 7)(2a + 9)$

5. Divide: $\dfrac{36x^2 - 42x + 60}{6}$

6. Subtract: $(5x^2 - 2x - 1) - (3x^2 - 5x + 7)$

7. Simplify: $(-3^2)^3$

8. Multiply: $(x^2 - 5x + 2)(x - 1)$

9. Multiply: $(a + 7)(a - 7)$

10. Evaluate: $\dfrac{6^2}{6^{-2}}$

11. Divide: $(x^2 + x - 42) \div (x + 7)$

12. Add: $(2x^3 + 7x^2 + x) + (2x^2 - 4x - 12)$

13. Multiply: $(6a^2b^5)(3a^6b)$

14. Multiply: $x^2y(3x^2 - 2x + 12)$

15. Multiply: $(2b - 3)(4b + 5)$

16. Divide: $\dfrac{16y^2 - 32y}{-4y}$

17. Subtract: $(13y^3 - 7y - 2) - (12y^2 - 2y - 1)$

18. Simplify: $(2^3)^2$

19. Multiply: $(3y^2 + 4y - 7)(2y + 3)$

20. Multiply: $(2b - 9)(2b + 9)$

21. Simplify: $(a^{-2}b^3c)^2$

22. Divide: $(6y^2 - 35y + 36) \div (3y - 4)$

23. Write 0.00000397 in scientific notation.

24. Multiply: $(xy^5z^3)(x^3y^3z)$

25. Multiply: $(6y^2 - 2y + 9)(-2y^3)$

26. Multiply: $(6x - 12)(3x - 2)$

27. Write 6.23×10^{-5} in decimal notation.

28. Subtract: $(8a^2 - a) - (15a^2 - 4)$

29. Simplify: $(-3x^2y^3)^2$

30. Multiply: $(4a^2 - 3)(3a - 2)$

31. Simplify: $(5y - 7)^2$

32. Simplify: $(-3x^{-2}y^{-3})^{-2}$

33. Divide: $(x^2 + 17x + 64) \div (x + 12)$

34. Write 2.4×10^5 in decimal notation.

35. Multiply: $(a^2b^7c^6)(ab^3c)(a^3bc^2)$

36. Multiply: $2ab^3(4a^2 - 2ab + 3b^2)$

37. Multiply: $(3x + 4y)(2x - 5y)$

38. Divide: $\dfrac{12b^7 + 36b^5 - 3b^3}{3b^3}$

39. Subtract: $(b^2 - 11b + 19) - (5b^2 + 2b - 9)$

40. Simplify: $(5a^7b^6)^2(4ab)$

41. Multiply: $(6b^3 - 2b^2 - 5)(2b^2 - 1)$

42. Multiply: $(6 - 5x)(6 + 5x)$

43. Simplify: $\dfrac{6x^{-2}y^4}{3xy}$

44. Divide: $(a^3 + a^2 + 18) \div (a + 3)$

45. Add: $(4b^3 - 7b^2 + 10) + (2b^2 - 9b - 3)$

46. Multiply: $(2a^{12}b^3)(-9b^2c^6)(3ac)$

47. Multiply: $-9x^2(2x^2 + 3x - 7)$

48. Multiply: $(10y - 3)(3y - 10)$

49. Write 9,176,000,000,000 in scientific notation.

50. Subtract: $(6y^2 + 2y + 7) - (8y^2 + y + 12)$

51. Simplify: $(6x^4y^7z^2)^2(-2x^3y^2z^6)^2$

52. Multiply: $(-3x^3 - 2x^2 + x - 9)(4x + 3)$

53. Simplify: $(8a + 1)^2$

54. Simplify: $\dfrac{4a^{-2}b^{-8}}{2a^{-1}b^{-2}}$

55. Divide: $(b^3 - 2b^2 - 33b - 7) \div (b - 7)$

56. **Geometry** The length of a rectangle is $5x$ m. The width is $(4x - 7)$ m. Find the area of the rectangle in terms of the variable x.

57. **Geometry** The length of a side of a square is $(5x + 4)$ in. Find the area of the square in terms of the variable x.

58. **Geometry** The base of a triangle is $(3x - 2)$ ft and the height is $(6x + 4)$ ft. Find the area of the triangle in terms of the variable x.

59. **Geometry** The radius of a circle is $(x - 6)$ cm. Find the area of the circle in terms of the variable x. Leave the answer in terms of π.

60. **Geometry** The width of a rectangle is $(3x - 8)$ mi. The length is $(5x + 4)$ mi. Find the area of the rectangle in terms of the variable x.

Chapter 7 Test

View the Chapter Test Videos for fully worked-out solutions to any exercise.

1. Add: $(3x^3 - 2x^2 - 4) + (8x^2 - 8x + 7)$

2. Multiply: $(-2x^3 + x^2 - 7)(2x - 3)$

3. Multiply: $2x(2x^2 - 3x)$

4. Simplify: $(-2a^2b)^3$

5. Simplify: $\dfrac{12x^2}{-3x^{-4}}$

6. Simplify: $(2ab^{-3})(3a^{-2}b^4)$

7. Subtract: $(3a^2 - 2a - 7) - (5a^3 + 2a - 10)$

8. Multiply: $(a - 2b)(a + 5b)$

9. Divide: $\dfrac{16x^5 - 8x^3 + 20x}{4x}$

10. Divide: $(4x^2 - 7) \div (2x - 3)$

11. Multiply: $(-2xy^2)(3x^2y^4)$

12. Multiply: $-3y^2(-2y^2 + 3y - 6)$

13. Simplify: $\dfrac{27xy^3}{3x^4y^3}$

14. Simplify: $(2x - 5)^2$

15. Multiply: $(2x - 7y)(5x - 4y)$

16. Multiply: $(x - 3)(x^2 - 4x + 5)$

17. Simplify: $(a^2b^{-3})^2$

18. Write 0.000029 in scientific notation.

19. Multiply: $(4y - 3)(4y + 3)$

20. Subtract: $(3y^3 - 5y + 8) - (-2y^2 + 5y + 8)$

21. Simplify: $(-3a^3b^2)^2$

22. Multiply: $(2a - 7)(5a^2 - 2a + 3)$

23. Simplify: $(3b + 2)^2$

24. Simplify: $\dfrac{-2a^2b^3}{8a^4b^8}$

25. Divide: $(8x^2 + 4x - 3) \div (2x - 3)$

26. Multiply: $(a^2b^5)(ab^2)$

27. Multiply: $(a - 3b)(a + 4b)$

28. Write 3.5×10^{-8} in decimal notation.

29. **Geometry** The length of a side of a square is $(2x + 3)$ m. Find the area of the square in terms of the variable x.

30. **Geometry** The radius of a circle is $(x - 5)$ in. Find the area of the circle in terms of the variable x. Leave the answer in terms of π.

Cumulative Review Exercises

1. Simplify: $\dfrac{3}{16} - \left(-\dfrac{3}{8}\right) - \dfrac{5}{9}$

2. Simplify: $-5^2 \cdot \left(\dfrac{2}{3}\right)^3 \cdot \left(-\dfrac{3}{8}\right)$

3. Simplify: $\left(-\dfrac{1}{2}\right)^2 \div \left(\dfrac{5}{8} - \dfrac{5}{6}\right) + 2$

4. Find the opposite of -87.

5. Write $\dfrac{31}{40}$ as a decimal.

6. Evaluate $\dfrac{b - (a - b)^2}{b^2}$ when $a = 3$ and $b = -2$.

7. Simplify: $-3x - (-xy) + 2x - 5xy$

8. Simplify: $(16x)\left(-\dfrac{3}{4}\right)$

9. Simplify: $-2[3x - 4(3 - 2x) + 2]$

10. Complete the statement by using the Inverse Property of Addition.
$-8 + ? = 0$

11. Solve: $12 = -\dfrac{2}{3}x$

12. Solve: $3x - 7 = 2x + 9$

13. Solve: $3 - 4(2 - x) = 3x + 7$

14. Solve: $-\dfrac{4}{5}x = 16 - x$

15. 38.4 is what percent of 160?

16. Solve: $7x - 8 \geq -29$

17. Find the slope of the line that contains the points whose coordinates are $(3, -4)$ and $(-2, 5)$.

18. Find the equation of the line that contains the point whose coordinates are $(1, -3)$ and has slope $-\dfrac{3}{2}$.

19. Graph: $3x - 2y = -6$

20. Graph the solution set of
$$y \le \frac{4}{5}x - 3.$$

21. Find the domain and range of the relation $\{(-8, -7), (-6, -5), (-4, -2), (-2, 0)\}$. Is the relation a function?

22. Evaluate $f(x) = -2x + 10$ at $x = 6$.

23. Solve by substitution: $x = 3y + 1$
$$2x + 5y = 13$$

24. Solve by the addition method: $9x - 2y = 17$
$$5x + 3y = -7$$

25. Subtract: $(5b^3 - 4b^2 - 7) - (3b^2 - 8b + 3)$

26. Multiply: $(3x - 4)(5x^2 - 2x + 1)$

27. Multiply: $(4b - 3)(5b - 8)$

28. Simplify: $(5b + 3)^2$

29. Simplify: $\dfrac{-3a^3b^2}{12a^4b^{-2}}$

30. Divide: $\dfrac{-15y^2 + 12y - 3}{-3y}$

31. Divide: $(a^2 - 3a - 28) \div (a + 4)$

32. Simplify: $(-3x^{-4}y)(-3x^{-2}y)$

33. Find the range of the function given by the equation $f(x) = -\dfrac{4}{3}x + 9$ if the domain is $\{-12, -9, -6, 0, 6\}$.

34. Translate and simplify "the product of five and the difference between a number and twelve."

35. Translate "the difference between eight times a number and twice the number is eighteen" into an equation and solve.

36. Geometry The width of a rectangle is 40% of the length. The perimeter of the rectangle is 42 m. Find the length and width of the rectangle.

L

$0.40L$

37. Markup A calculator costs a retailer $24. Find the selling price when the markup rate is 80%.

38. Food Mixtures Fifty ounces of pure orange juice are added to 200 oz of a fruit punch that is 10% orange juice. What is the percent concentration of orange juice in the resulting mixture?

39. Uniform Motion Problem A car traveling at 50 mph overtakes a cyclist who, riding at 10 mph, has had a 2-hour head start. How far from the starting point does the car overtake the cyclist?

40. Geometry The length of a side of a square is $(3x + 2)$ ft. Find the area of the square in terms of the variable x.

8 Factoring

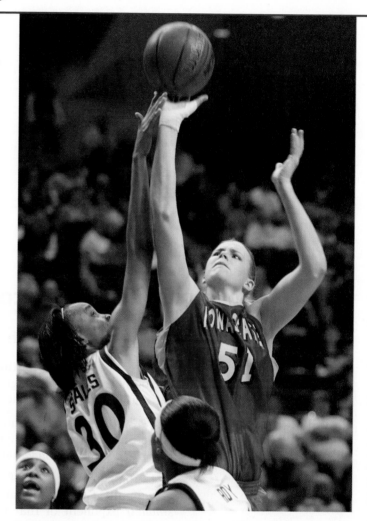

In 2008, Iowa State will host the first and second rounds of the NCAA Division I women's basketball tournament in Des Moines, Iowa. The teams who will compete in this tournament will be determined by their ranking after the 2008 regular season. Imagine that you have just gotten a job as the manager for NCAA Division I women's basketball, and that you have to organize the game schedule for the upcoming season. How would you go about creating this schedule? **Exercises 93 and 94 on page 457** show you how to use a formula to determine the number of league games that must be scheduled if each team is to play each of the other teams once.

DVD

SSM

Online Study Center

Need help? For online student resources, such as section quizzes, visit the Online Study Center at www.cengage.com/math/aufmann.

Prep Test

1. Write 30 as a product of prime numbers.

2. Simplify: $-3(4y - 5)$

3. Simplify: $-(a - b)$

4. Simplify: $2(a - b) - 5(a - b)$

5. Solve: $4x = 0$

6. Solve: $2x + 1 = 0$

7. Multiply: $(x + 4)(x - 6)$

8. Multiply: $(2x - 5)(3x + 2)$

9. Simplify: $\dfrac{x^5}{x^2}$

10. Simplify: $\dfrac{6x^4y^3}{2xy^2}$

8.1 Common Factors

OBJECTIVE 1 Factor a monomial from a polynomial

Take Note

12 is the GCF of 24 and 60 because 12 is the largest integer that divides evenly into both 24 and 60.

The **greatest common factor (GCF)** of two or more integers is the greatest integer that is a factor of all the integers.

$24 = 2 \cdot 2 \cdot 2 \cdot 3$
$60 = 2 \cdot 2 \cdot 3 \cdot 5$
$\text{GCF} = 2 \cdot 2 \cdot 3 = 12$

The GCF of two or more monomials is the product of the GCF of the coefficients and the common variable factors.

$6x^3y = 2 \cdot 3 \cdot x \cdot x \cdot x \cdot y$
$8x^2y^2 = 2 \cdot 2 \cdot 2 \cdot x \cdot x \cdot y \cdot y$
$\text{GCF} = 2 \cdot x \cdot x \cdot y = 2x^2y$

Note that the exponent of each variable in the GCF is the same as the *smallest* exponent of that variable in either of the monomials.

The GCF of $6x^3y$ and $8x^2y^2$ is $2x^2y$.

EXAMPLE 1 Find the GCF of $12a^4b$ and $18a^2b^2c$.

Solution $12a^4b = 2 \cdot 2 \cdot 3 \cdot a^4 \cdot b$ • **Factor each monomial.**
$18a^2b^2c = 2 \cdot 3 \cdot 3 \cdot a^2 \cdot b^2 \cdot c$

$\text{GCF} = 2 \cdot 3 \cdot a^2 \cdot b = 6a^2b$ • **The common variable factors are**
a^2 **and** b. c **is not a common factor.**

PROBLEM 1 Find the GCF of $4x^6y$ and $18x^2y^6$.

Solution See page S17.

The Distributive Property is used to multiply factors of a polynomial. To **factor a polynomial** means to write the polynomial as a product of other polynomials.

Multiply

Factors → Polynomial

$2x(x + 5) = 2x^2 + 10x$

Factor

In the example above, $2x$ is the GCF of the terms $2x^2$ and $10x$. It is a **common monomial factor** of the terms. $x + 5$ is a **binomial factor** of $2x^2 + 10x$.

EXAMPLE 2   Factor.   **A.** $5x^3 - 35x^2 + 10x$ **B.** $16x^2y + 8x^4y^2 - 12x^4y^5$

Solution   **A.** The GCF is $5x$.

$$\frac{5x^3}{5x} = x^2, \quad \frac{-35x^2}{5x} = -7x, \quad \frac{10x}{5x} = 2$$

$$5x^3 - 35x^2 + 10x$$

$$= 5x(x^2) + 5x(-7x) + 5x(2)$$

$$= 5x(x^2 - 7x + 2)$$

• Find the GCF of the terms of the polynomial.

• Divide each term of the polynomial by the GCF.

• Use the quotients to rewrite the polynomial, expressing each term as a product with the GCF as one of the factors.

• Use the Distributive Property to write the polynomial as a product of factors.

B. $16x^2y = 2 \cdot 2 \cdot 2 \cdot 2 \cdot x^2 \cdot y$
$8x^4y^2 = 2 \cdot 2 \cdot 2 \cdot x^4 \cdot y^2$
$12x^4y^5 = 2 \cdot 2 \cdot 3 \cdot x^4 \cdot y^5$
The GCF is $4x^2y$.

$$16x^2y + 8x^4y^2 - 12x^4y^5$$
$$= 4x^2y(4) + 4x^2y(2x^2y) + 4x^2y(-3x^2y^4)$$
$$= 4x^2y(4 + 2x^2y - 3x^2y^4)$$

PROBLEM 2   Factor.   **A.** $14a^2 - 21a^4b$ **B.** $6x^4y^2 - 9x^3y^2 + 12x^2y^4$

Solution   See page S17.

OBJECTIVE **2**   **Factor by grouping**

In the examples below, the binomials in parentheses are called **binomial factors.**

$$2a(a + b)$$
$$3xy(x - y)$$

The Distributive Property is used to factor a common binomial factor from an expression.

In the expression at the right, the common binomial factor is $y - 3$. The Distributive Property is used to write the expression as a product of factors.

$$x(y - 3) + 4(y - 3)$$
$$= (y - 3)(x + 4)$$

EXAMPLE 3   Factor: $y(x + 2) + 3(x + 2)$

Solution $y(x + 2) + 3(x + 2)$ • The common binomial factor is $x + 2$.
$$= (x + 2)(y + 3)$$

PROBLEM 3 Factor: $a(b-7) + b(b-7)$

Solution See page S17.

Sometimes a binomial factor must be rewritten before a common binomial factor can be found.

Factor: $a(a-b) + 5(b-a)$

$a-b$ and $b-a$ are different binomials.

Note that $(b-a) = (-a+b) = -(a-b)$.

Rewrite $(b-a)$ as $-(a-b)$ so that there is a common factor.

$$a(a-b) + 5(b-a) = a(a-b) + 5[-(a-b)]$$
$$= a(a-b) - 5(a-b)$$
$$= (a-b)(a-5)$$

EXAMPLE 4 Factor: $2x(x-5) + y(5-x)$

Solution $2x(x-5) + y(5-x)$
$$= 2x(x-5) - y(x-5)$$ • **Rewrite $5-x$ as $-(x-5)$ so that there is a common factor.**
$$= (x-5)(2x-y)$$ • **Write the expression as a product of factors.**

PROBLEM 4 Factor: $3y(5x-2) - 4(2-5x)$

Solution See page S17.

Some polynomials can be factored by grouping the terms so that a common binomial factor is found.

Factor: $2x^3 - 3x^2 + 4x - 6$

Group the first two terms and the last two terms.

$$2x^3 - 3x^2 + 4x - 6$$
$$= (2x^3 - 3x^2) + (4x - 6)$$

Factor out the GCF from each group.

$$= x^2(2x-3) + 2(2x-3)$$

Write the expression as a product of factors.

$$= (2x-3)(x^2+2)$$

EXAMPLE 5 Factor: $3y^3 - 4y^2 - 6y + 8$

Solution $3y^3 - 4y^2 - 6y + 8$
$$= (3y^3 - 4y^2) - (6y - 8)$$ • **Group the first two terms and the last two terms. Note that $-6y + 8 = -(6y - 8)$.**
$$= y^2(3y-4) - 2(3y-4)$$ • **Factor out the GCF from each group.**
$$= (3y-4)(y^2-2)$$ • **Write the expression as a product of factors.**

> **PROBLEM 5**   Factor: $y^5 - 5y^3 + 4y^2 - 20$
>
> **Solution**   See page S17.

8.1   Concept Review

Determine whether the statement is always true, sometimes true, or never true.

1. To factor a polynomial means to rewrite it as multiplication.

2. The expression $3x(x + 5)$ is a sum, and the expression $3x^2 + 15x$ is a product.

3. The greatest common factor of two numbers is the largest number that divides evenly into both numbers.

4. x is a monomial factor of $x(2x - 1)$. $2x - 1$ is a binomial factor of $x(2x - 1)$.

5. $y(y + 4) + 6$ is in factored form.

6. A common monomial factor is a factor of every term of a polynomial.

7. $a^2 - 8a - ab + 8b = a(a - 8) - b(a + 8)$

8. The binomial $d + 9$ is a common binomial factor of $2c(d + 9) - 7(d + 9)$.

8.1   Exercises

1   Factor a monomial from a polynomial

1. Explain the meaning of "a factor of a polynomial" and the meaning of "to factor a polynomial."

2. Explain why the statement is true.

   a. The terms of the binomial $3x - 6$ have a common factor.
   b. The expression $3x^2 + 15$ is not in factored form.
   c. $5y - 7$ is a factor of $y(5y - 7)$.

3. Use the three monomials $9x^3y^2$, $3xy^3z$, and $6x^2y^2z^2$.
   a. Of the variable factors x, y, and z, the one that is *not* a factor of the GCF of $9x^3y^2$, $3xy^3z$, and $6x^2y^2z^2$ is ___?___.
   b. The GCF of the coefficients 9, 3, and 6 is ___?___.
   c. The GCF of the factors x^3, x, and x^2 is ___?___.

d. The GCF of the factors y^2, y^3, and y^2 is _____?_____.

e. Use your answers to parts a to d to write the GCF of $9x^3y^2$, $3xy^3z$, and $6x^2y^2z^2$: _____?_____

4. a. Of the two expressions $25a^2 - 10a$ and $5a(5a - 2)$, the one that is written in *factored form* is _____?_____.

b. Use the Distributive Property to confirm that the two expressions in part a are equivalent:
$$5a(5a - 2) = (\underline{\quad?\quad})(5a) - (\underline{\quad?\quad})(2) = \underline{\quad?\quad} - \underline{\quad?\quad}.$$

c. The polynomial $25a^2 - 10a$ has a monomial factor and a binomial factor. The monomial factor is _____?_____ and the binomial factor is _____?_____.

Find the greatest common factor.

5. x^7, x^3

6. y^6, y^{12}

7. x^2y^4, xy^6

8. a^5b^3, a^3b^8

9. $x^2y^4z^6, xy^8z^2$

10. ab^2c^3, a^3b^2c

11. $14a^3, 49a^7$

12. $12y^2, 27y^4$

13. $3x^2y^2, 5ab^2$

14. $8x^2y^3, 7ab^4$

15. $9a^2b^4, 24a^4b^2$

16. $15a^4b^2, 9ab^5$

17. $ab^3, 4a^2b, 12a^2b^3$

18. $12x^2y, x^4y, 16x$

19. $2x^2y, 4xy, 8x$

20. $16x^2, 8x^4y^2, 12xy$

21. $3x^2y^2, 6x, 9x^3y^3$

22. $4a^2b^3, 8a^3, 12ab^4$

Factor.

23. $5a + 5$

24. $7b - 7$

25. $16 - 8a^2$

26. $12 + 12y^2$

27. $8x + 12$

28. $16a - 24$

29. $30a - 6$

30. $20b + 5$

31. $7x^2 - 3x$

32. $12y^2 - 5y$

33. $3a^2 + 5a^5$

34. $9x - 5x^2$

35. $14y^2 + 11y$

36. $6b^3 - 5b^2$

37. $2x^4 - 4x$

38. $3y^4 - 9y$

39. $10x^4 - 12x^2$

40. $12a^5 - 32a^2$

41. $x^2y - xy^3$

42. $a^2b + a^4b^2$

43. $2a^5b + 3xy^3$

44. $5x^2y - 7ab^3$

45. $6a^2b^3 - 12b^2$

46. $8x^2y^3 - 4x^2$

47. $6a^2bc + 4ab^2c$

48. $10x^2yz^2 + 15xy^3z$

49. $18x^2y^2 - 9a^2b^2$

50. $9a^2x - 27a^3x^3$

51. $6x^3y^3 - 12x^6y^6$

52. $3a^2b^2 - 12a^5b^5$

53. $x^3 - 3x^2 - x$

54. $a^3 + 4a^2 + 8a$

55. $2x^2 + 8x - 12$

56. $a^3 - 3a^2 + 5a$

57. $b^3 - 5b^2 - 7b$

58. $5x^2 - 15x + 35$

59. $8y^2 - 12y + 32$

60. $3x^3 + 6x^2 + 9x$

61. $5y^3 - 20y^2 + 10y$

62. $2x^4 - 4x^3 + 6x^2$

63. $3y^4 - 9y^3 - 6y^2$

64. $2x^3 + 6x^2 - 14x$

65. $3y^3 - 9y^2 + 24y$

66. $2y^5 - 3y^4 + 7y^3$

67. $6a^5 - 3a^3 - 2a^2$

68. $x^3y - 3x^2y^2 + 7xy^3$

69. $8x^2y^2 - 4x^2y + x^2$

70. $x^4y^4 - 3x^3y^3 + 6x^2y^2$

71. $4x^5y^5 - 8x^4y^4 + x^3y^3$

72. $16x^2y - 8x^3y^4 - 48x^2y^2$

For Exercises 73 and 74, use the polynomial $x^a + x^b + x^c$, where a, b, and c are all positive integers such that $a < b < c$.

73. What is the GCF of the terms of the polynomial $x^a + x^b + x^c$?

74. Suppose $b = a + 1$ and $c = a + 2$. Write $x^a + x^b + x^c$ in factored form.

2 Factor by grouping

75. a. The expression $5x(3x - 2) + 4(3x - 2)$ is the sum of two terms. One term is $5x(3x - 2)$ and the other term is ___?___. The terms have the common binomial factor ___?___.
b. To write the expression $5x(3x - 2) + 4(3x - 2)$ in factored form, factor out the common binomial factor: $5x(3x - 2) + 4(3x - 2) =$ $(3x - 2)(\underline{} + \underline{})$.

76. To factor $7a^2 - 7a + 6a - 6$ by grouping, start by factoring $7a$ from the first two terms and 6 from the second two terms: $7a^2 - 7a + 6a - 6 =$ $7a(\underline{} - \underline{}) + 6(\underline{} - \underline{}) = (\underline{})(7a + 6)$

Factor.

77. $x(a + b) + 2(a + b)$

78. $a(x + y) + 4(x + y)$

79. $x(b + 2) - y(b + 2)$

80. $d(z - 8) + 5(z - 8)$

81. $a(y - 4) - b(y - 4)$

82. $c(x - 6) - 7(x - 6)$

Rewrite the expression so that there is a common binomial factor.

83. $a(x - 2) - b(2 - x)$

84. $a(x - 2) + b(2 - x)$

85. $b(a - 7) + 3(7 - a)$

86. $b(a - 7) - 3(7 - a)$

87. $x(a - 2b) - y(2b - a)$

88. $x(a - 2b) + y(2b - a)$

Factor.

89. $a(x - 2) + 5(2 - x)$

90. $a(x - 7) + b(7 - x)$

91. $b(y - 3) + 3(3 - y)$

92. $c(a - 2) - b(2 - a)$

93. $a(x - y) - 2(y - x)$

94. $3(a - b) - x(b - a)$

95. $z(c + 5) - 8(5 + c)$

96. $y(ab + 4) - 7(4 + ab)$

97. $w(3x - 4) - (4 - 3x)$

98. $d(6y - 1) - (1 - 6y)$

99. $x^3 + 4x^2 + 3x + 12$

100. $x^3 - 4x^2 - 3x + 12$

101. $2y^3 + 4y^2 + 3y + 6$

102. $3y^3 - 12y^2 + y - 4$

103. $ab + 3b - 2a - 6$

104. $yz + 6z - 3y - 18$

105. $x^2a - 2x^2 - 3a + 6$

106. $x^2y + 4x^2 + 3y + 12$

107. $3ax - 3bx - 2ay + 2by$

108. $8 + 2c + 4a^2 + a^2c$

109. $x^2 - 3x + 4ax - 12a$

110. $t^2 + 4t - st - 4s$

111. $xy - 5y - 2x + 10$

112. $2y^2 - 10y + 7xy - 35x$

113. $21x^2 + 6xy - 49x - 14y$

114. $4a^2 + 5ab - 10b - 8a$

115. $2ra + a^2 - 2r - a$

116. $2ab - 3b^2 - 3b + 2a$

117. $4x^2 + 3xy - 12y - 16x$

118. $8s + 12r - 6s^2 - 9rs$

119. $10xy^2 - 15xy + 6y - 9$

120. $10a^2b - 15ab - 4a + 6$

121. Not all four-term expressions can be factored by grouping. Which of the following expressions can be factored by grouping?
I. $ab - 3a - 2b - 6$ **II.** $ab + 3a - 2b - 6$ **III.** $ab + 3a + 2b - 6$

122. **a.** Which of the following expressions are equivalent to $x^2 - 5x + 6$?
I. $x^2 - 15x + 10x + 6$ **II.** $x^2 - x - 4x + 6$ **III.** $x^2 - 2x - 3x + 6$
b. Which expression in part a can be factored by grouping?

8.1 Applying Concepts

Factor by grouping.

123. a. $2x^2 + 6x + 5x + 15$

  b. $2x^2 + 5x + 6x + 15$

124. a. $3x^2 + 3xy - xy - y^2$

  b. $3x^2 - xy + 3xy - y^2$

125. a. $2a^2 - 2ab - 3ab + 3b^2$

  b. $2a^2 - 3ab - 2ab + 3b^2$

Compare your answers to parts a and b of Exercises 123 to 125 in order to answer Exercise 126.

126. Do different groupings of the terms in a polynomial affect the binomial factoring?

A whole number is a perfect number if it is the sum of all of its factors that are less than itself. For example, 6 is a perfect number because all the factors of 6 that are less than 6 are 1, 2, and 3, and $1 + 2 + 3 = 6$.

127. Find a perfect number between 20 and 30.   **128.** Find a perfect number between 490 and 500.

Solve.

129. **Geometry** In the equation $P = 2L + 2W$, what is the effect on P when the quantity $L + W$ doubles?

130. **Geometry** Write an expression in factored form for the shaded portion in the diagram.

a.

b.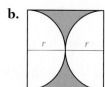

Factoring Polynomials of the Form $x^2 + bx + c$

OBJECTIVE 1 ## Factor trinomials of the form $x^2 + bx + c$

Trinomials of the form $x^2 + bx + c$, where b and c are integers, are shown at the right.

$$x^2 + 9x + 14, \quad b = 9, \quad c = 14$$
$$x^2 - x - 12, \quad b = -1, \quad c = -12$$
$$x^2 - 2x - 15, \quad b = -2, \quad c = -15$$

To factor a trinomial of this form means to express the trinomial as the product of two binomials. Some trinomials expressed as the product of binomials (factored form) are shown at the right.

Trinomial	Factored Form
$x^2 + 9x + 14$	$= (x + 2)(x + 7)$
$x^2 - x - 12$	$= (x + 3)(x - 4)$
$x^2 - 2x - 15$	$= (x + 3)(x - 5)$

The method by which the factors of a trinomial are found is based on FOIL. Consider the following binomial products, noting the relationship between the constant terms of the binomials and the terms of the trinomials.

Signs in the binomials are the same

$$(x + 6)(x + 2) = x^2 + 2x + 6x + (6)(2) = x^2 + 8x + 12$$
Sum of 6 and 2
Product of 6 and 2

$$(x - 3)(x - 4) = x^2 - 4x - 3x + (-3)(-4) = x^2 - 7x + 12$$
Sum of -3 and -4
Product of -3 and -4

Signs in the binomials are opposite

$$(x + 3)(x - 5) = x^2 - 5x + 3x + (3)(-5) = x^2 - 2x - 15$$
Sum of 3 and -5
Product of 3 and -5

$$(x - 4)(x + 6) = x^2 + 6x - 4x + (-4)(6) = x^2 + 2x - 24$$
Sum of -4 and 6
Product of -4 and 6

Points to Remember in Factoring $x^2 + bx + c$

1. In the trinomial, the coefficient of x is the sum of the constant terms of the binomials.

2. In the trinomial, the constant term is the product of the constant terms of the binomials.

3. When the constant term of the trinomial is positive, the constant terms of the binomials have the same sign as the coefficient of x in the trinomial.

4. When the constant term of the trinomial is negative, the constant terms of the binomials have opposite signs.

Success at factoring a trinomial depends on remembering these four points.

For example, to factor $x^2 - 2x - 24$, find two numbers whose sum is -2 and whose product is -24 [Points 1 and 2]. Because the constant term of the trinomial is negative (-24), the numbers will have opposite signs [Point 4].

A systematic method of finding these numbers involves listing the factors of the constant term of the trinomial and the sum of those factors.

Factors of -24	Sum of the Factors
1, -24	$1 + (-24) = -23$
-1, 24	$-1 + 24 = 23$
2, -12	$2 + (-12) = -10$
-2, 12	$-2 + 12 = 10$
3, -8	$3 + (-8) = -5$
-3, 8	$-3 + 8 = 5$
4, -6	**$4 + (-6) = -2$**
-4, 6	$-4 + 6 = 2$

Take Note

Always check your proposed factorization to ensure accuracy.

4 and -6 are two numbers whose sum is -2 and whose product is -24. Write the binomial factors of the trinomial.

$$x^2 - 2x - 24 = (x + 4)(x - 6)$$

Check: $(x + 4)(x - 6) = x^2 - 6x + 4x - 24 = x^2 - 2x - 24$

By the Commutative Property of Multiplication, the binomial factors can also be written as

$$x^2 - 2x - 24 = (x - 6)(x + 4)$$

EXAMPLE 1   Factor: $x^2 + 18x + 32$

Solution

Factors of 32	Sum
1, 32	33
2, 16	**18**
4, 8	12

$$x^2 + 18x + 32 = (x + 2)(x + 16)$$

- Try only positive factors of 32 [Point 3].

- Once the correct pair is found, the other factors need not be tried.

- Write the factors of the trinomial.

Check $(x + 2)(x + 16) = x^2 + 16x + 2x + 32$
$$= x^2 + 18x + 32$$

PROBLEM 1   Factor: $x^2 - 8x + 15$

Solution   See page S17.

EXAMPLE 2   Factor: $x^2 - 6x - 16$

Solution

Factors of -16	Sum
1, -16	-15
-1, 16	15
2, -8	**-6**
-2, 8	6
4, -4	0

- The factors must be of opposite signs [Point 4].

$$x^2 - 6x - 16 = (x + 2)(x - 8)$$

- Write the factors of the trinomial.

Check $(x + 2)(x - 8) = x^2 - 8x + 2x - 16$
$= x^2 - 6x - 16$

PROBLEM 2   Factor: $x^2 + 3x - 18$

Solution   See page S17.

Not all trinomials can be factored when using only integers. Consider the trinomial $x^2 - 6x - 8$.

Factors of −8	Sum
1, −8	−7
−1, 8	7
2, −4	−2
−2, 4	2

Because none of the pairs of factors of −8 have a sum of −6, the trinomial is not factorable using integers. The trinomial is said to be **nonfactorable over the integers.**

OBJECTIVE 2   **Factor completely**

A polynomial is **factored completely** when it is written as a product of factors that are nonfactorable over the integers.

Take Note

The first step in *any* factoring problem is to determine whether the terms of the polynomial have a *common factor*. If they do, factor it out first.

EXAMPLE 3   Factor: $3x^3 + 15x^2 + 18x$

Solution   The GCF of $3x^3$, $15x^2$, and $18x$ is $3x$.

• Find the GCF of the terms of the polynomial.

$3x^3 + 15x^2 + 18x$
$= 3x(x^2) + 3x(5x) + 3x(6)$
$= 3x(x^2 + 5x + 6)$

• Factor out the GCF.
• Write the polynomial as a product of factors.

Factors of 6	Sum
1, 6	7
2, 3	5

• Factor the trinomial $x^2 + 5x + 6$. Try only positive factors of 6.

$3x^3 + 15x^2 + 18x = 3x(x + 2)(x + 3)$

Check $3x(x + 2)(x + 3) = 3x(x^2 + 3x + 2x + 6)$
$= 3x(x^2 + 5x + 6)$
$= 3x^3 + 15x^2 + 18x$

PROBLEM 3   Factor: $3a^2b - 18ab - 81b$

Solution   See page S17.

EXAMPLE 4   Factor: $x^2 + 9xy + 20y^2$

Solution   There is no common factor.

Factors of 20	Sum
1, 20	21
2, 10	12
4, 5	9

• Try only positive factors of 20.

$$x^2 + 9xy + 20y^2 = (x + 4y)(x + 5y)$$

Check $(x + 4y)(x + 5y) = x^2 + 5xy + 4xy + 20y^2$
$$= x^2 + 9xy + 20y^2$$

PROBLEM 4   Factor: $4x^2 - 40xy + 84y^2$

Solution   See page S18.

Take Note

$4y$ and $5y$ are placed in the binomials. This is necessary so that the middle term contains xy and the last term contains y^2.

8.2   Concept Review

Determine whether the statement is always true, sometimes true, or never true.

1. The value of b in the trinomial $x^2 - 8x + 7$ is 8.

2. The factored form of $x^2 - 5x - 14$ is $(x - 7)(x + 2)$.

3. To factor a trinomial of the form $x^2 + bx + c$ means to rewrite the polynomial as a product of two binomials.

4. In the factoring of a trinomial, if the constant term is positive, then the signs in both binomial factors will be the same.

5. In the factoring of a trinomial, if the constant term is negative, then the signs in both binomial factors will be negative.

6. The first step in factoring a trinomial is to determine whether the terms of the trinomial have a common factor.

8.2 Exercises

1 Factor trinomials of the form $x^2 + bx + c$

Complete the table by listing the pairs of factors of the number and the sum of each pair.

1. Factors of 18	Sum

2. Factors of 12	Sum

3. Factors of −21	Sum

4. Factors of −10	Sum

5. Factors of −28	Sum

6. Factors of −32	Sum

Factor.

7. $x^2 + 3x + 2$ 8. $x^2 + 5x + 6$ 9. $x^2 - x - 2$ 10. $x^2 + x - 6$

11. $a^2 + a - 12$ 12. $a^2 - 2a - 35$ 13. $a^2 - 3a + 2$ 14. $a^2 - 5a + 4$

15. $a^2 + a - 2$ 16. $a^2 - 2a - 3$ 17. $b^2 - 6b + 9$ 18. $b^2 + 8b + 16$

19. $b^2 + 7b - 8$ 20. $y^2 - y - 6$ 21. $y^2 + 6y - 55$ 22. $z^2 - 4z - 45$

23. $y^2 - 5y + 6$ 24. $y^2 - 8y + 15$ 25. $z^2 - 14z + 45$ 26. $z^2 - 14z + 49$

27. $z^2 - 12z - 160$ 28. $p^2 + 2p - 35$ 29. $p^2 + 12p + 27$ 30. $p^2 - 6p + 8$

31. $x^2 + 20x + 100$ 32. $x^2 + 18x + 81$ 33. $b^2 + 9b + 20$ 34. $b^2 + 13b + 40$

35. $x^2 - 11x - 42$ 36. $x^2 + 9x - 70$ 37. $b^2 - b - 20$ 38. $b^2 + 3b - 40$

39. $y^2 - 14y - 51$ 40. $y^2 - y - 72$ 41. $p^2 - 4p - 21$ 42. $p^2 + 16p + 39$

43. $y^2 - 8y + 32$ 44. $y^2 - 9y + 81$ 45. $x^2 - 20x + 75$ 46. $p^2 + 24p + 63$

47. $x^2 - 15x + 56$ **48.** $x^2 + 21x + 38$ **49.** $x^2 + x - 56$ **50.** $x^2 + 5x - 36$

51. $a^2 - 21a - 72$ **52.** $a^2 - 7a - 44$ **53.** $a^2 - 15a + 36$ **54.** $a^2 - 21a + 54$

55. $z^2 - 9z - 136$ **56.** $z^2 + 14z - 147$ **57.** $c^2 - c - 90$ **58.** $c^2 - 3c - 180$

59. Suppose b and c are nonzero and n and m are positive constants such that $x^2 + bx + c = (x + n)(x + m)$.
  a. Is c positive or negative?
  b. Is b positive or negative?

60. Suppose b and c are nonzero and n and m are positive constants such that $x^2 + bx + c = (x - n)(x - m)$.
  a. Is c positive or negative?
  b. Is b positive or negative?

2 Factor completely

61. Use the trinomial $5x^2 - 10x - 40$.
  a. The first step in factoring the trinomial is to look for a __?__ factor of the three terms.
  b. The GCF of the terms of the trinomial $5x^2 - 10x - 40$ is __?__.
  c. Factor the GCF from the terms of the trinomial: $5x^2 - 10x - 40 =$ $5(\underline{})$
  d. Factor the trinomial completely: $5x^2 - 10x - 40 = 5(x^2 - 2x - 8) =$ $5(\underline{})(\underline{})$

62. To factor $x^2 + 2xy - 24y^2$, find binomials in the form $(x + ny)(x + my)$, where n and m are numbers whose product is __?__ and whose sum is __?__. Factors of -24 whose sum is 2 are __?__ and __?__. The trinomial $x^2 + 2x - 24y^2$ factors as $(\underline{})(\underline{})$.

Factor.

63. $2x^2 + 6x + 4$ **64.** $3x^2 + 15x + 18$ **65.** $3a^2 + 3a - 18$

66. $4x^2 - 4x - 8$ **67.** $ab^2 + 2ab - 15a$ **68.** $ab^2 + 7ab - 8a$

69. $xy^2 - 5xy + 6x$ **70.** $xy^2 + 8xy + 15x$ **71.** $z^3 - 7z^2 + 12z$

72. $2a^3 + 6a^2 + 4a$ **73.** $3y^3 - 15y^2 + 18y$ **74.** $4y^3 + 12y^2 - 72y$

75. $3x^2 + 3x - 36$ **76.** $2x^3 - 2x^2 - 4x$ **77.** $5z^2 - 15z - 140$

78. $6z^2 + 12z - 90$ **79.** $2a^3 + 8a^2 - 64a$ **80.** $3a^3 - 9a^2 - 54a$

81. $x^2 - 5xy + 6y^2$ **82.** $x^2 + 4xy - 21y^2$ **83.** $a^2 - 9ab + 20b^2$

84. $a^2 - 15ab + 50b^2$ **85.** $x^2 - 3xy - 28y^2$ **86.** $s^2 + 2st - 48t^2$

87. $y^2 - 15yz - 41z^2$

88. $y^2 + 85yz + 36z^2$

89. $z^4 - 12z^3 + 35z^2$

90. $z^4 + 2z^3 - 80z^2$

91. $b^4 - 22b^3 + 120b^2$

92. $b^4 - 3b^3 - 10b^2$

93. $2y^4 - 26y^3 - 96y^2$

94. $3y^4 + 54y^3 + 135y^2$

95. $x^4 + 7x^3 - 8x^2$

96. $x^4 - 11x^3 - 12x^2$

97. $4x^2y + 20xy - 56y$

98. $3x^2y - 6xy - 45y$

99. $8y^2 - 32y + 24$

100. $10y^2 - 100y + 90$

101. $c^3 + 13c^2 + 30c$

102. $c^3 + 18c^2 - 40c$

103. $3x^3 - 36x^2 + 81x$

104. $4x^3 + 4x^2 - 24x$

105. $x^2 - 8xy + 15y^2$

106. $y^2 - 7xy - 8x^2$

107. $a^2 - 13ab + 42b^2$

108. $y^2 + 4yz - 21z^2$

109. $y^2 + 8yz + 7z^2$

110. $y^2 - 16yz + 15z^2$

111. $3x^2y + 60xy - 63y$

112. $4x^2y - 68xy - 72y$

113. $3x^3 + 3x^2 - 36x$

114. $4x^3 + 12x^2 - 160x$

115. $4z^3 + 32z^2 - 132z$

116. $5z^3 - 50z^2 - 120z$

117. State whether or not the trinomial has a factor of $(x + 3)$.

   a. $3x^2 - 3x - 36$ **b.** $x^2y - xy - 12y$

118. State whether or not the trinomial has a factor of $(x + y)$.

   a. $2x^2 - 2xy - 4y^2$ **b.** $2x^2y - 4xy - 4y$

8.2 **Applying Concepts**

Factor.

119. $20 + c^2 + 9c$

120. $x^2y - 54y - 3xy$

121. $45a^2 + a^2b^2 - 14a^2b$

122. $12p^2 - 96p + 3p^3$

Find all integers k such that the trinomial can be factored over the integers.

123. $x^2 + kx + 35$

124. $x^2 + kx + 18$

125. $x^2 - kx + 21$

126. $x^2 - kx + 14$

Determine the positive integer values of k for which the following polynomials are factorable over the integers.

127. $y^2 + 4y + k$

128. $z^2 + 7z + k$

129. $a^2 - 6a + k$

130. $c^2 - 7c + k$

131. $x^2 - 3x + k$

132. $y^2 + 5y + k$

133. Exercises 127 to 132 included the requirement that $k > 0$. If k is allowed to be any integer, how many different values of k are possible for each polynomial? Explain your answer.

8.3   Factoring Polynomials of the Form $ax^2 + bx + c$

OBJECTIVE 1   **Factor trinomials of the form $ax^2 + bx + c$ using trial factors**

Trinomials of the form $ax^2 + bx + c$, where a, b, and c are integers and $a \neq 0$, are shown at the right.

$3x^2 - x + 4$, $a = 3$, $b = -1$, $c = 4$
$4x^2 + 5x - 8$, $a = 4$, $b = 5$, $c = -8$

These trinomials differ from those in the previous section in that the coefficient of x^2 is not 1. There are various methods of factoring these trinomials. The method described in this objective is factoring trinomials using trial factors.

To **factor a trinomial of the form $ax^2 + bx + c$** means to express the polynomial as the product of two binomials. Factoring such polynomials by trial and error may require testing many trial factors. To reduce the number of trial factors, remember the following points.

Points to Remember in Factoring $ax^2 + bx + c$

1. If the terms of the trinomial do not have a common factor, then the terms of a binomial factor cannot have a common factor.

2. When the constant term of the trinomial is positive, the constant terms of the binomials have the same sign as the coefficient of x in the trinomial.

3. When the constant term of the trinomial is negative, the constant terms of the binomials have opposite signs.

Factor: $10x^2 - x - 3$

The terms of the trinomial do not have a common factor; therefore, the terms of a binomial factor will not have a common factor [Point 1].

Because the constant term, c, of the trinomial is negative (-3), the constant terms of the binomial factors will have opposite signs [Point 3].

Find the factors of a (10) and the factors of c (-3).

Factors of 10	Factors of -3
1, 10	1, -3
2, 5	-1, 3

Using these factors, write trial factors, and use the Outer and Inner products of FOIL to check the middle term.

Trial Factors	Middle Term
$(x + 1)(10x - 3)$	$-3x + 10x = 7x$
$(x - 1)(10x + 3)$	$3x - 10x = -7x$
$\mathbf{(2x + 1)(5x - 3)}$	$\mathbf{-6x + 5x = -x}$
$(2x - 1)(5x + 3)$	$6x - 5x = x$
$(10x + 1)(x - 3)$	$-30x + x = -29x$
$(10x - 1)(x + 3)$	$30x - x = 29x$
$(5x + 1)(2x - 3)$	$-15x + 2x = -13x$
$(5x - 1)(2x + 3)$	$15x - 2x = 13x$

From the list of trial factors, $10x^2 - x - 3 = (2x + 1)(5x - 3)$.

Check: $(2x + 1)(5x - 3) = 10x^2 - 6x + 5x - 3 = 10x^2 - x - 3$

All the trial factors for this trinomial were listed in this example. However, once the correct binomial factors are found, it is not necessary to continue checking the remaining trial factors.

Factor: $4x^2 - 27x + 18$

The terms of the trinomial do not have a common factor; therefore, the terms of a binomial factor will not have a common factor [Point 1].

Because the constant term, c, of the trinomial is positive (18), the constant terms of the binomial factors will have the same sign as the coefficient of x. Because the coefficient of x is -27, both signs will be negative [Point 2].

Find the factors of a (4) and the negative factors of c (18).

Factors of 4	Factors of 18
1, 4	$-1, -18$
2, 2	$-2, -9$
	$-3, -6$

Using these factors, write trial factors, and use the Outer and Inner products of FOIL to check the middle term.

Trial Factors	Middle Term
$(x - 1)(4x - 18)$	Common factor
$(x - 2)(4x - 9)$	$-9x - 8x = -17x$
$(x - 3)(4x - 6)$	Common factor
$(2x - 1)(2x - 18)$	Common factor
$(2x - 2)(2x - 9)$	Common factor
$(2x - 3)(2x - 6)$	Common factor
$(4x - 1)(x - 18)$	$-72x - x = -73x$
$(4x - 2)(x - 9)$	Common factor
$\mathbf{(4x - 3)(x - 6)}$	$\mathbf{-24x - 3x = -27x}$

The correct factors have been found.

$$4x^2 - 27x + 18 = (4x - 3)(x - 6)$$

This last example illustrates that many of the trial factors may have common factors and thus need not be tried. For the remainder of this chapter, the trial factors with a common factor will not be listed.

EXAMPLE 1   Factor: $3x^2 + 20x + 12$

Solution

Factors of 3	Factors of 12
1, 3	1, 12
	2, 6
	3, 4

• Because 20 is positive, only the positive factors of 12 need be tried.

Trial Factors	Middle Term
$(x + 3)(3x + 4)$	$4x + 9x = 13x$
$(3x + 1)(x + 12)$	$36x + x = 37x$
$(3x + 2)(x + 6)$	$18x + 2x = 20x$

• Write the trial factors. Use FOIL to check the middle term.

$$3x^2 + 20x + 12 = (3x + 2)(x + 6)$$

Check $(3x + 2)(x + 6) = 3x^2 + 18x + 2x + 12$
$$= 3x^2 + 20x + 12$$

PROBLEM 1   Factor: $6x^2 - 11x + 5$

Solution   See page S18.

EXAMPLE 2   Factor: $6x^2 - 5x - 6$

Solution

Factors of 6	Factors of −6
1, 6	1, −6
2, 3	−1, 6
	2, −3
	−2, 3

• Find the factors of a (6) and the factors of c (−6).

Trial Factors	Middle Term
$(x - 6)(6x + 1)$	$x - 36x = -35x$
$(x + 6)(6x - 1)$	$-x + 36x = 35x$
$(2x - 3)(3x + 2)$	$4x - 9x = -5x$

• Write the trial factors. Use FOIL to check the middle term.

$$6x^2 - 5x - 6 = (2x - 3)(3x + 2)$$

Check $(2x - 3)(3x + 2) = 6x^2 + 4x - 9x - 6$
$$= 6x^2 - 5x - 6$$

PROBLEM 2   Factor: $8x^2 + 14x - 15$

Solution   See page S18.

EXAMPLE 3 Factor: $15 - 2x - x^2$

Solution

Factors of 15	Factors of −1
1, 15	1, −1
3, 5	

• The terms have no common factors. The coefficient of x^2 is −1.

Trial Factors	Middle Term
$(1 + x)(15 - x)$	$-x + 15x = 14x$
$(1 - x)(15 + x)$	$x - 15x = -14x$
$(3 + x)(5 - x)$	$-3x + 5x = 2x$
$(3 - x)(5 + x)$	$3x - 5x = -2x$

• Write the trial factors. Use FOIL to check the middle term.

$$15 - 2x - x^2 = (3 - x)(5 + x)$$

Check $(3 - x)(5 + x) = 15 + 3x - 5x - x^2$
$$= 15 - 2x - x^2$$

PROBLEM 3 Factor: $24 - 2y - y^2$

Solution See page S18.

The first step in factoring a trinomial is to determine whether there is a common factor. If there is a common factor, factor out the GCF of the terms.

EXAMPLE 4 Factor: $3x^3 - 23x^2 + 14x$

Solution The GCF of $3x^3$, $23x^2$, and $14x$ is x.

• Find the GCF of the terms of the polynomial.

$$3x^3 - 23x^2 + 14x = x(3x^2 - 23x + 14)$$

• Factor out the GCF.

Factors of 3	Factors of 14
1, 3	−1, −14
	−2, −7

• Factor the trinomial $3x^2 - 23x + 14$.

Trial Factors	Middle Term
$(x - 1)(3x - 14)$	$-14x - 3x = -17x$
$(x - 14)(3x - 1)$	$-x - 42x = -43x$
$(x - 2)(3x - 7)$	$-7x - 6x = -13x$
$(x - 7)(3x - 2)$	$-2x - 21x = -23x$

$$3x^3 - 23x^2 + 14x = x(x - 7)(3x - 2)$$

Check $x(x - 7)(3x - 2) = x(3x^2 - 2x - 21x + 14)$
$$= x(3x^2 - 23x + 14)$$
$$= 3x^3 - 23x^2 + 14x$$

PROBLEM 4 Factor: $4a^2b^2 - 30a^2b + 14a^2$

Solution See page S18.

OBJECTIVE **2**

Factor trinomials of the form $ax^2 + bx + c$ by grouping

Take Note

In this objective, we are using the skills taught in Objective 2 of Section 1 of this chapter. You may want to review that material before studying this objective.

In the previous objective, trinomials of the form $ax^2 + bx + c$ were factored using trial factors. In this objective, factoring by grouping is used.

To factor $ax^2 + bx + c$, first find two factors of $a \cdot c$ whose sum is b. Use the two factors to rewrite the middle term of the trinomial as the sum of two terms. Then use factoring by grouping to write the factorization of the trinomial.

Factor: $2x^2 + 13x + 15$

$a = 2, c = 15, a \cdot c = 2 \cdot 15 = 30$

Find two positive factors of 30 whose sum is 13.

Positive Factors of 30	Sum
1, 30	31
2, 15	17
3, 10	13
5, 6	11

The factors are 3 and 10.

Use the factors 3 and 10 to rewrite $13x$ as $3x + 10x$.

$$2x^2 + 13x + 15$$
$$= 2x^2 + 3x + 10x + 15$$

Factor by grouping.

$$= (2x^2 + 3x) + (10x + 15)$$
$$= x(2x + 3) + 5(2x + 3)$$
$$= (2x + 3)(x + 5)$$

Check: $(2x + 3)(x + 5) = 2x^2 + 10x + 3x + 15$
$$= 2x^2 + 13x + 15$$

Factor: $6x^2 - 11x - 10$

$a = 6, c = -10, a \cdot c = 6(-10) = -60$

Find two factors of -60 whose sum is -11.

Factors of -60	Sum
1, -60	-59
-1, 60	59
2, -30	-28
-2, 30	28
3, -20	-17
-3, 20	17
4, -15	-11

The required sum has been found. The remaining factors need not be checked. The factors are 4 and -15.

Use the factors 4 and -15 to rewrite $-11x$ as $4x - 15x$.

$$6x^2 - 11x - 10$$
$$= 6x^2 + 4x - 15x - 10$$

Factor by grouping.

Note: $-15x - 10 = -(15x + 10)$

$$= (6x^2 + 4x) - (15x + 10)$$
$$= 2x(3x + 2) - 5(3x + 2)$$
$$= (3x + 2)(2x - 5)$$

Check: $(3x + 2)(2x - 5) = 6x^2 - 15x + 4x - 10$
$$= 6x^2 - 11x - 10$$

Factor: $3x^2 - 2x - 4$

$a = 3, c = -4, a \cdot c = 3(-4) = -12$

Find two factors of -12 whose sum is -2.

Factors of -12	Sum
1, -12	-11
-1, 12	11
2, -6	-4
-2, 6	4
3, -4	-1
-3, 4	1

No integer factors of -12 have a sum of -2. Therefore, $3x^2 - 2x - 4$ is nonfactorable over the integers.

EXAMPLE 5   Factor: $2x^2 + 19x - 10$

Solution $a \cdot c = 2(-10) = -20$ • Find $a \cdot c$.

$-1(20) = -20$ • Find two numbers whose product is
$-1 + 20 = 19$ -20 and whose sum is 19.

$2x^2 + 19x - 10$
$\quad = 2x^2 - x + 20x - 10$ • Rewrite $19x$ as $-x + 20x$.
$\quad = (2x^2 - x) + (20x - 10)$ • Factor by grouping.
$\quad = x(2x - 1) + 10(2x - 1)$
$\quad = (2x - 1)(x + 10)$

PROBLEM 5   Factor: $2a^2 + 13a - 7$

Solution   See page S18.

EXAMPLE 6   Factor: $8y^2 - 10y - 3$

Solution $a \cdot c = 8(-3) = -24$ • Find $a \cdot c$.

$2(-12) = -24$ • Find two numbers whose product is
$2 + (-12) = -10$ -24 and whose sum is -10.

$8y^2 - 10y - 3$
$\quad = 8y^2 + 2y - 12y - 3$ • Rewrite $-10y$ as $2y - 12y$.
$\quad = (8y^2 + 2y) - (12y + 3)$ • Factor by grouping.
$\quad = 2y(4y + 1) - 3(4y + 1)$
$\quad = (4y + 1)(2y - 3)$

PROBLEM 6   Factor: $4a^2 - 11a - 3$

Solution   See page S18.

Remember that the first step in factoring a trinomial is to determine whether there is a common factor. If there is a common factor, factor out the GCF of the terms.

EXAMPLE 7 Factor: $24x^2y - 76xy + 40y$

Solution $24x^2y - 76xy + 40y$
$= 4y(6x^2 - 19x + 10)$

- The terms of the polynomial have a common factor, $4y$. Factor out the GCF.

$a \cdot c = 6(10) = 60$

- To factor $6x^2 - 19x + 10$, first find $a \cdot c$.

$-4(-15) = 60$
$-4 + (-15) = -19$

- Find two numbers whose product is 60 and whose sum is -19.

$6x^2 - 19x + 10$
$= 6x^2 - 4x - 15x + 10$
$= (6x^2 - 4x) - (15x - 10)$
$= 2x(3x - 2) - 5(3x - 2)$
$= (3x - 2)(2x - 5)$

- Rewrite $-19x$ as $-4x - 15x$.
- Factor by grouping.

$24x^2y - 76xy + 40y$
$= 4y(6x^2 - 19x + 10)$
$= 4y(3x - 2)(2x - 5)$

- Write the complete factorization of the given polynomial.

PROBLEM 7 Factor: $15x^3 + 40x^2 - 80x$

Solution See page S19.

8.3 Concept Review

Determine whether the statement is always true, sometimes true, or never true.

1. The value of a in the trinomial $3x^2 + 8x - 7$ is -7.

2. The factored form of $2x^2 - 7x - 15$ is $(2x + 3)(x - 5)$.

3. To check the factorization of a trinomial of the form $ax^2 + bx + c$, multiply the two binomial factors.

4. The terms of the binomial $3x - 9$ have a common factor.

5. If the terms of a trinomial of the form $ax^2 + bx + c$ do not have a common factor, then one of its binomial factors cannot have a common factor.

6. To factor a trinomial of the form $ax^2 + bx + c$ by grouping, first find two numbers whose product is ac and whose sum is b.

8.3 Exercises

1 Factor trinomials of the form $ax^2 + bx + c$ using trial factors

1. Use trial factors to factor $2x^2 - 7x - 15$.
  a. Complete the table of the factors of 2 and -15.

Factors of 2	Factors of -15
1, ___?___	1, ___?___
	-1, ___?___
	3, ___?___
	-3, ___?___

  b. Complete the table by finding the middle term for each pair of trial factors.

Trial Factors	Middle Term
$(x - 15)(2x + 1)$	___?___
$(x + 15)(2x - 1)$	___?___
$(x - 5)(2x + 3)$	___?___
$(x + 5)(2x - 3)$	___?___

  c. Use the results of part b to write the factored form of $2x^2 - 7x - 15$:
  $(\underline{\ \ ?\ \ })(\underline{\ \ ?\ \ })$.

2. Complete the factorization of $8x^2 - 14x + 3$:
  $8x^2 - 14x + 3 = (4x - 1)(\underline{\ \ ?\ \ })$.

Factor by the method of using trial factors.

3. $2x^2 + 3x + 1$ **4.** $5x^2 + 6x + 1$ **5.** $2y^2 + 7y + 3$ **6.** $3y^2 + 7y + 2$

7. $2a^2 - 3a + 1$ **8.** $3a^2 - 4a + 1$ **9.** $2b^2 - 11b + 5$ **10.** $3b^2 - 13b + 4$

11. $2x^2 + x - 1$ **12.** $4x^2 - 3x - 1$ **13.** $2x^2 - 5x - 3$ **14.** $3x^2 + 5x - 2$

15. $6z^2 - 7z + 3$ **16.** $9z^2 + 3z + 2$ **17.** $6t^2 - 11t + 4$ **18.** $10t^2 + 11t + 3$

19. $8x^2 + 33x + 4$ **20.** $7x^2 + 50x + 7$ **21.** $3b^2 - 16b + 16$ **22.** $6b^2 - 19b + 15$

23. $2z^2 - 27z - 14$ **24.** $4z^2 + 5z - 6$ **25.** $3p^2 + 22p - 16$ **26.** $7p^2 + 19p + 10$

27. $6x^2 - 17x + 12$ **28.** $15x^2 - 19x + 6$ **29.** $5b^2 + 33b - 14$ **30.** $8x^2 - 30x + 25$

31. $6a^2 + 7a - 24$ **32.** $14a^2 + 15a - 9$ **33.** $18t^2 - 9t - 5$ **34.** $12t^2 + 28t - 5$

35. $15a^2 + 26a - 21$ **36.** $6a^2 + 23a + 21$ **37.** $8y^2 - 26y + 15$ **38.** $18y^2 - 27y + 4$

39. $8z^2 + 2z - 15$

40. $10z^2 + 3z - 4$

41. $3x^2 + 14x - 5$

42. $15a^2 - 22a + 8$

43. $12x^2 + 25x + 12$

44. $10b^2 + 43b - 9$

45. $3z^2 + 95z + 10$

46. $8z^2 - 36z + 1$

47. $3x^2 + xy - 2y^2$

48. $6x^2 + 10xy + 4y^2$

49. $28 + 3z - z^2$

50. $15 - 2z - z^2$

51. $8 - 7x - x^2$

52. $12 + 11x - x^2$

53. $9x^2 + 33x - 60$

54. $16x^2 - 16x - 12$

55. $24x^2 - 52x + 24$

56. $60x^2 + 95x + 20$

57. $35a^4 + 9a^3 - 2a^2$

58. $15a^4 + 26a^3 + 7a^2$

59. $15b^2 - 115b + 70$

60. $25b^2 + 35b - 30$

61. $10x^3 + 12x^2 + 2x$

62. $9x^3 - 39x^2 + 12x$

63. $10y^3 - 44y^2 + 16y$

64. $14y^3 + 94y^2 - 28y$

65. $4yz^3 + 5yz^2 - 6yz$

66. $2yz^3 - 17yz^2 + 8yz$

67. $20b^4 + 41b^3 + 20b^2$

68. $6b^4 - 13b^3 + 6b^2$

69. $9x^3y + 12x^2y + 4xy$

70. $9a^3b - 9a^2b^2 - 10ab^3$

For Exercises 71 and 72, let $(nx + p)$ and $(mx + q)$ be factors of the trinomial $ax^2 + bx + c$, in which a and c are even and b is odd.

71. If n is even, which of the numbers p, m, and q must be odd?

72. If p is even, which of the numbers n, m, and q must be odd?

2 Factor trinomials of the form $ax^2 + bx + c$ by grouping

73. Complete the table of pairs of factors of -18.

Factors of -18	Sum of the Factors
1, ___?___	___?___
-1, ___?___	___?___
2, ___?___	___?___
-2, ___?___	___?___
3, ___?___	___?___
-3, ___?___	___?___

74. a. To factor $2x^2 - 3x - 9$ by grouping, first find two integers whose product is $2(-9) =$ ___?___ and whose sum is the coefficient of the middle term, ___?___. These two integers are ___?___ and ___?___.

   b. Complete the factoring by grouping:

$$2x^2 - 3x - 9 = 2x^2 - 6x + (\underline{\quad ? \quad}) - 9$$
$$= (\underline{\quad ? \quad}) + (\underline{\quad ? \quad})$$
$$= 2x(\underline{\quad ? \quad} - \underline{\quad ? \quad}) + 3(\underline{\quad ? \quad} - \underline{\quad ? \quad})$$
$$= (\underline{\quad ? \quad})(\underline{\quad ? \quad})$$

Factor by grouping.

75. $2t^2 - t - 10$

76. $2t^2 + 5t - 12$

77. $3p^2 - 16p + 5$

78. $6p^2 + 5p + 1$

79. $12y^2 - 7y + 1$

80. $6y^2 - 5y + 1$

81. $5x^2 - 62x - 7$

82. $9x^2 - 13x - 4$

83. $12y^2 + 19y + 5$

84. $5y^2 - 22y + 8$

85. $7a^2 + 47a - 14$

86. $11a^2 - 54a - 5$

87. $4z^2 + 11z + 6$

88. $6z^2 - 25z + 14$

89. $22p^2 + 51p - 10$

90. $14p^2 - 41p + 15$

91. $8y^2 + 17y + 9$

92. $12y^2 - 145y + 12$

93. $6b^2 - 13b + 6$

94. $20b^2 + 37b + 15$

95. $33b^2 + 34b - 35$

96. $15b^2 - 43b + 22$

97. $18y^2 - 39y + 20$

98. $24y^2 + 41y + 12$

99. $15x^2 - 82x + 24$

100. $13z^2 + 49z - 8$

101. $10z^2 - 29z + 10$

102. $15z^2 - 44z + 32$

103. $36z^2 + 72z + 35$

104. $16z^2 + 8z - 35$

105. $14y^2 - 29y + 12$

106. $8y^2 + 30y + 25$

107. $6x^2 + 35x - 6$

108. $4x^2 + 6x + 2$

109. $12x^2 + 33x - 9$

110. $15y^2 - 50y + 35$

111. $30y^2 + 10y - 20$

112. $2x^3 - 11x^2 + 5x$

113. $2x^3 - 3x^2 - 5x$

114. $3a^2 + 5ab - 2b^2$

115. $2a^2 - 9ab + 9b^2$

116. $4y^2 - 11yz + 6z^2$

117. $2y^2 + 7yz + 5z^2$

118. $12 - x - x^2$

119. $18 + 17x - x^2$

120. $21 - 20x - x^2$

121. $360y^2 + 4y - 4$

122. $10t^2 - 5t - 50$

123. $16t^2 + 40t - 96$

124. $3p^3 - 16p^2 + 5p$

125. $6p^3 + 5p^2 + p$

126. $26z^2 + 98z - 24$

127. $30z^2 - 87z + 30$

128. $12a^3 + 14a^2 - 48a$

129. $42a^3 + 45a^2 - 27a$

130. $36p^2 - 9p^3 - p^4$

131. $9x^2y - 30xy^2 + 25y^3$

132. $8x^2y - 38xy^2 + 35y^3$

133. $9x^3y - 24x^2y^2 + 16xy^3$

134. $45a^3b - 78a^2b^2 + 24ab^3$

In Exercises 135 to 138, information is given about the signs of b and c in $ax^2 + bx + c$, where $a > 0$. If you want to factor $ax^2 + bx + c$ by grouping, you look for factors of ac whose sum is b. In each case, state whether the factors of ac should be two positive numbers, two negative numbers, or one positive and one negative number.

135. $b > 0$ and $c > 0$

136. $b < 0$ and $c < 0$

137. $b < 0$ and $c > 0$

138. $b > 0$ and $c < 0$

8.3 Applying Concepts

Factor.

139. $6y + 8y^3 - 26y^2$

140. $22p^2 - 3p^3 + 16p$

141. $a^3b - 24ab - 2a^2b$

142. $3xy^2 - 14xy + 2xy^3$

143. $25t^2 + 60t - 10t^3$

144. $3xy^3 + 2x^3y - 7x^2y^2$

145. $2(y + 2)^2 - (y + 2) - 3$

146. $3(a + 2)^2 - (a + 2) - 4$

147. $10(x + 1)^2 - 11(x + 1) - 6$

148. $4(y - 1)^2 - 7(y - 1) - 2$

Find all integers k such that the trinomial can be factored over the integers.

149. $2x^2 + kx + 3$

150. $2x^2 + kx - 3$

151. $3x^2 + kx + 2$

152. $3x^2 + kx - 2$

153. $2x^2 + kx + 5$

154. $2x^2 + kx - 5$

155. Given that $x + 2$ is a factor of $x^3 - 2x^2 - 5x + 6$, factor $x^3 - 2x^2 - 5x + 6$ completely.

156. In your own words, explain how the signs of the last terms of the two binomial factors of a trinomial are determined.

157. **Geometry** The area of a rectangle is $(3x^2 + x - 2)$ ft². Find the dimensions of the rectangle in terms of the variable x. Given that $x > 0$, specify the dimension that is the length and the dimension that is the width. Can x be negative? Can $x = 0$? Explain your answers.

$A = 3x^2 + x - 2$

8.4   Special Factoring

OBJECTIVE **1**   **Factor the difference of two squares and perfect-square trinomials**

Recall from Objective 4 in Section 3 of the chapter on polynomials that the product of the sum and difference of the same two terms equals the square of the first term minus the square of the second term.

$$(a + b)(a - b) = a^2 - b^2$$

The expression $a^2 - b^2$ is the **difference of two squares.** The pattern above suggests the following rule for factoring the difference of two squares.

Rule for Factoring the Difference of Two Squares

Difference of Two Squares		**Sum and Difference of Two Terms**
$a^2 - b^2$	$=$	$(a + b)(a - b)$

$a^2 + b^2$ is the *sum* of two squares. It is nonfactorable over the integers.

Take Note

Convince yourself that the sum of two squares is nonfactorable over the integers by trying to factor $x^2 + 4$.

EXAMPLE 1   Factor.   **A.** $x^2 - 16$ **B.** $x^2 - 10$ **C.** $z^6 - 25$

Solution   **A.** $x^2 - 16 = x^2 - 4^2$ • Write $x^2 - 16$ as the difference of two squares.

$= (x + 4)(x - 4)$ • The factors are the sum and difference of the terms x and 4.

B. $x^2 - 10$ is nonfactorable over the integers.   • Because 10 is not the square of an integer, $x^2 - 10$ cannot be written as the difference of two squares.

C. $z^6 - 25 = (z^3)^2 - 5^2$ • Write $z^6 - 25$ as the difference of two squares.

$= (z^3 + 5)(z^3 - 5)$ • The factors are the sum and difference of the terms z^3 and 5.

PROBLEM 1   Factor.   **A.** $25a^2 - b^2$ **B.** $6x^2 - 1$ **C.** $n^8 - 36$

Solution   See page S19.

EXAMPLE 2   Factor: $z^4 - 16$

Solution $z^4 - 16 = (z^2)^2 - (4)^2$ • This is the difference of two squares.

$= (z^2 + 4)(z^2 - 4)$ • The factors are the sum and difference of the terms z^2 and 4.

$= (z^2 + 4)(z + 2)(z - 2)$ • Factor $z^2 - 4$, which is the difference of two squares. $z^2 + 4$ is nonfactorable over the integers.

PROBLEM 2   Factor: $n^4 - 81$

   Solution   See page S19.

Recall from Objective 4 in Section 3 in the chapter on polynomials the pattern for finding the square of a binomial.

$$(a + b)^2 = (a + b)(a + b) = a^2 + ab + ab + b^2$$
$$= a^2 + 2ab + b^2$$

Square the first term
Twice the product of the two terms
Square of last term

The square of a binomial is a **perfect-square trinomial.** The pattern above suggests the following rule for factoring a perfect-square trinomial.

Rule for Factoring a Perfect-Square Trinomial

Perfect-Square Trinomial				**Square of a Binomial**
$a^2 + 2ab + b^2$	$=$	$(a + b)(a + b)$	$=$	$(a + b)^2$
$a^2 - 2ab + b^2$	$=$	$(a - b)(a - b)$	$=$	$(a - b)^2$

Note in these patterns that the sign in the binomial is the sign of the middle term of the trinomial.

Factor: $4x^2 - 20x + 25$

Check that the first term and the last term are squares.	$4x^2 = (2x)^2, 25 = 5^2$
Use the squared terms to factor the trinomial as the square of a binomial. The sign of the binomial is the sign of the middle term of the trinomial.	$(2x - 5)^2$
Check the factorization.	$(2x - 5)^2$ $= (2x)^2 + 2(2x)(-5) + (-5)^2$ $= 4x^2 - 20x + 25$
The factorization is correct.	$4x^2 - 20x + 25 = (2x - 5)^2$

Factor: $9x^2 + 30x + 16$

Check that the first term and the last term are squares.	$9x^2 = (3x)^2, 16 = 4^2$
Use the squared terms to factor the trinomial as the square of a binomial. The sign of the binomial is the sign of the middle term of the trinomial.	$(3x + 4)^2$

Check the factorization.

$$(3x + 4)^2$$
$$= (3x)^2 + 2(3x)(4) + 4^2$$
$$= 9x^2 + 24x + 16$$

$$9x^2 + 24x + 16 \neq 9x^2 + 30x + 16$$

The proposed factorization is not correct.

In this case, the polynomial is not a perfect-square trinomial. It may, however, still factor. In fact, $9x^2 + 30x + 16 = (3x + 2)(3x + 8)$. If a trinomial does not check as a perfect-square trinomial, try to factor it by another method.

Take Note

A perfect-square trinomial can always be factored using either of the methods presented in Section 3 of this chapter. However, noticing that a trinomial is a perfect-square trinomial can save you a considerable amount of time.

EXAMPLE 3   Factor.   **A.** $9x^2 - 30x + 25$ **B.** $4x^2 + 37x + 9$

Solution   **A.** $9x^2 = (3x)^2$, $25 = 5^2$ — • Check that the first and last terms are squares.

$(3x - 5)^2$ — • Use the squared terms to factor the trinomial as the square of a binomial.

$(3x - 5)^2$ — • Check the factorization.
$$= (3x)^2 + 2(3x)(-5) + (-5)^2$$
$$= 9x^2 - 30x + 25$$
$$9x^2 - 30x + 25 = (3x - 5)^2$$ — • The factorization checks.

B. $4x^2 = (2x)^2$, $9 = 3^2$ — • Check that the first and last terms are squares.

$(2x + 3)^2$ — • Use the squared terms to factor the trinomial as the square of a binomial.

$(2x + 3)^2$ — • Check the factorization.
$$= (2x)^2 + 2(2x)(3) + 3^2$$
$$= 4x^2 + 12x + 9$$ — • The factorization does not check.

$$4x^2 + 37x + 9$$
$$= (4x + 1)(x + 9)$$ — • Use another method to factor the trinomial.

PROBLEM 3   Factor.   **A.** $16y^2 + 8y + 1$ **B.** $x^2 + 14x + 36$

Solution   See page S19.

OBJECTIVE 2   Factor completely

When factoring a polynomial completely, ask yourself the following questions about the polynomial.

1. Is there a common factor? If so, factor out the common factor.
2. Is the polynomial the difference of two squares? If so, factor.
3. Is the polynomial a perfect-square trinomial? If so, factor.
4. Is the polynomial a trinomial that is the product of two binomials? If so, factor.
5. Does the polynomial contain four terms? If so, try factoring by grouping.
6. Is each binomial factor nonfactorable over the integers? If not, factor.

Take Note

Remember that you may have to factor more than once in order to write the polynomial as a product of factors, each of which is nonfactorable over the integers.

| EXAMPLE 4 | Factor. | **A.** $3x^2 - 48$ | **B.** $x^3 - 3x^2 - 4x + 12$ |

C. $4x^2y^2 + 12xy^2 + 9y^2$

Solution

A. $3x^2 - 48$
$= 3(x^2 - 16)$
$= 3(x + 4)(x - 4)$

- The GCF of the terms is 3. Factor out the common factor.
- Factor the difference of two squares.

B. $x^3 - 3x^2 - 4x + 12$
$= (x^3 - 3x^2) - (4x - 12)$
$= x^2(x - 3) - 4(x - 3)$
$= (x - 3)(x^2 - 4)$
$= (x - 3)(x + 2)(x - 2)$

- The polynomial contains four terms. Factor by grouping.
- Factor the difference of two squares.

C. $4x^2y^2 + 12xy^2 + 9y^2$
$= y^2(4x^2 + 12x + 9)$
$= y^2(2x + 3)^2$

- The GCF of the terms is y^2. Factor out the common factor.
- Factor the perfect-square trinomial.

| PROBLEM 4 | Factor. | **A.** $12x^3 - 75x$ | **B.** $a^2b - 7a^2 - b + 7$ |

C. $4x^3 + 28x^2 - 120x$

Solution See page S19.

8.4 Concept Review

Determine whether the statement is always true, sometimes true, or never true.

1. The expression $x^2 - 12$ is an example of the difference of two squares.

2. The expression $(y + 8)(y - 8)$ is the product of the sum and difference of the same two terms. The two terms are y and 8.

3. A binomial is factorable.

4. A trinomial is factorable.

5. If a binomial is multiplied times itself, the result is a perfect-square trinomial.

6. In a perfect-square trinomial, the first and last terms are perfect squares.

7. If a polynomial contains four terms, try to factor it as a perfect-square trinomial.

8. The expression $x^2 + 9$ is the sum of two squares. It factors as $(x + 3)(x + 3)$.

8.4 Exercises

1 **Factor the difference of two squares and perfect-square trinomials**

1. a. The binomial $9x^2 - 4$ is in the form $a^2 - b^2$, where $a = $ ___?___ and $b = $ ___?___.
   b. Use the formula $a^2 - b^2 = (a + b)(a - b)$ to factor $9x^2 - 4$:
   $9x^2 - 4 = ($ ___?___ $)($ ___?___ $)$.

2. a. The trinomial $16y^2 - 8y + 1$ is in the form $a^2 - 2ab + b^2$, where $a = $ ___?___ and $b = $ ___?___.
   b. Use the formula $a^2 - 2ab + b^2 = (a - b)^2$ to factor $16y^2 - 8y + 1$:
   $16y^2 - 8y + 1 = ($ ___?___ $)^2$.

3. Provide an example of each of the following.
   a. the difference of two squares
   b. the product of the sum and difference of two terms
   c. a perfect-square trinomial
   d. the square of a binomial
   e. the sum of two squares

4. Explain the rule for factoring
   a. the difference of two squares.
   b. a perfect-square trinomial.

Which of the expressions are perfect squares?

5. 4; 8; $25x^6$; $12y^{10}$; $100x^4y^4$ **6.** 9; 18; $15a^8$; $49b^{12}$; $64a^{16}b^2$

Factor.

7. $x^2 - 4$ **8.** $x^2 - 9$ **9.** $a^2 - 81$ **10.** $a^2 - 49$

11. $4x^2 - 1$ **12.** $9x^2 - 16$ **13.** $y^2 + 2y + 1$ **14.** $y^2 + 14y + 49$

15. $a^2 - 2a + 1$ **16.** $x^2 + 8x - 16$ **17.** $z^2 - 18z - 81$ **18.** $x^2 - 12x + 36$

19. $x^6 - 9$ **20.** $y^{12} - 121$ **21.** $25x^2 - 1$ **22.** $9x^2 - 1$

23. $1 - 49x^2$ **24.** $1 - 64x^2$ **25.** $x^2 + 2xy + y^2$ **26.** $x^2 + 6xy + 9y^2$

27. $4a^2 + 4a + 1$ **28.** $25x^2 + 10x + 1$ **29.** $64a^2 - 16a + 1$ **30.** $9a^2 + 6a + 1$

31. $t^2 + 36$ **32.** $x^2 + 64$ **33.** $x^4 - y^2$ **34.** $b^4 - 16a^2$

35. $9x^2 - 16y^2$ **36.** $25z^2 - y^2$ **37.** $16b^2 + 8b + 1$ **38.** $4a^2 - 20a + 25$

39. $4b^2 + 28b + 49$ **40.** $9a^2 - 42a + 49$ **41.** $25a^2 + 30ab + 9b^2$

42. $4a^2 - 12ab + 9b^2$ **43.** $x^2y^2 - 4$ **44.** $a^2b^2 - 25$

45. $16 - x^2y^2$ **46.** $49x^2 + 28xy + 4y^2$ **47.** $4y^2 - 36yz + 81z^2$

48. $64y^2 - 48yz + 9z^2$ **49.** $9a^2b^2 - 6ab + 1$ **50.** $16x^2y^2 - 24xy + 9$

51. $m^4 - 256$ **52.** $81 - t^4$ **53.** $9x^2 + 13x + 4$

54. $x^2 + 10x + 16$ **55.** $y^8 - 81$ **56.** $9 + 24a + 16a^2$

57.   Which expressions are equivalent to $x^4 - 81$?

     a. $(x^2 + 9)(x + 3)(x - 3)$ **b.** $(2x + 9)(2x^2 - 9)$
     c. $(x^2 + 9)(x^2 - 9)$ **d.** $(x + 3)^2(x - 3)^2$

58.   Which expressions can be factored as the square of a binomial, given
     that a and b are positive numbers?
     a. $a^2x^2 - 2abx + b^2$ **b.** $a^2x^2 - 2abx - b^2$
     c. $a^2x^2 + 2abx + b^2$ **d.** $a^2x^2 + 2abx - b^2$

2   Factor completely

59. When factoring a polynomial, always look first for a ____?___ factor.

60. To factor a polynomial with four terms, try factoring by ____?___.

Factor.

61. $2x^2 - 18$ **62.** $y^3 - 10y^2 + 25y$ **63.** $x^4 + 2x^3 - 35x^2$ **64.** $a^4 - 11a^3 + 24a^2$

65. $5b^2 + 75b + 180$ **66.** $6y^2 - 48y + 72$ **67.** $3a^2 + 36a + 10$ **68.** $5a^2 - 30a + 4$

69. $2x^2y + 16xy - 66y$ **70.** $3a^2b + 21ab - 54b$ **71.** $x^3 - 6x^2 - 5x$ **72.** $b^3 - 8b^2 - 7b$

73. $3y^2 - 36$ **74.** $3y^2 - 147$ **75.** $20a^2 + 12a + 1$ **76.** $12a^2 - 36a + 27$

77. $x^2y^2 - 7xy^2 - 8y^2$ **78.** $a^2b^2 + 3a^2b - 88a^2$ **79.** $10a^2 - 5ab - 15b^2$

80. $16x^2 - 32xy + 12y^2$ **81.** $50 - 2x^2$ **82.** $72 - 2x^2$

83. $12a^3b - a^2b^2 - ab^3$ **84.** $2x^3y - 7x^2y^2 + 6xy^3$ **85.** $2ax - 2a + 2bx - 2b$

86. $4ax - 12a - 2bx + 6b$ **87.** $12a^3 - 12a^2 + 3a$ **88.** $18a^3 + 24a^2 + 8a$

89. $243 + 3a^2$ **90.** $75 + 27y^2$ **91.** $12a^3 - 46a^2 + 40a$

92. $24x^3 - 66x^2 + 15x$ **93.** $x^3 - 2x^2 - x + 2$ **94.** $ay^2 - by^2 - a + b$

95. $4a^3 + 20a^2 + 25a$ **96.** $2a^3 - 8a^2b + 8ab^2$ **97.** $27a^2b - 18ab + 3b$

98. $a^2b^2 - 6ab^2 + 9b^2$ **99.** $48 - 12x - 6x^2$ **100.** $21x^2 - 11x^3 - 2x^4$

101. $ax^2 - 4a + bx^2 - 4b$

102. $a^2x - b^2x - a^2y + b^2y$

103. $x^4 - x^2y^2$

104. $b^4 - a^2b^2$

105. $18a^3 + 24a^2 + 8a$

106. $32xy^2 - 48xy + 18x$

107. $2b + ab - 6a^2b$

108. $20x - 11xy - 3xy^2$

109. $4x - 20 - x^3 + 5x^2$

110. $ay^2 - by^2 - 9a + 9b$

111. $72xy^2 + 48xy + 8x$

112. $4x^2y + 8xy + 4y$

113. $15y^2 - 2xy^2 - x^2y^2$

114. $4x^4 - 38x^3 + 48x^2$

115. $y^3 - 9y$

116. $a^4 - 16$

117. $2x^4y^2 - 2x^2y^2$

118. $6x^5y - 6xy^5$

119. $x^9 - x^5$

120. $8b^5 - 2b^3$

121. $24x^3y + 14x^2y - 20xy$

122. $12x^3y - 60x^2y + 63xy$

123. $4x^4y^2 - 20x^3y^2 + 25x^2y^2$

124. $9x^4y^2 + 24x^3y^2 + 16x^2y^2$

125. $x^3 - 2x^2 - 4x + 8$

126. $24x^2y + 6x^3y - 45x^4y$

127. $8xy^2 - 20x^2y^2 + 12x^3y^2$

128. $45y^2 - 42y^3 - 24y^4$

129. $36a^3b - 62a^2b^2 + 12ab^3$

130. $18a^3b + 57a^2b^2 + 30ab^3$

131. $5x^2y^2 - 11x^3y^2 - 12x^4y^2$

132. $24x^2y^2 - 32x^3y^2 + 10x^4y^2$

133. $(4x - 3)^2 - y^2$

134. $(2a + 3)^2 - 25b^2$

135. $(x^2 - 4x + 4) - y^2$

136. $(4x^2 + 12x + 9) - 4y^2$

For Exercises 137 and 138, $x^2(x - a)(x + b)$, where $a > 0$ and $b > 0$, is the factored form of a polynomial P.

137. What is the degree of the polynomial P?

138. If the middle term of the polynomial P has a negative coefficient, is b greater than, less than, or equal to a?

8.4 Applying Concepts

Find all integers k such that the trinomial is a perfect-square trinomial.

139. $4x^2 - kx + 9$

140. $25x^2 - kx + 1$

141. $36x^2 + kxy + y^2$

142. $64x^2 + kxy + y^2$

143. $x^2 + 6x + k$

144. $x^2 - 4x + k$

145. $x^2 - 2x + k$

146. $x^2 + 10x + k$

147. **Number Problems** The prime factorization of a number is $2^3 \cdot 3^2$. How many of its whole-number factors are perfect squares?

148. **Number Problems** The product of two numbers is 48. One of the two numbers is a perfect square. The other is a prime number. Find the sum of the two numbers.

149. **Number Problems** What is the smallest whole number by which 300 can be multiplied so that the product will be a perfect square?

150. **Geometry** The area of a square is $(16x^2 + 24x + 9)$ ft². Find the dimensions of the square in terms of the variable x. Can $x = 0$? What are the possible values of x?

$A = 16x^2 + 24x + 9$

The cube of an integer is a **perfect cube.** Because $2^3 = 8$, 8 is a perfect cube. Because $4^3 = 64$, 64 is a perfect cube. A variable expression can be a perfect cube; the exponents on variables of perfect cubes are multiples of 3. Therefore, x^3, x^6, and x^9 are perfect cubes. The sum and the difference of two perfect cubes are factorable. They can be written as the product of a binomial and a trinomal. Their factoring patterns are shown below.

$a^3 + b^3$ is the sum of two cubes. $a^3 + b^3 = (a + b)(a^2 - ab + b^2)$
$a^3 - b^3$ is the difference of two cubes. $a^3 - b^3 = (a - b)(a^2 + ab + b^2)$

To factor $x^3 - 8$, write the binomial as $x^3 - 8 = (x)^3 - (2)^3$
the difference of two perfect cubes. Use $= (x - 2)(x^2 + 2x + 4)$
the factoring pattern shown above.
Replace a with x and b with 2.

Factor.

151. $x^3 + 8$ **152.** $y^3 + 27$ **153.** $y^3 - 27$ **154.** $x^3 - 1$

155. $y^3 + 64$ **156.** $x^3 - 125$ **157.** $8x^3 - 1$ **158.** $27y^3 + 1$

159. Select any odd integer greater than 1, square it, and then subtract 1. Is the result evenly divisible by 8? Prove that this procedure always produces a number divisible by 8. (*Suggestion:* Any odd integer greater than 1 can be expressed as $2n + 1$, where n is a natural number.)

8.5   Solving Equations

OBJECTIVE **1**   **Solve equations by factoring**

Recall that the Multiplication Property of Zero states that the product of a number and zero is zero.

If a is a real number, then $a \cdot 0 = 0$.

Consider the equation $a \cdot b = 0$. If this is a true equation, then either $a = 0$ or $b = 0$.

> **Principle of Zero Products**
>
> If the product of two factors is zero, then at least one of the factors must be zero.
>
> If $a \cdot b = 0$, then $a = 0$ or $b = 0$.

The Principle of Zero Products is used in solving equations.

Take Note

$x - 2$ is equal to a number. $x - 3$ is equal to a number. In $(x - 2)(x - 3)$, two numbers are being multiplied. Since their product is 0, one of the numbers must be equal to 0. The number $x - 2$ is equal to 0 or the number $x - 3$ is equal to 0.

Solve: $(x - 2)(x - 3) = 0$

If $(x - 2)(x - 3) = 0$, then $(x - 2) = 0$ or $(x - 3) = 0$.

$$(x - 2)(x - 3) = 0$$

Solve each equation for x.

$$x - 2 = 0 \qquad\qquad x - 3 = 0$$
$$x = 2 \qquad\qquad x = 3$$

Check:

$(x - 2)(x - 3) = 0$		$(x - 2)(x - 3) = 0$	
$(2 - 2)(2 - 3)$	0	$(3 - 2)(3 - 3)$	0
$0(-1)$	0	$1(0)$	0
$0 = 0$		$0 = 0$	

A true equation   A true equation

Write the solutions.   The solutions are 2 and 3.

An equation that can be written in the form $ax^2 + bx + c = 0$, $a \neq 0$, is a **quadratic equation.** A quadratic equation is in **standard form** when the polynomial is equal to 0 and its terms are in descending order.

$$3x^2 + 2x + 1 = 0$$

$$4x^2 - 3x + 2 = 0$$

A quadratic equation can be solved by using the Principle of Zero Products when the polynomial $ax^2 + bx + c$ is factorable.

Take Note

Note the steps involved in solving a quadratic equation by factoring:
(1) Write in standard form.
(2) Factor.
(3) Set each factor equal to 0.
(4) Solve each equation.
(5) Check.

EXAMPLE 1   Solve: $2x^2 + x = 6$

Solution

$$2x^2 + x = 6$$
$$2x^2 + x - 6 = 0 \qquad \text{• Write the equation in standard form.}$$
$$(2x - 3)(x + 2) = 0 \qquad \text{• Factor the trinomial.}$$
$$2x - 3 = 0 \qquad x + 2 = 0 \qquad \text{• Set each factor equal to zero (the Principle of Zero Products).}$$
$$2x = 3 \qquad x = -2 \qquad \text{• Solve each equation for } x.$$
$$x = \frac{3}{2}$$

Check

$2x^2 + x = 6$		$2x^2 + x = 6$	
$2\left(\frac{3}{2}\right)^2 + \frac{3}{2}$	6	$2(-2)^2 + (-2)$	6
$2\left(\frac{9}{4}\right) + \frac{3}{2}$	6	$2 \cdot 4 - 2$	6
$\frac{9}{2} + \frac{3}{2}$	6	$8 - 2$	6
$6 = 6$		$6 = 6$	

The solutions are $\frac{3}{2}$ and -2.   • **Write the solutions.**

PROBLEM 1   Solve: $2x^2 - 50 = 0$

Solution   See page S19.

Take Note

The Principle of Zero Products cannot be used unless 0 is on one side of the equation.

EXAMPLE 2   Solve: $(x - 3)(x - 10) = -10$

Solution

$$(x - 3)(x - 10) = -10$$
$$x^2 - 13x + 30 = -10$$ • Multiply $(x - 3)(x - 10)$.
$$x^2 - 13x + 40 = 0$$ • Write the equation in standard form.
$$(x - 8)(x - 5) = 0$$ • Factor.

$x - 8 = 0 \qquad x - 5 = 0$ • Set each factor equal to zero.
$\qquad x = 8 \qquad\qquad x = 5$ • Solve each equation for x.

The solutions are 8 and 5. • Write the solutions.

PROBLEM 2   Solve: $(x + 2)(x - 7) = 52$

Solution   See page S19.

OBJECTIVE 2   **Application problems**

EXAMPLE 3   The sum of the squares of two consecutive positive odd integers is equal to 130. Find the two integers.

Strategy   ▶ First positive odd integer: n
Second positive odd integer: $n + 2$
Square of the first positive odd integer: n^2
Square of the second positive odd integer: $(n + 2)^2$
▶ The sum of the square of the first positive odd integer and the square of the second positive odd integer is 130.

Solution

$$n^2 + (n + 2)^2 = 130$$
$$n^2 + n^2 + 4n + 4 = 130$$
$$2n^2 + 4n - 126 = 0$$
$$2(n^2 + 2n - 63) = 0$$
$$n^2 + 2n - 63 = 0$$ • Divide each side of the equation by 2.
$$(n - 7)(n + 9) = 0$$

$n - 7 = 0 \qquad n + 9 = 0$ • Because -9 is not a positive odd
$\qquad n = 7 \qquad\qquad n = -9$ integer, it is not a solution.

$n = 7$ • The first positive odd integer is 7.

$n + 2 = 7 + 2 = 9$ • Substitute the value of n into the variable expression for the second positive odd integer and evaluate.

The two integers are 7 and 9.

PROBLEM 3   The sum of the squares of two consecutive positive integers is 85. Find the two integers.

Solution   See page S19.

EXAMPLE 4   A stone is thrown into a well with an initial velocity of 8 ft/s. The well is 440 ft deep. How many seconds later will the stone hit the bottom of the well? Use the equation $d = vt + 16t^2$, where d is the distance in feet, v is the initial velocity in feet per second, and t is the time in seconds.

Strategy   To find the time for the stone to drop to the bottom of the well, replace the variables d and v by their given values and solve for t.

Solution $d = vt + 16t^2$

$440 = 8t + 16t^2$

$0 = 16t^2 + 8t - 440$ • Write the equation in standard
                              form.
$0 = 8(2t^2 + t - 55)$

$0 = 2t^2 + t - 55$ • Divide each side of the equation
                              by 8.
$0 = (2t + 11)(t - 5)$

$2t + 11 = 0$ $t - 5 = 0$

$2t = -11$ $t = 5$

$t = -\dfrac{11}{2}$ • Because the time cannot be a
                               negative number, $-\dfrac{11}{2}$ is not a
The time is 5 s.   solution.

PROBLEM 4   The length of a rectangle is 3 m
more than twice the width. The
area of the rectangle is 90 m².
Find the length and width of the
rectangle.

W

$2W + 3$

■   **Solution**   See page S19.

8.5   Concept Review

Determine whether the statement is always true, sometimes true, or never true.

1. If you multiply two numbers and the product is zero, then either one or
both of the numbers must be zero.

2. $2x^2 + 5x - 7$ is a quadratic equation.

3. $4x^2 - 9 = 0$ is a quadratic equation.

4. $3x + 1 = 0$ is a quadratic equation in standard form.

5. If $(x - 8)(x + 6) = 0$, then $x = -8$ or $x = 6$.

6. If a quadratic equation is not in standard form, the first step in solving the
equation by factoring is to write it in standard form.

8.5   Exercises

1   **Solve equations by factoring**

1. What does the Principle of Zero Products state?

2. Why is it possible to solve some quadratic equations by using the Principle of Zero Products?

3. Of the two quadratic equations $0 = x^2 + x - 2$ and $5x^2 + 2x = 3$, the one that is in standard form is ___?___.

4. Solve: $2x^2 - 5x - 3 = 0$

$$2x^2 - 5x - 3 = 0$$ • The equation is in ___?___ form.

$$(x - \underline{})(2x + \underline{}) = 0$$ • Factor the trinomial.

$$x - 3 = \underline{} \qquad 2x + 1 = \underline{}$$ • Use the Principle of Zero Products to set each factor equal to 0.

$$x = \underline{} \qquad\qquad x = \underline{}$$ • Solve each equation for x.

Solve.

5. $(y + 3)(y + 2) = 0$

6. $(y - 3)(y - 5) = 0$

7. $(z - 7)(z - 3) = 0$

8. $(z + 8)(z - 9) = 0$

9. $x(x - 5) = 0$

10. $x(x + 2) = 0$

11. $a(a - 9) = 0$

12. $a(a + 12) = 0$

13. $y(2y + 3) = 0$

14. $t(4t - 7) = 0$

15. $2a(3a - 2) = 0$

16. $4b(2b + 5) = 0$

17. $(b + 2)(b - 5) = 0$

18. $(b - 8)(b + 3) = 0$

19. $x^2 - 81 = 0$

20. $9x^2 - 1 = 0$

21. $16x^2 - 49 = 0$

22. $x^2 + 6x + 8 = 0$

23. $x^2 - 8x + 15 = 0$

24. $z^2 + 5z - 14 = 0$

25. $z^2 + z - 72 = 0$

26. $x^2 - 5x + 6 = 0$

27. $2y^2 - y - 1 = 0$

28. $2a^2 - 9a - 5 = 0$

29. $3a^2 + 14a + 8 = 0$

30. $2x^2 - 6x - 20 = 0$

31. $3y^2 + 12y - 63 = 0$

32. $a^2 - 5a = 0$

33. $x^2 - 7x = 0$

34. $2a^2 - 8a = 0$

35. $a^2 + 5a = -4$

36. $a^2 - 5a = 24$

37. $y^2 - 5y = -6$

38. $y^2 - 7y = 8$

39. $2t^2 + 7t = 4$

40. $3t^2 + t = 10$

41. $3t^2 - 13t = -4$

42. $5t^2 - 16t = -12$

43. $x(x - 12) = -27$

44. $x(x - 11) = 12$

45. $y(y - 7) = 18$

46. $y(y + 8) = -15$

47. $p(p + 3) = -2$

48. $p(p - 1) = 20$

49. $y(y + 4) = 45$

50. $y(y - 8) = -15$

51. $x(x + 3) = 28$

52. $p(p - 14) = 15$

53. $(x + 8)(x - 3) = -30$

54. $(x + 4)(x - 1) = 14$

55. $(y + 3)(y + 10) = -10$

56. $(z - 5)(z + 4) = 52$

57. $(z - 8)(z + 4) = -35$

58. $(z - 6)(z + 1) = -10$

59. $(a + 3)(a + 4) = 72$ **60.** $(a - 4)(a + 7) = -18$ **61.** $(z + 3)(z - 10) = -42$

62. $(2x + 5)(x + 1) = -1$ **63.** $(y + 3)(2y + 3) = 5$ **64.** $(y + 5)(3y - 2) = -14$

For Exercises 65 to 68, $ax^2 + bx + c = 0$, where $a > 0$, is a quadratic equation that can be solved by factoring and then using the Principle of Zero Products.

65. If $ax^2 + bx + c = 0$ has one positive solution and one negative solution, is c greater than, less than, or equal to 0?

66. If zero is one solution of $ax^2 + bx + c = 0$, is c greater than, less than, or equal to 0?

67. If $ax^2 + bx + c$ is a perfect-square trinomial, how many solutions does $0 = ax^2 + bx + c$ have?

68. If the solutions of $ax^2 + bx + c = 0$ are opposites, what kind of trinomial is $ax^2 + bx + c$?

2   Application problems

Complete Exercises 69 and 70 using this problem situation: The sum of the squares of two consecutive positive integers is 113. Find the two integers.

69. a. Let x represent a positive integer. Then the next consecutive positive integer is ____?____, and an expression that represents the sum of the squares of the two integers is ____?____.
   b. An equation that can be used to find the integers is ____?____ + ____?____ = ____?____.

70. The solutions of the equation you wrote in Exercise 69 are -8 and 7. Which solution should be eliminated and why?

71. Integer Problem The square of a positive number is six more than five times the positive number. Find the number.

72. Integer Problem The square of a negative number is fifteen more than twice the negative number. Find the number.

73. Integer Problem The sum of two numbers is six. The sum of the squares of the two numbers is twenty. Find the two numbers.

74. Integer Problem The sum of two numbers is eight. The sum of the squares of the two numbers is thirty-four. Find the two numbers.

75. Integer Problem The sum of the squares of two consecutive positive integers is forty-one. Find the two integers.

76. Integer Problem The sum of the squares of two consecutive positive even integers is one hundred. Find the two integers.

77. **Integer Problem** The product of two consecutive positive integers is two hundred forty. Find the two integers.

78. **Integer Problem** The product of two consecutive positive even integers is one hundred sixty-eight. Find the two integers.

79. **Geometry** The length of the base of a triangle is three times the height. The area of the triangle is 54 ft². Find the base and height of the triangle.

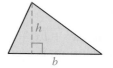

80. **Geometry** The height of a triangle is 4 m more than twice the length of the base. The area of the triangle is 35 m². Find the height of the triangle.

81. **Geometry** The length of a rectangle is two feet more than twice the width. The area is 144 ft². Find the length and width of the rectangle.

82. **Geometry** The width of a rectangle is 5 ft less than the length. The area of the rectangle is 176 ft². Find the length and width of the rectangle.

83. **Geometry** The length of each side of a square is extended 4 m. The area of the resulting square is 64 m². Find the length of a side of the original square.

84. **Geometry** The length of each side of a square is extended 2 cm. The area of the resulting square is 64 cm². Find the length of a side of the original square.

85. **Geometry** The radius of a circle is increased by 3 in., which increases the area by 100 in². Find the radius of the original circle. Round to the nearest hundredth.

86. **Geometry** The length of a rectangle is 5 cm, and the width is 3 cm. If both the length and the width are increased by equal amounts, the area of the rectangle is increased by 48 cm². Find the length and width of the larger rectangle.

87. **Geometry** The page of a book measures 6 in. by 9 in. A uniform border around the page leaves 28 in² for type. What are the dimensions of the type area?

88. **Geometry** A small garden measures 8 ft by 10 ft. A uniform border around the garden increases the total area to 143 ft². What is the width of the border?

Physics Use the formula $d = vt + 16t^2$, where d is the distance in feet, v is the initial velocity in feet per second, and t is the time in seconds.

89. An object is released from a plane at an altitude of 1600 ft. The initial velocity is 0 ft/s. How many seconds later will the object hit the ground?

90. An object is released from the top of a building 320 ft high. The initial velocity is 16 ft/s. How many seconds later will the object hit the ground?

Number Problems Use the formula $S = \dfrac{n^2 + n}{2}$, where S is the sum of the first n natural numbers.

91. How many consecutive natural numbers beginning with 1 will give a sum of 78?

92. How many consecutive natural numbers beginning with 1 will give a sum of 120?

Sports Use the formula $N = \dfrac{t^2 - t}{2}$, where N is the number of basketball games that must be scheduled in a league with t teams if each team is to play every other team once.

93. A league has 28 games scheduled. How many teams are in the league if each team plays every other team once?

94. A league has 45 games scheduled. How many teams are in the league if each team plays every other team once?

Sports Use the formula $h = vt - 16t^2$, where h is the height in feet an object will attain (neglecting air resistance) in t seconds and v is the initial velocity in feet per second.

95. A baseball player hits a "Baltimore chop," meaning the ball bounces off home plate after the batter hits it. The ball leaves home plate with an initial upward velocity of 32 ft/s. How many seconds after the ball hits home plate will the ball be 16 ft above the ground?

96. A golf ball is thrown onto a cement surface and rebounds straight up. The initial velocity of the rebound is 48 ft/s. How many seconds later will the golf ball return to the ground?

8.5 Applying Concepts

Solve.

97. $2y(y + 4) = -5(y + 3)$

98. $2y(y + 4) = 3(y + 4)$

99. $(a - 3)^2 = 36$

100. $(b + 5)^2 = 16$

101. $p^3 = 9p^2$

102. $p^3 = 7p^2$

103. $(2z - 3)(z + 5) = (z + 1)(z + 3)$

104. $(x + 3)(2x - 1) = (3 - x)(5 - 3x)$

105. Find $3n^2$ if $n(n + 5) = -4$.

106. Find $2n^3$ if $n(n + 3) = 4$.

107. Geometry The length of a rectangle is 7 cm, and the width is 4 cm. If both the length and the width are increased by equal amounts, the area of the rectangle is increased by 42 cm². Find the length and width of the larger rectangle.

7 cm
4 cm

108. Geometry A rectangular piece of cardboard is 10 in. longer than it is wide. Squares 2 in. on a side are to be cut from each corner, and then the sides will be folded up to make an open box with a volume of 192 in³. Find the length and width of the piece of cardboard.

109. Explain the error made in solving the equation at the right. Solve the equation correctly.

$$(x + 2)(x - 3) = 6$$
$$x + 2 = 6 \qquad x - 3 = 6$$
$$x = 4 \qquad\quad x = 9$$

110. Explain the error made in solving the equation at the right. Solve the equation correctly.

$$x^2 = x$$
$$\frac{x^2}{x} = \frac{x}{x}$$
$$x = 1$$

Focus on Problem Solving

The Trial-and-Error Method

A topic in Section 3 of this chapter is factoring trinomials using trial factors. This method involves writing trial factors and then using the FOIL method to determine which pair of factors is the correct one. The **trial-and-error method** of arriving at a solution to a problem involves performing repeated tests or experiments until a satisfactory conclusion is reached. However, not all problems solved using the trial-and-error method have a strategy by which to determine the answer. Here is an example:

Explain how you could cut through a cube so that the face of the resulting solid is **a.** a square, **b.** an equilateral triangle, **c.** a trapezoid, and **d.** a hexagon.

There is no formula to apply to this problem; there is no computation to perform. This problem requires picturing a cube and the results after cutting through it at different places on its surface and at different angles. For part a, cutting perpendicular to the top and bottom of the cube and parallel to two of its sides will result in a square. The other shapes may prove more difficult.

When solving problems of this type, keep an open mind. Sometimes when using the trial-and-error method, we are hampered by narrowness of vision; we cannot expand our thinking to include other possibilities. Then when we see someone else's solution, it appears so obvious! For example, for the question above, it is necessary to conceive of cutting through the cube at places other than the top surface; we need to be open to the idea of beginning the cut at one of the corner points of the cube.

Look at the letter A printed at the left. If the letter were folded along line ℓ, the two sides of the letter would match exactly. This letter has **symmetry** with respect to line ℓ. Line ℓ is called the **axis of symmetry.** Now consider the letter H printed below at the left. Both lines ℓ_1 and ℓ_2 are axes of symmetry for this letter; the letter could be folded along either line and the two sides would match exactly. Does the letter A have more than one axis of symmetry? Find axes of symmetry for other capital letters of the alphabet. Which lower-case letters have one axis of symmetry? Do any of the lower-case letters have more than one axis of symmetry?

How many axes of symmetry does a square have? In determining lines of symmetry for a square, begin by drawing a square as shown at the right. The horizontal line of symmetry and the vertical line of symmetry may be immediately obvious to you. But there are two others. Do you see that a line drawn through opposite corners of the square is also a line of symmetry?

Find the number of axes of symmetry for each of the following figures: equilateral triangle, rectangle, regular pentagon, regular hexagon, and circle.

Many of the questions in this text that require an answer of "always true," "sometimes true," or "never true" are best solved by the trial-and-error method. For example, consider the following statement:

If two rectangles have the same area, then they have the same perimeter.

Try some numbers. Each of two rectangles, one measuring 6 units by 2 units and another measuring 4 units by 3 units, has an area of 12 square units, but the perimeter of the first is 16 units and the perimeter of the second is 14 units. Thus the answer "always true" has been eliminated. We still need to determine whether there is a case when the statement is true. After experimenting with a lot of numbers, you may come to realize that we are trying to determine whether it is possible for two different pairs of factors of a number to have the same sum. Is it?

Don't be afraid to make many experiments, and remember that *errors*, or tests that "don't work," are a part of the trial-and-*error* process.

Projects & Group Activities

Prime and Composite Numbers

A **prime number** is a natural number greater than 1 whose only natural-number factors are itself and 1. The number 11 is a prime number because the only natural-number factors of 11 are 11 and 1.

Eratosthenes, a Greek philosopher and astronomer who lived from 270 to 190 B.C., devised a method of identifying prime numbers. It is called the **Sieve of Eratosthenes.** The procedure is illustrated on the next page.

List all the natural numbers from 1 to 100. Cross out the number 1, because it is not a prime number. The number 2 is prime; circle it. Cross out all the other multiples of 2 (4, 6, 8, . . .), because they are not prime. The number 3 is prime; circle it. Cross out all the other multiples of 3 (6, 9, 12, . . .) that are not already crossed out. The number 4, the next consecutive number in the list, has already been crossed out. The number 5 is prime; circle it. Cross out all the other multiples of 5 that are not already crossed out. Continue in this manner until all the prime numbers less than 100 are circled.

1	②	③	4	⑤	6	⑦	8	9	10
⑪	12	⑬	14	15	16	⑰	18	⑲	20
21	22	㉓	24	25	26	27	28	㉙	30
㉛	32	33	34	35	36	㊲	38	39	40
㊶	42	㊸	44	45	46	㊼	48	49	50
51	52	㊼53㊼	54	55	56	57	58	㊾	60
㊽	62	63	64	65	66	㊻	68	69	70
㉛71	72	㉝73	74	75	76	77	78	㉙79	80
81	82	㊱83	84	85	86	87	88	㊳89	90
91	92	93	94	95	96	㊲97	98	99	100

A **composite number** is a natural number greater than 1 that has a natural-number factor other than itself and 1. The number 21 is a composite number because it has factors of 3 and 7. All the numbers crossed out in the table above, except the number 1, are composite numbers.

Solve.

1. Use the Sieve of Eratosthenes to find the prime numbers between 100 and 200.

2. How many prime numbers are even numbers?

3. Find the "twin primes" between 1 and 200. Twin primes are two prime numbers whose difference is 2. For instance, 3 and 5 are twin primes; 5 and 7 are also twin primes.

4. **a.** List two prime numbers that are consecutive natural numbers.

   b. Can there be any other pairs of prime numbers that are consecutive natural numbers?

5. Some primes are the sum of a square and 1. For example, $5 = 2^2 + 1$. Find another prime p such that $p = n^2 + 1$, where n is a natural number.

6. Find a prime p such that $p = n^2 - 1$, where n is a natural number.

7. **a.** 4! (which is read "4 factorial") is equal to $4 \cdot 3 \cdot 2 \cdot 1$. Show that $4! + 2$, $4! + 3$, and $4! + 4$ are all composite numbers.

   b. 5! (which is read "5 factorial") is equal to $5 \cdot 4 \cdot 3 \cdot 2 \cdot 1$. Will $5! + 2$, $5! + 3, 5! + 4$, and $5! + 5$ generate four consecutive composite numbers?

   c. Use the notation 6! to represent a list of five consecutive composite numbers.

Chapter 8 Summary

Key Words

The **greatest common factor** (GCF) of two or more integers is the greatest integer that is a factor of all the integers. [8.1.1, p. 418]

To **factor a polynomial** means to write the polynomial as a product of other polynomials.   [8.1.1, p. 419]

To **factor a trinomial of the form** $ax^2 + bx + c$ means to express the trinomial as the product of two binomials. [8.3.1, p. 432]

A polynomial that does not factor using only integers is **nonfactorable over the integers.**   [8.2.1, p. 427]

An equation that can be written in the form $ax^2 + bx + c = 0$, $a \neq 0$, is a **quadratic equation.** A quadratic equation is in **standard form** when the polynomial is in descending order and equal to zero.   [8.5.1, p. 451]

Examples

The greatest common factor of 12 and 18 is 6 because 6 is the greatest integer that divides evenly into both 12 and 18.

To factor $8x + 12$ means to write it as the product $4(2x + 3)$. The expression $8x + 12$ is a sum. The expression $4(2x + 3)$ is a product (the polynomial $2x + 3$ is multiplied by 4).

To factor $3x^2 + 7x + 2$ means to write it as the product $(3x + 1)(x + 2)$.

The trinomial $x^2 + x + 2$ is nonfactorable over the integers. There are no two integers whose product is 2 and whose sum is 1.

The equation $2x^2 + 7x + 3 = 0$ is a quadratic equation in standard form.

Essential Rules and Procedures

Factoring the Difference of Two Squares
The difference of two squares is the product of the sum and difference of two terms.
$a^2 - b^2 = (a + b)(a - b)$ [8.4.1, p. 443]

$y^2 - 81 = (y + 9)(y - 9)$

Factoring a Perfect-Square Trinomial
A perfect-square trinomial is the square of a binomial.
$a^2 + 2ab + b^2 = (a + b)^2$
$a^2 - 2ab + b^2 = (a - b)^2$ [8.4.1, p. 444]

$x^2 + 10x + 25 = (x + 5)^2$
$x^2 - 10x + 25 = (x - 5)^2$

The Principle of Zero Products
If the product of two factors is zero, then at least one of the factors must be zero.

If $a \cdot b = 0$, then $a = 0$ or $b = 0$.

The Principle of Zero Products is used to solve a quadratic equation by factoring.   [8.5.1, p. 450]

$$x^2 + x = 12$$
$$x^2 + x - 12 = 0$$
$$(x + 4)(x - 3) = 0$$

$x + 4 = 0 \qquad x - 3 = 0$
$x = -4 \qquad\quad x = 3$

General Factoring Strategy

1. Is there a common factor? If so, factor out the common factor.

2. Is the polynomial the difference of two squares? If so, factor.

3. Is the polynomial a perfect-square trinomial? If so, factor.

4. Is the polynomial a trinomial that is the product of two binomials? If so, factor.

5. Does the polynomial contain four terms? If so, try factoring by grouping.

6. Is each binomial factor nonfactorable over the integers? If not, factor. [8.4.2, p. 445]

$24x + 6 = 6(4x + 1)$

$2x^2y + 6xy + 8y = 2y(x^2 + 3x + 4)$

$4x^2 - 49 = (2x + 7)(2x - 7)$

$9x^2 + 6x + 1 = (3x + 1)^2$

$2x^2 + 7x + 5 = (2x + 5)(x + 1)$

$$x^3 - 3x^2 + 2x - 6 = (x^3 - 3x^2) + (2x - 6)$$
$$= x^2(x - 3) + 2(x - 3)$$
$$= (x - 3)(x^2 + 2)$$

$$x^4 - 16 = (x^2 + 4)(x^2 - 4)$$
$$= (x^2 + 4)(x + 2)(x - 2)$$

Chapter 8 Review Exercises

1. Factor: $14y^9 - 49y^6 + 7y^3$

2. Factor: $3a^2 - 12a + ab - 4b$

3. Factor: $c^2 + 8c + 12$

4. Factor: $a^3 - 5a^2 + 6a$

5. Factor: $6x^2 - 29x + 28$

6. Factor: $3y^2 + 16y - 12$

7. Factor: $18a^2 - 3a - 10$

8. Factor: $a^2b^2 - 1$

9. Factor: $4y^2 - 16y + 16$

10. Solve: $a(5a + 1) = 0$

11. Factor: $12a^2b + 3ab^2$

12. Factor: $b^2 - 13b + 30$

13. Factor: $10x^2 + 25x + 4xy + 10y$

14. Factor: $3a^2 - 15a - 42$

15. Factor: $n^4 - 2n^3 - 3n^2$

16. Factor: $2x^2 - 5x + 6$

17. Factor: $6x^2 - 7x + 2$

18. Factor: $16x^2 + 49$

19. Solve: $(x - 2)(2x - 3) = 0$

20. Factor: $7x^2 - 7$

21. Factor: $3x^5 - 9x^4 - 4x^3$

22. Factor: $4x(x - 3) - 5(3 - x)$

23. Factor: $a^2 + 5a - 14$

24. Factor: $y^2 + 5y - 36$

25. Factor: $5x^2 - 50x - 120$

26. Solve: $(x + 1)(x - 5) = 16$

27. Factor: $7a^2 + 17a + 6$

28. Factor: $4x^2 + 83x + 60$

29. Factor: $9y^4 - 25z^2$

30. Factor: $5x^2 - 5x - 30$

31. Solve: $6 - 6y^2 = 5y$

32. Factor: $12b^3 - 58b^2 + 56b$

33. Factor: $5x^3 + 10x^2 + 35x$

34. Factor: $x^2 - 23x + 42$

35. Factor: $a(3a + 2) - 7(3a + 2)$

36. Factor: $8x^2 - 38x + 45$

37. Factor: $10a^2x - 130ax + 360x$

38. Factor: $2a^2 - 19a - 60$

39. Factor: $21ax - 35bx - 10by + 6ay$

40. Factor: $a^6 - 100$

41. Factor: $16a^2 + 8a + 1$

42. Solve: $4x^2 + 27x = 7$

43. Factor: $20a^2 + 10a - 280$

44. Factor: $6x - 18$

45. Factor: $3x^4y + 2x^3y + 6x^2y$

46. Factor: $d^2 + 3d - 40$

47. Factor: $24x^2 - 12xy + 10y - 20x$

48. Factor: $4x^3 - 20x^2 - 24x$

49. Solve: $x^2 - 8x - 20 = 0$

50. Factor: $3x^2 - 17x + 10$

51. Factor: $16x^2 - 94x + 33$

52. Factor: $9x^2 - 30x + 25$

53. Factor: $12y^2 + 16y - 3$

54. Factor: $3x^2 + 36x + 108$

55. Sports The length of a playing field is twice the width. The area is 5000 yd². Find the length and width of the playing field.

56. Sports The length of a hockey field is 20 yd less than twice the width. The area of the field is 6000 yd². Find the length and width of the hockey field.

57. Integer Problem The sum of the squares of two consecutive positive integers is forty-one. Find the two integers.

58. Motion Pictures The size of a motion picture on the screen is given by the equation $S = d^2$, where d is the distance between the projector and the screen. Find the distance between the projector and the screen when the size of the picture is 400 ft².

59. Gardens A rectangular garden plot has dimensions 15 ft by 12 ft. A uniform path around the garden increases the total area to 270 ft². What is the width of the larger rectangle?

60. Geometry The length of each side of a square is extended 4 ft. The area of the resulting square is 576 ft². Find the length of a side of the original square.

Chapter 8 Test

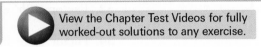

View the Chapter Test Videos for fully worked-out solutions to any exercise.

1. Factor: $6x^2y^2 + 9xy^2 + 12y^2$

2. Factor: $6x^3 - 8x^2 + 10x$

3. Factor: $p^2 + 5p + 6$

4. Factor: $a(x - 2) + b(2 - x)$

5. Solve: $(2a - 3)(a + 7) = 0$

6. Factor: $a^2 - 19a + 48$

7. Factor: $x^3 + 2x^2 - 15x$

8. Factor: $8x^2 + 20x - 48$

9. Factor: $ab + 6a - 3b - 18$

10. Solve: $4x^2 - 1 = 0$

11. Factor: $6x^2 + 19x + 8$

12. Factor: $x^2 - 9x - 36$

13. Factor: $2b^2 - 32$

14. Factor: $4a^2 - 12ab + 9b^2$

15. Factor: $px + x - p - 1$

16. Factor: $5x^2 - 45x - 15$

17. Factor: $2x^2 + 4x - 5$

18. Factor: $4x^2 - 49y^2$

19. Solve: $x(x - 8) = -15$

20. Factor: $p^2 + 12p + 36$

21. Factor: $18x^2 - 48xy + 32y^2$

22. Factor: $2y^4 - 14y^3 - 16y^2$

23. Geometry The length of a rectangle is 3 cm more than twice the width. The area of the rectangle is 90 cm². Find the length and width of the rectangle.

24. Geometry The length of the base of a triangle is three times the height. The area of the triangle is 24 in². Find the length of the base of the triangle.

25. Integer Problem The product of two consecutive negative integers is one hundred fifty-six. Find the two integers.

Cumulative Review Exercises

1. Subtract: $4 - (-5) - 6 - 11$

2. Divide: $0.372 \div (-0.046)$
Round to the nearest tenth.

3. Simplify: $(3 - 7)^2 \div (-2) - 3 \cdot (-4)$

4. Evaluate $-2a^2 \div (2b) - c$ when $a = -4$, $b = 2$, and $c = -1$.

5. Identify the property that justifies the statement.
$(3 + 8) + 7 = 3 + (8 + 7)$

6. Multiply: $-\dfrac{3}{4}(-24x^2)$

7. Simplify: $-2[3x - 4(3 - 2x) - 8x]$

8. Solve: $-\dfrac{5}{7}x = -\dfrac{10}{21}$

9. Solve: $4 + 3(x - 2) = 13$

10. Solve: $3x - 2 = 12 - 5x$

11. Solve: $-2 + 4[3x - 2(4 - x) - 3] = 4x + 2$

12. 120% of what number is 42?

13. Solve: $-4x - 2 \geq 10$

14. Solve: $9 - 2(4x - 5) < 3(7 - 6x)$

15. Graph: $y = \dfrac{3}{4}x - 2$

16. Graph: $f(x) = -3x - 3$

17. Find the domain and range of the relation $\{(-5, -4), (-3, -2), (-1, 0), (1, 2), (3, 4)\}$. Is the relation a function?

18. Evaluate $f(x) = 6x - 5$ at $x = 11$.

19. Graph the solution set of $x + 3y > 2$.

20. Solve by substitution: $6x + y = 7$
$\qquad\qquad\qquad\qquad\qquad x - 3y = 17$

21. Solve by the addition method: $2x - 3y = -4$
$\qquad\qquad\qquad\qquad\qquad\qquad\quad 5x + y = 7$

22. Add: $(3y^3 - 5y^2 - 6) + (2y^2 - 8y + 1)$

23. Simplify: $(-3a^4b^2)^3$

24. Multiply: $(x + 2)(x^2 - 5x + 4)$

25. Divide: $(8x^2 + 4x - 3) \div (2x - 3)$

26. Simplify: $(x^{-4}y^2)^3$

27. Factor: $3a - 3b - ax + bx$

28. Factor: $x^2 + 3xy - 10y^2$

29. Factor: $6a^4 + 22a^3 + 12a^2$

30. Factor: $25a^2 - 36b^2$

31. Factor: $12x^2 - 36xy + 27y^2$

32. Solve: $3x^2 + 11x - 20 = 0$

33. Find the range of the function given by the equation $f(x) = \dfrac{4}{5}x - 3$ if the domain is $\{-10, -5, 0, 5, 10\}$.

34. **Temperature** The daily high temperatures, in degrees Celsius, during one week were recorded as follows: $-4°$, $-7°$, $2°$, $0°$, $-1°$, $-6°$, $-5°$. Find the average daily high temperature for the week.

35. **Geometry** The width of a rectangle is 40% of the length. The perimeter of the rectangle is 42 cm. Find the length and width of the rectangle.

36. **Carpentry** A board 10 ft long is cut into two pieces. Four times the length of the shorter piece is 2 ft less than three times the length of the longer piece. Find the length of each piece.

37. **Rental Cars** Company A rents cars for $6 a day and 25¢ for every mile driven. Company B rents cars for $15 a day and 10¢ per mile driven. You want to rent a car for 6 days. What is the maximum number of miles you can drive a Company A car if it is to cost you less than a Company B car?

38. **Investments** An investment of $4000 is made at an annual simple interest rate of 8%. How much additional money must be invested at an annual simple interest rate of 11% so that the total interest earned is $1035?

39. **Discounts** A stereo that regularly sells for $165 is on sale for $99. Find the discount rate.

40. **Integer Problem** Find three consecutive even integers such that five times the middle integer is twelve more than twice the sum of the first and third.

CHAPTER

9 Rational Expressions

OBJECTIVES

9.1
1 Simplify rational expressions
2 Multiply rational expressions
3 Divide rational expressions

9.2
1 Find the least common multiple (LCM) of two or more polynomials
2 Express two fractions in terms of the LCM of their denominators

9.3
1 Add and subtract rational expressions with the same denominator
2 Add and subtract rational expressions with different denominators

9.4
1 Simplify complex fractions

9.5
1 Solve equations containing fractions
2 Solve proportions
3 Applications of proportions
4 Problems involving similar triangles

9.6
1 Solve a literal equation for one of the variables

9.7
1 Work problems
2 Uniform motion problems

DVD SSM

 Online Study Center

Need help? For online student resources, such as section quizzes, visit the Online Study Center at www.cengage.com/math/aufmann.

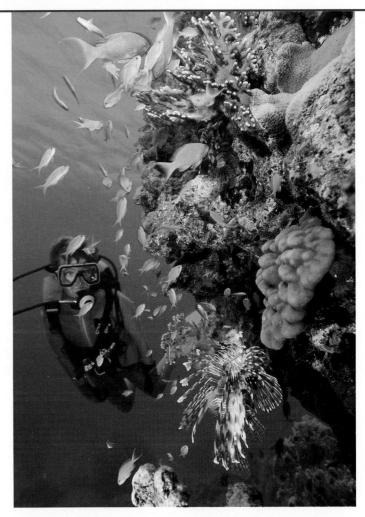

Deep-sea diving is not only a recreational sport enjoyed by tourists and adventure-seekers. Others decide to make deep-sea diving a career. Commercial deep-sea divers work on a variety of projects, including pipeline systems, offshore oilfield sites, and search-and-recovery missions. For any deep-sea diver, whether diving for recreation or for business, underwater survival depends on an oxygen tank. On land, the average adult at rest inhales and exhales about one cubic foot of air every four minutes. This air contains approximately 21% oxygen. The percent of oxygen needed by a person changes when he or she is underwater. **Exercise 104 on page 493** uses a variable expression that gives the recommended percent of oxygen for a diver as a function of the diver's depth.

467

Prep Test

1. Find the least common multiple (LCM) of 12 and 18.

2. Simplify: $\dfrac{9x^3y^4}{3x^2y^7}$

3. Subtract: $\dfrac{3}{4} - \dfrac{8}{9}$

4. Divide: $\left(-\dfrac{8}{11}\right) \div \dfrac{4}{5}$

5. If a is a nonzero number, are the expressions $\dfrac{0}{a}$ and $\dfrac{a}{0}$ equal?

6. Solve: $\dfrac{2}{3}x - \dfrac{3}{4} = \dfrac{5}{6}$

7. Line ℓ_1 is parallel to line ℓ_2. Find the measure of angle a.

8. Factor: $x^2 - 4x - 12$

9. Factor: $2x^2 - x - 3$

10. At 9:00 A.M., Anthony begins jogging on a park trail at a rate of 9 ft/s. Ten minutes later his sister Jean begins jogging on the same trail in pursuit of her brother at a rate of 12 ft/s. At what time will Jean catch up to Anthony?

9.1 Multiplication and Division of Rational Expressions

OBJECTIVE 1　Simplify rational expressions

A fraction in which the numerator and denominator are polynomials is called a **rational expression.** Examples of rational expressions are shown at the right.

$$\dfrac{5}{z} \qquad \dfrac{x^2 + 1}{2x - 1} \qquad \dfrac{y^2 - 3}{3xy + 1}$$

Care must be exercised with rational expressions to ensure that when the variables are replaced with numbers, the resulting denominator is not zero.

Consider the rational expression at the right. The value of x cannot be 2 because the denominator would then be zero.

$$\frac{3x + 1}{2x - 4}$$

$$\frac{3 \cdot 2 + 1}{2 \cdot 2 - 4} = \frac{7}{0} \leftarrow \text{Not a real number}$$

A **fraction** is **in simplest form** when the numerator and denominator have no common factors other than 1. The Multiplication Property of One is used to write a rational expression in simplest form.

Simplify: $\dfrac{x^2 - 4}{x^2 - 2x - 8}$

Factor the numerator and denominator.

$$\frac{x^2 - 4}{x^2 - 2x - 8} = \frac{(x - 2)(x + 2)}{(x - 4)(x + 2)}$$

$$= \frac{x - 2}{x - 4} \cdot \frac{\boxed{x + 2}}{\boxed{x + 2}}$$

$$= \frac{x - 2}{x - 4} \cdot 1$$

The restrictions $x \neq -2$ and $x \neq 4$ are necessary to prevent division by zero.

$$= \frac{x - 2}{x - 4}, x \neq -2, 4$$

This simplification is usually shown with slashes through the common factors. The preceding simplification would be shown as follows.

$$\frac{x^2 - 4}{x^2 - 2x - 8} = \frac{(x - 2)\overset{1}{\cancel{(x + 2)}}}{(x - 4)\underset{1}{\cancel{(x + 2)}}} = \frac{x - 2}{x - 4}, x \neq -2, 4$$

In this problem, it is stated that $x \neq -2, 4$. Look at the factored form of the original rational expression:

$$\frac{(x - 2)(x + 2)}{(x - 4)(x + 2)}$$

If either of the factors in the denominator is zero, then the denominator is zero.

$$\begin{array}{cc} x + 2 = 0 & x - 4 = 0 \\ x = -2 & x = 4 \end{array}$$

When x is -2 or 4, the denominator is 0. Therefore, for this fraction, $x \neq -2, 4$.

For the remaining examples, we will omit the restrictions on the variables that prevent division by zero and assume the values of the variables are such that division by zero is not possible.

Simplify: $\dfrac{10 + 3x - x^2}{x^2 - 4x - 5}$

Factor the numerator and denominator.

$$\frac{10 + 3x - x^2}{x^2 - 4x - 5} = \frac{(5 - x)(2 + x)}{(x - 5)(x + 1)}$$

Divide by the common factors. Remember that $5 - x = -(x - 5)$. Therefore,

$$\dfrac{5 - x}{x - 5} = \dfrac{-(x - 5)}{x - 5} = \dfrac{-1}{1} = -1$$

Write the answer in simplest form.

$$= \dfrac{\overset{-1}{(\cancel{5 - x})}(2 + x)}{\underset{1}{(\cancel{x - 5})}(x + 1)}$$

$$= -\dfrac{x + 2}{x + 1}$$

EXAMPLE 1 Simplify: **A.** $\dfrac{4x^3y^4}{6x^4y}$ **B.** $\dfrac{9 - x^2}{x^2 + x - 12}$

Solution **A.** $\dfrac{4x^3y^4}{6x^4y} = \dfrac{\overset{1}{\cancel{2}} \cdot 2x^3y^4}{\underset{1}{\cancel{2}} \cdot 3x^4y} = \dfrac{2y^3}{3x}$ • Simplify using the rules of exponents.

B. $\dfrac{9 - x^2}{x^2 + x - 12} = \dfrac{\overset{-1}{(\cancel{3 - x})}(3 + x)}{\underset{1}{(\cancel{x - 3})}(x + 4)} = -\dfrac{x + 3}{x + 4}$

PROBLEM 1 Simplify. **A.** $\dfrac{6x^5y}{12x^2y^3}$ **B.** $\dfrac{x^2 + 2x - 24}{16 - x^2}$

Solution See page S20.

OBJECTIVE 2 Multiply rational expressions

The product of two fractions is a fraction whose numerator is the product of the numerators of the two fractions and whose denominator is the product of the denominators of the two fractions.

$$\dfrac{a}{b} \cdot \dfrac{c}{d} = \dfrac{ac}{bd}$$

$$\dfrac{2}{3} \cdot \dfrac{4}{5} = \dfrac{8}{15}$$

$$\dfrac{3x}{y} \cdot \dfrac{2}{z} = \dfrac{6x}{yz}$$

$$\dfrac{x + 2}{x} \cdot \dfrac{3}{x - 2} = \dfrac{3(x + 2)}{x(x - 2)}$$

Multiply: $\dfrac{x^2 + 3x}{x^2 - 3x - 4} \cdot \dfrac{x^2 - 5x + 4}{x^2 + 2x - 3}$

$$\dfrac{x^2 + 3x}{x^2 - 3x - 4} \cdot \dfrac{x^2 - 5x + 4}{x^2 + 2x - 3}$$

Factor the numerator and denominator of each fraction.

$$= \dfrac{x(x + 3)}{(x - 4)(x + 1)} \cdot \dfrac{(x - 4)(x - 1)}{(x + 3)(x - 1)}$$

Multiply. Divide by the common factors.

$$= \dfrac{x\overset{1}{\cancel{(x + 3)}}\overset{1}{\cancel{(x - 4)}}\overset{1}{\cancel{(x - 1)}}}{\underset{1}{\cancel{(x - 4)}}(x + 1)\underset{1}{\cancel{(x + 3)}}\underset{1}{\cancel{(x - 1)}}}$$

Write the answer in simplest form.

$$= \dfrac{x}{x + 1}$$

EXAMPLE 2 Multiply.

A. $\dfrac{10x^2 - 15x}{12x - 8} \cdot \dfrac{3x - 2}{20x - 25}$ B. $\dfrac{x^2 + x - 6}{x^2 + 7x + 12} \cdot \dfrac{x^2 + 3x - 4}{4 - x^2}$

Solution A. $\dfrac{10x^2 - 15x}{12x - 8} \cdot \dfrac{3x - 2}{20x - 25}$

$= \dfrac{5x(2x - 3)}{4(3x - 2)} \cdot \dfrac{(3x - 2)}{5(4x - 5)}$ • Factor the numerator and denominator of each fraction.

$$= \dfrac{\overset{1}{\cancel{5}}x(2x - 3)\overset{1}{\cancel{(3x - 2)}}}{2 \cdot 2\cancel{(3x - 2)}\underset{1}{\cancel{5}}(4x - 5)}$$ • Multiply. Divide by the common factors.

$= \dfrac{x(2x - 3)}{4(4x - 5)}$ • Write the answer in simplest form.

B. $\dfrac{x^2 + x - 6}{x^2 + 7x + 12} \cdot \dfrac{x^2 + 3x - 4}{4 - x^2}$

$= \dfrac{(x + 3)(x - 2)}{(x + 3)(x + 4)} \cdot \dfrac{(x + 4)(x - 1)}{(2 - x)(2 + x)}$

$$= \dfrac{\overset{1}{\cancel{(x + 3)}}\overset{-1}{\cancel{(x - 2)}}\overset{1}{\cancel{(x + 4)}}(x - 1)}{\underset{1}{\cancel{(x + 3)}}\underset{1}{\cancel{(x + 4)}}\underset{1}{\cancel{(2 - x)}}(2 + x)}$$

$= -\dfrac{x - 1}{x + 2}$

PROBLEM 2 Multiply.

A. $\dfrac{12x^2 + 3x}{10x - 15} \cdot \dfrac{8x - 12}{9x + 18}$ B. $\dfrac{x^2 + 2x - 15}{9 - x^2} \cdot \dfrac{x^2 - 3x - 18}{x^2 - 7x + 6}$

Solution See page S20.

OBJECTIVE 3 Divide rational expressions

The **reciprocal** of a fraction is a fraction with the numerator and denominator interchanged.

$$\text{Fraction} \left\{ \begin{array}{cc} \dfrac{a}{b} & \dfrac{b}{a} \\[2mm] x^2 = \dfrac{x^2}{1} & \dfrac{1}{x^2} \\[2mm] \dfrac{x + 2}{x} & \dfrac{x}{x + 2} \end{array} \right\} \text{Reciprocal}$$

To divide two fractions, multiply by the reciprocal of the divisor.

$$\frac{a}{b} \div \frac{c}{d} = \frac{a}{b} \cdot \frac{d}{c} = \frac{ad}{bc}$$

$$\frac{4}{x} \div \frac{y}{5} = \frac{4}{x} \cdot \frac{5}{y} = \frac{20}{xy}$$

$$\frac{x+4}{x} \div \frac{x-2}{4} = \frac{x+4}{x} \cdot \frac{4}{x-2} = \frac{4(x+4)}{x(x-2)}$$

The basis for the division rule is shown below.

$$\underbrace{\frac{a}{b} \div \frac{c}{d}}_{} = \frac{\dfrac{a}{b}}{\dfrac{c}{d}} = \frac{\dfrac{a}{b} \cdot \dfrac{d}{c}}{\dfrac{c}{d} \cdot \dfrac{d}{c}} = \frac{\dfrac{a}{b} \cdot \dfrac{d}{c}}{1} = \underbrace{\frac{a}{b} \cdot \frac{d}{c}}_{}$$

EXAMPLE 3   Divide.

A. $\dfrac{xy^2 - 3x^2y}{z^2} \div \dfrac{6x^2 - 2xy}{z^3}$

B. $\dfrac{2x^2 + 5x + 2}{2x^2 + 3x - 2} \div \dfrac{3x^2 + 13x + 4}{2x^2 + 7x - 4}$

Solution   **A.** $\dfrac{xy^2 - 3x^2y}{z^2} \div \dfrac{6x^2 - 2xy}{z^3} = \dfrac{xy^2 - 3x^2y}{z^2} \cdot \dfrac{z^3}{6x^2 - 2xy}$

$$= \frac{xy(y - 3x) \cdot z^3}{z^2 \cdot 2x(3x - y)}$$

$$= -\frac{yz}{2}$$

B. $\dfrac{2x^2 + 5x + 2}{2x^2 + 3x - 2} \div \dfrac{3x^2 + 13x + 4}{2x^2 + 7x - 4} = \dfrac{2x^2 + 5x + 2}{2x^2 + 3x - 2} \cdot \dfrac{2x^2 + 7x - 4}{3x^2 + 13x + 4}$

$$= \frac{(2x + 1)(x + 2)}{(2x - 1)(x + 2)} \cdot \frac{(2x - 1)(x + 4)}{(3x + 1)(x + 4)}$$

$$= \frac{2x + 1}{3x + 1}$$

PROBLEM 3   Divide.

A. $\dfrac{a^2}{4bc^2 - 2b^2c} \div \dfrac{a}{6bc - 3b^2}$

B. $\dfrac{3x^2 + 26x + 16}{3x^2 - 7x - 6} \div \dfrac{2x^2 + 9x - 5}{x^2 + 2x - 15}$

Solution   See page S20.

9.1 Concept Review

Determine whether the statement is always true, sometimes true, or never true.

1. The numerator and denominator of a rational expression are polynomials.

2. A rational expression is in simplest form when the only factor common to both the numerator and the denominator is 1.

3. Before multiplying two rational expressions, we must write the expressions in terms of a common denominator.

4. The expression $\dfrac{x}{x + 2}$ is not a real number if $x = 0$.

5. The procedure for multiplying rational expressions is the same as that for multiplying arithmetic fractions.

6. When a rational expression is rewritten in simplest form, its value is less than it was before it was rewritten in simplest form.

7. To divide two rational expressions, multiply the reciprocal of the first expression by the second expression.

9.1 Exercises

1 Simplify rational expressions

1. What is a rational expression? Provide an example.

2. When is a rational expression in simplest form?

3. For the rational expression $\dfrac{x + 7}{x - 4}$, explain why the value of x cannot be 4.

4. Explain why the following simplification is incorrect.

$$\frac{x + 3}{x} = \frac{\overset{1}{\cancel{x}} + 3}{\underset{1}{\cancel{x}}} = 4$$

5. a. To simplify $\dfrac{9x^2y^5}{3x^3y^2}$, first identify the common factors of the numerator and denominator. The greatest common factor of 9 and 3 is ___?___. The greatest common factor of x^2 and x^3 is ___?___. The greatest common factor of y^5 and y^2 is ___?___.

b. When the numerator and denominator of $\dfrac{9x^2y^5}{3x^3y^2}$ are divided by the greatest common factor $3x^2y^2$, the result is $\dfrac{?}{?}$.

6. Simplify: $\dfrac{x^2 - 4}{2x^2 + 4x}$

$\dfrac{x^2 - 4}{2x^2 + 4x} = \dfrac{(x + \underline{\ ?\ })(x - \underline{\ ?\ })}{(\underline{\ ?\ })(x + 2)}$

• Factor the numerator and denominator.

$= \dfrac{?}{?}$

• Divide the numerator and denominator by the common factor ___?___.

Simplify.

7. $\dfrac{9x^3}{12x^4}$

8. $\dfrac{16x^2y}{24xy^3}$

9. $\dfrac{(x + 3)^2}{(x + 3)^3}$

10. $\dfrac{(2x - 1)^5}{(2x - 1)^4}$

11. $\dfrac{3n - 4}{4 - 3n}$

12. $\dfrac{5 - 2x}{2x - 5}$

13. $\dfrac{6y(y + 2)}{9y^2(y + 2)}$

14. $\dfrac{12x^2(3 - x)}{18x(3 - x)}$

15. $\dfrac{6x(x - 5)}{8x^2(5 - x)}$

16. $\dfrac{14x^3(7 - 3x)}{21x(3x - 7)}$

17. $\dfrac{a^2 + 4a}{ab + 4b}$

18. $\dfrac{x^2 - 3x}{2x - 6}$

19. $\dfrac{4 - 6x}{3x^2 - 2x}$

20. $\dfrac{5xy - 3y}{9 - 15x}$

21. $\dfrac{y^2 - 3y + 2}{y^2 - 4y + 3}$

22. $\dfrac{x^2 + 5x + 6}{x^2 + 8x + 15}$

23. $\dfrac{x^2 + 3x - 10}{x^2 + 2x - 8}$

24. $\dfrac{a^2 + 7a - 8}{a^2 + 6a - 7}$

25. $\dfrac{x^2 + x - 12}{x^2 - 6x + 9}$

26. $\dfrac{x^2 + 8x + 16}{x^2 - 2x - 24}$

27. $\dfrac{x^2 - 3x - 10}{25 - x^2}$

28. $\dfrac{4 - y^2}{y^2 - 3y - 10}$

29. $\dfrac{2x^3 + 2x^2 - 4x}{x^3 + 2x^2 - 3x}$

30. $\dfrac{3x^3 - 12x}{6x^3 - 24x^2 + 24x}$

31. $\dfrac{6x^2 - 7x + 2}{6x^2 + 5x - 6}$

32. $\dfrac{2n^2 - 9n + 4}{2n^2 - 5n - 12}$

33. True or false? $\dfrac{3x^2 - 6x}{9 - 6x} = \dfrac{x^2}{3}$

34. True or false? $\dfrac{3x + 1}{9x + 3} = \dfrac{1}{3}$

2   Multiply rational expressions

Multiply.

35. $\dfrac{8x^2}{9y^3} \cdot \dfrac{3y^2}{4x^3}$

36. $\dfrac{4a^2b^3}{15x^5y^2} \cdot \dfrac{25x^3y}{16ab}$

37. $\dfrac{12x^3y^4}{7a^2b^3} \cdot \dfrac{14a^3b^4}{9x^2y^2}$

38. $\dfrac{18a^4b^2}{25x^2y^3} \cdot \dfrac{50x^5y^6}{27a^6b^2}$

39. $\dfrac{3x - 6}{5x - 20} \cdot \dfrac{10x - 40}{27x - 54}$

40. $\dfrac{8x - 12}{14x + 7} \cdot \dfrac{42x + 21}{32x - 48}$

41. $\dfrac{3x^2 + 2x}{3xy - 3y} \cdot \dfrac{3xy^3 - 3y^3}{3x^3 + 2x^2}$

42. $\dfrac{4a^2x - 3a^2}{2by + 5b} \cdot \dfrac{2b^3y + 5b^3}{4ax - 3a}$

43. $\dfrac{x^2 + 5x + 4}{x^3y^2} \cdot \dfrac{x^2y^3}{x^2 + 2x + 1}$

44. $\dfrac{x^2 + x - 2}{xy^2} \cdot \dfrac{x^3y}{x^2 + 5x + 6}$

45. $\dfrac{x^4y^2}{x^2 + 3x - 28} \cdot \dfrac{x^2 - 49}{xy^4}$

46. $\dfrac{x^5y^3}{x^2 + 13x + 30} \cdot \dfrac{x^2 + 2x - 3}{x^7y^2}$

47. $\dfrac{2x^2 - 5x}{2xy + y} \cdot \dfrac{2xy^2 + y^2}{5x^2 - 2x^3}$

48. $\dfrac{3a^3 + 4a^2}{5ab - 3b} \cdot \dfrac{3b^3 - 5ab^3}{3a^2 + 4a}$

49. $\dfrac{x^2 - 2x - 24}{x^2 - 5x - 6} \cdot \dfrac{x^2 + 5x + 6}{x^2 + 6x + 8}$

50. $\dfrac{x^2 - 8x + 7}{x^2 + 3x - 4} \cdot \dfrac{x^2 + 3x - 10}{x^2 - 9x + 14}$

51. $\dfrac{x^2 + 2x - 35}{x^2 + 4x - 21} \cdot \dfrac{x^2 + 3x - 18}{x^2 + 9x + 18}$

52. $\dfrac{y^2 + y - 20}{y^2 + 2y - 15} \cdot \dfrac{y^2 + 4y - 21}{y^2 + 3y - 28}$

53. $\dfrac{x^2 - 3x - 4}{x^2 + 6x + 5} \cdot \dfrac{x^2 + 5x + 6}{8 + 2x - x^2}$

54. $\dfrac{25 - n^2}{n^2 - 2n - 35} \cdot \dfrac{n^2 - 8n - 20}{n^2 - 3n - 10}$

55. $\dfrac{12x^2 - 6x}{x^2 + 6x + 5} \cdot \dfrac{2x^4 + 10x^3}{4x^2 - 1}$

56. $\dfrac{8x^3 + 4x^2}{x^2 - 3x + 2} \cdot \dfrac{x^2 - 4}{16x^2 + 8x}$

57. $\dfrac{16 + 6x - x^2}{x^2 - 10x - 24} \cdot \dfrac{x^2 - 6x - 27}{x^2 - 17x + 72}$

58. $\dfrac{x^2 - 11x + 28}{x^2 - 13x + 42} \cdot \dfrac{x^2 + 7x + 10}{20 - x - x^2}$

59. $\dfrac{2x^2 + 5x + 2}{2x^2 + 7x + 3} \cdot \dfrac{x^2 - 7x - 30}{x^2 - 6x - 40}$

60. $\dfrac{x^2 - 4x - 32}{x^2 - 8x - 48} \cdot \dfrac{3x^2 + 17x + 10}{3x^2 - 22x - 16}$

61. $\dfrac{2x^2 + x - 3}{2x^2 - x - 6} \cdot \dfrac{2x^2 - 9x + 10}{2x^2 - 3x + 1}$

62. $\dfrac{3y^2 + 14y + 8}{2y^2 + 7y - 4} \cdot \dfrac{2y^2 + 9y - 5}{3y^2 + 16y + 5}$

63. $\dfrac{6x^2 - 11x + 4}{6x^2 + x - 2} \cdot \dfrac{12x^2 + 11x + 2}{8x^2 + 14x + 3}$

64. $\dfrac{6 - x - 2x^2}{4x^2 + 3x - 10} \cdot \dfrac{3x^2 + 7x - 20}{2x^2 + 5x - 12}$

For Exercises 65 to 68, use the product $\dfrac{x^a}{y^b} \cdot \dfrac{y^c}{x^d}$, where a, b, c, and d are positive integers.

65. Suppose $a > d$ and $c > b$. What is the denominator of the simplified product?

66. Suppose $a > d$ and $b > c$. Which variable appears in the denominator of the simplified product?

67. Suppose $a = 2d$ and $b > c$. What is the numerator of the simplified product?

68. Suppose $a < d$ and $b = c$. What is the numerator of the simplified product?

3   Divide rational expressions

69. The reciprocal of $\dfrac{5a}{a - 5}$ is $\dfrac{?}{?}$.

70. Write the first step of this division:
$\dfrac{x - 8}{y + 1} \div \dfrac{x^2 - 6x - 16}{3y + 3} = \dfrac{x - 8}{y + 1} \cdot \dfrac{?}{?}$.

Divide.

71. $\dfrac{4x^2y^3}{15a^2b^3} \div \dfrac{6xy}{5a^3b^5}$

72. $\dfrac{9x^3y^4}{16a^4b^2} \div \dfrac{45x^4y^2}{14a^7b}$

73. $\dfrac{6x - 12}{8x + 32} \div \dfrac{18x - 36}{10x + 40}$

74. $\dfrac{28x + 14}{45x - 30} \div \dfrac{14x + 7}{30x - 20}$

75. $\dfrac{6x^3 + 7x^2}{12x - 3} \div \dfrac{6x^2 + 7x}{36x - 9}$

76. $\dfrac{5a^2y + 3a^2}{2x^3 + 5x^2} \div \dfrac{10ay + 6a}{6x^3 + 15x^2}$

77. $\dfrac{x^2 + 4x + 3}{x^2y} \div \dfrac{x^2 + 2x + 1}{xy^2}$

78. $\dfrac{x^3y^2}{x^2 - 3x - 10} \div \dfrac{xy^4}{x^2 - x - 20}$

79. $\dfrac{x^2 - 49}{x^4y^3} \div \dfrac{x^2 - 14x + 49}{x^4y^3}$

80. $\dfrac{x^2y^5}{x^2 - 11x + 30} \div \dfrac{xy^6}{x^2 - 7x + 10}$

81. $\dfrac{4ax - 8a}{c^2} \div \dfrac{2y - xy}{c^3}$

82. $\dfrac{3x^2y - 9xy}{a^2b} \div \dfrac{3x^2 - x^3}{ab^2}$

83. $\dfrac{x^2 - 5x + 6}{x^2 - 9x + 18} \div \dfrac{x^2 - 6x + 8}{x^2 - 9x + 20}$

84. $\dfrac{x^2 + 3x - 40}{x^2 + 2x - 35} \div \dfrac{x^2 + 2x - 48}{x^2 + 3x - 18}$

85. $\dfrac{x^2 + 2x - 15}{x^2 - 4x - 45} \div \dfrac{x^2 + x - 12}{x^2 - 5x - 36}$

86. $\dfrac{y^2 - y - 56}{y^2 + 8y + 7} \div \dfrac{y^2 - 13y + 40}{y^2 - 4y - 5}$

87. $\dfrac{8 + 2x - x^2}{x^2 + 7x + 10} \div \dfrac{x^2 - 11x + 28}{x^2 - x - 42}$

88. $\dfrac{x^2 - x - 2}{x^2 - 7x + 10} \div \dfrac{x^2 - 3x - 4}{40 - 3x - x^2}$

89. $\dfrac{2x^2 - 3x - 20}{2x^2 - 7x - 30} \div \dfrac{2x^2 - 5x - 12}{4x^2 + 12x + 9}$

90. $\dfrac{6n^2 + 13n + 6}{4n^2 - 9} \div \dfrac{6n^2 + n - 2}{4n^2 - 1}$

91. $\dfrac{9x^2 - 16}{6x^2 - 11x + 4} \div \dfrac{6x^2 + 11x + 4}{8x^2 + 10x + 3}$

92. $\dfrac{15 - 14x - 8x^2}{4x^2 + 4x - 15} \div \dfrac{4x^2 + 13x - 12}{3x^2 + 13x + 4}$

93. $\dfrac{8x^2 + 18x - 5}{10x^2 - 9x + 2} \div \dfrac{8x^2 + 22x + 15}{10x^2 + 11x - 6}$

94. $\dfrac{10 + 7x - 12x^2}{8x^2 - 2x - 15} \div \dfrac{6x^2 - 13x + 5}{10x^2 - 13x + 4}$

For Exercises 95 to 98, state whether or not the given division is equivalent
to $\dfrac{x^2 - 3x - 4}{x^2 + 5x - 6}$.

95. $\dfrac{x - 4}{x + 6} \div \dfrac{x - 1}{x + 1}$

96. $\dfrac{x + 1}{x + 6} \div \dfrac{x - 1}{x - 4}$

97. $\dfrac{x + 1}{x - 1} \div \dfrac{x + 6}{x - 4}$

98. $\dfrac{x - 1}{x + 1} \div \dfrac{x - 4}{x + 6}$

9.1   Applying Concepts

For what values of x is the rational expression undefined? (*Hint:* Set the denominator equal to zero and solve for x.)

99. $\dfrac{x}{(x + 6)(x - 1)}$

100. $\dfrac{x}{(x - 2)(x + 5)}$

101. $\dfrac{8}{x^2 - 1}$

102. $\dfrac{7}{x^2 - 16}$

103. $\dfrac{x - 4}{x^2 - x - 6}$

104. $\dfrac{x + 5}{x^2 - 4x - 5}$

105. $\dfrac{3x}{x^2 + 6x + 9}$

106. $\dfrac{3x - 8}{3x^2 - 10x - 8}$

107. $\dfrac{4x + 7}{6x^2 - 5x - 4}$

Simplify.

108. $\dfrac{y^2}{x} \cdot \dfrac{x}{2} \div \dfrac{y}{x}$

109. $\dfrac{ab}{3} \cdot \dfrac{a}{b^2} \div \dfrac{a}{4}$

110. $\left(\dfrac{2x}{y}\right)^3 \div \left(\dfrac{x}{3y}\right)^2$

111. $\left(\dfrac{c}{3}\right)^2 \div \left(\dfrac{c}{2} \cdot \dfrac{c}{4}\right)$

112. $\left(\dfrac{a - 3}{b}\right)^2 \left(\dfrac{b}{3 - a}\right)^3$

113. $\left(\dfrac{x - 4}{y^2}\right)^3 \cdot \left(\dfrac{y}{4 - x}\right)^2$

114. $\dfrac{x^2 + 3x - 40}{x^2 + 2x - 35} \div \dfrac{x^2 + 2x - 48}{x^2 + 3x - 18} \cdot \dfrac{x^2 - 36}{x^2 - 9}$

115. $\dfrac{x^2 + x - 6}{x^2 + 7x + 12} \cdot \dfrac{x^2 + 3x - 4}{x^2 + x - 2} \div \dfrac{x^2 - 16}{x^2 - 4}$

Write in simplest form the ratio of the shaded area of the figure to the total area of the figure.

116.

117.

118. Given the expression $\dfrac{9}{x^2 + 1}$, choose some values of x and evaluate the expression for those values. Is it possible to choose a value of x for which the value of the expression is greater than 10? If so, give such a value. If not, explain why it is not possible.

119. Given the expression $\dfrac{1}{y - 3}$, choose some values of y and evaluate the expression for those values. Is it possible to choose a value of y for which the value of the expression is greater than 10,000,000? If so, give such a value. Explain your answer.

9.2

Expressing Fractions in Terms of the Least Common Multiple of Their Denominators

OBJECTIVE **1**   **Find the least common multiple (LCM) of two or more polynomials**

The **least common multiple (LCM)** of two or more numbers is the smallest number that contains the prime factorization of each number.

The LCM of 12 and 18 is 36. 36 contains the prime factors of 12 and the prime factors of 18.

$$12 = 2 \cdot 2 \cdot 3$$
$$18 = 2 \cdot 3 \cdot 3$$

$$\text{LCM} = 36 = \underbrace{2 \cdot \overbrace{2 \cdot 3} \cdot 3}$$

Factors of 12

Factors of 18

The least common multiple of two or more polynomials is the simplest polynomial that contains the factors of each polynomial.

To find the LCM of two or more polynomials, first factor each polynomial completely. The LCM is the product of each factor the greatest number of times it occurs in any one factorization.

Take Note

The LCM must contain the factors of each polynomial. As shown with braces at the right, the LCM contains the factors of $4x^2 + 4x$ and the factors of $x^2 + 2x + 1$.

Find the LCM of $4x^2 + 4x$ and $x^2 + 2x + 1$.

The LCM of $4x^2 + 4x$ and $x^2 + 2x + 1$ is the product of the LCM of the numerical coefficients and each variable factor the greatest number of times it occurs in any one factorization.

$$4x^2 + 4x = 4x(x + 1) = 2 \cdot 2 \cdot x(x + 1)$$
$$x^2 + 2x + 1 = (x + 1)(x + 1)$$

Factors of $4x^2 + 4x$

$$\text{LCM} = \overbrace{2 \cdot 2 \cdot x\underbrace{(x + 1)(x + 1)}} = 4x(x + 1)(x + 1)$$

Factors of $x^2 + 2x + 1$

EXAMPLE 1   Find the LCM of $4x^2y$ and $6xy^2$.

Solution $4x^2y = 2 \cdot 2 \cdot x \cdot x \cdot y$
$6xy^2 = 2 \cdot 3 \cdot x \cdot y \cdot y$

• **Factor each polynomial completely.**

$\text{LCM} = 2 \cdot 2 \cdot 3 \cdot x \cdot x \cdot y \cdot y$
$= 12x^2y^2$

• **Write the product of the LCM of the numerical coefficients and each variable factor the greatest number of times it occurs in any one factorization.**

PROBLEM 1   Find the LCM of $8uv^2$ and $12uw$.

Solution   See page S20.

EXAMPLE 2   Find the LCM of $x^2 - x - 6$ and $9 - x^2$.

Solution $x^2 - x - 6 = (x - 3)(x + 2)$
$9 - x^2 = -(x^2 - 9) = -(x + 3)(x - 3)$

$\text{LCM} = (x - 3)(x + 2)(x + 3)$

PROBLEM 2   Find the LCM of $m^2 - 6m + 9$ and $m^2 - 2m - 3$.

Solution   See page S20.

OBJECTIVE 2   Express two fractions in terms of the LCM of their denominators

When adding and subtracting fractions, it is often necessary to express two or more fractions in terms of a common denominator. This common denominator is the LCM of the denominators of the fractions.

Write the fractions $\dfrac{x + 1}{4x^2}$ and $\dfrac{x - 3}{6x^2 - 12x}$ in terms of the LCM of the denominators.

Find the LCM of the denominators.

The LCM is $12x^2(x - 2)$.

Take Note

$\dfrac{3(x - 2)}{3(x - 2)} = 1$ and $\dfrac{2x}{2x} = 1$. We are multiplying each fraction by 1, so we are not changing the value of either fraction.

For each fraction, multiply the numerator and denominator by the factors whose product with the denominator is the LCM.

$\dfrac{x + 1}{4x^2} = \dfrac{x + 1}{4x^2} \cdot \dfrac{3(x - 2)}{3(x - 2)} = \dfrac{3x^2 - 3x - 6}{12x^2(x - 2)}$ ⟵

$\dfrac{x - 3}{6x^2 - 12x} = \dfrac{x - 3}{6x(x - 2)} \cdot \dfrac{2x}{2x} = \dfrac{2x^2 - 6x}{12x^2(x - 2)}$ ⟵ $\Big\}$ LCM

EXAMPLE 3   Write the fractions $\dfrac{x + 2}{3x^2}$ and $\dfrac{x - 1}{8xy}$ in terms of the LCM of the denominators.

Solution   The LCM is $24x^2y$.

$\dfrac{x + 2}{3x^2} = \dfrac{x + 2}{3x^2} \cdot \dfrac{8y}{8y} = \dfrac{8xy + 16y}{24x^2y}$ • The product of $3x^2$ and $8y$ is the LCM.

$\dfrac{x - 1}{8xy} = \dfrac{x - 1}{8xy} \cdot \dfrac{3x}{3x} = \dfrac{3x^2 - 3x}{24x^2y}$ • The product of $8xy$ and $3x$ is the LCM.

PROBLEM 3   Write the fractions $\dfrac{x - 3}{4xy^2}$ and $\dfrac{2x + 1}{9y^2z}$ in terms of the LCM of the denominators.

Solution   See page S20.

EXAMPLE 4 Write the fractions $\dfrac{2x-1}{2x-x^2}$ and $\dfrac{x}{x^2+x-6}$ in terms of the LCM of the denominators.

Solution $\dfrac{2x-1}{2x-x^2} = \dfrac{2x-1}{-(x^2-2x)} = -\dfrac{2x-1}{x^2-2x}$

• Rewrite $\dfrac{2x-1}{2x-x^2}$ with a denominator of x^2-2x.

The LCM is $x(x-2)(x+3)$.

$$\dfrac{2x-1}{2x-x^2} = -\dfrac{2x-1}{x(x-2)} \cdot \dfrac{x+3}{x+3} = -\dfrac{2x^2+5x-3}{x(x-2)(x+3)}$$

$$\dfrac{x}{x^2+x-6} = \dfrac{x}{(x-2)(x+3)} \cdot \dfrac{x}{x} = \dfrac{x^2}{x(x-2)(x+3)}$$

PROBLEM 4 Write the fractions $\dfrac{x+4}{x^2-3x-10}$ and $\dfrac{2x}{25-x^2}$ in terms of the LCM of the denominators.

Solution See page S20.

9.2   Concept Review

Determine whether the statement is always true, sometimes true, or never true.

1. The least common multiple of two numbers is the smallest number that contains all the prime factors of both numbers.

2. The least common denominator is the least common multiple of the denominators of two or more fractions.

3. The LCM of x^2, x^5, and x^8 is x^2.

4. We can rewrite $\dfrac{x}{y}$ as $\dfrac{4x}{4y}$ by using the Multiplication Property of One.

5. Rewriting two fractions in terms of the LCM of their denominators is the reverse process of simplifying the fractions.

6. To rewrite a rational expression in terms of a common denominator, determine what factor you must multiply the denominator by so that the denominator will be the common denominator. Then multiply the numerator and denominator of the fraction by that factor.

9.2   Exercises

1   **Find the least common multiple (LCM) of two or more polynomials**

1. a. In the LCM of $12x^4y^3$ and $15x^2y^5$, the exponent on x is ____?____ and the exponent on y is ____?____.
  b. Because $12 = 3 \cdot 4$, and $15 = 3 \cdot 5$, the coefficient in the LCM of $12x^4y^3$ and $15x^2y^5$ is (____?____)(____?____)(____?____) = (____?____).
  c. The LCM of $12x^4y^3$ and $15x^2y^5$ is ____?____.

2. To find the LCM of $x^2 - 4x + 4$ and $x^2 - 4$, first factor each polynomial:

$x^2 - 4x + 4 = ($____?____$)^2$ • $x^2 - 4x + 4$ factors as a perfect-square trinomial.

$x^2 - 4 = ($____?____$)($____?____$)$ • $x^2 - 4$ factors as the difference of two perfect squares.

The LCM will use the factor $x - 2$ ____?____ time(s) and the factor $x + 2$ ____?____ time(s). The LCM is ____?____.

Find the LCM of the expressions.

3. $8x^3y$
   $12xy^2$

4. $6ab^2$
   $18ab^3$

5. $10x^4y^2$
   $15x^3y$

6. $12a^2b$
   $18ab^3$

7. $8x^2$
   $4x^2 + 8x$

8. $6y^2$
   $4y + 12$

9. $2x^2y$
   $3x^2 + 12x$

10. $4xy^2$
   $6xy^2 + 12y^2$

11. $8x^2(x - 1)^2$
   $10x^3(x - 1)$

12. $3x + 3$
   $2x^2 + 4x + 2$

13. $4x - 12$
   $2x^2 - 12x + 18$

14. $(x - 1)(x + 2)$
   $(x - 1)(x + 3)$

15. $(2x - 1)(x + 4)$
   $(2x + 1)(x + 4)$

16. $(2x + 3)^2$
   $(2x + 3)(x - 5)$

17. $(x - 7)(x + 2)$
   $(x - 7)^2$

18. $x - 1$
   $x - 2$
   $(x - 1)(x - 2)$

19. $(x + 4)(x - 3)$
   $x + 4$
   $x - 3$

20. $x^2 - x - 6$
   $x^2 + x - 12$

21. $x^2 + 3x - 10$
   $x^2 + 5x - 14$

22. $x^2 + 5x + 4$
   $x^2 - 3x - 28$

23. $x^2 - 10x + 21$
   $x^2 - 8x + 15$

24. $x^2 - 2x - 24$
   $x^2 - 36$

25. $x^2 + 7x + 10$
   $x^2 - 25$

26. $x^2 - 7x - 30$
   $x^2 - 5x - 24$

27. $2x^2 - 7x + 3$
   $2x^2 + x - 1$

28. $3x^2 - 11x + 6$
   $3x^2 + 4x - 4$

29. $2x^2 - 9x + 10$
   $2x^2 + x - 15$

30. $6 + x - x^2$
   $x + 2$
   $x - 3$

31. $15 + 2x - x^2$
   $x - 5$
   $x + 3$

32. $5 + 4x - x^2$
   $x - 5$
   $x + 1$

33. $x^2 + 3x - 18$
   $3 - x$
   $x + 6$

34. $x^2 - 5x + 6$
   $1 - x$
   $x - 6$

35. How many factors of $x - 3$ are in the LCM of each pair of expressions?

a. $x^2 + x - 12$ and $x^2 - 9$ **b.** $x^2 - x - 12$ and $x^2 + 6x + 9$

c. $x^2 - 6x + 9$ and $x^2 + x - 12$

36. How many factors of a are in the LCM of $(a^3b^2)^2$ and a^4b^6? How many factors of b?

2   **Express two fractions in terms of the LCM of their denominators**

For Exercises 37 to 40, use the fractions $\dfrac{x^2}{y(y - 3)}$ and $\dfrac{x}{(y - 3)^2}$.

37. The LCM of the denominators of the fractions is ___?___.

38. To write the first fraction in terms of the LCM of the denominators, multiply its numerator and its denominator by ___?___.

39. To write the second fraction in terms of the LCM of the denominators, multiply its numerator and its denominator by ___?___.

40. Write the two fractions in terms of the LCM of their denominators: ___?___ and ___?___.

Write each fraction in terms of the LCM of the denominators.

41. $\dfrac{4}{x}; \dfrac{3}{x^2}$

42. $\dfrac{5}{ab^2}; \dfrac{6}{ab}$

43. $\dfrac{x}{3y^2}; \dfrac{z}{4y}$

44. $\dfrac{5y}{6x^2}; \dfrac{7}{9xy}$

45. $\dfrac{y}{x(x - 3)}; \dfrac{6}{x^2}$

46. $\dfrac{a}{y^2}; \dfrac{6}{y(y + 5)}$

47. $\dfrac{9}{(x - 1)^2}; \dfrac{6}{x(x - 1)}$

48. $\dfrac{a^2}{y(y + 7)}; \dfrac{a}{(y + 7)^2}$

49. $\dfrac{3}{x - 3}; -\dfrac{5}{x(3 - x)}$

50. $\dfrac{b}{y(y - 4)}; \dfrac{b^2}{4 - y}$

51. $\dfrac{3}{(x - 5)^2}; \dfrac{2}{5 - x}$

52. $\dfrac{3}{7 - y}; \dfrac{2}{(y - 7)^2}$

53. $\dfrac{3}{x^2 + 2x}; \dfrac{4}{x^2}$

54. $\dfrac{2}{y - 3}; \dfrac{3}{y^3 - 3y^2}$

55. $\dfrac{x - 2}{x + 3}; \dfrac{x}{x - 4}$

56. $\dfrac{x^2}{2x - 1}; \dfrac{x + 1}{x + 4}$

57. $\dfrac{3}{x^2 + x - 2}; \dfrac{x}{x + 2}$

58. $\dfrac{3x}{x - 5}; \dfrac{4}{x^2 - 25}$

59. $\dfrac{5}{2x^2 - 9x + 10}; \dfrac{x - 1}{2x - 5}$

60. $\dfrac{x - 3}{3x^2 + 4x - 4}; \dfrac{2}{x + 2}$

61. $\dfrac{x}{x^2 + x - 6}; \dfrac{2x}{x^2 - 9}$

62. $\dfrac{x - 1}{x^2 + 2x - 15}; \dfrac{x}{x^2 + 6x + 5}$

63. $\dfrac{x}{9 - x^2}; \dfrac{x - 1}{x^2 - 6x + 9}$

64. $\dfrac{2x}{10 + 3x - x^2}; \dfrac{x + 2}{x^2 - 8x + 15}$

65. $\dfrac{3x}{x - 5}; \dfrac{x}{x + 4}; \dfrac{3}{20 + x - x^2}$

66. $\dfrac{x + 1}{x + 5}; \dfrac{x + 2}{x - 7}; \dfrac{3}{35 + 2x - x^2}$

9.2   Applying Concepts

Write each expression in terms of the LCM of the denominators.

67. $\dfrac{3}{10^2}; \dfrac{5}{10^4}$

68. $\dfrac{8}{10^3}; \dfrac{9}{10^5}$

69. $b; \dfrac{5}{b}$

70. $3; \dfrac{2}{n}$

71. $1; \dfrac{y}{y - 1}$

72. $x; \dfrac{x}{x^2 - 1}$

73. $\dfrac{x^2 + 1}{(x - 1)^3}; \dfrac{x + 1}{(x - 1)^2}; \dfrac{1}{x - 1}$

74. $\dfrac{a^2 + a}{(a + 1)^3}; \dfrac{a + 1}{(a + 1)^2}; \dfrac{1}{a + 1}$

75. $\dfrac{b}{4a^2 - 4b^2}; \dfrac{a}{8a - 8b}$

76. $\dfrac{c}{6c^2 + 7cd + d^2}; \dfrac{d}{3c^2 - 3d^2}$

77. $\dfrac{1}{x^2 + 2x + xy + 2y}; \dfrac{1}{x^2 + xy - 2x - 2y}$

78. $\dfrac{1}{ab + 3a - 3b - b^2}; \dfrac{1}{ab + 3a + 3b + b^2}$

79. When is the LCM of two expressions equal to their product?

9.3 Addition and Subtraction of Rational Expressions

OBJECTIVE 1

Add and subtract rational expressions with the same denominator

When adding rational expressions in which the denominators are the same, add the numerators. The denominator of the sum is the common denominator.

$$\frac{a}{b} + \frac{c}{b} = \frac{a+c}{b}$$

$$\frac{5x}{18} + \frac{7x}{18} = \frac{12x}{18} = \frac{2x}{3}$$

$$\frac{x}{x^2 - 1} + \frac{1}{x^2 - 1} = \frac{x+1}{x^2 - 1} = \frac{\overset{1}{\cancel{(x+1)}}}{(x-1)\underset{1}{\cancel{(x+1)}}} = \frac{1}{x-1}$$

Note that the sum is written in simplest form.

When subtracting rational expressions in which the denominators are the same, subtract the numerators. The denominator of the difference is the common denominator. Write the answer in simplest form.

$$\frac{2x}{x-2} - \frac{4}{x-2} = \frac{2x-4}{x-2} = \frac{2\overset{1}{\cancel{(x-2)}}}{\underset{1}{\cancel{x-2}}} = 2$$

$$\frac{3x-1}{x^2 - 5x + 4} - \frac{2x+3}{x^2 - 5x + 4} = \frac{(3x-1) - (2x+3)}{x^2 - 5x + 4}$$

$$= \frac{x-4}{x^2 - 5x + 4}$$

$$= \frac{\overset{1}{\cancel{(x-4)}}}{\underset{1}{\cancel{(x-4)}}(x-1)}$$

$$= \frac{1}{x-1}$$

Take Note

Be careful with signs when subtracting rational expressions. Note that we must subtract the *entire* numerator $2x + 3$.

$(3x - 1) - (2x + 3) =$
$3x - 1 - 2x - 3$

EXAMPLE 1 Add or subtract. **A.** $\dfrac{7}{x^2} + \dfrac{9}{x^2}$ **B.** $\dfrac{3x^2}{x^2 - 1} - \dfrac{x+4}{x^2 - 1}$

Solution **A.** $\dfrac{7}{x^2} + \dfrac{9}{x^2} = \dfrac{7+9}{x^2}$

$= \dfrac{16}{x^2}$

• The denominators are the same. Add the numerators.

B. $\dfrac{3x^2}{x^2 - 1} - \dfrac{x + 4}{x^2 - 1} = \dfrac{3x^2 - (x + 4)}{x^2 - 1}$ • The denominators are the same. Subtract the numerators.

$\qquad\qquad\qquad\qquad = \dfrac{3x^2 - x - 4}{x^2 - 1}$

$\qquad\qquad\qquad\qquad = \dfrac{\overset{1}{\cancel{(3x - 4)(x + 1)}}}{(x - 1)\underset{1}{\cancel{(x + 1)}}}$ • Write the answer in simplest form.

$\qquad\qquad\qquad\qquad = \dfrac{3x - 4}{x - 1}$

PROBLEM 1 Add or subtract. **A.** $\dfrac{3}{xy} + \dfrac{12}{xy}$ **B.** $\dfrac{2x^2}{x^2 - x - 12} - \dfrac{7x + 4}{x^2 - x - 12}$

Solution See page S20.

OBJECTIVE 2   Add and subtract rational expressions with different denominators

Take Note

This objective requires using the skills learned in the objective on writing two fractions in terms of the LCM of their denominators and the objective on adding and subtracting rational expressions with the same denominator.

Before two fractions with different denominators can be added or subtracted, each fraction must be expressed in terms of a common denominator. This common denominator is the LCM of the denominators of the fractions.

Add: $\dfrac{x - 3}{x^2 - 2x} + \dfrac{6}{x^2 - 4}$

Find the LCM of the denominators.

$x^2 - 2x = x(x - 2)$
$x^2 - 4 = (x - 2)(x + 2)$

The LCM is $x(x - 2)(x + 2)$.

$\dfrac{x - 3}{x^2 - 2x} + \dfrac{6}{x^2 - 4}$

Write each fraction in terms of the LCM of the denominators.

$= \dfrac{x - 3}{x(x - 2)} \cdot \dfrac{x + 2}{x + 2} + \dfrac{6}{(x - 2)(x + 2)} \cdot \dfrac{x}{x}$

Multiply the factors in the numerator.

$= \dfrac{x^2 - x - 6}{x(x - 2)(x + 2)} + \dfrac{6x}{x(x - 2)(x + 2)}$

Add the fractions.

$= \dfrac{x^2 - x - 6 + 6x}{x(x - 2)(x + 2)}$

$= \dfrac{x^2 + 5x - 6}{x(x - 2)(x + 2)}$

Factor the numerator to determine whether there are common factors in the numerator and denominator.

$= \dfrac{(x + 6)(x - 1)}{x(x - 2)(x + 2)}$

EXAMPLE 2 Add or subtract.

$$\textbf{A. } \frac{y}{x} - \frac{4y}{3x} + \frac{3y}{4x} \qquad \textbf{B. } \frac{2x}{x-3} - \frac{5}{3-x} \qquad \textbf{C. } x - \frac{3}{5x}$$

Solution **A.** The LCM of the denominators is $12x$.

• Find the LCM of the denominators.

$$\frac{y}{x} - \frac{4y}{3x} + \frac{3y}{4x}$$

$$= \frac{y}{x} \cdot \frac{12}{12} - \frac{4y}{3x} \cdot \frac{4}{4} + \frac{3y}{4x} \cdot \frac{3}{3}$$

• Write each fraction in terms of the LCM.

$$= \frac{12y}{12x} - \frac{16y}{12x} + \frac{9y}{12x}$$

$$= \frac{12y - 16y + 9y}{12x}$$

$$= \frac{5y}{12x}$$

B. The LCM of $x - 3$ and $3 - x$ is $x - 3$.

• $3 - x = -(x - 3)$

$$\frac{2x}{x-3} - \frac{5}{3-x}$$

$$= \frac{2x}{x-3} - \frac{5}{-(x-3)} \cdot \frac{-1}{-1}$$

• Multiply $\dfrac{5}{-(x-3)}$ by $\dfrac{-1}{-1}$ so that the denominator will be $x - 3$.

$$= \frac{2x}{x-3} - \frac{-5}{x-3}$$

$$= \frac{2x - (-5)}{x-3}$$

$$= \frac{2x + 5}{x-3}$$

C. The LCM of the denominators is $5x$.

$$x - \frac{3}{5x} = \frac{x}{1} - \frac{3}{5x}$$

$$= \frac{x}{1} \cdot \frac{5x}{5x} - \frac{3}{5x}$$

$$= \frac{5x^2}{5x} - \frac{3}{5x}$$

$$= \frac{5x^2 - 3}{5x}$$

PROBLEM 2 Add or subtract.

$$\textbf{A. } \frac{z}{8y} - \frac{4z}{3y} + \frac{5z}{4y} \qquad \textbf{B. } \frac{5x}{x-2} - \frac{3}{2-x} \qquad \textbf{C. } y + \frac{5}{y-7}$$

Solution See page S21.

EXAMPLE 3 Add or subtract. **A.** $\dfrac{2x}{2x - 3} - \dfrac{1}{x + 1}$

B. $\dfrac{x + 3}{x^2 - 2x - 8} + \dfrac{3}{4 - x}$

Solution **A.** The LCM is $(2x - 3)(x + 1)$.

$$\dfrac{2x}{2x - 3} - \dfrac{1}{x + 1} = \dfrac{2x}{2x - 3} \cdot \dfrac{x + 1}{x + 1} - \dfrac{1}{x + 1} \cdot \dfrac{2x - 3}{2x - 3}$$

$$= \dfrac{2x^2 + 2x}{(2x - 3)(x + 1)} - \dfrac{2x - 3}{(2x - 3)(x + 1)}$$

$$= \dfrac{(2x^2 + 2x) - (2x - 3)}{(2x - 3)(x + 1)}$$

$$= \dfrac{2x^2 + 3}{(2x - 3)(x + 1)}$$

B. The LCM is $(x - 4)(x + 2)$.

$$\dfrac{x + 3}{x^2 - 2x - 8} + \dfrac{3}{4 - x}$$

$$= \dfrac{x + 3}{(x - 4)(x + 2)} + \dfrac{3}{-(x - 4)} \cdot \dfrac{-1 \cdot (x + 2)}{-1 \cdot (x + 2)}$$

$$= \dfrac{x + 3}{(x - 4)(x + 2)} + \dfrac{-3(x + 2)}{(x - 4)(x + 2)}$$

$$= \dfrac{(x + 3) + (-3)(x + 2)}{(x - 4)(x + 2)}$$

$$= \dfrac{x + 3 - 3x - 6}{(x - 4)(x + 2)}$$

$$= \dfrac{-2x - 3}{(x - 4)(x + 2)}$$

PROBLEM 3 Add or subtract. **A.** $\dfrac{4x}{3x - 1} - \dfrac{9}{x + 4}$ **B.** $\dfrac{2x - 1}{x^2 - 25} + \dfrac{2}{5 - x}$

Solution See page S21.

9.3 Concept Review

Determine whether the statement is always true, sometimes true, or never true.

1. To add two fractions, add the numerators and the denominators.

2. The procedure for subtracting two rational expressions is the same as that for subtracting two arithmetic fractions.

3. To add two rational expressions, first multiply both expressions by the LCM of their denominators.

4. If $x \neq -2$ and $x \neq 0$, then $\dfrac{x}{x+2} + \dfrac{3}{x+2} = \dfrac{x+3}{x+2} = \dfrac{3}{2}$.

5. If $y \neq 8$, then $\dfrac{y}{y-8} - \dfrac{8}{y-8} = \dfrac{y-8}{y-8} = 1$.

6. If $x \neq 0$, then $\dfrac{4x-3}{x} - \dfrac{3x+1}{x} = \dfrac{4x-3-3x+1}{x} = \dfrac{x-2}{x}$.

9.3 Exercises

1 Add and subtract rational expressions with the same denominator

1. Add: $\dfrac{6a+1}{a-4} + \dfrac{2a-1}{a-4}$

$\dfrac{6a+1}{a-4} + \dfrac{2a-1}{a-4} = \dfrac{6a+1+2a-1}{a-4}$

$= \dfrac{?}{a-4}$

- The denominators are the same. Add the ___?___.

- Simplify the numerator. The result is in simplest form because the numerator and denominator have no common ___?___.

2. Subtract: $\dfrac{5x}{x^2+5x-14} - \dfrac{2x-21}{x^2+5x-14}$

$\dfrac{5x}{x^2+5x-14} - \dfrac{2x-21}{x^2+5x-14}$

$= \dfrac{?-(\quad?\quad)}{x^2+5x-14}$

$= \dfrac{5x-\quad?\quad+\quad?\quad}{x^2+5x-14}$

$= \dfrac{?}{x^2+5x-14}$

$= \dfrac{3(\quad?\quad)}{(\quad?\quad)(\quad?\quad)}$

$= \dfrac{?}{?}$

- The ___?___ are the same.

- Subtract the numerators.

- Remove the parentheses.

- Simplify the numerator.

- Factor the numerator and denominator.

- Divide the numerator and denominator by the common factor, ___?___.

Add or subtract.

3. $\dfrac{3}{y^2} + \dfrac{8}{y^2}$

4. $\dfrac{6}{ab} - \dfrac{2}{ab}$

5. $\dfrac{3}{x+4} - \dfrac{10}{x+4}$

6. $\dfrac{x}{x+6} - \dfrac{2}{x+6}$

7. $\dfrac{3x}{2x+3} + \dfrac{5x}{2x+3}$

8. $\dfrac{6y}{4y+1} - \dfrac{11y}{4y+1}$

9. $\dfrac{2x+1}{x-3} + \dfrac{3x+6}{x-3}$

10. $\dfrac{4x+3}{2x-7} + \dfrac{3x-8}{2x-7}$

11. $\dfrac{5x-1}{x+9} - \dfrac{3x+4}{x+9}$

12. $\dfrac{6x-5}{x-10} - \dfrac{3x-4}{x-10}$

13. $\dfrac{x-7}{2x+7} - \dfrac{4x-3}{2x+7}$

14. $\dfrac{2n}{3n+4} - \dfrac{5n-3}{3n+4}$

15. $\dfrac{x}{x^2+2x-15} - \dfrac{3}{x^2+2x-15}$

16. $\dfrac{3x}{x^2+3x-10} - \dfrac{6}{x^2+3x-10}$

17. $\dfrac{2x+3}{x^2-x-30} - \dfrac{x-2}{x^2-x-30}$

18. $\dfrac{3x-1}{x^2+5x-6} - \dfrac{2x-7}{x^2+5x-6}$

19. $\dfrac{4y+7}{2y^2+7y-4} - \dfrac{y-5}{2y^2+7y-4}$

20. $\dfrac{x+1}{2x^2-5x-12} + \dfrac{x+2}{2x^2-5x-12}$

21. $\dfrac{2x^2+3x}{x^2-9x+20} + \dfrac{2x^2-3}{x^2-9x+20} - \dfrac{4x^2+2x+1}{x^2-9x+20}$

22. $\dfrac{2x^2+3x}{x^2-2x-63} - \dfrac{x^2-3x+21}{x^2-2x-63} - \dfrac{x-7}{x^2-2x-63}$

2   Add and subtract rational expressions with different denominators

23. To add or subtract rational expressions that have different denominators, you must first express each fraction in terms of a ___?___, which can be the ___?___ of the denominators of the rational expressions.

24. Subtract: $\dfrac{3}{x-1} - \dfrac{2}{x+5}$

$\dfrac{3}{x-1} - \dfrac{2}{x+5}$

$= \dfrac{3}{x-1} \cdot \dfrac{x+5}{x+5} - \dfrac{2}{x+5} \cdot \dfrac{x-1}{x-1}$

$= \dfrac{?}{(x-1)(x+5)} - \dfrac{?}{(x-1)(x+5)}$

$= \dfrac{(\;\;?\;\;) - (\;\;?\;\;)}{(x-1)(x+5)}$

$= \dfrac{3x+15 - \;\;?\;\; + \;\;?\;\;}{(x-1)(x+5)}$

$= \dfrac{?}{(x-1)(x+5)}$

- The denominators are different.
- Write each fraction in terms of the ___?___ of the denominators, $(x-1)(x+5)$.
- Simplify each product. Multiply the numerators. Leave the denominators in factored form.
- Subtract the ___?___. The denominator is the common denominator.
- Remove the parentheses.

- Simplify the numerator. The result is in simplest form because the numerator and denominator have no common ___?___.

25. 🗨 True or false? To add $\dfrac{5}{8x^3} + \dfrac{7}{12x^5}$, use a common denominator of $4x^3$.

26. 🗨 True or false? $\dfrac{3}{x - 8} + \dfrac{3}{8 - x} = 0$.

Add or subtract.

27. $\dfrac{4}{x} + \dfrac{5}{y}$

28. $\dfrac{7}{a} + \dfrac{5}{b}$

29. $\dfrac{12}{x} - \dfrac{5}{2x}$

30. $\dfrac{5}{3a} - \dfrac{3}{4a}$

31. $\dfrac{1}{2x} - \dfrac{5}{4x} + \dfrac{7}{6x}$

32. $\dfrac{7}{4y} + \dfrac{11}{6y} - \dfrac{8}{3y}$

33. $\dfrac{5}{3x} - \dfrac{2}{x^2} + \dfrac{3}{2x}$

34. $\dfrac{6}{y^2} + \dfrac{3}{4y} - \dfrac{2}{5y}$

35. $\dfrac{2}{x} - \dfrac{3}{2y} + \dfrac{3}{5x} - \dfrac{1}{4y}$

36. $\dfrac{5}{2a} + \dfrac{7}{3b} - \dfrac{2}{b} - \dfrac{3}{4a}$

37. $\dfrac{2x + 1}{3x} + \dfrac{x - 1}{5x}$

38. $\dfrac{4x - 3}{6x} + \dfrac{2x + 3}{4x}$

39. $\dfrac{x - 3}{6x} + \dfrac{x + 4}{8x}$

40. $\dfrac{2x - 3}{2x} + \dfrac{x + 3}{3x}$

41. $\dfrac{2x + 9}{9x} - \dfrac{x - 5}{5x}$

42. $\dfrac{3y - 2}{12y} - \dfrac{y - 3}{18y}$

43. $\dfrac{x + 4}{2x} - \dfrac{x - 1}{x^2}$

44. $\dfrac{x - 2}{3x^2} - \dfrac{x + 4}{x}$

45. $\dfrac{x - 10}{4x^2} + \dfrac{x + 1}{2x}$

46. $\dfrac{x + 5}{3x^2} + \dfrac{2x + 1}{2x}$

47. $y + \dfrac{8}{3y}$

48. $\dfrac{7}{2n} - n$

49. $\dfrac{4}{x + 4} + x$

50. $x + \dfrac{3}{x + 2}$

51. $5 - \dfrac{x - 2}{x + 1}$

52. $3 + \dfrac{x - 1}{x + 1}$

53. $\dfrac{2x + 1}{6x^2} - \dfrac{x - 4}{4x}$

54. $\dfrac{x + 3}{6x} - \dfrac{x - 3}{8x^2}$

55. $\dfrac{x + 2}{xy} - \dfrac{3x - 2}{x^2y}$

56. $\dfrac{3x - 1}{xy^2} - \dfrac{2x + 3}{xy}$

57. $\dfrac{4x - 3}{3x^2y} + \dfrac{2x + 1}{4xy^2}$

58. $\dfrac{5x + 7}{6xy^2} - \dfrac{4x - 3}{8x^2y}$

59. $\dfrac{x-2}{8x^2} - \dfrac{x+7}{12xy}$

60. $\dfrac{3x-1}{6y^2} - \dfrac{x+5}{9xy}$

61. $\dfrac{4}{x-2} + \dfrac{5}{x+3}$

62. $\dfrac{2}{x-3} + \dfrac{5}{x-4}$

63. $\dfrac{6}{x-7} - \dfrac{4}{x+3}$

64. $\dfrac{3}{y+6} - \dfrac{4}{y-3}$

65. $\dfrac{2x}{x+1} + \dfrac{1}{x-3}$

66. $\dfrac{3x}{x-4} + \dfrac{2}{x+6}$

67. $\dfrac{4x}{2x-1} - \dfrac{5}{x-6}$

68. $\dfrac{6x}{x+5} - \dfrac{3}{2x+3}$

69. $\dfrac{2a}{a-7} + \dfrac{5}{7-a}$

70. $\dfrac{4x}{6-x} + \dfrac{5}{x-6}$

71. $\dfrac{x}{x^2-9} + \dfrac{3}{x-3}$

72. $\dfrac{y}{y^2-16} + \dfrac{1}{y-4}$

73. $\dfrac{2x}{x^2-x-6} - \dfrac{3}{x+2}$

74. $\dfrac{5x}{x^2+2x-8} - \dfrac{2}{x+4}$

75. $\dfrac{3x-1}{x^2-10x+25} - \dfrac{3}{x-5}$

76. $\dfrac{2a+3}{a^2-7a+12} - \dfrac{2}{a-3}$

77. $\dfrac{x+4}{x^2-x-42} + \dfrac{3}{7-x}$

78. $\dfrac{x+3}{x^2-3x-10} + \dfrac{2}{5-x}$

79. $\dfrac{x}{2x+4} - \dfrac{2}{x^2+2x}$

80. $\dfrac{x+2}{4x+16} - \dfrac{2}{x^2+4x}$

81. $\dfrac{x-1}{x^2-x-2} + \dfrac{3}{x^2-3x+2}$

82. $\dfrac{a+2}{a^2+a-2} + \dfrac{3}{a^2+2a-3}$

83. $\dfrac{1}{x+1} + \dfrac{x}{x-6} - \dfrac{5x-2}{x^2-5x-6}$

84. $\dfrac{x}{x-4} + \dfrac{5}{x+5} - \dfrac{11x-8}{x^2+x-20}$

85. $\dfrac{3x+1}{x-1} - \dfrac{x-1}{x-3} + \dfrac{x+1}{x^2-4x+3}$

86. $\dfrac{4x+1}{x-8} - \dfrac{3x+2}{x+4} - \dfrac{49x+4}{x^2-4x-32}$

9.3   Applying Concepts

Simplify.

87. $\dfrac{a}{a-b} + \dfrac{b}{b-a} + 1$

88. $\dfrac{y}{x-y} + 2 - \dfrac{x}{y-x}$

89. $b - 3 + \dfrac{5}{b+4}$

90. $2y - 1 + \dfrac{6}{y+5}$

91. $\dfrac{(n+1)^2}{(n-1)^2} - 1$

92. $1 - \dfrac{(y-2)^2}{(y+2)^2}$

93. $\dfrac{2x+9}{3-x} + \dfrac{x+5}{x+7} - \dfrac{2x^2+3x-3}{x^2+4x-21}$

94. $\dfrac{3x+5}{x+5} - \dfrac{x+1}{2-x} - \dfrac{4x^2-3x-1}{x^2+3x-10}$

95. $\dfrac{x^2+x-6}{x^2+2x-8} \cdot \dfrac{x^2+5x+4}{x^2+2x-3} - \dfrac{2}{x-1}$

96. $\dfrac{x^2+9x+20}{x^2+4x-5} \div \dfrac{x^2-49}{x^2+6x-7} - \dfrac{x}{x-7}$

97. $\dfrac{x^2-9}{x^2+6x+9} \div \dfrac{x^2+x-20}{x^2-x-12} + \dfrac{1}{x+1}$

98. $\dfrac{x^2-25}{x^2+10x+25} \cdot \dfrac{x^2-7x+10}{x^2-x-2} + \dfrac{1}{x+1}$

99. Find the sum of the following:

$$\dfrac{1}{1\cdot 2} + \dfrac{1}{2\cdot 3}$$

$$\dfrac{1}{1\cdot 2} + \dfrac{1}{2\cdot 3} + \dfrac{1}{3\cdot 4}$$

$$\dfrac{1}{1\cdot 2} + \dfrac{1}{2\cdot 3} + \dfrac{1}{3\cdot 4} + \dfrac{1}{4\cdot 5}$$

Note the pattern for these sums, and then find the sum of 50 terms, of 100 terms, and of 1000 terms.

Rewrite the expression as the sum of two fractions in simplest form.

100. $\dfrac{5b+4a}{ab}$

101. $\dfrac{6x+7y}{xy}$

102. $\dfrac{3x^2+4xy}{x^2y^2}$

103. $\dfrac{2mn^2+8m^2n}{m^3n^3}$

104. Deep-Sea Diving A recommended percent of oxygen (by volume) in the air that a deep-sea diver breathes is given by $\dfrac{660}{d+33}$, where d is the depth, in feet, at which the diver is working.

a. What is the recommended percent of oxygen for a diver working at a depth of 50 ft? Round to the nearest percent.

b. As the depth of the diver increases, does the recommended amount of oxygen increase or decrease?

c. At sea level, the oxygen content of air is approximately 21%. Is this less than or more than the recommended amount of oxygen for a diver working at the water's surface?

Complex Fractions

OBJECTIVE **1**   **Simplify complex fractions**

A **complex fraction** is a fraction whose numerator or denominator contains one or more fractions. Examples of complex fractions are shown at the right.

$$\dfrac{3}{2 - \dfrac{1}{2}}, \qquad \dfrac{4 + \dfrac{1}{x}}{3 + \dfrac{2}{x}}, \qquad \dfrac{\dfrac{1}{x - 1} + x + 3}{x - 3 + \dfrac{1}{x + 4}}$$

■   Simplify: $\dfrac{1 - \dfrac{4}{x^2}}{1 + \dfrac{2}{x}}$

Find the LCM of the denominators of the fractions in the numerator and denominator.

The LCM of x^2 and x is x^2.

Multiply the numerator and denominator of the complex fraction by the LCM.

$$\dfrac{1 - \dfrac{4}{x^2}}{1 + \dfrac{2}{x}} = \dfrac{1 - \dfrac{4}{x^2}}{1 + \dfrac{2}{x}} \cdot \dfrac{x^2}{x^2}$$

$$= \dfrac{1 \cdot x^2 - \dfrac{4}{x^2} \cdot x^2}{1 \cdot x^2 + \dfrac{2}{x} \cdot x^2}$$

$$= \dfrac{x^2 - 4}{x^2 + 2x}$$

Simplify.

$$= \dfrac{(x - 2)\overset{1}{\cancel{(x + 2)}}}{x\underset{1}{\cancel{(x + 2)}}}$$

$$= \dfrac{x - 2}{x}$$

The method shown above of simplifying a complex fraction by multiplying the numerator and denominator by the LCM of the denominators is used in Example 1. However, a different approach is to rewrite the numerator and denominator of the complex fraction as single fractions and then divide the numerator by the denominator. The example shown above is simplified below using this alternative method.

Rewrite the numerator and denominator of the complex fraction as single fractions.

$$\dfrac{1 - \dfrac{4}{x^2}}{1 + \dfrac{2}{x}} = \dfrac{1 \cdot \dfrac{x^2}{x^2} - \dfrac{4}{x^2}}{1 \cdot \dfrac{x}{x} + \dfrac{2}{x}} = \dfrac{\dfrac{x^2}{x^2} - \dfrac{4}{x^2}}{\dfrac{x}{x} + \dfrac{2}{x}} = \dfrac{\dfrac{x^2 - 4}{x^2}}{\dfrac{x + 2}{x}}$$

Divide the numerator of the complex fraction by the denominator.

$$= \dfrac{x^2 - 4}{x^2} \div \dfrac{x + 2}{x} = \dfrac{x^2 - 4}{x^2} \cdot \dfrac{x}{x + 2}$$

Multiply the fractions.
Factor the numerator.

$$= \frac{(x^2 - 4)x}{x^2(x + 2)} = \frac{(x + 2)(x - 2)x}{x^2(x + 2)}$$

Simplify.

$$= \frac{x - 2}{x}$$

Note that this is the same result as shown above.

EXAMPLE 1   Simplify.   **A.** $\dfrac{\dfrac{1}{x} + \dfrac{1}{2}}{\dfrac{1}{x^2} - \dfrac{1}{4}}$ **B.** $\dfrac{1 - \dfrac{2}{x} - \dfrac{15}{x^2}}{1 - \dfrac{11}{x} + \dfrac{30}{x^2}}$

Solution   **A.** The LCM of x, 2, x^2, and 4 is $4x^2$.

$$\frac{\dfrac{1}{x} + \dfrac{1}{2}}{\dfrac{1}{x^2} - \dfrac{1}{4}} = \frac{\dfrac{1}{x} + \dfrac{1}{2}}{\dfrac{1}{x^2} - \dfrac{1}{4}} \cdot \frac{4x^2}{4x^2}$$

$$= \frac{\dfrac{1}{x} \cdot 4x^2 + \dfrac{1}{2} \cdot 4x^2}{\dfrac{1}{x^2} \cdot 4x^2 - \dfrac{1}{4} \cdot 4x^2}$$

$$= \frac{4x + 2x^2}{4 - x^2}$$

$$= \frac{\overset{1}{2x(2 + x)}}{\underset{1}{(2 - x)(2 + x)}}$$

$$= \frac{2x}{2 - x}$$

B. The LCM of x and x^2 is x^2.

$$\frac{1 - \dfrac{2}{x} - \dfrac{15}{x^2}}{1 - \dfrac{11}{x} + \dfrac{30}{x^2}} = \frac{1 - \dfrac{2}{x} - \dfrac{15}{x^2}}{1 - \dfrac{11}{x} + \dfrac{30}{x^2}} \cdot \frac{x^2}{x^2}$$

$$= \frac{1 \cdot x^2 - \dfrac{2}{x} \cdot x^2 - \dfrac{15}{x^2} \cdot x^2}{1 \cdot x^2 - \dfrac{11}{x} \cdot x^2 + \dfrac{30}{x^2} \cdot x^2}$$

$$= \frac{x^2 - 2x - 15}{x^2 - 11x + 30}$$

$$= \frac{\overset{1}{(x - 5)(x + 3)}}{\underset{1}{(x - 5)(x - 6)}}$$

$$= \frac{x + 3}{x - 6}$$

PROBLEM 1   Simplify.   **A.** $\dfrac{\dfrac{1}{3} - \dfrac{1}{x}}{\dfrac{1}{9} - \dfrac{1}{x^2}}$ **B.** $\dfrac{1 + \dfrac{4}{x} + \dfrac{3}{x^2}}{1 + \dfrac{10}{x} + \dfrac{21}{x^2}}$

Solution   See page S21.

9.4   Concept Review

Determine whether the statement is always true, sometimes true, or never true.

1. A complex fraction is a fraction that has fractions in the numerator and denominator.

2. We can simplify a complex fraction by first finding the least common multiple of the denominators of the fractions in the numerator and denominator of the complex fraction.

3. To simplify a complex fraction, multiply the complex fraction by the LCM of the denominators of the fractions in the numerator and denominator of the complex fraction.

4. When we multiply the numerator and denominator of a complex fraction by the same expression, we are using the Multiplication Property of One.

5. Our goal in simplifying a complex fraction is to rewrite it so that there are no fractions in the numerator or in the denominator. We then express the fraction in simplest form.

6. For the complex fraction $\dfrac{1 + \dfrac{4}{x} + \dfrac{3}{x^2}}{1 + \dfrac{10}{x} + \dfrac{21}{x^2}}$, x can be any real number except 0.

9.4   Exercises

1   Simplify complex fractions

For Exercises 1 to 4, use the complex fraction $\dfrac{1 - \dfrac{5}{x} + \dfrac{6}{x^2}}{1 - \dfrac{4}{x^2}}$.

1. To simplify the complex fraction, multiply the numerator and denominator of the complex fraction by the LCM of the denominators of the fractions ___?___ , ___?___ , and ___?___ . The LCM is ___?___ .

2. When you multiply the numerator of the complex fraction by x^2, the numerator of the complex fraction simplifies to ___?___, which factors as (___?___)(___?___).

3. When you multiply the denominator of the complex fraction by x^2, the denominator of the complex fraction simplifies to ___?___, which factors as (___?___)(___?___).

4. The numerator from Exercise 2 and the denominator from Exercise 3 have a common factor of ___?___, so the simplified form of the complex fraction is (___?___).

Simplify.

5. $\dfrac{1 + \dfrac{3}{x}}{1 - \dfrac{9}{x^2}}$

6. $\dfrac{1 + \dfrac{4}{x}}{1 - \dfrac{16}{x^2}}$

7. $\dfrac{2 - \dfrac{8}{x + 4}}{3 - \dfrac{12}{x + 4}}$

8. $\dfrac{5 - \dfrac{25}{x + 5}}{1 - \dfrac{3}{x + 5}}$

9. $\dfrac{1 + \dfrac{5}{y - 2}}{1 - \dfrac{2}{y - 2}}$

10. $\dfrac{2 - \dfrac{11}{2x - 1}}{3 - \dfrac{17}{2x - 1}}$

11. $\dfrac{4 - \dfrac{2}{x + 7}}{5 + \dfrac{1}{x + 7}}$

12. $\dfrac{5 + \dfrac{3}{x - 8}}{2 - \dfrac{1}{x - 8}}$

13. $\dfrac{\dfrac{3}{x - 2} + 3}{\dfrac{4}{x - 2} + 4}$

14. $\dfrac{\dfrac{3}{2x + 1} - 3}{2 - \dfrac{4x}{2x + 1}}$

15. $\dfrac{2 - \dfrac{3}{x} - \dfrac{2}{x^2}}{2 + \dfrac{5}{x} + \dfrac{2}{x^2}}$

16. $\dfrac{2 + \dfrac{5}{x} - \dfrac{12}{x^2}}{4 - \dfrac{4}{x} - \dfrac{3}{x^2}}$

17. $\dfrac{1 - \dfrac{1}{x} - \dfrac{6}{x^2}}{1 - \dfrac{9}{x^2}}$

18. $\dfrac{1 + \dfrac{4}{x} + \dfrac{4}{x^2}}{1 - \dfrac{2}{x} - \dfrac{8}{x^2}}$

19. $\dfrac{1 - \dfrac{5}{x} - \dfrac{6}{x^2}}{1 + \dfrac{6}{x} + \dfrac{5}{x^2}}$

20. $\dfrac{1 - \dfrac{7}{a} + \dfrac{12}{a^2}}{1 + \dfrac{1}{a} - \dfrac{20}{a^2}}$

21. $\dfrac{1 - \dfrac{6}{x} + \dfrac{8}{x^2}}{\dfrac{4}{x^2} + \dfrac{3}{x} - 1}$

22. $\dfrac{1 + \dfrac{3}{x} - \dfrac{18}{x^2}}{\dfrac{21}{x^2} - \dfrac{4}{x} - 1}$

23. $\dfrac{x - \dfrac{4}{x + 3}}{1 + \dfrac{1}{x + 3}}$

24. $\dfrac{y + \dfrac{1}{y - 2}}{1 + \dfrac{1}{y - 2}}$

25. $\dfrac{1 - \dfrac{x}{2x + 1}}{x - \dfrac{1}{2x + 1}}$

26. $\dfrac{1 - \dfrac{2x - 2}{3x - 1}}{x - \dfrac{4}{3x - 1}}$

27. $\dfrac{x - 5 + \dfrac{14}{x + 4}}{x + 3 - \dfrac{2}{x + 4}}$

28. $\dfrac{a + 4 + \dfrac{5}{a - 2}}{a + 6 + \dfrac{15}{a - 2}}$

29. $\dfrac{x + 3 - \dfrac{10}{x - 6}}{x + 2 - \dfrac{20}{x - 6}}$

30. $\dfrac{x - 7 + \dfrac{5}{x - 1}}{x - 3 + \dfrac{1}{x - 1}}$

31. $\dfrac{y - 6 + \dfrac{22}{2y + 3}}{y - 5 + \dfrac{11}{2y + 3}}$

32. $\dfrac{x + 2 - \dfrac{12}{2x - 1}}{x + 1 - \dfrac{9}{2x - 1}}$

33. $\dfrac{x - \dfrac{2}{2x - 3}}{2x - 1 - \dfrac{8}{2x - 3}}$

34. $\dfrac{x + 3 - \dfrac{18}{2x + 1}}{x - \dfrac{6}{2x + 1}}$

35. $\dfrac{1 - \dfrac{2}{x + 1}}{1 + \dfrac{1}{x - 2}}$

36. $\dfrac{1 - \dfrac{1}{x + 2}}{1 + \dfrac{2}{x - 1}}$

37. $\dfrac{1 - \dfrac{2}{x + 4}}{1 + \dfrac{3}{x - 1}}$

38. $\dfrac{1 + \dfrac{1}{x - 2}}{1 - \dfrac{3}{x + 2}}$

39. $\dfrac{\dfrac{1}{x} - \dfrac{2}{x - 1}}{\dfrac{3}{x} + \dfrac{1}{x - 1}}$

40. $\dfrac{\dfrac{3}{n + 1} + \dfrac{1}{n}}{\dfrac{2}{n + 1} + \dfrac{3}{n}}$

41. $\dfrac{\dfrac{3}{2x - 1} - \dfrac{1}{x}}{\dfrac{4}{x} + \dfrac{2}{2x - 1}}$

42. $\dfrac{\dfrac{4}{3x + 1} + \dfrac{3}{x}}{\dfrac{6}{x} - \dfrac{2}{3x + 1}}$

43. $\dfrac{\dfrac{3}{b - 4} - \dfrac{2}{b + 1}}{\dfrac{5}{b + 1} - \dfrac{1}{b - 4}}$

44. $\dfrac{\dfrac{5}{x - 5} - \dfrac{3}{x - 1}}{\dfrac{6}{x - 1} + \dfrac{2}{x - 5}}$

45. True or false? The reciprocal of the complex fraction $\dfrac{1}{1 - \dfrac{1}{x}}$ is $\dfrac{x - 1}{x}$.

46. True or false? If the denominator of a complex fraction is the reciprocal of its numerator, then the complex fraction is equal to the square of the numerator of the complex fraction.

9.4 Applying Concepts

Simplify.

47. $1 + \dfrac{1}{1 + \dfrac{1}{2}}$

48. $1 + \dfrac{1}{1 + \dfrac{1}{1 + \dfrac{1}{2}}}$

49. $1 - \dfrac{1}{1 - \dfrac{1}{x}}$

50. $1 - \dfrac{1}{1 - \dfrac{1}{y + 1}}$

51. $\dfrac{a^{-1} - b^{-1}}{a^{-2} - b^{-2}}$

52. $\dfrac{x^{-2} - y^{-2}}{x^{-2}y^{-2}}$

53. $\left(\dfrac{y}{4} - \dfrac{4}{y} \right) \div \left(\dfrac{4}{y} - 3 + \dfrac{y}{2} \right)$

54. $\left(\dfrac{b}{8} - \dfrac{8}{b} \right) \div \left(\dfrac{8}{b} - 5 + \dfrac{b}{2} \right)$

55. How would you explain to a classmate why we multiply the numerator and denominator of a complex fraction by the LCM of the denominators of the fractions in the numerator and denominator?

9.5 Equations Containing Fractions

OBJECTIVE 1 **Solve equations containing fractions**

In the chapter "Solving Equations and Inequalities," equations containing fractions were solved by the method of clearing denominators. Recall that to **clear denominators,** we multiply each side of an equation by the LCM of the denominators. The result is an equation that contains no fractions. In this section, we will again solve equations containing fractions by multiplying each side of the equation by the LCM of the denominators. The difference between this section and the chapter "Solving Equations and Inequalities" is that the fractions in these equations contain variables in the denominators.

Take Note

Note that we are now solving *equations,* not operating on *expressions.* We are not writing each fraction in terms of the LCM of the denominators; we are multiplying both sides of the equation by the LCM of the denominators.

Solve: $\dfrac{3x - 1}{4x} + \dfrac{2}{3x} = \dfrac{7}{6x}$

Find the LCM of the denominators.

The LCM of $4x$, $3x$, and $6x$ is $12x$.

$$\frac{3x - 1}{4x} + \frac{2}{3x} = \frac{7}{6x}$$

Multiply each side of the equation by the LCM of the denominators.

$$12x \left(\frac{3x - 1}{4x} + \frac{2}{3x} \right) = 12x \left(\frac{7}{6x} \right)$$

Simplify using the Distributive Property.

$$12x \left(\frac{3x - 1}{4x} \right) + 12x \left(\frac{2}{3x} \right) = 12x \left(\frac{7}{6x} \right)$$

$$\frac{12x}{1} \left(\frac{3x - 1}{4x} \right) + \frac{12x}{1} \left(\frac{2}{3x} \right) = \frac{12x}{1} \left(\frac{7}{6x} \right)$$

$$3(3x - 1) + 4(2) = 2(7)$$

Solve for x.

$$9x - 3 + 8 = 14$$
$$9x + 5 = 14$$
$$9x = 9$$
$$x = 1$$

1 checks as a solution.
The solution is 1.

EXAMPLE 1   Solve: $\dfrac{4}{x} - \dfrac{x}{2} = \dfrac{7}{2}$

Solution
$$\frac{4}{x} - \frac{x}{2} = \frac{7}{2}$$
• **The LCM of x and 2 is 2x.**

$$2x\left(\frac{4}{x} - \frac{x}{2}\right) = 2x\left(\frac{7}{2}\right)$$

$$\frac{2x}{1} \cdot \frac{4}{x} - \frac{2x}{1} \cdot \frac{x}{2} = \frac{2x}{1} \cdot \frac{7}{2}$$

$$8 - x^2 = 7x$$
• **This is a quadratic equation.**

$$0 = x^2 + 7x - 8$$

$$0 = (x + 8)(x - 1)$$

$$x + 8 = 0 \qquad x - 1 = 0$$
$$x = -8 \qquad x = 1$$

Both −8 and 1 check as solutions.
The solutions are −8 and 1.

PROBLEM 1   Solve: $x + \dfrac{1}{3} = \dfrac{4}{3x}$

Solution   See page S21.

Occasionally, a value of a variable in a fractional equation makes one of the denominators zero. In this case, that value of the variable is not a solution of the equation.

Solve: $\dfrac{2x}{x - 2} = 1 + \dfrac{4}{x - 2}$

Find the LCM of the denominators.

The LCM is $x - 2$.

$$\frac{2x}{x - 2} = 1 + \frac{4}{x - 2}$$

Multiply each side of the equation by the LCM of the denominators.

$$(x - 2)\frac{2x}{x - 2} = (x - 2)\left(1 + \frac{4}{x - 2}\right)$$

Simplify using the Distributive Property.

$$(x - 2)\left(\frac{2x}{x - 2}\right) = (x - 2) \cdot 1 + (x - 2) \cdot \frac{4}{x - 2}$$

Solve for x.

$$2x = x - 2 + 4$$
$$2x = x + 2$$
$$x = 2$$

When x is replaced by 2, the denominators of $\dfrac{2x}{x - 2}$ and $\dfrac{4}{x - 2}$ are zero. Therefore, 2 is not a solution of the equation.

The equation has no solution.

EXAMPLE 2 Solve: $\dfrac{3x}{x-4} = 5 + \dfrac{12}{x-4}$

Solution $\dfrac{3x}{x-4} = 5 + \dfrac{12}{x-4}$ • **The LCM is $x - 4$.**

$$(x-4)\cdot\dfrac{3x}{x-4} = (x-4)\left(5 + \dfrac{12}{x-4}\right)$$

$$3x = (x-4)5 + 12$$

$$3x = 5x - 20 + 12$$

$$3x = 5x - 8$$

$$-2x = -8$$

$$x = 4$$

4 does not check as a solution.
The equation has no solution.

PROBLEM 2 Solve: $\dfrac{5x}{x+2} = 3 - \dfrac{10}{x+2}$

Solution   See page S22.

OBJECTIVE **2**   ## Solve proportions

Quantities such as 4 meters, 15 seconds, and 8 gallons are number quantities written with **units.** In these examples, the units are meters, seconds, and gallons.

A **ratio** is the quotient of two quantities that have the same unit.

The length of a living room is 16 ft, and the width is 12 ft. The ratio of the length to the width is written

$\dfrac{16\text{ ft}}{12\text{ ft}} = \dfrac{16}{12} = \dfrac{4}{3}$ A ratio is in simplest form when the two numbers do not have a common factor. Note that the units are not written.

A **rate** is the quotient of two quantities that have different units.

There are 2 lb of salt in 8 gal of water. The salt-to-water rate is

$\dfrac{2\text{ lb}}{8\text{ gal}} = \dfrac{1\text{ lb}}{4\text{ gal}}$ A rate is in simplest form when the two numbers do not have a common factor. The units are written as part of the rate.

A **proportion** is an equation that states the equality of two ratios or rates.

Examples of proportions are shown below.

$$\dfrac{30\text{ mi}}{4\text{ h}} = \dfrac{15\text{ mi}}{2\text{ h}} \qquad \dfrac{4}{6} = \dfrac{20}{30} \qquad \dfrac{3}{4} = \dfrac{x}{12}$$

Because a proportion is an equation containing fractions, the same method used to solve an equation containing fractions is used to solve a proportion. Multiply each side of the equation by the LCM of the denominators. Then solve for the variable.

■

Solve the proportion $\dfrac{4}{x} = \dfrac{2}{3}$.

$$\dfrac{4}{x} = \dfrac{2}{3}$$

Multiply each side of the proportion by the LCM of the denominators.

$$3x\left(\dfrac{4}{x}\right) = 3x\left(\dfrac{2}{3}\right)$$

$$12 = 2x$$

Solve the equation.

$$6 = x$$

The solution is 6.

■

EXAMPLE 3 Solve.   **A.** $\dfrac{8}{x+3} = \dfrac{4}{x}$ **B.** $\dfrac{6}{x+4} = \dfrac{12}{5x-13}$

Solution **A.** $\dfrac{8}{x+3} = \dfrac{4}{x}$

$$x(x+3)\dfrac{8}{x+3} = x(x+3)\dfrac{4}{x}$$ • **Multiply each side of the proportion by the LCM of the denominators.**

$$8x = (x+3)4$$

$$8x = 4x + 12$$

$$4x = 12$$

$$x = 3$$ • **Remember to check the solution because it is a fractional equation.**

The solution is 3.

B. $\dfrac{6}{x+4} = \dfrac{12}{5x-13}$

$$(5x-13)(x+4)\dfrac{6}{x+4} = (5x-13)(x+4)\dfrac{12}{5x-13}$$

$$(5x-13)6 = (x+4)12$$

$$30x - 78 = 12x + 48$$

$$18x - 78 = 48$$

$$18x = 126$$

$$x = 7$$

The solution is 7.

PROBLEM 3 Solve.   **A.** $\dfrac{2}{x+3} = \dfrac{6}{5x+5}$ **B.** $\dfrac{5}{2x-3} = \dfrac{10}{x+3}$

Solution See page S22.

OBJECTIVE 3   Applications of proportions

EXAMPLE 4 The monthly loan payment for a car is $29.50 for each $1000 borrowed. At this rate, find the monthly payment for a $9000 car loan.

Strategy To find the monthly payment, write and solve a proportion using P to represent the monthly car payment.

Solution

$$\frac{29.50}{1000} = \frac{P}{9000}$$

$$9000\left(\frac{29.50}{1000}\right) = 9000\left(\frac{P}{9000}\right)$$

$$265.50 = P$$

• **The monthly payments are in the numerators. The loan amounts are in the denominators.**

The monthly payment is $265.50.

PROBLEM 4 Nine ceramic tiles are required to tile a 4-square-foot area. At this rate, how many square feet can be tiled with 270 ceramic tiles?

Solution See page S22.

EXAMPLE 5 An investment of $1200 earns $96 each year. At the same rate, how much additional money must be invested to earn $128 each year?

Strategy To find the additional amount of money that must be invested, write and solve a proportion using x to represent the additional money. Then $1200 + x$ is the total amount invested.

Solution

$$\frac{1200}{96} = \frac{1200 + x}{128}$$

$$\frac{25}{2} = \frac{1200 + x}{128}$$

$$128\left(\frac{25}{2}\right) = 128\left(\frac{1200 + x}{128}\right)$$

$$1600 = 1200 + x$$

$$400 = x$$

• **The amounts invested are in the numerators. The amounts earned are in the denominators.**

• **Simplify** $\frac{1200}{96}$.

An additional $400 must be invested.

PROBLEM 5 Three ounces of a medication are required for a 120-pound adult. At the same rate, how many additional ounces of the medication are required for a 180-pound adult?

Solution See page S22.

OBJECTIVE **Problems involving similar triangles**

Similar objects have the same shape but not necessarily the same size. A tennis ball is similar to a basketball. A model ship is similar to an actual ship.

Similar objects have corresponding parts; for example, the rudder on the model ship corresponds to the rudder on the actual ship. The relationship between the sizes of each of the corresponding parts can be written as a ratio, and each ratio will be the same. If the rudder on the model ship is $\frac{1}{100}$ the size of the rudder on the actual ship, then the model wheelhouse is $\frac{1}{100}$ the size of the actual wheelhouse, the width of the model is $\frac{1}{100}$ the width of the actual ship, and so on.

The two triangles *ABC* and *DEF* shown at the right are similar triangles. Side *AB* corresponds to *DE*, side *BC* corresponds to *EF*, and side *AC* corresponds to *DF*. The height *CH* corresponds to the height *FK*. The ratios of corresponding parts are equal.

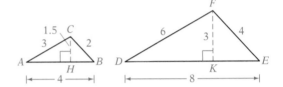

$$\frac{AB}{DE} = \frac{4}{8} = \frac{1}{2}, \quad \frac{AC}{DF} = \frac{3}{6} = \frac{1}{2}, \quad \frac{BC}{EF} = \frac{2}{4} = \frac{1}{2}, \quad \text{and} \quad \frac{CH}{FK} = \frac{1.5}{3} = \frac{1}{2}$$

Because the ratios of corresponding parts are equal, three proportions can be formed using the sides of the triangles.

$$\frac{AB}{DE} = \frac{AC}{DF}, \quad \frac{AB}{DE} = \frac{BC}{EF}, \quad \text{and} \quad \frac{AC}{DF} = \frac{BC}{EF}$$

Three proportions can also be formed by using the sides and heights of the triangles.

$$\frac{AB}{DE} = \frac{CH}{FK}, \quad \frac{AC}{DF} = \frac{CH}{FK}, \quad \text{and} \quad \frac{BC}{EF} = \frac{CH}{FK}$$

The corresponding angles in similar triangles are equal. Therefore,

$$\angle A = \angle D, \quad \angle B = \angle E, \quad \text{and} \quad \angle C = \angle F$$

Triangles *ABC* and *DEF* at the right are similar. Find the area of triangle *ABC*.

Solve a proportion to find
the height of triangle *ABC*.

$$\frac{AB}{DE} = \frac{CH}{FG}$$

$$\frac{5}{12} = \frac{CH}{3}$$

$$12 \cdot \frac{5}{12} = 12 \cdot \frac{CH}{3}$$

$$5 = 4(CH)$$

$$1.25 = CH$$

The height is 1.25 in. The
base is 5 in.

Use the formula for the area
of a triangle.

$$A = \frac{1}{2}bh = \frac{1}{2}(5)(1.25) = 3.125$$

The area of triangle *ABC* is 3.125 in².

It is also true that if the three angles of one triangle are equal, respectively, to
the three angles of another triangle, then the two triangles are similar.

A line segment $\overline{DE}$ is drawn parallel to the
base *AB* in the triangle at the right. $\angle x = \angle m$
and $\angle y = \angle n$ because corresponding angles
are equal. Because $\angle C = \angle C$, the three angles
of triangle *DEC* are equal, respectively, to the
three angles of triangle *ABC*. Triangle *DEC* is
similar to triangle *ABC*.

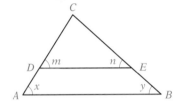

The sum of the three angles of a triangle is 180°. If two angles of one triangle
are equal to two angles of another triangle, then the third angles must be
equal. Thus we can say that if two angles of one triangle are equal to two angles
of another triangle, then the two triangles are similar.

The line segments $\overline{AB}$ and $\overline{CD}$ intersect at
point *O* in the figure at the right. Angles *C*
and *D* are right angles. Find the length of
DO.

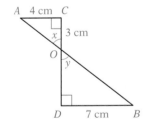

First determine whether triangle *AOC* is similar to triangle *BOD*.

Angle *C* = angle *D* because they are right angles. Angle *x* = angle *y*
because they are vertical angles. Therefore, triangle *AOC* is similar to
triangle *BOD* because two angles of one triangle are equal to two
angles of the other triangle.

Use a proportion to find the length of the unknown side.

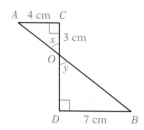

$$\frac{AC}{DB} = \frac{CO}{DO}$$

$$\frac{4}{7} = \frac{3}{DO}$$

$$7(DO)\frac{4}{7} = 7(DO)\frac{3}{DO}$$

$$4(DO) = 7(3)$$

$$4(DO) = 21$$

$$DO = 5.25$$

The length of DO is 5.25 cm.

EXAMPLE 6   In the figure at the right, $\overline{AB}$ is parallel to $\overline{DC}$, and angles B and D are right angles. $AB = 12$ m, $CD = 4$ m, and $AC = 18$ m. Find the length of CO.

Strategy   Triangle AOB is similar to triangle COD. Solve a proportion to find the length of CO. Let x represent the length of CO. Then $18 - x$ represents the length of AO.

Solution

$$\frac{CD}{AB} = \frac{CO}{AO}$$

$$\frac{4}{12} = \frac{x}{18 - x}$$

$$12(18 - x) \cdot \frac{4}{12} = 12(18 - x) \cdot \frac{x}{18 - x}$$

$$(18 - x)4 = 12x$$

$$72 - 4x = 12x$$

$$72 = 16x$$

$$4.5 = x$$

The length of CO is 4.5 m.

PROBLEM 6   In the figure at the right, $\overline{AB}$ is parallel to $\overline{DC}$, and angles A and D are right angles. $AB = 10$ cm, $CD = 4$ cm, and $DO = 3$ cm. Find the area of triangle AOB.

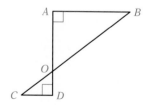

Solution   See page S22.

9.5 Concept Review

Determine whether the statement is always true, sometimes true, or never true.

1. The process of clearing denominators in an equation containing fractions is an application of the Multiplication Property of Equations.

2. If the denominator of a fraction is $x + 3$, then $x \neq 3$ for that fraction.

3. The first step in solving an equation containing fractions is to find the LCM of the denominators.

4. The solutions to an equation containing rational expressions must be checked because a solution might make one of the denominators equal to zero.

5. Suppose, after the clearing of denominators, a fractional equation results in a quadratic equation. Then the equation has two solutions.

6. Both sides of an equation containing fractions can be multiplied by the same number without changing the solution of the equation.

7. To solve a proportion, multiply each side of the proportion by the LCM of the denominators.

9.5 Exercises

1 Solve equations containing fractions

1. In solving an equation containing fractions, why do we first multiply each side of the equation by the LCM of the denominators?

2. After solving an equation containing fractions, why must we check the solution?

For Exercises 3 to 6, use the equation $\dfrac{7}{x} = \dfrac{3}{x - 4}$.

3. The first step in solving the equation is to clear denominators by multiplying each side of the equation by the LCM of the denominators _____?_____ and _____?_____. The LCM is _____?_____.

4. **a.** When you multiply the left side of the equation by the LCM $x(x - 4)$, the left side simplifies to _____?_____.
   b. When you multiply the right side of the equation by the LCM $x(x - 4)$, the right side simplifies to _____?_____.

5. Use your answers to Exercise 2 to write the equation that results from clearing the denominators: ___?___ = ___?___. The solution of this equation is ___?___.

6. The solution of a rational equation must be checked in the original equation. To check the solution you found in Exercise 3 in the original equation, substitute ___?___ for x in the original equation: $\dfrac{7}{7} = \dfrac{3}{7-4}$ simplifies to ___?___ = ___?___. The solution checks.

When a proposed solution of a rational equation does not check in the original equation, it is because it results in an expression involving division by zero. For each equation, state the values of x that would result in division by zero when substituted into the original equation.

7. $\dfrac{1}{x+5} = \dfrac{x}{x-3} + \dfrac{2}{x^2+2x-15}$

8. $\dfrac{3}{x-9} = \dfrac{1}{x^2-9x} + 2$

9. $\dfrac{6x}{x+1} - \dfrac{x}{x-2} = 4$

Solve.

10. $2 + \dfrac{5}{x} = 7$

11. $3 + \dfrac{8}{n} = 5$

12. $1 - \dfrac{9}{x} = 4$

13. $3 - \dfrac{12}{x} = 7$

14. $\dfrac{2}{y} + 5 = 9$

15. $\dfrac{6}{x} + 3 = 11$

16. $\dfrac{4x}{x-4} + 5 = \dfrac{5x}{x-4}$

17. $\dfrac{2x}{x+2} - 5 = \dfrac{7x}{x+2}$

18. $2 + \dfrac{3}{a-3} = \dfrac{a}{a-3}$

19. $\dfrac{x}{x+4} = 3 - \dfrac{4}{x+4}$

20. $\dfrac{x}{x-1} = \dfrac{8}{x+2}$

21. $\dfrac{x}{x+12} = \dfrac{1}{x+5}$

22. $\dfrac{2x}{x+4} = \dfrac{3}{x-1}$

23. $\dfrac{5}{3n-8} = \dfrac{n}{n+2}$

24. $x + \dfrac{6}{x-2} = \dfrac{3x}{x-2}$

25. $x - \dfrac{6}{x-3} = \dfrac{2x}{x-3}$

26. $\dfrac{x}{x+2} + \dfrac{2}{x-2} = \dfrac{x+6}{x^2-4}$

27. $\dfrac{x}{x+4} = \dfrac{11}{x^2-16} + 2$

28. $\dfrac{8}{y} = \dfrac{2}{y-2} + 1$

29. $\dfrac{8}{r} + \dfrac{3}{r-1} = 3$

2 Solve proportions

30. The quotient of two quantities that have the same unit is called a ___?___. The quotient of two quantities that have different units is called a ___?___.

31. An equation that states the equality of two ratios or rates is called a _____?_____.

Solve.

32. $\dfrac{x}{12} = \dfrac{3}{4}$

33. $\dfrac{6}{x} = \dfrac{2}{3}$

34. $\dfrac{4}{9} = \dfrac{x}{27}$

35. $\dfrac{16}{9} = \dfrac{64}{x}$

36. $\dfrac{x+3}{12} = \dfrac{5}{6}$

37. $\dfrac{3}{5} = \dfrac{x-4}{10}$

38. $\dfrac{18}{x+4} = \dfrac{9}{5}$

39. $\dfrac{2}{11} = \dfrac{20}{x-3}$

40. $\dfrac{2}{x} = \dfrac{4}{x+1}$

41. $\dfrac{16}{x-2} = \dfrac{8}{x}$

42. $\dfrac{x+3}{4} = \dfrac{x}{8}$

43. $\dfrac{x-6}{3} = \dfrac{x}{5}$

44. $\dfrac{2}{x-1} = \dfrac{6}{2x+1}$

45. $\dfrac{9}{x+2} = \dfrac{3}{x-2}$

46. $\dfrac{2x}{7} = \dfrac{x-2}{14}$

47. True or false? If $\dfrac{a}{b} = \dfrac{c}{d}$, then $\dfrac{d}{b} = \dfrac{c}{a}$.

48. True or false? If $\dfrac{a}{b} = \dfrac{c}{d}$, then $\dfrac{b}{a} = \dfrac{d}{c}$.

3 Applications of proportions

49. The scale on a map shows that a distance of 3 cm on the map represents an actual distance of 10 mi. This rate can be expressed as the quotient $\dfrac{?}{?}$ or as the quotient $\dfrac{?}{?}$.

50. Let x be the distance (in miles) represented by 12 cm on the map described in Exercise 49. Use a proportion to find x.

$\dfrac{10}{3} = \dfrac{?}{?}$ • Write the proportion so that each side is the ratio of miles to centimeters.

$(12)\left(\dfrac{10}{3}\right) = (12)\left(\dfrac{x}{12}\right)$ • Multiply each side of the proportion by _____?_____, the LCM of the denominators.

$\underline{\quad?\quad} = x$ • Simplify.

12 cm on the map represents _____?_____ mi.

51. Could the proportion used in Exercise 50 have been written so that each side was the ratio of centimeters to miles, instead of miles to centimeters?

52. On the map described in Exercise 49, would a distance of 8 cm represent an actual distance that is greater than 30 mi or less than 30 mi?

53. Elections An exit poll showed that 4 out of every 7 voters cast a ballot in favor of an amendment to a city charter. At this rate, how many people voted in favor of the amendment if 35,000 people voted?

54. Business A quality control inspector found 3 defective transistors in a shipment of 500 transistors. At this rate, how many transistors would be defective in a shipment of 2000 transistors?

55. Construction An air conditioning specialist recommends 2 air vents for every 300 ft² of floor space. At this rate, how many air vents are required for an office building of 21,000 ft²?

56. Television In a city of 25,000 homes, a survey was taken to determine the number with cable television. Of the 300 homes surveyed, 210 had cable television. Estimate the number of homes in the city that have cable television.

57. Cooking A simple syrup is made by dissolving 2 c of sugar in $\frac{2}{3}$ c of boiling water. At this rate, how many cups of sugar are required for 2 c of boiling water?

58. Energy The lighting for a billboard is provided by solar energy. If 3 energy panels generate 10 watts of power, how many panels are needed to provide 600 watts of power?

59. Conservation As part of a conservation effort for a lake, 40 fish were caught, tagged, and then released. Later, 80 fish were caught from the lake. Four of these 80 fish were found to have tags. Estimate the number of fish in the lake.

60. Business A company will accept a shipment of 10,000 computer disks if there are 2 or fewer defects in a sample of 100 randomly chosen disks. Assume that there are 300 defective disks in the shipment and that the rate of defective disks in the sample is the same as the rate in the shipment. Will the shipment be accepted?

61. Business A company will accept a shipment of 20,000 precision bearings if there are 3 or fewer defects in a sample of 100 randomly chosen bearings. Assume that there are 400 defective bearings in the shipment and that the rate of defective bearings in the sample is the same as the rate in the shipment. Will the shipment be accepted?

62. Art Leonardo da Vinci measured various distances on the human body in order to make accurate drawings. He determined that in general, the ratio of the kneeling height of a person to his or her standing height is $\frac{3}{4}$. Using this ratio, determine the standing height of a person who has a kneeling height of 48 in.

63. **Art** In one of Leonardo da Vinci's notebooks, he wrote that ". . . from the top to the bottom of the chin is the sixth part of a face, and it is the fifty-fourth part of the man." Suppose the distance from the top to the bottom of a person's chin is 1.25 in. Using da Vinci's measurements, find the height of the person.

64. **Cartography** On a map, two cities are $2\frac{5}{8}$ in. apart. If $\frac{3}{8}$ in. on the map represents 25 mi, find the number of miles between the two cities.

65. **Cartography** On a map, two cities are $5\frac{5}{8}$ in. apart. If $\frac{3}{4}$ in. on the map represents 100 mi, find the number of miles between the two cities.

66. **Rocketry** The engine of a small rocket burns 170,000 lb of fuel in 1 min. At this rate, how many pounds of fuel does the rocket burn in 45 s?

67. **Construction** To conserve energy and still allow for as much natural lighting as possible, an architect suggests that the ratio of the area of a window to the area of the total wall surface be 5 to 12. Using this ratio, determine the recommended area of a window to be installed in a wall that measures 8 ft by 12 ft.

68. **Paint Mixtures** A green paint is created by mixing 3 parts of yellow with every 5 parts of blue. How many gallons of yellow paint are needed to make 60 gal of this green paint?

69. **Food Industry** A soft drink is made by mixing 4 parts of carbonated water with every 3 parts of syrup. How many milliliters of carbonated water are in 280 ml of soft drink?

70. **Redecorating** A painter estimates that 5 gal of paint will cover 1200 ft² of wall surface. How many additional gallons are required to cover 1680 ft²?

71. **Agriculture** A 50-acre field yields 1100 bushels of wheat annually. How many additional acres must be planted so that the annual yield will be 1320 bushels?

72. **Taxes** The sales tax on a car that sold for $12,000 is $780. At the same rate, how much higher is the sales tax on a car that sells for $13,500?

73. **Catering** A caterer estimates that 5 gal of coffee will serve 50 people. How much additional coffee is necessary to serve 70 people?

4 Problems involving similar triangles

For Exercises 74 and 75, use the pair of similar triangles shown at the right. Triangle *PQR* is similar to triangle *XYZ*.

74. **a.** The corresponding part for side *RP* is ___?___.
    b. The corresponding part for side *YX* is ___?___.
    c. The corresponding part for ∠*X* is ___?___.

75. a. Complete this proportion: $\dfrac{QR}{?} = \dfrac{PR}{XZ}$.

   b. Complete this equality: $\angle Z = \underline{\quad ? \quad}$.

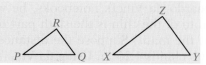

Solve. Triangles *ABC* and *DEF* in Exercises 76 to 83 are similar. Round answers to the nearest tenth.

76. Find side *AC*.

77. Find side *DE*.

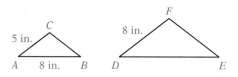

78. Find the height of triangle *ABC*.

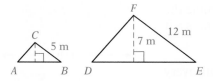

79. Find the height of triangle *DEF*.

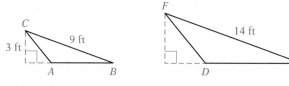

80. Find the perimeter of triangle *DEF*.

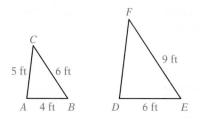

81. Find the perimeter of triangle *ABC*.

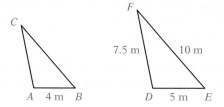

82. Find the area of triangle *ABC*.

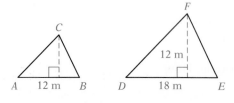

83. Find the area of triangle *ABC*.

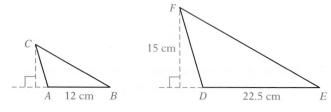

84. True or false? If the ratio of the corresponding sides of two similar triangles is $\frac{2}{3}$, the ratio of the perimeters of the two triangles is also $\frac{2}{3}$.

85. True or false? If the ratio of the corresponding sides of two similar triangles is $\frac{5}{4}$, the ratio of the areas of the two triangles is also $\frac{5}{4}$.

86. Look at the diagram in Exercise 88, in which BD is parallel to AE.
   a. Triangle CBD is similar to triangle __?__.
   b. Complete this proportion: $\dfrac{BD}{AE} = \dfrac{CD}{\underline{\;?\;}}$.

87. Look at the diagram in Exercise 92.
   a. Triangle MNO is similar to triangle __?__.
   b. Complete this proportion: $\dfrac{OP}{\underline{\;?\;}} = \dfrac{PQ}{NM}$.

88. Given $\overline{BD}\|\overline{AE}$, BD measures 5 cm, AE measures 8 cm, and AC measures 10 cm, find the length of BC.

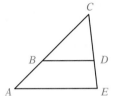

89. Given $\overline{AC}\|\overline{DE}$, BD measures 8 m, AD measures 12 m, and BE measures 6 m, find the length of BC.

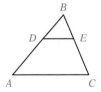

90. Given $\overline{DE}\|\overline{AC}$, DE measures 6 in., AC measures 10 in., and AB measures 15 in., find the length of DA.

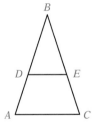

91. Given $\overline{MP}$ and $\overline{NQ}$ intersect at O, NO measures 25 ft, MO measures 20 ft, and PO measures 8 ft, find the length of QO.

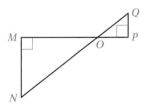

92. Given $\overline{MP}$ and $\overline{NQ}$ intersect at O, NO measures 24 cm, MN measures 10 cm, MP measures 39 cm, and QO measures 12 cm, find the length of OP.

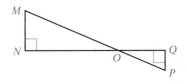

93. Given $\overline{MQ}$ and $\overline{NP}$ intersect at O, NO measures 12 m, MN measures 9 m, PQ measures 3 m, and MQ measures 20 m, find the perimeter of triangle OPQ.

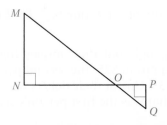

94. Similar triangles can be used as an indirect way to measure inaccessible distances. The diagram at the right represents a river of width DC. The triangles AOB and DOC are similar. The distances AB, BO, and OC can be measured. Find the width of the river.

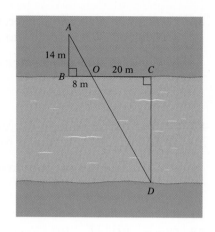

95. The sun's rays cast a shadow as shown in the diagram at the right. Find the height of the flagpole. Write the answer in terms of feet.

9.5 Applying Concepts

Solve.

96. $\dfrac{2}{3}(x + 2) - \dfrac{x + 1}{6} = \dfrac{1}{2}$

97. $\dfrac{3}{4}a = \dfrac{1}{2}(3 - a) + \dfrac{a - 2}{4}$

98. $\dfrac{x}{2x^2 - x - 1} = \dfrac{3}{x^2 - 1} + \dfrac{3}{2x + 1}$

99. $\dfrac{x + 1}{x^2 + x - 2} = \dfrac{x + 2}{x^2 - 1} + \dfrac{3}{x + 2}$

100. Number Problem The sum of a number and its reciprocal is $\dfrac{26}{5}$. Find the number.

101. Number Problem The sum of the multiplicative inverses of two consecutive integers is $-\dfrac{7}{12}$. Find the integers.

102. Number Problem The denominator of a fraction is 2 more than the numerator. If both the numerator and denominator of the fraction are increased by 3, the new fraction is $\dfrac{4}{5}$. Find the original fraction.

103. Lotteries Three people put their money together to buy lottery tickets. The first person put in $25, the second person put in $30, and the third person put in $35. One of their tickets was a winning ticket. If they won $4.5 million, what was the first person's share of the winnings?

104. sports A basketball player has made 5 out of every 6 foul shots attempted. If 42 foul shots were missed in the player's career, how many foul shots were made in the player's career?

105. Photography The "sitting fee" for school pictures is $4. If 10 photos cost $10, including the sitting fee, what would 24 photos cost, including the sitting fee?

106. Fundraising No one belongs to both the Math Club and the Photography Club, but the two clubs join to hold a car wash. Ten members of the Math Club and 6 members of the Photography Club participate. The profits from the car wash are $120. If each club's profits are proportional to the number of members participating, what share of the profits does the Math Club receive?

107. History Eratosthenes, the fifth librarian of Alexandria (230 B.C.), was familiar with certain astronomical data that enabled him to calculate the circumference of Earth by using a proportion. He knew that on a midsummer day, the sun was directly overhead at Syene, as shown in the diagram. At the same time, at Alexandria, the sun was at a 7.5° angle from the zenith. The distance from Syene to Alexandria was 5000 stadia, or about 520 mi. Eratosthenes reasoned that the ratio of the 7.5° angle to one revolution was equal to the ratio of the arc length of 520 mi to the circumference of Earth. From this, he wrote and solved a proportion.
a. What did Eratosthenes calculate to be the circumference of Earth?

b. Find the difference between his calculation and the accepted value of 24,800 mi.

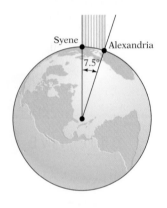

108. Population The table below shows the projected population of people age 65 and older and the projected total population of the United States each decade from 2010 to 2050.

Year	Population 65+, in thousands	Total Population, in thousands
2010	40,243	308,936
2020	54,632	335,805
2030	71,453	363,584
2040	80,049	391,948
2050	86,705	419,854

a. What is the percent increase, for each 10-year period, in the population of people age 65 and older? Round to the nearest tenth of a percent.

b. What is the percent increase, for each 10-year period, in the total population of the United States?

c. Are there any 10-year periods during which the total population of the United States is increasing more rapidly (at a faster rate) than the population of people age 65 and older?

d. Many people, as they age, need more medical care. The population of people in the 20-to-44-year age group who provide that care is given below. For each decade, find the ratio of the number of potential caregivers to the number of people in the 65 and older age group. Round to the nearest whole number.

Year	2010	2020	2030	2040	2050
Population 20–44, in millions	104,444	108,632	114,747	121,659	130,897

e. Write a sentence that explains the meaning of the ratios you found in part d. Are the ratios increasing or decreasing?

f. Write a few sentences that summarize the calculations in parts a through d.

9.6 Literal Equations

OBJECTIVE **1**   **Solve a literal equation for one of the variables**

A **literal equation** is an equation that contains more than one variable. Examples of literal equations are shown at the right.

$$2x + 3y = 6$$
$$4w - 2x + z = 0$$

Formulas are used to express a relationship among physical quantities. A **formula** is a literal equation that states rules about measurements. Examples of formulas are shown below.

$$\frac{1}{R_1} + \frac{1}{R_2} = \frac{1}{R} \qquad \text{(Physics)}$$
$$s = a + (n - 1)d \qquad \text{(Mathematics)}$$
$$A = P + Prt \qquad \text{(Business)}$$

The Addition and Multiplication Properties can be used to solve a literal equation for one of the variables. The goal is to rewrite the equation so that the letter being solved for is alone on one side of the equation and all numbers and other variables are on the other side.

■   Solve $A = P(1 + i)$ for i.

The goal is to rewrite the equation so that i is on one side of the equation and all other variables are on the other side.

$$A = P(1 + i)$$

Use the Distributive Property to remove parentheses.

$$A = P + Pi$$

Subtract P from each side of the equation.

$$A - P = P - P + Pi$$
$$A - P = Pi$$

Divide each side of the equation by P.

$$\frac{A - P}{P} = \frac{Pi}{P}$$

$$\frac{A - P}{P} = i$$

EXAMPLE 1 **A.** Solve $I = \dfrac{E}{R + r}$ for R.   **B.** Solve $L = a(1 + ct)$ for c.

Solution **A.**
$$I = \frac{E}{R + r}$$

$$(R + r)I = (R + r)\frac{E}{R + r}$$

$$RI + rI = E$$

$$RI + rI - rI = E - rI$$

$$RI = E - rI$$

$$\frac{RI}{I} = \frac{E - rI}{I}$$

$$R = \frac{E - rI}{I}$$

B.
$$L = a(1 + ct)$$

$$L = a + act$$

$$L - a = a - a + act$$

$$L - a = act$$

$$\frac{L - a}{at} = \frac{act}{at}$$

$$\frac{L - a}{at} = c$$

PROBLEM 1 **A.** Solve $s = \dfrac{A + L}{2}$ for L.   **B.** Solve $S = a + (n - 1)d$ for n.

Solution See page S22.

EXAMPLE 2 Solve $S = C - rC$ for C.

Solution
$$S = C - rC$$

$$S = C(1 - r) \qquad \bullet \text{ Factor } C \text{ from } C - rC.$$

$$\frac{S}{1 - r} = \frac{C(1 - r)}{1 - r} \qquad \bullet \text{ Divide each side of the equation by } 1 - r.$$

$$\frac{S}{1 - r} = C$$

PROBLEM 2 Solve $S = rS + C$ for S.

Solution See page S23.

9.6 Concept Review

Determine whether the statement is always true, sometimes true, or never true.

1. An equation that contains more than one variable is a literal equation.

2. The linear equation $y = 4x - 5$ is not a literal equation.

3. Literal equations are solved using the same properties of equations that are used to solve equations in one variable.

4. In solving a literal equation, the goal is to get the variable being solved for alone on one side of the equation and all numbers and other variables on the other side of the equation.

5. In solving $L = a(1 + ct)$ for c, you need to use the Distributive Property. In solving $S = C - rC$ for C, you need to factor.

6. We can divide both sides of a literal equation by the same nonzero expression.

9.6 Exercises

1 Solve a literal equation for one of the variables

Solve the formula for the variable given.

1. $A = \frac{1}{2}bh; h$ (Geometry)

2. $P = a + b + c; b$ (Geometry)

3. $d = rt; t$ (Physics)

4. $E = IR; R$ (Physics)

5. $PV = nRT; T$ (Chemistry)

6. $A = bh; h$ (Geometry)

7. $P = 2L + 2W; L$ (Geometry)

8. $F = \frac{9}{5}C + 32; C$ (Temperature conversion)

9. $A = \frac{1}{2}h(b_1 + b_2); b_1$ (Geometry)

10. $C = \frac{5}{9}(F - 32); F$ (Temperature conversion)

11. $V = \frac{1}{3}Ah; h$ (Geometry)

12. $P = R - C; C$ (Business)

13. $R = \frac{C - S}{t}; S$ (Business)

14. $P = \frac{R - C}{n}; R$ (Business)

15. $A = P + Prt; P$ (Business)

16. $T = fm - gm; m$ (Engineering)

17. $A = Sw + w; w$ (Physics)

18. $a = S - Sr; S$ (Mathematics)

19. When asked to solve $A = P(1 + i)$ for i, one student answered $i = \dfrac{A}{P} - 1$ and another student answered $i = \dfrac{A - P}{P}$. Are the two answers equivalent?

20. When asked to solve $A = P(1 + i)$ for i, one student answered $i = -\dfrac{P - A}{P}$ and another student answered $i = \dfrac{A - P}{P}$. Are the two answers equivalent?

9.6 Applying Concepts

Geometry The surface area of a right circular cylinder is given by the formula $S = 2\pi rh + 2\pi r^2$, where r is the radius of the base and h is the height of the cylinder.

21. **a.** Solve the formula $S = 2\pi rh + 2\pi r^2$ for h.
 b. Use your answer to part a to find the height of a right circular cylinder when the surface area is 12π in^2 and the radius is 1 in.
 c. Use your answer to part a to find the height of a right circular cylinder when the surface area is 24π in^2 and the radius is 2 in.

1 in.

$S = 12\pi$ in^2

Business Break-even analysis is a method used to determine the sales volume required for a company to break even, or experience neither a profit nor a loss, on the sale of its product. The break-even point represents the number of units that must be made and sold for income from sales to equal the cost of producing the product. The break-even point can be calculated using the formula $B = \dfrac{F}{S - V}$, where F is the fixed costs, S is the selling price per unit, and V is the variable costs per unit.

22. **a.** Solve the formula $B = \dfrac{F}{S - V}$ for S.
 b. Use your answer to part a to find the selling price per desk required for a company to break even. The fixed costs are $40,000, the variable costs per desk are $160, and the company plans to make and sell 200 desks.
 c. Use your answer to part a to find the selling price per camera required for a company to break even. The fixed costs are $30,000, the variable costs per camera are $100, and the company plans to make and sell 600 cameras.

Business When markup is based on selling price, the selling price of a product is given by the formula $S = C + rC$, where C is the cost of the product and r is the markup rate.

23. **a.** Solve the formula $S = C + rC$ for r.
 b. Use your answer to part a to find the markup rate on a tennis racket when the cost is $108 and the selling price is $180.
 c. Use your answer to part a to find the markup rate on a car radio when the cost is $120 and the selling price is $172.

Electricity Resistors are used to control the flow of current. The total resistance of two resistors in a circuit can be given by the formula $R = \dfrac{1}{\dfrac{1}{R_1} + \dfrac{1}{R_2}}$, where

Generator

R_1 and R_2 are the resistances of the two resistors in the circuit. Resistance is measured in ohms.

24. **a.** Solve the formula $R = \dfrac{1}{\dfrac{1}{R_1} + \dfrac{1}{R_2}}$ for R_1.

  b. Use your answer to part a to find the resistance in R_1 if the resistance in R_2 is 30 ohms and the total resistance is 12 ohms.

  c. Use your answer to part a to find the resistance in R_1 if the resistance in R_2 is 15 ohms and the total resistance is 6 ohms.

9.7 Application Problems

OBJECTIVE 1   Work problems

If a painter can paint a room in 4 h, then in 1 h the painter can paint $\frac{1}{4}$ of the room. The painter's rate of work is $\frac{1}{4}$ of the room each hour. The **rate of work** is that part of a task that is completed in 1 unit of time.

A pipe can fill a tank in 30 min. This pipe can fill $\frac{1}{30}$ of the tank in 1 min. The rate of work is $\frac{1}{30}$ of the tank each minute. If a second pipe can fill the tank in x min, the rate of work for the second pipe is $\frac{1}{x}$ of the tank each minute.

In solving a work problem, the goal is to determine the time it takes to complete a task. The basic equation that is used to solve work problems is

Rate of work · Time worked = Part of task completed

For example, if a faucet can fill a sink in 6 min, then in 5 min the faucet will fill $\frac{1}{6} \cdot 5 = \frac{5}{6}$ of the sink. In 5 min, the faucet completes $\frac{5}{6}$ of the task.

Solve: A painter can paint a ceiling in 60 min. The painter's apprentice can paint the same ceiling in 90 min. How long will it take them to paint the ceiling if they work together?

> **STRATEGY**   **for solving a work problem**
>
> ▶ For each person or machine, write a numerical or variable expression for the rate of work, the time worked, and the part of the task completed. The results can be recorded in a table.

Unknown time to paint the ceiling working together: t

	Rate of work	·	Time worked	=	Part of task completed
Painter	$\dfrac{1}{60}$	·	t	=	$\dfrac{t}{60}$
Apprentice	$\dfrac{1}{90}$	·	t	=	$\dfrac{t}{90}$

▶ Determine how the parts of the task completed are related. Use the fact that the sum of the parts of the task completed must equal 1, the complete task.

$$\frac{t}{60} + \frac{t}{90} = 1$$

• The part of the task completed by the painter plus the part of the task completed by the apprentice must equal 1.

$$180\left(\frac{t}{60} + \frac{t}{90}\right) = 180 \cdot 1$$

• Multiply each side of the equation by the LCM of 60 and 90.

$$3t + 2t = 180$$
$$5t = 180$$
$$t = 36$$

Working together, they will paint the ceiling in 36 min.

EXAMPLE 1 A small water pipe takes four times longer to fill a tank than does a large water pipe. With both pipes open, it takes 3 h to fill the tank. Find the time it would take the small pipe, working alone, to fill the tank.

Strategy ▶ Time for large pipe to fill the tank: t

▶ Time for small pipe to fill the tank: $4t$

Fills tank in $4t$ hours

Fills tank in t hours

Fills $\frac{3}{4t}$ of the tank in 3 hours

Fills $\frac{3}{t}$ of the tank in 3 hours

	Rate	Time	Part
Small pipe	$\dfrac{1}{4t}$	3	$\dfrac{3}{4t}$
Large pipe	$\dfrac{1}{t}$	3	$\dfrac{3}{t}$

▶ The sum of the parts of the task completed must equal 1.

Solution

$$\frac{3}{4t} + \frac{3}{t} = 1$$

• The part of the task completed by the small pipe plus the part of the task completed by the large pipe must equal 1.

$$4t\left(\frac{3}{4t} + \frac{3}{t}\right) = 4t \cdot 1$$

$$3 + 12 = 4t$$

$$15 = 4t$$

$$\frac{15}{4} = t$$

• t is the time for the large pipe to fill the tank.

$$4t = 4\left(\frac{15}{4}\right) = 15$$

• Substitute the value of t into the variable expression for the time for the small pipe to fill the tank.

The small pipe, working alone, takes 15 h to fill the tank.

PROBLEM 1   Two computer printers that work at the same rate are working together to print the payroll checks for a corporation. After they work together for 3 h, one of the printers quits. The second requires 2 more hours to complete the checks. Find the time it would take one printer, working alone, to print the checks.

■ **Solution**   See page S23.

OBJECTIVE 2   **Uniform motion problems**

A car that travels constantly in a straight line at 30 mph is in uniform motion. When an object is in **uniform motion**, its speed does not change.

The basic equation used to solve uniform motion problems is

Distance = Rate · Time

An alternative form of this equation is written by solving the equation for time:

$$\frac{\textbf{Distance}}{\textbf{Rate}} = \textbf{Time}$$

This form of the equation is useful when the total time of travel for two objects is known or the times of travel for two objects are equal.

Solve: The speed of a boat in still water is 20 mph. The boat traveled 120 mi down a river in the same amount of time it took the boat to travel 80 mi up the river. Find the rate of the river's current.

STRATEGY   for solving a uniform motion problem

▶ For each object, write a numerical or variable expression for the distance, rate, and time. The results can be recorded in a table.

The unknown rate of the river's current: r

Take Note

Use the information given in the problem to fill in the distance and rate columns of the table. Fill in the time column by dividing the two expressions you wrote in each row.

	Distance	÷	Rate	=	Time
Down river	120	÷	$20 + r$	=	$\dfrac{120}{20 + r}$
Up river	80	÷	$20 - r$	=	$\dfrac{80}{20 - r}$

▶ Determine how the times traveled by the two objects are related. For example, it may be known that the times are equal, or the total time may be known.

$$\frac{120}{20 + r} = \frac{80}{20 - r}$$

$$(20 + r)(20 - r)\frac{120}{20 + r} = (20 + r)(20 - r)\frac{80}{20 - r}$$

$$(20 - r)120 = (20 + r)80$$

$$2400 - 120r = 1600 + 80r$$

$$-200r = -800$$

$$r = 4$$

• The time spent traveling down the river is equal to the time spent traveling up the river.

The rate of the river's current is 4 mph.

EXAMPLE 2   A cyclist rode the first 20 mi of a trip at a constant rate. For the next 16 mi, the cyclist reduced the speed by 2 mph. The total time for the 36 mi was 4 h. Find the rate of the cyclist for each leg of the trip.

Strategy   ▶ Rate for the first 20 mi: r

▶ Rate for the next 16 mi: $r - 2$

20 mi   16 mi

36 mi in 4 h

	Distance	Rate	Time
First 20 mi	20	r	$\dfrac{20}{r}$
Next 16 mi	16	$r - 2$	$\dfrac{16}{r - 2}$

▶ The total time for the trip was 4 h.

Solution

$$\frac{20}{r} + \frac{16}{r - 2} = 4$$

$$r(r - 2)\left[\frac{20}{r} + \frac{16}{r - 2}\right] = r(r - 2) \cdot 4$$

$$(r - 2)20 + 16r = (r^2 - 2r)4$$

$$20r - 40 + 16r = 4r^2 - 8r$$

$$36r - 40 = 4r^2 - 8r$$

$$0 = 4r^2 - 44r + 40$$

$$0 = 4(r^2 - 11r + 10)$$

$$0 = r^2 - 11r + 10$$

$$0 = (r - 10)(r - 1)$$

$$r - 10 = 0 \qquad r - 1 = 0$$

$$r = 10 \qquad\quad r = 1$$

• The time spent riding the first 20 mi plus the time spent riding the next 16 mi is equal to 4 h.

• This is a quadratic equation.

• Divide each side by 4.
• Solve by factoring.

$$r - 2 = 10 - 2 \qquad r - 2 = 1 - 2$$
$$= 8 \qquad\qquad\quad = -1$$

• **Find the rate for the last 16 mi. The solution $r = 1$ mph is not possible, because the rate on the last 16 mi would be -1 mph.**

10 mph was the rate for the first 20 mi.
8 mph was the rate for the next 16 mi.

PROBLEM 2   The total time for a sailboat to sail back and forth across a lake 6 km wide was 3 h. The rate sailing back was twice the rate sailing across the lake. Find the rate of the sailboat going across the lake.

Solution   See page S23.

9.7   Concept Review

Determine whether the statement is always true, sometimes true, or never true.

1. The work problems in this section require use of the equation
Rate of work · Time worked = 1.

2. If it takes a janitorial crew 5 h to clean a company's offices, then in x hours the crew has completed $\dfrac{x}{5}$ of the job.

3. If it takes an automotive crew x min to service a car, then the rate of work is $\dfrac{1}{x}$ of the job each minute.

4. If only two people worked on a job and together they completed it, and one person completed $\dfrac{t}{30}$ of the job and the other person completed $\dfrac{t}{20}$ of the job, then $\dfrac{t}{30} + \dfrac{t}{20} = 1$.

5. Uniform motion problems are based on the equation
Distance · Rate = Time.

6. If a plane flies 300 mph in calm air and the rate of the wind is r mph, then the rate of the plane flying with the wind can be represented as $300 - r$, and the rate of the plane flying against the wind can be represented as $300 + r$.

9.7 Exercises

1 Work problems

1. Explain the meaning of the phrase "rate of work."

2. a. If $\frac{2}{5}$ of a room can be painted in 1 h, what is the rate of work?

b. At the same rate, how long will it take to paint the entire room?

3. One electrician can do a wiring job in 10 h. It would take the electrician's assistant 12 h to complete the same wiring job. Let t represent the amont of time it would take the electrician and the assistant to complete the job if they worked together. Complete the following table.

	Rate of work	·	Time worked	=	Part of task completed
Electrician	?	·	?	=	?
Assistant	?	·	?	=	?

4. Refer to the situation presented in Exercise 3. When the wiring job is finished, the "part of task completed" is the whole task, so the sum of the parts completed by the electrician and the assistant is ___?___. Use this fact and the expressions in the table in Exercise 3 to write an equation that can be solved to find the amount of time it takes for the electrician and the assistant to complete the job together: ___?___ + ___?___ = ___?___.

5. A park has two sprinklers that are used to fill a fountain. One sprinkler can fill the fountain in 3 h, whereas the second sprinkler can fill the fountain in 6 h. How long will it take to fill the fountain with both sprinklers operating?

6. One grocery clerk can stock a shelf in 20 min. A second clerk requires 30 min to stock the same shelf. How long would it take to stock the shelf if the two clerks worked together?

7. One person with a skiploader requires 12 h to transfer a large quantity of earth. With a larger skiploader, the same amount of earth can be transferred in 4 h. How long would it take to transfer the earth if both skiploaders were operated together?

8. It takes Doug 6 days to reroof a house. If Doug's son helps him, the job can be completed in 4 days. How long would it take Doug's son, working alone, to do the job?

9. One computer can solve a complex prime factorization problem in 75 h. A second computer can solve the same problem in 50 h. How long would it take both computers, working together, to solve the problem?

10. A new machine makes 10,000 aluminum cans three times faster than an older machine. With both machines operating, it takes 9 h to make 10,000 cans. How long would it take the new machine, working alone, to make 10,000 cans?

11. A small air conditioner can cool a room 5°F in 60 min. A larger air conditioner can cool the room 5°F in 40 min. How long would it take to cool the room 5°F with both air conditioners working?

12. One printing press can print the first edition of a book in 55 min. A second printing press requires 66 min to print the same number of copies. How long would it take to print the first edition of the book with both presses operating?

13. Two welders working together can complete a job in 6 h. One of the welders, working alone, can complete the task in 10 h. How long would it take the second welder, working alone, to complete the task?

14. Working together, Pat and Chris can reseal a driveway in 6 h. Working alone, Pat can reseal the driveway in 15 h. How long would it take Chris, working alone, to reseal the driveway?

15. Two oil pipelines can fill a small tank in 30 min. Using one of the pipelines would require 45 min to fill the tank. How long would it take the second pipeline, working alone, to fill the tank?

16. A cement mason can construct a retaining wall in 8 h. A second mason requires 12 h to do the same job. After working alone for 4 h, the first mason quits. How long will it take the second mason to complete the wall?

17. With two reapers operating, a field can be harvested in 1 h. If only the newer reaper is used, the crop can be harvested in 1.5 h. How long would it take to harvest the field using only the older reaper?

18. A manufacturer of prefabricated homes has the company's employees work in teams. Team 1 can erect the Silvercrest model in 15 h. Team 2 can erect the same model in 10 h. How long would it take for Team 1 and Team 2, working together, to erect the Silvercrest model home?

19. One computer technician can wire a modem in 4 h. A second technician requires 6 h to do the same job. After working alone for 2 h, the first technician quits. How long will it take the second technician to complete the wiring?

20. A wallpaper hanger requires 2 h to hang the wallpaper on one wall of a room. A second wallpaper hanger requires 4 h to hang the same amount of wallpaper. The first wallpaper hanger works alone for 1 h and then quits. How long will it take the second hanger, working alone, to finish papering the wall?

21. A large heating unit and a small heating unit are being used to heat the water in a pool. The large unit, working alone, requires 8 h to heat the pool. After both units have been operating for 2 h, the large unit is turned off. The small unit requires 9 more hours to heat the pool. How long would it take the small unit, working alone, to heat the pool?

22. Two machines fill cereal boxes at the same rate. After the two machines work together for 7 h, one machine breaks down. The second machine requires 14 more hours to finish filling the boxes. How long would it have taken one of the machines, working alone, to fill the boxes?

23. Two welders who work at the same rate are riveting the girders of a building. After they work together for 10 h, one of the welders quits. The second welder requires 20 more hours to complete the welds. Find the time it would have taken one of the welders, working alone, to complete the welds.

24. A large drain and a small drain are opened to drain a pool. The large drain can empty the pool in 6 h. After both drains have been open 1 h, the large drain becomes clogged and is closed. The small drain remains open and requires 9 more hours to empty the pool. How long would it have taken the small drain, working alone, to empty the pool?

25. It takes Sam h hours to rake the yard and it takes Emma k hours to rake the yard, where $h > k$. Let t be the amount of time it takes Sam and Emma to rake the yard together. Is t less than k, between k and h, or greater than k?

26. Zachary and Eli picked a row of peas together in m minutes. It would have taken Zachary n minutes to pick the row of peas by himself. What fraction of the row of peas did Zachary pick? What fraction of the row of peas did Eli pick?

2   Uniform motion problems

27. a. A plane can fly 380 mph in calm air. In the time it takes the plane to fly 1440 mi against a headwind, it could fly 1600 mi if it were flying with the wind. Let *r* represent the rate of the wind. Complete the following table.

	Distance	÷	Rate	=	Time
Against the wind	?	÷	?	=	?
With the wind	?	÷	?	=	?

    b. Use the relationship between the expressions in the last column of the table to write an equation that can be solved to find the rate of the wind: ____?____ = ____?____ .

28. Use the equation from part b of Exercise 27. The first step in solving this equation is to multiply each side of the equation by ____?____ .

29. A camper drove 80 mi to a recreational area and then hiked 4 mi into the woods. The rate of the camper while driving was ten times the rate while hiking. The time spent hiking and driving was 3 h. Find the rate at which the camper hiked.

30. The president of a company traveled 1800 mi by jet and 300 mi on a prop plane. The rate of the jet was four times the rate of the prop plane. The entire trip took 5 h. Find the rate of the jet plane.

31. To assess the damage done by a fire, a forest ranger traveled 1080 mi by jet and then an additional 180 mi by helicopter. The rate of the jet was four times the rate of the helicopter. The entire trip took 5 h. Find the rate of the jet.

32. An engineer traveled 165 mi by car and then an additional 660 mi by plane. The rate of the plane was four times the rate of the car. The total trip took 6 h. Find the rate of the car.

33. After sailing 15 mi, a sailor changed direction and increased the boat's speed by 2 mph. An additional 19 mi was sailed at the increased speed. The total sailing time was 4 h. Find the rate of the boat for the first 15 mi.

34. On a recent trip, a trucker traveled 330 mi at a constant rate. Because of road conditions, the trucker then reduced the speed by 25 mph. An additional 30 mi was traveled at the reduced rate. The entire trip took 7 h. Find the rate of the trucker for the first 330 mi.

35. In calm water, the rate of a small rental motorboat is 15 mph. The rate of the current on the river is 3 mph. How far down the river can a family travel and still return the boat in 3 h?

36. The rate of a small aircraft in calm air is 125 mph. If the wind is currently blowing south at a rate of 15 mph, how far north can a pilot fly the plane and return it within 2 h?

37. Commuting from work to home, a lab technician traveled 10 mi at a constant rate through congested traffic. Upon reaching the expressway, the technician increased the speed by 20 mph. An additional 20 mi was traveled at the increased speed. The total time for the trip was 1 h. How fast did the technician travel through the congested traffic?

38. As part of a conditioning program, a jogger ran 8 mi in the same amount of time as it took a cyclist to ride 20 mi. The rate of the cyclist was 12 mph faster than the rate of the jogger. Find the rate of the jogger and the rate of the cyclist.

39. The speed of a boat in still water is 20 mph. The Jacksons traveled 75 mi down the Woodset River in the same amount of time as it took them to return 45 mi up the river. Find the rate of the river's current.

40. A backpacker hiking into a wilderness area walked 9 mi at a constant rate and then reduced this rate by 1 mph. Another 4 mi was hiked at this reduced rate. The time required to hike the 4 mi was 1 h less than the time required to walk the 9 mi. Find the rate at which the hiker walked the first 9 mi.

41. An express train traveled 600 mi in the same amount of time as it took a freight train to travel 360 mi. The rate of the express train was 20 mph faster than the rate of the freight train. Find the rate of each train.

42. A twin-engine plane flies 800 mi in the same amount of time as it takes a single-engine plane to fly 600 mi. The rate of the twin-engine plane is 50 mph faster than the rate of the single-engine plane. Find the rate of the twin-engine plane.

43. A car is traveling at a rate that is 36 mph faster than the rate of a cyclist. The car travels 384 mi in the same time as it takes the cyclist to travel 96 mi. Find the rate of the car.

44. A small motor on a fishing boat can move the boat at a rate of 6 mph in calm water. Traveling with the current, the boat can travel 24 mi in the same amount of time as it takes to travel 12 mi against the current. Find the rate of the current.

45. A commercial jet can fly 550 mph in calm air. Traveling with the jet stream, the plane flew 2400 mi in the same amount of time as it takes to fly 2000 mi against the jet stream. Find the rate of the jet stream.

46. A cruise ship can sail 28 mph in calm water. Sailing with the Gulf Stream, the ship can sail 170 mi in the same amount of time as it takes to sail 110 mi against the Gulf Stream. Find the rate of the Gulf Stream.

47. Rowing with the current of a river, a rowing team can row 25 mi in the same amount of time as it takes to row 15 mi against the current. The rate of the rowing team in calm water is 20 mph. Find the rate of the current.

48. A plane can fly 180 mph in calm air. Flying with the wind, the plane can fly 600 mi in the same amount of time as it takes to fly 480 mi against the wind. Find the rate of the wind.

9.7 Applying Concepts

49. Work Problem One pipe can fill a tank in 2 h, a second pipe can fill the tank in 4 h, and a third pipe can fill the tank in 5 h. How long would it take to fill the tank with all three pipes operating?

50. Work Problem A mason can construct a retaining wall in 10 h. The mason's more experienced apprentice can do the same job in 15 h. How long would it take the mason's less experienced apprentice to do the job if, working together, all three can complete the wall in 5 h?

51. Uniform Motion An Outing Club traveled 18 mi by canoe and then hiked 3 mi. The rate by boat was three times the rate on foot. The time spent walking was 1 h less than the time spent canoeing. Find the amount of time spent traveling by canoe.

52. Uniform Motion A motorist drove 120 mi before running out of gas and walking 4 mi to a gas station. The rate of the motorist in the car was ten times the rate walking. The time spent walking was 2 h less than the time spent driving. How long did it take for the motorist to drive the 120 mi?

53. Uniform Motion Because of bad weather, a bus driver reduced the usual speed along a 150-mile bus route by 10 mph. The bus arrived only 30 min later than its usual arrival time. How fast does the bus usually travel?

Focus on Problem Solving

Calculators A calculator is an important tool for problem solving. It can be used as an aide to guessing or estimating a solution to a problem. Here are a few problems to solve with a calculator.

1. Choose any positive integer less than 9. Multiply the number by 1507. Now multiply the result by 7519. What is the answer? Choose another positive single-digit number and again multiply by 1507 and 7519. What is the answer? What pattern do you see? Why does this work?

2. Are there enough people in the United States so that if they held hands in a line, they would stretch around the world at the equator? To answer this question, begin by determining what information you need. What assumptions must you make?

3. Which of the reciprocals of the first 16 natural numbers have a terminating decimal representation and which have a repeating decimal representation?

4. What is the largest natural number n for which $4^n > 1 \cdot 2 \cdot \cdots \cdot n$?

5. Calculate 15^2, 35^2, 65^2, and 85^2. Study the results. Make a conjecture about a relationship between a number ending in 5 and its square. Use your conjecture to find 75^2 and 95^2. Does your conjecture work for 125^2?

6. Find the sum of the first 1000 natural numbers. (*Hint:* You could just start adding $1 + 2 + 3 + 4 + \cdots$, but even if you performed one operation each second, it would take over 15 minutes to find the sum. Instead, try pairing the numbers and then adding the numbers in each pair. Pair 1 and 1000, 2 and 999, 3 and 998, and so on. What is the sum of each pair? How many pairs are there? Use this information to answer the original question.)

7. For a borrower to qualify for a home loan, a bank requires that the monthly mortgage payment be less than 25% of the borrower's monthly take-home income. A laboratory technician has deductions for taxes, insurance, and retirement that amount to 25% of the technician's monthly gross income. What minimum gross monthly income must this technician earn to receive a bank loan that has a mortgage payment of $1200 per month?

Projects & Group Activities

Scale Model of the Solar system

The table below lists the diameters of the sun and each of its nine planets, as well as the average distance of each planet from the sun.

Body	Body Diameter (in kilometers)	Average Distance from the Sun (in millions of kilometers)
Sun	1,391,900	
Mercury	4,878	58.05
Venus	12,104	108.45
Earth	12,756	150.0
Mars	6,787	228.6
Jupiter	142,800	780.45
Saturn	120,660	1,430.85
Uranus	51,118	2,877.0
Neptune	49,528	4,509.0
Pluto	2,300	5,929.5

Source: http://pds.jpl.nasa.gov/planets/welcome

To make a scale model of our solar system, begin by choosing the diameter of the sun in the scale model. Use the chosen ratio to determine the diameters of the planets and the distances between the sun and each of the planets.

Chapter 9 Summary

Key Words

A **rational expression** is a fraction in which the numerator or denominator is a variable expression. A rational expression is in simplest form when the numerator and denominator have no common factors other than 1. [9.1.1, pp. 468–469]

The **reciprocal** of a fraction is that fraction with the numerator and denominator interchanged. [9.1.3, p. 471]

The **least common multiple** (LCM) of two or more numbers is the smallest number that contains the prime factorization of each number. [9.2.1, p. 479]

A **complex fraction** is a fraction whose numerator or denominator contains one or more fractions. [9.4.1, p. 494]

A **ratio** is the quotient of two quantities that have the same unit. A **rate** is the quotient of two quantities that have different units. A **proportion** is an equation that states the equality of two ratios or rates. [9.5.2, p. 501]

A **literal equation** is an equation that contains more than one variable. A **formula** is a literal equation that states rules about measurements. [9.6.1, p. 516]

Examples

$\dfrac{x + 4}{x - 3}$ is a rational expression in simplest form.

The reciprocal of $\dfrac{x - 7}{y}$ is $\dfrac{y}{x - 7}$.

The LCM of 8 and 12 is 24 because 24 is the smallest number that is a multiple of both 8 and 12.

$\dfrac{x + \dfrac{1}{x}}{2 - \dfrac{3}{x}}$ is a complex fraction.

$\dfrac{3}{8} = \dfrac{15}{40}$ and $\dfrac{20 \text{ m}}{5 \text{ s}} = \dfrac{80 \text{ m}}{20 \text{ s}}$ are examples of proportions.

$2x + 3y = 6$ is an example of a literal equation. $A = \pi r^2$ is a literal equation that is also a formula.

Essential Rules and Procedures

Simplifying Rational Expressions
Factor the numerator and denominator. Divide by the common factors. [9.1.1, p. 469]

$\dfrac{x^2 - 3x - 10}{x^2 - 25} = \dfrac{(x + 2)(x - 5)}{(x + 5)(x - 5)}$
$= \dfrac{x + 2}{x + 5}$

Multiplying Rational Expressions
Multiply the numerators. Multiply the denominators. Write the answer in simplest form.
$\dfrac{a}{b} \cdot \dfrac{c}{d} = \dfrac{ac}{bd}$ [9.1.2, p. 470]

$\dfrac{x^2 - 3x}{x^2 + x} \cdot \dfrac{x^2 + 5x + 4}{x^2 - 4x + 3}$
$= \dfrac{x(x - 3)}{x(x + 1)} \cdot \dfrac{(x + 4)(x + 1)}{(x - 3)(x - 1)}$
$= \dfrac{x(x - 3)(x + 4)(x + 1)}{x(x + 1)(x - 3)(x - 1)} = \dfrac{x + 4}{x - 1}$

Dividing Rational Expressions
To divide two fractions, multiply by the reciprocal of the divisor.
$$\frac{a}{b} \div \frac{c}{d} = \frac{a}{b} \cdot \frac{d}{c} = \frac{ad}{bc}$$ [9.1.3, p. 472]

$$\frac{3x^3y^2}{8a^4b^5} \div \frac{6x^4y}{4a^3b^2} = \frac{3x^3y^2}{8a^4b^5} \cdot \frac{4a^3b^2}{6x^4y}$$
$$= \frac{3x^3y^2 \cdot 4a^3b^2}{8a^4b^5 \cdot 6x^4y} = \frac{y}{4ab^3x}$$

Adding and Subtracting Rational Expressions

1. Find the LCM of the denominators.

2. Write each fraction with the LCM as the denominator.

3. Add or subtract the numerators. The denominator of the sum or difference is the common denominator.

4. Write the answer in simplest form.

[9.3.2, p. 482]

$$\frac{4x-2}{3x+12} - \frac{x-2}{x+4} = \frac{4x-2}{3(x+4)} - \frac{x-2}{x+4}$$
$$= \frac{4x-2}{3(x+4)} - \frac{x-2}{x+4} \cdot \frac{3}{3}$$
$$= \frac{4x-2}{3(x+4)} - \frac{3x-6}{3(x+4)}$$
$$= \frac{4x-2-(3x-6)}{3(x+4)}$$
$$= \frac{x+4}{3(x+4)} = \frac{1}{3}$$

Simplifying Complex Fractions
Multiply the numerator and denominator of the complex fraction by the LCM of the denominators of the fractions in the numerator and denominator. [9.4.1, p. 494]

$$\frac{\frac{1}{x}+\frac{1}{y}}{\frac{1}{x}-\frac{1}{y}} = \frac{\frac{1}{x}+\frac{1}{y}}{\frac{1}{x}-\frac{1}{y}} \cdot \frac{xy}{xy} = \frac{\frac{1}{x} \cdot xy + \frac{1}{y} \cdot xy}{\frac{1}{x} \cdot xy - \frac{1}{y} \cdot xy}$$
$$= \frac{y+x}{y-x}$$

Solving Equations Containing Fractions
Clear denominators by multiplying each side of the equation by the LCM of the denominators. Then solve for the variable. [9.5.1, p. 499]

$$\frac{1}{2a} = \frac{2}{a} - \frac{3}{8}$$
$$8a\left(\frac{1}{2a}\right) = 8a\left(\frac{2}{a} - \frac{3}{8}\right)$$
$$4 = 16 - 3a$$
$$-12 = -3a$$
$$4 = a$$

Similar Triangles
Similar triangles have the same shape but not necessarily the same size. The ratios of corresponding sides of similar triangles are equal. The ratio of corresponding heights is equal to the ratio of corresponding sides. [9.5.4, p. 504]

Triangles *ABC* and *DEF* are similar triangles. The ratio of corresponding sides and of corresponding heights is $\frac{1}{3}$.

Solving Literal Equations

Rewrite the equation so that the letter being solved for is alone on one side of the equation and all numbers and other variables are on the other side.   [9.6.1, p. 516]

Solve $A = \frac{1}{2}bh$ for b.

$$2(A) = 2\left(\frac{1}{2}bh\right)$$

$$2A = bh$$

$$\frac{2A}{h} = \frac{bh}{h}$$

$$\frac{2A}{h} = b$$

Work Problems

Rate of work · Time worked = Part of task completed
[9.7.1, p. 520]

Pat can do a certain job in 3 h. Chris can do the same job in 5 h. How long would it take them, working together, to get the job done?

$$\frac{t}{3} + \frac{t}{5} = 1$$

Uniform Motion Problems

Distance ÷ Rate = Time   [9.7.2, p. 522]

Train A's speed is 15 mph faster than Train B's speed. Train A travels 150 mi in the same amount of time as it takes Train B to travel 120 mi. Find the rate of Train B.

$$\frac{120}{r} = \frac{150}{r + 15}$$

Chapter 9 Review Exercises

1. Multiply: $\dfrac{8ab^2}{15x^3y} \cdot \dfrac{5xy^4}{16a^2b}$

2. Add: $\dfrac{5}{3x - 4} + \dfrac{4}{2x + 3}$

3. Solve $4x + 3y = 12$ for x.

4. Simplify: $\dfrac{16x^5y^3}{24xy^{10}}$

5. Divide: $\dfrac{20x^2 - 45x}{6x^3 + 4x^2} \div \dfrac{40x^3 - 90x^2}{12x^2 + 8x}$

6. Simplify: $\dfrac{x - \dfrac{16}{5x - 2}}{3x - 4 - \dfrac{88}{5x - 2}}$

7. Find the LCM of $24a^2b^5$ and $36a^3b$.

8. Subtract: $\dfrac{5x}{3x + 7} - \dfrac{x}{3x + 7}$

9. Write each fraction in terms of the LCM of the denominators.

$$\frac{3}{16x}, \frac{5}{8x^2}$$

10. Simplify: $\dfrac{2x^2 - 13x - 45}{2x^2 - x - 15}$

11. Divide: $\dfrac{x^2 - 5x - 14}{x^2 - 3x - 10} \div \dfrac{x^2 - 4x - 21}{x^2 - 9x + 20}$

12. Add: $\dfrac{2y}{5y - 7} + \dfrac{3}{7 - 5y}$

13. Multiply: $\dfrac{3x^3 + 10x^2}{10x - 2} \cdot \dfrac{20x - 4}{6x^4 + 20x^3}$

14. Subtract: $\dfrac{5x + 3}{2x^2 + 5x - 3} - \dfrac{3x + 4}{2x^2 + 5x - 3}$

15. Find the LCM of $5x^4(x - 7)^2$ and $15x(x - 7)$.

16. Solve: $\dfrac{6}{x - 7} = \dfrac{8}{x - 6}$

17. Solve: $\dfrac{x + 8}{x + 4} = 1 + \dfrac{5}{x + 4}$

18. Simplify: $\dfrac{12a^2b(4x - 7)}{15ab^2(7 - 4x)}$

19. Simplify: $\dfrac{5x - 1}{x^2 - 9} + \dfrac{4x - 3}{x^2 - 9} - \dfrac{8x - 1}{x^2 - 9}$

20. Triangles *ABC* and *DEF* below are similar. Find the perimeter of triangle *ABC*.

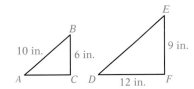

21. Solve: $\dfrac{20}{2x + 3} = \dfrac{17x}{2x + 3} - 5$

22. Simplify: $\dfrac{\dfrac{5}{x - 1} - \dfrac{3}{x + 3}}{\dfrac{6}{x + 3} + \dfrac{2}{x - 1}}$

23. Add: $\dfrac{x - 1}{x + 2} + \dfrac{3x - 2}{5 - x} + \dfrac{5x^2 + 15x - 11}{x^2 - 3x - 10}$

24. Divide: $\dfrac{18x^2 + 25x - 3}{9x^2 - 28x + 3} \div \dfrac{2x^2 + 9x + 9}{x^2 - 6x + 9}$

25. Simplify: $\dfrac{x^2 + x - 30}{15 + 2x - x^2}$

26. Solve: $\dfrac{5}{7} + \dfrac{x}{2} = 2 - \dfrac{x}{7}$

27. Simplify: $\dfrac{x + \dfrac{6}{x - 5}}{1 + \dfrac{2}{x - 5}}$

28. Multiply: $\dfrac{3x^2 + 4x - 15}{x^2 - 11x + 28} \cdot \dfrac{x^2 - 5x - 14}{3x^2 + x - 10}$

29. Solve: $\dfrac{x}{5} = \dfrac{x + 12}{9}$

30. Solve: $\dfrac{3}{20} = \dfrac{x}{80}$

31. Simplify: $\dfrac{1 - \dfrac{1}{x}}{1 - \dfrac{8x - 7}{x^2}}$

32. Solve $x - 2y = 15$ for x.

33. Add: $\dfrac{6}{a} + \dfrac{9}{b}$

34. Find the LCM of $10x^2 - 11x + 3$ and $20x^2 - 17x + 3$.

35. Solve $i = \dfrac{100m}{c}$ for c.

36. Solve: $\dfrac{15}{x} = \dfrac{3}{8}$

37. Solve: $\dfrac{22}{2x + 5} = 2$

38. Add: $\dfrac{x + 7}{15x} + \dfrac{x - 2}{20x}$

39. Multiply: $\dfrac{16a^2 - 9}{16a^2 - 24a + 9} \cdot \dfrac{8a^2 - 13a - 6}{4a^2 - 5a - 6}$

40. Write each fraction in terms of the LCM of the denominators.

$$\dfrac{x}{12x^2 + 16x - 3}, \dfrac{4x^2}{6x^2 + 7x - 3}$$

41. Add: $\dfrac{3}{4ab} + \dfrac{5}{4ab}$

42. Solve: $\dfrac{20}{x + 2} = \dfrac{5}{16}$

43. Solve: $\dfrac{5x}{3} - \dfrac{2}{5} = \dfrac{8x}{5}$

44. Divide: $\dfrac{6a^2b^7}{25x^3y} \div \dfrac{12a^3b^4}{5x^2y^2}$

45. **Masonry** A brick mason can construct a patio in 3 h. If the mason works with an apprentice, they can construct the patio in 2 h. How long would it take the apprentice, working alone, to construct the patio?

46. **Physics** A weight of 21 lb stretches a spring 14 in. At the same rate, how far would a weight of 12 lb stretch the spring?

47. **Uniform Motion** The rate of a jet is 400 mph in calm air. Traveling with the wind, the jet can fly 2100 mi in the same amount of time as it takes to fly 1900 mi against the wind. Find the rate of the wind.

48. **Gardening** A gardener uses 4 oz of insecticide to make 2 gal of garden spray. At this rate, how much additional insecticide is necessary to make 10 gal of the garden spray?

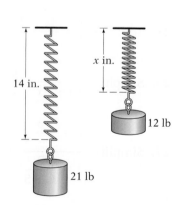

49. Work Problem One hose can fill a pool in 15 h. A second hose can fill the pool in 10 h. How long would it take to fill the pool using both hoses?

50. Uniform Motion A car travels 315 mi in the same amount of time as it takes a bus to travel 245 mi. The rate of the car is 10 mph faster than that of the bus. Find the rate of the car.

Chapter 9 Test

 View the Chapter Test Videos for fully worked-out solutions to any exercise.

1. Divide: $\dfrac{x^2 + 3x + 2}{x^2 + 5x + 4} \div \dfrac{x^2 - x - 6}{x^2 + 2x - 15}$

2. Subtract: $\dfrac{2x}{x^2 + 3x - 10} - \dfrac{4}{x^2 + 3x - 10}$

3. Find the LCM of $6x - 3$ and $2x^2 + x - 1$.

4. Solve: $\dfrac{3}{x + 4} = \dfrac{5}{x + 6}$

5. Multiply: $\dfrac{x^3 y^4}{x^2 - 4x + 4} \cdot \dfrac{x^2 - x - 2}{x^6 y^4}$

6. Simplify: $\dfrac{1 + \dfrac{1}{x} - \dfrac{12}{x^2}}{1 + \dfrac{2}{x} - \dfrac{8}{x^2}}$

7. Write each fraction in terms of the LCM of the denominators.

$\dfrac{3}{x^2 - 2x}; \dfrac{x}{x^2 - 4}$

8. Solve $3x + 5y + 15 = 0$ for x.

9. Solve: $\dfrac{6}{x} - 2 = 1$

10. Subtract: $\dfrac{2}{2x - 1} - \dfrac{3}{3x + 1}$

11. Divide: $\dfrac{x^2 - x - 56}{x^2 + 8x + 7} \div \dfrac{x^2 - 13x + 40}{x^2 - 4x - 5}$

12. Subtract: $\dfrac{3x}{x^2 + 5x - 24} - \dfrac{9}{x^2 + 5x - 24}$

13. Find the LCM of $3x^2 + 6x$ and $2x^2 + 8x + 8$.

14. Simplify: $\dfrac{x^2 - 7x + 10}{25 - x^2}$

15. Solve: $\dfrac{3x}{x - 3} - 2 = \dfrac{10}{x - 3}$

16. Solve $f = v + at$ for t.

17. Simplify: $\dfrac{12x^4 y^2}{18xy^7}$

18. Subtract: $\dfrac{2}{2x - 1} - \dfrac{1}{x + 1}$

19. Solve: $\dfrac{2}{x - 2} = \dfrac{12}{x + 3}$

20. Multiply: $\dfrac{x^5 y^3}{x^2 - x - 6} \cdot \dfrac{x^2 - 9}{x^2 y^4}$

21. Write each fraction in terms of the LCM of the denominators.

$$\frac{3y}{x(1-x)}; \frac{x}{(x+1)(x-1)}$$

22. Simplify: $\dfrac{1 - \dfrac{2}{x} - \dfrac{15}{x^2}}{1 - \dfrac{25}{x^2}}$

23. Mixture Problem A salt solution is formed by mixing 4 lb of salt with 10 gal of water. At this rate, how many additional pounds of salt are required for 15 gal of water?

24. Uniform Motion A small plane can fly at 110 mph in calm air. Flying with the wind, the plane can fly 260 mi in the same amount of time as it takes to fly 180 mi against the wind. Find the rate of the wind.

25. Work Problem One pipe can fill a tank in 9 min. A second pipe requires 18 min to fill the tank. How long would it take both pipes, working together, to fill the tank?

Cumulative Review Exercises

1. Evaluate: $-|-17|$

2. Evaluate: $-\dfrac{3}{4} \cdot (2)^3$

3. Simplify: $\left(\dfrac{2}{3}\right)^2 \div \left(\dfrac{3}{2} - \dfrac{2}{3}\right) + \dfrac{1}{2}$

4. Evaluate $-a^2 + (a - b)^2$ when $a = -2$ and $b = 3$.

5. Simplify: $-2x - (-3y) + 7x - 5y$

6. Simplify: $2[3x - 7(x - 3) - 8]$

7. Solve: $3 - \dfrac{1}{4}x = 8$

8. Solve: $3[x - 2(x - 3)] = 2(3 - 2x)$

9. Find $16\dfrac{2}{3}\%$ of 60.

10. Solve: $\dfrac{5}{9}x < 1$

11. Solve: $x - 2 \geq 4x - 47$

12. Graph: $y = 2x - 1$

13. Graph: $f(x) = 3x + 2$

14. Graph: $x = 3$

15. Graph the solution set of $5x + 2y < 6$.

16. Find the range of the function given by the equation $f(x) = -2x + 11$ if the domain is $\{-8, -4, 0, 3, 7\}$.

17. Evaluate $f(x) = 4x - 3$ at $x = 10$.

18. Solve by substitution: $6x - y = 1$
$y = 3x + 1$

19. Solve by the addition method: $2x - 3y = 4$
$4x + y = 1$

20. Multiply: $(3xy^4)(-2x^3y)$

21. Simplify: $(a^4b^3)^5$

22. Simplify: $\dfrac{a^2b^{-5}}{a^{-1}b^{-3}}$

23. Multiply: $(a - 3b)(a + 4b)$

24. Divide: $\dfrac{15b^4 - 5b^2 + 10b}{5b}$

25. Divide: $(x^3 - 8) \div (x - 2)$

26. Factor: $12x^2 - x - 1$

27. Factor: $y^2 - 7y + 6$

28. Factor: $2a^3 + 7a^2 - 15a$

29. Factor: $4b^2 - 100$

30. Solve: $(x + 3)(2x - 5) = 0$

31. Simplify: $\dfrac{x^2 + 3x - 28}{16 - x^2}$

32. Divide: $\dfrac{x^2 - 3x - 10}{x^2 - 4x - 12} \div \dfrac{x^2 - x - 20}{x^2 - 2x - 24}$

33. Subtract: $\dfrac{6}{3x - 1} - \dfrac{2}{x + 1}$

34. Solve: $\dfrac{4x}{x - 3} - 2 = \dfrac{8}{x - 3}$

35. Solve $f = v + at$ for a.

36. Translate "the difference between five times a number and eighteen is the opposite of three" into an equation and solve.

37. Investments An investment of \$5000 is made at an annual simple interest rate of 7%. How much additional money must be invested at an annual simple interest rate of 11% so that the total interest earned is 9% of the total investment?

38. Metallurgy A silversmith mixes 60 g of an alloy that is 40% silver with 120 g of another silver alloy. The resulting alloy is 60% silver. Find the percent of silver in the 120-gram alloy.

39. Geometry The length of the base of a triangle is 2 in. less than twice the height. The area of the triangle is 30 in². Find the base and height of the triangle.

40. Work Problem One water pipe can fill a tank in 12 min. A second pipe requires 24 min to fill the tank. How long would it take both pipes, working together, to fill the tank?

h

$2h - 2$

OBJECTIVES

10.1
1 Simplify numerical radical expressions
2 Simplify variable radical expressions

10.2
1 Add and subtract radical expressions

10.3
1 Multiply radical expressions
2 Divide radical expressions

10.4
1 Solve equations containing one or more radical expressions
2 Application problems

Civil engineers design expressways with efficiency and, most importantly, safety in mind. They have to take into account the speed of drivers entering and exiting these busy roadways. An on- or off-ramp cannot have too sharp a curve, or the drivers may be in danger of skidding off the road. However, a ramp with too wide a curve requires more building material, takes longer to travel, and uses more land. A radical equation is used to determine the maximum speed at which a car can travel around a curve without skidding. This equation is used in the **Projects & Group Activities on page 575.**

DVD **SSM** **Online Study Center**

Need help? For online student resources, such as section quizzes, visit the Online Study Center at www.cengage.com/math/aufmann.

Prep Test

1. Evaluate $-|-14|$.

2. Simplify: $3x^2y - 4xy^2 - 5x^2y$

3. Solve: $1.5h = 21$

4. Solve: $3x - 2 = 5 - 2x$

5. Simplify: $x^3 \cdot x^3$

6. Simplify: $(x + y)^2$

7. Simplify: $(2x - 3)^2$

8. Simplify: $(a - 5)(a + 5)$

9. Simplify: $(2 - 3v)(2 + 3v)$

10. Simplify: $\dfrac{2x^4y^3}{18x^2y}$

10.1 Introduction to Radical Expressions

OBJECTIVE 1 Simplify numerical radical expressions

A **square root** of a positive number x is a number whose square is x.

A square root of 16 is 4 because $4^2 = 16$.

A square root of 16 is -4 because $(-4)^2 = 16$.

Every positive number has two square roots, one a positive number and one a negative number. The symbol $\sqrt{}$, called a **radical sign,** is used to indicate the positive or **principal square root** of a number. For example, $\sqrt{16} = 4$ and $\sqrt{25} = 5$. The number or variable expression under the radical sign is called the **radicand.**

When the negative square root of a number is to be found, a negative sign is placed in front of the radical. For example, $-\sqrt{16} = -4$ and $-\sqrt{25} = -5$.

The square of an integer is a **perfect square.** 49, 81, and 144 are examples of perfect squares.

$$7^2 = 49$$
$$9^2 = 81$$
$$12^2 = 144$$

The principal square root of a perfect-square integer is a positive integer.

$$\sqrt{49} = 7$$
$$\sqrt{81} = 9$$
$$\sqrt{144} = 12$$

If an integer is not a perfect square, its square root can only be approximated. For example, 2 and 7 are not perfect squares. Thus their square roots can only be approximated. These numbers are **irrational numbers.** Their decimal representations never terminate or repeat.

$$\sqrt{2} \approx 1.4142135\ldots$$

$$\sqrt{7} \approx 2.6457513\ldots$$

The approximate square roots of numbers that are not perfect squares can be found using a calculator. The square roots can be rounded to any given place value.

Radical expressions that contain radicands that are not perfect squares are generally written in *simplest form*. A radical expression is in **simplest form** when the radicand contains no factor greater than 1 that is a perfect square. For example, $\sqrt{50}$ is not in simplest form because 25 is a perfect-square factor of 50. The radical expression $\sqrt{15}$ is in simplest form because there is no perfect-square factor of 15 that is greater than 1.

The Product Property of Square Roots and a knowledge of perfect squares are used to simplify radical expressions.

> ## Take Note
>
> Recall that a factor of a number divides the number evenly. For example, 6 is a factor of 18. 9 is also a factor of 18. Note that 9 is a *perfect-square factor* of 18, whereas 6 is not a perfect-square factor of 18.

The Product Property of Square Roots

If a and b are positive real numbers, then $\sqrt{ab} = \sqrt{a} \cdot \sqrt{b}.$

The chart below shows square roots of some perfect squares.

Square Roots of Perfect Squares			
$\sqrt{1} = 1$	$\sqrt{16} = 4$	$\sqrt{49} = 7$	$\sqrt{100} = 10$
$\sqrt{4} = 2$	$\sqrt{25} = 5$	$\sqrt{64} = 8$	$\sqrt{121} = 11$
$\sqrt{9} = 3$	$\sqrt{36} = 6$	$\sqrt{81} = 9$	$\sqrt{144} = 12$

Simplify: $\sqrt{72}$

$$\sqrt{72} = \sqrt{36 \cdot 2}$$ • Write the radicand as the product of a perfect square and a factor that does not contain a perfect square.

$$= \sqrt{36}\,\sqrt{2}$$ • Use the Product Property of Square Roots to write the expression as a product.

$$= 6\sqrt{2}$$ • Simplify $\sqrt{36}$.

Note in the example on the previous page that 72 must be written as the product of a perfect square and *a factor that does not contain a perfect square.* Therefore, it would not be correct to rewrite $\sqrt{72}$ as $\sqrt{9 \cdot 8}$ and simplify the expression as shown at the right. Although 9 is a perfect-square factor of 72, 8 contains a perfect square ($8 = 4 \cdot 2$), and $\sqrt{4}$ can be simplified. Therefore, $\sqrt{8}$ is not in simplest form. Remember to find the *largest* perfect square that is a factor of the radicand.

$$\sqrt{72} = \sqrt{9 \cdot 8}$$
$$= \sqrt{9}\,\sqrt{8}$$
$$= 3\sqrt{8}$$

Not in simplest form

Simplify: $\sqrt{147}$

$\sqrt{147} = \sqrt{49 \cdot 3}$ • Write the radicand as the product of a perfect square and a factor that does not contain a perfect square.

$= \sqrt{49}\,\sqrt{3}$ • Use the Product Property of Square Roots to write the expression as a product.

$= 7\sqrt{3}$ • Simplify $\sqrt{49}$.

Simplify: $\sqrt{360}$

$\sqrt{360} = \sqrt{36 \cdot 10}$ • Write the radicand as the product of a perfect square and a factor that does not contain a perfect square.

$= \sqrt{36}\,\sqrt{10}$ • Use the Product Property of Square Roots to write the expression as a product.

$= 6\sqrt{10}$ • Simplify $\sqrt{36}$.

From the last example, note that $\sqrt{360} = 6\sqrt{10}$. The two expressions are different representations of the same number. Using a calculator, we find that $\sqrt{360} \approx 18.973666$ and $6\sqrt{10} \approx 6(3.1622777) = 18.973666$.

Simplify: $\sqrt{-16}$

Because the square of any real number is positive, there is no real number whose square is -16.

$\sqrt{-16}$ is not a real number.

EXAMPLE 1 Simplify: $3\sqrt{90}$

Solution $3\sqrt{90} = 3\sqrt{9 \cdot 10}$ • Write the radicand as the product of a perfect square and a factor that does not contain a perfect square.

$= 3\sqrt{9}\,\sqrt{10}$ • Use the Product Property of Square Roots to write the expression as a product.

$= 3 \cdot 3\sqrt{10}$ • Simplify $\sqrt{9}$.

$= 9\sqrt{10}$ • Multiply $3 \cdot 3$.

PROBLEM 1 Simplify: $-5\sqrt{32}$

Solution See page S23.

EXAMPLE 2   Simplify: $\sqrt{252}$

Solution $\sqrt{252} = \sqrt{36 \cdot 7}$ • **Write the radicand as the product of a perfect square and a factor that does not contain a perfect square.**

$= \sqrt{36}\,\sqrt{7}$ • **Use the Product Property of Square Roots to write the expression as a product.**

$= 6\sqrt{7}$ • **Simplify $\sqrt{36}$.**

PROBLEM 2   Simplify: $\sqrt{216}$

Solution   See page S23.

OBJECTIVE **2**   **Simplify variable radical expressions**

Variable expressions that contain radicals do not always represent real numbers.

The variable expression at the right does not represent a real number when x is a negative number, such as -4.

$$\sqrt{x^3}$$
$$\sqrt{(-4)^3} = \sqrt{-64} \leftarrow \text{Not a real number}$$

Now consider the expression $\sqrt{x^2}$ and evaluate this expression for $x = -2$ and $x = 2$.

$$\sqrt{x^2}$$
$$\sqrt{(-2)^2} = \sqrt{4} = 2 = |-2|$$
$$\sqrt{2^2}\ \ \ = \sqrt{4} = 2 = |2|$$

This suggests the following.

The Square Root of a^2

For any real number a, $\sqrt{a^2} = |a|$.

If $a \geq 0$, then $\sqrt{a^2} = a.$

In order to avoid variable expressions that do not represent real numbers, and so that absolute value signs are not needed for certain expressions, the variables in this chapter will represent *positive* numbers unless otherwise stated.

A variable or a product of variables written in exponential form is a **perfect square** when each exponent is an even number.

To find the square root of a perfect square, remove the radical sign, and divide each exponent by 2.

Simplify: $\sqrt{a^6}$

Remove the radical sign, and divide the exponent by 2. $\sqrt{a^6} = a^3$

A variable radical expression is not in simplest form when the radicand contains a factor greater than 1 that is a perfect square.

Simplify: $\sqrt{x^7}$

Write x^7 as the product of x and a perfect square. $\sqrt{x^7} = \sqrt{x^6 \cdot x}$

Use the Product Property of Square Roots. $= \sqrt{x^6}\,\sqrt{x}$

Simplify the square root of the perfect square. $= x^3\sqrt{x}$

EXAMPLE 3 Simplify: $\sqrt{b^{15}}$

Solution $\sqrt{b^{15}} = \sqrt{b^{14} \cdot b} = \sqrt{b^{14}} \cdot \sqrt{b} = b^7\sqrt{b}$

PROBLEM 3 Simplify: $\sqrt{y^{19}}$

Solution See page S23.

Simplify: $3x\sqrt{8x^3y^{13}}$

Write the radicand as the product of a perfect square and factors that do not contain a perfect square. $3x\sqrt{8x^3y^{13}} = 3x\sqrt{4x^2y^{12}(2xy)}$

Use the Product Property of Square Roots. $= 3x\sqrt{4x^2y^{12}}\,\sqrt{2xy}$

Simplify. $= 3x \cdot 2xy^6\sqrt{2xy}$
$= 6x^2y^6\sqrt{2xy}$

EXAMPLE 4 Simplify.   **A.** $\sqrt{24x^5}$ **B.** $2a\sqrt{18a^3b^{10}}$

Solution **A.** $\sqrt{24x^5} = \sqrt{4x^4 \cdot 6x}$ **B.** $2a\sqrt{18a^3b^{10}} = 2a\sqrt{9a^2b^{10} \cdot 2a}$
$= \sqrt{4x^4}\,\sqrt{6x}$ $= 2a\sqrt{9a^2b^{10}}\,\sqrt{2a}$
$= 2x^2\sqrt{6x}$ $= 2a \cdot 3ab^5\sqrt{2a}$
            $= 6a^2b^5\sqrt{2a}$

PROBLEM 4 Simplify.   **A.** $\sqrt{45b^7}$ **B.** $3a\sqrt{28a^9b^{18}}$

Solution See page S23.

Simplify: $\sqrt{25(x+2)^2}$

25 is a perfect square. $(x+2)^2$ is a perfect square. $\sqrt{25(x+2)^2} = 5(x+2)$
$= 5x + 10$

EXAMPLE 5 Simplify: $\sqrt{16(x+5)^2}$

Solution $\sqrt{16(x+5)^2} = 4(x+5) = 4x + 20$

PROBLEM 5 Simplify: $\sqrt{25(a+3)^2}$

Solution See page S23.

10.1   Concept Review

Determine whether the statement is always true, sometimes true, or never true.

1. The square root of a positive number is a positive number, and the square root of a negative number is a negative number.

2. Every positive number has two square roots, one of which is the additive inverse of the other.

3. The square root of an integer that is not a perfect square is an irrational number.

4. If the radicand of a radical expression is evenly divisible by a perfect square greater than 1, then the radical expression is not in simplest form.

5. Suppose a and b are real numbers. Then $\sqrt{ab} = \sqrt{a} \cdot \sqrt{b}$.

6. When a perfect square is written in exponential form, the exponents are multiples of 2.

10.1   Exercises

1   Simplify numerical radical expressions

1. Show by example that a positive number has two square roots.

2. Why is the square root of a negative number not a real number?

3. Which of the numbers 2, 9, 20, 25, 50, 81, and 100 are *not* perfect squares?

4. Write down a number that has a perfect-square factor that is greater than 1.

5. Write a sentence or two that you could email a friend to explain the concept of a perfect-square factor.

6. Name the perfect-square factors of 540. What is the largest perfect-square factor of 540?

7. In the expression $\sqrt{a}$, the symbol $\sqrt{}$ is called the _____?_____, and a is called the _____?_____.

8. Simplify: $\sqrt{98}$

$\sqrt{98} = \sqrt{\underline{\quad ? \quad} \cdot 2}$ • Write 98 as the product of a perfect-square factor and a factor that does not contain a perfect square.

$\quad\quad = \sqrt{\underline{\quad ? \quad}}\,\sqrt{\underline{\quad ? \quad}}$ • Use the Product Property of Radicals to write the expression as the product of two square roots.

$\quad\quad = \underline{\quad ? \quad}\,\sqrt{2}$ • Take the square root of the perfect square.

Simplify.

9. $\sqrt{16}$ **10.** $\sqrt{64}$ **11.** $\sqrt{49}$ **12.** $\sqrt{144}$ **13.** $\sqrt{32}$ **14.** $\sqrt{50}$

15. $\sqrt{8}$ **16.** $\sqrt{12}$ **17.** $6\sqrt{18}$ **18.** $-3\sqrt{48}$ **19.** $5\sqrt{40}$ **20.** $2\sqrt{28}$

21. $\sqrt{15}$ **22.** $\sqrt{21}$ **23.** $\sqrt{29}$ **24.** $\sqrt{13}$ **25.** $-9\sqrt{72}$ **26.** $11\sqrt{80}$

27. $\sqrt{45}$ **28.** $\sqrt{225}$ **29.** $\sqrt{0}$ **30.** $\sqrt{210}$ **31.** $6\sqrt{128}$ **32.** $9\sqrt{288}$

33. $\sqrt{105}$ **34.** $\sqrt{55}$ **35.** $\sqrt{900}$ **36.** $\sqrt{300}$ **37.** $5\sqrt{180}$ **38.** $7\sqrt{98}$

39. $\sqrt{250}$ **40.** $\sqrt{120}$ **41.** $\sqrt{96}$ **42.** $\sqrt{160}$ **43.** $\sqrt{324}$ **44.** $\sqrt{444}$

Complete Exercises 45 and 46 without using a calculator.

45. Is the given number a rational number, an irrational number, or a number that is not a real number?

     a. $\sqrt{0.16}$ **b.** $-\sqrt{18}$ **c.** $\sqrt{\sqrt{36}}$ **d.** $\sqrt{-25}$

46. Find consecutive integers m and n such that the given number is between m and n, or state that the given number is not a real number.

     a. $-\sqrt{115}$ **b.** $-\sqrt{-90}$ **c.** $\sqrt{\sqrt{64}}$ **d.** $\sqrt{200}$

Find the decimal approximation to the nearest thousandth.

47. $\sqrt{240}$ **48.** $\sqrt{300}$ **49.** $\sqrt{288}$ **50.** $\sqrt{600}$

51. $\sqrt{245}$ **52.** $\sqrt{525}$ **53.** $\sqrt{352}$ **54.** $\sqrt{363}$

2 **Simplify variable radical expressions**

55. How can you tell whether a variable exponential expression is a perfect square?

56. When is a radical expression in simplest form?

57. $16x^6y^8$ is a perfect square because $16 = (\underline{\quad ? \quad})^2$, $x^6 = (\underline{\quad ? \quad})^2$, and $y^8 = (\underline{\quad ? \quad})^2$.

58. To simplify $\sqrt{75x^{15}}$, write $75x^{15}$ as the product of a perfect square and a factor that does not contain a perfect square. Then use the Product Property of Radicals and simplify:

$$\sqrt{75x^{15}} = \sqrt{\underline{\quad ? \quad}} \cdot 3x = \sqrt{\underline{\quad ? \quad}} \, \sqrt{3x} = \underline{\quad ? \quad}\sqrt{3x}$$

Simplify.

59. $\sqrt{x^6}$

60. $\sqrt{x^{12}}$

61. $\sqrt{y^{15}}$

62. $\sqrt{y^{11}}$

63. $\sqrt{a^{20}}$

64. $\sqrt{a^{16}}$

65. $\sqrt{x^4 y^4}$

66. $\sqrt{x^{12} y^8}$

67. $\sqrt{4x^4}$

68. $\sqrt{25y^8}$

69. $\sqrt{24x^2}$

70. $\sqrt{x^3 y^{15}}$

71. $\sqrt{x^3 y^7}$

72. $\sqrt{a^{15} b^5}$

73. $\sqrt{a^3 b^{11}}$

74. $\sqrt{24y^7}$

75. $\sqrt{60x^5}$

76. $\sqrt{72y^7}$

77. $\sqrt{49a^4 b^8}$

78. $\sqrt{144x^2 y^8}$

79. $\sqrt{18x^5 y^7}$

80. $\sqrt{32a^5 b^{15}}$

81. $\sqrt{40x^{11} y^7}$

82. $\sqrt{72x^9 y^3}$

83. $\sqrt{80a^9 b^{10}}$

84. $\sqrt{96a^5 b^7}$

85. $2\sqrt{16a^2 b^3}$

86. $5\sqrt{25a^4 b^7}$

87. $x\sqrt{x^4 y^2}$

88. $y\sqrt{x^3 y^6}$

89. $4\sqrt{20a^4 b^7}$

90. $5\sqrt{12a^3 b^4}$

91. $3x\sqrt{12x^2 y^7}$

92. $4y\sqrt{18x^5 y^4}$

93. $2x^2\sqrt{8x^2 y^3}$

94. $3y^2\sqrt{27x^4 y^3}$

95. $\sqrt{25(a + 4)^2}$

96. $\sqrt{81(x + y)^4}$

97. $\sqrt{4(x + 2)^4}$

98. $\sqrt{9(x + 2)^2}$

99. $\sqrt{x^2 + 4x + 4}$

100. $\sqrt{b^2 + 8b + 16}$

101. $\sqrt{y^2 + 2y + 1}$

102. $\sqrt{a^2 + 6a + 9}$

For Exercises 103 to 106, a is a positive integer. State whether the expression represents a rational number or an irrational number.

103. $\sqrt{100a^6}$

104. $\sqrt{9a^9}$

105. $\sqrt{\sqrt{25a^{16}}}$

106. $\sqrt{\sqrt{81a^8}}$

10.1 Applying Concepts

107. **Traffic Safety** Traffic accident investigators can estimate the speed S, in miles per hour, of a car from the length of its skid mark by using the formula $S = \sqrt{30\,fl}$, where f is the coefficient of friction (which depends on the type of road surface) and l is the length of the skid mark in feet. Suppose the coefficient of friction is 1.2 and the length of a skid mark is 60 ft. Determine the speed of the car **a.** as a radical in simplest form and **b.** rounded to the nearest integer.

108. **Aviation** The distance a pilot in an airplane can see to the horizon can be approximated by the equation $d = 1.2\sqrt{h}$, where d is the distance to the horizon in miles and h is the height of the plane in feet. For a pilot flying at an altitude of 5000 ft, what is the distance to the horizon? Round to the nearest tenth.

Simplify.

109. $\sqrt{0.0025a^3b^5}$

110. $-\dfrac{3y}{4}\sqrt{64x^4y^2}$

111. Given $f(x) = \sqrt{2x - 1}$, find each of the following. Write your answer in simplest form.
   a. $f(1)$ **b.** $f(5)$ **c.** $f(14)$

112. Use the roster method to list the whole numbers between $\sqrt{8}$ and $\sqrt{90}$.

113. **Geometry** The area of a square is 76 cm². Find the length of a side of the square. Round to the nearest tenth.

Assuming x can be any real number, for what values of x is the radical expression a real number? Write the answer as an inequality or write "all real numbers."

114. $\sqrt{x}$

115. $\sqrt{4x}$

116. $\sqrt{x - 2}$

117. $\sqrt{x + 5}$

118. $\sqrt{6 - 4x}$

119. $\sqrt{5 - 2x}$

120. $\sqrt{x^2 + 7}$

121. $\sqrt{x^2 + 1}$

122. Describe in your own words how to simplify a radical expression.

123. Explain why $2\sqrt{2}$ is in simplest form and $\sqrt{8}$ is not in simplest form.

10.2 Addition and Subtraction of Radical Expressions

OBJECTIVE **1**   **Add and subtract radical expressions**

The Distributive Property is used to simplify the sum or difference of radical expressions with the same radicand.

$$5\sqrt{2} + 3\sqrt{2} = (5 + 3)\sqrt{2} = 8\sqrt{2}$$

$$6\sqrt{2x} - 4\sqrt{2x} = (6 - 4)\sqrt{2x} = 2\sqrt{2x}$$

Radical expressions that are in simplest form and have different radicands cannot be simplified by the Distributive Property.

$2\sqrt{3} + 4\sqrt{2}$ cannot be simplified by the Distributive Property.

To simplify the sum or difference of radical expressions, simplify each term. Then use the Distributive Property.

Subtract: $4\sqrt{8} - 10\sqrt{2}$

Simplify each term.

$$\begin{aligned}
4\sqrt{8} - 10\sqrt{2} &= 4\sqrt{4 \cdot 2} - 10\sqrt{2} \\
&= 4\sqrt{4}\sqrt{2} - 10\sqrt{2} \\
&= 4 \cdot 2\sqrt{2} - 10\sqrt{2} \\
&= 8\sqrt{2} - 10\sqrt{2}
\end{aligned}$$

Subtract by using the Distributive Property.

$$\begin{aligned}
&= (8 - 10)\sqrt{2} \\
&= -2\sqrt{2}
\end{aligned}$$

EXAMPLE 1   Simplify.   **A.** $5\sqrt{2} - 3\sqrt{2} + 12\sqrt{2}$ **B.** $3\sqrt{12} - 5\sqrt{27}$

Solution   **A.** $5\sqrt{2} - 3\sqrt{2} + 12\sqrt{2}$

$= (5 - 3 + 12)\sqrt{2}$ • **Use the Distributive Property.**

$= 14\sqrt{2}$

B. $\begin{aligned}
3\sqrt{12} - 5\sqrt{27} &= 3\sqrt{4 \cdot 3} - 5\sqrt{9 \cdot 3} \\
&= 3\sqrt{4}\,\sqrt{3} - 5\sqrt{9}\,\sqrt{3} \\
&= 3 \cdot 2\sqrt{3} - 5 \cdot 3\sqrt{3} \\
&= 6\sqrt{3} - 15\sqrt{3} \\
&= -9\sqrt{3}
\end{aligned}$

PROBLEM 1   Simplify.   **A.** $9\sqrt{3} + 3\sqrt{3} - 18\sqrt{3}$ **B.** $2\sqrt{50} - 5\sqrt{32}$

Solution   See page S23.

Subtract: $8\sqrt{18x} - 2\sqrt{32x}$

Simplify each term.

$$\begin{aligned}
8\sqrt{18x} - 2\sqrt{32x} &= 8\sqrt{9}\,\sqrt{2x} - 2\sqrt{16}\,\sqrt{2x} \\
&= 8 \cdot 3\sqrt{2x} - 2 \cdot 4\sqrt{2x} \\
&= 24\sqrt{2x} - 8\sqrt{2x}
\end{aligned}$$

Subtract the radical expressions.

$$= 16\sqrt{2x}$$

EXAMPLE 2   Simplify.

A. $3\sqrt{12x^3} - 2x\sqrt{3x}$ B. $2x\sqrt{8y} - 3\sqrt{2x^2y} + 2\sqrt{32x^2y}$

Solution   A. $3\sqrt{12x^3} - 2x\sqrt{3x} = 3\sqrt{4x^2}\sqrt{3x} - 2x\sqrt{3x}$
$$= 3 \cdot 2x\sqrt{3x} - 2x\sqrt{3x}$$
$$= 6x\sqrt{3x} - 2x\sqrt{3x}$$
$$= 4x\sqrt{3x}$$

B. $2x\sqrt{8y} - 3\sqrt{2x^2y} + 2\sqrt{32x^2y}$
$$= 2x\sqrt{4}\sqrt{2y} - 3\sqrt{x^2}\sqrt{2y} + 2\sqrt{16x^2}\sqrt{2y}$$
$$= 2x \cdot 2\sqrt{2y} - 3 \cdot x\sqrt{2y} + 2 \cdot 4x\sqrt{2y}$$
$$= 4x\sqrt{2y} - 3x\sqrt{2y} + 8x\sqrt{2y}$$
$$= 9x\sqrt{2y}$$

PROBLEM 2   Simplify.

A. $y\sqrt{28y} + 7\sqrt{63y^3}$ B. $2\sqrt{27a^5} - 4a\sqrt{12a^3} + a^2\sqrt{75a}$

Solution   See page S24.

10.2   Concept Review

Determine whether the statement is always true, sometimes true, or never true.

1. $5\sqrt{2} + 6\sqrt{3} = 11\sqrt{5}$

2. The Distributive Property is used to add or subtract radical expressions with the same radicand.

3. $4\sqrt{7}$ and $\sqrt{7}$ are examples of like radical expressions.

4. The expressions $3\sqrt{12}$ and $5\sqrt{3}$ cannot be subtracted until $3\sqrt{12}$ is rewritten in simplest form.

5. $5\sqrt{32x} + 4\sqrt{18x} = 5(4\sqrt{2x}) + 4(3\sqrt{2x}) = 20\sqrt{2x} + 12\sqrt{2x} = 32\sqrt{2x}$

6. The expressions $9\sqrt{11}$ and $10\sqrt{13}$ can be added after each radical is written in simplest form.

10.2   Exercises

1   Add and subtract radical expressions

1. Simplify: $5\sqrt{5} - 8\sqrt{5}$

$5\sqrt{5} - 8\sqrt{5} = (\underline{\quad?\quad} - \underline{\quad?\quad})\sqrt{5}$ • **The radicands are the same. Use the Distributive Property.**

$= \underline{\quad?\quad}\sqrt{5}$ • **Subtract.**

Simplify.

2. $2\sqrt{2} + \sqrt{2}$

3. $3\sqrt{5} + 8\sqrt{5}$

4. $-3\sqrt{7} + 2\sqrt{7}$

5. $4\sqrt{5} - 10\sqrt{5}$

6. $-3\sqrt{11} - 8\sqrt{11}$

7. $-3\sqrt{3} - 5\sqrt{3}$

8. $2\sqrt{x} + 8\sqrt{x}$

9. $3\sqrt{y} + 2\sqrt{y}$

10. $8\sqrt{y} - 10\sqrt{y}$

11. $-5\sqrt{2a} + 2\sqrt{2a}$

12. $-2\sqrt{3b} - 9\sqrt{3b}$

13. $-7\sqrt{5a} - 5\sqrt{5a}$

14. $3x\sqrt{2} - x\sqrt{2}$

15. $2y\sqrt{3} - 9y\sqrt{3}$

16. $2a\sqrt{3a} - 5a\sqrt{3a}$

17. $-5b\sqrt{3x} - 2b\sqrt{3x}$

18. $3\sqrt{xy} - 8\sqrt{xy}$

19. $-4\sqrt{xy} + 6\sqrt{xy}$

20. $\sqrt{45} + \sqrt{125}$

21. $\sqrt{32} - \sqrt{98}$

22. $2\sqrt{2} + 3\sqrt{8}$

23. $4\sqrt{128} - 3\sqrt{32}$

24. $5\sqrt{18} - 2\sqrt{75}$

25. $5\sqrt{75} - 2\sqrt{18}$

26. $5\sqrt{4x} - 3\sqrt{9x}$

27. $-3\sqrt{25y} + 8\sqrt{49y}$

28. Simplify: $3\sqrt{x^3} + 2x\sqrt{x}$

$3\sqrt{x^3} + 2x\sqrt{x} = 3\sqrt{\underline{}}\sqrt{x} + 2x\sqrt{x}$

- Write $\sqrt{x^3}$ as the product of the square root of a perfect square and $\sqrt{x}$.

$= 3\underline{}\sqrt{x} + 2x\sqrt{x}$

- Simplify $\sqrt{x^2}$.

$= (\underline{} + \underline{})\sqrt{x}$

- Use the Distributive Property.

$= \underline{}\sqrt{x}$

- Add.

29. $3\sqrt{3x^2} - 5\sqrt{27x^2}$

30. $-2\sqrt{8y^2} + 5\sqrt{32y^2}$

31. $2x\sqrt{xy^2} - 3y\sqrt{x^2y}$

32. $4a\sqrt{b^2a} - 3b\sqrt{a^2b}$

33. $3x\sqrt{12x} - 5\sqrt{27x^3}$

34. $2a\sqrt{50a} + 7\sqrt{32a^3}$

35. $4y\sqrt{8y^3} - 7\sqrt{18y^5}$

36. $2a\sqrt{8ab^2} - 2b\sqrt{2a^3}$

37. $b^2\sqrt{a^5b} + 3a^2\sqrt{ab^5}$

38. $y^2\sqrt{x^5y} + x\sqrt{x^3y^5}$

39. $4\sqrt{2} - 5\sqrt{2} + 8\sqrt{2}$

40. $3\sqrt{3} + 8\sqrt{3} - 16\sqrt{3}$

41. $5\sqrt{x} - 8\sqrt{x} + 9\sqrt{x}$

42. $\sqrt{x} - 7\sqrt{x} + 6\sqrt{x}$

43. $8\sqrt{2} - 3\sqrt{y} - 8\sqrt{2}$

44. $8\sqrt{3} - 5\sqrt{2} - 5\sqrt{3}$

45. $8\sqrt{8} - 4\sqrt{32} - 9\sqrt{50}$

46. $2\sqrt{12} - 4\sqrt{27} + \sqrt{75}$

47. $-2\sqrt{3} + 5\sqrt{27} - 4\sqrt{45}$

48. $-2\sqrt{8} - 3\sqrt{27} + 3\sqrt{50}$

49. $4\sqrt{75} + 3\sqrt{48} - \sqrt{99}$

50. $2\sqrt{75} - 5\sqrt{20} + 2\sqrt{45}$

51. $\sqrt{25x} - \sqrt{9x} + \sqrt{16x}$

52. $\sqrt{4x} - \sqrt{100x} - \sqrt{49x}$

53. $3\sqrt{3x} + \sqrt{27x} - 8\sqrt{75x}$

54. $5\sqrt{5x} + 2\sqrt{45x} - 3\sqrt{80x}$

55. $2a\sqrt{75b} - a\sqrt{20b} + 4a\sqrt{45b}$

56. $2b\sqrt{75a} - 5b\sqrt{27a} + 2b\sqrt{20a}$

57. $x\sqrt{3y^2} - 2y\sqrt{12x^2} + xy\sqrt{3}$

58. $a\sqrt{27b^2} + 3b\sqrt{147a^2} - ab\sqrt{3}$

59. $3\sqrt{ab^3} + 4a\sqrt{a^2b} - 5b\sqrt{4ab}$

60. $5\sqrt{a^3b} + a\sqrt{4ab} - 3\sqrt{49a^3b}$

61. $3a\sqrt{2ab^2} - \sqrt{a^2b^2} + 4b\sqrt{3a^2b}$

62. $2\sqrt{4a^2b^2} - 3a\sqrt{9ab^2} + 4b\sqrt{a^2b}$

63. Determine whether the statement is true or false.

    a. $7x\sqrt{x} + x\sqrt{x} = 7x^2\sqrt{x}$

    c. $\sqrt{9 + y^2} = 3 + y$

    b. $\sqrt{10a} - \sqrt{a} = \sqrt{a}(\sqrt{10} - 1)$

    d. $\sqrt{27x^4} + \sqrt{3} = \sqrt{3}(3x^2 + 1)$

64. Which expression is equivalent to $\sqrt{2ab} + \sqrt{2ab}$?

    a. $2\sqrt{ab}$ **b.** $\sqrt{4ab}$ **c.** $2ab$ **d.** $\sqrt{8ab}$

10.2   Applying Concepts

Add or subtract.

65. $5\sqrt{x + 2} + 3\sqrt{x + 2}$

66. $8\sqrt{a + 5} - 4\sqrt{a + 5}$

67. $\dfrac{1}{2}\sqrt{8x^2y} + \dfrac{1}{3}\sqrt{18x^2y}$

68. $\dfrac{1}{4}\sqrt{48ab^2} + \dfrac{1}{5}\sqrt{75ab^2}$

69. $\dfrac{a}{3}\sqrt{54ab^3} + \dfrac{b}{4}\sqrt{96a^3b}$

70. $\dfrac{x}{6}\sqrt{72xy^5} + \dfrac{y}{7}\sqrt{98x^3y^3}$

71. $2\sqrt{8x + 4y} - 5\sqrt{18x + 9y}$

72. $3\sqrt{a^3 + a^2} + 5\sqrt{4a^3 + 4a^2}$

73. **Geometry** The lengths of the sides of a triangle are $4\sqrt{3}$ cm, $2\sqrt{3}$ cm, and $2\sqrt{15}$ cm. Find the perimeter of the triangle.

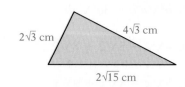

74. **Geometry** The length of a rectangle is $3\sqrt{2}$ cm. The width is $\sqrt{2}$ cm. Find the perimeter of the rectangle.

75. **Geometry** The length of a rectangle is $4\sqrt{5}$ cm. The width is $\sqrt{5}$ cm. Find the decimal approximation of the perimeter. Round to the nearest tenth.

$\sqrt{5}$ cm

76. Given $G(x) = \sqrt{x + 5} + \sqrt{5x + 3}$, write $G(3)$ in simplest form.

77. Use complete sentences to explain the steps in simplifying the radical expression $a\sqrt{32ab^2} + b\sqrt{50a^3}$.

10.3 Multiplication and Division of Radical Expressions

OBJECTIVE 1 **Multiply radical expressions**

The Product Property of Square Roots is used to multiply variable radical expressions.

$$\sqrt{2x}\,\sqrt{3y} = \sqrt{2x \cdot 3y}$$
$$= \sqrt{6xy}$$

Multiply: $\sqrt{2x^2}\,\sqrt{32x^5}$

Use the Product Property of Square Roots to multiply the radicands.

$$\sqrt{2x^2}\,\sqrt{32x^5} = \sqrt{2x^2 \cdot 32x^5}$$
$$= \sqrt{64x^7}$$

Simplify.

$$= \sqrt{64x^6}\,\sqrt{x}$$
$$= 8x^3\sqrt{x}$$

EXAMPLE 1 Multiply: $\sqrt{3x^4}\,\sqrt{2x^2y}\,\sqrt{6xy^2}$

Solution $\sqrt{3x^4}\,\sqrt{2x^2y}\,\sqrt{6xy^2} = \sqrt{3x^4 \cdot 2x^2y \cdot 6xy^2}$
$$= \sqrt{36x^7y^3}$$
$$= \sqrt{36x^6y^2}\,\sqrt{xy}$$
$$= 6x^3y\sqrt{xy}$$

PROBLEM 1 Multiply: $\sqrt{5a}\,\sqrt{15a^3b^4}\,\sqrt{3b^5}$

Solution See page S24.

When the expression $(\sqrt{x})^2$ is simplified by using the Product Property of Square Roots, the result is x.

$$(\sqrt{x})^2 = \sqrt{x}\,\sqrt{x}$$
$$= \sqrt{x \cdot x}$$
$$= \sqrt{x^2}$$
$$= x$$

For $a > 0$, $(\sqrt{a})^2 = \sqrt{a^2} = a$.

Multiply: $\sqrt{2x}\,(x + \sqrt{2x})$

Use the Distributive Property to remove parentheses.

$$\sqrt{2x}\,(x + \sqrt{2x}) = \sqrt{2x}\,(x) + \sqrt{2x}\,\sqrt{2x}$$
$$= x\sqrt{2x} + (\sqrt{2x})^2$$
$$= x\sqrt{2x} + 2x$$

EXAMPLE 2 Multiply: $\sqrt{3ab}\left(\sqrt{3a} + \sqrt{9b}\right)$

Solution $\sqrt{3ab}\left(\sqrt{3a} + \sqrt{9b}\right) = \sqrt{3ab}\left(\sqrt{3a}\right) + \sqrt{3ab}\left(\sqrt{9b}\right)$

$$= \sqrt{9a^2b} + \sqrt{27ab^2}$$
$$= \sqrt{9a^2}\sqrt{b} + \sqrt{9b^2}\sqrt{3a}$$
$$= 3a\sqrt{b} + 3b\sqrt{3a}$$

PROBLEM 2 Multiply: $\sqrt{5x}\left(\sqrt{5x} - \sqrt{25y}\right)$

Solution See page S24.

To multiply $\left(\sqrt{2} - 3x\right)\left(\sqrt{2} + x\right)$, use the FOIL method.

$$\left(\sqrt{2} - 3x\right)\left(\sqrt{2} + x\right) = \left(\sqrt{2}\right)^2 + x\sqrt{2} - 3x\sqrt{2} - 3x^2$$
$$= 2 + (x - 3x)\sqrt{2} - 3x^2$$
$$= 2 - 2x\sqrt{2} - 3x^2$$

EXAMPLE 3 Multiply: $\left(2\sqrt{x} - \sqrt{y}\right)\left(5\sqrt{x} - 2\sqrt{y}\right)$

Solution $\left(2\sqrt{x} - \sqrt{y}\right)\left(5\sqrt{x} - 2\sqrt{y}\right)$

$$= 10\left(\sqrt{x}\right)^2 - 4\sqrt{xy} - 5\sqrt{xy} + 2\left(\sqrt{y}\right)^2$$
$$= 10x - 9\sqrt{xy} + 2y$$

PROBLEM 3 Multiply: $\left(3\sqrt{x} - \sqrt{y}\right)\left(5\sqrt{x} - 2\sqrt{y}\right)$

Solution See page S24.

The expressions $a + b$ and $a - b$, which are the sum and difference of two terms, are called **conjugates** of each other.

The product of conjugates is the difference of two squares.

$$(a + b)(a - b) = a^2 - b^2$$
$$\left(2 + \sqrt{7}\right)\left(2 - \sqrt{7}\right) = 2^2 - \left(\sqrt{7}\right)^2 = 4 - 7 = -3$$
$$\left(3 + \sqrt{y}\right)\left(3 - \sqrt{y}\right) = 3^2 - \left(\sqrt{y}\right)^2 = 9 - y$$

EXAMPLE 4 Multiply: $\left(\sqrt{a} - \sqrt{b}\right)\left(\sqrt{a} + \sqrt{b}\right)$

Solution $\left(\sqrt{a} - \sqrt{b}\right)\left(\sqrt{a} + \sqrt{b}\right) = \left(\sqrt{a}\right)^2 - \left(\sqrt{b}\right)^2 = a - b$

PROBLEM 4 Multiply: $\left(2\sqrt{x} + 7\right)\left(2\sqrt{x} - 7\right)$

Solution See page S24.

OBJECTIVE 2 **Divide radical expressions**

The square root of a quotient is equal to the quotient of the square roots.

The Quotient Property of Square Roots

If a and b are positive real numbers, then $\sqrt{\dfrac{a}{b}} = \dfrac{\sqrt{a}}{\sqrt{b}}$.

Point of Interest

A radical expression that occurs in Einstein's Theory of Relativity is

$$\frac{1}{\sqrt{1 - \dfrac{v^2}{c^2}}}$$

where v is the velocity of an object and c is the speed of light.

Simplify: $\sqrt{\dfrac{4x^2}{z^6}}$

Rewrite the radical expression as the quotient of the square roots.

Take the square roots of the perfect squares.

$$\sqrt{\frac{4x^2}{z^6}} = \frac{\sqrt{4x^2}}{\sqrt{z^6}}$$
$$= \frac{2x}{z^3}$$

Simplify: $\sqrt{\dfrac{24x^3y^7}{3x^7y^2}}$

Simplify the radicand.

Rewrite the radical expression as the quotient of the square roots.

Simplify.

$$\sqrt{\frac{24x^3y^7}{3x^7y^2}} = \sqrt{\frac{8y^5}{x^4}}$$
$$= \frac{\sqrt{8y^5}}{\sqrt{x^4}}$$
$$= \frac{\sqrt{4y^4}\,\sqrt{2y}}{\sqrt{x^4}}$$
$$= \frac{2y^2\sqrt{2y}}{x^2}$$

Simplify: $\dfrac{\sqrt{4x^2y}}{\sqrt{xy}}$

Use the Quotient Property of Square Roots.

Simplify the radicand.

Simplify the radical expression.

$$\frac{\sqrt{4x^2y}}{\sqrt{xy}} = \sqrt{\frac{4x^2y}{xy}}$$
$$= \sqrt{4x}$$
$$= \sqrt{4}\,\sqrt{x}$$
$$= 2\sqrt{x}$$

A radical expression is not in simplest form if a radical remains in the denominator. The procedure used to remove a radical from the denominator is called **rationalizing the denominator.**

Simplify: $\dfrac{2}{\sqrt{3}}$

The expression $\dfrac{2}{\sqrt{3}}$ has a radical expression in the denominator. Multiply the expression by $\dfrac{\sqrt{3}}{\sqrt{3}}$, which equals 1.

Simplify.

$$\frac{2}{\sqrt{3}} = \frac{2}{\sqrt{3}} \cdot \frac{\sqrt{3}}{\sqrt{3}}$$
$$= \frac{2\sqrt{3}}{(\sqrt{3})^2}$$
$$= \frac{2\sqrt{3}}{3}$$

Thus $\dfrac{2}{\sqrt{3}} = \dfrac{2\sqrt{3}}{3}$, but $\dfrac{2}{\sqrt{3}}$ is not in simplest form. Because no radical remains in the denominator and the radical in the numerator contains no perfect-square factors other than 1, $\dfrac{2\sqrt{3}}{3}$ is in simplest form.

When the denominator contains a radical expression with two terms, simplify the radical expression by multiplying the numerator and denominator by the conjugate of the denominator.

Simplify: $\dfrac{\sqrt{2y}}{\sqrt{y} + 3}$

Multiply the numerator and denominator by $\sqrt{y} - 3$, the conjugate of $\sqrt{y} + 3$.

$$\dfrac{\sqrt{2y}}{\sqrt{y} + 3} = \dfrac{\sqrt{2y}}{\sqrt{y} + 3} \cdot \dfrac{\sqrt{y} - 3}{\sqrt{y} - 3}$$

Simplify.

$$= \dfrac{\sqrt{2y^2} - 3\sqrt{2y}}{(\sqrt{y})^2 - 3^2}$$

$$= \dfrac{y\sqrt{2} - 3\sqrt{2y}}{y - 9}$$

The following list summarizes the discussions about radical expressions in simplest form.

Radical Expressions in Simplest Form

A radical expression is in simplest form if:

1. The radicand contains no factor greater than 1 that is a perfect square.

2. There is no fraction under the radical sign.

3. There is no radical in the denominator of a fraction.

EXAMPLE 5   Simplify.   **A.** $\dfrac{\sqrt{4x^2y^5}}{\sqrt{3x^4y}}$ **B.** $\dfrac{\sqrt{2}}{\sqrt{2} - \sqrt{x}}$ **C.** $\dfrac{3 - \sqrt{5}}{2 + 3\sqrt{5}}$

Solution   **A.** $\dfrac{\sqrt{4x^2y^5}}{\sqrt{3x^4y}} = \sqrt{\dfrac{4x^2y^5}{3x^4y}} = \sqrt{\dfrac{4y^4}{3x^2}} = \dfrac{\sqrt{4y^4}}{\sqrt{3x^2}} = \dfrac{2y^2}{x\sqrt{3}} \cdot \dfrac{\sqrt{3}}{\sqrt{3}} = \dfrac{2y^2\sqrt{3}}{3x}$

B. $\dfrac{\sqrt{2}}{\sqrt{2} - \sqrt{x}} = \dfrac{\sqrt{2}}{\sqrt{2} - \sqrt{x}} \cdot \dfrac{\sqrt{2} + \sqrt{x}}{\sqrt{2} + \sqrt{x}} = \dfrac{2 + \sqrt{2x}}{2 - x}$

C. $\dfrac{3 - \sqrt{5}}{2 + 3\sqrt{5}} = \dfrac{3 - \sqrt{5}}{2 + 3\sqrt{5}} \cdot \dfrac{2 - 3\sqrt{5}}{2 - 3\sqrt{5}}$

$$= \dfrac{6 - 9\sqrt{5} - 2\sqrt{5} + 3 \cdot 5}{4 - 9 \cdot 5}$$

$$= \dfrac{21 - 11\sqrt{5}}{-41}$$

$$= -\dfrac{21 - 11\sqrt{5}}{41}$$

> **PROBLEM 5** Simplify. **A.** $\dfrac{\sqrt{15x^6y^7}}{\sqrt{3x^7y^9}}$ **B.** $\dfrac{\sqrt{y}}{\sqrt{y}+3}$ **C.** $\dfrac{5+\sqrt{y}}{1-2\sqrt{y}}$
>
> ■ **Solution** See page S24.

10.3 Concept Review

Determine whether the statement is always true, sometimes true, or never true.

1. By the Product Property of Square Roots, if $a > 0$ and $b > 0$, then $\sqrt{a} \cdot \sqrt{b} = \sqrt{ab}$.

2. When we square a square root, the result is the radicand.

3. The procedure for rationalizing the denominator is used when a fraction has a radical expression in the denominator.

4. The square root of a fraction is equal to the square root of the numerator over the square root of the denominator.

5. A radical expression is in simplest form if the radicand contains no factor other than 1 that is a perfect square.

6. The conjugate of $5 - \sqrt{3}$ is $\sqrt{3} - 5$.

10.3 Exercises

1 Multiply radical expressions

1. $\sqrt{3} \cdot \sqrt{3} = \sqrt{\underline{\quad?\quad}}$ • Use the Product Property of Square Roots to multiply the radicands.

     $= \underline{\quad?\quad}$ • Simplify.

2. $\sqrt{3} \cdot \sqrt{15} = \sqrt{\underline{\quad?\quad}}$ • Use the Product Property of Square Roots to multiply the radicands.

     $= \sqrt{9 \cdot \underline{\quad?\quad}}$ • Write the radicand as the product of a perfect square and a factor that does not contain a perfect square.

     $= \sqrt{9}\sqrt{\underline{\quad?\quad}}$ • Use the Product Property of Square Roots.

     $= \underline{\quad?\quad}\sqrt{\underline{\quad?\quad}}$ • Simplify the square root of the perfect square.

Multiply.

3. $\sqrt{5}\,\sqrt{5}$ **4.** $\sqrt{11}\,\sqrt{11}$ **5.** $\sqrt{3}\,\sqrt{12}$ **6.** $\sqrt{2}\,\sqrt{8}$

7. $\sqrt{x}\,\sqrt{x}$ **8.** $\sqrt{y}\,\sqrt{y}$ **9.** $\sqrt{xy^3}\,\sqrt{x^5y}$ **10.** $\sqrt{a^3b^5}\,\sqrt{ab^5}$

11. $\sqrt{3a^2b^5}\,\sqrt{6ab^7}$ **12.** $\sqrt{5x^3y}\,\sqrt{10x^2y}$ **13.** $\sqrt{6a^3b^2}\,\sqrt{24a^5b}$ **14.** $\sqrt{8ab^5}\,\sqrt{12a^7b}$

15. $\sqrt{2}\left(\sqrt{2}-\sqrt{3}\right)$ **16.** $3\left(\sqrt{12}-\sqrt{3}\right)$ **17.** $\sqrt{x}\left(\sqrt{x}-\sqrt{y}\right)$ **18.** $\sqrt{b}\left(\sqrt{a}-\sqrt{b}\right)$

19. $\sqrt{5}\left(\sqrt{10}-\sqrt{x}\right)$ **20.** $\sqrt{6}\left(\sqrt{y}-\sqrt{18}\right)$ **21.** $\sqrt{8}\left(\sqrt{2}-\sqrt{5}\right)$ **22.** $\sqrt{10}\left(\sqrt{20}-\sqrt{a}\right)$

23. $\left(\sqrt{x}-3\right)^2$ **24.** $\left(2\sqrt{a}-y\right)^2$ **25.** $\sqrt{3a}\left(\sqrt{3a}-\sqrt{3b}\right)$

26. $\sqrt{5x}\left(\sqrt{10x}-\sqrt{x}\right)$ **27.** $\sqrt{2ac}\,\sqrt{5ab}\,\sqrt{10cb}$ **28.** $\sqrt{3xy}\,\sqrt{6x^3y}\,\sqrt{2y^2}$

29. $\left(3\sqrt{x}-2y\right)\left(5\sqrt{x}-4y\right)$ **30.** $\left(5\sqrt{x}+2\sqrt{y}\right)\left(3\sqrt{x}-\sqrt{y}\right)$ **31.** $\left(\sqrt{x}-\sqrt{y}\right)\left(\sqrt{x}+\sqrt{y}\right)$

32. $\left(\sqrt{3x}+y\right)\left(\sqrt{3x}-y\right)$ **33.** $\left(2\sqrt{x}+\sqrt{y}\right)\left(5\sqrt{x}+4\sqrt{y}\right)$ **34.** $\left(5\sqrt{x}-2\sqrt{y}\right)\left(3\sqrt{x}-4\sqrt{y}\right)$

35. For $a > 0$, is $(\sqrt{a}-1)(\sqrt{a}+1)$ less than, equal to, or greater than a?

36. For $a > 0$, is $\sqrt{a}\,(\sqrt{2a}-\sqrt{a})$ less than, equal to, or greater than a?

2 ### Divide radical expressions

37. Explain why $\dfrac{\sqrt{5}}{5}$ is in simplest form and $\dfrac{1}{\sqrt{5}}$ is not in simplest form.

38. Why can we multiply $\dfrac{1}{\sqrt{3}}$ by $\dfrac{\sqrt{3}}{\sqrt{3}}$ without changing the value of $\dfrac{1}{\sqrt{3}}$?

39. State whether the expression is in simplest form.

     a. $\dfrac{a}{\sqrt{b}}$ **b.** $\dfrac{\sqrt{a}}{b}$ **c.** $\sqrt{\dfrac{a}{b}}$ **d.** $\dfrac{\sqrt{a}}{\sqrt{b}}$

40. By what expression should the numerator and denominator be multiplied in order to rationalize the denominator?

     a. $\dfrac{2}{\sqrt{5}}$ **b.** $\dfrac{3}{\sqrt{y}}$ **c.** $\dfrac{14}{\sqrt{3xy}}$ **d.** $\dfrac{\sqrt{5}}{4\sqrt{6}}$

Simplify.

41. $\dfrac{\sqrt{32}}{\sqrt{2}}$

42. $\dfrac{\sqrt{45}}{\sqrt{5}}$

43. $\dfrac{\sqrt{98}}{\sqrt{2}}$

44. $\dfrac{\sqrt{48}}{\sqrt{3}}$

45. $\dfrac{\sqrt{27a}}{\sqrt{3a}}$

46. $\dfrac{\sqrt{72x^5}}{\sqrt{2x}}$

47. $\dfrac{\sqrt{15x^3y}}{\sqrt{3xy}}$

48. $\dfrac{\sqrt{40x^5y^2}}{\sqrt{5xy}}$

49. $\dfrac{\sqrt{2a^5b^4}}{\sqrt{98ab^4}}$

50. $\dfrac{\sqrt{48x^5y^2}}{\sqrt{3x^3y}}$

51. $\dfrac{1}{\sqrt{3}}$

52. $\dfrac{1}{\sqrt{8}}$

53. $\dfrac{15}{\sqrt{75}}$

54. $\dfrac{6}{\sqrt{72}}$

55. $\dfrac{6}{\sqrt{12x}}$

56. $\dfrac{14}{\sqrt{7y}}$

57. $\dfrac{8}{\sqrt{32x}}$

58. $\dfrac{15}{\sqrt{50x}}$

59. $\dfrac{3}{\sqrt{x}}$

60. $\dfrac{4}{\sqrt{2x}}$

61. $\dfrac{\sqrt{8x^2y}}{\sqrt{2x^4y^2}}$

62. $\dfrac{\sqrt{4x^2}}{\sqrt{9y}}$

63. $\dfrac{\sqrt{16a}}{\sqrt{49ab}}$

64. $\dfrac{5\sqrt{8}}{4\sqrt{50}}$

65. $\dfrac{5\sqrt{18}}{9\sqrt{27}}$

66. $\dfrac{\sqrt{12a^3b}}{\sqrt{24a^2b^2}}$

67. $\dfrac{\sqrt{3xy}}{\sqrt{27x^3y^2}}$

68. $\dfrac{\sqrt{9xy^2}}{\sqrt{27x}}$

69. $\dfrac{\sqrt{4x^2y}}{\sqrt{3xy^3}}$

70. $\dfrac{\sqrt{16x^3y^2}}{\sqrt{8x^3y}}$

71. $\dfrac{1}{\sqrt{2}-3}$

72. $\dfrac{5}{\sqrt{7}-3}$

73. $\dfrac{3}{5+\sqrt{5}}$

74. $\dfrac{7}{\sqrt{2}-7}$

75. $\dfrac{\sqrt{xy}}{\sqrt{x}-\sqrt{y}}$

76. $\dfrac{\sqrt{x}}{\sqrt{x}-\sqrt{y}}$

77. $\dfrac{5\sqrt{x^2y}}{\sqrt{75xy^2}}$

78. $\dfrac{3\sqrt{ab}}{a\sqrt{6b}}$

79. $\dfrac{\sqrt{2}}{\sqrt{2}-\sqrt{3}}$

80. $\dfrac{1+\sqrt{2}}{1-\sqrt{2}}$

81. $\dfrac{\sqrt{5}}{\sqrt{2}-\sqrt{5}}$

82. $\dfrac{\sqrt{6}}{\sqrt{3}-\sqrt{2}}$

83. $\dfrac{\sqrt{x}}{\sqrt{x}+3}$

84. $\dfrac{\sqrt{y}}{2-\sqrt{y}}$

85. $\dfrac{5\sqrt{3}-7\sqrt{3}}{4\sqrt{3}}$

86. $\dfrac{10\sqrt{7}-2\sqrt{7}}{2\sqrt{7}}$

87. $\dfrac{5\sqrt{8}-3\sqrt{2}}{\sqrt{2}}$

88. $\dfrac{5\sqrt{12}-\sqrt{3}}{\sqrt{27}}$

89. $\dfrac{3\sqrt{2}-8\sqrt{2}}{\sqrt{2}}$

90. $\dfrac{5\sqrt{3}-2\sqrt{3}}{2\sqrt{3}}$

91. $\dfrac{2\sqrt{8}+3\sqrt{2}}{\sqrt{32}}$

92. $\dfrac{3-\sqrt{6}}{5-2\sqrt{6}}$

93. $\dfrac{6-2\sqrt{3}}{4+3\sqrt{3}}$

94. $\dfrac{\sqrt{2}+2\sqrt{6}}{2\sqrt{2}-3\sqrt{6}}$

95. $\dfrac{2\sqrt{3} - \sqrt{6}}{5\sqrt{3} + 2\sqrt{6}}$

96. $\dfrac{3 + \sqrt{x}}{2 - \sqrt{x}}$

97. $\dfrac{\sqrt{a} - 4}{2\sqrt{a} + 2}$

98. $\dfrac{3 + 2\sqrt{y}}{2 - \sqrt{y}}$

99. $\dfrac{2 + \sqrt{y}}{\sqrt{y} - 3}$

100. $\dfrac{\sqrt{x} + \sqrt{y}}{\sqrt{x} - \sqrt{y}}$

10.3 Applying Concepts

Simplify.

101. $-\sqrt{1.3}\,\sqrt{1.3}$

102. $\sqrt{\dfrac{5}{8}}\,\sqrt{\dfrac{5}{8}}$

103. $-\sqrt{\dfrac{16}{81}}$

104. $\sqrt{1\dfrac{9}{16}}$

105. $\sqrt{2\dfrac{1}{4}}$

106. $-\sqrt{6\dfrac{1}{4}}$

Geometry Find the area of the geometric figure. All dimensions are given in meters.

107.

$8 - \sqrt{5}$

$8 + \sqrt{5}$

108.

$12 + \sqrt{2}$

$10 + \sqrt{8}$

109. Is the equation true or false? If the equation is false, correct the right side.

a. $\left(\sqrt{y}\right)^4 = y^2$
b. $\left(2\sqrt{x}\right)^3 = 8x\sqrt{x}$
c. $\left(\sqrt{x} + 1\right)^2 = x + 1$
d. $\dfrac{1}{2 - \sqrt{3}} = 2 + \sqrt{3}$

110. Show that 2 is a solution of the equation $\sqrt{x + 2} + \sqrt{x - 1} = 3$.

111. Is 16 a solution of the equation $\sqrt{x} - \sqrt{x + 9} = 1$?

112. Show that $1 + \sqrt{6}$ and $1 - \sqrt{6}$ are solutions of the equation $x^2 - 2x - 5 = 0$.

113. In your own words, describe the process of rationalizing the denominator.

114. The number $\dfrac{\sqrt{5} + 1}{2}$ is called the golden ratio. Research the golden ratio and write a few paragraphs about this number and its applications.

10.4 Solving Equations Containing Radical Expressions

OBJECTIVE **1**

Solve equations containing one or more radical expressions

An equation that contains a variable expression in a radicand is a **radical equation.**

$$\left.\begin{array}{l} \sqrt{x} = 4 \\ \sqrt{x + 2} = \sqrt{x - 7} \end{array}\right\} \begin{array}{l} \text{Radical} \\ \text{equations} \end{array}$$

The following property of equality states that if two numbers are equal, then the squares of the numbers are equal. This property is used to solve radical equations.

Property of Squaring Both Sides of an Equation

If a and b are real numbers and $a = b$, then $a^2 = b^2$.

Solve: $\sqrt{x - 2} - 7 = 0$

Rewrite the equation with the radical on one side of the equation and the constant on the other side.

$$\sqrt{x - 2} - 7 = 0$$
$$\sqrt{x - 2} = 7$$

Square both sides of the equation.

$$\left(\sqrt{x - 2}\right)^2 = 7^2$$

Solve the resulting equation.

$$x - 2 = 49$$
$$x = 51$$

Take Note

Any time each side of an equation is squared, you must check the proposed solution of the equation.

Check the solution. When both sides of an equation are squared, the resulting equation may have a solution that is not a solution of the original equation.

Check:
$$\sqrt{x - 2} - 7 = 0$$
$$\begin{array}{c|c} \sqrt{51 - 2} - 7 & 0 \\ \sqrt{49} - 7 & 0 \\ 7 - 7 & 0 \\ 0 = 0 \end{array}$$

The solution is 51.

EXAMPLE 1   Solve: $\sqrt{3x} + 2 = 5$

Solution
$$\sqrt{3x} + 2 = 5$$
$$\sqrt{3x} = 3$$

• **Rewrite the equation so that the radical is alone on one side of the equation.**

$$\left(\sqrt{3x}\right)^2 = 3^2$$
$$3x = 9$$
$$x = 3$$

• **Square both sides of the equation.**
• **Solve for x.**

Check
$$\sqrt{3x} + 2 = 5$$
$$\begin{array}{c|c} \sqrt{3 \cdot 3} + 2 & 5 \\ \sqrt{9} + 2 & 5 \\ 3 + 2 & 5 \\ 5 = 5 \end{array}$$

• **Both sides of the equation were squared. The solution must be checked.**

• **This is a true equation. The solution checks.**

The solution is 3.

PROBLEM 1 Solve: $\sqrt{4x} + 3 = 7$

Solution See page S24.

EXAMPLE 2 Solve. **A.** $0 = 3 - \sqrt{2x - 3}$ **B.** $\sqrt{2x - 5} + 3 = 0$

Solution **A.**
$$0 = 3 - \sqrt{2x - 3}$$
$$\sqrt{2x - 3} = 3$$

- Rewrite the equation so that the radical is alone on one side of the equation.

$$\left(\sqrt{2x - 3}\right)^2 = 3^2$$
$$2x - 3 = 9$$
$$2x = 12$$
$$x = 6$$

- Square both sides of the equation.

Check $0 = 3 - \sqrt{2x - 3}$

0	$3 - \sqrt{2 \cdot 6 - 3}$
0	$3 - \sqrt{12 - 3}$
0	$3 - \sqrt{9}$
0	$3 - 3$
$0 = 0$	

- This is a true equation. The solution checks.

The solution is 6.

B. $\sqrt{2x - 5} + 3 = 0$
$$\sqrt{2x - 5} = -3$$

- Rewrite the equation so that the radical is alone on one side of the equation.

$$\left(\sqrt{2x - 5}\right)^2 = (-3)^2$$
$$2x - 5 = 9$$
$$2x = 14$$
$$x = 7$$

- Square each side of the equation.
- Solve for x.

Check $\sqrt{2x - 5} + 3 = 0$

$\sqrt{2 \cdot 7 - 5} + 3$	0
$\sqrt{14 - 5} + 3$	0
$\sqrt{9} + 3$	0
$3 + 3$	0
$6 \neq 0$	

- This is not a true equation. The solution does not check.

There is no solution.

PROBLEM 2 Solve. **A.** $\sqrt{3x - 2} - 5 = 0$ **B.** $\sqrt{4x - 7} + 5 = 0$

Solution See page S24.

The following example illustrates the procedure for solving a radical equation containing two radical expressions. Note that the process of squaring both sides of the equation is perfomed twice.

Solve: $\sqrt{5 + x} + \sqrt{x} = 5$

Solve for one of the radical expressions. Square each side.

$$\sqrt{5 + x} + \sqrt{x} = 5$$
$$\sqrt{5 + x} = 5 - \sqrt{x}$$
$$\left(\sqrt{5 + x}\right)^2 = \left(5 - \sqrt{x}\right)^2$$

Recall that $(a - b)^2 = a^2 - 2ab + b^2$.

$$5 + x = 25 - 10\sqrt{x} + x$$

Simplify.

$$-20 = -10\sqrt{x}$$

This is still a radical equation.

$$2 = \sqrt{x}$$

Square each side.

$$2^2 = \left(\sqrt{x}\right)^2$$
$$4 = x$$

4 checks as the solution.   The solution is 4.

EXAMPLE 3   Solve: $\sqrt{x} - \sqrt{x - 5} = 1$

Solution $\sqrt{x} - \sqrt{x - 5} = 1$
$$\sqrt{x} = 1 + \sqrt{x - 5}$$
$$\left(\sqrt{x}\right)^2 = \left(1 + \sqrt{x - 5}\right)^2$$
$$x = 1 + 2\sqrt{x - 5} + (x - 5)$$
$$4 = 2\sqrt{x - 5}$$
$$2 = \sqrt{x - 5}$$

$$2^2 = \left(\sqrt{x - 5}\right)^2$$
$$4 = x - 5$$
$$9 = x$$

- Solve for one of the radical expressions.
- Square each side.
- Simplify.

- This is a radical equation.
- Square each side.
- Simplify.

Check $\dfrac{\sqrt{x} - \sqrt{x - 5} = 1}{}$

$\sqrt{9} - \sqrt{9 - 5}$	1
$3 - \sqrt{4}$	1
$3 - 2$	1
$1 = 1$	

The solution is 9.

PROBLEM 3   Solve: $\sqrt{x} + \sqrt{x + 9} = 9$

Solution   See page S24.

OBJECTIVE [2]   Application problems

A **right triangle** contains one 90° angle. The side opposite the 90° angle is called the **hypotenuse.** The other two sides are called **legs.**

The angles in a right triangle are usually labeled with the capital letters A, B, and C, with C reserved for the right angle. The side opposite angle A is side a, the side opposite side B is side b, and c is the hypotenuse.

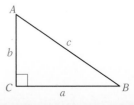

Pythagoras (c. 580 B.C.–520 B.C.)

The Greek mathematician Pythagoras is generally credited with the discovery that the square of the hypotenuse of a right triangle is equal to the sum of the squares of the two legs. This is called the **Pythagorean Theorem.**

The figure at the left is a right triangle with legs measuring 3 units and 4 units and a hypotenuse measuring 5 units. Each side of the triangle is also the side of a square. The number of square units in the area of the largest square is equal to the sum of the numbers of square units in the areas of the smaller squares.

Square of the hypotenuse	$=$	Sum of the squares of the two legs

$$5^2 = 3^2 + 4^2$$
$$25 = 9 + 16$$
$$25 = 25$$

Point of Interest

The first known proof of this theorem occurs in a Chinese text, Arithmetic Classic, which was written around 600 B.C. (but there are no existing copies) and revised over a period of 500 years. The earliest known copy of this text dates from approximately 100 B.C.

Pythagorean Theorem

If a and b are the lengths of the legs of a right triangle and c is the length of the hypotenuse, then $c^2 = a^2 + b^2.$

If the lengths of two sides of a right triangle are known, the Pythagorean Theorem can be used to find the length of the third side.

The Pythagorean Theorem is used to find the hypotenuse when the two legs are known.

Take Note

If we let $a = 12$ and $b = 5$, the result is the same.

$$\text{Hypotenuse} = \sqrt{(\text{leg})^2 + (\text{leg})^2}$$
$$c = \sqrt{a^2 + b^2}$$
$$c = \sqrt{(5)^2 + (12)^2}$$
$$c = \sqrt{25 + 144}$$
$$c = \sqrt{169}$$
$$c = 13$$

The Pythagorean Theorem is used to find the length of a leg when one leg and the hypotenuse are known.

$$\text{Leg} = \sqrt{(\text{hypotenuse})^2 - (\text{leg})^2}$$
$$a = \sqrt{c^2 - b^2}$$
$$a = \sqrt{(25)^2 - (20)^2}$$
$$a = \sqrt{625 - 400}$$
$$a = \sqrt{225}$$
$$a = 15$$

Example 4 and Problem 4 illustrate the use of the Pythagorean Theorem. Example 5 and Problem 5 illustrate other applications of radical equations.

EXAMPLE 4 A guy wire is attached to a point 22 m above the ground on a telephone pole that is perpendicular to the ground. The wire is anchored to the ground at a point 9 m from the base of the pole. Find the length of the guy wire. Round to the nearest hundredth.

Strategy To find the length of the guy wire, use the Pythagorean Theorem. One leg is the distance from the bottom of the wire to the base of the telephone pole. The other leg is the distance from the top of the wire to the base of the telephone pole. The guy wire is the hypotenuse. Solve the Pythagorean Theorem for the hypotenuse.

Solution
$$c = \sqrt{a^2 + b^2}$$
$$c = \sqrt{(22)^2 + (9)^2}$$
$$c = \sqrt{484 + 81}$$
$$c = \sqrt{565}$$
$$c \approx 23.77$$

The guy wire has a length of 23.77 m.

PROBLEM 4 A ladder 12 ft long is resting against a building. How high on the building will the ladder reach when the bottom of the ladder is 5 ft from the building? Round to the nearest hundredth.

Solution See page S25.

EXAMPLE 5 How far would a submarine periscope have to be above the water for the lookout to locate a ship 5 mi away? The equation for the distance in miles that the lookout can see is $d = \sqrt{1.5h}$, where h is the height in feet above the surface of the water. Round to the nearest hundredth.

Strategy To find the height above water, replace d in the equation with the given value. Then solve for h.

Solution
$$d = \sqrt{1.5h}$$
$$5 = \sqrt{1.5h}$$
$$5^2 = \left(\sqrt{1.5h}\right)^2$$
$$25 = 1.5h$$
$$\frac{25}{1.5} = h$$
$$16.67 \approx h$$

The periscope must be 16.67 ft above the water.

PROBLEM 5 Find the length of a pendulum that makes one swing in 1.5 s. The equation for the time of one swing is $T = 2\pi\sqrt{\dfrac{L}{32}}$, where T is the time in seconds and L is the length in feet. Round to the nearest hundredth.

Solution See page S25.

10.4 Concept Review

Determine whether the statement is always true, sometimes true, or never true.

1. A radical equation is an equation that contains a radical.

2. We can square both sides of an equation without changing the solutions of the equation.

3. We use the Property of Squaring Both Sides of an Equation in order to eliminate a radical expression from an equation.

4. The first step in solving a radical equation is to square both sides of the equation.

5. Suppose $a^2 = b^2$. Then $a = b$.

6. The Pythagorean Theorem is used to find the length of a side of a triangle.

10.4 Exercises

1 Solve equations containing one or more radical expressions

1. Which of the following equations are radical equations?
 a. $8 = \sqrt{5} + x$
 b. $\sqrt{x - 7} = 9$
 c. $\sqrt{x} + 4 = 6$
 d. $12 = \sqrt{3x}$

2. What does the Property of Squaring Both Sides of an Equation state?

3. Solve: $\sqrt{x - 2} = 5$. You will check the solution in Exercise 4.

$$\sqrt{x - 2} = 5$$ • The radical is alone on one side.

$$(\sqrt{x - 2})^{\underline{?}} = 5^{\underline{?}}$$ • Square each side of the equation.

$$\underline{\quad?\quad} = \underline{\quad?\quad}$$ • Simplify.

$$x = \underline{\quad?\quad}$$ • Add $\underline{\quad?\quad}$ to each side of the equation.

4. Check the solution of the equation $\sqrt{x} - 2 = 5$ that you found in Exercise 3.

$$\sqrt{x} - 2 = 5$$

$\sqrt{27} - 2$	5	• Replace x with _____?_____.
$\sqrt{?}$	5	• Subtract.
$? = 5$		• Simplify the radical expression. This is a _____?_____ equation. The solution checks.

Solve and check.

5. $\sqrt{x} = 5$ **6.** $\sqrt{y} = 7$ **7.** $\sqrt{a} = 12$ **8.** $\sqrt{a} = 9$

9. $\sqrt{5x} = 5$ **10.** $\sqrt{3x} = 4$ **11.** $\sqrt{4x} = 8$ **12.** $\sqrt{6x} = 3$

13. $\sqrt{2x} - 4 = 0$ **14.** $3 - \sqrt{5x} = 0$ **15.** $\sqrt{4x} + 5 = 2$ **16.** $\sqrt{3x} + 9 = 4$

17. $\sqrt{3x} - 2 = 4$ **18.** $\sqrt{5x + 6} = 1$ **19.** $\sqrt{2x + 1} = 7$ **20.** $\sqrt{5x + 4} = 3$

21. $0 = 2 - \sqrt{3 - x}$ **22.** $0 = 5 - \sqrt{10 + x}$ **23.** $\sqrt{5x + 2} = 0$ **24.** $\sqrt{3x - 7} = 0$

25. $\sqrt{3x} - 6 = -4$ **26.** $\sqrt{5x} + 8 = 23$ **27.** $0 = \sqrt{3x - 9} - 6$ **28.** $0 = \sqrt{2x + 7} - 3$

29. $\sqrt{5x - 1} = \sqrt{3x + 9}$ **30.** $\sqrt{3x + 4} = \sqrt{12x - 14}$

31. $\sqrt{5x - 3} = \sqrt{4x - 2}$ **32.** $\sqrt{5x - 9} = \sqrt{2x - 3}$

33. $\sqrt{x^2 - 5x + 6} = \sqrt{x^2 - 8x + 9}$ **34.** $\sqrt{x^2 - 2x + 4} = \sqrt{x^2 + 5x - 12}$

35. $\sqrt{x} = \sqrt{x + 3} - 1$ **36.** $\sqrt{x + 5} = \sqrt{x} + 1$

37. $\sqrt{2x + 5} = 5 - \sqrt{2x}$ **38.** $\sqrt{2x} + \sqrt{2x + 9} = 9$

39. $\sqrt{3x} - \sqrt{3x + 7} = 1$ **40.** $\sqrt{x} - \sqrt{x + 9} = 1$

41. Without actually solving the equations, identify which equation has no solution.

   a. $-\sqrt{2x - 5} = -3$ **b.** $\sqrt{2x} - 5 = -3$ **c.** $\sqrt{2x - 5} = -3$

42. How many times will the Property of Squaring Both Sides of an Equation be used in the solving of each equation? Do not solve.

   a. $\sqrt{x - 3} = \sqrt{4x - 7}$ **b.** $\sqrt{x - 6} = \sqrt{x} - 3$

2   Application problems

43. Integer Problem Five added to the square root of the product of four and a number is equal to seven. Find the number.

44. **Integer Problem** The product of a number and the square root of three is equal to the square root of twenty-seven. Find the number.

45. **Integer Problem** Two added to the square root of the sum of a number and five is equal to six. Find the number.

46. **Integer Problem** The product of a number and the square root of seven is equal to the square root of twenty-eight. Find the number.

47. In a right triangle, the hypotenuse is the side opposite the ____?____ angle. The other two sides are called ____?____ .

48. Label the right triangle shown at the right. Include the right angle symbol, the three angles, the two legs, and the hypotenuse.

49. What does the Pythagorean Theorem state?

50. A 20-foot ladder leans against the side of a building with its bottom d foot from the building. The ladder reaches a height of h feet. Which of the following distances is not possible as a value for h?
a. 4 ft   **b.** 10 ft   **c.** 16 ft   **d.** 22 ft

Solve. Round to the nearest hundredth.

51. **Geometry** The two legs of a right triangle measure 5 cm and 9 cm. Find the length of the hypotenuse.

5 cm

9 cm

52. **Geometry** The two legs of a right triangle measure 8 in. and 4 in. Find the length of the hypotenuse.

53. **Geometry** The hypotenuse of a right triangle measures 12 ft. One leg of the triangle measures 7 ft. Find the length of the other leg of the triangle.

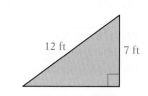

12 ft   7 ft

54. **Geometry** The hypotenuse of a right triangle measures 20 cm. One leg of the triangle measures 16 cm. Find the length of the other leg of the triangle.

55. **Geometry** The diagonal of a rectangle is a line drawn from one vertex to the opposite vertex. Find the length of the diagonal in the rectangle shown at the right. Round to the nearest tenth.

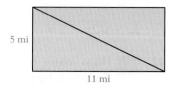

5 mi

11 mi

56. The equation $v = 4\sqrt{d}$ gives the speed, v, in feet per second, of a dropped object after the object has fallen d feet. A stone is dropped from a bridge. To find the distance the stone has fallen when it reaches a speed of 48 feet per second, replace ____?____ with 48 and solve for ____?____ .

57. Is the equation equivalent to the equation $C = \sqrt{32H}$, given in Exercise 59? Assume C and H are positive.

a. $\dfrac{C^2}{H} = 32$ **b.** $C = 4\sqrt{2H}$ **c.** $\dfrac{C^2}{32} = H$ **d.** $\left(\dfrac{C}{4}\right)^2 = 2H$

58. **Education** One method used to "curve" the grades on an exam is to use the formula $R = 10\sqrt{O}$, where R is the revised score and O is the original score. Use this formula to find the original score on an exam that has a revised score of 75. Round to the nearest whole number.

59. **Physics** A formula used in the study of shallow-water wave motion is $C = \sqrt{32H}$, where C is the wave velocity in feet per second and H is the depth in feet. Use this formula to find the depth of the water when the wave velocity is 20 ft/s.

60. **Sports** The infield of a baseball diamond is a square. The distance between successive bases is 90 ft. The pitcher's mound is on the diagonal between home plate and second base at a distance of 60.5 ft from home plate. Is the pitcher's mound more or less than halfway between home plate and second base?

61. **Sports** The infield of a softball diamond is a square. The distance between successive bases is 60 ft. The pitcher's mound is on the diagonal between home plate and second base at a distance of 46 ft from home plate. Is the pitcher's mound more or less than halfway between home plate and second base?

62. **Communications** Marta Lightfoot leaves a dock in her sailboat and sails 2.5 mi due east. She then tacks and sails 4 mi due north. The walkie-talkie Marta has on board has a range of 5 mi. Will she be able to call a friend on the dock from her location using the walkie-talkie?

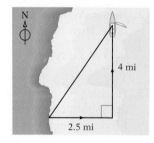

63. **Navigation** How far would a submarine periscope have to be above the water for the lookout to locate a ship 4 mi away? The equation for the distance in miles that the lookout can see is $d = \sqrt{1.5h}$, where h is the height in feet above the surface of the water.

64. **Navigation** How far would a submarine periscope have to be above the water for the lookout to locate a ship 7 mi away? The equation for the distance in miles that the lookout can see is $d = \sqrt{1.5h}$, where h is the height in feet above the surface of the water.

65. **Home Maintenance** Rick Wyman needs to clean the gutters of his home. The gutters are 24 ft above the ground. For safety, the distance a ladder reaches up a wall should be four times the distance from the bottom of the ladder to the base of the side of the house. Therefore, the bottom of the ladder must be 6 ft from the base of the house. Will a 25-foot ladder be long enough to reach the gutters?

66. **Physics** The speed of a child riding a merry-go-round at a carnival is given by the equation $v = \sqrt{12r}$, where v is the speed in feet per second and r is the distance in feet from the center of the merry-go-round to the rider. If a child is moving at 15 ft/s, how far is the child from the center of the merry-go-round?

67. **Physics** Find the length of a pendulum that makes one swing in 3 s. The equation for the time of one swing is $T = 2\pi\sqrt{\dfrac{L}{32}}$, where T is the time in seconds and L is the length in feet.

68. **Physics** Find the length of a pendulum that makes one swing in 2 s. The equation for the time of one swing is $T = 2\pi\sqrt{\dfrac{L}{32}}$, where T is the time in seconds and L is the length in feet.

69. **Parks** An L-shaped sidewalk from the parking lot to a memorial is shown in the figure at the right. The distance directly across the grass to the memorial is 650 ft. The distance to the corner is 600 ft. Find the distance from the corner to the memorial.

70. **Aviation** A commuter plane leaves an airport traveling due south at 400 mph. Another plane leaving at the same time travels due east at 300 mph. Find the distance between the two planes after 2 h.

71. **Physics** A stone is dropped from a bridge and hits the water 2 s later. How high is the bridge? The equation for the distance an object falls in T seconds is $T = \sqrt{\dfrac{d}{16}}$, where d is the distance in feet.

72. **Physics** A stone is dropped into a mine shaft and hits the bottom 3.5 s later. How deep is the mine shaft? The equation for the distance an object falls in T seconds is $T = \sqrt{\dfrac{d}{16}}$, where d is the distance in feet.

73. **Television** The measure of a television screen is given by the length of a diagonal across the screen. A 36-inch television has a width of 28.8 in. Find the height of the screen.

74. **Television** The measure of a television screen is given by the length of a diagonal across the screen. A 33-inch television has a width of 26.4 in. Find the height of the screen.

10.4 Applying Concepts

Solve.

75. $\sqrt{\dfrac{5y + 2}{3}} = 3$

76. $\sqrt{\dfrac{3y}{5}} - 1 = 2$

77. $\sqrt{9x^2 + 49} + 1 = 3x + 2$

78. **Geometry** In the coordinate plane, a triangle is formed by drawing lines between the points (0, 0) and (5, 0), (5, 0) and (5, 12), and (5, 12) and (0, 0). Find the number of units in the perimeter of the triangle.

79. **Geometry** The hypotenuse of a right triangle is $5\sqrt{2}$ cm, and the length of one leg is $4\sqrt{2}$ cm.
  a. Find the perimeter of the triangle.   **b.** Find the area of the triangle.

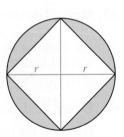

  Geometry Write an expression in factored form for the shaded region in the diagram at the right.

81. Geometry A circular fountain is being designed for a triangular plaza in a cultural center. The fountain is placed so that each side of the triangle touches the fountain as shown in the diagram at the right. Find the area of the fountain. The formula for the radius of the circle is given by

$$r = \sqrt{\frac{(s-a)(s-b)(s-c)}{s}}$$

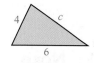

where $s = \frac{1}{2}(a + b + c)$ and a, b, and c are the lengths of the sides of the triangle. Round to the nearest hundredth.

82. Can the Pythagorean Theorem be used to find the length of side c of the triangle at the right? If so, determine c. If not, explain why the theorem cannot be used.

83. What is a Pythagorean triple? Provide at least three examples of Pythagorean triples.

84. Complete the statement using the symbol $<$, $=$, or $>$. Explain how you determined which symbol to use.
  a. For an acute triangle with side c the longest side, $a^2 + b^2$ _____ c^2.
  b. For a right triangle with side c the longest side, $a^2 + b^2$ _____ c^2.
  c. For an obtuse triangle with side c the longest side, $a^2 + b^2$ _____ c^2.

Focus on Problem Solving

Deductive Reasoning   Deductive reasoning uses a rule or statement of fact to reach a conclusion. In the section Equations Containing Fractions in the "Rational Expressions" chapter, we established the rule that if two angles of one triangle are equal to two angles of another triangle, then the two triangles are similar. Thus any time we establish this fact about two triangles, we know that the triangles are similar. Two examples of deductive reasoning follow.

Given that △△△ = ◊◊◊◊ and ◊◊◊◊ = ÓÓ, then △△△△△△ is equivalent to how many Ós?

Because 3 △s = 4 ◊s and 4 ◊s = 2 Ós, 3 △s = 2 Ós.

6 △s is twice 3 △s. We need to find twice 2 Ós, which is 4 Ós.

Therefore, △△△△△△ = ÓÓÓÓ.

Lomax, Parish, Thorpe, and Wong are neighbors. Each drives a different type of vehicle: a compact car, a sedan, a sports car, or a station wagon. From the following statements, determine which type of vehicle each of the neighbors drives.

a. Although the vehicle owned by Lomax has more mileage on it than does either the sedan or the sports car, it does not have the highest mileage of all four cars. (Use Xa in the chart below to eliminate whatever possibilities this statement enables you to rule out.)

b. Wong and the owner of the sports car live on one side of the street, and Thorpe and the owner of the compact car live on the other side of the street. (Use Xb to eliminate possibilities that this statement rules out.)

c. Thorpe owns the vehicle with the most mileage on it. (Use Xc to eliminate possibilities that this statement rules out.)

	Compact	Sedan	Sports Car	Wagon
Lomax	√	Xa	Xa	Xb
Parish	Xb	Xb	√	Xb
Thorpe	Xb	Xc	Xb	√
Wong	Xb	√	Xb	

Lomax drives the compact car, Parish drives the sports car, Thorpe drives the station wagon, and Wong drives the sedan.

Try the following exercises.

1. Given that ‡‡ = ••••• and ••••• = △△, then ‡‡‡‡ = how many △'s?

2. Given that ▽▽▽▽▽▽ = ◆◆◆◆ and ◆◆◆◆ = ⊕⊕, then ▽▽▽ = how many ⊕'s?

3. Given that ♣♣♣♣ = ⊗⊗⊗ and ⊗⊗⊗ = ♥♥, then ♥♥♥♥ = how many ♣'s?

4. Given that ◊◊◊◊◊◊ = ÓÓ and ÓÓ = ♠♠♠, then ♠♠♠♠♠♠ = how many ◊'s?

5. Anna, Kay, Megan, and Nicole decide to travel together during spring break, but they need to find a destination where each of them will be able to participate in her favorite sport (golf, horseback riding, sailing, or tennis). From the following statements, determine the favorite sport of each student.

a. Anna and the student whose favorite sport is sailing both like to swim, whereas Nicole and the student whose favorite sport is tennis would prefer to scuba dive.

b. Megan and the student whose favorite sport is sailing are roommates. Nicole and the student whose favorite sport is golf both live in a single.

6. Chang, Nick, Pablo, and Saul all take different forms of transportation (bus, car, subway, or taxi) from the office to the airport. From the following statements, determine which form of transportation each takes.

a. Chang spent more on transportation than the fellow who took the bus but less than the fellow who took the taxi.

b. Pablo, who did not travel by bus and who spent the least on transportation, arrived at the airport after Nick but before the fellow who took the subway.

c. Saul spent less on transportation than either Chang or Nick.

Projects & Group Activities

Expressway On-Ramp Curves

Highway engineers design expressway on-ramps with both efficiency and safety in mind. An on-ramp cannot be built with too sharp a curve, or the speed at which drivers take the curve will cause them to skid off the road. However, an on-ramp built with too wide a curve requires more building material, takes longer to travel, and uses more land. The following formula states the relationship between the maximum speed at which a car can travel around a curve without skidding: $v = \sqrt{2.5r}$. In this formula, v is speed in miles per hour and r is the radius, in feet, of an unbanked curve.

1. Use a graphing calculator to graph this equation. Use a window of Xmin = 0, Xmax = 2000, Ymin = 0, Ymax = 100. What do the values used for Xmin, Xmax, Ymin, and Ymax represent?

2. As the radius of the curve increases, does the maximum safe speed increase or decrease? Explain your answer on the basis of the graph of the equation.

3. Use the graph to approximate the maximum safe speed when the radius of the curve is 100 ft. Round to the nearest whole number.

4. Use the graph to approximate the radius of the curve for which the maximum safe speed is 40 mph. Round to the nearest whole number.

5. Dan Wheldon won the Indianapolis 500 in 2005 driving at an average speed of 157.603 mph. At this speed, should the radius of an unbanked curve be more or less than 1 mi?

Chapter 10 Summary

Key Words

A **square root** of a positive number x is a number whose square is x. The square root of a negative number is not a real number.   [10.1.1, pp. 542, 544]

Examples

A square root of 25 is 5 because $5^2 = 25$.

A square root of 25 is -5 because $(-5)^2 = 25$.

$\sqrt{-9}$ is not a real number.

The **principal square root** of a number is the positive square root. The symbol $\sqrt{}$ is called a **radical sign** and is used to indicate the principal square root of a number. The negative square root of a number is indicated by placing a negative sign in front of the radical. The **radicand** is the expression under the radical symbol.   [10.1.1, p. 542]

$\sqrt{25} = 5$

$-\sqrt{25} = -5$

In the expression $\sqrt{25}$, 25 is the radicand.

The square of an integer is a **perfect square.** If a number is not a perfect square, its square root can only be approximated. Such numbers are **irrational numbers.** Their decimal representations never terminate or repeat.
[10.1.1, pp. 542–543]

$2^2 = 4$, $3^2 = 9$, $4^2 = 16$, $5^2 = 25$, $6^2 = 36$, ... 4, 9, 16, 25, 36, ... are perfect squares.

5 is not a perfect square. $\sqrt{5}$ is an irrational number.

Conjugates are expressions with two terms that differ only in the sign of the second term. The expressions $a + b$ and $a - b$ are conjugates.   [10.3.1, p. 556]

$3 + \sqrt{7}$ and $3 - \sqrt{7}$ are conjugates.

$\sqrt{x} + 2$ and $\sqrt{x} - 2$ are conjugates.

A **radical equation** is an equation that contains a variable expression in a radicand.   [10.4.1, p. 563]

$\sqrt{2x} + 8 = 12$ is a radical equation. $2x + \sqrt{8} = 12$ is not a radical equation.

Essential Rules and Procedures

The Product Property of Square Roots
If a and b are positive real numbers, then $\sqrt{ab} = \sqrt{a} \cdot \sqrt{b}$.
[10.1.1, p. 543]

$\sqrt{12} = \sqrt{4 \cdot 3} = \sqrt{4}\sqrt{3} = 2\sqrt{3}$

Adding and Subtracting Radical Expressions
The Distributive Property is used to simplify the sum or difference of like radical expressions.   [10.2.1, p. 551]

$16\sqrt{3x} - 4\sqrt{3x} = (16 - 4)\sqrt{3x}$
$\qquad = 12\sqrt{3x}$

Multiplying Radical Expressions
The Product Property of Square Roots is used to multiply radical expressions.

$\sqrt{5x}\sqrt{7y} = \sqrt{5x \cdot 7y} = \sqrt{35xy}$

Use the Distributive Property to remove parentheses.

$\sqrt{y}(2 + \sqrt{3x}) = 2\sqrt{y} + \sqrt{3xy}$

Use the FOIL method to multiply radical expressions with two terms.   [10.3.1, pp. 555–556]

$(5 - \sqrt{x})(11 + \sqrt{x})$
$\quad = 55 + 5\sqrt{x} - 11\sqrt{x} - (\sqrt{x})^2$
$\quad = 55 - 6\sqrt{x} - x$

The Quotient Property of Square Roots
If a and b are positive real numbers, then $\sqrt{\dfrac{a}{b}} = \dfrac{\sqrt{a}}{\sqrt{b}}$.
[10.3.2, p. 556]

$\sqrt{\dfrac{9x^2}{y^8}} = \dfrac{\sqrt{9x^2}}{\sqrt{y^8}} = \dfrac{3x}{y^4}$

Dividing Radical Expressions
The Quotient Property of Square Roots is used to divide radical expressions.   [10.3.2, p. 557]

$\dfrac{\sqrt{3x^5y}}{\sqrt{75xy^3}} = \sqrt{\dfrac{3x^5y}{75xy^3}} = \sqrt{\dfrac{x^4}{25y^2}}$
$\qquad = \dfrac{\sqrt{x^4}}{\sqrt{25y^2}} = \dfrac{x^2}{5y}$

Rationalizing the Denominator
A radical is not in simplest form if there is a radical in the denominator. The procedure used to remove a radical from the denominator is called rationalizing the denominator.
[10.3.2, p. 557]

$\dfrac{5}{\sqrt{7}} = \dfrac{5}{\sqrt{7}} \cdot \dfrac{\sqrt{7}}{\sqrt{7}} = \dfrac{5\sqrt{7}}{7}$

Radical Expressions in Simplest Form

A radical expression is in simplest form if:
1. The radicand contains no factor greater than 1 that is a perfect square.
2. There is no fraction under the radical sign.
3. There is no radical in the denominator of a fraction. [10.3.2, p. 558]

$\sqrt{12}$, $\sqrt{\dfrac{3}{4}}$, and $\dfrac{1}{\sqrt{2}}$ are not in simplest form.

$2\sqrt{3}$, $\dfrac{\sqrt{3}}{2}$, and $\dfrac{\sqrt{2}}{2}$ are in simplest form.

Property of Squaring Both Sides of an Equation

If a and b are real numbers and $a = b$, then $a^2 = b^2$. [10.4.1, p. 563]

$$\sqrt{x+3} = 4$$
$$\left(\sqrt{x+3}\right)^2 = 4^2$$
$$x + 3 = 16$$
$$x = 13$$

Solving Radical Equations

When an equation contains one radical expression, write the equation with the radical alone on one side of the equation. Square both sides of the equation. Solve for the variable. Whenever both sides of an equation are squared, the solutions must be checked. [10.4.1, p. 563]

$$\sqrt{2x} - 1 = 5$$
$$\sqrt{2x} = 6$$
$$\left(\sqrt{2x}\right)^2 = 6^2$$
$$2x = 36$$
$$x = 18 \quad \text{The solution checks.}$$

Pythagorean Theorem

If a and b are the lengths of the legs of a right triangle and c is the length of the hypotenuse, then $c^2 = a^2 + b^2$. [10.4.2, p. 566]

Two legs of a right triangle measure 4 cm and 7 cm. To find the length of the hypotenuse, use the equation

$$c = \sqrt{a^2 + b^2}$$
$$c = \sqrt{4^2 + 7^2} = \sqrt{16 + 49} = \sqrt{65}$$

The hypotenuse measures $\sqrt{65}$ cm.

Chapter 10 Review Exercises

1. Subtract: $5\sqrt{3} - 16\sqrt{3}$

2. Simplify: $\dfrac{2x}{\sqrt{3} - \sqrt{5}}$

3. Simplify: $\sqrt{x^2 + 16x + 64}$

4. Solve: $3 - \sqrt{7x} = 5$

5. Simplify: $\dfrac{5\sqrt{y} - 2\sqrt{y}}{3\sqrt{y}}$

6. Add: $6\sqrt{7} + \sqrt{7}$

7. Multiply: $\left(6\sqrt{a} + 5\sqrt{b}\right)\left(2\sqrt{a} + 3\sqrt{b}\right)$

8. Simplify: $\sqrt{49(x + 3)^4}$

9. Simplify: $2\sqrt{36}$

10. Solve: $\sqrt{b} = 4$

11. Subtract: $9x\sqrt{5} - 5x\sqrt{5}$

12. Multiply: $\left(\sqrt{5ab} - \sqrt{7}\right)\left(\sqrt{5ab} + \sqrt{7}\right)$

13. Solve: $\sqrt{2x + 9} = \sqrt{8x - 9}$

14. Simplify: $\sqrt{35}$

15. Add: $2x\sqrt{60x^3y^3} + 3x^2y\sqrt{15xy}$

16. Simplify: $\dfrac{\sqrt{3x^3y}}{\sqrt{27xy^5}}$

17. Simplify: $\left(3\sqrt{x} - \sqrt{y}\right)^2$

18. Simplify: $\sqrt{(a+4)^2}$

19. Simplify: $5\sqrt{48}$

20. Add: $3\sqrt{12x} + 5\sqrt{48x}$

21. Simplify: $\dfrac{8}{\sqrt{x}-3}$

22. Multiply: $\sqrt{6a}\left(\sqrt{3a} + \sqrt{2a}\right)$

23. Simplify: $3\sqrt{18a^5b}$

24. Simplify: $-3\sqrt{120}$

25. Subtract: $\sqrt{20a^5b^9} - 2ab^2\sqrt{45a^3b^5}$

26. Simplify: $\dfrac{\sqrt{98x^7y^9}}{\sqrt{2x^3y}}$

27. Solve: $\sqrt{5x+1} = \sqrt{20x-8}$

28. Simplify: $\sqrt{c^{18}}$

29. Simplify: $\sqrt{450}$

30. Simplify: $6a\sqrt{80b} - \sqrt{180a^2b} + 5a\sqrt{b}$

31. Simplify: $\dfrac{16}{\sqrt{a}}$

32. Solve: $6 - \sqrt{2y} = 2$

33. Multiply: $\sqrt{a^3b^4c}\,\sqrt{a^7b^2c^3}$

34. Simplify: $7\sqrt{630}$

35. Simplify: $y\sqrt{24y^6}$

36. Simplify: $\dfrac{\sqrt{250}}{\sqrt{10}}$

37. Solve: $\sqrt{x^2+5x+4} = \sqrt{x^2+7x-6}$

38. Multiply: $\left(4\sqrt{y} - \sqrt{5}\right)\left(2\sqrt{y} + 3\sqrt{5}\right)$

39. Find the decimal approximation of $\sqrt{9900}$ to the nearest thousandth.

40. Multiply: $\sqrt{7}\,\sqrt{7}$

41. Simplify: $5x\sqrt{150x^7}$

42. Simplify: $2x^2\sqrt{18x^2y^5} + 6y\sqrt{2x^6y^3} - 9xy^2\sqrt{8x^4y}$

43. Simplify: $\dfrac{\sqrt{54a^3}}{\sqrt{6a}}$

44. Simplify: $4\sqrt{250}$

45. Solve: $\sqrt{5x} = 10$

46. Simplify: $\dfrac{3a\sqrt{3} + 2\sqrt{12a^2}}{\sqrt{27}}$

47. Multiply: $\sqrt{2}\,\sqrt{50}$

48. Simplify: $\sqrt{36x^4y^5}$

49. Simplify: $4y\sqrt{243x^{17}y^9}$

50. Solve: $\sqrt{x+1} - \sqrt{x-2} = 1$

51. Simplify: $\sqrt{400}$

52. Simplify: $-4\sqrt{8x} + 7\sqrt{18x} - 3\sqrt{50x}$

53. Solve: $0 = \sqrt{10x+4} - 8$

54. Multiply: $\sqrt{3}\left(\sqrt{12} - \sqrt{3}\right)$

55. **Integer Problem** The square root of the sum of two consecutive odd integers is equal to 10. Find the larger integer.

56. **Space Travel** The weight of an object is related to the object's distance from the surface of Earth. An equation for this relationship is

$$d = 4000\sqrt{\dfrac{W_0}{W_a}},$$ where W_0 is the object's weight on the surface of Earth

and W_a is the object's weight at a distance of d miles above Earth's surface. A space explorer weighs 36 lb when 8000 mi above Earth's surface. Find the explorer's weight on the surface of Earth.

57. Geometry The hypotenuse of a right triangle measures 18 cm. One leg of the triangle measures 11 cm. Find the length of the other leg of the triangle. Round to the nearest hundredth.

58. Bicycling A bicycle will overturn if it rounds a corner too sharply or too quickly. The equation for the maximum velocity at which a cyclist can turn a corner without tipping over is given by the equation $v = 4\sqrt{r}$, where v is the velocity of the bicycle in miles per hour and r is the radius of the corner in feet. Find the radius of the sharpest corner that a cyclist can safely turn when riding at a speed of 20 mph.

59. Tsunamis A tsunami is a great sea wave produced by underwater earthquakes or volcanic eruption. The velocity of a tsunami as it approaches land is approximated by the equation $v = 3\sqrt{d}$, where v is the velocity in feet per second and d is the depth of the water in feet. Find the depth of the water when the velocity of a tsunami is 30 ft/s.

60. Guy Wires A guy wire is attached to a point 25 ft above the ground on a telephone pole that is perpendicular to the ground. The wire is anchored to the ground at a point 8 ft from the base of the pole. Find the length of the guy wire. Round to the nearest hundredth.

Chapter 10 Test

 View the Chapter Test Videos for fully worked-out solutions to any exercise.

1. Simplify: $\sqrt{121x^8y^2}$

2. Subtract: $5\sqrt{8} - 3\sqrt{50}$

3. Multiply: $\sqrt{3x^2y}\ \sqrt{6x^2}\ \sqrt{2x}$

4. Simplify: $\sqrt{45}$

5. Simplify: $\sqrt{72x^7y^2}$

6. Simplify: $3\sqrt{8y} - 2\sqrt{72x} + 5\sqrt{18x}$

7. Multiply: $\left(\sqrt{y} + 3\right)\left(\sqrt{y} + 5\right)$

8. Simplify: $\dfrac{4}{\sqrt{8}}$

9. Simplify: $\dfrac{\sqrt{162}}{\sqrt{2}}$

10. Solve: $\sqrt{5x - 6} = 7$

11. Find the decimal approximation of $\sqrt{500}$ to the nearest thousandth.

12. Simplify: $\sqrt{32a^5b^{11}}$

13. Multiply: $\sqrt{a}\left(\sqrt{a} - \sqrt{b}\right)$

14. Multiply: $\sqrt{8x^3y}\ \sqrt{10xy^4}$

15. Simplify: $\dfrac{\sqrt{98a^6b^4}}{\sqrt{2a^3b^2}}$

16. Solve: $\sqrt{9x} + 3 = 18$

17. Simplify: $\sqrt{192x^{13}y^5}$

18. Simplify: $2a\sqrt{2ab^3} + b\sqrt{8a^3b} - 5ab\sqrt{ab}$

19. Multiply: $\left(\sqrt{a} - 2\right)\left(\sqrt{a} + 2\right)$

20. Simplify: $\dfrac{3}{2 - \sqrt{5}}$

21. Solve: $3 = 8 - \sqrt{5x}$

22. Multiply: $\sqrt{3}\left(\sqrt{6} - \sqrt{x^2}\right)$

23. Subtract: $3\sqrt{a} - 9\sqrt{a}$

24. Simplify: $\sqrt{108}$

25. Find the decimal approximation of $\sqrt{63}$ to the nearest thousandth.

26. Simplify: $\dfrac{\sqrt{108a^7b^3}}{\sqrt{3a^4b}}$

27. Solve: $\sqrt{x} - \sqrt{x + 3} = 1$

28. **Integer Problem** The square root of the sum of two consecutive integers is equal to 9. Find the smaller integer.

29. **Physics** Find the length of a pendulum that makes one swing in 2.5 s. The equation for the time of one swing of a pendulum is $T = 2\pi\sqrt{\dfrac{L}{32}}$, where T is the time in seconds and L is the length in feet. Round to the nearest hundredth.

30. **Home Maintenance** A ladder 16 ft long is resting against a building. How high on the building will the ladder reach when the bottom of the ladder is 5 ft from the building? Round to the nearest tenth.

Cumulative Review Exercises

1. Simplify: $\left(\dfrac{2}{3}\right)^2\left(\dfrac{3}{4} - \dfrac{3}{2}\right) + \left(\dfrac{1}{2}\right)^2$

2. Simplify: $-3[x - 2(3 - 2x) - 5x] + 2x$

3. Solve: $2x - 4[3x - 2(1 - 3x)] = 2(3 - 4x)$

4. Solve: $3(x - 7) \geq 5x - 12$

5. Find the slope of the line that contains the points whose coordinates are $(2, -5)$ and $(-4, 3)$.

6. Find the equation of the line that contains the point whose coordinates are $(-2, -3)$ and has slope $\dfrac{1}{2}$.

7. Evaluate $f(x) = \dfrac{5}{2}x - 8$ at $x = -4$.

8. Graph: $f(x) = -4x + 2$

9. Graph the solution set of $2x + y < -2$.

10. Solve by graphing: $3x - 2y = 8$
$4x + 5y = 3$

11. Solve by substitution: $\;4x - 3y = 1$
$2x + y = 3$

12. Solve by the addition method: $5x + 4y = 7$
$3x - 2y = 13$

13. Simplify: $(-3x^2y)(-2x^3y^{-4})$

14. Simplify: $\dfrac{12b^4 - 6b^2 + 2}{-6b^2}$

15. Factor: $12x^3y^2 - 9x^2y^3$

16. Factor: $9b^2 + 3b - 20$

17. Factor: $2a^3 - 16a^2 + 30a$

18. Multiply: $\dfrac{3x^3 - 6x^2}{4x^2 + 4x} \cdot \dfrac{3x - 9}{9x^3 - 45x^2 + 54x}$

19. Simplify: $\dfrac{1 - \dfrac{2}{x} - \dfrac{15}{x^2}}{1 - \dfrac{9}{x^2}}$

20. Subtract: $\dfrac{x + 2}{x - 4} - \dfrac{6}{(x - 4)(x - 3)}$

21. Solve: $\dfrac{x}{2x - 5} - 2 = \dfrac{3x}{2x - 5}$

22. Simplify: $2\sqrt{27a} - 5\sqrt{49a} + 8\sqrt{48a}$

23. Simplify: $\dfrac{\sqrt{320}}{\sqrt{5}}$

24. Solve: $\sqrt{2x - 3} - 5 = 0$

25. **Integer Problem** Three-eighths of a number is less than negative twelve. Find the largest integer that satisfies the inequality.

26. **Markup** The selling price of a book is $29.40. The markup rate used by the bookstore is 20% of the cost. Find the cost of the book.

27. **Mixture Problem** How many ounces of pure water must be added to 40 oz of a 12% salt solution to make a salt solution that is 5% salt?

28. **Integer Problem** The sum of two numbers is twenty-one. Three more than twice the smaller number is equal to the larger. Find the two numbers.

29. **Work Problem** A small water pipe takes twice as long to fill a tank as does a larger water pipe. With both pipes open, it takes 16 h to fill the tank. Find the time it would take the small pipe, working alone, to fill the tank.

30. **Integer Problem** The square root of the sum of two consecutive integers is equal to 7. Find the smaller integer.

11 Quadratic Equations

DVD   SSM

Online Study Center

Need help? For online student resources, such as section quizzes, visit the Online Study Center at www.cengage.com/math/aufmann.

Businesses take into account the cost of producing and selling their products, as well as the prices customers pay for them. Profit is the difference between a company's revenue (the total amount of money the company earns by selling its products or services) and its costs (the total amount of money the company spends doing business). Quadratic equations are used in the **Focus on Problem Solving on pages 635–636** to determine the maximum profit companies can earn. You will be asked to determine the maximum monthly profit for a company that sells guitars like the one being purchased in this photo.

Prep Test

1. Evaluate $b^2 - 4ac$ when $a = 2$, $b = -3$, and $c = -4$.

2. Solve: $5x + 4 = 3$

3. Factor: $x^2 + x - 12$

4. Factor: $4x^2 - 12x + 9$

5. Is $x^2 - 10x + 25$ a perfect square trinomial?

6. Solve: $\dfrac{5}{x - 2} = \dfrac{15}{x}$

7. Graph: $y = -2x + 3$

8. Simplify: $\sqrt{28}$

9. If a is *any* real number, simplify $\sqrt{a^2}$.

10. Walking at a constant speed of 4.5 mph, Lucy and Sam walked from the beginning to the end of a hiking trail. When they reached the end, they immediately started back along the same path at a constant speed of 3 mph. If the round trip took 2 h, what is the length of the hiking trail?

Solving Quadratic Equations by Factoring or by Taking Square Roots

OBJECTIVE 1   Solve quadratic equations by factoring

In Section 5 of the chapter on factoring, we solved quadratic equations by factoring. In this section, we will review that material and then solve quadratic equations by taking square roots.

An equation of the form $ax^2 + bx + c = 0$, $a \neq 0$, is a **quadratic equation.**

$$4x^2 - 3x + 1 = 0, \qquad a = 4, b = -3, c = 1$$
$$3x^2 - 4 = 0, \qquad a = 3, b = 0, \quad c = -4$$

A quadratic equation is also called a **second-degree equation.**

A quadratic equation is in **standard form** when the polynomial is in descending order and equal to zero.

Recall that the Principle of Zero Products states that if the product of two factors is zero, then at least one of the factors must be zero.

If $a \cdot b = 0$, then $a = 0$ or $b = 0$.

The Principle of Zero Products can be used in solving quadratic equations.

Solve by factoring: $2x^2 - x = 1$

$$2x^2 - x = 1$$

Write the equation in standard form. $2x^2 - x - 1 = 0$

Factor the left side of the equation. $(2x + 1)(x - 1) = 0$

If $(2x + 1)(x - 1) = 0$, then either $2x + 1 = 0$ $x - 1 = 0$
$2x + 1 = 0$ or $x - 1 = 0$.

Solve each equation for x. $2x = -1$ $x = 1$

$$x = -\frac{1}{2}$$

The solutions are $-\dfrac{1}{2}$ and 1.

 A graphing calculator can be used to check the solutions of a quadratic equation. Consider the preceding example. The solutions appear to be $-\dfrac{1}{2}$

and 1. To check these solutions, store one value of x, $-\dfrac{1}{2}$, in the calculator. Note

 that after you store $-\dfrac{1}{2}$ in the calculator's memory, your calculator rewrites the

fraction as the decimal -0.5. Evaluate the expression on the left side of the original equation: $2x^2 - x$. The result is 1, which is the number on the right side of the original equation. The solution -0.5 checks. Now store the other value of x, 1, in the calculator. Evaluate the expression on the left side of the original equation: $2x^2 - x$. The result is 1, which is the number on the right side of the equation. The solution 1 checks.

Solve by factoring: $x^2 = 10x - 25$

$$x^2 = 10x - 25$$

Write the equation in standard form. $x^2 - 10x + 25 = 0$

Factor the left side of the equation. $(x - 5)(x - 5) = 0$

Let each factor equal 0. $x - 5 = 0$ $x - 5 = 0$

Solve each equation for x. $x = 5$ $x = 5$

The factorization in this example produced two identical factors. Because $x - 5$ occurs twice in the factored form of the equation, 5 is a **double root** of the equation.

EXAMPLE 1 Solve by factoring: $\dfrac{z^2}{2} + \dfrac{z}{3} - \dfrac{1}{6} = 0$

Solution

$$\dfrac{z^2}{2} + \dfrac{z}{3} - \dfrac{1}{6} = 0$$

$$6\left(\dfrac{z^2}{2} + \dfrac{z}{3} - \dfrac{1}{6}\right) = 6(0)$$

$$3z^2 + 2z - 1 = 0$$

$$(3z - 1)(z + 1) = 0$$

$$3z - 1 = 0 \qquad z + 1 = 0$$
$$3z = 1 \qquad\qquad z = -1$$

$$z = \dfrac{1}{3}$$

The solutions are $\dfrac{1}{3}$ and -1.

- To eliminate the fractions, multiply each side of the equation by **6**.
- The quadratic equation is in standard form.
- Factor the left side of the equation.
- Let each factor equal zero.
- Solve each equation for *z*.

- $\dfrac{1}{3}$ and -1 check as solutions.

PROBLEM 1 Solve by factoring: $\dfrac{3y^2}{2} + y - \dfrac{1}{2} = 0$

Solution See page S25.

OBJECTIVE 2 **Solve quadratic equations by taking square roots**

Consider a quadratic equation of the form $x^2 = a$. This equation can be solved by factoring.

$$x^2 = 25$$
$$x^2 - 25 = 0$$
$$(x + 5)(x - 5) = 0$$

$$x + 5 = 0 \qquad x - 5 = 0$$
$$x = -5 \qquad\qquad x = 5$$

The solutions are -5 and 5.

Solutions that are plus or minus the same number are frequently written using $\pm$. For the example above, this would be written: "The solutions are ± 5." Because the solutions ± 5 can be written as $\pm\sqrt{25}$, an alternative method of solving this equation is suggested.

> **Take Note**
>
> Recall that the solution of the equation $|x| = 5$ is ± 5. This principle is used when solving an equation by taking square roots. Remember that $\sqrt{x^2} = |x|$. Therefore,
>
> $$x^2 = 25$$
> $$\sqrt{x^2} = \sqrt{25}$$
> $$|x| = 5 \qquad \bullet\ \sqrt{x^2} = |x|$$
> $$x = \pm 5 \qquad \bullet\ \text{If } |x| = 5,$$
> $$\text{then } x = \pm 5.$$

Principle of Taking the Square Root of Each Side of an Equation

If $x^2 = a$, then $x = \pm\sqrt{a}$.

Solve by taking square roots: $x^2 = 25$

Take the square root of each side of the equation.

$$x^2 = 25$$
$$\sqrt{x^2} = \sqrt{25}$$

Simplify.

$$x = \pm\sqrt{25} = \pm 5$$

Write the solutions.

The solutions are 5 and -5.

■ Solve by taking square roots: $3x^2 = 36$

$$3x^2 = 36$$

Solve for x^2. $$x^2 = 12$$

Take the square root of each
side of the equation. $$\sqrt{x^2} = \sqrt{12}$$

Simplify. $$x = \pm\sqrt{12} = \pm 2\sqrt{3}$$

Check:

$$
\begin{array}{c|c}
3x^2 = 36 & 3x^2 = 36 \\
\hline
3(2\sqrt{3})^2 \;\big|\; 36 & 3(-2\sqrt{3})^2 \;\big|\; 36 \\
3(12) \;\big|\; 36 & 3(12) \;\big|\; 36 \\
36 = 36 & 36 = 36
\end{array}
$$

These are true equations.
The solutions check.

Write the solutions.   The solutions are $2\sqrt{3}$ and $-2\sqrt{3}$. ■

Take Note

You should always check your
solutions by substituting them
back into the *original* equation.

A graphing calculator can be used to check irrational solutions of a quadratic equation. Consider the preceding example; the solutions $2\sqrt{3}$ and $-2\sqrt{3}$ checked. To check these solutions on a calculator, store one value of x, $2\sqrt{3}$, in the calculator. Note that after you store this number in the calculator's memory, the calculator rewrites the expression as the decimal 3.464101615, which is an approximation of $2\sqrt{3}$. Evaluate the expression on the left side of the original equation. The result is 36, which is the number on the right side of the original equation. The solution $2\sqrt{3}$ checks. Now store the other value of x, $-2\sqrt{3}$, in the calculator. Note that after you store this number in the calculator's memory, the calculator rewrites the expression as the decimal -3.464101615, which is an approximation of $-2\sqrt{3}$. Evaluate the expression on the left side of the original equation. The result is 36, which is the number on the right side of the equation. The solution $-2\sqrt{3}$ checks.

```
-2√(3)→X
              -3.464101615
3X²
                        36
```

EXAMPLE 2   Solve by taking square roots.

A. $2x^2 - 72 = 0$ **B.** $x^2 + 16 = 0$

Solution   **A.** $2x^2 - 72 = 0$

$$2x^2 = 72$$ • **Solve for x^2.**
$$x^2 = 36$$
$$\sqrt{x^2} = \sqrt{36}$$ • **Take the square root of each**
$$x = \pm\sqrt{36}$$ **side of the equation.**
$$x = \pm 6$$

The solutions are 6 and -6.

B. $x^2 + 16 = 0$

$$x^2 = -16$$
$$\sqrt{x^2} = \sqrt{-16}$$ • $\sqrt{-16}$ **is not a real number.**

The equation has no real number solution.

PROBLEM 2   Solve by taking square roots.

A. $4x^2 - 96 = 0$ **B.** $x^2 + 81 = 0$

Solution   See page S25.

An equation containing the square of a binomial can be solved by taking square roots.

Solve by taking square roots: $2(x - 1)^2 - 36 = 0$

Solve for $(x - 1)^2$.
$$2(x - 1)^2 - 36 = 0$$
$$2(x - 1)^2 = 36$$
$$(x - 1)^2 = 18$$

Take the square root of each side of the equation.
$$\sqrt{(x - 1)^2} = \sqrt{18}$$

Simplify.
$$x - 1 = \pm\sqrt{18}$$
$$x - 1 = \pm 3\sqrt{2}$$

Solve for x.

$$x - 1 = 3\sqrt{2} \qquad x - 1 = -3\sqrt{2}$$
$$x = 1 + 3\sqrt{2} \qquad x = 1 - 3\sqrt{2}$$

Check:
$$\begin{array}{r|l} 2(x - 1)^2 - 36 = 0 & \\ \hline 2\left(1 + 3\sqrt{2} - 1\right)^2 - 36 & 0 \\ 2\left(3\sqrt{2}\right)^2 - 36 & 0 \\ 2(18) - 36 & 0 \\ 36 - 36 & 0 \\ 0 = 0 & \end{array}$$

$$\begin{array}{r|l} 2(x - 1)^2 - 36 = 0 & \\ \hline 2\left(1 - 3\sqrt{2} - 1\right)^2 - 36 & 0 \\ 2\left(-3\sqrt{2}\right)^2 - 36 & 0 \\ 2(18) - 36 & 0 \\ 36 - 36 & 0 \\ 0 = 0 & \end{array}$$

Write the solutions.   The solutions are $1 + 3\sqrt{2}$ and $1 - 3\sqrt{2}$.

EXAMPLE 3   Solve by taking square roots: $(x - 6)^2 = 12$

Solution
$$(x - 6)^2 = 12$$
$$\sqrt{(x - 6)^2} = \sqrt{12}$$
$$x - 6 = \pm\sqrt{12}$$
$$x - 6 = \pm 2\sqrt{3}$$

• Take the square root of each side of the equation.

$$x - 6 = 2\sqrt{3} \qquad x - 6 = -2\sqrt{3}$$
$$x = 6 + 2\sqrt{3} \qquad x = 6 - 2\sqrt{3}$$

• Solve for x.

The solutions are $6 + 2\sqrt{3}$ and $6 - 2\sqrt{3}$.

PROBLEM 3   Solve by taking square roots: $(x + 5)^2 = 20$

Solution   See page S25.

11.1   Concept Review

Determine whether the statement is always true, sometimes true, or never true.

1. $2x^2 - 3x + 9$ is a quadratic equation.

2. By the Principle of Zero Products, if $(3x + 4)(x - 7) = 0$, then $3x + 4 = 0$ or $x - 7 = 0$.

3. A quadratic equation has two distinct solutions.

4. To solve the equation $3x^2 - 26x = 9$ by factoring, first write the equation in standard form.

5. To say that the solutions are ± 6 means that the solutions are 6 and -6.

6. If we take the square root of the square of a binomial, the result is the binomial.

11.1   Exercises

1   Solve quadratic equations by factoring

For the given quadratic equation, find the values of a, b, and c.

1. $3x^2 - 4x + 1 = 0$

2. $x^2 + 2x - 5 = 0$

3. $2x^2 - 5 = 0$

4. $4x^2 + 1 = 0$

5. $6x^2 - 3x = 0$

6. $-x^2 + 7x = 0$

Write the quadratic equation in standard form.

7. $x^2 - 8 = 3x$

8. $2x^2 = 4x - 1$

9. $x^2 = 16$

10. $x + 5 = x(x - 3)$

11. $2(x + 3)^2 = 5$

12. $4(x - 1)^2 = 3$

13. How does a quadratic equation differ from a linear equation?

14. What does the Principle of Zero Products state?

15. Explain why the equation $x(x + 5) = 12$ cannot be solved by saying $x = 12$ or $x + 5 = 12$.

16. What is a double root of a quadratic equation?

17. Solve: $x^2 - 36 = 0$

$$x^2 - 36 = 0$$
$$(\underline{})(\underline{}) = 0$$
$$x + 6 = \underline{} \qquad x - 6 = \underline{}$$
$$x = \underline{} \qquad\qquad x = \underline{}$$

- The equation is in ___?___ form.
- Factor the difference of two squares.
- Use the Principle of ___?___ to set each factor equal to 0.
- Solve each equation for x.

18. Solve: $x^2 + 4x - 12 = 0$

$$x^2 + 4x - 12 = 0$$
$$(x + \underline{})(x - \underline{}) = 0$$
$$\underline{} = 0 \qquad \underline{} = 0$$
$$x = \underline{} \qquad x = \underline{}$$

- The equation is in ___?___ form.
- Factor the trinomial.
- Use the Principle of Zero Products to set each factor equal to 0.
- Solve each equation for x.

Solve for x.

19. $(x + 3)(x - 5) = 0$

20. $(x - 9)(x + 11) = 0$

21. $x(x - 7) = 0$

22. $x(x + 10) = 0$

23. $(2x + 5)(3x - 1) = 0$

24. $(2x - 7)(3x + 4) = 0$

Solve by factoring.

25. $x^2 + 2x - 15 = 0$

26. $t^2 + 3t - 10 = 0$

27. $z^2 - 4z + 3 = 0$

28. $s^2 - 5s + 4 = 0$

29. $p^2 + 3p + 2 = 0$

30. $v^2 + 6v + 5 = 0$

31. $x^2 - 6x + 9 = 0$

32. $y^2 - 8y + 16 = 0$

33. $6x^2 - 9x = 0$

34. $12y^2 + 8y = 0$

35. $r^2 - 10 = 3r$

36. $t^2 - 12 = 4t$

37. $3v^2 - 5v + 2 = 0$

38. $2p^2 - 3p - 2 = 0$

39. $3s^2 + 8s = 3$

40. $3x^2 + 5x = 12$

41. $6r^2 = 12 - r$

42. $4t^2 = 4t + 3$

43. $5y^2 + 11y = 12$

44. $4v^2 - 4v + 1 = 0$

45. $9s^2 - 6s + 1 = 0$

46. $x^2 - 9 = 0$

47. $t^2 - 16 = 0$

48. $4y^2 - 1 = 0$

49. $9z^2 - 4 = 0$

50. $x + 15 = x(x - 1)$

51. $\dfrac{3x^2}{2} = 4x - 2$

52. $\dfrac{2x^2}{5} = 3x - 5$

53. $\dfrac{2x^2}{9} + x = 2$

54. $\dfrac{3x^2}{8} - x = 2$

55. $\dfrac{3}{4}z^2 - z = -\dfrac{1}{3}$

56. $\dfrac{r^2}{2} = 1 - \dfrac{r}{12}$

57. $p + 18 = p(p - 2)$

58. $r^2 - r - 2 = (2r - 1)(r - 3)$

59. $s^2 + 5s - 4 = (2s + 1)(s - 4)$

60. $x^2 + x + 5 = (3x + 2)(x - 4)$

61. $ax^2 + bx + c = 0$ is a quadratic equation that can be solved by factoring. For each case, state whether the equation has two positive solutions, two negative solutions, or one positive and one negative solution.
a. $a > 0, b < 0, c > 0$ **b.** $a > 0, b < 0, c < 0$ **c.** $a > 0, b > 0, c < 0$

62. Let a be a positive integer. Which equation has a positive double root?

a. $x^2 - a^2 = 0$ **b.** $x^2 + 2ax - a^2 = 0$
c. $x^2 + 2ax + a^2 = 0$ **d.** $x^2 - 2ax + a^2 = 0$

2 Solve quadratic equations by taking square roots

63. The notation $x = \pm 3$ means $x =$ _____?_____ or $x =$ _____?_____.

64. Solve by taking square roots: $4x^2 - 9 = 0$

$4x^2 - 9 = 0$

$4x^2 =$ ____?____   • Add ____?____ to each side of the equation.

$x^2 =$ ____?____   • Divide each side of the equation by ____?____.

$\sqrt{x^2} = \sqrt{\dfrac{9}{4}}$ • Take the ____?____ of each side of the equation.

$x =$ ____?____ $\sqrt{\dfrac{9}{4}}$ • There are two square roots, one positive and one negative.

$x = \pm$ ____?____   • Simplify.

Solve by taking square roots.

65. $x^2 = 36$ **66.** $y^2 = 49$ **67.** $v^2 - 1 = 0$ **68.** $z^2 - 64 = 0$

69. $4x^2 - 49 = 0$ **70.** $9w^2 - 64 = 0$ **71.** $9y^2 = 4$ **72.** $4z^2 = 25$

73. $16v^2 - 9 = 0$ **74.** $25x^2 - 64 = 0$ **75.** $y^2 + 81 = 0$ **76.** $z^2 + 49 = 0$

77. $w^2 - 24 = 0$ **78.** $v^2 - 48 = 0$ **79.** $(x - 1)^2 = 36$ **80.** $(y + 2)^2 = 49$

81. $2(x + 5)^2 = 8$ **82.** $4(z - 3)^2 = 100$ **83.** $2(x + 1)^2 = 50$

84. $3(x - 4)^2 = 27$ **85.** $4(x + 5)^2 = 64$ **86.** $9(x - 3)^2 = 81$

87. $2(x - 9)^2 = 98$ **88.** $5(x + 5)^2 = 125$ **89.** $12(x + 3)^2 = 27$

90. $8(x - 4)^2 = 50$ **91.** $9(x - 1)^2 - 16 = 0$ **92.** $4(y + 3)^2 - 81 = 0$

93. $49(v + 1)^2 - 25 = 0$ **94.** $81(y - 2)^2 - 64 = 0$ **95.** $(x - 4)^2 - 20 = 0$

96. $(y + 5)^2 - 50 = 0$ **97.** $(x + 1)^2 + 36 = 0$ **98.** $(y - 7)^2 + 49 = 0$

99. $2\left(z - \dfrac{1}{2}\right)^2 = 12$ **100.** $3\left(v + \dfrac{3}{4}\right)^2 = 36$ **101.** $4\left(x - \dfrac{2}{3}\right)^2 = 16$

For Exercises 102 to 105, a and b are both positive numbers. In each case, state how many solutions the equation has.

102. $(x + a)^2 = 0$ **103.** $ax^2 + b = 0$

104. $(x + a)^2 = b$ **105.** $ax^2 - b = 0$

11.1   Applying Concepts

106. Evaluate $2n^2 - 7n - 4$ given $n(n - 2) = 15$.   **107.** Evaluate $3y^2 + 5y - 2$ given $y(y + 3) = 28$.

Solve for x.

108. $(x^2 - 1)^2 = 9$ **109.** $(x^2 + 3)^2 = 25$

110. $(6x^2 - 5)^2 = 1$ **111.** $x^2 = x$

112. $ax^2 - bx = 0, a > 0$ and $b > 0$ **113.** $ax^2 - b = 0, a > 0$ and $b > 0$

114. **Investments** The value P of an initial investment of A dollars after 2 years is given by $P = A(1 + r)^2$, where r is the annual percentage rate earned by the investment. If an initial investment of \$1500 grew to a value of \$1782.15 in 2 years, what was the annual percentage rate?

115. **Energy** The kinetic energy of a moving body is given by $E = \frac{1}{2}mv^2$, where E is the kinetic energy in newton-meters, m is the mass in kilograms, and v is the speed in meters per second. What is the speed of a moving body whose mass is 5 kg and whose kinetic energy is 250 newton-meters?

116. **Automobiles** On a certain type of street surface, the equation $d = 0.055v^2$ can be used to approximate the distance d, in feet, a car traveling v miles per hour will slide when its brakes are applied. After applying the brakes, the owner of a car involved in an accident skidded 40 ft. Did the traffic officer investigating the accident issue the car owner a ticket for speeding if the speed limit was 30 mph?

11.2 Solving Quadratic Equations by Completing the Square

OBJECTIVE 1 **Solve quadratic equations by completing the square**

Recall that a perfect-square trinomial is the square of a binomial.

Perfect-square Trinomial		Square of a Binomial
$x^2 + 6x + 9$	$=$	$(x + 3)^2$
$x^2 - 10x + 25$	$=$	$(x - 5)^2$
$x^2 + 8x + 16$	$=$	$(x + 4)^2$

For each perfect-square trinomial above, the square of $\frac{1}{2}$ of the coefficient of x equals the constant term.

$$x^2 + 6x + 9, \qquad \left(\frac{1}{2} \cdot 6\right)^2 = 9$$

$$x^2 - 10x + 25, \qquad \left[\frac{1}{2}(-10)\right]^2 = 25 \qquad \left(\frac{1}{2} \text{ coefficient of } x\right)^2 = \textbf{Constant term}$$

$$x^2 + 8x + 16, \qquad \left(\frac{1}{2} \cdot 8\right)^2 = 16$$

This relationship can be used to write the constant term for a perfect-square trinomial. Adding to a binomial the constant term that makes it a perfect-square trinomial is called **completing the square.**

Complete the square of $x^2 - 8x$. Write the resulting perfect-square trinomial as the square of a binomial.

$$x^2 - 8x$$

Find the constant term.

$$\left[\frac{1}{2}(-8)\right]^2 = 16$$

Complete the square of $x^2 - 8x$ by adding the constant term.

$$x^2 - 8x + 16$$

Write the resulting perfect-square trinomial as the square of a binomial.

$$x^2 - 8x + 16 = (x - 4)^2$$

Complete the square of $y^2 + 5y$. Write the resulting perfect-square trinomial as the square of a binomial.

$$y^2 + 5y$$

Find the constant term.

$$\left(\frac{1}{2} \cdot 5\right)^2 = \left(\frac{5}{2}\right)^2 = \frac{25}{4}$$

Complete the square of $y^2 + 5y$ by adding the constant term.

$$y + 5y + \frac{25}{4}$$

Write the resulting perfect-square trinomial as the square of a binomial.

$$y^2 + 5y + \frac{25}{4} = \left(y + \frac{5}{2}\right)^2$$

A quadratic equation of the form $x^2 + bx + c = 0$, $x \neq 0$, that cannot be solved by factoring can be solved by completing the square. The procedure is:

1. Write the equation in the form $x^2 + bx = c$.

2. Add to each side of the equation the term that completes the square on $x^2 + bx$.

3. Factor the perfect-square trinomial. Write it as the square of a binomial.

4. Take the square root of each side of the equation.

5. Solve for x.

Solve by completing the square: $x^2 - 6x - 3 = 0$

Add the opposite of the constant term to each side of the equation.

$$x^2 - 6x - 3 = 0$$
$$x^2 - 6x = 3$$

Find the constant term that completes the square of $x^2 - 6x$.

$$\left[\frac{1}{2}(-6)\right]^2 = 9$$

Add this term to each side of the equation.

$$x^2 - 6x + 9 = 3 + 9$$

Factor the perfect-square trinomial.

$$(x - 3)^2 = 12$$

Take the square root of each side of the equation.

$$\sqrt{(x-3)^2} = \sqrt{12}$$

Simplify.

$$x - 3 = \pm\sqrt{12}$$
$$x - 3 = \pm 2\sqrt{3}$$

Solve for x.

$$x - 3 = 2\sqrt{3} \qquad x - 3 = -2\sqrt{3}$$
$$x = 3 + 2\sqrt{3} \qquad x = 3 - 2\sqrt{3}$$

Check:

$$x^2 - 6x - 3 = 0$$
$$\begin{array}{c|c} \left(3 + 2\sqrt{3}\right)^2 - 6\left(3 + 2\sqrt{3}\right) - 3 & 0 \\ 9 + 12\sqrt{3} + 12 - 18 - 12\sqrt{3} - 3 & 0 \\ & 0 = 0 \end{array}$$

$$x^2 - 6x - 3 = 0$$
$$\begin{array}{c|c} \left(3 - 2\sqrt{3}\right)^2 - 6\left(3 - 2\sqrt{3}\right) - 3 & 0 \\ 9 - 12\sqrt{3} + 12 - 18 + 12\sqrt{3} - 3 & 0 \\ & 0 = 0 \end{array}$$

Write the solutions.

The solutions are $3 + 2\sqrt{3}$ and $3 - 2\sqrt{3}$.

For the method of completing the square to be used, the coefficient of the x^2 term must be 1. If it is not 1, we must multiply each side of the equation by the reciprocal of the coefficient of x^2. This is illustrated in the example below.

Solve by completing the square: $2x^2 - x - 1 = 0$

Add the opposite of the constant term to each side of the equation.

$$2x^2 - x - 1 = 0$$
$$2x^2 - x = 1$$

The coefficient of the x^2 term must be 1. Multiply each side by the reciprocal of the coefficient of x^2.

$$\frac{1}{2}(2x^2 - x) = \frac{1}{2} \cdot 1$$

$$x^2 - \frac{1}{2}x = \frac{1}{2}$$

Find the constant term that completes the square of $x^2 - \frac{1}{2}x$.

$$\left[\frac{1}{2}\left(-\frac{1}{2}\right)\right]^2 = \left(-\frac{1}{4}\right)^2 = \frac{1}{16}$$

Add this term to each side of the equation.

$$x^2 - \frac{1}{2}x + \frac{1}{16} = \frac{1}{2} + \frac{1}{16}$$

Factor the perfect-square trinomial.

$$\left(x - \frac{1}{4}\right)^2 = \frac{9}{16}$$

Take the square root of each side of the equation.

$$\sqrt{\left(x - \frac{1}{4}\right)^2} = \sqrt{\frac{9}{16}}$$

Simplify.

$$x - \frac{1}{4} = \pm\sqrt{\frac{9}{16}}$$

$$x - \frac{1}{4} = \pm\frac{3}{4}$$

Solve for x.

$$x - \frac{1}{4} = \frac{3}{4} \qquad x - \frac{1}{4} = -\frac{3}{4}$$

$$x = 1 \qquad x = -\frac{1}{2}$$

Check:

$$\begin{array}{r|l} 2x^2 - x - 1 = 0 \\ \hline 2(1)^2 - 1 - 1 & 0 \\ 2(1) - 1 - 1 & 0 \\ 2 - 1 - 1 & 0 \\ 0 = 0 \end{array}$$

$$\begin{array}{r|l} 2x^2 - x - 1 = 0 \\ \hline 2\left(-\frac{1}{2}\right)^2 - \left(-\frac{1}{2}\right) - 1 & 0 \\ 2\left(\frac{1}{4}\right) - \left(-\frac{1}{2}\right) - 1 & 0 \\ \frac{1}{2} + \frac{1}{2} - 1 & 0 \\ 0 = 0 \end{array}$$

Write the solutions.

The solutions are 1 and $-\frac{1}{2}$.

EXAMPLE 1   Solve by completing the square.

A. $2x^2 - 4x - 1 = 0$ **B.** $p^2 - 4p + 6 = 0$

Solution   **A.** $2x^2 - 4x - 1 = 0$

$$2x^2 - 4x = 1$$

• Add the opposite of -1 to each side of the equation.

$$\frac{1}{2}(2x^2 - 4x) = \frac{1}{2} \cdot 1$$

• The coefficient of the x^2 term must be 1.

$$x^2 - 2x = \frac{1}{2}$$

$$x^2 - 2x + 1 = \frac{1}{2} + 1$$

• Complete the square of $x^2 - 2x$. Add 1 to each side of the equation.

$$(x - 1)^2 = \frac{3}{2}$$

• Factor the perfect-square trinomial.

$$\sqrt{(x - 1)^2} = \sqrt{\frac{3}{2}}$$

• Take the square root of each side of the equation.

$$x - 1 = \pm\sqrt{\frac{3}{2}}$$

$$x - 1 = \pm\frac{\sqrt{3}}{\sqrt{2}}$$

$$x - 1 = \pm\frac{\sqrt{6}}{2}$$

• Rationalize the denominator.
$$\frac{\sqrt{3}}{\sqrt{2}} = \frac{\sqrt{3}}{\sqrt{2}} \cdot \frac{\sqrt{2}}{\sqrt{2}} = \frac{\sqrt{6}}{2}$$

$$x - 1 = \frac{\sqrt{6}}{2} \qquad x - 1 = -\frac{\sqrt{6}}{2}$$

$$x = 1 + \frac{\sqrt{6}}{2} \qquad x = 1 - \frac{\sqrt{6}}{2}$$

$$= \frac{2}{2} + \frac{\sqrt{6}}{2} \qquad = \frac{2}{2} - \frac{\sqrt{6}}{2}$$

$$= \frac{2 + \sqrt{6}}{2} \qquad = \frac{2 - \sqrt{6}}{2}$$

The solutions are $\dfrac{2 + \sqrt{6}}{2}$ and $\dfrac{2 - \sqrt{6}}{2}$.

B. $p^2 - 4p + 6 = 0$

$$p^2 - 4p = -6$$

• Add the opposite of the constant term to each side of the equation.

$$p^2 - 4p + 4 = -6 + 4$$

• Complete the square of $p^2 - 4p$. Add 4 to each side of the equation.

$$(p - 2)^2 = -2$$

• Factor the perfect-square trinomial.

$$\sqrt{(p - 2)^2} = \sqrt{-2}$$

• Take the square root of each side of the equation.

$\sqrt{-2}$ is not a real number.
The equation has no real number solution.

PROBLEM 1   Solve by completing the square.

A. $3x^2 - 6x - 2 = 0$ **B.** $y^2 - 6y + 10 = 0$

Solution   See page S25.

EXAMPLE 2   Solve by completing the square: $x^2 + 6x + 4 = 0$
Approximate the solutions to the nearest thousandth.

Solution
$$x^2 + 6x + 4 = 0$$
$$x^2 + 6x = -4$$
$$x^2 + 6x + 9 = -4 + 9$$ • **Complete the square of $x^2 + 6x$. Add 9 to each side of the equation.**
$$(x + 3)^2 = 5$$
$$\sqrt{(x + 3)^2} = \sqrt{5}$$
$$x + 3 = \pm\sqrt{5}$$
$$x + 3 \approx \pm 2.2361$$

$x + 3 \approx 2.2361$	$x + 3 \approx -2.2361$
$x \approx -3 + 2.2361$	$x \approx -3 - 2.2361$
≈ -0.764	≈ -5.236

The solutions are approximately -0.764 and -5.236.

PROBLEM 2   Solve by completing the square: $x^2 + 8x + 8 = 0$
Approximate the solutions to the nearest thousandth.

Solution   See page S26.

11.2   Concept Review

Determine whether the statement is always true, sometimes true, or never true.

1. When we square a binomial, the result is a perfect-square trinomial.

2. The constant term in a perfect-square trinomial is equal to the square of one-half the coefficient of x.

3. To "complete the square" means to add to $x^2 + bx$ the constant term that will make it a perfect-square trinomial.

4. To complete the square of $x^2 + 4x$, add 16 to it.

5. To complete the square of $3x^2 + 6x$, add 9 to it.

6. In solving a quadratic equation by completing the square, the next step after writing the equation in the form $(x + a)^2 = b$ is to take the square root of each side of the equation.

11.2   Exercises

1   Solve quadratic equations by completing the square

1. **a.** To complete the square of $x^2 + 18x$, find the constant c that makes $x^2 + 18x + c$ a ___?___ trinomial.
The constant term c will be the square of half the coefficient of

___?___ , so $c = \left[\dfrac{1}{2}(\underline{})\right]^2 = \underline{}$.

b. Complete the square of $x^2 + 18x$ and write the result as the square of a binomial:

$x^2 + 18x +$ ___?___ $= ($ ___?___ $)^2$

2. Rewrite the equation $5x^2 - 10x + 2 = 0$ in the form $(x - m)^2 = n$.

$5x^2 - 10x + 2 = 0$

$5x^2 - 10x =$ ___?___   • Subtract 2 from each side of the equation.

$x^2 -$ ___?___ $x =$ ___?___   • To make the coefficient of x^2 equal to 1, divide each side of the equation by 5.

$x^2 - 2x +$ ___?___ $= -\dfrac{2}{5} +$ ___?___   • Add $\left[\dfrac{1}{2}(\underline{\quad?\quad})\right]^2$ to each side of the equation.

$(x -$ ___?___ $)^2 =$ ___?___   • Factor the left side of the equation. Simplify the right side of the equation.

Complete the square. Write the resulting perfect-square trinomial as the square of a binomial.

3. $x^2 + 12x$

4. $x^2 - 4x$

5. $x^2 + 10x$

6. $x^2 + 3x$

7. $x^2 - x$

8. $x^2 + 5x$

Solve by completing the square.

9. $x^2 + 2x - 3 = 0$

10. $y^2 + 4y - 5 = 0$

11. $v^2 + 4v + 1 = 0$

12. $y^2 - 2y - 5 = 0$

13. $v^2 - 6v + 13 = 0$

14. $x^2 + 4x + 13 = 0$

15. $x^2 + 6x = 5$

16. $w^2 - 8w = 3$

17. $x^2 = 4x - 4$

18. $z^2 = 8z - 16$

19. $z^2 = 2z + 1$

20. $y^2 = 10y - 20$

Solve. First try to solve the equation by factoring. If you are unable to solve the equation by factoring, solve the equation by completing the square.

21. $p^2 + 3p = 1$

22. $r^2 + 5r = 2$

23. $w^2 + 7w = 8$

24. $y^2 + 5y = -4$

25. $x^2 + 6x + 4 = 0$

26. $y^2 - 8y - 1 = 0$

27. $r^2 - 8r = -2$

28. $s^2 + 6s = 5$

29. $t^2 - 3t = -2$

30. $y^2 = 4y + 12$

31. $w^2 = 3w + 5$

32. $x^2 = 1 - 3x$

33. $x^2 - x - 1 = 0$

34. $x^2 - 7x = -3$

35. $y^2 - 5y + 3 = 0$

36. $z^2 - 5z = -2$

37. $v^2 + v - 3 = 0$

38. $x^2 - x = 1$

39. $y^2 = 7 - 10y$

40. $v^2 = 14 + 16v$

41. $s^2 + 3s = -1$

42. $r^2 - 3r = 5$

43. $t^2 - t = 4$

44. $y^2 + y - 4 = 0$

45. $x^2 - 3x + 5 = 0$

46. $z^2 + 5z + 7 = 0$

47. $2t^2 - 3t + 1 = 0$

48. $2x^2 - 7x + 3 = 0$

49. $2r^2 + 5r = 3$

50. $2y^2 - 3y = 9$

51. $4v^2 - 4v - 1 = 0$

52. $2s^2 - 4s - 1 = 0$

53. $4z^2 - 8z = 1$

54. $3r^2 - 2r = 2$

55. $3y - 5 = (y - 1)(y - 2)$

56. $4p + 2 = (p - 1)(p + 3)$

57. $\dfrac{x^2}{4} - \dfrac{x}{2} = 3$

58. $\dfrac{x^2}{6} - \dfrac{x}{3} = 1$

59. $\dfrac{2x^2}{3} = 2x + 3$

60. $\dfrac{3x^2}{2} = 3x + 2$

61. $\dfrac{x}{3} + \dfrac{3}{x} = \dfrac{8}{3}$

62. $\dfrac{x}{4} - \dfrac{2}{x} = \dfrac{3}{4}$

Complete Exercises 63 and 64 without using a calculator.

63. A quadratic equation has solutions $-3 \pm \sqrt{5}$. Are both of these solutions negative, are both positive, or is one negative and one positive?

64. A quadratic equation has solutions $2 \pm \sqrt{7}$. Are both of these solutions negative, are both positive, or is one negative and one positive?

Solve by completing the square. Approximate the solutions to the nearest thousandth.

65. $y^2 + 3y = 5$

66. $w^2 + 5w = 2$

67. $2z^2 - 3z = 7$

68. $2x^2 + 3x = 11$

69. $4x^2 + 6x - 1 = 0$

70. $4x^2 + 2x - 3 = 0$

11.2 Applying Concepts

71. Evaluate $2b^2$ given $b^2 - 6b + 7 = 0$.

72. Evaluate $2y^2$ given $y^2 - 2y - 7 = 0$.

Solve.

73. $\sqrt{2x + 7} - 4 = x$

74. $\dfrac{x + 1}{2} + \dfrac{3}{x - 1} = 4$

75. $\dfrac{x - 2}{3} + \dfrac{2}{x + 2} = 4$

76. Explain why the equation $(x - 2)^2 = -4$ does not have a real number solution.

11.3 Solving Quadratic Equations by Using the Quadratic Formula

OBJECTIVE 1   **Solve quadratic equations by using the quadratic formula**

Any quadratic equation can be solved by completing the square. Applying this method to the standard form of a quadratic equation produces a formula that can be used to solve any quadratic equation.

To solve $ax^2 + bx + c = 0$, $a \neq 0$, by completing the square, subtract the constant term from each side of the equation.

$$ax^2 + bx + c = 0$$
$$ax^2 + bx + c - c = 0 - c$$
$$ax^2 + bx = -c$$

Multiply each side of the equation by the reciprocal of a, the coefficient of x^2.

$$\frac{1}{a}(ax^2 + bx) = \frac{1}{a}(-c)$$
$$x^2 + \frac{b}{a}x = -\frac{c}{a}$$

Complete the square by adding $\left(\dfrac{1}{2} \cdot \dfrac{b}{a}\right)^2$ to each side of the equation.

$$x^2 + \frac{b}{a}x + \left(\frac{1}{2} \cdot \frac{b}{a}\right)^2 = \left(\frac{1}{2} \cdot \frac{b}{a}\right)^2 - \frac{c}{a}$$
$$x^2 + \frac{b}{a}x + \frac{b^2}{4a^2} = \frac{b^2}{4a^2} - \frac{c}{a}$$

Simplify the right side of the equation.

$$x^2 + \frac{b}{a}x + \frac{b^2}{4a^2} = \frac{b^2}{4a^2} - \left(\frac{c}{a} \cdot \frac{4a}{4a}\right)$$
$$x^2 + \frac{b}{a}x + \frac{b^2}{4a^2} = \frac{b^2}{4a^2} - \frac{4ac}{4a^2}$$
$$x^2 + \frac{b}{a}x + \frac{b^2}{4a^2} = \frac{b^2 - 4ac}{4a^2}$$

Factor the perfect-square trinomial on the left side of the equation.

$$\left(x + \frac{b}{2a}\right)^2 = \frac{b^2 - 4ac}{4a^2}$$

Take the square root of each side of the equation.

$$\sqrt{\left(x + \frac{b}{2a}\right)^2} = \sqrt{\frac{b^2 - 4ac}{4a^2}}$$

$$x + \frac{b}{2a} = \pm\frac{\sqrt{b^2 - 4ac}}{2a}$$

Solve for x.

$$x + \frac{b}{2a} = \frac{\sqrt{b^2 - 4ac}}{2a} \qquad\qquad x + \frac{b}{2a} = -\frac{\sqrt{b^2 - 4ac}}{2a}$$

$$x = -\frac{b}{2a} + \frac{\sqrt{b^2 - 4ac}}{2a} \qquad\qquad x = -\frac{b}{2a} - \frac{\sqrt{b^2 - 4ac}}{2a}$$

$$x = \frac{-b + \sqrt{b^2 - 4ac}}{2a} \qquad\qquad x = \frac{-b - \sqrt{b^2 - 4ac}}{2a}$$

The Quadratic Formula

The solution of $ax^2 + bx + c = 0$, $a \neq 0$, is

$$x = \frac{-b + \sqrt{b^2 - 4ac}}{2a} \quad\text{or}\quad x = \frac{-b - \sqrt{b^2 - 4ac}}{2a}$$

The quadratic formula is frequently written in the form

$$x = \frac{-b \pm \sqrt{b^2 - 4ac}}{2a}$$

Solve by using the quadratic formula: $2x^2 = 4x - 1$

$$2x^2 = 4x - 1$$

Write the equation in standard form. $a = 2$, $b = -4$, and $c = 1$.

$$2x^2 - 4x + 1 = 0$$

Replace a, b, and c in the quadratic formula by their values.

$$x = \frac{-b \pm \sqrt{b^2 - 4ac}}{2a}$$

$$= \frac{-(-4) \pm \sqrt{(-4)^2 - 4 \cdot 2 \cdot 1}}{2 \cdot 2}$$

Simplify.

$$= \frac{4 \pm \sqrt{16 - 8}}{4}$$

$$= \frac{4 \pm \sqrt{8}}{4}$$

$$= \frac{4 \pm 2\sqrt{2}}{4} = \frac{2(2 \pm \sqrt{2})}{2 \cdot 2} = \frac{2 \pm \sqrt{2}}{2}$$

Check:

$$2x^2 = 4x - 1 \qquad\qquad\qquad 2x^2 = 4x - 1$$

$2\left(\dfrac{2 + \sqrt{2}}{2}\right)^2$	$4\left(\dfrac{2 + \sqrt{2}}{2}\right) - 1$	$2\left(\dfrac{2 - \sqrt{2}}{2}\right)^2$	$4\left(\dfrac{2 - \sqrt{2}}{2}\right) - 1$
$2\left(\dfrac{4 + 4\sqrt{2} + 2}{4}\right)$	$2(2 + \sqrt{2}) - 1$	$2\left(\dfrac{4 - 4\sqrt{2} + 2}{4}\right)$	$2(2 - \sqrt{2}) - 1$
$2\left(\dfrac{6 + 4\sqrt{2}}{4}\right)$	$4 + 2\sqrt{2} - 1$	$2\left(\dfrac{6 - 4\sqrt{2}}{4}\right)$	$4 - 2\sqrt{2} - 1$
$\dfrac{6 + 4\sqrt{2}}{2}$	$3 + 2\sqrt{2}$	$\dfrac{6 - 4\sqrt{2}}{2}$	$3 - 2\sqrt{2}$
$3 + 2\sqrt{2} = 3 + 2\sqrt{2}$		$3 - 2\sqrt{2} = 3 - 2\sqrt{2}$	

Write the solutions.   The solutions are $\dfrac{2 + \sqrt{2}}{2}$ and $\dfrac{2 - \sqrt{2}}{2}$. ∎

EXAMPLE 1   Solve by using the quadratic formula.

A. $2x^2 - 3x + 1 = 0$ **B.** $2x^2 = 8x - 5$
C. $t^2 - 3t + 7 = 0$

Solution   **A.** $2x^2 - 3x + 1 = 0$ • $a = 2, b = -3, c = 1$

$$x = \frac{-(-3) \pm \sqrt{(-3)^2 - 4(2)(1)}}{2 \cdot 2}$$

$$= \frac{3 \pm \sqrt{9 - 8}}{4} = \frac{3 \pm \sqrt{1}}{4} = \frac{3 \pm 1}{4}$$

$$x = \frac{3 + 1}{4} \qquad x = \frac{3 - 1}{4}$$

$$= \frac{4}{4} = 1 \qquad = \frac{2}{4} = \frac{1}{2}$$

The solutions are 1 and $\dfrac{1}{2}$.

B. $\qquad\qquad 2x^2 = 8x - 5$
$\qquad 2x^2 - 8x + 5 = 0$ • **Write the equation in standard form.**
                                 $a = 2, b = -8, c = 5$

$$x = \frac{-(-8) \pm \sqrt{(-8)^2 - 4(2)(5)}}{2 \cdot 2}$$

$$= \frac{8 \pm \sqrt{64 - 40}}{4}$$

$$= \frac{8 \pm \sqrt{24}}{4}$$

$$= \frac{8 \pm 2\sqrt{6}}{4}$$

$$= \frac{2(4 \pm \sqrt{6})}{2 \cdot 2} = \frac{4 \pm \sqrt{6}}{2}$$

The solutions are $\dfrac{4 + \sqrt{6}}{2}$ and $\dfrac{4 - \sqrt{6}}{2}$.

C. $t^2 - 3t + 7 = 0$ • $a = 1, b = -3, c = 7$

$$t = \frac{-(-3) \pm \sqrt{(-3)^2 - 4(1)(7)}}{2(1)}$$

$$= \frac{3 \pm \sqrt{9 - 28}}{2} = \frac{3 \pm \sqrt{-19}}{2}$$

$\sqrt{-19}$ is not a real number.

The equation has no real number solution.

PROBLEM 1   Solve by using the quadratic formula.

A. $3x^2 + 4x - 4 = 0$ **B.** $x^2 + 2x = 1$

C. $z^2 + 2z + 6 = 0$

■ **Solution**   See page S26.

11.3   Concept Review

Determine whether the statement is always true, sometimes true, or never true.

1. Any quadratic equation can be solved by using the quadratic formula.

2. The solutions of a quadratic equation can be written as

$$x = \frac{-b + \sqrt{b^2 - 4ac}}{2a} \text{ and } x = \frac{-b - \sqrt{b^2 - 4ac}}{2a}.$$

3. The equation $4x^2 - 3x = 9$ is a quadratic equation in standard form.

4. In the quadratic formula $x = \dfrac{-b \pm \sqrt{b^2 - 4ac}}{2a}$, b is the coefficient of x^2.

5. $\dfrac{6 \pm 2\sqrt{3}}{2}$ simplifies to $3 \pm 2\sqrt{3}$.

11.3   Exercises

1   Solve quadratic equations by using the quadratic formula

1. Write the quadratic formula. Explain what each variable in the formula represents.

2. Explain what the quadratic formula is used for.

3. To write the equation $x^2 = 4x + 2$ in standard form, subtract ____?____ and ____?____ from each side of the equation. The resulting equation is ____?____ $= 0$. Then $a =$ ____?____ , $b =$ ____?____ , and $c =$ ____?____ .

4. Use the values of a, b, and c that you found in Exercise 3 to evaluate the quadratic formula for the equation $x^2 = 4x + 2$.

$x = \dfrac{-b \pm \sqrt{b^2 - 4ac}}{2a}$ • Write the ____?____ formula.

$= \dfrac{-(-4) \pm \sqrt{(-4)^2 - 4(1)(-2)}}{2(1)}$ • Replace b with ____?____ , a with ____?____ , and c with ____?____ .

$= \dfrac{\underline{\ ?\ } \pm \sqrt{\underline{\ ?\ } + \underline{\ ?\ }}}{\underline{\ ?\ }}$ • Simplify.

$= \dfrac{4 \pm \sqrt{\underline{\ ?\ }}}{2}$ • Simplify the number under the radical sign.

$= \dfrac{4 \pm \underline{\ ?\ }\sqrt{\underline{\ ?\ }}}{2}$ • Simplify the radical.

$= \underline{\ ?\ } \pm \underline{\ ?\ }$ • Divide each term of the numerator by the 2 in the denominator.

Solve by using the quadratic formula.

5. $z^2 + 6z - 7 = 0$ **6.** $s^2 + 3s - 10 = 0$ **7.** $w^2 = 3w + 18$ **8.** $r^2 = 5 - 4r$

9. $t^2 - 2t = 5$ **10.** $y^2 - 4y = 6$ **11.** $t^2 + 6t - 1 = 0$ **12.** $z^2 + 4z + 1 = 0$

13. $w^2 + 3w + 5 = 0$ **14.** $x^2 - 2x + 6 = 0$ **15.** $w^2 = 4w + 9$ **16.** $y^2 = 8y + 3$

Solve. First try to solve the equation by factoring. If you are unable to solve the equation by factoring, solve the equation by using the quadratic formula.

17. $p^2 - p = 0$ **18.** $2v^2 + v = 0$ **19.** $4t^2 - 4t - 1 = 0$

20. $4x^2 - 8x - 1 = 0$ **21.** $4t^2 - 9 = 0$ **22.** $4s^2 - 25 = 0$

23. $3x^2 - 6x + 2 = 0$ **24.** $5x^2 - 6x = 3$ **25.** $3t^2 = 2t + 3$

26. $4n^2 = 7n - 2$ **27.** $2x^2 + x + 1 = 0$ **28.** $3r^2 - r + 2 = 0$

29. $2y^2 + 3 = 8y$ **30.** $5x^2 - 1 = x$ **31.** $3t^2 = 7t + 6$

32. $3x^2 = 10x + 8$

33. $3y^2 - 4 = 5y$

34. $6x^2 - 5 = 3x$

35. $3x^2 = x + 3$

36. $2n^2 = 7 - 3n$

37. $5d^2 - 2d - 8 = 0$

38. $x^2 - 7x - 10 = 0$

39. $5z^2 + 11z = 12$

40. $4v^2 = v + 3$

41. $v^2 + 6v + 1 = 0$

42. $s^2 + 4s - 8 = 0$

43. $4t^2 - 12t - 15 = 0$

44. $4w^2 - 20w + 5 = 0$

45. $2x^2 = 4x - 5$

46. $3r^2 = 5r - 6$

47. $9y^2 + 6y - 1 = 0$

48. $9s^2 - 6s - 2 = 0$

49. $6s^2 - s - 2 = 0$

50. $6y^2 + 5y - 4 = 0$

51. $4p^2 + 16p = -11$

52. $4y^2 - 12y = -1$

53. $4x^2 = 4x + 11$

54. $4s^2 + 12s = 3$

55. $4p^2 = -12p - 9$

56. $3y^2 + 6y = -3$

57. $9v^2 = -30v - 23$

58. $9t^2 = 30t + 17$

59. $\dfrac{x^2}{2} - \dfrac{x}{3} = 1$

60. $\dfrac{x^2}{4} - \dfrac{x}{2} = 5$

61. $\dfrac{2x^2}{5} = x + 1$

62. $\dfrac{3x^2}{2} + 2x = 1$

63. $\dfrac{x}{5} + \dfrac{5}{x} = \dfrac{12}{5}$

64. $\dfrac{x}{4} + \dfrac{3}{x} = \dfrac{5}{2}$

65. True or false? If you solve $ax^2 + bx + c = 0$ by using the quadratic formula and the solutions are rational numbers, then the equation could have been solved by factoring.

66. True or false? If the value of $b^2 - 4ac$ in the quadratic formula is 0, then $ax^2 + bx + c = 0$ has one solution, a double root.

Solve by using the quadratic formula. Approximate the solutions to the nearest thousandth.

67. $x^2 - 2x - 21 = 0$

68. $y^2 + 4y - 11 = 0$

69. $s^2 - 6s - 13 = 0$

70. $w^2 + 8w - 15 = 0$

71. $2p^2 - 7p - 10 = 0$

72. $3t^2 - 8t - 1 = 0$

73. $4z^2 + 8z - 1 = 0$

74. $4x^2 + 7x + 1 = 0$

75. $5v^2 - v - 5 = 0$

11.3 Applying Concepts

Solve.

76. $\sqrt{x^2 + 2x + 1} = x - 1$

77. $\dfrac{x + 2}{3} - \dfrac{4}{x - 2} = 2$

78. $\dfrac{x + 1}{5} - \dfrac{3}{x - 1} = 2$

79. True or false?
  a. The equations $x = \sqrt{12 - x}$ and $x^2 = 12 - x$ have the same solution.
  b. If $\sqrt{a} + \sqrt{b} = c$, then $a + b = c^2$.
  c. $\sqrt{9} = \pm 3$
  d. $\sqrt{x^2} = |x|$

80. Factoring, completing the square, and using the quadratic formula are three methods of solving quadratic equations. Describe each method, and cite the advantages and disadvantages of using each.

81. Explain why the equation $0x^2 + 3x + 4 = 0$ cannot be solved by the quadratic formula.

11.4 Complex Numbers

OBJECTIVE 1 Simplify complex numbers

Recall that $\sqrt{16} = 4$ because $4^2 = 16$. Now consider the expression $\sqrt{-16}$. To find $\sqrt{-16}$, we need to find a number n such that $n^2 = -16$. However, the square of any real number (except zero) is a *positive* number. To find a number n such that $n^2 = -16$, we introduce a new number.

> **Definition of *i***
>
> The **imaginary unit,** designated by the letter i, is the number whose square is -1. Symbolically, this is written as follows:
>
> $$i^2 = -1$$

Using this definition, we can now write that $\sqrt{-16} = 4i$ because

$(4i)^2 = 4^2 i^2$ • **Use the Rule for Simplifying Powers of Products.**

$\qquad = 16(-1)$ • $i^2 = -1$

$\qquad = -16$

The principal square root of a negative number is defined in terms of i.

Principal Square Root of a Negative Number

If a is a positive real number, then $\sqrt{-a} = \sqrt{a}\,i = i\sqrt{a}$. The number $i\sqrt{a}$ is called an **imaginary number.** When $a = 1$, we have $\sqrt{-1} = i$.

Examples of imaginary numbers are $-12i$, $\frac{3}{2}i$, and $i\sqrt{15}$. Note that we wrote $i\sqrt{15}$ rather than $\sqrt{15}i$. It is customary, when a radical occurs in an imaginary number, to write the i in front of the radical. This is done to avoid confusion of $\sqrt{15}i$ with $\sqrt{15i}$.

EXAMPLE 1 Write each expression in terms of i.

A. $\sqrt{-23}$ **B.** $\sqrt{-36}$ **C.** $\sqrt{-45}$ **D.** $5\sqrt{-27}$

Solution **A.** $\sqrt{-23} = \sqrt{-1 \cdot 23} = \sqrt{-1}\sqrt{23} = i\sqrt{23}$

B. $\sqrt{-36} = \sqrt{-1 \cdot 36} = \sqrt{-1}\sqrt{36} = i\sqrt{36} = i \cdot 6 = 6i$

C. $\sqrt{-45} = \sqrt{-1 \cdot 45} = \sqrt{-1}\sqrt{45} = i\sqrt{45} = i\sqrt{9 \cdot 5}$
$= i\sqrt{9}\sqrt{5} = i \cdot 3\sqrt{5} = 3i\sqrt{5}$

D. $5\sqrt{-18} = 5\sqrt{-1 \cdot 18} = 5\sqrt{-1}\sqrt{18} = 5i\sqrt{18}$
$= 5i\sqrt{9 \cdot 2} = 5i\sqrt{9}\sqrt{2} = 5i \cdot 3\sqrt{2} = 15i\sqrt{2}$

PROBLEM 1 Write each expression in terms of i.
A. $\sqrt{-17}$ **B.** $\sqrt{-81}$ **C.** $\sqrt{-63}$ **D.** $4\sqrt{-50}$

Solution See page S26.

The real numbers and the imaginary numbers make up the *complex numbers*.

Complex Numbers

A **complex number** is a number of the form $a + bi$, where a and b are real numbers and $i = \sqrt{-1}$, the imaginary unit. The number a is the **real part of a complex number** and b is the **imaginary part of a complex number.**

Here are examples of complex numbers and their real and imaginary parts.

$-3 + 5i$ • **Real part: -3; imaginary part: 5**

$2 - 6i$ • **Real part: 2; imaginary part: -6. Note that $2 - 6i = 2 + (-6)i$.**

5 • **Real part: 5; imaginary part: 0. Note that $5 = 5 + 0i$.**

$7i$ • **Real part: 0; imaginary part: 7. Note that $7i = 0 + 7i$.**

From these examples, note that a real number, such as 5, is a complex number whose imaginary part is zero and that an imaginary number, such as $7i$, is a complex number whose real part is zero.

Although $3 + \sqrt{-4}$ is a complex number, the preferred form is $3 + 2i$. This is called the **standard form of a complex number.** If the imaginary part of a complex number is negative, such as $2 + (-5i)$, we normally write $2 - 5i$, for example, as the standard form of the complex number.

Write $7 - 2\sqrt{-20}$ in standard form.

$$7 - 2\sqrt{-20} = 7 - 2i\sqrt{20}$$ • $\sqrt{-20} = i\sqrt{20}$

$$= 7 - 2i\sqrt{4}\,\sqrt{5} = 7 - 2i \cdot 2\sqrt{5}$$ • **Simplify** $\sqrt{20}$.

$$= 7 - 4i\sqrt{5}$$ • **Multiply** $2i$ **times 2.**

EXAMPLE 2   Write $\dfrac{4 + 8\sqrt{-45}}{6}$ in standard form.

Solution $\dfrac{4 + 8\sqrt{-45}}{6} = \dfrac{4 + 8i\sqrt{45}}{6}$ • $\sqrt{-45} = i\sqrt{45}$

$$= \dfrac{4 + 8i\sqrt{9}\sqrt{5}}{6} = \dfrac{4 + 24i\sqrt{5}}{6}$$

$$= \dfrac{4}{6} + \dfrac{24i\sqrt{5}}{6} = \dfrac{2}{3} + 4i\sqrt{5}$$

PROBLEM 2   Write $\dfrac{5 - 3\sqrt{-50}}{10}$ in standard form.

Solution   See page S26.

OBJECTIVE 2   Add and subtract complex numbers

Operations on complex numbers can be related to operations on binomials. To add two complex numbers, add the real parts and add the imaginary parts. To subtract two complex numbers, subtract the real parts and subtract the imaginary parts.

EXAMPLE 3   Simplify.

     A. $(-3 + 2i) + (5 - 6i)$ **B.** $(-9 + 4i) - (2 - 6i)$

Solution   **A.** Add the real parts.

$$(-3 + 2i) + (5 - 6i) = (-3 + 5) + (2 + (-6))i$$
$$= 2 + (-4)i$$

Add the imaginary parts. $= 2 - 4i$

     B. Subtract the real parts.

$$(-9 + 4i) - (2 - 6i) = (-9 - 2) + (4 - (-6))i$$
$$= -11 + 10i$$

Subtract the imaginary parts.

PROBLEM 3   Simplify.

        A. $(7 - 3i) + (-8 + i)$ **B.** $(-5 + 4i) - (-3 - 7i)$

   Solution   See page S26.

OBJECTIVE **3**   **Multiply complex numbers**

When multiplying complex numbers, recall that $i^2 = -1$. Here are some examples.

$$3i(5i) = 15i^2 = 15(-1) = -15$$
$$-2i(6i) = -12i^2 = -12(-1) = 12$$

EXAMPLE 4   Multiply: $3i(2 - 4i)$

   Solution $3i(2 - 4i) = 6i - 12i^2$ • Use the Distributive Property to remove parentheses.

              $= 6i - 12(-1)$ • Replace i^2 with -1.

              $= 6i + 12$

              $= 12 + 6i$ • Write the answer in the form $a + bi$.

PROBLEM 4   Multiply: $5i(3 + 6i)$

   Solution   See page S26.

The product of two complex numbers of the form $a + bi$, $a \neq 0$, $b \neq 0$, can be found by using the FOIL method and the fact that $i^2 = -1$.

EXAMPLE 5   Multiply: $(5 - 4i)(2 + 3i)$

   Solution $(5 - 4i)(2 + 3i)$

         $= 5(2) + 5(3i) + (-4i)2 + (-4i)3i$ • Use the FOIL method.

         $= 10 + 15i - 8i - 12i^2$

         $= 10 + 7i - 12i^2$ • Combine like terms.

         $= 10 + 7i - 12(-1)$ • Replace i^2 with -1.

         $= 10 + 7i + 12$

         $= 22 + 7i$ • Write the answer in the form $a + bi$.

PROBLEM 5   Multiply: $(-1 + 5i)(2 - 3i)$

   Solution   See page S27.

The square of a complex number is found by using FOIL.

Write $(2 - 3i)^2$ in standard form.

$(2 - 3i)^2 = (2 - 3i)(2 - 3i)$ • Multiply $2 - 3i$ times itself.

       $= 4 - 6i - 6i + 9i^2$ • Use the FOIL method.

       $= 4 - 12i + 9i^2$ • Combine like terms.

       $= 4 - 12i + 9(-1)$ • Replace i^2 with -1.

       $= 4 - 12i - 9$

       $= -5 - 12i$ • Write in the form $a + bi$.

The complex numbers $a + bi$ and $a - bi$ are called **complex conjugates** or **conjugates** of each other. Here are some examples.

Number	Conjugate
$2 + 5i$	$2 - 5i$
$-3 + 6i$	$-3 - 6i$
$5 - 4i$	$5 + 4i$

Consider the product of a complex number and its conjugate. For instance,

$$
\begin{aligned}
(2 + 5i)(2 - 5i) &= 4 - 10i + 10i - 25i^2 \\
&= 4 - 25i^2 \\
&= 4 - 25(-1) \\
&= 4 + 25 = 29
\end{aligned}
$$

Note that the product of complex conjugates is a *real* number. This is always true.

Product of Complex Conjugates

The product of a complex number and its conjugate is a real number. That is, $(a + bi)(a - bi) = a^2 + b^2$.

For instance, $(5 + 3i)(5 - 3i) = 5^2 + 3^2 = 25 + 9 = 34$.

EXAMPLE 6   Multiply: $(8 + 3i)(8 - 3i)$

Solution $(8 + 3i)(8 - 3i) = 8^2 + 3^2$ • $(a + bi)(a - bi) = a^2 + b^2$
                                                 $a = 8, b = 3$

                                   $= 64 + 9$

                                   $= 73$

PROBLEM 6   Multiply: $(-2 + 5i)(-2 - 5i)$

Solution   See page S27.

OBJECTIVE   **4**   ## Divide complex numbers

Recall that the number $\dfrac{3}{\sqrt{2}}$ is not in simplest form because there is a radical expression in the denominator. Similarly, $\dfrac{3}{i}$ is not in simplest form because $i = \sqrt{-1}$. To write this expression in simplest form, multiply the numerator and denominator by i.

$$
\frac{3}{i} \cdot \frac{i}{i} = \frac{3i}{i^2} = \frac{3i}{-1} = -3i
$$

This process is used to divide a complex number by an imaginary number.

EXAMPLE 7 Divide: $\dfrac{3 - 6i}{2i}$

Solution $\dfrac{3 - 6i}{2i} = \dfrac{3 - 6i}{2i} \cdot \dfrac{i}{i}$ • **Multiply the numerator and denominator by i.**

$$= \frac{3i - 6i^2}{2i^2} = \frac{3i - 6(-1)}{2(-1)}$$ • $i^2 = -1$

$$= \frac{3i + 6}{-2} = \frac{3}{-2}i + \frac{6}{-2} = -3 - \frac{3}{2}i$$ • **Write in the form a + bi.**

PROBLEM 7 Divide: $\dfrac{-12 + 8i}{-4i}$

Solution See page S27.

Recall that to simplify the quotient $\dfrac{2 + \sqrt{3}}{5 + 2\sqrt{3}}$, multiply the numerator and denominator by the conjugate of $5 + 2\sqrt{3}$, which is $5 - 2\sqrt{3}$. In a similar manner, to simplify the quotient of the two complex numbers, multiply the numerator and denominator by the conjugate of the complex number in the denominator.

The next example shows how the quotient of two complex numbers is determined by using conjugates.

EXAMPLE 8 Divide: $\dfrac{3 - 6i}{4 - 3i}$

Solution $\dfrac{3 - 6i}{4 - 3i} = \dfrac{3 - 6i}{4 - 3i} \cdot \dfrac{4 + 3i}{4 + 3i}$ • **Multiply the numerator and denominator by the conjugate of the denominator.**

$$= \frac{12 + 9i - 24i - 18i^2}{4^2 + 3^2}$$

$$= \frac{12 - 15i - 18i^2}{16 + 9}$$ • **Combine like terms in the numerator.**

$$= \frac{12 - 15i - 18(-1)}{25}$$ • **Replace i^2 with -1.**

$$= \frac{12 - 15i + 18}{25}$$

$$= \frac{30 - 15i}{25}$$

$$= \frac{30}{25} - \frac{15}{25}i = \frac{6}{5} - \frac{3}{5}i$$ • **Write in the form a + bi.**

PROBLEM 8 Divide: $\dfrac{16 - 11i}{5 + 2i}$

Solution See page S27.

OBJECTIVE **5**   **Solve quadratic equations with complex number solutions**

Allowing complex numbers to be solutions of quadratic equations enables us to solve quadratic equations that in previous sections we stated have "no real number solutions."

Solve: $2x^2 + 128 = 0$

$2x^2 + 128 = 0$

$\quad\quad 2x^2 = -128$
• Subtract 128 from each side of the equation.

$\quad\quad\quad x^2 = -64$
• Divide each side of the equation by 2.

$\quad\quad \sqrt{x^2} = \sqrt{-64}$
• Take the square root of each side of the equation.

$\quad\quad\quad x = \pm\sqrt{-64} = \pm i\sqrt{64}$
• Rewrite $\sqrt{-64}$ as $i\sqrt{64}$.

$\quad\quad\quad x = \pm 8i$
• Simplify $\sqrt{64}$.

The solutions are $-8i$ and $8i$.

Solve $(x - 1)^2 + 9 = 1$ and check.

$(x - 1)^2 + 9 = 1$

$\quad (x - 1)^2 = -8$
• Subtract 9 from each side of the equation.

$\sqrt{(x - 1)^2} = \sqrt{-8}$
• Take the square root of each side of the equation.

$\quad x - 1 = \pm\sqrt{-8} = \pm i\sqrt{8}$
• Rewrite $\sqrt{-8}$ as $i\sqrt{8}$.

$\quad x - 1 = \pm 2i\sqrt{2}$
• Simplify $\sqrt{8}$.

$\quad\quad\quad x = 1 \pm 2i\sqrt{2}$
• Add 1 to each side of the equation.

Check:

$(x - 1)^2 + 9 = 1$	
$(1 + 2i\sqrt{2} - 1)^2 + 9$	1
$(2i\sqrt{2})^2 + 9$	1
$2^2(i^2)(\sqrt{2})^2 + 9$	1
$4(-1)(2) + 9$	1
$-8 + 9$	1
	$1 = 1$

$(x - 1)^2 + 9 = 1$	
$(1 - 2i\sqrt{2} - 1)^2 + 9$	1
$(-2i\sqrt{2})^2 + 9$	1
$(-2)^2(i^2)(\sqrt{2})^2 + 9$	1
$4(-1)(2) + 9$	1
$-8 + 9$	1
	$1 = 1$

The solutions are $1 + 2i\sqrt{2}$ and $1 - 2i\sqrt{2}$.

EXAMPLE 9   Solve $(2x + 1)^2 + 5 = 1$ and check.

Solution $(2x + 1)^2 + 5 = 1$

$\quad\quad (2x + 1)^2 = -4$
• Subtract 5 from each side of the equation.

$\sqrt{(2x + 1)^2} = \sqrt{-4}$
• Take the square root of each side of the equation.

$$2x + 1 = \pm 2i$$

• Rewrite $\sqrt{-4}$ as $2i$.

$$2x = -1 \pm 2i$$

• Subtract 1 from each side of the equation.

$$x = \frac{-1 \pm 2i}{2}$$

• Divide each side of the equation by 2.

$$x = -\frac{1}{2} \pm \frac{2i}{2}$$

• Write the solution in standard form by dividing each term by 2.

$$x = -\frac{1}{2} \pm i$$

Check

$(2x + 1)^2 + 5 = 1$		$(2x + 1)^2 + 5 = 1$	
$\left(2\left(-\dfrac{1}{2} + i\right) + 1\right)^2 + 5$	1	$\left(2\left(-\dfrac{1}{2} - i\right) + 1\right)^2 + 5$	1
$(-1 + 2i + 1)^2 + 5$	1	$(-1 - 2i + 1)^2 + 5$	1
$(2i)^2 + 5$	1	$(-2i)^2 + 5$	1
$2^2 i^2 + 5$	1	$(-2)^2 i^2 + 5$	1
$4(-1) + 5$	1	$4(-1) + 5$	1
$-4 + 5$	1	$-4 + 5$	1
$1 = 1$		$1 = 1$	

The solutions are $-\dfrac{1}{2} + i$ and $-\dfrac{1}{2} - i$.

PROBLEM 9   Solve: $8z^2 + 17 = -7$ and check.

Solution   See page S27.

In Example 9 we were able to solve the equation by taking the square root of each side of the equation. In many instances, however, using the quadratic formula will be the best choice for solving a quadratic equation with complex number solutions. We restate the quadratic formula here for your reference.

The solutions of the quadratic equation $ax^2 + bx + c = 0, a \neq 0$, are given by

$$x = \frac{-b \pm \sqrt{b^2 - 4ac}}{2a}$$

Solve: $4x^2 - 4x + 2 = 0$

$$x = \frac{-b \pm \sqrt{b^2 - 4ac}}{2a}$$

• $a = 4, b = -4, c = 2$

$$x = \frac{-(-4) \pm \sqrt{(-4)^2 - 4(4)(2)}}{2(4)}$$

$$= \frac{4 \pm \sqrt{16 - 32}}{8} = \frac{4 \pm \sqrt{-16}}{8}$$

$$= \frac{4 \pm i\sqrt{16}}{8} = \frac{4 \pm 4i}{8}$$

• Rewrite $\sqrt{-16}$ as $i\sqrt{16}$. $\sqrt{16} = 4$

$$= \frac{4}{8} \pm \frac{4i}{8} = \frac{1}{2} \pm \frac{1}{2}i$$

• Write the solution as a complex number in standard form.

Check:

$$4x^2 - 4x + 2 = 0$$

$$4\left(\frac{1}{2} + \frac{1}{2}i\right)^2 - 4\left(\frac{1}{2} + \frac{1}{2}i\right) + 2 \;\Big|\; 0$$

$$4\left(\frac{1}{4} + \frac{1}{4}i + \frac{1}{4}i + \frac{1}{4}i^2\right) - 2 - 2i + 2 \;\Big|\; 0$$

$$1 + i + i + i^2 - 2 - 2i + 2 \;\Big|\; 0$$

$$1 + 2i + (-1) - 2i \;\Big|\; 0$$

$$0 = 0$$

$$4x^2 - 4x + 2 = 0$$

$$4\left(\frac{1}{2} - \frac{1}{2}i\right)^2 - 4\left(\frac{1}{2} - \frac{1}{2}i\right) + 2 \;\Big|\; 0$$

$$4\left(\frac{1}{4} - \frac{1}{4}i - \frac{1}{4}i + \frac{1}{4}i^2\right) - 2 + 2i + 2 \;\Big|\; 0$$

$$1 - i - i + i^2 - 2 + 2i + 2 \;\Big|\; 0$$

$$1 - 2i + (-1) + 2i \;\Big|\; 0$$

$$0 = 0$$

The solutions are $\dfrac{1}{2} + \dfrac{1}{2}i$ and $\dfrac{1}{2} - \dfrac{1}{2}i$.

EXAMPLE 10   Solve $x^2 + 4x + 6 = 0$ and check.

Solution $x = \dfrac{-b \pm \sqrt{b^2 - 4ac}}{2a}$

$$= \frac{-4 \pm \sqrt{4^2 - 4(1)(6)}}{2(1)}$$ • $a = 1, b = 4, c = 6$

$$= \frac{-4 \pm \sqrt{16 - 24}}{2} = \frac{-4 \pm \sqrt{-8}}{2}$$

$$= \frac{-4 \pm i\sqrt{8}}{2} = \frac{-4 \pm 2i\sqrt{2}}{2}$$ • Rewrite $\sqrt{-8}$ as $i\sqrt{8}$ and then rewrite $i\sqrt{8}$ as $2i\sqrt{2}$.

$$= -\frac{4}{2} \pm \frac{2i\sqrt{2}}{2} = -2 \pm i\sqrt{2}$$ • Write the solution as a complex number in standard form.

Check

$$x^2 + 4x + 6 = 0$$

$$(-2 + i\sqrt{2})^2 + 4(-2 + i\sqrt{2}) + 6 \;\Big|\; 0$$

$$4 - 2i\sqrt{2} - 2i\sqrt{2} + i^2(\sqrt{2})^2 - 8 + 4i\sqrt{2} + 6 \;\Big|\; 0$$

$$4 - 4i\sqrt{2} + (-1)2 - 8 + 4i\sqrt{2} + 6 \;\Big|\; 0$$

$$4 - 4i\sqrt{2} + (-2) - 8 + 4i\sqrt{2} + 6 \;\Big|\; 0$$

$$0 = 0$$

$$x^2 + 4x + 6 = 0$$

$$\begin{array}{c|c}
(-2 - i\sqrt{2})^2 + 4(-2 - i\sqrt{2}) + 6 & 0 \\
4 + 2i\sqrt{2} + 2i\sqrt{2} + i^2(\sqrt{2})^2 - 8 - 4i\sqrt{2} + 6 & 0 \\
4 + 4i\sqrt{2} + (-1)2 - 8 - 4i\sqrt{2} + 6 & 0 \\
4 + 4i\sqrt{2} + (-2) - 8 - 4i\sqrt{2} + 6 & 0 \\
& 0 = 0
\end{array}$$

The solutions are $-2 + i\sqrt{2}$ and $-2 - i\sqrt{2}$.

PROBLEM 10   Solve $x^2 - 6x + 4 = -6$

Solution   See page S27.

11.4   Concept Review

Determine whether each statement is always true, sometimes true, or never true.

1. Given that i is the imaginary unit, $i^2 = -1$.

2. All real numbers are complex numbers.

3. For the complex number $3 - 4i$, the real part is 3 and the imaginary part is 4.

4. The equation $\sqrt{-15} = i\sqrt{15}$ is a true equation.

5. The complex conjugate of $-3 + 4i$ is $3 - 4i$.

6. Quadratic equations have imaginary number solutions.

11.4   Exercises

1   Simplify complex numbers

1. a. The real part of the complex number $5 - 8i$ is ___?___.
   b. The imaginary part of the complex number $5 - 8i$ is ___?___.

2. a. If the complex number $a + bi$ is a real number, then ___?___ = 0.
   b. If the complex number $a + bi$ is an imaginary number, then ___?___ = 0.

3. Write $\sqrt{-100}$ in terms of i.

$\sqrt{-100} = \sqrt{\underline{\quad ? \quad}} \cdot 100 = \sqrt{\underline{\quad ? \quad}}\sqrt{100} = \underline{\quad ? \quad}\sqrt{100} = \underline{\quad ? \quad} i$

4. Write $8 - 3\sqrt{-98}$ in standard form.

$8 - 3\sqrt{-98} = 8 - 3(\underline{\quad ? \quad})\sqrt{98}$ • Write $\sqrt{-98}$ in terms of i.

$\phantom{8 - 3\sqrt{-98}} = 8 - 3i\sqrt{\underline{\quad ? \quad}}\sqrt{2}$ • Use the Product Property of Square Roots to simplify $\sqrt{98}$.

$\phantom{8 - 3\sqrt{-98}} = 8 - 3i(\underline{\quad ? \quad})\sqrt{2}$ • Take the square root of 49.

$\phantom{8 - 3\sqrt{-98}} = 8 - \underline{\quad ? \quad}i\sqrt{2}$ • Multiply 3 times 7.

Write each expression in terms of i.

5. $\sqrt{-81}$ **6.** $\sqrt{-64}$ **7.** $5\sqrt{-49}$ **8.** $-3\sqrt{-16}$ **9.** $\sqrt{-13}$

10. $\sqrt{-26}$ **11.** $\sqrt{-75}$ **12.** $\sqrt{-90}$ **13.** $-4\sqrt{-54}$ **14.** $3\sqrt{-80}$

15. Let a and b be positive numbers. Is $a - bi$ equivalent to $a + \sqrt{-b^2}$ or to $a - \sqrt{-b^2}$?

16. Let a be a positive number. Which expression is equivalent to $\sqrt{a^2} + \sqrt{-a^2}$?

   a. 0   **b.** $a + ai$ **c.** $a - ai$ **d.** $2ai$

Write each number in standard form.

17. $5 + \sqrt{-4}$ **18.** $-3 + \sqrt{-25}$ **19.** $-7 - 2\sqrt{-36}$ **20.** $5 - 3\sqrt{-100}$

21. $5 + 3\sqrt{-48}$ **22.** $2 - 2\sqrt{-50}$ **23.** $7 - 6\sqrt{-28}$ **24.** $-2 + 5\sqrt{-72}$

25. $\dfrac{6 + 5\sqrt{-4}}{2}$ **26.** $\dfrac{5 - 3\sqrt{-25}}{5}$ **27.** $\dfrac{-6 + 2\sqrt{-54}}{6}$

28. $\dfrac{-4 + 2\sqrt{-72}}{4}$ **29.** $\dfrac{-2 - 4\sqrt{-90}}{5}$ **30.** $\dfrac{4 - 5\sqrt{-63}}{6}$

2   **Add and subtract complex numbers**

31. Add: $(6 - 8i) + (-2 + 3i)$

$(6 - 8i) + (-2 + 3i)$

$ = (6 + \underline{\quad ? \quad}) + (-8 + \underline{\quad ? \quad})i$ • Add the real parts. Add the imaginary parts.

$ = \underline{\quad ? \quad}$ • Simplify.

32. Subtract: $10 - (8 - 7i)$

$10 - (8 - 7i) = (10 - \underline{\quad ? \quad}) - \underline{\quad ? \quad}i$ • Subtract the real parts.

$ = \underline{\quad ? \quad}$ • Simplify.

Add or subtract.

33. $3i + 7i$

34. $-9i + 6i$

35. $-2i - 7i$

36. $5i - (-4i)$

37. $6i + (7 + 3i)$

38. $3 + (4 + 2i)$

39. $-2i - (8 - 9i)$

40. $5 - (7 + 6i)$

41. $(7 + 4i) + (6 - 2i)$

42. $(-2 + 12i) + (7 - 15i)$

43. $(5 - 8i) - (3 + 2i)$

44. $(-7 - i) - (6 - 2i)$

45. $(-10 + 4i) - (-2 + 6i)$

46. $(6 - 11i) + (-7 - i)$

47. $(8 + 4i) + (-2 - 4i)$

48. $(7 - 8i) + (-7 + 3i)$

49. $(-2 + 11i) - (-2 + 11i)$

50. $(3 - 13i) - (3 + 13i)$

For Exercises 51 to 54, use the complex numbers $m = a - bi$ and $n = c + di$.

51. True or false? If $a = c$ and $b = d$, then $m - n = 0$.

52. True or false? If $m - n$ is a real number, then b and d are opposites.

53. Suppose $b > 0, d > 0$, and $b > d$. Is the imaginary part of $m + n$ positive or negative?

54. Suppose $a > 0, c > 0$, and $a > c$. Is the real part of $m - n$ positive or negative?

3   Multiply complex numbers

55. Multiply: $-8i(1 + 7i)$

$$-8i(1 + 7i) = (\underline{\quad ? \quad})(1) + (\underline{\quad ? \quad})(7i)$$ • Use the Distributive Property.

$$= \underline{\quad ? \quad} - (\underline{\quad ? \quad})i^2$$ • Simplify.

$$= -8i - 56(\underline{\quad ? \quad})$$ • $i^2 = \underline{\quad ? \quad}$.

$$= \underline{\quad ? \quad}$$ • Write the answer in the form $a + bi$.

56. Multiply: $(1 + 9i)(2 - 3i)$

$$(1 + 9i)(2 - 3i) = (1)(\underline{\quad ? \quad}) + (1)(\underline{\quad ? \quad})$$ • Use the FOIL method.
$$+ 9i(\underline{\quad ? \quad}) + 9i(\underline{\quad ? \quad})$$

$$= \underline{\quad ? \quad} + \underline{\quad ? \quad}$$ • Simplify each term.
$$+ \underline{\quad ? \quad} - \underline{\quad ? \quad}$$

$$= 2 + \underline{\quad ? \quad} - 27i^2$$ • Combine like terms.

$$= 2 + 15i - 27(\underline{\quad ? \quad})$$ • Replace i^2 by $\underline{\quad ? \quad}$.

$$= 2 + 15i + \underline{\quad ? \quad}$$ • Simplify.

$$= \underline{\quad ? \quad}$$ • Write in the form $a + bi$.

Multiply.

57. $4i \cdot 5i$

58. $6i \cdot 8i$

59. $(-2i)(9i)$

60. $6i(-9i)$

61. $5i(2 + 4i)$

62. $3i(2 - 7i)$

63. $(3 + 2i)(4 + 5i)$

64. $(4 - 3i)(2 + i)$

65. $(-3 + 2i)(1 + 3i)$

66. $(5 - 3i)(-2 + 4i)$

67. $(3 - 7i)(-2 - 5i)$

68. $(-5 - 3i)(4 - 6i)$

69. $(2 + 5i)^2$

70. $(-3 + 2i)^2$

71. $(1 - 2i)^2$

72. $(-4 - 3i)^2$

73. $(2 - 5i)(-5 + 2i)$

74. $(-1 + 3i)(3 - i)$

75. $(2 + 4i)(2 - 4i)$

76. $(-3 + 4i)(-3 - 4i)$

77. $(4 - i)(4 + i)$

78. True or false? For all nonzero real numbers a and b, the product $(a + bi)(a - bi)$ is a positive real number.

79. True or false? The product of two imaginary numbers is never a positive real number.

4 Divide complex numbers

80. Simplify: $\dfrac{2 - i}{-3i}$

$\dfrac{2 - i}{-3i} = \dfrac{2 - i}{-3i} \cdot \dfrac{?}{?}$
- To remove i from the denominator, multiply the expression by 1 in the form $\dfrac{i}{i}$.

$= \dfrac{2i - ?}{-3i^2}$
- Multiply the numerators. Multiply the denominators.

$= \dfrac{2i - ()}{-3()}$
- Replace i^2 by -1.

$= \dfrac{2i + ?}{?}$
- Simplify.

$= \underline{} + \underline{} \, i$
- Write the answer in the form $a + bi$.

81. To simplify $\dfrac{3i}{1 - 4i}$, multiply the numerator and denominator by $\underline{}$.

Divide.

82. $\dfrac{2 + 3i}{i}$

83. $\dfrac{6 + i}{i}$

84. $\dfrac{3 - 5i}{i}$

85. $\dfrac{-2 + 7i}{-i}$

86. $\dfrac{-5 - 9i}{-i}$

87. $\dfrac{-9 + 15i}{3i}$

88. $\dfrac{6 - 4i}{2i}$

89. $\dfrac{6 + 12i}{8i}$

90. $\dfrac{4 - 10i}{6i}$

91. $\dfrac{-15 + 6i}{-9i}$

92. $\dfrac{4 - 15i}{-6i}$

93. $\dfrac{3}{1 + i}$

94. $\dfrac{-4}{1 - 2i}$

95. $\dfrac{-10i}{3 + i}$

96. $\dfrac{12i}{2 - 2i}$

97. $\dfrac{13 - i}{2 + i}$

98. $\dfrac{12 + i}{1 - 2i}$

99. $\dfrac{18 + 4i}{1 + 3i}$

100. $\dfrac{-18 + 13i}{1 + 4i}$

101. $\dfrac{8 - 14i}{-2 - 3i}$

102. $\dfrac{5 + 15i}{3 + 4i}$

103. True or false? The quotient of two imaginary numbers is a real number.

104. True or false? The reciprocal of an imaginary number is a real number.

5 Solve quadratic equations with complex number solutions

Solve.

105. $x^2 + 16 = 0$

106. $z^2 + 25 = 0$

107. $2z^2 + 49 = -49$

108. $3x^2 + 108 = 0$

109. $x^2 + 11 = -16$

110. $z^2 + 12 = -28$

111. $3z^2 + 16 = -20$

112. $4z^2 - 13 = -21$

113. $(x + 1)^2 + 36 = 0$

114. $(x - 3)^2 + 81 = 0$

115. $(x - 2)^2 + 12 = 0$

116. $(z + 4)^2 + 18 = 0$

117. $(z + 2)^2 + 27 = -23$

118. $(x - 5)^2 + 17 = 9$

119. $(2x + 3)^2 + 9 = 5$

120. $(2z - 1)^2 + 25 = 9$

121. $z^2 - 2z + 2 = 0$

122. $z^2 - 2z + 5 = 0$

123. $x^2 + 4x = -5$

124. $x^2 + 4x = -8$

125. $x^2 - 6x + 13 = 0$

126. $x^2 + 10 = 2x$

127. $x^2 - 2x + 3 = 0$

128. $x^2 + 2x + 13 = 0$

129. $4x^2 + 8x = -5$

130. $4x^2 + 12x + 25 = 0$

131. $4x^2 - 4x + 13 = 0$

For Exercises 132 and 133, a is a positive real number. State how many solutions the equation has and whether the solutions are real, imaginary, or complex numbers.

132. $x^2 + a = 0$

133. $(x + a)^2 = 0$

11.4 Applying Concepts

134. We can evaluate i^3 as $i^3 = (i \cdot i) \cdot i = i^2 \cdot i = (-1) \cdot i = -i$. Using a similar method, evaluate each of the following.
   a. i^4 **b.** i^5 **c.** i^6 **d.** i^7

135. Using the fact that $i^9 = i$, find i^{18}.

Write each of the following in the form $a + bi$.

136. $(1 - i)(1 + i)(2 - 3i)$

137. $(2 - i)(2 + i)(1 + 5i)$

138. $(1 + i)^3$

139. $(2 - 3i)^3$

140. $(4 - 3i)(1 + 2i) + (3 - 2i)(2 - i)$

141. $(2 + 5i)(1 - 3i) - (3 + i)(4 - 2i)$

Solve.

142. $(x - 1)(x + 1) + 5 = 0$

143. $(x + 2)(x - 2) + 12 = 0$

144. $(x + 4)(x + 6) + 4 = 0$

145. $(x - 5)(x + 1) = -14$

146. $(x - 2)(x - 4) + 4 = 0$

147. $(x - 4)(x - 2) = -6$

Graphing Quadratic Equations in Two Variables

OBJECTIVE **1** **Graph a quadratic equation of the form $y = ax^2 + bx + c$**

An equation of the form $y = ax^2 + bx + c$, $a \neq 0$, is a **quadratic equation in two variables.** Examples of quadratic equations in two variables are shown at the right.

$$y = 3x^2 - x + 1$$
$$y = -x^2 - 3$$
$$y = 2x^2 - 5x$$

For these equations, y is a function of x, and we can write $f(x) = ax^2 + bx + c$. This equation represents a **quadratic function.**

Evaluate $f(x) = 2x^2 - 3x + 4$ when $x = -2$.

$$f(x) = 2x^2 - 3x + 4$$
$$f(-2) = 2(-2)^2 - 3(-2) + 4$$ • **Replace x with -2.**
$$= 2(4) - 3(-2) + 4$$ • **Simplify.**
$$= 8 + 6 + 4$$
$$= 18$$

The value of the function when $x = -2$ is 18.

The graph of $y = ax^2 + bx + c$ or $f(x) = ax^2 + bx + c$ is a **parabola.** The graph is ∪-shaped and opens up when a is positive and down when a is negative. The graphs of two parabolas are shown below.

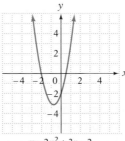

$y = 2x^2 + 3x - 2$
$a = 2$, a positive number
Parabola opens up

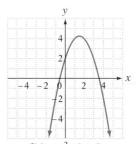

$f(x) = -x^2 + 3x + 2$
$a = -1$, a negative number
Parabola opens down

Graph $y = x^2 - 2x - 3$.

x	y
-2	5
-1	0
0	-3
1	-4
2	-3
3	0
4	5

• **Find several solutions of the equation. Because the graph is not a straight line, several solutions must be found in order to determine the ∪-shape. Record the ordered pairs in a table.**

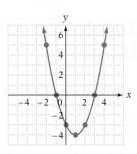

• **Graph the ordered-pair solutions on a rectangular coordinate system. Draw a parabola through the points.**

Note that the graph of $y = x^2 - 2x - 3$ crosses the x-axis at $(-1, 0)$ and at $(3, 0)$. These points are confirmed in the table of values. The x-intercepts of the graph are $(-1, 0)$ and $(3, 0)$.

The y-intercept is the point at which the graph crosses the y-axis. At this point, $x = 0$. From the graph or the table, we can see that the y-intercept is $(0, -3)$.

We can find the x-intercepts algebraically by letting $y = 0$ and solving for x.

$$y = x^2 - 2x - 3$$
$$0 = x^2 - 2x - 3$$
$$0 = (x + 1)(x - 3)$$

• **Replace y with 0 and solve for x.**
• **This equation can be solved by factoring. However, it will be necessary to use the quadratic formula to solve some quadratic equations.**

$$x + 1 = 0 \qquad x - 3 = 0$$
$$x = -1 \qquad x = 3$$

When $y = 0$, $x = -1$ or $x = 3$. The x-intercepts are $(-1, 0)$ and $(3, 0)$.

We can find the y-intercept algebraically by letting $x = 0$ and solving for y.

$$y = x^2 - 2x - 3$$
$$y = 0^2 - 2(0) - 3$$
$$y = 0 - 0 - 3$$
$$y = -3$$

• **Replace x with 0 and simplify.**

When $x = 0$, $y = -3$. The y-intercept is $(0, -3)$.

Using a graphing utility, enter the equation $y = x^2 - 2x - 3$ and verify the graph shown above. (Refer to the Appendix for instructions on using a graphing calculator to graph a quadratic equation.) Verify that $(-1, 0)$, $(3, 0)$, and $(0, -3)$ are coordinates of points on the graph.

The graph of $y = -2x^2 + 1$ is shown below.

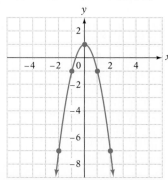

x	y
0	1
1	−1
−1	−1
2	−7
−2	−7

```
Plot1 Plot2 Plot3
\Y1 ▆ -2X²+1
\Y2 =
\Y3 =
\Y4 =
\Y5 =
\Y6 =
\Y7 =
```

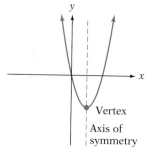

Use a graphing utility to verify the graph of $y = -2x^2 + 1$ shown at the bottom of the preceding page.

Note that the graph of $y = x^2 - 2x - 3$, shown on the previous page, opens up and that the coefficient of x^2 is positive. The graph of $y = -2x^2 + 1$ opens down, and the coefficient of x^2 is negative. As stated earlier, for any quadratic equation in two variables, the coefficient of x^2 determines whether the parabola opens up or down. When a is positive, the parabola opens up. When a is negative, the parabola opens down.

Point of Interest

Mirrors in some telescopes are ground into the shape of a parabola. The mirror at the Mount Palomar Observatory is 2 ft thick at the ends and weighs 14.75 tons. The mirror has been ground to a true paraboloid (the three-dimensional version of a parabola) to within 0.0000015 in.

Every parabola has an **axis of symmetry** and a **vertex** that is on the axis of symmetry. If the parabola opens up, the vertex is the lowest point on the graph. If the parabola opens down, the vertex is the highest point on the graph.

To understand the axis of symmetry, think of folding the paper along that axis. The two halves of the graph will match up.

When graphing a quadratic equation in two variables, use the value of a to determine whether the parabola opens up or down. After graphing ordered-pair solutions of the equation, use symmetry to help you draw the parabola.

EXAMPLE 1   Graph.   **A.** $y = x^2 - 2x$ **B.** $y = -x^2 + 4x - 4$

Solution   **A.** $a = 1$. a is positive.
The parabola opens up.

x	y
0	0
1	−1
−1	3
2	0
3	3

B. $a = -1$. a is negative.
The parabola opens down.

x	y
0	−4
1	−1
2	0
3	−1
4	−4

PROBLEM 1   Graph.   **A.** $y = x^2 + 2$ **B.** $y = -x^2 - 2x + 3$

Solution   See page S27.

EXAMPLE 2 Find the x- and y-intercepts of the graph of $y = x^2 - 2x - 5$.

Solution To find the x-intercepts, let $y = 0$ and solve for x.

$$y = x^2 - 2x - 5$$
$$0 = x^2 - 2x - 5$$

$$x = \frac{-b \pm \sqrt{b^2 - 4ac}}{2a}$$ • $x^2 - 2x - 5$ is nonfactorable over the integers. Use the quadratic formula.

$$= \frac{-(-2) \pm \sqrt{(-2)^2 - 4(1)(-5)}}{2(1)}$$

$$= \frac{2 \pm \sqrt{24}}{2} = \frac{2 \pm 2\sqrt{6}}{2} = 1 \pm \sqrt{6}$$

The x-intercepts are $\left(1 + \sqrt{6}, 0\right)$ and $\left(1 - \sqrt{6}, 0\right)$.

To find the y-intercept, let $x = 0$ and solve for y.

$$y = x^2 - 2x - 5$$
$$y = 0^2 - 2(0) - 5 = -5$$

The y-intercept is $(0, -5)$.

PROBLEM 2 Find the x- and y-intercepts of the graph of $y = x^2 - 6x + 9$.

Solution See page S28.

11.5 Concept Review

Determine whether the statement is always true, sometimes true, or never true.

1. The equation $y = 3x^2 - 2x + 1$ is an example of a quadratic equation in two variables.

2. The graph of an equation of the form $y = ax^2 + bx + c, a \neq 0$, is a parabola.

3. The graph of an equation of the form $y = ax^2 + c, a \neq 0$, is a straight line.

4. For the equation $y = -x^2 + 2x - 1$, when $x = 1, y = 2$.

5. The graph of the equation $y = -\frac{1}{2}x^2 + 5x$ is a parabola opening up.

6. If a parabola opens down, then the vertex is the highest point on the graph.

11.5 Exercises

1 Graph a quadratic equation of the form $y = ax^2 + bx + c$

1. What is a parabola?

2. Explain how you know whether the graph of the equation $y = -2x^2 + 3x + 4$ opens up or down.

3. Explain the axis of symmetry of a parabola.

4. What is the vertex of a parabola?

Determine whether the graph of the equation opens up or down.

5. $y = x^2 - 3$

6. $y = -x^2 + 4$

7. $y = \dfrac{1}{2}x^2 - 2$

8. $y = -\dfrac{1}{3}x^2 + 5$

9. $y = x^2 - 2x + 3$

10. $y = -x^2 + 4x - 1$

11. Use the quadratic equation $y = -x^2 + 9$.
   a. The equation is in the standard form $y = ax^2 + bx + c$, where $a =$ ___?___ , $b =$ ___?___ , and $c =$ ___?___ .
   b. The graph of the equation is a ___?___ . Because $a < 0$, the graph of the equation opens ___?___ .
   c. The equation can be written in function notation as $f(x) = -x^2 + 9$. To evaluate the function for $x = 2$, find $f(2) = -($ ___?___ $)^2 + 9$ $=$ ___?___ $+ 9 =$ ___?___ .
   d. Use the results of part c to name one point on the graph of $y = -x^2 + 9$: (___?___ , ___?___).

12. a. To find the x-intercepts of the graph of $y = x^2 - 3x - 4$, let ___?___ $= 0$ and solve for ___?___ .
   b. The equation $0 = x^2 - 3x - 4$ can be solved by factoring: $0 = (x -$ ___?___ $)(x +$ ___?___ $)$. The solutions are ___?___ and ___?___ .
   c. The x-intercepts of the graph of $y = x^2 - 3x - 4$ are (___?___ , ___?___) and (___?___ , ___?___).

Evaluate the function for the given value of x.

13. $f(x) = x^2 - 2x + 1; x = 3$

14. $f(x) = 2x^2 + x - 1; x = -2$

15. $f(x) = 4 - x^2; x = -3$

16. $f(x) = x^2 + 6x + 9; x = -3$

17. $f(x) = -x^2 + 5x - 6; x = -4$

18. $f(x) = -2x^2 + 2x - 1; x = -1$

Graph.

19. $y = x^2$

20. $y = -x^2$

21. $y = -x^2 + 1$

22. $y = x^2 - 1$

23. $y = 2x^2$

24. $y = \dfrac{1}{2}x^2$

25. $y = -\dfrac{1}{2}x^2 + 1$

26. $y = 2x^2 - 1$

27. $y = x^2 - 4x$

28. $y = x^2 + 4x$

29. $y = x^2 - 2x + 3$

30. $y = x^2 - 4x + 2$

31. $y = -x^2 + 2x + 3$

32. $y = x^2 + 2x + 1$

33. $y = -x^2 + 3x - 4$

34. $y = -x^2 + 6x - 9$

35. $y = 2x^2 + x - 3$

36. $y = -2x^2 - 3x + 3$

For Exercises 37 and 38, $y = ax^2 + bx + c$ is a quadratic equation whose graph is a parabola that has only one x-intercept, $(n, 0)$.

37. True or false? If $a < 0$, then for all real numbers $x, y \geq 0$.

38. True or false? The point on the parabola with x-coordinate $n - m$ has the same y-coordinate as the point on the parabola with x-coordinate $n + m$.

Determine the x- and y-intercepts of the graph of the equation.

39. $y = x^2 - 5x + 6$

40. $y = x^2 + 5x - 6$

41. $f(x) = 9 - x^2$

42. $f(x) = x^2 + 12x + 36$

43. $y = x^2 + 2x - 6$

44. $y = x^2 + 4x - 2$

45. $f(x) = 2x^2 - x - 3$

46. $f(x) = 2x^2 - 13x + 15$

47. $y = 4 - x - x^2$ **48.** $y = 2 - 3x - 3x^2$

Graph using a graphing utility. Verify that the graph is a graph of a parabola opening up if a is positive or opening down if a is negative.

49. $y = x^2 - 2$ **50.** $y = -x^2 + 3$ **51.** $y = x^2 + 2x$

52. $y = -2x^2 + 4x$ **53.** $y = \dfrac{1}{2}x^2 - x$ **54.** $y = -\dfrac{1}{2}x^2 + 2$

55. $y = x^2 - x - 2$ **56.** $y = x^2 - 3x + 2$ **57.** $y = 2x^2 - x - 5$

58. $y = -2x^2 - 3x + 2$ **59.** $y = -x^2 - 2x - 1$ **60.** $y = \dfrac{1}{2}x^2 - 2x - 1$

11.5   Applying Concepts

Show that the equation is a quadratic equation in two variables by writing it in the form $y = ax^2 + bx + c$.

61. $y + 1 = (x - 4)^2$ **62.** $y - 2 = 3(x + 1)^2$

63. $y - 4 = 2(x - 3)^2$ **64.** $y + 3 = 3(x - 1)^2$

Find the x-intercepts of the graph of the equation.

65. $y = x^3 - x^2 - 6x$ **66.** $y = x^3 - 4x^2 - 5x$

67. $y = x^3 + x^2 - 4x - 4$ (*Hint:* Factor by grouping.)   **68.** $y = x^3 + 3x^2 - x - 3$ (*Hint:* Factor by grouping.)

State whether the graph is the graph of a linear function, a quadratic function, or neither.

69.

70.

71.

72.

73.

74.

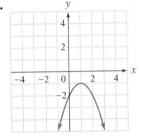

75. **The Postal Service** The graph below shows the cost of a first-class postage stamp from 1950 to 2006. A quadratic function that approximately models the data is $0.0034x^2 + 0.2509x - 24.7909$, where $x \geq 50$ and $x = 50$ for the year 1950, and y is the cost in cents of a first-class stamp. What does the model predict will be the cost of a first-class stamp in 2020? Round to the nearest cent.

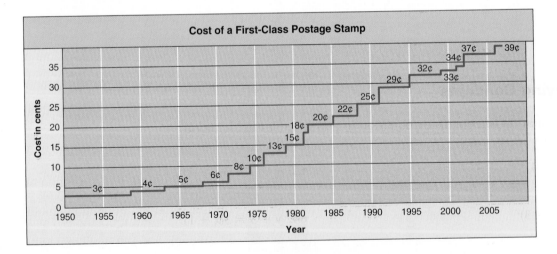

76. The point whose coordinates are (x_1, y_1) lies in quadrant I and is a point on the graph of the equation $y = 2x^2 - 2x + 1$. Given $y_1 = 13$, find x_1.

77. The point whose coordinates are (x_1, y_1) lies in quadrant II and is a point on the graph of the equation $y = 2x^2 - 3x - 2$. Given $y_1 = 12$, find x_1.

11.6   Application Problems

OBJECTIVE **1**   **Application problems**

The application problems in this section are varieties of those problems solved earlier in the text. Each of the strategies for the problems in this section results in a quadratic equation.

Solve: It took a motorboat a total of 7 h to travel 48 mi down a river and then 48 mi back again. The rate of the current was 2 mph. Find the rate of the motorboat in calm water.

> **STRATEGY**   **for solving an application problem**
>
> ▶ Determine the type of problem. For example, is it a uniform motion problem, a geometry problem, or a work problem?

The problem is a uniform motion problem.

> ▶ Choose a variable to represent the unknown quantity. Write numerical or variable expressions for all the remaining quantities. These results can be recorded in a table.

The unknown rate of the motorboat: r

Down river: $r + 2$
Up river: $r - 2$
48 mi

	Distance	÷	Rate	=	Time
Down river	48	÷	$r + 2$	=	$\dfrac{48}{r + 2}$
Up river	48	÷	$r - 2$	=	$\dfrac{48}{r - 2}$

> ▶ Determine how the quantities are related. If necessary, review the strategies presented in the chapter "Solving Equations and Inequalities: Applications."

The total time of the trip was 7 h.

$$\frac{48}{r+2} + \frac{48}{r-2} = 7$$

$$(r+2)(r-2)\left(\frac{48}{r+2} + \frac{48}{r-2}\right) = (r+2)(r-2)7$$

$$(r-2)48 + (r+2)48 = (r^2 - 4)7$$

$$48r - 96 + 48r + 96 = 7r^2 - 28$$

$$96r = 7r^2 - 28$$

$$0 = 7r^2 - 96r - 28$$

$$0 = (7r + 2)(r - 14)$$

$$7r + 2 = 0 \qquad\qquad r - 14 = 0$$
$$7r = -2 \qquad\qquad\quad r = 14$$
$$r = -\frac{2}{7}$$

The solution $-\frac{2}{7}$ is not possible, because the rate cannot be negative.

The rate of the motorboat in calm water is 14 mph.

EXAMPLE 1   Working together, a painter and the painter's apprentice can paint a room in 4 h. Working alone, the apprentice requires 6 more hours to paint the room than the painter requires working alone. How long does it take the painter, working alone, to paint the room?

Strategy   ▶ This is a work problem.

▶ Time for the painter to paint the room: t
Time for the apprentice to paint the room: $t + 6$

	Rate	Time	Part
Painter	$\dfrac{1}{t}$	4	$\dfrac{4}{t}$
Apprentice	$\dfrac{1}{t+6}$	4	$\dfrac{4}{t+6}$

▶ The sum of the parts of the task completed must equal 1.

Solution
$$\frac{4}{t} + \frac{4}{t+6} = 1$$

$$t(t+6)\left(\frac{4}{t} + \frac{4}{t+6}\right) = t(t+6) \cdot 1$$

$$(t+6)4 + t(4) = t(t+6)$$

$$4t + 24 + 4t = t^2 + 6t$$

$$0 = t^2 - 2t - 24$$

$$0 = (t-6)(t+4)$$

$$t - 6 = 0 \qquad\qquad t + 4 = 0$$
$$t = 6 \qquad\qquad\quad t = -4 \qquad$$ • The solution $t = -4$ is not possible.

Working alone, the painter requires 6 h to paint the room.

PROBLEM 1	The length of a rectangle is 3 m more than the width. The area is 40 m². Find the width.
Solution	See page S28.

11.6   Concept Review

Determine whether the statement is always true, sometimes true, or never true.

1. If the length of a rectangle is three more than twice the width and the width is represented by W, then the length is represented by $3W + 2$.

2. The sum of the squares of two consecutive odd integers can be represented as $n^2 + (n + 1)^2$.

3. If it takes one pipe 15 min longer to fill a tank than it does a second pipe, then the rate of work for the second pipe can be represented by $\frac{1}{t}$ and the rate of work for the first pipe can be represented by $\frac{1}{t + 15}$.

4. If a plane's rate of speed is r and the rate of the wind is 30 mph, then the plane's rate of speed flying with the wind is $30 + r$ and the plane's rate of speed flying against the wind is $30 - r$.

5. The graph of the equation $h = 48t - 16t^2$ is the graph of a parabola opening down.

6. A number that is a solution to a quadratic equation may not be a possible answer to the application problem it models. Such a solution is disregarded.

11.6   Exercises

1   Application problems

1. The length of a rectangle is 2 ft less than twice the width. Let w be the width of the rectangle.
   a. In terms of w, the length of the rectangle is ___?___ .
   b. In terms of w, the area of the rectangle is ___?___ .
   c. The area of the rectangle is 84 ft². Use your answer to part b and the fact that the area of the rectangle is 84 ft² to write an equation that can be solved to find the width of the rectangle: ___?___ = ___?___ .

2. a. Solve the equation that you wrote in part c of Exercise 1.

$$w(2w - 2) = 84$$

$$\underline{\quad ? \quad} - \underline{\quad ? \quad} = 84 \qquad \bullet \text{ Use the Distributive Property.}$$

$$2w^2 - 2w - 84 = 0 \qquad \bullet \text{ Subtract } \underline{\quad ? \quad} \text{ from each side of the equation.}$$

$$w^2 - w - 42 = 0 \qquad \bullet \text{ Divide each side of the equation by } \underline{\quad ? \quad}.$$

$$(w - \underline{\quad ? \quad})(w + \underline{\quad ? \quad}) = 0 \qquad \bullet \text{ Factor the left side.}$$

$$\underline{\quad ? \quad} = 0 \qquad \underline{\quad ? \quad} = 0 \qquad \bullet \text{ Use the Principle of Zero Products.}$$

$$w = \underline{\quad ? \quad} \qquad w = \underline{\quad ? \quad} \qquad \bullet \text{ Solve for } w.$$

b. Only one solution from part a makes sense as the width of the rectangle described in Exercise 1. The width of the rectangle is _____?_____. The length of the rectangle is _____?_____.

3. **Integer Problem** The sum of the squares of two positive consecutive odd integers is 130. Find the two integers.

4. **Integer Problem** The sum of two integers is 12. The product of the two integers is 35. Find the two integers.

5. **Integer Problem** The difference between two integers is 4. The product of the two integers is 60. Find the integers.

6. **Integer Problem** Twice an integer equals the square of the integer. Find the integer.

7. **Sports** The area of the batter's box on a major-league baseball field is 24 ft². The length of the batter's box is 2 ft more than the width. Find the length and width of the rectangular batter's box.

8. **Sports** The length of the batter's box on a softball field is 1 ft more than twice the width. The area of the batter's box is 21 ft². Find the length and width of the rectangular batter's box.

9. **Recreation** The length of a children's playground is twice the width. The area is 5000 ft². Find the length and width of the rectangular playground.

10. **Work Problem** A tank has two drains. One drain takes 16 min longer to empty the tank than does the second drain. With both drains open, the tank is emptied in 6 min. How long would it take each drain, working alone, to empty the tank?

11. **Work Problem** One computer takes 21 min longer than a second computer to calculate the value of a complex expression. Working together, these computers can complete the calculation in 10 min. How long would it take each computer, working alone, to calculate the value?

12. **Sports** The length of a singles tennis court is 24 ft more than twice the width. The area is 2106 ft². Find the length and width of the singles tennis court.

13. **Work Problem** It takes 6 h longer to cross a channel in a ferryboat when one engine of the boat is used alone than when a second engine is used alone. Using both engines, the ferryboat can make the crossing in 4 h. How long would it take each engine, working alone, to power the ferryboat across the channel?

14. **Work Problem** An apprentice mason takes 8 h longer than an experienced mason to build a small fireplace. Working together, they can build the fireplace in 3 h. How long would it take the experienced mason, working alone, to build the fireplace?

15. **Uniform Motion** It took a small plane 2 h longer to fly 375 mi against the wind than it took the plane to fly the same distance with the wind. The rate of the wind was 25 mph. Find the rate of the plane in calm air.

16. **Uniform Motion** It took a motorboat 1 h longer to travel 36 mi against the current than it took the boat to travel 36 mi with the current. The rate of the current was 3 mph. Find the rate of the boat in calm water.

17. **Uniform Motion** A motorcycle traveled 150 mi at a constant rate before its speed was decreased by 15 mph. Another 35 mi was driven at the decreased speed. The total time for the 185-mile trip was 4 h. Find the cyclist's rate during the first 150 mi.

18. **Uniform Motion** A cruise ship sailed through a 20-mile inland passageway at a constant rate before its speed was increased by 15 mph. Another 75 mi was traveled at the increased rate. The total time for the 95-mile trip was 5 h. Find the rate of the ship during the last 75 mi.

19. **Physics** An arrow is projected into the air with an initial velocity of 48 ft/s. At what times will the arrow be 32 ft above the ground? Use the equation $h = 48t - 16t^2$, where h is the height, in feet, above the ground after t seconds.

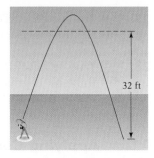

20. **Physics** A model rocket is launched with an initial velocity of 200 ft/s. The height, h, of the rocket t seconds after launch is given by $h = -16t^2 + 200t$. How many seconds after the launch will the rocket be 300 ft above the ground? Round to the nearest hundredth.

21. ⬤ **Travel** In Germany there are no speed limits on some portions of the autobahn (highway). Other portions have a speed limit of 180 km/h (approximately 112 mph). The distance, d (in meters), required to stop a car traveling at v kilometers per hour is $d = 0.0056v^2 + 0.14v$. What is the maximum speed a driver can be traveling and still be able to stop within 150 m? Round to the nearest tenth.

German Autobahn System

22. **Sports** In a slow-pitch softball game, the height of the ball thrown by a pitcher can be modeled by the equation $h = -16t^2 + 24t + 4$, where h is the height of the ball in feet, and t is the time, in seconds, since it was released by the pitcher. If the batter hits the ball when it is 2 ft off the ground, how many seconds has the ball been in the air? Round to the nearest hundredth.

23. Safety The path of water from a hose on a fire tugboat can be modeled by the equation $y = -0.005x^2 + 1.2x + 10$, where y is the height in feet of the water above the ocean when it is x feet from the tugboat. At what distance from the tugboat is the water from the hose when the water from the hose is 5 ft above the ocean? Round to the nearest tenth.

24. Sports A baseball player hits a ball. The height, in feet, of the ball above the ground at time t, in seconds, can be approximated by the equation $h = -16t^2 + 76t + 5$. When will the ball hit the ground? Round to the nearest hundredth. (*Hint:* The ball strikes the ground when $h = 0$ ft.)

5 ft

25. Sports A basketball player shoots at a basket 25 ft away. The height h, in feet, of the ball above the ground at time t, in seconds, is given by $h = -16t^2 + 32t + 6.5$. How many seconds after the ball is released does it hit the basket? Round to the nearest hundredth. (*Hint:* When it hits the basket, $h = 10$ ft.)

26. Sports The hang time of a football that is kicked on the opening kickoff is given by $s = -16t^2 + 88t + 1$, where s is the height, in feet, of the football t seconds after leaving the kicker's foot. What is the hang time of a kickoff that hits the ground without being caught? Round to the nearest tenth.

Complete Exercises 27 and 28 *without* writing and solving an equation. Use this situation: A small pipe takes 12 min longer to fill a tank than does a larger pipe. Working together, the pipes can fill the tank in 4 min.

27. True or false? The amount of time that it takes the larger pipe to fill the tank is less than 4 min.

28. True or false? The amount of time that it takes the small pipe to fill the tank is greater than 16 min.

11.6 Applying Concepts

29. Geometry A tin can has a volume of 1500 cm^3 and a height of 15 cm. Find the radius of the base of the tin can. Round to the nearest hundredth.

15 cm

30. Geometry The hypotenuse of a right triangle measures $\sqrt{13}$ cm. One leg is 1 cm shorter than twice the length of the other leg. Find the lengths of the legs of the right triangle.

31. Integer Problem The sum of the squares of four consecutive integers is 86. Find the four integers.

32. Geometry Find the radius of a right circular cone that has a volume of 800 cm^3 and a height of 12 cm. Round to the nearest hundredth.

12 cm

33. Food Industry The radius of a large pizza is 1 in. less than twice the radius of a small pizza. The difference between the areas of the two pizzas is 33π in^2. Find the radius of the large pizza.

34. Gardening The perimeter of a rectangular garden is 54 ft. The area of the garden is 180 ft². Find the length and width of the garden.

35. Food Industry A square piece of cardboard is to be formed into a box to transport pizzas. The box is formed by cutting 2-inch square corners from the cardboard and folding them up as shown in the figure at the right. If the volume of the box is 512 in³, what are the dimensions of the cardboard?

36. Metalwork A wire 8 ft long is cut into two pieces. A circle is formed from one piece and a square is formed from the other. The total area of both figures is given by $A = \dfrac{1}{16}(8 - x)^2 + \dfrac{x^2}{4\pi}$. What is the length of each piece of wire if the total area is 4.5 ft²? Round to the nearest thousandth.

Focus on Problem Solving

Applying Algebraic Manipulation and Graphing Techniques to Business

Problem solving is often easier when we have both algebraic manipulation and graphing techniques at our disposal. Solving quadratic equations and graphing quadratic equations in two variables are used here to solve problems involving profit.

A company's **revenue,** R, is the total amount of money the company earned by selling its products. The **cost,** C, is the total amount of money the company spent to manufacture and sell its products. A company's **profit,** P, is the difference between the revenue and cost: $P = R - C$. A company's revenue and cost may be represented by equations.

A company manufactures and sells wood stoves. The total monthly cost, in dollars, to produce n wood stoves is $C = 30n + 2000$. Write a variable expression for the company's monthly profit if the revenue, in dollars, obtained from selling all n wood stoves is $R = 150n - 0.4n^2$.

$$P = R - C$$
$$P = 150n - 0.4n^2 - (30n + 2000)$$ • Replace R by $150n - 0.4n^2$ and C by $30n + 2000$. Then simplify.
$$P = -0.4n^2 + 120n - 2000$$

The company's monthly profit is $P = -0.4n^2 + 120n - 2000$.

How many wood stoves must the company manufacture and sell in order to make a profit of $6000 a month?

$$P = -0.4n^2 + 120n - 2000$$
$$6000 = -0.4n^2 + 120n - 2000$$ • Substitute 6000 for P.
$$0 = -0.4n^2 + 120n - 8000$$ • Write the equation in standard form.
$$0 = n^2 - 300n + 20,000$$ • Divide each side of the equation by -0.4.
$$0 = (n - 100)(n - 200)$$ • Factor.

$$n - 100 = 0 \qquad n - 200 = 0$$ • Solve for n.
$$n = 100 \qquad\qquad n = 200$$

The company will make a monthly profit of $6000 if either 100 or 200 wood stoves are manufactured and sold.

The graph of $P = -0.4n^2 + 120n - 2000$ is shown at the left. Note that when $P = 6000$, the values of n are 100 and 200.

Also note that the coordinates of the highest point on the graph are $(150, 7000)$. This means that the company makes a *maximum* profit of $7000 per month when 150 wood stoves are manufactured and sold.

1. The total cost, in dollars, for a company to produce and sell n guitars per month is $C = 240n + 1200$. The company's revenue, in dollars, from selling all n guitars is $R = 400n - 2n^2$.

   a. How many guitars must the company produce and sell each month in order to make a monthly profit of $1200?

   b. Graph the profit equation. What is the maximum monthly profit the company can make?

2. A company's total monthly cost, in dollars, for manufacturing and selling n videotapes per month is $C = 35n + 2000$. The company's revenue, in dollars, from selling all n videotapes is $R = 175n - 0.2n^2$.

   a. How many videotapes must be produced and sold each month in order for the company to make a monthly profit of $18,000?

   b. Graph the profit equation. How many videotapes must the company produce and sell in order to make the maximum monthly profit?

Projects & Group Activities

Graphical Solutions of Quadratic Equations

A real number x is called a **zero of a function** if the value of the function when evaluated at x is 0. That is, if $f(x) = 0$, then x is called a zero of the function. For instance, evaluating $f(x) = x^2 + x - 6$ at $x = -3$, we have

$$f(x) = x^2 + x - 6$$
$$f(-3) = (-3)^2 + (-3) - 6 \qquad \bullet \text{ Replace } x \text{ with } -3.$$
$$f(-3) = 9 - 3 - 6$$
$$f(-3) = 0$$

For this function, $f(-3) = 0$, so -3 is a zero of the function.

You can verify that 2 is also a zero of $f(x) = x^2 + x - 6$ by showing that $f(2) = 0$.

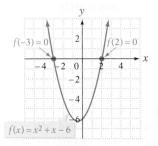

The graph of $y = x^2 + x - 6$ is shown at the left. Note that the graph crosses the x-axis at -3 and 2, the two zeros of the function. The points $(-3, 0)$ and $(2, 0)$ are x-intercepts of the graph.

Now consider the equation $0 = x^2 + x - 6$, which is $f(x) = x^2 + x - 6$ with $f(x)$ replaced with 0. Solving $0 = x^2 + x - 6$ for x, we have

$$0 = x^2 + x - 6$$
$$0 = (x + 3)(x - 2)$$ • **Solve by factoring and using the Principle of Zero Products.**

$$x + 3 = 0 \qquad x - 2 = 0$$
$$x = -3 \qquad x = 2$$

The solutions are -3 and 2.

Observe that the solutions of the equation are the zeros of the function. This important connection among the real zeros of a function, the x-intercepts of its graph, and the solutions of its equation is the basis for using a graphing calculator to solve an equation.

The following method of solving a quadratic equation using a graphing calculator is based on a TI-83/TI-83 Plus/TI-84 Plus calculator. Other calculators will require a slightly different approach.

Approximate the solutions of $x^2 + 4x = 6$ by using a graphing calculator.

a. Write the equation in standard form.

$$x^2 + 4x = 6$$
$$x^2 + 4x - 6 = 0$$

b. Press $\boxed{\text{Y=}}$ and enter $x^2 + 4x - 6$ for Y1.

c. Press $\boxed{\text{GRAPH}}$. If the graph does not appear on the screen, press $\boxed{\text{ZOOM}}$ 6.

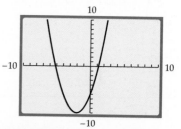

d. Press $\boxed{\text{2nd}}$ CALC 2. Note that the selection for 2 says **zero**. This will begin the calculation of the zeros of the function, which are the solutions of the equation.

e. At the bottom of the screen you will see **Left Bound?** This is asking you to move the blinking cursor so that it is to the *left* of the first x-intercept. Use the left arrow key to move the cursor to the left of the first x-intercept. The values of x and y that appear on your calculator may be different from the ones shown here. Just be sure you are to the left of the x-intercept. When you have done that, press ENTER .

f. At the bottom of the screen you will see **Right Bound**? This is asking you to move the blinking cursor so that it is to the *right* of the x-intercept. Use the right arrow key to move the cursor to the right of the x-intercept. The values of x and y that appear on your calculator may be different from the ones shown here. Just be sure you are to the right of the x-intercept. When you have done that, press ENTER .

g. At the bottom of the screen you will see **Guess**? This is asking you to move the blinking cursor to the approximate x-intercept. Use the arrow keys to move the cursor to the approximate x-intercept. The values of x and y that appear on your calculator may be different from the ones shown here. When you have done that, press ENTER .

h. The zero of the function is approximately -5.162278. Thus one solution of $x^2 + 4x = 6$ is approximately -5.162278. Also note that the value of y is given as $Y = -1E{-}12$. This is the way the calculator writes a number in scientific notation. We would normally write $Y = -1.0 \times 10^{-12}$. This number is very close to zero.

i. To find the other solution, repeat Steps d through g. The screens are shown below and at the top of the next page.

A second zero of the function is approximately 1.1622777.

Thus the two solutions of $x^2 + 4x = 6$ are approximately -5.162278 and 1.1622777.

Use a graphing calculator to approximate the solutions of the equation.

1. $x^2 + 3x - 4 = 0$

2. $2x^2 - 3x - 7 = 0$

3. $x^2 + 5x = 1$

4. $x^2 + 3.4x = 4.15$

5. $\pi x^2 - \sqrt{17}x - 2 = 0$

6. $\sqrt{2}x^2 + x = \sqrt{7}$

Chapter 11 Summary

Key Words

Examples

A **quadratic equation** is an equation that can be written in the form $ax^2 + bx + c = 0$, $a \neq 0$. A quadratic equation is also called a **second-degree equation.**   [11.1.1, p. 584]

The equation $4x^2 - 3x + 6 = 0$ is a quadratic equation. In this equation, $a = 4$, $b = -3$, and $c = 6$.

A quadratic equation is in **standard form** when the polynomial is in descending order and equal to zero.   [11.1.1, p. 584]

The quadratic equation $5x^2 + 3x - 1 = 0$ is in standard form.

Adding to a binomial the constant term that makes it a perfect-square trinomial is called **completing the square.** [11.2.1, p. 593]

Adding to $x^2 - 6x$ the constant term 9 results in a perfect-square trinomial:

$x^2 - 6x + 9 = (x - 3)(x - 3) = (x - 3)^2$

A **complex number** is a number of the form $a + bi$, where a and b are real numbers and $i = \sqrt{-1}$. For the complex number $a + bi$, a is the **real part** of the complex number and b is the **imaginary part** of the complex number.   [11.4.1, p. 607]

$5 + 2i$ is a complex number. 5 is the real part and 2 is the imaginary part of the complex number.

The graph of an equation of the form $y = ax^2 + bx + c$ is a **parabola**. The graph is U-shaped and opens up when a is positive and down when a is negative. The **vertex** is the lowest point on a parabola that opens up, or the highest point on a parabola that opens down.   [11.5.1, pp. 621, 623]

Parabola that opens up   Parabola that opens down

Essential Rules and Procedures

Solving a Quadratic Equation by Factoring
Write the equation in standard form, factor the left side of the equation, apply the Principle of Zero Products, and solve for the variable.   [11.1.1, p. 585]

$$x^2 + 2x = 15$$
$$x^2 + 2x - 15 = 0$$
$$(x - 3)(x + 5) = 0$$

$x - 3 = 0$	$x + 5 = 0$
$x = 3$	$x = -5$

Principle of Taking the Square Root of Each Side of an Equation
If $x^2 = a$, then $x = \pm\sqrt{a}$.

This principle is used to solve quadratic equations by taking square roots.   [11.1.2, p. 586]

$$3x^2 - 48 = 0$$
$$3x^2 = 48$$
$$x^2 = 16$$
$$\sqrt{x^2} = \sqrt{16}$$
$$x = \pm\sqrt{16}$$
$$x = \pm 4$$

Solving a Quadratic Equation by Completing the Square
When the quadratic equation is in the form $x^2 + bx = c$, add to each side of the equation the term that completes the square of $x^2 + bx$. Factor the perfect-square trinomial, and write it as the square of a binomial. Take the square root of each side of the equation and solve for x.   [11.2.1, p. 594]

$$x^2 + 6x = 5$$
$$x^2 + 6x + 9 = 5 + 9$$
$$(x + 3)^2 = 14$$
$$\sqrt{(x + 3)^2} = \sqrt{14}$$
$$x + 3 = \pm\sqrt{14}$$
$$x = -3 \pm \sqrt{14}$$

The Quadratic Formula
The solutions of $ax^2 + bx + c = 0$, $a \neq 0$, are
$$x = \frac{-b \pm \sqrt{b^2 - 4ac}}{2a}.$$ [11.3.1, p. 601]

$$3x^2 = x + 5$$
$$3x^2 - x - 5 = 0$$
$$x = \frac{-b \pm \sqrt{b^2 - 4ac}}{2a}$$
$$= \frac{-(-1) \pm \sqrt{(-1)^2 - 4(3)(-5)}}{2(3)}$$
$$= \frac{1 \pm \sqrt{1 + 60}}{6} = \frac{1 \pm \sqrt{61}}{6}$$

Principal Square Root of a Negative Number
If a is a positive real number, then the **principal square root of negative a** is the imaginary number $i\sqrt{a}$: $\sqrt{-a} = i\sqrt{a}$. The number $i\sqrt{a}$ is called an **imaginary number.** When $a = 1$, we have $\sqrt{-1} = i$.   [11.4.1, p. 607]

$$\sqrt{-8} = i\sqrt{8} = 2i\sqrt{2}$$

Addition and Subtraction of Complex Numbers

To add two complex numbers, add the real parts and add the imaginary parts. To subtract two complex numbers, subtract the real parts and subtract the imaginary parts. [11.4.2, p. 608]

$$(3 + 5i) + (2 + 4i) = (3 + 2) + (5 + 4)i$$
$$= 5 + 9i$$
$$(5 + 2i) - (8 + 4i) = (5 - 8) + (2 - 4)i$$
$$= -3 - 2i$$

Multiplication of Complex Numbers

The product of two complex numbers of the form $a + bi$, $a \neq 0$, $b \neq 0$, can be found by using the FOIL method and the fact that $i^2 = -1$. [11.4.3, p. 609]

$$(2 - 3i)(5 + 4i) = 10 + 8i - 15i - 12i^2$$
$$= 10 - 7i - 12(-1)$$
$$= 22 - 7i$$

Product of Complex Conjugates

$(a + bi)(a - bi) = a^2 + b^2$ [11.4.4, p. 611]

$$(3 + 5i)(3 - 5i) = 3^2 + 5^2$$
$$= 9 + 25$$
$$= 34$$

Graphing a Quadratic Equation in Two Variables

Find several solutions of the equation. Graph the ordered-pair solutions on a rectangular coordinate system. Draw a parabola through the points. [11.5.1, pp. 621–622]

To find the x-intercepts of the graph of a parabola, let $y = 0$ and solve for x. The x-intercepts of the graph at the right are $(-1, 0)$ and $(2, 0)$. To find the y-intercept, let $x = 0$ and solve for y. The y-intercept of the graph at the right is $(0, -2)$. [11.5.1, p. 622]

$$y = x^2 - x - 2$$

x	y
0	-2
1	-2
-1	0
2	0
-2	4
3	4

Chapter 11 Review Exercises

1. Solve: $b^2 - 16 = 0$

2. Solve: $x^2 - x - 3 = 0$

3. Solve: $x^2 - 3x - 5 = 0$

4. Solve: $49x^2 = 25$

5. Graph: $y = -\dfrac{1}{4}x^2$

6. Graph: $y = -3x^2$

7. Simplify: $3\sqrt{-28}$

8. Solve: $6x(x + 1) = x - 1$

9. Solve: $4y^2 + 9 = 0$

10. Solve: $5x^2 + 20x + 12 = 0$

11. Add: $(-4 + i) + (6 - 5i)$

12. Solve: $x^2 - x = 30$

13. Solve: $6x^2 + 13x - 28 = 0$

14. Solve: $x^2 = 40$

15. Subtract: $(-1 + 2i) - (2 - 3i)$

16. Solve: $x^2 - 2x - 10 = 0$

17. Solve: $x^2 - 12x + 27 = 0$

18. Solve: $(x - 7)^2 = 81$

19. Graph: $y = 2x^2 + 1$

20. Graph: $y = \dfrac{1}{2}x^2 - 1$

21. Solve: $(y + 4)^2 - 25 = 0$

22. Solve: $4x^2 + 16x = 7$

23. Solve: $24x^2 + 34x + 5 = 0$

24. Solve: $x^2 = 4x - 8$

25. Multiply: $4i(3 - 5i)$

26. Solve: $25(2x^2 - 2x + 1) = (x + 3)^2$

27. Solve: $\left(x - \dfrac{1}{2}\right)^2 = \dfrac{9}{4}$

28. Multiply: $(-2 + 4i)(3 - i)$

29. Solve: $x^2 + 7x = 3$

30. Solve: $12x^2 + 10 = 29x$

31. Solve: $4(x - 3)^2 = 20$

32. Solve: $x^2 + 8x - 3 = 0$

33. Graph: $y = x^2 - 3x$

34. Graph: $y = x^2 - 4x + 3$

35. Solve: $(x + 9)^2 = x + 11$

36. Divide: $\dfrac{3 - i}{2 - 4i}$

37. Solve: $x^2 + 6x + 12 = 0$

38. Solve: $x^2 + 6x - 2 = 0$

39. Solve: $18x^2 - 52x = 6$

40. Solve: $2x^2 + 5x = 1$

41. Graph: $y = -x^2 + 4x - 5$

42. Divide: $\dfrac{2 - 6i}{2i}$

43. Solve: $2x^2 + 5 = 7x$

44. Graph: $y = 4 - x^2$

45. **Uniform Motion** It took an air balloon 1 h longer to fly 60 mi against the wind than it took to fly 60 mi with the wind. The rate of the wind was 5 mph. Find the rate of the air balloon in calm air.

46. **Geometry** The height of a triangle is 2 m more than twice the length of the base. The area of the triangle is 20 m². Find the height of the triangle and the length of the base.

47. Integer Problem The sum of the squares of two consecutive positive odd integers is thirty-four. Find the two integers.

48. Uniform Motion In 5 h, two campers rowed 12 mi down a stream and then rowed back to their campsite. The rate of the stream's current was 1 mph. Find the rate of the boat in still water.

49. Physics An object is thrown into the air with an initial velocity of 32 ft/s. At what times will the object be 12 ft above the ground? Use the equation $h = 32t - 16t^2$, where h is the height, in feet, above the ground after t seconds.

50. Work Problem A smaller drain takes 8 h longer to empty a tank than does a larger drain. Working together, the drains can empty the tank in 3 h. How long would it take each drain, working alone, to empty the tank?

Chapter 11 Test

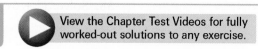

View the Chapter Test Videos for fully worked-out solutions to any exercise.

1. Solve: $3(x + 4)^2 - 60 = 0$

2. Solve: $2x^2 + 8x = 3$

3. Solve: $3x^2 + 7x = 20$

4. Simplify: $4\sqrt{-45}$

5. Solve: $x^2 + 4x - 16 = 0$

6. Graph: $y = x^2 + 2x - 4$

7. Solve: $x^2 + 4x + 2 = 0$

8. Subtract: $(-5 + 6i) - (3 - 7i)$

9. Solve: $2x^2 - 5x - 3 = 0$

10. Solve: $2x^2 - 6x + 1 = 0$

11. Multiply: $6i(5 - 4i)$

12. Solve: $2(x - 5)^2 = 36$

13. Solve: $x^2 - 6x - 5 = 0$

14. Multiply: $(-5 + 2i)(4 - i)$

15. Solve: $x^2 - 5x = 2$

16. Solve: $6x^2 - 17x = -5$

17. Solve: $x^2 + 3x - 7 = 0$

18. Divide: $\dfrac{3 - i}{2i}$

19. Solve: $x^2 - 8x + 17 = 0$

20. Graph: $y = x^2 - 2x - 3$

21. Divide: $\dfrac{4 - 2i}{1 - i}$

22. Geometry The length of a rectangle is 2 ft less than twice the width. The area of the rectangle is 40 ft². Find the length and width of the rectangle.

23. Uniform Motion It took a motorboat 1 h more to travel 60 mi against the current than it took to go 60 mi with the current. The rate of the current was 1 mph. Find the rate of the boat in calm water.

24. Integer Problem The sum of the squares of three consecutive odd integers is 83. Find the middle odd integer.

25. Uniform Motion A jogger ran 7 mi at a constant rate and then reduced the rate by 3 mph. An additional 8 mi was run at the reduced rate. The total time spent jogging the 15 mi was 3 h. Find the rate for the last 8 mi.

Cumulative Review Exercises

1. Simplify: $2x - 3[2x - 4(3 - 2x) + 2] - 3$

2. Solve: $-\dfrac{3}{5}x = -\dfrac{9}{10}$

3. Solve: $2x - 3(4x - 5) = -3x - 6$

4. Solve: $2x - 3(2 - 3x) > 2x - 5$

5. Find the x- and y-intercepts of the line $4x - 3y = 12$.

6. Find the equation of the line that contains the point whose coordinates are $(-3, 2)$ and has slope $-\dfrac{4}{3}$.

7. Find the domain and range of the relation $\{(-2, -8),\ (-1, -1),\ (0, 0),\ (1, 1),\ (2, 8)\}$. Is the relation a function?

8. Evaluate $f(x) = -3x + 10$ at $x = -9$.

9. Graph: $y = \dfrac{1}{4}x - 2$

10. Graph the solution set of $2x - 3y > 6$.

11. Solve by substitution: $3x - y = 5$
$y = 2x - 3$

12. Solve by the addition method: $3x + 2y = 2$
$5x - 2y = 14$

13. Simplify: $\dfrac{(2a^{-2}b)^2}{-3a^{-5}b^4}$

14. Divide: $(x^2 - 8) \div (x - 2)$

15. Factor: $4y(x - 4) - 3(x - 4)$

16. Factor: $3x^3 + 2x^2 - 8x$

17. Divide: $\dfrac{3x^2 - 6x}{4x - 6} \div \dfrac{2x^2 + x - 6}{6x^2 - 24x}$

18. Subtract: $\dfrac{x}{2(x - 1)} - \dfrac{1}{(x - 1)(x + 1)}$

19. Simplify: $\dfrac{1 - \dfrac{7}{x} + \dfrac{12}{x^2}}{2 - \dfrac{1}{x} - \dfrac{15}{x^2}}$

20. Solve: $\dfrac{x}{x + 6} = \dfrac{3}{x}$

21. Multiply: $\left(\sqrt{a} - \sqrt{2}\right)\left(\sqrt{a} + \sqrt{2}\right)$

22. Solve: $3 = 8 - \sqrt{5x}$

23. Solve: $2x^2 - 7x = -3$

24. Solve: $3(x - 2)^2 = 36$

25. Solve: $3x^2 - 4x - 5 = 0$

26. Graph: $y = x^2 - 3x - 2$

27. Taxes In a certain state, the sales tax is $7\frac{1}{4}\%$. The sales tax on a chemistry textbook is $5.22. Find the cost of the textbook before the tax is added.

28. Mixture Problem Find the cost per pound of a mixture made from 20 lb of cashews that cost $7 per pound and 50 lb of peanuts that cost $3.50 per pound.

29. Investments A stock investment of 100 shares paid a dividend of $215. At this rate, how many additional shares are required to earn a dividend of $752.50?

30. Uniform Motion A 720-mile trip from one city to another takes 3 h when a plane is flying with the wind. The return trip, against the wind, takes 4.5 h. Find the rate of the plane in calm air and the rate of the wind.

31. Test Scores A student received a 70, a 91, an 85, and a 77 on four tests in a math class. What scores on the fifth test will enable the student to receive a minimum of 400 points?

32. Guy Wires A guy wire is attached to a point 30 m above the ground on a telephone pole that is perpendicular to the ground. The wire is anchored to the ground at a point 10 m from the base of the pole. Find the length of the guy wire. Round to the nearest hundredth.

33. Integer Problem The sum of the squares of three consecutive odd integers is 155. Find the middle odd integer.

Final Exam

1. Evaluate: $-|-3|$

2. Subtract: $-15 - (-12) - 3$

3. Write $\dfrac{1}{8}$ as a percent.

4. Simplify: $-2^4 \cdot (-2)^4$

5. Simplify: $-7 - \dfrac{12 - 15}{2 - (-1)} \cdot (-4)$

6. Evaluate $\dfrac{a^2 - 3b}{2a - 2b^2}$ when $a = 3$ and $b = -2$.

7. Simplify: $6x - (-4y) - (-3x) + 2y$

8. Multiply: $(-15z)\left(-\dfrac{2}{5}\right)$

9. Simplify: $-2[5 - 3(2x - 7) - 2x]$

10. Solve: $20 = -\dfrac{2}{5}x$

11. Solve: $4 - 2(3x + 1) = 3(2 - x) + 5$

12. Find 19% of 80.

13. Solve: $4 - x \geq 7$

14. Solve: $2 - 2(y - 1) \leq 2y - 6$

15. Find the slope of the line that contains the points whose coordinates are $(-1, -3)$ and $(2, -1)$.

16. Find the equation of the line that contains the point whose coordinates are $(3, -4)$ and has slope $-\dfrac{2}{3}$.

17. Graph the line with slope $-\dfrac{1}{2}$ and y-intercept $(0, -3)$.

18. Graph: $f(x) = \dfrac{2}{3}x - 4$

19. Find the range of the function given by the equation $f(x) = -x + 5$ if the domain is $\{-6, -3, 0, 3, 6\}$.

20. Graph the solution set of $3x - 2y \geq 6$.

21. Solve by substitution: $y = 4x - 7$ $\quad\quad y = 2x + 5$

22. Solve by the addition method: $4x - 3y = 11$ $\quad\quad 2x + 5y = -1$

23. Subtract: $(2x^2 - 5x + 1) - (5x^2 - 2x - 7)$

24. Simplify: $(-3xy^3)^4$

25. Multiply: $(3x^2 - x - 2)(2x + 3)$

26. Simplify: $\dfrac{(-2x^2y^3)^3}{(-4x^{-1}y^4)^2}$

27. Simplify: $(4x^{-2}y)^3(2xy^{-2})^{-2}$

28. Divide: $\dfrac{12x^3y^2 - 16x^2y^2 - 20y^2}{4xy^2}$

29. Divide: $(5x^2 - 2x - 1) \div (x + 2)$

30. Write 0.000000039 in scientific notation.

31. Factor: $2a(4 - x) - 6(x - 4)$

32. Factor: $x^2 - 5x - 6$

33. Factor: $2x^2 - x - 3$

34. Factor: $6x^2 - 5x - 6$

35. Factor: $8x^3 - 28x^2 + 12x$

36. Factor: $25x^2 - 16$

37. Factor: $75y - 12x^2y$

38. Solve: $2x^2 = 7x - 3$

39. Multiply: $\dfrac{2x^2 - 3x + 1}{4x^2 - 2x} \cdot \dfrac{4x^2 + 4x}{x^2 - 2x + 1}$

40. Subtract: $\dfrac{5}{x + 3} - \dfrac{3x}{2x - 5}$

41. Simplify: $\dfrac{x - \dfrac{3}{2x - 1}}{1 - \dfrac{2}{2x - 1}}$

42. Solve: $\dfrac{5x}{3x - 5} - 3 = \dfrac{7}{3x - 5}$

43. Solve $a = 3a - 2b$ for a.

44. Simplify: $\sqrt{49x^6}$

45. Add: $2\sqrt{27a} + 8\sqrt{48a}$

46. Simplify: $\dfrac{\sqrt{3}}{\sqrt{5} - 2}$

47. Solve: $\sqrt{x + 4} - \sqrt{x - 1} = 1$

48. Solve: $(x - 3)^2 = 7$

49. Solve: $4x^2 - 2x - 1 = 0$

50. Graph: $y = x^2 - 4x + 3$

51. Translate and simplify "the sum of twice a number and three times the difference between the number and two."

52. **Depreciation** Because of depreciation, the value of an office machine is now $2400. This is 80% of its original value. Find the original value of the machine.

53. **Coins** A coin bank contains quarters and dimes. There are three times as many dimes as quarters. The total value of the coins in the bank is $11. Find the number of dimes in the bank.

54. **Geometry** The measure of one angle of a triangle is 10° more than the measure of the second angle. The measure of the third angle is 10° more than the measure of the first angle. Find the measure of each angle of the triangle.

55. **Markup** The manufacturer's cost for a laser printer is $900. The manufacturer sells the printer for $1485. Find the markup rate.

56. **Investments** An investment of $3000 is made at an annual simple interest rate of 8%. How much additional money must be invested at 11% so that the total interest earned is 10% of the total investment?

57. **Food Mixtures** A grocer mixes 4 lb of peanuts that cost $2 per pound with 2 lb of walnuts that cost $5 per pound. What is the cost per pound of the resulting mixture?

58. **Mixture Problem** A pharmacist mixes 20 L of a solution that is 60% acid with 30 L of a solution that is 20% acid. What is the percent concentration of acid in the resulting mixture?

59. **Uniform Motion** A small plane flew at a constant rate for 1 h. The pilot then doubled the plane's speed. An additional 1.5 h were flown at the increased speed. If the entire flight was 860 km, how far did the plane travel during the first hour?

60. **Uniform Motion** With the current, a motorboat travels 50 mi in 2.5 h. Against the current, it takes twice as long to travel 50 mi. Find the rate of the boat in calm water and the rate of the current.

61. **Geometry** The length of a rectangle is 5 m more than the width. The area of the rectangle is 50 m². Find the dimensions of the rectangle.

62. **Paint** A paint formula requires 2 oz of dye for every 15 oz of base paint. How many ounces of dye are required for 120 oz of base paint?

63. **Work Problem** It takes a chef 1 h to prepare a dinner. The chef's apprentice can prepare the same dinner in 1.5 h. How long would it take the chef and the apprentice, working together, to prepare the dinner?

64. **Geometry** The hypotenuse of a right triangle measures 14 cm. One leg of the triangle measures 8 cm. Find the length of the other leg of the triangle. Round to the nearest tenth.

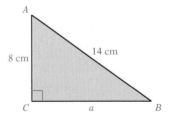

65. **Uniform Motion** It took a plane $\frac{1}{2}$ h more to fly 500 mi against the wind than it took to fly the same distance with the wind. The rate of the plane in calm air is 225 mph. Find the rate of the wind.

Table of Properties

Properties of Real Numbers

The Associative Property of Addition

If a, b, and c are real numbers, then $(a + b) + c = a + (b + c)$.

The Commutative Property of Addition

If a and b are real numbers, then $a + b = b + a$.

The Addition Property of Zero

If a is a real number, then $a + 0 = 0 + a = a$.

The Multiplication Property of Zero

If a is a real number, then $a \cdot 0 = 0 \cdot a = 0$.

The Inverse Property of Addition

If a is a real number, then
$a + (-a) = (-a) + a = 0$.

The Associative Property of Multiplication

If a, b, and c are real numbers, then $(a \cdot b) \cdot c = a \cdot (b \cdot c)$.

The Commutative Property of Multiplication

If a and b are real numbers, then $a \cdot b = b \cdot a$.

The Multiplication Property of One

If a is a real number, then $a \cdot 1 = 1 \cdot a = a$.

The Inverse Property of Multiplication

If a is a real number and $a \neq 0$, then
$$a \cdot \frac{1}{a} = \frac{1}{a} \cdot a = 1.$$

Distributive Property

If a, b, and c are real numbers, then
$a(b + c) = ab + ac$ or $(b + c)a = ba + ca$.

Properties of Equations

Addition Property of Equations

The same number or variable term can be added to each side of an equation without changing the solution of the equation.

Multiplication Property of Equations

Each side of an equation can be multiplied by the same nonzero number without changing the solution of the equation.

Properties of Inequalities

Addition Property of Inequalities

If $a > b$, then $a + c > b + c$.

If $a < b$, then $a + c < b + c$.

Multiplication Property of Inequalities

If $a > b$ and $c > 0$, then $ac > bc$.

If $a < b$ and $c > 0$, then $ac < bc$.

If $a > b$ and $c < 0$, then $ac < bc$.

If $a < b$ and $c < 0$, then $ac > bc$.

Table of Properties (*continued*)

Properties of Exponents

If m and n are integers, then $x^m \cdot x^n = x^{m+n}$.

If m and n are integers, then $(x^m)^n = x^{mn}$.

If $x \neq 0$, then $x^0 = 1$.

If m and n are integers and $x \neq 0$, then
$\dfrac{x^m}{x^n} = x^{m-n}$.

If m, n, and p are integers, then
$(x^m \cdot y^n)^p = x^{mp} y^{np}$.

If n is a positive integer and $x \neq 0$, then
$x^{-n} = \dfrac{1}{x^n}$ and $\dfrac{1}{x^{-n}} = x^n$.

If m, n, and p are integers and $y \neq 0$, then
$\left(\dfrac{x^m}{y^n}\right)^p = \dfrac{x^{mp}}{y^{np}}$.

Principle of Zero Products

If $a \cdot b = 0$, then $a = 0$ or $b = 0$.

Properties of Radical Expressions

If a and b are positive real numbers, then
$\sqrt[n]{ab} = \sqrt[n]{a}\,\sqrt[n]{b}$.

If a and b are positive real numbers, then
$$\sqrt[n]{\dfrac{a}{b}} = \dfrac{\sqrt[n]{a}}{\sqrt[n]{b}}.$$

Property of Squaring Both Sides of an Equation

If a and b are real numbers and $a = b$, then $a^2 = b^2$.

Keystroke Guide for the TI-83 and TI-83 Plus/TI-84 Plus

Basic Operations

Numerical calculations are performed on the **home screen.** You can always return to the home screen by pressing `2nd` QUIT. Pressing `CLEAR` erases the home screen.

To evaluate the expression $-2(3 + 5) - 8 \div 4$, use the following keystrokes.

`(-)` 2 `(` 3 `+` 5 `)` `-` 8 `÷` 4 `ENTER`

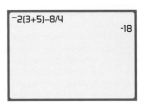

Note: There is a difference between the key to enter a negative number, `(-)`, and the key for subtraction, `-`. You cannot use these keys interchangeably.

The `2nd` key is used to access the commands in gold writing above a key. For instance, to evaluate the $\sqrt{49}$, press `2nd` $\sqrt{\ }$ 49 `)` `ENTER`.

The `ALPHA` key is used to place a letter on the screen. One reason to do this is to store a value of a variable. The following keystrokes give A the value of 5.

5 `STO▶` `ALPHA` A `ENTER`

This value is now available in calculations. For instance, we can find the value of $3a^2$ by using the following keystrokes: 3 `ALPHA` A `x²`. To display the value of the variable on the screen, press `2nd` RCL `ALPHA` A.

Note: When you use the `ALPHA` key, only capital letters are available on the TI calculators.

Evaluating Functions

There are various methods of evaluating a function, but all methods require that the expression be entered as one of the ten functions Y_1 to Y_0. To evaluate $f(x) = \dfrac{x^2}{x - 1}$ when $x = -3$, enter the expression into, for instance, Y_1, and then press `VARS` `▶` 11 `(` `(-)` 3 `)` `ENTER`.

Note: If you try to evaluate a function at a number that is not in the domain of the function, you will get an error message. For instance, 1 is not in the domain of $f(x) = \dfrac{x^2}{x - 1}$. If we try to evaluate the function at 1, the error screen at the right appears.

Evaluating Variable Expressions

To evaluate a variable expression, first store the values of each variable. Then enter the variable expression. For instance, to evaluate $s^2 + 2sl$ when $s = 4$ and $l = 5$, use the following keystrokes.

4 STO► ALPHA S ENTER 5 STO► ALPHA L ENTER ALPHA S

x^2 + 2 ALPHA S ALPHA L ENTER

Graph

To graph a function, use the Y= key to enter the expression for the function, select a suitable viewing window, and then press GRAPH . For instance, to graph $f(x) = 0.1x^3 - 2x - 1$ in the standard viewing window, use the following keystrokes.

Y= 0.1 X,T,θ,n ^ 3 − 2 X,T,θ,n − 1 ZOOM (scroll to 6) ENTER

 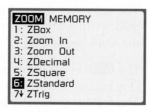

Note: For the keystrokes above, you do not have to scroll to 6. Alternatively, use ZOOM 6. This will select the standard viewing window and automatically start the graph. Use the WINDOW key to create a custom window for a graph.

Graphing Inequalities

To illustrate this feature, we will graph $y \leq 2x - 1$. Enter $2x - 1$ into Y_1. Because $y \leq 2x - 1$, we want to shade below the graph. Move the cursor to the left of Y_1 and press ENTER three times. Press GRAPH .

Note: To shade above the graph, move the cursor to the left of Y_1 and press ENTER two times. An inequality with the symbol $\leq$ or $\geq$ should be graphed with a solid line, and an inequality with the symbol $<$ or $>$ should be graphed with a dashed line. However, the graph of a linear inequality on a graphing calculator does not distinguish between a solid line and a dashed line.

To graph the solution set of a system of inequalities, solve each inequality for y and graph each inequality. The solution set is the intersection of the two inequalities. The solution set of $\begin{array}{l} 3x + 2y > 10 \\ 4x - 3y \leq 5 \end{array}$ is shown at the right.

Intersect The INTERSECT feature is used to solve a system of equations. To illustrate this feature, we will use the system of equations $\dfrac{2x - 3y = 13}{3x + 4y = -6}$.

> *Note:* Some equations can be solved by this method. See the section "Solve an equation" below. Also, this method is used to find a number in the domain of a function for a given number in the range. See the section "Find a domain element."

Solve each of the equations in the system of equations for y. In this case, we have $y = \dfrac{2}{3}x - \dfrac{13}{3}$ and $y = -\dfrac{3}{4}x - \dfrac{3}{2}$.

Use the (Y=) editor to enter $\dfrac{2}{3}x - \dfrac{13}{3}$ into Y₁ and $-\dfrac{3}{4}x - \dfrac{3}{2}$ into Y₂. Graph the two functions in the standard viewing window. (If the window does not show the point of intersection of the two graphs, adjust the window until you can see the point of intersection.)

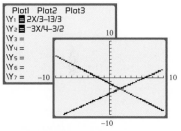

Press (2nd) CALC (scroll to 5, intersect) (ENTER).

Alternatively, you can just press (2nd) CALC 5.

First curve? is shown at the bottom of the screen and identifies one of the two graphs on the screen. Press (ENTER).

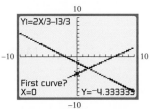

Second curve? is shown at the bottom of the screen and identifies the second of the two graphs on the screen. Press (ENTER).

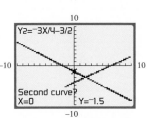

Guess? shown at the bottom of the screen asks you to use the left or right arrow key to move the cursor to the *approximate* location of the point of intersection. (If there are two or more points of intersection, it does not matter which one you choose first.) Press (ENTER).

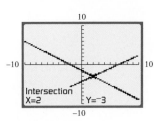

The solution of the system of equations is $(2, -3)$.

Solve an equation To illustrate the steps involved, we will solve the equation $2x + 4 = -3x - 1$. The idea is to write the equation as the system of equations $\begin{aligned} y &= 2x + 4 \\ y &= -3x - 1 \end{aligned}$ and then use the steps for solving a system of equations.

Use the Y= editor to enter the left and right sides of the equation into Y_1 and Y_2. Graph the two functions and then follow the steps for Intersect.

The solution is -1, the x-coordinate of the point of intersection.

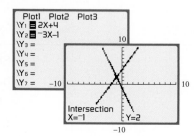

Find a domain element For this example, we will find a number in the domain of $f(x) = -\frac{2}{3}x + 2$ that corresponds to 4 in the range of the function. This is like solving the system of equations $y = -\frac{2}{3}x + 2$ and $y = 4$.

Use the Y= editor to enter the expression for the function in Y_1 and the desired output, 4, in Y_2. Graph the two functions and then follow the steps for Intersect.

The point of intersection is $(-3, 4)$. The number -3 in the domain of f produces an output of 4 in the range of f.

Math Pressing MATH gives you access to many built-in functions. The following keystrokes will convert 0.125 to a fraction: .125 MATH 1 ENTER .

Additional built-in functions under MATH can be found by pressing MATH ◗. For instance, to evaluate $-|-25|$, press (-) MATH ◗ 1 (-) 25) ENTER .

See your owner's manual for assistance with other functions under the MATH key.

Radical Expressions

To evaluate a square-root expression, press √ .

For instance, to evaluate $0.15\sqrt{p^2 + 4p + 10}$ when $p = 100{,}000$, first store 100,000 in P. Then press 0.15 `2nd` √ `ALPHA` P `x²` `+` 4 `ALPHA` P `+` 10 `)` `ENTER`.

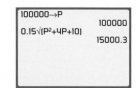

To evaluate a radical expression other than a square root, access $\sqrt[x]{}$ by pressing `MATH`. For instance, to evaluate $\sqrt[4]{67}$, press 4 (the index of the radical) `MATH` (scroll to 5) `ENTER` 67 `ENTER`.

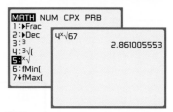

Scientific Notation

To enter a number in scientific notation, use `2nd` EE. For instance, to find $\dfrac{3.45 \times 10^{-12}}{1.5 \times 10^{25}}$, press 3.45 `2nd` EE `(-)` 12 `÷` 1.5 `2nd` EE 25 `ENTER`. The answer is 2.3×10^{-37}.

Table

There are three steps in creating an input/output table for a function. First use the `Y=` editor to input the function. The second step is setting up the table, and the third step is displaying the table.

To set up the table, press `2nd` TBLSET. **TblStart** is the first value of the independent variable in the input/output table. **△Tbl** is the difference between successive values. Setting this to 1 means that, for this table, the input values are $-2, -1, 0, 1, 2, \ldots$. If △Tbl $= 0.5$, then the input values are $-2, -1.5, -1, -0.5, 0, 0.5, \ldots$.

Indpnt is the independent variable. When this is set to **Auto**, values of the independent variable are automatically entered into the table. **Depend** is the dependent variable. When this is set to **Auto**, values of the dependent variable are automatically entered into the table.

To display the table, press `2nd` TABLE. An input/output table for $f(x) = x^2 - 1$ is shown at the right.

Once the table is on the screen, the up and down arrow keys can be used to display more values in the table. For the table at the right, we used the up arrow key to move to $x = -7$.

An input/output table for any given input can be created by selecting **Ask** for the independent variable. The table at the right shows an input/output table for $f(x) = \dfrac{4x}{x - 2}$ for selected values of x. Note that the word **ERROR** or **ERR:** appeared when 2 was entered. This occurred because f is not defined when $x = 2$.

Note: Using the table feature in **Ask** mode is the same as evaluating a function for given values of the independent variable. For instance, from the table on the preceding page, we have $f(4) = 8$.

Test   The TEST feature has many uses, one of which is to graph the solution set of a linear inequality in one variable. To illustrate this feature, we will graph the solution set of $x - 1 < 4$. Press ⬤ Y= ⬤ X,T,θ,n ⬤ – 1 ⬤ 2nd ⬤ TEST (scroll to 5) ENTER 4 GRAPH .

Trace   Once a graph is drawn, pressing TRACE will place a cursor on the screen, and the coordinates of the point below the cursor are shown at the bottom of the screen. Use the left and right arrow keys to move the cursor along the graph. For the graph at the right, we have $f(4.8) = 3.4592$, where $f(x) = 0.1x^3 - 2x + 2$ is shown at the top left of the screen.

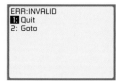

In TRACE mode, you can evaluate a function at any value of the independent variable that is within Xmin and Xmax. To do this, first graph the function. Now press TRACE (the value of x) ENTER . For the graph at the left below, we used $x = -3.5$. If a value of x is chosen outside the window, an error message is displayed.

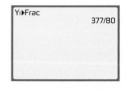

In the example above where we entered -3.5 for x, the value of the function was calculated as 4.7125. This means that $f(-3.5) = 4.7125$. The keystrokes 2nd QUIT VARS ▶ 11 MATH 1 ENTER will convert the decimal value to a fraction.

When the TRACE feature is used with two or more graphs, the up and down arrow keys are used to move between the graphs. The following two graphs are for the functions $f(x) = 0.1x^3 - 2x + 2$ and $g(x) = 2x - 3$. By using the up and down arrows, we can place the cursor on either graph. The right and left arrows are used to move along the graph.

Window The viewing window for a graph is controlled by pressing WINDOW . Xmin and Xmax are the minimum value and maximum value, respectively, of the independent variable shown on the graph. Xscl is the distance between tick marks on the *x*-axis. Ymin and Ymax are the minimum value and maximum value, respectively, of the dependent variable shown on the graph. Yscl is the distance between tick marks on the *y*-axis. Leave Xres as 1.

Note: In the standard viewing window, the distance between tick marks on the *x*-axis is different from the distance between tick marks on the *y*-axis. This will distort a graph. A more accurate picture of a graph can be created by using a square viewing window. See **ZOOM**.

Y= The Y= editor is used to enter the expression for a function. There are ten possible functions, labeled Y_1 to Y_0, that can be active at any one time. For instance, to enter $f(x) = x^2 + 3x - 2$ as Y_1, use the following keystrokes.

 X,T,θ,n x² + 3 X,T,θ,n − 2

Note: If an expression is already entered for Y_1, place the cursor anywhere on that expression and press CLEAR .

To enter $s = \dfrac{2v - 1}{v^3 - 3}$ into Y_2, place the cursor to the right of the equals sign for Y_2. Then press (2 X,T,θ,n −

1 (÷ (X,T,θ,n ^ 3 − 3) .

Note: When we enter an equation, the independent variable (*v* in the expression above) is entered using X,T,θ,n . The dependent variable (*s* in the expression above) is one of Y_1 to Y_0. Also note the use of parentheses to ensure the correct order of operations.

Observe the black rectangle that covers the equals sign for the two examples we have shown. This rectangle means that the function is "active." If we were to press GRAPH , then the graph of both functions would appear. You can make a function inactive by using the arrow keys to move the cursor over the equals sign of that function and then pressing ENTER . This will remove the black rectangle. We have done that for Y_2, as shown at the right. Now if GRAPH is pressed, only Y_1 will be graphed.

It is also possible to control the appearance of the graph by moving the cursor on the [Y=] screen to the left of any Y. With the cursor in this position, pressing [ENTER] will change the appearance of the graph. The options are shown at the right.

```
Plot1  Plot2  Plot3
\Y₁ = Default graph line
\Y₂ = Bold graph line
▀Y₃ = Shade above graph
▄Y₄ = Shade below graph
-₀Y₅ = Draw path of graph
₀Y₆ = Travel path of graph
\Y₇ = Dashed graph line
```

Zero   The ZERO feature of a graphing calculator is used for various calculations: to find the x-intercepts of a function, to solve some equations, and to find the zero of a function.

x-intercepts   To illustrate the procedure for finding x-intercepts, we will use $f(x) = x^2 + x - 2$.

First, use the [Y=] editor to enter the expression for the function and then graph the function in the standard viewing window. (It may be necessary to adjust this window so that the intercepts are visible.) Once the graph is displayed, use the keystrokes below to find the x-intercepts of the graph of the function.

Press [2nd] CALC (scroll to 2 for **zero** of the function) [ENTER].

Alternatively, you can just press [2nd] CALC 2.

```
CALCULATE
1: value
2: zero
3: minimum
4: maximum
5: intersect
6: dy/dx
7: ∫f(x)dx
```

Left Bound? shown at the bottom of the screen asks you to use the left or right arrow key to move the cursor to the *left* of the desired x-intercept. Press [ENTER].

Right Bound? shown at the bottom of the screen asks you to use the left or right arrow key to move the cursor to the *right* of the desired x-intercept. Press [ENTER].

Guess? shown at the bottom of the screen asks you to use the left or right arrow key to move the cursor to the *approximate* location of the desired x-intercept. Press [ENTER].

The x-coordinate of an x-intercept is −2. Therefore, an x-intercept is (−2, 0).

To find the other x-intercept, follow the same steps as above. The screens for this calculation are shown at the top of the next page.

A second x-intercept is $(1, 0)$.

Solve an equation   To use the ZERO feature to solve an equation, first rewrite the equation with all terms on one side. For instance, one way to solve the equation $x^3 - x + 1 = -2x + 3$ is first to rewrite it as $x^3 + x - 2 = 0$. Enter $x^3 + x - 2$ into Y1 and then follow the steps for finding x-intercepts.

Find the real zeros of a function   To find the real zeros of a function, follow the steps for finding x-intercepts.

Zoom   Pressing ⟨ZOOM⟩ allows you to select some preset viewing windows. This key also gives you access to ZBox, Zoom In, and Zoom Out. These functions enable you to redraw a selected portion of a graph in a new window. Some windows that are used frequently in this text are shown below.

Photo Credits

Solutions to Chapter Problems

Solutions to Chapter 1 Problems

SECTION 1.1

Problem 1
$A = \{1, 2, 3, 4\}$

Problem 2
$-5 < -1$
$-1 = -1$
$5 > -1$

The element 5 is greater than -1.

Problem 3
A. 9   **B.** -62

Problem 4
A. $|-5| = 5$ **B.** $-|-9| = -9$

SECTION 1.2

Problem 1
A. $-162 + 98 = -64$

B. $-154 + (-37) = -191$

C. $-36 + 17 + (-21) = -19 + (-21)$
$= -40$

Problem 2
$-8 - 14 = -8 + (-14)$
$= -22$

Problem 3
$4 - (-3) - 12 - (-7) - 20$
$= 4 + 3 + (-12) + 7 + (-20)$
$= 7 + (-12) + 7 + (-20)$
$= -5 + 7 + (-20)$
$= 2 + (-20)$
$= -18$

Problem 4
A. $-38 \cdot 51 = -1938$

B. $-7(-8)(9)(-2) = 56(9)(-2)$
$= 504(-2)$
$= -1008$

Problem 5
A. $(-135) \div (-9) = 15$

B. $\dfrac{84}{-6} = -14$

C. $-\dfrac{36}{-12} = -(-3) = 3$

Problem 6
Strategy To find the average daily high temperature:
   ▶ Add the seven temperature readings.
   ▶ Divide the sum by 7.

Solution $-5 + (-6) + 3 + 0 + (-4) + (-7) + (-2)$
$= -11 + 3 + 0 + (-4) + (-7) + (-2)$
$= -8 + 0 + (-4) + (-7) + (-2)$
$= -8 + (-4) + (-7) + (-2)$
$= -12 + (-7) + (-2)$
$= -19 + (-2)$
$= -21$

$-21 \div 7 = -3$

The average daily high temperature was $-3°C$.

SECTION 1.3

Problem 1
$$\begin{array}{r} 0.16 \\ 25\overline{)4.00} \\ \underline{-2\ 5} \\ 1\ 50 \\ \underline{-1\ 50} \\ 0 \end{array}$$

$\dfrac{4}{25} = 0.16$

Problem 2
$$\begin{array}{r} 0.444 \\ 9\overline{)4.000} \\ \underline{-3\ 6} \\ 40 \\ \underline{-36} \\ 40 \\ \underline{-36} \\ 4 \end{array}$$

$\dfrac{4}{9} = 0.\overline{4}$

Problem 3
$$-\frac{7}{12} \cdot \frac{9}{14} = -\frac{7 \cdot 9}{12 \cdot 14} = -\frac{\overset{1}{\cancel{7}} \cdot \overset{1}{\cancel{3}} \cdot 3}{2 \cdot 2 \cdot \underset{1}{\cancel{3}} \cdot 2 \cdot \underset{1}{\cancel{7}}}$$
$$= -\frac{3}{8}$$

Problem 4
$$-\frac{3}{8} \div \left(-\frac{5}{12}\right) = \frac{3}{8} \cdot \frac{12}{5}$$
$$= \frac{3 \cdot 12}{8 \cdot 5} = \frac{3 \cdot \overset{1}{\cancel{2}} \cdot \overset{1}{\cancel{2}} \cdot 3}{\underset{1}{\cancel{2}} \cdot \underset{1}{\cancel{2}} \cdot 2 \cdot 5} = \frac{9}{10}$$

Problem 5

$$
\begin{array}{r}
5.44 \\
\times \quad 3.8 \\
\hline
4352 \\
1632 \\
\hline
20.672
\end{array}
$$

$(-5.44)(3.8) = -20.672$

Problem 6

$$
\begin{array}{r}
0.231 \\
1.7\overline{)0.3.940} \\
-3\,4 \\
\hline
54 \\
-51 \\
\hline
30 \\
-17 \\
\hline
13
\end{array}
$$

$-0.394 \div 1.7 \approx -0.23$

Problem 7

Prime factorization of 9 and 12:

$9 = 3 \cdot 3 \qquad 12 = 2 \cdot 2 \cdot 3$

$\text{LCM} = 2 \cdot 2 \cdot 3 \cdot 3 = 36$

$$
\frac{5}{9} - \frac{11}{12} = \frac{20}{36} - \frac{33}{36} = \frac{20}{36} + \frac{-33}{36}
$$
$$
= \frac{20 + (-33)}{36} = \frac{-13}{36} = -\frac{13}{36}
$$

Problem 8

$$
-\frac{7}{8} - \frac{5}{6} + \frac{1}{2} = -\frac{21}{24} - \frac{20}{24} + \frac{12}{24}
$$
$$
= \frac{-21}{24} + \frac{-20}{24} + \frac{12}{24}
$$
$$
= \frac{-21 + (-20) + 12}{24} = \frac{-29}{24} = -\frac{29}{24}
$$

Problem 9

$$
\begin{array}{r}
3.097 \\
4.9 \\
+\ 3.09 \\
\hline
11.087
\end{array}
$$

Problem 10

$$
\begin{array}{r}
67.910 \\
-16.127 \\
\hline
51.783
\end{array}
$$

$16.127 - 67.91 = -51.783$

Problem 11

$$
125\% = 125\left(\frac{1}{100}\right) = \frac{125}{100} = 1\frac{1}{4}
$$
$$
125\% = 125(0.01) = 1.25
$$

Problem 12

$$
16\frac{2}{3}\% = 16\frac{2}{3}\left(\frac{1}{100}\right) = \frac{50}{3}\left(\frac{1}{100}\right) = \frac{1}{6}
$$

Problem 13

$6.08\% = 6.08(0.01) = 0.0608$

Problem 14

A. $0.043 = 0.043(100\%) = 4.3\%$

B. $2.57 = 2.57(100\%) = 257\%$

Problem 15

$$
\frac{5}{9} = \frac{5}{9}(100\%) = \frac{500}{9}\% \approx 55.6\%
$$

Problem 16

$$
\frac{9}{16} = \frac{9}{16}(100\%) = \frac{900}{16}\% = 56\frac{1}{4}\%
$$

SECTION 1.4

Problem 1

$(-5)^3 = (-5)(-5)(-5) = 25(-5) = -125$

$-5^3 = -(5 \cdot 5 \cdot 5) = -(25 \cdot 5) = -125$

Problem 2

$(-3)^3 = (-3)(-3)(-3) = 9(-3) = -27$

$(-3)^4 = (-3)(-3)(-3)(-3)$
$\quad = 9(-3)(-3) = -27(-3) = 81$

Problem 3

$(3^3)(-2)^3 = (3)(3)(3) \cdot (-2)(-2)(-2)$
$\quad\quad = 27 \cdot (-8) = -216$

$$
\left(-\frac{2}{5}\right)^2 = \left(-\frac{2}{5}\right)\left(-\frac{2}{5}\right) = \frac{2 \cdot 2}{5 \cdot 5} = \frac{4}{25}
$$

Problem 4

$36 \div (8 - 5)^2 - (-3)^2 \cdot 2$
$\quad = 36 \div (3)^2 - (-3)^2 \cdot 2$
$\quad = 36 \div 9 - 9 \cdot 2$
$\quad = 4 - 9 \cdot 2$
$\quad = 4 - 18$
$\quad = -14$

Problem 5

$27 \div 3^2 + (-3)^2 \cdot 4$
$\quad = 27 \div 9 + 9 \cdot 4$
$\quad = 3 + 9 \cdot 4$
$\quad = 3 + 36$
$\quad = 39$

Problem 6

$4 - 3[4 - 2(6 - 3)] \div 2$
$\quad = 4 - 3[4 - 2(3)] \div 2$
$\quad = 4 - 3[4 - 6] \div 2$
$\quad = 4 - 3(-2) \div 2$
$\quad = 4 - (-6) \div 2$
$\quad = 4 - (-3)$
$\quad = 7$

SECTION 1.5

Problem 1

To find the complement of 87°, subtract 87° from 90°.
$$90° - 87° = 3°$$
3° is the complement of 87°.

Problem 2

To find the supplement of 87°, subtract 87° from 180°.
$$180° - 87° = 93°$$
93° is the supplement of 87°.

Problem 3

$m\angle x$ is the sum of the measures of two angles.
$$m\angle x = 34° + 95° = 129°$$

Problem 4

Perimeter = 4 · side
$$= 4 \cdot 4.2 \text{ m} = 16.8 \text{ m}$$

Problem 5

Circumference = π · diameter
$$\approx 3.14 \cdot 5 \text{ in.}$$
$$= 15.7 \text{ in.}$$

Problem 6

Strategy To find the cost of the metal strip:
- ▶ Find the circumference of the table in inches.
- ▶ Convert inches to feet.
- ▶ Multiply the circumference by the per-foot cost of the metal strip.

Solution Circumference = π · diameter
$$\approx 3.14 \cdot 36 \text{ in.}$$
$$= 113.04 \text{ in.}$$

$$\frac{113.04}{12} = 9.42 \text{ ft}$$

Cost: 9.42(3.21) = 30.2382
The cost is $30.24.

Problem 7

Area $= \dfrac{1}{2}$ · base · height
$$= \frac{1}{2} \cdot 5 \text{ ft} \cdot 3 \text{ ft} = 7.5 \text{ ft}^2$$

Problem 8

Area $= \pi$ · (radius)^2
$$\approx 3.14 \cdot (6 \text{ in.})^2$$
$$= 113.04 \text{ in}^2$$

Problem 9

Area = base · height
$$= 28 \text{ in.} \cdot 15 \text{ in.} = 420 \text{ in}^2$$

Problem 10

Strategy To find how much more expensive the wool rug is than the nylon rug:
- ▶ Find the area of the rug.
- ▶ Multiply the area of the rug by the per-square-foot cost of the wool rug.
- ▶ Multiply the area of the rug by the per-square-foot cost of the nylon rug.
- ▶ Find the difference between the two costs.

Solution Area = length · width
$$= 15 \text{ ft} \cdot 4 \text{ ft} = 60 \text{ ft}^2$$

Cost of wool rug = $1.93 · 60 = $115.80

Cost of nylon rug = $1.25 · 60 = $75

Difference in cost = $115.80 − $75 = $40.80

The difference in cost is $40.80.

Solutions to Chapter 2 Problems

SECTION 2.1

Problem 1
−4

Problem 2
$2xy + y^2$
$$2(-4)(2) + (2)^2 = 2(-4)(2) + 4$$
$$= -8(2) + 4$$
$$= -16 + 4$$
$$= -12$$

Problem 3
$$\frac{a^2 + b^2}{a + b}$$
$$\frac{(5)^2 + (-3)^2}{5 + (-3)} = \frac{25 + 9}{5 + (-3)}$$
$$= \frac{34}{2}$$
$$= 17$$

Problem 4
$x^3 - 2(x + y) + z^2$
$$(2)^3 - 2[2 + (-4)] + (-3)^2$$
$$= (2)^3 - 2(-2) + (-3)^2$$
$$= 8 - 2(-2) + 9$$
$$= 8 + 4 + 9$$
$$= 12 + 9$$
$$= 21$$

Problem 5
$$V = \frac{1}{3}\pi r^2 h$$
$$V = \frac{1}{3}\pi(4.5)^2(9.5) \qquad \bullet \, r = \frac{1}{2}d = \frac{1}{2}(9) = 4.5$$

$V = \dfrac{1}{3}\pi(20.25)(9.5)$

$V \approx 201.5$

The volume is approximately 201.5 cm³.

SECTION 2.2

Problem 1
$7 + (-7) = 0$

Problem 2
The Associative Property of Addition

Problem 3
A. $9x + 6x = (9 + 6)x = 15x$

B. $-4y - 7y = [-4 + (-7)]y = -11y$

Problem 4
A. $3a - 2b + 5a = 3a + 5a - 2b$
$= (3a + 5a) - 2b$
$= 8a - 2b$

B. $x^2 - 7 + 9x^2 - 14$
$= x^2 + 9x^2 - 7 - 14$
$= (x^2 + 9x^2) + (-7 - 14)$
$= 10x^2 - 21$

Problem 5
A. $-7(-2a) = [-7(-2)]a$
$= 14a$

B. $-\dfrac{5}{6}(-30y^2) = \left[-\dfrac{5}{6}(-30)\right]y^2$
$= 25y^2$

C. $(-5x)(-2) = (-2)(-5x)$
$= [-2(-5)]x$
$= 10x$

Problem 6
A. $7(4 + 2y) = 7(4) + 7(2y)$
$= 28 + 14y$

B. $-(5x - 12) = -1(5x - 12)$
$= -1(5x) - (-1)(12)$
$= -5x + 12$

C. $(3a - 1)5 = (3a)(5) - (1)(5)$
$= 15a - 5$

D. $-3(6a^2 - 8a + 9)$
$= -3(6a^2) - (-3)(8a) + (-3)(9)$
$= -18a^2 + 24a - 27$

Problem 7
$7(x - 2y) - 3(-x - 2y)$
$= 7x - 14y + 3x + 6y$
$= 10x - 8y$

Problem 8
$3y - 2[x - 4(2 - 3y)]$
$= 3y - 2[x - 8 + 12y]$
$= 3y - 2x + 16 - 24y$
$= -2x - 21y + 16$

SECTION 2.3

Problem 1
A. eighteen less than the cube of x
$x^3 - 18$

B. y decreased by the sum of z and nine
$y - (z + 9)$

C. the difference between the square of q
and the sum of r and t
$q^2 - (r + t)$

Problem 2
the unknown number: n
the square of the number: n^2
the product of five and the square of the number: $5n^2$

$5n^2 + n$

Problem 3
the unknown number: n
twice the number: $2n$
the sum of seven and twice the number: $7 + 2n$

$3(7 + 2n)$

Problem 4
the unknown number: n
twice the number: $2n$
the difference between twice the number and 17:
$2n - 17$

$n - (2n - 17) = n - 2n + 17$
$= -n + 17$

Problem 5
the unknown number: n

three-fourths of the number: $\dfrac{3}{4}n$

one-fifth of the number: $\dfrac{1}{5}n$

$\dfrac{3}{4}n + \dfrac{1}{5}n = \dfrac{15}{20}n + \dfrac{4}{20}n$
$= \dfrac{19}{20}n$

Problem 6
the time required by the newer model: t
the time required by the older model is twice the time
 required for the newer model: $2t$

Problem 7
the length of one piece: L
the length of the second piece: $6 - L$

Solutions to Chapter 3 Problems

SECTION 3.1

Problem 1

$$5 - 4x = 8x + 2$$

$$\begin{array}{c|c} 5 - 4\left(\dfrac{1}{4}\right) & 8\left(\dfrac{1}{4}\right) + 2 \\ 5 - 1 & 2 + 2 \\ \multicolumn{2}{c}{4 = 4} \end{array}$$

Yes, $\dfrac{1}{4}$ is a solution.

Problem 2

$$10x - x^2 = 3x - 10$$

$$\begin{array}{c|c} 10(5) - (5)^2 & 3(5) - 10 \\ 50 - 25 & 15 - 10 \\ \multicolumn{2}{c}{25 \neq 5} \end{array}$$

No, 5 is not a solution.

Problem 3

$$x - \dfrac{1}{3} = -\dfrac{3}{4}$$

$$x - \dfrac{1}{3} + \dfrac{1}{3} = -\dfrac{3}{4} + \dfrac{1}{3}$$

$$x + 0 = -\dfrac{9}{12} + \dfrac{4}{12}$$

$$x = -\dfrac{5}{12}$$

Check

$$x - \dfrac{1}{3} = -\dfrac{3}{4}$$

$$\begin{array}{c|c} -\dfrac{5}{12} - \dfrac{1}{3} & -\dfrac{3}{4} \\ -\dfrac{3}{4} & = -\dfrac{3}{4} \end{array}$$

The solution is $-\dfrac{5}{12}$.

Problem 4

$$-8 = 5 + x$$

$$-8 - 5 = 5 - 5 + x$$

$$-13 = x$$

The solution is -13.

Problem 5

$$-\dfrac{2x}{5} = 6$$

$$\left(-\dfrac{5}{2}\right)\left(-\dfrac{2}{5}x\right) = \left(-\dfrac{5}{2}\right)(6)$$

$$1x = -15$$

$$x = -15$$

The solution is -15.

Problem 6

$$6x = 10$$

$$\dfrac{6x}{6} = \dfrac{10}{6}$$

$$x = \dfrac{5}{3}$$

Check

$$6x = 10$$

$$\begin{array}{c|c} 6\left(\dfrac{5}{3}\right) & 10 \\ 10 & = 10 \end{array}$$

The solution is $\dfrac{5}{3}$.

Problem 7

$$4x - 8x = 16$$

$$-4x = 16$$

$$\dfrac{-4x}{-4} = \dfrac{16}{-4}$$

$$x = -4$$

The solution is -4.

Problem 8

Strategy The distance is 80 mi. Therefore, $d = 80$. The cyclists are moving in opposite directions, so the rate at which the distance between them is changing is the sum of the rates of the two cyclists. The rate is 18 mph + 14 mph = 32 mph. Therefore, $r = 32$. To find the time, solve the equation $d = rt$ for t.

Solution

$$d = rt$$

$$80 = 32t$$

$$\dfrac{80}{32} = \dfrac{32t}{32}$$

$$2.5 = t$$

They will meet 2.5 h after they begin.

Problem 9

Strategy Because the plane is flying against the wind, the rate of the plane is its speed in calm air (250 mph) minus the speed of the headwind (25 mph): 250 mph − 25 mph = 225 mph. Therefore, $r = 225$. The time is 3 h, so $t = 3$. To find the distance, solve the equation $d = rt$ for d.

Solution

$$d = rt$$

$$d = 225(3)$$

$$d = 675$$

The plane can fly 675 mi in 3 h.

Problem 10

$$PB = A$$
$$P(60) = 27$$
$$60P = 27$$
$$\frac{60P}{60} = \frac{27}{60}$$
$$P = 0.45$$

27 is 45% of 60.

Problem 11

Strategy To find the percent of the questions answered correctly, solve the basic percent equation using $B = 80$ and $A = 72$. The percent is unknown.

Solution
$$PB = A$$
$$P(80) = 72$$
$$80P = 72$$
$$\frac{80P}{80} = \frac{72}{80}$$
$$P = 0.9$$

90% of the questions were answered correctly.

Problem 12

Strategy To determine the sales tax, solve the basic percent equation using $B = 895$ and $P = 6\% = 0.06$. The amount is unknown.

Solution
$$PB = A$$
$$0.06(895) = A$$
$$53.7 = A$$

The sales tax is $53.70.

Problem 13

Strategy To determine how much she must deposit into the bank account:

▶ Find the amount of interest earned on the municipal bond by solving the equation $I = Prt$ for I using $P = 1000$, $r = 6.4\% = 0.064$, and $t = 1$.

▶ Solve $I = Prt$ for P using the amount of interest earned on the municipal bond for I, $r = 8\% = 0.08$, and $t = 1$.

Solution $I = Prt$
$$I = 1000(0.064)(1)$$
$$I = 64$$

The interest earned on the municipal bond is $64.

$$I = Prt$$
$$64 = P(0.08)(1)$$
$$64 = 0.08P$$

$$\frac{64}{0.08} = \frac{0.08P}{0.08}$$
$$800 = P$$

Clarissa must deposit $800 into the bank account.

Problem 14

Strategy To find the number of ounces of cereal in the bowl, solve the equation $Q = Ar$ for A using $Q = 2$ and $r = 25\% = 0.25$.

Solution
$$Q = Ar$$
$$2 = A(0.25)$$
$$\frac{2}{0.25} = \frac{A(0.25)}{0.25}$$
$$8 = A$$

The cereal bowl contains 8 oz of cereal.

SECTION 3.2

Problem 1

$$5x + 7 = 10$$
$$5x + 7 - 7 = 10 - 7$$
$$5x = 3$$
$$\frac{5x}{5} = \frac{3}{5}$$
$$x = \frac{3}{5}$$

The solution is $\frac{3}{5}$.

Problem 2

$$11 = 11 + 3x$$
$$11 - 11 = 11 - 11 + 3x$$
$$0 = 3x$$
$$\frac{0}{3} = \frac{3x}{3}$$
$$0 = x$$

The solution is 0.

Problem 3

$$\frac{5}{2} - \frac{2}{3}x = \frac{1}{2}$$
$$6\left(\frac{5}{2} - \frac{2}{3}x\right) = 6\left(\frac{1}{2}\right)$$
$$6\left(\frac{5}{2}\right) - 6\left(\frac{2}{3}x\right) = 3$$
$$15 - 4x = 3$$
$$15 - 15 - 4x = 3 - 15$$
$$-4x = -12$$
$$\frac{-4x}{-4} = \frac{-12}{-4}$$
$$x = 3$$

The solution is 3.

Problem 4

$$5x + 4 = 6 + 10x$$
$$5x - 10x + 4 = 6 + 10x - 10x$$
$$-5x + 4 = 6$$
$$-5x + 4 - 4 = 6 - 4$$
$$-5x = 2$$
$$\frac{-5x}{-5} = \frac{2}{-5}$$
$$x = -\frac{2}{5}$$

The solution is $-\frac{2}{5}$.

Problem 5

$$5x - 4(3 - 2x) = 2(3x - 2) + 6$$
$$5x - 12 + 8x = 6x - 4 + 6$$
$$13x - 12 = 6x + 2$$
$$13x - 6x - 12 = 6x - 6x + 2$$
$$7x - 12 = 2$$
$$7x - 12 + 12 = 2 + 12$$
$$7x = 14$$
$$\frac{7x}{7} = \frac{14}{7}$$
$$x = 2$$

The solution is 2.

Problem 6

$$-2[3x - 5(2x - 3)] = 3x - 8$$
$$-2[3x - 10x + 15] = 3x - 8$$
$$-2[-7x + 15] = 3x - 8$$
$$14x - 30 = 3x - 8$$
$$14x - 3x - 30 = 3x - 3x - 8$$
$$11x - 30 = -8$$
$$11x - 30 + 30 = -8 + 30$$
$$11x = 22$$
$$\frac{11x}{11} = \frac{22}{11}$$
$$x = 2$$

The solution is 2.

Problem 7

Strategy To find the number of years, replace V with 10,200 in the given equation and solve for t.

Solution
$$V = 450t + 7500$$
$$10,200 = 450t + 7500$$
$$10,200 - 7500 = 450t + 7500 - 7500$$
$$2700 = 450t$$
$$\frac{2700}{450} = \frac{450t}{450}$$
$$6 = t$$

The value of the investment will be $10,200 in 6 years.

Problem 8

Strategy The lever is 14 ft long, so $d = 14$. One force is 6 ft from the fulcrum, so $x = 6$. The one force is 40 lb, so $F_1 = 40$. To find the other force when the system balances, replace the variables F_1, x, and d in the lever system equation with the given values, and solve for F_2.

Solution
$$F_1 x = F_2(d - x)$$
$$40(6) = F_2(14 - 6)$$
$$240 = F_2(8)$$
$$240 = 8F_2$$
$$\frac{240}{8} = \frac{8F_2}{8}$$
$$30 = F_2$$

A 30-pound force must be applied to the other end.

SECTION 3.3

Problem 1

The solution set is the numbers greater than -2.

Problem 2

$$x + 2 < -2$$
$$x + 2 - 2 < -2 - 2$$
$$x < -4$$

Problem 3

$$5x + 3 > 4x + 5$$
$$5x - 4x + 3 > 4x - 4x + 5$$
$$x + 3 > 5$$
$$x + 3 - 3 > 5 - 3$$
$$x > 2$$

Problem 4

$$3x < 9$$
$$\frac{3x}{3} < \frac{9}{3}$$
$$x < 3$$

Problem 5

$$-\frac{3}{4}x \geq 18$$
$$-\frac{4}{3}\left(-\frac{3}{4}x\right) \leq -\frac{4}{3}(18)$$
$$x \leq -24$$

Problem 6

$$5 - 4x > 9 - 8x$$
$$5 - 4x + 8x > 9 - 8x + 8x$$
$$5 + 4x > 9$$
$$5 - 5 + 4x > 9 - 5$$
$$4x > 4$$
$$\frac{4x}{4} > \frac{4}{4}$$
$$x > 1$$

Problem 7

$$8 - 4(3x + 5) \le 6(x - 8)$$
$$8 - 12x - 20 \le 6x - 48$$
$$-12 - 12x \le 6x - 48$$
$$-12 - 12x - 6x \le 6x - 6x - 48$$
$$-12 - 18x \le -48$$
$$-12 + 12 - 18x \le -48 + 12$$
$$-18x \le -36$$
$$\frac{-18x}{-18} \ge \frac{-36}{-18}$$
$$x \ge 2$$

Solutions to Chapter 4 Problems

SECTION 4.1

Problem 1

the unknown number: n

nine less than twice a number	is	five times the sum of the number and twelve

$$2n - 9 = 5(n + 12)$$
$$2n - 9 = 5n + 60$$
$$2n - 5n - 9 = 5n - 5n + 60$$
$$-3n - 9 = 60$$
$$-3n - 9 + 9 = 60 + 9$$
$$-3n = 69$$
$$\frac{-3n}{-3} = \frac{69}{-3}$$
$$n = -23$$

The number is -23.

Problem 2

Strategy To find the number of carbon atoms, write and solve an equation using n to represent the number of carbon atoms.

Solution

eight	represents	twice the number of carbon atoms

$$8 = 2n$$
$$\frac{8}{2} = \frac{2n}{2}$$
$$4 = n$$

There are 4 carbon atoms in a butane gas molecule.

Problem 3

Strategy To find the number of 10-speed bicycles made each day, write and solve an equation using n to represent the number of 10-speed bicycles and $160 - n$ to represent the number of 3-speed bicycles.

Solution

four times the number of 3-speed bicycles made	equals	30 less than the number of 10-speed bicycles made

$$4(160 - n) = n - 30$$
$$640 - 4n = n - 30$$
$$640 - 4n - n = n - n - 30$$
$$640 - 5n = -30$$
$$640 - 640 - 5n = -30 - 640$$
$$-5n = -670$$
$$\frac{-5n}{-5} = \frac{-670}{-5}$$
$$n = 134$$

There are 134 10-speed bicycles made each day.

SECTION 4.2

Problem 1

Strategy ▶ First consecutive integer: n
Second consecutive integer: $n + 1$
Third consecutive integer: $n + 2$

▶ The sum of the three integers is -12.

Solution $n + (n + 1) + (n + 2) = -12$
$$3n + 3 = -12$$
$$3n = -15$$
$$n = -5$$

$$n + 1 = -5 + 1 = -4$$
$$n + 2 = -5 + 2 = -3$$

The three consecutive integers are -5, -4, and -3.

Problem 2

Strategy ▶ Number of dimes: x
Number of nickels: $5x$
Number of quarters: $x + 6$

Coin	Number	Value	Total value
Dime	x	10	$10x$
Nickel	$5x$	5	$5(5x)$
Quarter	$x + 6$	25	$25(x + 6)$

▶ The sum of the total values of the individual denominations of coins equals the total value of all the coins (630 cents).

Solution $10x + 5(5x) + 25(x + 6) = 630$
$$10x + 25x + 25x + 150 = 630$$
$$60x + 150 = 630$$
$$60x = 480$$
$$x = 8$$

$5x = 5(8) = 40$
$x + 6 = 8 + 6 = 14$

The bank contains 8 dimes, 40 nickels, and 14 quarters.

SECTION 4.3

Problem 1

Strategy ▶ Each equal side: s

▶ Use the equation for the perimeter of a square.

Solution $P = 4s$
$$52 = 4s$$
$$13 = s$$

The length of each side is 13 ft.

Problem 2

Strategy To find the supplement, let x represent the supplement of a 107° angle. Use the fact that supplementary angles are two angles whose sum is 180° to write an equation. Solve for x.

Solution $107° + x = 180°$
$$x = 73°$$

The supplement of a 107° angle is a 73° angle.

Problem 3

Strategy The angles labeled are adjacent angles of intersecting lines and are therefore supplementary angles. To find x, write an equation and solve for x.

Solution $x + (3x + 20°) = 180°$
$$4x + 20° = 180°$$
$$4x = 160°$$
$$x = 40°$$

Problem 4

Strategy $2x = y$ because alternate exterior angles have the same measure.

$y + (x + 15°) = 180°$ because adjacent angles of intersecting lines are supplementary angles. Substitute $2x$ for y and solve for x.

Solution $y + (x + 15°) = 180°$
$$2x + (x + 15°) = 180°$$
$$3x + 15° = 180°$$
$$3x = 165°$$
$$x = 55°$$

Problem 5

Strategy ▶ To find the measure of $\angle a$, use the fact that $\angle a$ and $\angle y$ are vertical angles.

▶ To find the measure of $\angle b$, use the fact that the sum of the interior angles of a triangle is 180°.

▶ To find the measure of $\angle d$, use the fact that $\angle b$ and $\angle d$ are supplementary angles.

Solution $\angle a = \angle y = 55°$

$\angle a + \angle b + 90° = 180°$
$$55° + \angle b + 90° = 180°$$
$$145° + \angle b = 180°$$
$$\angle b = 35°$$

$\angle b + \angle d = 180°$
$$35° + \angle d = 180°$$
$$\angle d = 145°$$

Problem 6

Strategy To find the measure of the third angle, use the fact that the sum of the measures of the interior angles of a triangle is 180°. Write an equation using x to represent the measure of the third angle. Solve the equation for x.

Solution $x + 90° + 27° = 180°$
$$x + 117° = 180°$$
$$x = 63°$$

The measure of the third angle is 63°.

SECTION 4.4

Problem 1

Strategy Given: $C = \$120$
$\qquad\qquad S = \$180$
Unknown markup rate: r
Use the equation $S = C + rC$.

Solution $S = C + rC$
$$180 = 120 + 120r$$
$$60 = 120r$$
$$0.5 = r$$

The markup rate is 50%.

Problem 2

Strategy Given: $r = 40\% = 0.40$
$\qquad\qquad S = \$266$
Unknown cost: C
Use the equation $S = C + rC$.

Solution $S = C + rC$
$$266 = C + 0.4C$$
$$266 = 1.40C$$
$$190 = C$$

The cost is $190.

Problem 3

Strategy Given: $R = \$39.80$
$\qquad\qquad S = \$29.85$
Unknown discount rate: r
Use the equation $S = R - rR$.

Solution
$$S = R - rR$$
$$29.85 = 39.80 - 39.80r$$
$$-9.95 = -39.80r$$
$$0.25 = r$$

The discount rate is 25%.

Problem 4

Strategy Given: $S = \$43.50$
$r = 25\% = 0.25$
Unknown regular price: R
Use the equation $S = R - rR$.

Solution
$$S = R - rR$$
$$43.50 = R - 0.25R$$
$$43.50 = 0.75R$$
$$58 = R$$

The regular price is $58.

SECTION 4.5

Problem 1

Strategy ▶ Additional amount: x

	Principal	·	Rate	=	Interest
Amount at 7%	2500	·	0.07	=	0.07(2500)
Amount at 10%	x	·	0.10	=	0.10x
Amount at 9%	2500 + x	·	0.09	=	0.09(2500 + x)

▶ The sum of the interest earned by the two investments equals the interest earned on the total investment.

Solution
$$0.07(2500) + 0.10x = 0.09(2500 + x)$$
$$175 + 0.10x = 225 + 0.09x$$
$$175 + 0.01x = 225$$
$$0.01x = 50$$
$$x = 5000$$

$5000 more must be invested at 10%.

SECTION 4.6

Problem 1

Strategy ▶ Pounds of $.75 fertilizer: x

	Amount	Cost	Value
$.90 fertilizer	20	0.90	0.90(20)
$.75 fertilizer	x	0.75	0.75x
$.85 fertilizer	20 + x	0.85	0.85(20 + x)

▶ The sum of the values before mixing equals the value after mixing.

Solution
$$0.90(20) + 0.75x = 0.85(20 + x)$$
$$18 + 0.75x = 17 + 0.85x$$
$$18 - 0.10x = 17$$
$$-0.10x = -1$$
$$x = 10$$

10 lb of the $.75 fertilizer must be added.

Problem 2

Strategy ▶ Pure orange juice is 100% orange juice.
$100\% = 1.00$

Amount of pure orange juice: x

	Amount	Percent	Quantity
Pure orange juice	x	1.00	1.00x
Fruit drink	5	0.10	0.10(5)
Orange drink	$x + 5$	0.25	0.25($x + 5$)

▶ The sum of the quantities before mixing is equal to the quantity after mixing.

Solution
$$1.00x + 0.10(5) = 0.25(x + 5)$$
$$1.00x + 0.5 = 0.25x + 1.25$$
$$0.75x + 0.5 = 1.25$$
$$0.75x = 0.75$$
$$x = 1$$

To make the orange drink, 1 qt of pure orange juice is added to the fruit drink.

SECTION 4.7

Problem 1

Strategy ▶ Rate of the first train: r
Rate of the second train: $2r$

	Rate	Time	Distance
First train	r	3	$3r$
Second train	$2r$	3	$3(2r)$

▶ The sum of the distances traveled by each train equals 306 mi.

Solution
$$3r + 3(2r) = 306$$
$$3r + 6r = 306$$
$$9r = 306$$
$$r = 34$$

$$2r = 2(34) = 68$$

The first train is traveling at 34 mph. The second train is traveling at 68 mph.

Problem 2

Strategy ▶ Time spent flying out: t
Time spent flying back: $7 - t$

	Rate	Time	Distance
Out	120	t	$120t$
Back	90	$7 - t$	$90(7 - t)$

▶ The distance out equals the distance back.

Solution
$$120t = 90(7 - t)$$
$$120t = 630 - 90t$$
$$210t = 630$$
$$t = 3 \quad \text{(The time out was 3 h.)}$$

$\text{Distance} = 120t = 120(3) = 360$ mi

The parcel of land was 360 mi away.

SECTION 4.8

Problem 1

Strategy To find the minimum selling price, write and solve an inequality using S to represent the selling price.

Solution
$$340 < 0.70S$$
$$\frac{340}{0.70} < \frac{0.70S}{0.70}$$
$$485.71429 < S$$

The minimum selling price is $485.72.

Problem 2

Strategy To find the maximum number of miles:

▶ Write an expression for the cost of each car, using x to represent the number of miles driven during the week.

▶ Write and solve an inequality.

Solution

cost of a Company A car	is less than	cost of a Company B car

$$9(7) + 0.10x < 12(7) + 0.08x$$
$$63 + 0.10x < 84 + 0.08x$$
$$63 + 0.10x - 0.08x < 84 + 0.08x - 0.08x$$
$$63 + 0.02x < 84$$
$$63 - 63 + 0.02x < 84 - 63$$
$$0.02x < 21$$
$$\frac{0.02x}{0.02} < \frac{21}{0.02}$$
$$x < 1050$$

The maximum number of miles is 1049.

Solutions to Chapter 5 Problems

SECTION 5.1

Problem 1

Problem 2

$A(4, 2)$, $B(-3, 4)$, $C(-3, 0)$, $D(0, 0)$

Problem 3

Problem 4

In 1900, the population was 76 million: (1900, 76)
In 2000, the population was 281 million: (2000, 281)

Average rate of change

$$= \frac{\text{change in } y}{\text{change in } x}$$

$$= \frac{\text{population in 2000} - \text{population in 1900}}{2000 - 1900}$$

$$= \frac{281 - 76}{2000 - 1900}$$

$$= \frac{205}{100} = 2.05$$

The average rate of change in the population was 2.05 million people per year.

Problem 5

28 weeks after conception, the weight is 3 lb: (28, 3)
38 weeks after conception, the weight is 7.5 lb: (38, 7.5)

Average rate of change

$$= \frac{\text{change in } y}{\text{change in } x}$$

$$= \frac{\text{weight after 38 weeks} - \text{weight after 28 weeks}}{38 - 28}$$

$$= \frac{7.5 - 3}{38 - 28}$$

$$= \frac{4.5}{10} = 0.45$$

The average rate of change in weight is 0.45 lb per week.

SECTION 5.2

Problem 1

$$y = -\frac{1}{2}x - 3$$

$$
\begin{array}{c|c}
-4 & -\frac{1}{2}(2) - 3 \\
& -1 - 3 \\
& -4
\end{array}
$$

$$-4 = -4$$

Yes, $(2, -4)$ is a solution of $y = -\frac{1}{2}x - 3$.

Problem 2

$$y = -\frac{1}{4}x + 1$$

$$= -\frac{1}{4}(4) + 1$$

$$= -1 + 1$$

$$= 0$$

The ordered-pair solution is $(4, 0)$.

Problem 3

Problem 4

Problem 5

$$5x - 2y = 10$$

$$5x - 5x - 2y = -5x + 10$$

$$-2y = -5x + 10$$

$$\frac{-2y}{-2} = \frac{-5x + 10}{-2}$$

$$y = \frac{-5x}{-2} + \frac{10}{-2}$$

$$y = \frac{5}{2}x - 5$$

Problem 6

A. $5x - 2y = 10$

$$-2y = -5x + 10$$

$$y = \frac{5}{2}x - 5$$

B. $x - 3y = 9$

$$-3y = -x + 9$$

$$y = \frac{1}{3}x - 3$$

Problem 7

x-intercept: $4x - y = 4$

$$4x - 0 = 4$$

$$4x = 4$$

$$x = 1$$

The x-intercept is $(1, 0)$.

y-intercept: $4x - y = 4$

$$4(0) - y = 4$$

$$-y = 4$$

$$y = -4$$

The y-intercept is $(0, -4)$.

Problem 8

A.

B.

SECTION 5.3

Problem 1

A. $m = \dfrac{y_2 - y_1}{x_2 - x_1} = \dfrac{3 - 2}{1 - (-1)} = \dfrac{1}{2}$

The slope is $\dfrac{1}{2}$.

B. $m = \dfrac{y_2 - y_1}{x_2 - x_1} = \dfrac{-5 - 2}{4 - 1} = \dfrac{-7}{3}$

The slope is $-\dfrac{7}{3}$.

C. $m = \dfrac{y_2 - y_1}{x_2 - x_1} = \dfrac{7 - 3}{2 - 2} = \dfrac{4}{0}$

The slope is undefined.

D. $m = \dfrac{y_2 - y_1}{x_2 - x_1} = \dfrac{-3 - (-3)}{-5 - 1} = \dfrac{0}{-6} = 0$

The slope is 0.

Problem 2

Find the slope of the line through $(-2, -3)$ and $(7, 1)$.

$$m = \frac{y_2 - y_1}{x_2 - x_1} = \frac{1 - (-3)}{7 - (-2)} = \frac{4}{9}$$

Find the slope of the line through $(1, 4)$ and $(-5, 6)$.

$$m = \frac{y_2 - y_1}{x_2 - x_1} = \frac{6 - 4}{-5 - 1} = \frac{2}{-6} = -\frac{1}{3}$$

$$\frac{4}{9} \neq -\frac{1}{3}$$

The slopes are not equal.
The lines are not parallel.

Problem 3

$$m = \frac{8650 - 6100}{1 - 4} = \frac{2550}{-3} = -850$$

A slope of -850 means that the value of the car is decreasing at a rate of $850 per year.

Problem 4

y-intercept $= (0, b) = (0, -1)$

$$m = -\frac{1}{4}$$

Problem 5

Solve the equation for y.

$$x - 2y = 4$$
$$-2y = -x + 4$$
$$y = \frac{1}{2}x - 2$$

y-intercept $= (0, b) = (0, -2)$

$$m = \frac{1}{2}$$

SECTION 5.4

Problem 1

$$y = \frac{3}{2}x + b$$

$$-2 = \frac{3}{2}(4) + b$$

$$-2 = 6 + b$$
$$-8 = b$$

$$y = \frac{3}{2}x - 8$$

Problem 2

$$m = \frac{2}{5} \quad (x_1, y_1) = (5, 4)$$

$$y - y_1 = m(x - x_1)$$

$$y - 4 = \frac{2}{5}(x - 5)$$

$$y - 4 = \frac{2}{5}x - 2$$

$$y = \frac{2}{5}x + 2$$

Problem 3

Let $(x_1, y_1) = (-3, -9)$ and $(x_2, y_2) = (1, -1)$.

$$m = \frac{y_2 - y_1}{x_2 - x_1} = \frac{-1 - (-9)}{1 - (-3)} = \frac{8}{4} = 2$$

$$y - y_1 = m(x - x_1)$$
$$y - (-9) = 2(x - (-3)) \quad \bullet \; m = 2; (x_1, y_1) = (-3, -9)$$
$$y + 9 = 2(x + 3)$$
$$y + 9 = 2x + 6$$
$$y = 2x - 3$$

The equation of the line is $y = 2x - 3$.

SECTION 5.5

Problem 1

The domain is $\{1\}$.
The range is $\{0, 1, 2, 3, 4\}$.
There are ordered pairs with the same first coordinate and different second coordinates. The relation is not a function.

Problem 2

$$f(x) = -5x + 1$$
$$f(2) = -5(2) + 1$$
$$f(2) = -10 + 1$$
$$f(2) = -9$$

The ordered pair $(2, -9)$ is an element of the function.

Problem 3

$$f(x) = 4x - 3$$
$$f(-5) = 4(-5) - 3 = -20 - 3 = -23$$
$$f(-3) = 4(-3) - 3 = -12 - 3 = -15$$
$$f(-1) = 4(-1) - 3 = -4 - 3 = -7$$
$$f(1) = 4(1) - 3 = 4 - 3 = 1$$

The range is $\{-23, -15, -7, 1\}$.
The ordered pairs $(-5, -23)$, $(-3, -15)$, $(-1, -7)$, and $(1, 1)$ belong to the function.

Problem 4

$$f(x) = -\frac{1}{2}x - 3$$

$$y = -\frac{1}{2}x - 3$$

Problem 5

A. $d = 40t$ **B.**
$f(t) = 40t$

C. The ordered pair (3, 120) means that in 3 h, the car travels a distance of 120 mi.

SECTION 5.6

Problem 1

$$x - 3y < 2$$
$$x - x - 3y < -x + 2$$
$$-3y < -x + 2$$
$$\frac{-3y}{-3} > \frac{-x + 2}{-3}$$
$$y > \frac{1}{3}x - \frac{2}{3}$$

Problem 2

$$x < 3$$

Solutions to Chapter 6 Problems

SECTION 6.1

Problem 1

$2x - 5y = 8$		$-x + 3y = -5$	
$2(-1) - 5(-2)$	8	$-(-1) + 3(-2)$	-5
$-2 + 10$	8	$1 + (-6)$	-5
$8 = 8$		$-5 = -5$	

Yes, $(-1, -2)$ is a solution of the system of equations.

Problem 2

A.

The solution is $(-3, 2)$.

B.

No solution

The lines are parallel and therefore do not intersect. The system of equations is inconsistent and has no solution.

SECTION 6.2

Problem 1

(1) $7x - y = 4$
(2) $3x + 2y = 9$

$$7x - y = 4$$
$$-y = -7x + 4$$
$$y = 7x - 4$$

• Solve equation (1) for **y.**

$$3x + 2y = 9$$
$$3x + 2(7x - 4) = 9$$
$$3x + 14x - 8 = 9$$
$$17x - 8 = 9$$
$$17x = 17$$
$$x = 1$$

• Substitute $7x - 4$ for **y** in equation (2).

$$7x - y = 4$$
$$7(1) - y = 4$$
$$7 - y = 4$$
$$-y = -3$$
$$y = 3$$

• Substitute the value of **x** in equation (1).

The solution is $(1, 3)$.

Problem 2

$$3x - y = 4$$
$$y = 3x + 2$$

$$3x - y = 4$$
$$3x - (3x + 2) = 4$$
$$3x - 3x - 2 = 4$$
$$-2 = 4$$

The system of equations is inconsistent and has no solution.

Problem 3

$$y = -2x + 1$$
$$6x + 3y = 3$$

$$6x + 3y = 3$$
$$6x + 3(-2x + 1) = 3$$
$$6x - 6x + 3 = 3$$
$$3 = 3$$

The system of equations is dependent. The solutions are the ordered pairs that satisfy the equation $y = -2x + 1$.

SECTION 6.3

Problem 1

(1) $x - 2y = 1$
(2) $2x + 4y = 0$

$2(x - 2y) = 2 \cdot 1$ • **Eliminate y.**
$2x + 4y = 0$

$2x - 4y = 2$
$2x + 4y = 0$
$\underline{\qquad\qquad}$
$4x \quad = 2$ • **Add the equations.**

$x = \dfrac{2}{4} = \dfrac{1}{2}$

$2x + 4y = 0$ • **Replace x in equation (2).**

$2\left(\dfrac{1}{2}\right) + 4y = 0$

$1 + 4y = 0$
$4y = -1$
$y = -\dfrac{1}{4}$

The solution is $\left(\dfrac{1}{2}, -\dfrac{1}{4}\right)$.

Problem 2

(1) $2x - 3y = 4$
(2) $-4x + 6y = -8$

$2(2x - 3y) = 2 \cdot 4$ • **Eliminate y.**
$-4x + 6y = -8$

$4x - 6y = 8$
$-4x + 6y = -8$
$\underline{\qquad\qquad}$
$0 + 0 = 0$ • **Add the equations.**
$0 = 0$

The system of equations is dependent. The solutions are the ordered pairs that satisfy the equation $2x - 3y = 4$.

SECTION 6.4

Problem 1

Strategy ▶ Rate of the current: c
Rate of the canoeist in calm water: r

	Rate	Time	Distance
With current	$r + c$	3	$3(r + c)$
Against current	$r - c$	4	$4(r - c)$

▶ The distance traveled with the current is 24 mi.
The distance traveled against the current is 24 mi.

Solution

$3(r + c) = 24$ ➡ $\dfrac{3(r + c)}{3} = \dfrac{24}{3}$ ➡ $r + c = 8$

$4(r - c) = 24$ ➡ $\dfrac{4(r - c)}{4} = \dfrac{24}{4}$ ➡ $r - c = 6$

$\underline{\qquad\qquad}$
$2r = 14$
$r = 7$

$r + c = 8$
$7 + c = 8$
$c = 1$

The rate of the current is 1 mph.
The rate of the canoeist in calm water is 7 mph.

Problem 2

Strategy ▶ The number of dimes in the first bank: d
The number of quarters in the first bank: q

First bank

	Number	Value	Total value
Dimes	d	10	$10d$
Quarters	q	25	$25q$

Second bank

	Number	Value	Total value
Dimes	$2d$	10	$20d$
Quarters	$\frac{1}{2}q$	25	$\frac{25}{2}q$

▶ The total value of the coins in the first bank is \$3.90.
The total value of the coins in the second bank is \$3.30.

Solution

$10d + 25q = 390 \qquad\qquad 10d + 25q = 390$

$20d + \dfrac{25}{2}q = 330 \qquad -2\left(20d + \dfrac{25}{2}q\right) = -2(330)$

$10d + 25q = 390$

$-40d - 25q = -660$
$\underline{\qquad\qquad}$
$-30d = -270$
$d = 9$

$10d + 25q = 390$
$10(9) + 25q = 390$
$90 + 25q = 390$
$25q = 300$
$q = 12$

There are 9 dimes and 12 quarters in the first bank.

Solutions to Chapter 7 Problems

SECTION 7.1

Problem 1

$$2x^2 + 4x - 3$$
$$\underline{5x^2 - 6x}$$
$$7x^2 - 2x - 3$$

Problem 2

$$(-4x^2 - 3xy + 2y^2) + (3x^2 - 4y^2)$$
$$= (-4x^2 + 3x^2) - 3xy + (2y^2 - 4y^2)$$
$$= -x^2 - 3xy - 2y^2$$

Problem 3

The opposite of $2y^2 - xy + 5x^2$ is $-2y^2 + xy - 5x^2$.

$$8y^2 - 4xy + x^2$$
$$\underline{-2y^2 + xy - 5x^2}$$
$$6y^2 - 3xy - 4x^2$$

Problem 4

$$(-3a^2 - 4a + 2) - (5a^3 + 2a - 6)$$
$$= (-3a^2 - 4a + 2) + (-5a^3 - 2a + 6)$$
$$= -5a^3 - 3a^2 + (-4a - 2a) + (2 + 6)$$
$$= -5a^3 - 3a^2 - 6a + 8$$

SECTION 7.2

Problem 1

$$(3x^2)(6x^3) = (3 \cdot 6)(x^2 \cdot x^3) = 18x^5$$

Problem 2

$$(-3xy^2)(-4x^2y^3)$$
$$= [(-3)(-4)](x \cdot x^2)(y^2 \cdot y^3)$$
$$= 12x^3y^5$$

Problem 3

$$(3x)(2x^2y)^3 = (3x)(2^3x^6y^3) = (3x)(8x^6y^3)$$
$$= (3 \cdot 8)(x \cdot x^6)y^3 = 24x^7y^3$$

SECTION 7.3

Problem 1

A. $(-2y + 3)(-4y) = 8y^2 - 12y$

B. $-a^2(3a^2 + 2a - 7) = -3a^4 - 2a^3 + 7a^2$

Problem 2

$$2y^3 + 2y^2 - 3$$
$$\underline{ 3y - 1}$$
$$-2y^3 - 2y^2 + 3$$
$$\underline{6y^4 + 6y^3 - 9y}$$
$$6y^4 + 4y^3 - 2y^2 - 9y + 3$$

Problem 3

$$3x^3 - 2x^2 + x - 3$$
$$\underline{ 2x + 5}$$
$$15x^3 - 10x^2 + 5x - 15$$
$$\underline{6x^4 - 4x^3 + 2x^2 - 6x}$$
$$6x^4 + 11x^3 - 8x^2 - x - 15$$

Problem 4

$$(4y - 5)(3y - 3)$$
$$= 12y^2 - 12y - 15y + 15$$
$$= 12y^2 - 27y + 15$$

Problem 5

$$(3a + 2b)(3a - 5b)$$
$$= 9a^2 - 15ab + 6ab - 10b^2$$
$$= 9a^2 - 9ab - 10b^2$$

Problem 6

$$(2a + 5c)(2a - 5c) = (2a)^2 - (5c)^2$$
$$= 4a^2 - 25c^2$$

Problem 7

$$(3x + 2y)^2 = (3x)^2 + 2(3x)(2y) + (2y)^2$$
$$= 9x^2 + 12xy + 4y^2$$

Problem 8

$$(6x - y)^2 = (6x)^2 + 2(6x)(-y) + (-y)^2$$
$$= 36x^2 - 12xy + y^2$$

Problem 9

Strategy To find the area in terms of x, replace the variables L and W in the equation $A = LW$ with the given values, and solve for A.

Solution $A = LW$
$A = (x + 7)(x - 4)$
$A = x^2 - 4x + 7x - 28$
$A = x^2 + 3x - 28$

The area is $(x^2 + 3x - 28)$ m².

Problem 10

Strategy To find the area of the triangle in terms of x, replace the variables b and h in the equation $A = \frac{1}{2}bh$ with the given values, and solve for A.

Solution $A = \frac{1}{2}bh$

$A = \frac{1}{2}(x + 3)(4x - 6)$

$A = \frac{1}{2}(4x^2 + 6x - 18)$

$A = 2x^2 + 3x - 9$

The area is $(2x^2 + 3x - 9)$ cm².

SECTION 7.4

Problem 1

$$\frac{2^{-2}}{2^3} = 2^{-2-3} = 2^{-5} = \frac{1}{2^5} = \frac{1}{32}$$

Problem 2

$$\frac{b^8}{a^{-5}b^6} = a^5b^{8-6} = a^5b^2$$

Problem 3

A. $\dfrac{12x^{-8}y^4}{-16xy^{-3}} = -\dfrac{3x^{-9}y^7}{4} = -\dfrac{3y^7}{4x^9}$

B. $(-3ab)(2a^3b^{-2})^{-3} = (-3ab)(2^{-3}a^{-9}b^6)$

$= -\dfrac{3a^{-8}b^7}{2^3} = -\dfrac{3b^7}{8a^8}$

Problem 4

A. $57{,}000{,}000{,}000 = 5.7 \times 10^{10}$

B. $0.000000017 = 1.7 \times 10^{-8}$

Problem 5

A. $5 \times 10^{12} = 5{,}000{,}000{,}000{,}000$

B. $4.0162 \times 10^{-9} = 0.0000000040162$

Problem 6

A. $(2.4 \times 10^{-9})(1.6 \times 10^3) = 3.84 \times 10^{-6}$

B. $\dfrac{5.4 \times 10^{-2}}{1.8 \times 10^{-4}} = 3 \times 10^2$

SECTION 7.5

Problem 1

$\dfrac{4x^3y + 8x^2y^2 - 4xy^3}{2xy} = \dfrac{4x^3y}{2xy} + \dfrac{8x^2y^2}{2xy} - \dfrac{4xy^3}{2xy}$

$= 2x^2 + 4xy - 2y^2$

Problem 2

$\dfrac{24x^2y^2 - 18xy + 6y}{6xy} = \dfrac{24x^2y^2}{6xy} - \dfrac{18xy}{6xy} + \dfrac{6y}{6xy}$

$= 4xy - 3 + \dfrac{1}{x}$

Problem 3

$$
\begin{array}{r}
x^2 + 2x + 2 \\
x - 2\overline{)x^3 + 0x^2 - 2x - 4} \\
\underline{x^3 - 2x^2} \\
2x^2 - 2x \\
\underline{2x^2 - 4x} \\
2x - 4 \\
\underline{2x - 4} \\
0
\end{array}
$$

$(x^3 - 2x - 4) \div (x - 2) = x^2 + 2x + 2$

Solutions to Chapter 8 Problems

SECTION 8.1

Problem 1

$4x^6y = 2 \cdot 2 \cdot x^6 \cdot y$
$18x^2y^6 = 2 \cdot 3 \cdot 3 \cdot x^2 \cdot y^6$
$\text{GCF} = 2 \cdot x^2 \cdot y = 2x^2y$

Problem 2

A. $14a^2 = 2 \cdot 7 \cdot a^2$
$21a^4b = 3 \cdot 7 \cdot a^4 \cdot b$
The GCF is $7a^2$.

$14a^2 - 21a^4b = 7a^2(2) + 7a^2(-3a^2b)$
$= 7a^2(2 - 3a^2b)$

B. $6x^4y^2 = 2 \cdot 3 \cdot x^4 \cdot y^2$
$9x^3y^2 = 3 \cdot 3 \cdot x^3 \cdot y^2$
$12x^2y^4 = 2 \cdot 2 \cdot 3 \cdot x^2 \cdot y^4$
The GCF is $3x^2y^2$.

$6x^4y^2 - 9x^3y^2 + 12x^2y^4$
$= 3x^2y^2(2x^2) + 3x^2y^2(-3x) + 3x^2y^2(4y^2)$
$= 3x^2y^2(2x^2 - 3x + 4y^2)$

Problem 3

$a(b - 7) + b(b - 7) = (b - 7)(a + b)$

Problem 4

$3y(5x - 2) - 4(2 - 5x)$
$= 3y(5x - 2) + 4(5x - 2)$
$= (5x - 2)(3y + 4)$

Problem 5

$y^5 - 5y^3 + 4y^2 - 20$
$= (y^5 - 5y^3) + (4y^2 - 20)$
$= y^3(y^2 - 5) + 4(y^2 - 5)$
$= (y^2 - 5)(y^3 + 4)$

SECTION 8.2

Problem 1

Factors of 15	Sum
$-1, -15$	-16
$-3, -5$	-8

$x^2 - 8x + 15 = (x - 3)(x - 5)$

Problem 2

Factors of -18	Sum
$1, -18$	-17
$-1, \ 18$	17
$2, -9$	-7
$-2, \ 9$	7
$3, -6$	-3
$-3, \ 6$	3

$x^2 + 3x - 18 = (x + 6)(x - 3)$

Problem 3

The GCF is $3b$.

$3a^2b - 18ab - 81b = 3b(a^2 - 6a - 27)$

Factors of -27	Sum
$1, -27$	-26
$-1, \ 27$	26
$3, -9$	-6
$-3, \ 9$	6

$3a^2b - 18ab - 81b = 3b(a + 3)(a - 9)$

Problem 4

The GCF is 4.

$4x^2 - 40xy + 84y^2$
$\quad = 4(x^2 - 10xy + 21y^2)$

Factors of 21	Sum
$-1, -21$	-22
$-3, -7$	-10

$4x^2 - 40xy + 84y^2 = 4(x - 3y)(x - 7y)$

SECTION 8.3

Problem 1

Factors of 6	Factors of 5
$1, 6$	$-1, -5$
$2, 3$	

Trial Factors	Middle Term
$(x - 1)(6x - 5)$	$-5x - 6x = -11x$

$6x^2 - 11x + 5 = (x - 1)(6x - 5)$

Problem 2

Factors of 8	Factors of -15
$1, 8$	$1, -15$
$2, 4$	$-1, \ 15$
	$3, -5$
	$-3, \ 5$

Trial Factors	Middle Term
$(x + 1)(8x - 15)$	$-15x + 8x = -7x$
$(x - 1)(8x + 15)$	$15x - 8x = 7x$
$(x + 3)(8x - 5)$	$-5x + 24x = 19x$
$(x - 3)(8x + 5)$	$5x - 24x = -19x$
$(2x + 1)(4x - 15)$	$-30x + 4x = -26x$
$(2x - 1)(4x + 15)$	$30x - 4x = 26x$
$(2x + 3)(4x - 5)$	$-10x + 12x = 2x$
$(2x - 3)(4x + 5)$	$10x - 12x = -2x$
$(8x + 1)(x - 15)$	$-120x + x = -119x$
$(8x - 1)(x + 15)$	$120x - x = 119x$
$(8x + 3)(x - 5)$	$-40x + 3x = -37x$
$(8x - 3)(x + 5)$	$40x - 3x = 37x$

$(4x + 1)(2x - 15)$	$-60x + 2x = -58x$
$(4x - 1)(2x + 15)$	$60x - 2x = 58x$
$(4x + 3)(2x - 5)$	$-20x + 6x = -14x$
$(4x - 3)(2x + 5)$	$20x - 6x = 14x$

$8x^2 + 14x - 15 = (4x - 3)(2x + 5)$

Problem 3

Factors of 24	Factors of -1
$1, 24$	$1, -1$
$2, 12$	
$3, 8$	
$4, 6$	

Trial Factors	Middle Term
$(1 - y)(24 + y)$	$y - 24y = -23y$
$(2 - y)(12 + y)$	$2y - 12y = -10y$
$(3 - y)(8 + y)$	$3y - 8y = -5y$
$(4 - y)(6 + y)$	$4y - 6y = -2y$

$24 - 2y - y^2 = (4 - y)(6 + y)$

Problem 4

The GCF is $2a^2$.

$4a^2b^2 - 30a^2b + 14a^2$
$\quad = 2a^2(2b^2 - 15b + 7)$

Factors of 2	Factors of 7
$1, 2$	$-1, -7$

Trial Factors	Middle Term
$(b - 1)(2b - 7)$	$-7b - 2b = -9b$
$(b - 7)(2b - 1)$	$-b - 14b = -15b$

$4a^2b^2 - 30a^2b + 14a^2$
$\quad = 2a^2(b - 7)(2b - 1)$

Problem 5

$a \cdot c = -14$
$-1(14) = -14, \ -1 + 14 = 13$

$2a^2 + 13a - 7$
$\quad = 2a^2 - a + 14a - 7$
$\quad = (2a^2 - a) + (14a - 7)$
$\quad = a(2a - 1) + 7(2a - 1)$
$\quad = (2a - 1)(a + 7)$

Problem 6

$a \cdot c = -12$
$1(-12) = -12, \ 1 - 12 = -11$

$4a^2 - 11a - 3$
$\quad = 4a^2 + a - 12a - 3$
$\quad = (4a^2 + a) - (12a + 3)$
$\quad = a(4a + 1) - 3(4a + 1)$
$\quad = (4a + 1)(a - 3)$

Problem 7

The GCF is $5x$.

$15x^3 + 40x^2 - 80x = 5x(3x^2 + 8x - 16)$
$3(-16) = -48$
$-4(12) = -48, -4 + 12 = 8$

$3x^2 + 8x - 16$
$\quad = 3x^2 - 4x + 12x - 16$
$\quad = (3x^2 - 4x) + (12x - 16)$
$\quad = x(3x - 4) + 4(3x - 4)$
$\quad = (3x - 4)(x + 4)$

$15x^3 + 40x^2 - 80x = 5x(3x^2 + 8x - 16)$
$\qquad\qquad\qquad\quad = 5x(3x - 4)(x + 4)$

SECTION 8.4

Problem 1

A. $25a^2 - b^2 = (5a)^2 - b^2$
$\qquad\qquad = (5a + b)(5a - b)$

B. $6x^2 - 1$ is nonfactorable over the integers.

C. $n^8 - 36 = (n^4)^2 - 6^2$
$\qquad\quad = (n^4 + 6)(n^4 - 6)$

Problem 2

$n^4 - 81 = (n^2 + 9)(n^2 - 9)$
$\qquad\quad = (n^2 + 9)(n + 3)(n - 3)$

Problem 3

A. $16y^2 = (4y)^2, 1 = 1^2$

$(4y + 1)^2 = (4y)^2 + 2(4y)(1) + (1)^2$
$\qquad\qquad = 16y^2 + 8y + 1$

$16y^2 + 8y + 1 = (4y + 1)^2$

B. $x^2 = (x)^2, 36 = 6^2$

$(x + 6)^2 = x^2 + 2(x)(6) + 6^2$
$\qquad\qquad = x^2 + 12x + 36$

The polynomial is not a perfect square.

$x^2 + 14x + 36$ is nonfactorable over the integers.

Problem 4

A. $12x^3 - 75x = 3x(4x^2 - 25)$
$\qquad\qquad\quad = 3x(2x + 5)(2x - 5)$

B. $a^2b - 7a^2 - b + 7$
$\quad = (a^2b - 7a^2) - (b - 7)$
$\quad = a^2(b - 7) - (b - 7)$
$\quad = (b - 7)(a^2 - 1)$
$\quad = (b - 7)(a + 1)(a - 1)$

C. $4x^3 + 28x^2 - 120x = 4x(x^2 + 7x - 30)$
$\qquad\qquad\qquad\qquad = 4x(x + 10)(x - 3)$

SECTION 8.5

Problem 1

$\qquad 2x^2 - 50 = 0$
$\qquad 2(x^2 - 25) = 0$
$\qquad\quad x^2 - 25 = 0 \qquad$ • **Divide each side by 2.**
$(x + 5)(x - 5) = 0$

$x + 5 = 0 \qquad x - 5 = 0$
$\quad x = -5 \qquad\quad x = 5$

The solutions are -5 and 5.

Problem 2

$(x + 2)(x - 7) = 52$
$\quad x^2 - 5x - 14 = 52$
$\quad x^2 - 5x - 66 = 0$
$(x - 11)(x + 6) = 0$

$x - 11 = 0 \qquad x + 6 = 0$
$\quad x = 11 \qquad\quad x = -6$

The solutions are -6 and 11.

Problem 3

Strategy First positive integer: n
Second positive integer: $n + 1$
Square of the first positive integer: n^2
Square of the second positive integer: $(n + 1)^2$

The sum of the squares of the two integers is 85.

Solution $\qquad n^2 + (n + 1)^2 = 85$
$\qquad n^2 + n^2 + 2n + 1 = 85$
$\qquad\quad 2n^2 + 2n - 84 = 0$
$\qquad\quad 2(n^2 + n - 42) = 0$
$\qquad\qquad n^2 + n - 42 = 0$
$\qquad\quad (n + 7)(n - 6) = 0$

$n + 7 = 0 \qquad n - 6 = 0$
$\quad n = -7 \qquad\quad n = 6$

-7 is not a positive integer.

$n + 1 = 6 + 1 = 7$

The two integers are 6 and 7.

Problem 4

Strategy Width $= W$
Length $= 2W + 3$

The area of the rectangle is 90 m^2.
Use the equation $A = LW$.

Solution $\quad A = LW$
$\quad 90 = (2W + 3)W$
$\quad 90 = 2W^2 + 3W$
$\quad\; 0 = 2W^2 + 3W - 90$
$\quad\; 0 = (2W + 15)(W - 6)$

$$2W + 15 = 0 \qquad W - 6 = 0$$
$$2W = -15 \qquad W = 6$$
$$W = -\frac{15}{2}$$

The width cannot be a negative number.

$$2W + 3 = 2(6) + 3 = 12 + 3 = 15$$

The width is 6 m. The length is 15 m.

Solutions to Chapter 9 Problems

SECTION 9.1

Problem 1

A. $\dfrac{6x^5y}{12x^2y^3} = \dfrac{\overset{1}{\cancel{2}} \cdot \overset{1}{\cancel{3}} \cdot x^5y}{\underset{1}{\cancel{2}} \cdot 2 \cdot \underset{1}{\cancel{3}} \cdot x^2y^3} = \dfrac{x^3}{2y^2}$

B. $\dfrac{x^2 + 2x - 24}{16 - x^2} = \dfrac{\overset{-1}{\cancel{(x - 4)}}(x + 6)}{\underset{1}{\cancel{(4 - x)}}(4 + x)} = -\dfrac{x + 6}{x + 4}$

Problem 2

A. $\dfrac{12x^2 + 3x}{10x - 15} \cdot \dfrac{8x - 12}{9x + 18}$

$= \dfrac{3x(4x + 1)}{5(2x - 3)} \cdot \dfrac{4(2x - 3)}{9(x + 2)}$

$= \dfrac{\overset{1}{\cancel{3}}x(4x + 1) \cdot 2 \cdot 2\overset{1}{\cancel{(2x - 3)}}}{5\underset{1}{\cancel{(2x - 3)}} \cdot \underset{1}{\cancel{3}} \cdot 3(x + 2)}$

$= \dfrac{4x(4x + 1)}{15(x + 2)}$

B. $\dfrac{x^2 + 2x - 15}{9 - x^2} \cdot \dfrac{x^2 - 3x - 18}{x^2 - 7x + 6}$

$= \dfrac{(x - 3)(x + 5)}{(3 - x)(3 + x)} \cdot \dfrac{(x + 3)(x - 6)}{(x - 1)(x - 6)}$

$= \dfrac{\overset{-1}{\cancel{(x - 3)}}(x + 5) \cdot \overset{1}{\cancel{(x + 3)}}\overset{1}{\cancel{(x - 6)}}}{\underset{1}{\cancel{(3 - x)}}\underset{1}{\cancel{(3 + x)}} \cdot (x - 1)\underset{1}{\cancel{(x - 6)}}}$

$= -\dfrac{x + 5}{x - 1}$

Problem 3

A. $\dfrac{a^2}{4bc^2 - 2b^2c} \div \dfrac{a}{6bc - 3b^2}$

$= \dfrac{a^2}{4bc^2 - 2b^2c} \cdot \dfrac{6bc - 3b^2}{a}$

$= \dfrac{a^2 \cdot 3b\overset{1}{\cancel{(2c - b)}}}{2bc\underset{1}{\cancel{(2c - b)}} \cdot a} = \dfrac{3a}{2c}$

B. $\dfrac{3x^2 + 26x + 16}{3x^2 - 7x - 6} \div \dfrac{2x^2 + 9x - 5}{x^2 + 2x - 15}$

$= \dfrac{3x^2 + 26x + 16}{3x^2 - 7x - 6} \cdot \dfrac{x^2 + 2x - 15}{2x^2 + 9x - 5}$

$= \dfrac{\overset{1}{\cancel{(3x + 2)}}(x + 8)}{\underset{1}{\cancel{(3x + 2)}}\underset{1}{\cancel{(x - 3)}}} \cdot \dfrac{\overset{1}{\cancel{(x + 5)}}\overset{1}{\cancel{(x - 3)}}}{(2x - 1)\underset{1}{\cancel{(x + 5)}}}$

$= \dfrac{x + 8}{2x - 1}$

SECTION 9.2

Problem 1

$8uv^2 = 2 \cdot 2 \cdot 2 \cdot u \cdot v \cdot v$
$12uw = 2 \cdot 2 \cdot 3 \cdot u \cdot w$

$\text{LCM} = 2 \cdot 2 \cdot 2 \cdot 3 \cdot u \cdot v \cdot v \cdot w$
$\qquad\ = 24uv^2w$

Problem 2

$m^2 - 6m + 9 = (m - 3)(m - 3)$
$m^2 - 2m - 3 = (m + 1)(m - 3)$

$\text{LCM} = (m - 3)(m - 3)(m + 1)$

Problem 3

The LCM is $36xy^2z$.

$\dfrac{x - 3}{4xy^2} = \dfrac{x - 3}{4xy^2} \cdot \dfrac{9z}{9z} = \dfrac{9xz - 27z}{36xy^2z}$

$\dfrac{2x + 1}{9y^2z} = \dfrac{2x + 1}{9y^2z} \cdot \dfrac{4x}{4x} = \dfrac{8x^2 + 4x}{36xy^2z}$

Problem 4

$\dfrac{2x}{25 - x^2} = \dfrac{2x}{-(x^2 - 25)} = -\dfrac{2x}{x^2 - 25}$

The LCM is $(x + 2)(x - 5)(x + 5)$.

$\dfrac{x + 4}{x^2 - 3x - 10} = \dfrac{x + 4}{(x + 2)(x - 5)} \cdot \dfrac{x + 5}{x + 5}$

$\qquad\qquad = \dfrac{x^2 + 9x + 20}{(x + 2)(x - 5)(x + 5)}$

$\dfrac{2x}{25 - x^2} = -\dfrac{2x}{(x - 5)(x + 5)} \cdot \dfrac{x + 2}{x + 2}$

$\qquad\ = -\dfrac{2x^2 + 4x}{(x + 2)(x - 5)(x + 5)}$

SECTION 9.3

Problem 1

A. $\dfrac{3}{xy} + \dfrac{12}{xy} = \dfrac{3 + 12}{xy} = \dfrac{15}{xy}$

B. $\dfrac{2x^2}{x^2 - x - 12} - \dfrac{7x + 4}{x^2 - x - 12} = \dfrac{2x^2 - (7x + 4)}{x^2 - x - 12}$

$= \dfrac{2x^2 - 7x - 4}{x^2 - x - 12} = \dfrac{(2x + 1)(x - 4)}{(x + 3)(x - 4)} = \dfrac{2x + 1}{x + 3}$

Problem 2

A. The LCM of the denominators is $24y$.

$\dfrac{z}{8y} - \dfrac{4z}{3y} + \dfrac{5z}{4y} = \dfrac{z}{8y} \cdot \dfrac{3}{3} - \dfrac{4z}{3y} \cdot \dfrac{8}{8} + \dfrac{5z}{4y} \cdot \dfrac{6}{6}$

$= \dfrac{3z}{24y} - \dfrac{32z}{24y} + \dfrac{30z}{24y} = \dfrac{3z - 32z + 30z}{24y} = \dfrac{z}{24y}$

B. The LCM is $x - 2$.

$\dfrac{5x}{x - 2} - \dfrac{3}{2 - x} = \dfrac{5x}{x - 2} - \dfrac{3}{-(x - 2)} \cdot \dfrac{-1}{-1}$

$= \dfrac{5x}{x - 2} - \dfrac{-3}{x - 2} = \dfrac{5x - (-3)}{x - 2} = \dfrac{5x + 3}{x - 2}$

C. The LCM is $y - 7$.

$y + \dfrac{5}{y - 7} = \dfrac{y}{1} + \dfrac{5}{y - 7} = \dfrac{y}{1} \cdot \dfrac{y - 7}{y - 7} + \dfrac{5}{y - 7}$

$= \dfrac{y^2 - 7y}{y - 7} + \dfrac{5}{y - 7} = \dfrac{y^2 - 7y + 5}{y - 7}$

Problem 3

A. The LCM is $(3x - 1)(x + 4)$.

$\dfrac{4x}{3x - 1} - \dfrac{9}{x + 4}$

$= \dfrac{4x}{3x - 1} \cdot \dfrac{x + 4}{x + 4} - \dfrac{9}{x + 4} \cdot \dfrac{3x - 1}{3x - 1}$

$= \dfrac{4x^2 + 16x}{(3x - 1)(x + 4)} - \dfrac{27x - 9}{(3x - 1)(x + 4)}$

$= \dfrac{(4x^2 + 16x) - (27x - 9)}{(3x - 1)(x + 4)}$

$= \dfrac{4x^2 + 16x - 27x + 9}{(3x - 1)(x + 4)} = \dfrac{4x^2 - 11x + 9}{(3x - 1)(x + 4)}$

B. The LCM is $(x + 5)(x - 5)$.

$\dfrac{2x - 1}{x^2 - 25} + \dfrac{2}{5 - x}$

$= \dfrac{2x - 1}{(x + 5)(x - 5)} + \dfrac{2}{-(x - 5)} \cdot \dfrac{-1(x + 5)}{-1(x + 5)}$

$= \dfrac{2x - 1}{(x + 5)(x - 5)} + \dfrac{-2(x + 5)}{(x + 5)(x - 5)}$

$= \dfrac{(2x - 1) + (-2)(x + 5)}{(x + 5)(x - 5)}$

$= \dfrac{2x - 1 - 2x - 10}{(x + 5)(x - 5)}$

$= \dfrac{-11}{(x + 5)(x - 5)} = -\dfrac{11}{(x + 5)(x - 5)}$

SECTION 9.4

Problem 1

A. The LCM of 3, x, 9, and x^2 is $9x^2$.

$\dfrac{\dfrac{1}{3} - \dfrac{1}{x}}{\dfrac{1}{9} - \dfrac{1}{x^2}} = \dfrac{\dfrac{1}{3} - \dfrac{1}{x}}{\dfrac{1}{9} - \dfrac{1}{x^2}} \cdot \dfrac{9x^2}{9x^2} = \dfrac{\dfrac{1}{3} \cdot 9x^2 - \dfrac{1}{x} \cdot 9x^2}{\dfrac{1}{9} \cdot 9x^2 - \dfrac{1}{x^2} \cdot 9x^2}$

$= \dfrac{3x^2 - 9x}{x^2 - 9} = \dfrac{3x(x - 3)}{(x - 3)(x + 3)} = \dfrac{3x}{x + 3}$

B. The LCM of x and x^2 is x^2.

$\dfrac{1 + \dfrac{4}{x} + \dfrac{3}{x^2}}{1 + \dfrac{10}{x} + \dfrac{21}{x^2}} = \dfrac{1 + \dfrac{4}{x} + \dfrac{3}{x^2}}{1 + \dfrac{10}{x} + \dfrac{21}{x^2}} \cdot \dfrac{x^2}{x^2}$

$= \dfrac{1 \cdot x^2 + \dfrac{4}{x} \cdot x^2 + \dfrac{3}{x^2} \cdot x^2}{1 \cdot x^2 + \dfrac{10}{x} \cdot x^2 + \dfrac{21}{x^2} \cdot x^2}$

$= \dfrac{x^2 + 4x + 3}{x^2 + 10x + 21}$

$= \dfrac{(x + 1)(x + 3)}{(x + 3)(x + 7)} = \dfrac{x + 1}{x + 7}$

SECTION 9.5

Problem 1

The LCM of 3 and $3x$ is $3x$.

$$x + \dfrac{1}{3} = \dfrac{4}{3x}$$

$$3x\left(x + \dfrac{1}{3}\right) = 3x\left(\dfrac{4}{3x}\right)$$

$$3x \cdot x + \dfrac{3x}{1} \cdot \dfrac{1}{3} = \dfrac{3x}{1} \cdot \dfrac{4}{3x}$$

$$3x^2 + x = 4$$

$$3x^2 + x - 4 = 0$$

$$(3x + 4)(x - 1) = 0$$

$3x + 4 = 0 \qquad x - 1 = 0$

$3x = -4 \qquad\qquad x = 1$

$x = -\dfrac{4}{3}$

Both $-\dfrac{4}{3}$ and 1 check as solutions. The solutions are $-\dfrac{4}{3}$ and 1.

Problem 2

The LCM is $x + 2$.

$$\frac{5x}{x + 2} = 3 - \frac{10}{x + 2}$$

$$\frac{(x + 2)}{1} \cdot \frac{5x}{x + 2} = \frac{(x + 2)}{1}\left(3 - \frac{10}{x + 2}\right)$$

$$5x = (x + 2)3 - 10$$
$$5x = 3x + 6 - 10$$
$$5x = 3x - 4$$
$$2x = -4$$
$$x = -2$$

-2 does not check as a solution. The equation has no solution.

Problem 3

A.
$$\frac{2}{x + 3} = \frac{6}{5x + 5}$$

$$(x + 3)(5x + 5)\frac{2}{x + 3} = (x + 3)(5x + 5)\frac{6}{5x + 5}$$
$$(5x + 5)2 = (x + 3)6$$
$$10x + 10 = 6x + 18$$
$$4x + 10 = 18$$
$$4x = 8$$
$$x = 2$$

The solution is 2.

B.
$$\frac{5}{2x - 3} = \frac{10}{x + 3}$$

$$(x + 3)(2x - 3)\frac{5}{2x - 3} = (x + 3)(2x - 3)\frac{10}{x + 3}$$
$$(x + 3)5 = (2x - 3)10$$
$$5x + 15 = 20x - 30$$
$$-15x + 15 = -30$$
$$-15x = -45$$
$$x = 3$$

The solution is 3.

Problem 4

Strategy To find the total area that 270 ceramic tiles will cover, write and solve a proportion using x to represent the number of square feet that 270 tiles will cover.

Solution
$$\frac{4}{9} = \frac{x}{270}$$

$$270\left(\frac{4}{9}\right) = 270\left(\frac{x}{270}\right)$$
$$120 = x$$

A 120-square-foot area can be tiled using 270 ceramic tiles.

Problem 5

Strategy To find the additional amount of medication required for a 180-pound adult, write and solve a proportion using x to represent the additional medication. Then $3 + x$ is the total amount required for a 180-pound adult.

Solution
$$\frac{120}{3} = \frac{180}{3 + x}$$

$$\frac{40}{1} = \frac{180}{3 + x}$$

$$(3 + x)40 = (3 + x)\frac{180}{3 + x}$$
$$120 + 40x = 180$$
$$40x = 60$$
$$x = 1.5$$

1.5 additional ounces are required for a 180-pound adult.

Problem 6

Strategy Triangle AOB is similar to triangle DOC. Solve a proportion to find the length of AO. Then use the formula for the area of a triangle to find the area of triangle AOB.

Solution
$$\frac{CD}{AB} = \frac{DO}{AO}$$

$$\frac{4}{10} = \frac{3}{x}$$

• Let x represent the length of AO.

$$10x\left(\frac{4}{10}\right) = 10x\left(\frac{3}{x}\right)$$
$$4x = 30$$
$$x = 7.5$$

$$A = \frac{1}{2}bh$$

$$A = \frac{1}{2}(10)(7.5)$$

$$A = 37.5$$

The area of triangle AOB is 37.5 cm².

SECTION 9.6

Problem 1

A.
$$s = \frac{A + L}{2}$$

$$2 \cdot s = 2\left(\frac{A + L}{2}\right)$$
$$2s = A + L$$
$$2s - A = A - A + L$$
$$2s - A = L$$

B.
$$S = a + (n - 1)d$$
$$S = a + nd - d$$
$$S - a = a - a + nd - d$$
$$S - a = nd - d$$
$$S - a + d = nd - d + d$$
$$S - a + d = nd$$

$$\frac{S - a + d}{d} = \frac{nd}{d}$$

$$\frac{S - a + d}{d} = n$$

Problem 2

$$S = rS + C$$
$$S - rS = C$$
$$S(1 - r) = C$$
$$S = \frac{C}{1 - r}$$

SECTION 9.7

Problem 1

Strategy ▶ Time for one printer to complete the job: t

	Rate	Time	Part
1st printer	$\frac{1}{t}$	3	$\frac{3}{t}$
2nd printer	$\frac{1}{t}$	5	$\frac{5}{t}$

▶ The sum of the parts of the task completed must equal 1.

Solution
$$\frac{3}{t} + \frac{5}{t} = 1$$

$$t\left(\frac{3}{t} + \frac{5}{t}\right) = t \cdot 1$$

$$3 + 5 = t$$
$$8 = t$$

Working alone, one printer takes 8 h to print the payroll.

Problem 2

Strategy ▶ Rate sailing across the lake: r
Rate sailing back: $2r$

	Distance	Rate	Time
Across	6	r	$\frac{6}{r}$
Back	6	$2r$	$\frac{6}{2r}$

▶ The total time for the trip was 3 h.

Solution
$$\frac{6}{r} + \frac{6}{2r} = 3$$

$$2r\left(\frac{6}{r} + \frac{6}{2r}\right) = 2r(3)$$

$$2r \cdot \frac{6}{r} + 2r \cdot \frac{6}{2r} = 6r$$

$$12 + 6 = 6r$$
$$18 = 6r$$
$$3 = r$$

The rate across the lake was 3 km/h.

Solutions to Chapter 10 Problems

SECTION 10.1

Problem 1

$$-5\sqrt{32} = -5\sqrt{16 \cdot 2}$$
$$= -5\sqrt{16}\,\sqrt{2}$$
$$= -5 \cdot 4\sqrt{2}$$
$$= -20\sqrt{2}$$

Problem 2

$$\sqrt{216} = \sqrt{36 \cdot 6}$$
$$= \sqrt{36}\,\sqrt{6}$$
$$= 6\sqrt{6}$$

Problem 3

$$\sqrt{y^{19}} = \sqrt{y^{18} \cdot y} = \sqrt{y^{18}}\,\sqrt{y} = y^9\sqrt{y}$$

Problem 4

A. $\sqrt{45b^7} = \sqrt{9b^6 \cdot 5b} = \sqrt{9b^6}\,\sqrt{5b} = 3b^3\sqrt{5b}$

B. $3a\sqrt{28a^9b^{18}} = 3a\sqrt{4a^8b^{18} \cdot 7a}$
$$= 3a\sqrt{4a^8b^{18}}\,\sqrt{7a}$$
$$= 3a \cdot 2a^4b^9\sqrt{7a}$$
$$= 6a^5b^9\sqrt{7a}$$

Problem 5

$$\sqrt{25(a + 3)^2} = 5(a + 3) = 5a + 15$$

SECTION 10.2

Problem 1

A. $9\sqrt{3} + 3\sqrt{3} - 18\sqrt{3}$
$$= (9 + 3 - 18)\sqrt{3} = -6\sqrt{3}$$

B. $2\sqrt{50} - 5\sqrt{32} = 2\sqrt{25 \cdot 2} - 5\sqrt{16 \cdot 2}$
$$= 2\sqrt{25}\,\sqrt{2} - 5\sqrt{16}\,\sqrt{2}$$
$$= 2 \cdot 5\sqrt{2} - 5 \cdot 4\sqrt{2}$$
$$= 10\sqrt{2} - 20\sqrt{2} = -10\sqrt{2}$$

Problem 2

A. $y\sqrt{28y} + 7\sqrt{63y^3}$
$= y\sqrt{4}\,\sqrt{7y} + 7\sqrt{9y^2}\,\sqrt{7y}$
$= y \cdot 2\sqrt{7y} + 7 \cdot 3y\sqrt{7y}$
$= 2y\sqrt{7y} + 21y\sqrt{7y} = 23y\sqrt{7y}$

B. $2\sqrt{27a^5} - 4a\sqrt{12a^3} + a^2\sqrt{75a}$
$= 2\sqrt{9a^4}\,\sqrt{3a} - 4a\sqrt{4a^2}\,\sqrt{3a} + a^2\sqrt{25}\,\sqrt{3a}$
$= 2 \cdot 3a^2\sqrt{3a} - 4a \cdot 2a\sqrt{3a} + a^2 \cdot 5\sqrt{3a}$
$= 6a^2\sqrt{3a} - 8a^2\sqrt{3a} + 5a^2\sqrt{3a} = 3a^2\sqrt{3a}$

SECTION 10.3

Problem 1

$\sqrt{5a}\,\sqrt{15a^3b^4}\,\sqrt{3b^5} = \sqrt{225a^4b^9}$
$\qquad = \sqrt{225a^4b^8}\,\sqrt{b}$
$\qquad = 15a^2b^4\sqrt{b}$

Problem 2

$\sqrt{5x}\left(\sqrt{5x} - \sqrt{25y}\right) = \left(\sqrt{5x}\right)^2 - \sqrt{125xy}$
$= 5x - \sqrt{25}\,\sqrt{5xy} = 5x - 5\sqrt{5xy}$

Problem 3

$\left(3\sqrt{x} - \sqrt{y}\right)\left(5\sqrt{x} - 2\sqrt{y}\right)$
$= 15\left(\sqrt{x}\right)^2 - 6\sqrt{xy} - 5\sqrt{xy} + 2\left(\sqrt{y}\right)^2$
$= 15x - 11\sqrt{xy} + 2y$

Problem 4

$\left(2\sqrt{x} + 7\right)\left(2\sqrt{x} - 7\right)$
$= \left(2\sqrt{x}\right)^2 - 7^2 = 4x - 49$

Problem 5

A. $\dfrac{\sqrt{15x^6y^7}}{\sqrt{3x^7y^9}} = \sqrt{\dfrac{15x^6y^7}{3x^7y^9}} = \sqrt{\dfrac{5}{xy^2}} = \dfrac{\sqrt{5}}{\sqrt{xy^2}}$
$= \dfrac{\sqrt{5}}{y\sqrt{x}} = \dfrac{\sqrt{5}}{y\sqrt{x}} \cdot \dfrac{\sqrt{x}}{\sqrt{x}} = \dfrac{\sqrt{5x}}{xy}$

B. $\dfrac{\sqrt{y}}{\sqrt{y} + 3} = \dfrac{\sqrt{y}}{\sqrt{y} + 3} \cdot \dfrac{\sqrt{y} - 3}{\sqrt{y} - 3} = \dfrac{y - 3\sqrt{y}}{y - 9}$

C. $\dfrac{5 + \sqrt{y}}{1 - 2\sqrt{y}} = \dfrac{5 + \sqrt{y}}{1 - 2\sqrt{y}} \cdot \dfrac{1 + 2\sqrt{y}}{1 + 2\sqrt{y}}$
$= \dfrac{5 + 10\sqrt{y} + \sqrt{y} + 2y}{1 - 4y}$
$= \dfrac{5 + 11\sqrt{y} + 2y}{1 - 4y}$

SECTION 10.4

Problem 1

$\sqrt{4x} + 3 = 7$
$\sqrt{4x} = 4$
$\left(\sqrt{4x}\right)^2 = 4^2$
$4x = 16$
$x = 4$

Check $\sqrt{4x} + 3 = 7$

$$
\begin{array}{c|c}
\sqrt{4 \cdot 4} + 3 & 7 \\
\sqrt{16} + 3 & 7 \\
4 + 3 & 7 \\
\end{array}
$$
$7 = 7$

The solution is 4.

Problem 2

A. $\sqrt{3x - 2} - 5 = 0$
$\sqrt{3x - 2} = 5$
$\left(\sqrt{3x - 2}\right)^2 = 5^2$
$3x - 2 = 25$
$3x = 27$
$x = 9$

Check $\sqrt{3x - 2} - 5 = 0$

$$
\begin{array}{c|c}
\sqrt{3 \cdot 9 - 2} - 5 & 0 \\
\sqrt{27 - 2} - 5 & 0 \\
\sqrt{25} - 5 & 0 \\
5 - 5 & 0 \\
\end{array}
$$
$0 = 0$

The solution is 9.

B. $\sqrt{4x - 7} + 5 = 0$
$\sqrt{4x - 7} = -5$
$\left(\sqrt{4x - 7}\right)^2 = (-5)^2$
$4x - 7 = 25$
$4x = 32$
$x = 8$

Check $\sqrt{4x - 7} + 5 = 0$

$$
\begin{array}{c|c}
\sqrt{4 \cdot 8 - 7} + 5 & 0 \\
\sqrt{32 - 7} + 5 & 0 \\
\sqrt{25} + 5 & 0 \\
5 + 5 & 0 \\
\end{array}
$$
$10 \neq 0$

There is no solution.

Problem 3

$\sqrt{x} + \sqrt{x + 9} = 9$
$\sqrt{x} = 9 - \sqrt{x + 9}$
$\left(\sqrt{x}\right)^2 = \left(9 - \sqrt{x + 9}\right)^2$
$x = 81 - 18\sqrt{x + 9} + (x + 9)$
$18\sqrt{x + 9} = 90$
$\sqrt{x + 9} = 5$
$\left(\sqrt{x + 9}\right)^2 = 5^2$
$x + 9 = 25$
$x = 16$

Check $\sqrt{x} + \sqrt{x + 9} = 9$

$$
\begin{array}{c|c}
\sqrt{16} + \sqrt{16 + 9} & 9 \\
4 + \sqrt{25} & 9 \\
4 + 5 & 9 \\
\end{array}
$$
$9 = 9$

The solution is 16.

Problem 4

Strategy To find the distance, use the Pythagorean Theorem. The hypotenuse is the length of the ladder. One leg is the distance from the bottom of the ladder to the base of the building. The distance along the building from the ground to the top of the ladder is the unknown leg.

Solution
$$a = \sqrt{c^2 - b^2}$$
$$a = \sqrt{(12)^2 - (5)^2}$$
$$a = \sqrt{144 - 25}$$
$$a = \sqrt{119}$$
$$a \approx 10.91$$

The distance is 10.91 ft.

Problem 5

Strategy To find the length of the pendulum, replace T in the equation with the given value and solve for L.

Solution
$$T = 2\pi\sqrt{\frac{L}{32}}$$
$$1.5 = 2\pi\sqrt{\frac{L}{32}}$$
$$\frac{1.5}{2\pi} = \sqrt{\frac{L}{32}}$$
$$\left(\frac{1.5}{2\pi}\right)^2 = \left(\sqrt{\frac{L}{32}}\right)^2$$
$$\left(\frac{1.5}{2\pi}\right)^2 = \frac{L}{32}$$
$$32\left(\frac{1.5}{2\pi}\right)^2 = L \quad \bullet \text{ Use the } \pi \text{ key on your calculator.}$$
$$1.82 \approx L$$

The length of the pendulum is 1.82 ft.

Solutions to Chapter 11 Problems

SECTION 11.1

Problem 1

$$\frac{3y^2}{2} + y - \frac{1}{2} = 0$$
$$2\left(\frac{3y^2}{2} + y - \frac{1}{2}\right) = 2(0)$$
$$3y^2 + 2y - 1 = 0$$
$$(3y - 1)(y + 1) = 0$$

$$3y - 1 = 0 \qquad y + 1 = 0$$
$$3y = 1 \qquad\qquad y = -1$$
$$y = \frac{1}{3}$$

The solutions are $\frac{1}{3}$ and -1.

Problem 2

A. $4x^2 - 96 = 0$
$$4x^2 = 96$$
$$x^2 = 24$$
$$\sqrt{x^2} = \sqrt{24}$$
$$x = \pm\sqrt{24}$$
$$x = \pm 2\sqrt{6}$$

The solutions are $2\sqrt{6}$ and $-2\sqrt{6}$.

B. $x^2 + 81 = 0$
$$x^2 = -81$$
$$\sqrt{x^2} = \sqrt{-81} \quad \text{(not a real number)}$$

The equation has no real number solution.

Problem 3

$$(x + 5)^2 = 20$$
$$\sqrt{(x + 5)^2} = \sqrt{20}$$
$$x + 5 = \pm\sqrt{20}$$
$$x + 5 = \pm 2\sqrt{5}$$

$$x + 5 = 2\sqrt{5} \qquad\qquad x + 5 = -2\sqrt{5}$$
$$x = -5 + 2\sqrt{5} \qquad\qquad x = -5 - 2\sqrt{5}$$

The solutions are $-5 + 2\sqrt{5}$ and $-5 - 2\sqrt{5}$.

SECTION 11.2

Problem 1

A. $3x^2 - 6x - 2 = 0$
$$3x^2 - 6x = 2$$
$$\frac{1}{3}(3x^2 - 6x) = \frac{1}{3} \cdot 2$$
$$x^2 - 2x = \frac{2}{3}$$

Complete the square.

$$x^2 - 2x + 1 = \frac{2}{3} + 1$$
$$(x - 1)^2 = \frac{5}{3}$$
$$\sqrt{(x - 1)^2} = \sqrt{\frac{5}{3}}$$
$$x - 1 = \pm\sqrt{\frac{5}{3}}$$
$$x - 1 = \pm\frac{\sqrt{15}}{3}$$

$$x - 1 = \frac{\sqrt{15}}{3} \qquad\qquad x - 1 = -\frac{\sqrt{15}}{3}$$
$$x = 1 + \frac{\sqrt{15}}{3} \qquad\qquad x = 1 - \frac{\sqrt{15}}{3}$$
$$= \frac{3 + \sqrt{15}}{3} \qquad\qquad = \frac{3 - \sqrt{15}}{3}$$

The solutions are $\dfrac{3 + \sqrt{15}}{3}$ and $\dfrac{3 - \sqrt{15}}{3}$.

B. $y^2 - 6y + 10 = 0$
$$y^2 - 6y = -10$$

Complete the square.

$$y^2 - 6y + 9 = -10 + 9$$
$$(y - 3)^2 = -1$$
$$\sqrt{(y - 3)^2} = \sqrt{-1}$$

$\sqrt{-1}$ is not a real number.

The equation has no real number solution.

Problem 2

$$x^2 + 8x + 8 = 0$$
$$x^2 + 8x = -8$$
$$x^2 + 8x + 16 = -8 + 16$$
$$(x + 4)^2 = 8$$
$$\sqrt{(x + 4)^2} = \sqrt{8}$$
$$x + 4 = \pm\sqrt{8}$$
$$x + 4 \approx \pm 2.828$$

$x + 4 \approx 2.828$	$x + 4 \approx -2.828$
$x \approx -4 + 2.828$	$x \approx -4 - 2.828$
≈ -1.172	≈ -6.828

The solutions are approximately -1.172 and -6.828.

SECTION 11.3

Problem 1

A. $3x^2 + 4x - 4 = 0$
$$a = 3, b = 4, c = -4$$
$$x = \frac{-(4) \pm \sqrt{(4)^2 - 4(3)(-4)}}{2 \cdot 3}$$
$$= \frac{-4 \pm \sqrt{16 + 48}}{6}$$
$$= \frac{-4 \pm \sqrt{64}}{6} = \frac{-4 \pm 8}{6}$$

$x = \dfrac{-4 + 8}{6}$	$x = \dfrac{-4 - 8}{6}$
$= \dfrac{4}{6} = \dfrac{2}{3}$	$= \dfrac{-12}{6} = -2$

The solutions are $\frac{2}{3}$ and -2.

B. $\quad x^2 + 2x = 1$
$$x^2 + 2x - 1 = 0$$
$$a = 1, b = 2, c = -1$$
$$x = \frac{-(2) \pm \sqrt{(2)^2 - 4(1)(-1)}}{2 \cdot 1}$$
$$= \frac{-2 \pm \sqrt{4 + 4}}{2}$$
$$= \frac{-2 \pm \sqrt{8}}{2}$$

$$= \frac{-2 \pm 2\sqrt{2}}{2}$$
$$= \frac{2(-1 \pm \sqrt{2})}{2} = -1 \pm \sqrt{2}$$

The solutions are $-1 + \sqrt{2}$ and $-1 - \sqrt{2}$.

C. $z^2 + 2z + 6 = 0$
$$a = 1, b = 2, c = 6$$
$$z = \frac{-(2) \pm \sqrt{2^2 - 4(1)(6)}}{2(1)}$$
$$= \frac{-2 \pm \sqrt{4 - 24}}{2} = \frac{-2 \pm \sqrt{-20}}{2}$$

$\sqrt{-20}$ is not a real number.

The equation has no real number solution.

SECTION 11.4

Problem 1

A. $\sqrt{-17} = \sqrt{-1 \cdot 17} = \sqrt{-1}\sqrt{17} = i\sqrt{17}$

B. $\sqrt{-81} = \sqrt{-1 \cdot 81} = \sqrt{-1}\sqrt{81} = i\sqrt{81} = i \cdot 9 = 9i$

C. $\sqrt{-63} = \sqrt{-1 \cdot 63} = \sqrt{-1}\sqrt{63} = i\sqrt{63} = i\sqrt{9 \cdot 7}$
$$= i\sqrt{9}\sqrt{7} = i \cdot 3\sqrt{7} = 3i\sqrt{7}$$

D. $4\sqrt{-50} = 4\sqrt{-1 \cdot 50} = 4\sqrt{-1}\sqrt{50} = 4i\sqrt{50}$
$$= 4i\sqrt{25 \cdot 2} = 4i\sqrt{25}\sqrt{2} = 4i \cdot 5\sqrt{2} = 20i\sqrt{2}$$

Problem 2

$$\frac{5 - 3\sqrt{-50}}{10} = \frac{5 - 3i\sqrt{50}}{10} \qquad \bullet\ \sqrt{-50} = i\sqrt{50}$$
$$= \frac{5 - 3i\sqrt{25}\sqrt{2}}{10} = \frac{5 - 15i\sqrt{2}}{10}$$
$$= \frac{5}{10} - \frac{15i\sqrt{2}}{10} = \frac{1}{2} - \frac{3i\sqrt{2}}{2} = \frac{1}{2} - \frac{3\sqrt{2}}{2}i$$

Problem 3

A. $(7 - 3i) + (-8 + i) = (7 + (-8)) + (-3 + 1)i$
$$= -1 - 2i$$

B. $(-5 + 4i) - (-3 - 7i) = (-5 - (-3)) + (4 - (-7))i$
$$= -2 + 11i$$

Problem 4

$5i(3 + 6i) = 15i + 30i^2$ 　　• **Use the Distributive Property to remove parentheses.**

$\qquad\qquad = 15i + 30(-1)$ 　• **Replace i^2 with -1.**

$\qquad\qquad = 15i + (-30)$ 　• **Write the answer in the form**

$\qquad\qquad = -30 + 15i$ 　　$a + bi$**.**

Problem 5

$(-1 + 5i)(2 - 3i)$

$$= (-1)(2) + (-1)(-3i)$$
$$+ 5i(2) + 5i(-3i)$$ • **Use the FOIL method.**

$$= -2 + 3i + 10i - 15i^2$$

$$= -2 + 13i - 15i^2$$ • **Combine like terms.**

$$= -2 + 13i - 15(-1)$$ • **Replace i^2 with -1.**

$$= -2 + 13i + 15$$ • **Write the answer in the**
$$= 13 + 13i$$ **form $a + bi$.**

Problem 6

$(-2 + 5i)(-2 - 5i) = (-2)^2 + 5^2 = 4 + 25 = 29$

Problem 7

$$\frac{-12 + 8i}{-4i} = \frac{-12 + 8i}{-4i} \cdot \frac{i}{i}$$ • **Multiply the numerator and denominator by i.**

$$= \frac{-12i + 8i^2}{-4i^2}$$

$$= \frac{-12i + 8(-1)}{(-4)(-1)}$$ • **$i^2 = -1$**

$$= \frac{-12i - 8}{4} = \frac{-12i}{4} - \frac{8}{4}$$ • **Write in the form $a + bi$.**

$$= -2 - 3i$$

Problem 8

$$\frac{16 - 11i}{5 + 2i} = \frac{16 - 11i}{5 + 2i} \cdot \frac{5 - 2i}{5 - 2i}$$ • **Multiply the numerator and denominator by the conjugate of the denominator.**

$$= \frac{80 - 32i - 55i + 22i^2}{5^2 + 2^2}$$

$$= \frac{80 - 87i + 22i^2}{25 + 4}$$ • **Combine like terms.**

$$= \frac{80 - 87i + 22(-1)}{29}$$ • **$i^2 = -1$**

$$= \frac{80 - 87i - 22}{29}$$

$$= \frac{58 - 87i}{29}$$

$$= \frac{58}{29} - \frac{87i}{29} = 2 - 3i$$ • **Write in the form $a + bi$.**

Problem 9

$8z^2 + 17 = -7$

$$8z^2 = -24$$ • **Subtract 17 from each side of the equation.**

$$z^2 = -3$$ • **Divide each side of the equation by 8.**

$$\sqrt{z^2} = \sqrt{-3}$$ • **Take the square root of each side of the equation.**

$$z = \pm\sqrt{-3}$$

$$= \pm i\sqrt{3}$$ • **Rewrite $\sqrt{-3}$ as $i\sqrt{3}$.**

Check

$8z^2 + 17 = -7$		$8z^2 + 17 = -7$	
$8(i\sqrt{3})^2 + 17$	-7	$8(-i\sqrt{3})^2 + 17$	-7
$8(i)^2(\sqrt{3})^2 + 17$	-7	$8(-i)^2(\sqrt{3})^2 + 17$	-7
$8(-1)3 + 17$	-7	$8(-1)3 + 17$	-7
$-7 = -7$		$-7 = -7$	

The solutions are $i\sqrt{3}$ and $-i\sqrt{3}$.

Problem 10

$x^2 - 6x + 4 = -6$

$$x^2 - 6x + 10 = 0$$ • **Add 6 to each side of the equation.**

$$x = \frac{-b \pm \sqrt{b^2 - 4ac}}{2a}$$

$$x = \frac{-(-6) \pm \sqrt{(-6)^2 - 4(1)(10)}}{2(1)}$$ • **$a = 1, b = -6,$ $c = 10$**

$$= \frac{6 \pm \sqrt{36 - 40}}{2} = \frac{6 \pm \sqrt{-4}}{2}$$

$$= \frac{6 \pm i\sqrt{4}}{2} = \frac{6 \pm 2i}{2}$$ • **Rewrite $\sqrt{-4}$ as $i\sqrt{4}$ and then rewrite $i\sqrt{4}$ as $2i$.**

$$= \frac{6}{2} \pm \frac{2i}{2} = 3 \pm i$$ • **Write as a complex number in standard form.**

Check

$x^2 - 6x + 4 = -6$	
$(3 + i)^2 - 6(3 + i) + 4$	-6
$9 + 6i + i^2 - 18 - 6i + 4$	-6
$9 + 6i + (-1) - 18 - 6i + 4$	-6
$-6 = -6$	

$x^2 - 6x + 4 = -6$	
$(3 - i)^2 - 6(3 - i) + 4$	-6
$9 - 6i + i^2 - 18 + 6i + 4$	-6
$9 - 6i + (-1) - 18 + 6i + 4$	-6
$-6 = -6$	

The solutions are $3 + i$ and $3 - i$.

SECTION 11.5

Problem 1

A. $y = x^2 + 2$

$a = 1$. a is positive.

The parabola opens up.

x	y
0	2
1	3
-1	3
2	6
-2	6

B. $y = -x^2 - 2x + 3$
$a = -1.$ a is negative.
The parabola opens down.

x	y
0	3
1	0
−1	4
2	−5
−2	3
−3	0
−4	−5

Problem 2

To find the x-intercepts, let $y = 0$ and solve for x.

$y = x^2 - 6x + 9$
$0 = x^2 - 6x + 9$
$0 = (x - 3)(x - 3)$

$x - 3 = 0 \qquad x - 3 = 0$
$\qquad x = 3 \qquad\qquad x = 3$

The x-intercept is $(3, 0)$.

To find the y-intercept, let $x = 0$ and solve for y.

$y = x^2 - 6x + 9$
$y = 0^2 - 6(0) + 9 = 9$

The y-intercept is $(0, 9)$.

SECTION 11.6

Problem 1

Strategy ▶ This is a geometry problem.

▶ Width of the rectangle: W
Length of the rectangle: $W + 3$

▶ Use the equation $A = LW$.

Solution $A = LW$
$40 = (W + 3)W$
$40 = W^2 + 3W$
$0 = W^2 + 3W - 40$
$0 = (W + 8)(W - 5)$

$W + 8 = 0 \qquad W - 5 = 0$
$\qquad W = -8 \qquad\quad W = 5$

The solution −8 is not possible.
The width is 5 m.

Answers to Selected Exercises

Answers to Chapter 1 Selected Exercises

PREP TEST

1. 127.16   **2.** 49,743   **3.** 4517   **4.** 11,396   **5.** 24   **6.** 24   **7.** 4   **8.** $3 \cdot 7$
9. $\dfrac{2}{5}$

CONCEPT REVIEW 1.1

1. Sometimes true   **3.** Never true   **5.** Sometimes true   **7.** Always true   **9.** Always true

SECTION 1.1

3. natural   **5.** is greater than or equal to   **7.** >   **9.** <   **11.** >   **13.** >   **15.** <
17. >   **19.** >   **21.** <   **23.** a   **25.** Yes   **27.** $\{1, 2, 3, 4, 5, 6, 7, 8\}$
29. $\{1, 2, 3, 4, 5, 6, 7, 8\}$ **31.** $\{-6, -5, -4, -3, -2, -1\}$ **33.** 5   **35.** $-23, -18$ **37.** 21, 37
39. $-52, -46, 0$ **41.** $-17, 0, 4, 29$ **43.** 5, 6, 7, 8, 9   **45.** $-10, -9, -8, -7, -6, -5$ **49.** positive
51. absolute value   **53.** -22 **55.** 31   **57.** 168   **59.** -630 **61.** 18   **63.** -49
65. 16   **67.** 12   **69.** -29 **71.** -14 **73.** 0   **75.** -34 **77. a.** 8, 5, 2, $-1, -3$
b. 8, 5, 2, 1, 3   **79.** True   **81.** >   **83.** <   **85.** >   **87.** <   **89.** $-19, -|-8|, |-5|, 6$
91. $-22, -(-3), |-14|, |-25|$ **93. a.** 5°F with a 20 mph wind feels colder.   **b.** -25°F with a 10 mph wind
feels colder.   **95.** $-4, 4$ **97.** $-3, 11$ **99.** Negative   **101.** 0   **103.** True

CONCEPT REVIEW 1.2

1. Sometimes true   **3.** Always true   **5.** Always true   **7.** Never true   **9.** Never true

SECTION 1.2

3. 8; -3; 5   **5.** -11 **7.** -9 **9.** -3 **11.** 1   **13.** -5 **15.** -30 **17.** 9
19. 1   **21.** -10 **23.** -28 **25.** -392 **27.** Positive   **31.** $(-4); -14$ **33.** 8
35. -7 **37.** 7   **39.** -2 **41.** -28 **43.** -13 **45.** 6   **47.** -9 **49.** 2
51. -138 **53.** -8 **55.** Negative   **61.** $-10; 7; -70$ **63.** positive; 48   **65.** 42   **67.** -20
69. -16 **71.** 25   **73.** 0   **75.** -72 **77.** -102 **79.** 140   **81.** -70 **83.** 162
85. 120   **87.** 36   **89.** 192   **91.** -108 **93.** 0   **95.** Negative   **97.** $-15; 3$
99. $3(-12) = -36$ **101.** $-5(11) = -55$ **103.** -2 **105.** 8   **107.** 0   **109.** -9
111. -9 **113.** 9   **115.** -24 **117.** -12 **119.** -13 **121.** -18 **123.** 19
125. 26   **127.** 11   **129.** -13 **131.** 13   **133.** Positive   **135.** b
137. The temperature is 3°C.   **139.** The difference is 14°C.   **141.** The difference is 399°C.
143. The difference in elevation is 5662 m.   **145.** The difference in elevation is 6028 m.   **147.** The
difference in elevation is 9244 m.   **149.** The average daily high temperature is -3°C.   **151.** The
temperature dropped 100°F.   **153.** The average temperature at 30,000 ft is 36°F colder than at 20,000 ft.
155. The student's score is 93.   **157.** The 5-day moving average for the Disney stock is $-24, -18, -2, 2, 8$.
159. 17   **161.** 3   **163.** $-4, -9, -14$ **165.** $-16, 4, -1$ **167.** 5436   **169.** b   **171.** a
173. No. $10 - (-8) = 18$

CONCEPT REVIEW 1.3

1. Never true   **3.** Sometimes true   **5.** Always true   **7.** Never true   **9.** Always true

SECTION 1.3

1. 2; 3; repeating   **3.** $0.\overline{3}$ **5.** 0.25   **7.** 0.4   **9.** $0.1\overline{6}$ **11.** 0.125   **13.** $0.\overline{2}$

15. $0.\overline{45}$ **17.** $0.58\overline{3}$ **19.** $0.2\overline{6}$ **21.** 0.4375   **23.** 0.24   **25.** 0.225   **27.** $0.6\overline{81}$

29. $0.458\overline{3}$ **31.** $0.\overline{15}$ **33.** No   **35.** 4   **37.** $-\dfrac{3}{8}$ **39.** $\dfrac{1}{10}$ **41.** $\dfrac{15}{64}$ **43.** $\dfrac{3}{2}$

45. $-\dfrac{8}{9}$ **47.** $\dfrac{2}{3}$ **49.** 4.164   **51.** 4.347   **53.** -4.028 **55.** -2.22 **57.** 12.26448

59. a. Less than one   **b.** Greater than one   **61.** 0.75   **63.** -2060.55 **65.** 0.09

67. 6   **69.** $\dfrac{1}{2}$ **71.** -1 **73.** $-\dfrac{25}{18}$ **75.** $\dfrac{1}{24}$ **77.** $\dfrac{17}{18}$ **79.** $-\dfrac{47}{48}$ **81.** $\dfrac{3}{8}$

83. $-\dfrac{7}{60}$ **85.** $-\dfrac{1}{16}$ **87.** $-\dfrac{7}{24}$ **89.** 7.29   **91.** -3.049 **93.** -1.06 **95.** -23.845

97. -10.7893 **99.** 11.56   **101.** -60.03 **103.** -34.99 **105.** 239.2351   **107. a.** 2

b. 0   **c.** 1   **d.** -1 **111.** $\dfrac{1}{100}; \dfrac{1}{100}; \dfrac{4}{5}$ **113.** 100%; 100%; 30%   **115.** $\dfrac{3}{4}$, 0.75

117. $\dfrac{1}{2}$, 0.5   **119.** $\dfrac{16}{25}$, 0.64   **121.** $1\dfrac{3}{4}$, 1.75   **123.** $\dfrac{19}{100}$, 0.19   **125.** $\dfrac{1}{20}$, 0.05

127. $4\dfrac{1}{2}$, 4.5   **129.** $\dfrac{2}{25}$, 0.08   **131.** $\dfrac{1}{9}$ **133.** $\dfrac{5}{16}$ **135.** $\dfrac{1}{200}$ **137.** $\dfrac{1}{16}$ **139.** 0.073

141. 0.158   **143.** 0.0915   **145.** 0.1823   **147.** 15%   **149.** 5%   **151.** 17.5%

153. 115%   **155.** 0.8%   **157.** 6.5%   **159.** 54%   **161.** 33.3%   **163.** 44.4%

165. 250%   **167.** $37\dfrac{1}{2}$%   **169.** $35\dfrac{5}{7}$%   **171.** 125%   **173.** $155\dfrac{5}{9}$%   **175.** Greater than

100%   **177.** $\dfrac{2}{5}$ of the respondents found their most recent jobs on the Internet.   **179.** Less than one-

quarter of the respondents found their most recent jobs through a newspaper ad.   **181.** Natural number, integer, positive integer, rational number, real number   **183.** Rational number, real number   **185.** Irrational number, real number   **187.** The cost is $1.35.   **189.** The difference is $138.499 billion.   **191.** The deficit in 1985 was 4 times greater than in 1975.   **193.** The average deficit for the years 1995 through 2000 was $-\$4,579$ million.   **195.** The new fraction is greater than $\dfrac{2}{5}$.   **197.** $1.06x$ **199.** 53¢

201. Yes. For example, $c = \dfrac{a + b}{2}$.

CONCEPT REVIEW 1.4

1. Never true   **3.** Never true   **5.** Always true   **7.** Never true   **9.** Never true

SECTION 1.4

1. base; exponent; -5; -5; 25   **3.** 36   **5.** -49 **7.** 9   **9.** 81   **11.** $\dfrac{1}{4}$ **13.** 0.09

15. 12   **17.** 0.216   **19.** -12 **21.** 16   **23.** -864 **25.** -1008 **27.** 3

29. $-77,760$ **31.** Positive   **35.** -2; 4; 20; -17 **37.** 9   **39.** 12   **41.** 1   **43.** 7

45. -36 **47.** 13   **49.** 4   **51.** 15   **53.** -1 **55.** 4   **57.** 1.7   **59.** $\dfrac{17}{48}$ **61. b**

63. $<$ **65.** $>$ **67.** 100   **69.** 120   **71.** It will take the computer 17 s.   **73.** 6   **75.** 9

CONCEPT REVIEW 1.5

1. Never true   **3.** Always true   **5.** Never true

SECTION 1.5

1. 90°   **3.** 90°   **5.** Less than   **7.** 28°   **9.** 132°   **11.** 83°   **13.** 91°   **15.** 132°
17. 51°   **19.** 77°   **21.** 79°   **23.** 292°   **25.** triangle   **27.** 9.71 cm   **29.** 14 ft 2 in.
31. 52 in.   **33.** 131.88 cm   **35.** 3.768 m   **37.** The wood framing would cost $76.96.   **39.** The
cost of the binding is $19.78.   **41.** 22 units   **43.** width   **45.** 32 ft²   **47.** 378 cm²
49. 50.24 in²   **51.** 16.81 m²   **53.** 52.5 cm²   **55.** 226.865 in²   **57.** 138.6 gal of water should be
used.   **59.** The cost to build the design is $172.   **61.** The cost to plaster the room is $990.72.
63. 4 times   **65.** Perimeter: 265.6 m; area: 4056 m²   **67.** Perimeter: 340 m; area: 1600 m²
69. a. 39 in²   **b.** 87 in²

CHAPTER 1 REVIEW EXERCISES*

1. {1, 2, 3, 4, 5, 6} [1.1.1]   **2.** 62.5% [1.3.4]   **3.** −4 [1.1.2]   **4.** 4 [1.2.2]   **5.** 18 cm² [1.5.3]
6. $0.\overline{7}$ [1.3.1]   **7.** −5.3578 [1.3.2]   **8.** 8 [1.4.2]   **9.** 4 [1.1.2]   **10.** −14 [1.2.2]
11. 67.2% [1.3.4]   **12.** $\frac{159}{200}$ [1.3.4]   **13.** −9 [1.2.4]   **14.** 0.85 [1.3.1]   **15.** $-\frac{1}{2}$ [1.3.2]
16. 9 [1.4.2]   **17.** 37° [1.5.1]   **18.** −16 [1.2.1]   **19.** 90 [1.2.3]   **20.** −6.881 [1.3.3]
21. −5, −3 [1.1.1]   **22.** 0.07 [1.3.4]   **23.** 12 [1.4.1]   **24.** > [1.1.1]   **25.** −3 [1.2.1]
26. 34° [1.5.1]   **27.** $\frac{1}{15}$ [1.3.3]   **28.** −108 [1.4.1]   **29.** 277.8% [1.3.4]   **30.** 2.4 [1.3.4]
31. 152° [1.5.1]   **32.** −8 [1.2.4]   **33.** 28.26 m² [1.5.3]   **34.** 12 [1.4.2]   **35.** 3 [1.1.2]
36. $288\frac{8}{9}\%$ [1.3.4]   **37. a.** 12, 8, 1, −7   **b.** 12, 8, 1, 7 [1.1.2]   **38.** $0.\overline{63}$ [1.3.1]
39. −11.5 [1.3.2]   **40.** 8 [1.4.2]   **41.** −8 [1.2.1]   **42.** $-\frac{11}{24}$ [1.3.3]   **43.** −17, −9, 0, 4
[1.1.1]   **44.** 0.2% [1.3.4]   **45.** −4 [1.4.1]   **46.** 3.561 [1.3.3]   **47.** −17 [1.1.2]   **48.** −27
[1.2.2]   **49.** $-\frac{1}{10}$ [1.3.2]   **50.** < [1.1.1]   **51.** 44 in. [1.5.2]   **52.** −128 [1.4.1]
53. 7.5% [1.3.4]   **54.** $54\frac{2}{7}\%$ [1.3.4]   **55.** −18 [1.2.1]   **56.** 0 [1.2.3]   **57.** 9 [1.4.2]
58. $\frac{7}{8}$ [1.3.3]   **59.** 16 [1.2.4]   **60.** < [1.1.1]   **61.** −3 [1.4.1]   **62.** −6 [1.2.1]
63. 300 [1.2.3]   **64.** {−3, −2, −1} [1.1.1]   **65.** The cost is $240.96. [1.5.3]   **66.** The temperature
is 8°C. [1.2.5]   **67.** The average low temperature was −2°C. [1.2.5]   **68.** The difference is 106°F. [1.2.5]
69. The temperature is −6°C. [1.2.5]   **70.** The difference is 714°C. [1.2.5]

CHAPTER 1 TEST

1. $\frac{11}{20}$ [1.3.4]   **2.** −6, −8 [1.1.1]   **3.** 47° [1.5.1]   **4.** 0.15 [1.3.1]   **5.** $-\frac{1}{14}$ [1.3.2]
6. −15 [1.2.4]   **7.** $-\frac{8}{3}$ [1.4.1]   **8.** 2 [1.2.1]   **9.** {1, 2, 3, 4, 5, 6} [1.1.1]   **10.** 159% [1.3.4]

*The numbers in brackets following the answers in the Chapter Review Exercises refer to the objective that corresponds to
that problem. For example, the reference [1.2.1] stands for Section 1.2, Objective 1. This notation will be used for all Pretests,
Chapter Review Exercises, Chapter Tests, and Cumulative Review Exercises throughout the text.

11. 29 [1.1.2]   **12.** > [1.1.1]   **13.** $-\dfrac{23}{18}$ [1.3.3]   **14.** 90 cm² [1.5.3]   **15.** 3 [1.4.2]

16. $\dfrac{5}{6}$ [1.3.2]   **17.** 23.1% [1.3.4]   **18.** 0.062 [1.3.4]   **19.** 14 [1.2.2]   **20.** $0.4\overline{3}$ [1.3.1]

21. −2.43 [1.3.2]   **22.** 62° [1.5.1]   **23.** 640 [1.4.1]   **24.** −34 [1.1.2]   **25.** 84.78 in. [1.5.2]

26. a. 17, 6, −5, −9   **b.** 17, 6, 5, 9 [1.1.2]   **27.** $69\dfrac{13}{23}$% [1.3.4]   **28.** −11.384 [1.3.3]

29. 160 [1.2.3]   **30.** −2 [1.4.2]   **31.** The temperature is 4°C. [1.2.5]   **32.** The average is −48°F. [1.2.5]   **33.** The cost is $4564. [1.5.3]

Answers to Chapter 2 Selected Exercises

PREP TEST

1. 3 [1.2.2]   **2.** 4 [1.2.4]   **3.** $\dfrac{1}{12}$ [1.3.3]   **4.** $-\dfrac{4}{9}$ [1.3.2]   **5.** $\dfrac{3}{10}$ [1.3.2]

6. −16 [1.4.1]   **7.** $\dfrac{8}{27}$ [1.4.1]   **8.** 48 [1.4.1]   **9.** 1 [1.4.2]   **10.** 12 [1.4.2]

CONCEPT REVIEW 2.1

1. Always true   **3.** Sometimes true   **5.** Always true

SECTION 2.1

1. $-4x$; -7; $3x^2$; $-4x$; -7 **3.** $2x^2$, $5x$, $\underline{-8}$ **5.** $-a^4$, $\underline{6}$ **7.** $7x^2y$, $6xy^2$ **9.** 1, −9   **11.** 1, −4, −1
15. 10   **17.** 32   **19.** 21   **21.** 16   **23.** −9   **25.** 3   **27.** −7   **29.** 13
31. −15   **33.** 41   **35.** 1   **37.** 5   **39.** 1   **41.** 57   **43.** 5   **45.** 12   **47.** 6
49. 10   **51.** 8   **53.** −3   **55.** −2   **57.** −22   **59.** 4   **61.** 20   **63.** 24
65. 4.96   **67.** −5.68   **69. a.** No, V cannot be a whole number.   **b.** No, volume is not measured in
square units.   **71.** The volume is 25.8 in³.   **73.** The area is 93.7 cm².   **75.** The volume is 484.9 m³.
77. 41   **79.** 21   **81.** 24   **83.** $\dfrac{1}{2}$ **85.** 13   **87.** −1   **89.** 4   **91.** 81

CONCEPT REVIEW 2.2

1. Never true   **3.** Always true   **5.** Always true   **7.** Never true

SECTION 2.2

1. Commutative   **3.** reciprocal (or multiplicative inverse)   **5.** 2   **7.** 5   **9.** 6   **11.** −8
13. −4   **15.** The Inverse Property of Addition   **17.** The Commutative Property of Addition
19. The Associative Property of Addition   **21.** The Commutative Property of Multiplication
23. The Associative Property of Multiplication   **27.** $3x$, $5x$ **29.** $-8a$; Distributive; −3   **31.** $14x$

33. $5a$ **35.** $-6y$ **37.** $-3b - 7$ **39.** $5a$ **41.** $-2ab$ **43.** $5xy$ **45.** 0   **47.** $-\dfrac{5}{6}x$

49. $-\dfrac{1}{24}x^2$ **51.** $11x$ **53.** $7a$ **55.** $-14x^2$ **57.** $-x + 3y$ **59.** $17x - 3y$

61. $-2a - 6b$ **63.** $-3x - 8y$ **65.** $-4x^2 - 2x$ **67. a.** Negative   **b.** Positive   **c.** 0
69. Associative; $-48x$ **71.** $12x$ **73.** $-21a$ **75.** $6y$ **77.** $8x$ **79.** $-6a$ **81.** $12b$
83. $-15x^2$ **85.** x^2 **87.** x **89.** n **91.** x **93.** n **95.** $2x$ **97.** $-2x$

99. $-15a^2$ **101.** $6y$ **103.** $3y$ **105.** $-2x$ **107.** Less than one **109.** Distributive; -24; 16
111. $-x - 2$ **113.** $8x - 6$ **115.** $-2a - 14$ **117.** $-6y + 24$ **119.** $35 - 21b$
121. $-9 + 15x$ **123.** $15x^2 + 6x$ **125.** $2y - 18$ **127.** $-15x - 30$ **129.** $-6x^2 - 28$
131. $-6y^2 + 21$ **133.** $-6a^2 + 7b^2$ **135.** $4x^2 - 12x + 20$ **137.** $-3y^2 + 9y + 21$
139. $-12a^2 - 20a + 28$ **141.** $12x^2 - 9x + 12$ **143.** $10x^2 - 20xy - 5y^2$ **145.** $-8b^2 + 6b - 9$
147. 3 **149.** m; 3 **151.** $a - 7$ **153.** $-11x + 13$ **155.** $-4y - 4$ **157.** $-2x - 16$
159. $18y - 51$ **161.** $a + 7b$ **163.** $6x + 28$ **165.** $5x - 75$ **167.** $4x - 4$ **169.** $38x - 63$
171. b **173.** $20x + y$ **175.** **b** **177.** $-3x + y$ **179.** 0 **181.** $-a + b$ **183.** **a.** Yes
b. No

CONCEPT REVIEW 2.3

1. Never true **3.** Never true **5.** Always true **7.** Never true

SECTION 2.3

1. Sum, times **3.** Total, divided by **5.** $19 - d$ **7.** $r - 12$ **9.** $28a$ **11.** $5(n - 7)$

13. $y - 3y$ **15.** $-6b$ **17.** $\dfrac{4}{p - 6}$ **19.** $\dfrac{x - 9}{2x}$ **21.** $-4s - 21$ **23.** $\dfrac{d + 8}{d}$

25. $\dfrac{3}{8}(t + 15)$ **27.** $w + \dfrac{7}{w}$ **29.** $d + (16d - 3)$ **31.** $\dfrac{n}{19}$ **33.** $n + 40$ **35.** $(n - 90)^2$

37. $\dfrac{4}{9}n + 20$ **39.** $n(n + 10)$ **41.** $7n + 14$ **43.** $\dfrac{12}{n + 2}$ **45.** $\dfrac{2}{n + 1}$ **47.** $60 - \dfrac{n}{50}$

49. $n^2 + 3n$ **51.** $(n + 3) + n^3$ **53.** $n - \dfrac{1}{4}n^2$ **55.** $n - \dfrac{7}{n}$ **57.** $n^3 - 12n$ **59.** **c**

61. $\dfrac{1}{2}; \dfrac{3}{4}; \dfrac{5}{4}n$ **63.** $n + (n + 10); 2n + 10$ **65.** $n - (9 - n); 2n - 9$ **67.** $\dfrac{1}{5}n - \dfrac{3}{8}n; -\dfrac{7}{40}n$

69. $(n + 9) + 4; n + 13$ **71.** $2(3n + 40); 6n + 80$ **73.** $7(5n); 35n$ **75.** $17n + 2n; 19n$

77. $n + 12n; 13n$ **79.** $3(n^2 + 4); 3n^2 + 12$ **81.** $\dfrac{3}{4}(16n + 4); 12n + 3$ **83.** $16 - (n + 9); -n + 7$

85. $\dfrac{4n}{2} + 5; 2n + 5$ **87.** $6(n + 8); 6n + 48$ **89.** $7 - (n + 2); -n + 5$ **91.** $\dfrac{1}{3}(n + 6n); \dfrac{7n}{3}$

93. $(8 + n^3) + 2n^3; 3n^3 + 8$ **95.** $(n - 6) + (n + 12); 2n + 6$ **97.** $(n - 20) + (n + 9); 2n - 11$

99. $14 + (n - 3)10; 10n - 16$ **101.** $25 - x$ **103.** $\dfrac{1}{2}L$ **105.** Let x be one number; x and $18 - x$

107. Let G be the number of genes in the roundworm genome; $G + 11{,}000$ **109.** Let N be the total number of

Americans; $\dfrac{3}{4}N$ **111.** Let s be the number of points awarded for a safety; $3s$ **113.** Let d be the diameter of

Dione; $d + 253$ **115.** Let p be the pounds of pecans produced in Texas; $\dfrac{1}{2}p$ **117.** Let p be the world

population in 1980; $2p$ **119.** Let L be the measure of the largest angle; $\dfrac{1}{2}L - 10$ **121.** Let n be either the

number of nickels or the number of dimes; n and $35 - n$ **123.** Let h be the number of hours of overtime

worked; $720 + 27h$ **125.** Let m be the number of minutes of phone calls; $19.95 + 0.08m$ **127.** $\dfrac{1}{4}x$

CHAPTER 2 REVIEW EXERCISES

1. y^2 [2.2.2]   **2.** $3x$ [2.2.3]   **3.** $-10a$ [2.2.3]   **4.** $-4x + 8$ [2.2.4]   **5.** $7x + 38$ [2.2.5]
6. 16 [2.1.1]   **7.** 9 [2.2.1]   **8.** $36y$ [2.2.3]   **9.** $6y - 18$ [2.2.4]   **10.** $-3x + 21y$ [2.2.5]
11. $-8x^2 + 12y^2$ [2.2.4]   **12.** $5x$ [2.2.2]   **13.** 22 [2.1.1]   **14.** $2x$ [2.2.3]
15. $15 - 35b$ [2.2.4]   **16.** $-7x + 33$ [2.2.5]   **17.** The Commutative Property of Multiplication [2.2.1]
18. $24 - 6x$ [2.2.4]   **19.** $5x^2$ [2.2.2]   **20.** $-7x + 14$ [2.2.5]   **21.** $-9y^2 + 9y + 21$ [2.2.4]
22. $2x + y$ [2.2.5]   **23.** 3 [2.1.1]   **24.** $36y$ [2.2.3]   **25.** $5x - 43$ [2.2.5]   **26.** $2x$ [2.2.3]
27. $-6x^2 + 21y^2$ [2.2.4]   **28.** 6 [2.1.1]   **29.** $-x + 6$ [2.2.5]   **30.** $-5a - 2b$ [2.2.2]
31. $-10x^2 + 15x - 30$ [2.2.4]   **32.** $-9x - 7y$ [2.2.2]   **33.** $6a$ [2.2.3]   **34.** $17x - 24$ [2.2.5]
35. $-2x - 5y$ [2.2.2]   **36.** $30b$ [2.2.3]   **37.** 21 [2.2.1]   **38.** $-2x^2 + 4x$ [2.2.2]
39. $-6x^2$ [2.2.3]   **40.** $15x - 27$ [2.2.5]   **41.** $-8a^2 + 3b^2$ [2.2.4]
42. The Multiplication Property of Zero [2.2.1]   **43.** $b - 7b$ [2.3.1]   **44.** $n + 2n^2$ [2.3.1]
45. $\dfrac{6}{n} - 3$ [2.3.1]   **46.** $\dfrac{10}{y - 2}$ [2.3.1]   **47.** $8\left(\dfrac{2n}{16}\right); n$ [2.3.2]   **48.** $4(2 + 5n); 8 + 20n$ [2.3.2]
49. Let h be the height of the triangle; $h + 15$ [2.3.3]   **50.** Let b be the amount of either espresso beans or
mocha java beans; b and $20 - b$ [2.3.3]

CHAPTER 2 TEST

1. $36y$ [2.2.3]   **2.** $4x - 3y$ [2.2.2]   **3.** $10n - 6$ [2.2.5]   **4.** 2 [2.1.1]   **5.** The Multiplication
Property of One [2.2.1]   **6.** $4x - 40$ [2.2.4]   **7.** $\dfrac{1}{12}x^2$ [2.2.2]   **8.** $4x$ [2.2.3]
9. $-24y^2 + 48$ [2.2.4]   **10.** 19 [2.2.1]   **11.** 6 [2.1.1]   **12.** $-3x + 13y$ [2.2.5]
13. b [2.2.2]   **14.** $78a$ [2.2.3]   **15.** $3x^2 - 15x + 12$ [2.2.4]   **16.** -32 [2.1.1]
17. $37x - 5y$ [2.2.5]   **18.** $\dfrac{n + 8}{17}$ [2.3.1]   **19.** $(a + b) - b^2$ [2.3.1]   **20.** $n^2 + 11n$ [2.3.1]
21. $20(n + 9); 20n + 180$ [2.3.2]   **22.** $(n - 3) + (n + 2); 2n - 1$ [2.3.2]   **23.** $n - \dfrac{1}{4}(2n); \dfrac{1}{2}n$ [2.3.2]
24. Let d be the distance from Earth to the sun; $30d$ [2.3.3]
25. Let L be the length of one piece; L and $9 - L$ [2.3.3]

CUMULATIVE REVIEW EXERCISES

1. -7 [1.2.1]   **2.** 5 [1.2.2]   **3.** 24 [1.2.3]   **4.** -5 [1.2.4]   **5.** 1.25 [1.3.1]
6. $\dfrac{3}{5}, 0.60$ [1.3.4]   **7.** $\{-4, -3, -2, -1\}$ [1.1.1]   **8.** 8% [1.3.4]   **9.** $\dfrac{11}{48}$ [1.3.3]
10. $\dfrac{5}{18}$ [1.3.2]   **11.** $\dfrac{1}{4}$ [1.3.2]   **12.** $\dfrac{8}{3}$ [1.4.1]   **13.** -5 [1.4.2]   **14.** $\dfrac{53}{48}$ [1.4.2]
15. -8 [2.1.1]   **16.** $5x^2$ [2.2.2]   **17.** $-a - 12b$ [2.2.2]   **18.** $3a$ [2.2.3]   **19.** $20b$ [2.2.3]
20. $20 - 10x$ [2.2.4]   **21.** $6y - 21$ [2.2.4]   **22.** $-6x^2 + 8y^2$ [2.2.4]   **23.** $-8y^2 + 20y + 32$ [2.2.4]
24. $-10x + 15$ [2.2.5]   **25.** $5x - 17$ [2.2.5]   **26.** $13x - 16$ [2.2.5]   **27.** $6x + 29y$ [2.2.5]
28. $6 - 12n$ [2.3.1]   **29.** $5 + (n - 7); n - 2$ [2.3.2]
30. Let s be the speed of the dial-up connection; $10s$ [2.3.3]

Answers to Chapter 3 Selected Exercises

PREP TEST

1. −4 [1.2.2] **2.** 1 [1.3.2] **3.** −10 [1.3.2] **4.** 0.9 [1.3.4] **5.** 75% [1.3.4]
6. 63 [2.1.1] **7.** $10x - 5$ [2.2.2] **8.** −9 [2.2.2] **9.** $9x - 18$ [2.2.5]

CONCEPT REVIEW 3.1

1. Sometimes true **3.** Always true **5.** Always true **7.** Always true

SECTION 3.1

1. a. equation **b.** expression **3.** Yes **5.** No **7.** No **9.** Yes **11.** Yes **13.** Yes
15. No **17.** No **19.** No **21.** Yes **23.** No **25.** No **29.** 30; 87 **33.** 2
35. 15 **37.** 6 **39.** −6 **41.** 3 **43.** 0 **45.** −2 **47.** −7 **49.** −7
51. −12 **53.** 2 **55.** −5 **57.** 15 **59.** 9 **61.** 14 **63.** −1 **65.** 1
67. $-\dfrac{1}{2}$ **69.** $-\dfrac{3}{4}$ **71.** $\dfrac{1}{12}$ **73.** $-\dfrac{7}{12}$ **75.** $-\dfrac{5}{7}$ **77.** $-\dfrac{1}{3}$ **79.** 1.869 **81.** 0.884
85. divide; 7 **89.** 7 **91.** −7 **93.** −4 **95.** 5 **97.** 9 **99.** −8 **101.** 0
103. −7 **105.** 8 **107.** 12 **109.** 12 **111.** −18 **113.** −18 **115.** 6
117. −12 **119.** 32 **121.** −12 **123.** 15 **125.** 25 **127.** $\dfrac{8}{7}$ **129.** 2 **131.** 3
133. −3 **135.** −22.62 **137.** 1.05 **139.** −3.4 **141.** No **143.** distance; rate; time
145. $3t$; $2.5t$ **147. a.** Greater than **b.** Equal to **c.** 2 mi **149.** The train travels 245 mi in the 5-hour period. **151.** The dietician's average rate of speed is 30 mph. **153.** It will take 4 h to complete the trip. **155.** It would take 31.25 s to walk from one end of the moving sidewalk to the other. **157.** The two joggers will meet 40 min after they start. **159.** It will take her 0.5 h to travel 4 mi upstream. **163.** 24%
165. 7.2 **167.** 400 **169.** 9 **171.** 25% **173.** 5 **175.** 200% **177.** 400
179. 7.7 **181.** 200 **183.** 400 **185.** 20 **187.** 80% **189.** 40% of 80 is equal to 80% of 40. **191.** unknown; 30; 24 **193.** unknown; 32; 0.1 **195.** 250 seats are reserved for wheelchair accessibility. **197.** In the average single-family home, 74 gal of water are used per person per day.
199. 82.1% of the vacation cost is charged. **201.** There is insufficient information. **203.** 12% of the deaths were not attributed to motor vehicle accidents. **205.** In this country 96.1 billion kilowatt-hours of electricity are used for home lighting per year. **207. a.** 25% of the people watching the commercial would have to buy one can of the soft drink. **b.** 4.2% of the people watching the commercial would have to purchase one six-pack of the soft drink. **209.** The price of the less expensive model is $1423.41. **211.** The annual simple interest rate is 9%. **213.** Sal earned $240 in interest from the two accounts. **215.** Makana earned $63 in one year. **217.** The interest rate on the combined investment is between 6% and 9%. **219.** The percent concentration of the hydrogen peroxide is 2%. **221.** Apple Dan's has the greater concentration of apple juice. **223.** 12.5 g of the cream are not glycerine. **225.** The percent concentration of salt in the remaining solution is 12.5%. **227.** −21 **229.** −27 **231.** 21 **233.** 22° **235.** The cost of the dinner was $80. **237.** The new value is two times the original value. **239.** One possible answer is $5x = -10$.

CONCEPT REVIEW 3.2

1. Always true **3.** Never true **5.** Never true **7.** Sometimes true

SECTION 3.2

1. 5; 8 **3.** Negative **5.** 3 **7.** 6 **9.** −1 **11.** 1 **13.** −9 **15.** 3 **17.** 3

19. 3   **21.** 2   **23.** 2   **25.** 4   **27.** $\dfrac{6}{7}$ **29.** $\dfrac{2}{3}$ **31.** -1 **33.** $\dfrac{3}{4}$ **35.** $\dfrac{1}{3}$

37. $-\dfrac{3}{4}$ **39.** $\dfrac{1}{3}$ **41.** $-\dfrac{1}{6}$ **43.** 1   **45.** 0   **47.** $\dfrac{2}{5}$ **49.** $-\dfrac{3}{2}$ **51.** 18   **53.** 8

55. -16 **57.** 25   **59.** 21   **61.** 15   **63.** -16 **65.** $\dfrac{7}{6}$ **67.** $\dfrac{1}{8}$ **69.** $\dfrac{15}{2}$

71. $-\dfrac{18}{5}$ **73.** 2   **75.** 3   **77.** 1   **79.** 2   **81.** 3.95   **83.** -0.8 **85.** -11

87. 0   **89.** 12; 12; Distributive; 2; 84; $2x$; $2x$; 7; Divide; 7; -12 **91.** -2 **93.** 3   **95.** 8

97. 2   **99.** -2 **101.** -3 **103.** 2   **105.** -2 **107.** -2 **109.** -7 **111.** 0

113. -2 **115.** -2 **117.** 4   **119.** 10   **121.** 3   **123.** $\dfrac{3}{4}$ **125.** $\dfrac{2}{7}$ **127.** $-\dfrac{3}{4}$

129. 3   **131.** 10   **133.** $\dfrac{4}{3}$ **135.** 3   **137.** -14 **139.** 7   **141.** $3x$; 18   **143.** a, c

145. 3   **147.** 4   **149.** 2   **151.** 2   **153.** 2   **155.** -7 **157.** $\dfrac{4}{7}$ **159.** $\dfrac{1}{2}$

161. $-\dfrac{1}{3}$ **163.** $\dfrac{10}{3}$ **165.** $-\dfrac{1}{4}$ **167.** 0.5   **169.** 0   **171.** -1 **173.** The car will slide

168 ft.   **175.** The depth of the diver is 40 ft.   **177.** The initial velocity is 8 ft/s.   **179.** The height of

the adult is approximately 182.5 cm.   **181.** The passenger was driven 6 mi.   **183.** He made 8 errors.

185. The population is approximately 51,000 people.   **187.** The break-even point is 350 television sets.

191. 5 ft   **193.** No   **195.** No, the seesaw is not balanced.   **197.** A force of 25 lb must be applied to

the other end of the lever.   **199.** The fulcrum must be placed 10 ft from the 128-pound acrobat.   **201.** No

solution   **203.** $-\dfrac{11}{4}$ **205.** 62   **207.** One possible answer is $3x - 6 = 2x - 2$.

CONCEPT REVIEW 3.3

1. Always true   **3.** Sometimes true   **5.** Never true   **7.** Always true   **9.** Sometimes true

SECTION 3.3

1. includes; $\leq$ **3.**   **5.**   **7.** a, c

9. $x < 2$ **11.** $x > 3$

13. $n \geq 3$ **15.** $x \leq -4$

17. $x \geq -1$ **19.** Only negative numbers   **21.** Only positive numbers

23. $y \geq -9$ **25.** $x < 12$ **27.** $x \geq 5$ **29.** $x < -11$ **31.** $x \leq 10$ **33.** $x \geq -6$

35. $x > 2$ **37.** $d < -\dfrac{1}{6}$ **39.** $x \geq -\dfrac{31}{24}$ **41.** $x < \dfrac{5}{4}$ **43.** $x > \dfrac{5}{24}$ **45.** $x \leq -1.2$

47. $x \leq 0.70$ **49.** $x < -7.3$ **51.** a, b, c   **53.** is reversed   **55.** $x \leq -3$

57. $x > -2$ **59.** $x > 0$

61. $n \geq 4$ **63.** $x > -2$ **65.** $x < \dfrac{5}{3}$

67. $x \geq 5$ **69.** $x > -\dfrac{5}{2}$ **71.** $x \leq -\dfrac{2}{3}$ **73.** $x < -18$ **75.** $x > -16$ **77.** $y \geq 6$

79. $x \geq -6$ **81.** $b \leq 33$ **83.** $n < \dfrac{3}{4}$ **85.** $x \leq -\dfrac{6}{7}$ **87.** $y \leq \dfrac{5}{6}$ **89.** $x \leq \dfrac{27}{28}$

91. $y > -\dfrac{3}{2}$ **93.** $x > -0.5$ **95.** $y \geq -0.8$ **97.** $x \leq 4.2$ **99.** $x \leq 5$ **101.** $x < -5.4$

103. d   **107.** $2x$; $2x$; $3x$; 0; 9; $-3x$; -9, -3; $\leq$; -3; 3   **109.** $x < 4$ **111.** $x < -4$ **113.** $x \geq 1$

115. $x \leq 5$ **117.** $x < 0$ **119.** $x < 20$ **121.** $x > 500$ **123.** $x > 2$ **125.** $x \leq -5$

127. $y \leq \dfrac{5}{2}$ **129.** $x < \dfrac{25}{11}$ **131.** $x > 11$ **133.** $n \leq \dfrac{11}{18}$ **135.** $x \geq 6$ **137.** $x \leq \dfrac{2}{5}$

139. $t < 1$ **141.** $n > \dfrac{7}{10}$ **143.** 3   **145.** c, d   **147.** {1, 2}   **149.** {1, 2, 3}

151. {3, 4, 5}   **153.** {10, 11, 12, 13}   **155.**   **157.**

CHAPTER 3 REVIEW EXERCISES

1. No [3.1.1]   **2.** 20 [3.1.2]   **3.** -7 [3.1.3]   **4.** 7 [3.2.1]   **5.** 4 [3.2.2]

6. $-\dfrac{1}{5}$ [3.2.3]   **7.** 405 [3.1.5]   **8.** 25 [3.1.5]   **9.** 67.5% [3.1.5]

10. [3.3.1]   **11.** $x > 2$ [3.3.1]

12. $x > -4$ [3.3.2]   **13.** $x \geq -4$ [3.3.3]   **14.** $x \geq 4$ [3.3.3]

15. Yes [3.1.1]   **16.** 2.5 [3.1.2]   **17.** -49 [3.1.3]   **18.** $\dfrac{1}{2}$ [3.2.1]

19. $\dfrac{1}{3}$ [3.2.2]   **20.** 10 [3.2.3]   **21.** 16 [3.1.5]   **22.** 125 [3.1.5]   **23.** $16\dfrac{2}{3}\%$ [3.1.5]

24. $x < -4$ [3.3.1]   **25.** $x \leq -2$ [3.3.2]

26. -2 [3.2.3]   **27.** $\dfrac{5}{6}$ [3.1.2]   **28.** 20 [3.1.3]   **29.** 6 [3.2.1]   **30.** 0 [3.2.3]

31. $x < 12$ [3.3.3]   **32.** 15 [3.1.5]   **33.** 5 [3.2.1]   **34.** $x > 5$ [3.3.3]   **35.** 4% [3.1.5]

36. $x > -18$ [3.3.3]   **37.** $x < \dfrac{1}{2}$ [3.3.3]   **38.** The measure of the third angle is 110°. [3.2.4]

39. A force of 24 lb must be applied to the other end of the lever. [3.2.4]   **40.** The width is 6 ft. [3.2.4]
41. The discount is $31.99. [3.2.4]   **42.** Approximately 11,065 plants and animals are at risk of extinction on Earth. [3.1.5]   **43.** The depth is 80 ft. [3.2.4]   **44.** The fulcrum is 3 ft from the 25-pound force. [3.2.4]
45. The length of the rectangle is 24 ft. [3.2.4]   **46.** It will take the motorboat 1.5 h to travel 30 mi. [3.1.4]
47. She must invest $625 in an account that earns an annual simple interest rate of 8%. [3.1.5]
48. The percent concentration of hydrochloric acid is 6%. [3.1.5]

CHAPTER 3 TEST

1. -12 [3.1.3]   **2.** $-\dfrac{1}{2}$ [3.2.2]   **3.** -3 [3.2.1]   **4.** No [3.1.1]   **5.** $\dfrac{1}{8}$ [3.1.2]

6. $-\dfrac{1}{3}$ [3.2.3]   **7.** 5 [3.2.1]   **8.** $\dfrac{1}{2}$ [3.2.2]   **9.** -5 [3.1.2]   **10.** -5 [3.2.2]

11. $-\dfrac{40}{3}$ [3.1.3]   **12.** $-\dfrac{22}{7}$ [3.2.3]   **13.** 2 [3.2.3]   **14.** $\dfrac{12}{11}$ [3.2.3]   **15.** -3 [3.2.3]

16. 125% [3.1.5]   **17.** 40 [3.1.5]   **18.** [3.3.1]

19. $x \leq -1$ [3.3.1]   **20.** $x > -2$ [3.3.2]

21. $x > \dfrac{1}{2}$ [3.3.1]   **22.** $x \leq -\dfrac{9}{2}$ [3.3.3]   **23.** $x \geq -16$ [3.3.2]   **24.** $x \leq 2$ [3.3.3]

25. $x \leq -3$ [3.3.3]   **26.** $x > 2$ [3.3.3]   **27.** 4 [3.2.2]   **28.** 24 [3.1.5]

29. $x \geq 3$ [3.3.2]   **30.** Yes [3.1.1]   **31.** The astronaut would weigh 30 lb on the moon. [3.1.5]   **32.** The final temperature of the water after mixing is 60°C. [3.2.4]
33. The number of calculators produced was 200. [3.2.4]   **34.** They will meet 2 h after they begin. [3.1.4]

35. He must invest $930 in the second account. [3.1.5] **36.** The percent concentration of chocolate syrup in the chocolate milk is 25%. [3.1.5]

CUMULATIVE REVIEW EXERCISES

1. 6 [1.2.2] **2.** −48 [1.2.3] **3.** $-\dfrac{19}{48}$ [1.3.3] **4.** −2 [1.3.2] **5.** 54 [1.4.1]

6. 24 [1.4.2] **7.** 6 [2.1.1] **8.** −17x [2.2.2] **9.** −5a − 2b [2.2.2] **10.** 2x [2.2.3]

11. 36y [2.2.3] **12.** $2x^2 + 6x − 4$ [2.2.4] **13.** −4x + 14 [2.2.5] **14.** 6x − 34 [2.2.5]

15. {−7, −6, −5, −4, −3, −2, −1} [1.1.1] **16.** $87\dfrac{1}{2}\%$ [1.3.4] **17.** 3.42 [1.3.4] **18.** $\dfrac{5}{8}$ [1.3.4]

19. Yes [3.1.1] **20.** −5 [3.1.2] **21.** −25 [3.1.3] **22.** 3 [3.2.1] **23.** −3 [3.2.2]

24. 13 [3.2.3] **25.** $x < -\dfrac{8}{9}$ [3.3.2] **26.** $x \geq 12$ [3.3.3] **27.** $x > 9$ [3.3.3] **28.** $8 - \dfrac{n}{12}$

[2.3.1] **29.** n + (n + 2); 2n + 2 [2.3.2] **30.** b and 35 − b [2.3.3] **31.** Let L be the length of the longer piece; 3 − L [2.3.3] **32.** 17% of the computer programmer's salary is deducted for income tax. [3.1.5] **33.** The equation predicts that the first 4-minute mile was run in 1952. [3.2.4] **34.** The final temperature of the water after mixing is 60°C. [3.2.4] **35.** A force of 24 lb must be applied to the other end of the lever. [3.2.4]

Answers to Chapter 4 Selected Exercises

PREP TEST
1. 0.65R [2.2.2] **2.** 0.03x + 20 [2.2.5] **3.** 3n + 6 [2.2.2] **4.** 5 − 2x [2.3.1]
5. 40% [1.3.4] **6.** 2 [3.2.3] **7.** 0.25 [3.2.1] **8.** x < 4 [3.3.3] **9.** 20 − n [2.3.3]

CONCEPT REVIEW 4.1
1. Always true **3.** Always true **5.** Never true

SECTION 4.1
1. equals **3.** n − 15 = 7; n = 22 **5.** 7n = −21; n = −3 **7.** 3n − 4 = 5; n = 3
9. 4(2n + 3) = 12; n = 0 **11.** 12 = 6(n − 3); n = 5 **13.** 22 = 6n − 2; n = 4
15. 4n + 7 = 2n + 3; n = −2 **17.** 5n − 8 = 8n + 4; n = −4 **19.** 2(n − 25) = 3n; n = −50
21. 3n = 2(20 − n); 8 and 12 **23.** 3n + 2(18 − n) = 44; 8 and 10 **25.** Answers may vary. For example:
n + n + 10 = 14; n + n − 10 = 14 **27.** whole; low-fat **29.** The original value was $16,000.
31. There are 58 calories in a medium-size orange. **33.** The amount of mulch is 15 lb. **35.** The intensity
of the sound is 140 decibels. **37.** The monthly payment is $117.75. **39.** The length is 80 ft. The width is
50 ft. **41.** To replace the water pump, 5 h of labor were required. **43.** You are purchasing 9 tickets.
45. The length of the patio is 15 ft. **47.** The union member worked 168 h during the month of March.
49. The customer used the service for 11 min. **51.** One-third of the container is filled at 3:39 P.M.
53. The package weighs more than 12 oz but not over 13 oz. **55.** There are 60 coins in the bank.

CONCEPT REVIEW 4.2
1. Always true **3.** Always true **5.** Never true

SECTION 4.2
1. consecutive **5.** The integers are 17, 18, and 19. **7.** The integers are 26, 28, and 30. **9.** The
integers are 17, 19, and 21. **11.** The integers are 8 and 10. **13.** The integers are 7 and 9. **15.** The

integers are −9, −8, and −7.   **17.** The integers are 10, 12, and 14.   **19.** No solution   **21. b**
25. Row 1: 5; 5n; Row 2: 32 − n; 10; 10(32 − n)   **27. a.** 100d **b.** 20d **c.** 4d **29.** There are
12 dimes and 15 quarters in the bank.   **31.** The executive bought eight 24¢ stamps and thirty-two 39¢ stamps.
33. There are five 29¢ stamps in the drawer.   **35.** There are 28 quarters in the bank.   **37.** There are 20
one-dollar bills and 6 five-dollar bills in the cash box.   **39.** There are 11 pennies in the bank.   **41.** There
are twenty-seven 22¢ stamps in the collection.   **43.** There are thirteen 3¢ stamps, eighteen 7¢ stamps, and nine
12¢ stamps in the collection.   **45.** There are eighteen 6¢ stamps, six 8¢ stamps, and twenty-four 15¢ stamps.
47. The integers are −12, −10, −8, and −6.   **49.** There is $6.70 in the bank.   **51.** For any three
consecutive odd integers, the sum of the first and third integers is twice the second integer.

CONCEPT REVIEW 4.3
1. Always true   **3.** Always true   **5.** Never true

SECTION 4.3
3. $2x − 3$ **5.** True   **7.** The sides measure 50 ft, 50 ft, and 25 ft.   **9.** The length is 13 m. The width is
8 m.   **11.** The length is 40 ft. The width is 20 ft.   **13.** The sides measure 40 cm, 20 cm, and 50 cm.
15. The length is 130 ft. The width is 39 ft.   **17.** The width is 12 ft.   **19.** Each side measures 12 in.
21. a. 90°   **b.** 180°   **c.** 360°   **d.** between 0° and 90°   **e.** between 90° and 180°   **f.** 90°
g. 180°   **23.** 90; 37; 37°   **25.** The complement of a 28° angle is 62°.   **27.** The supplement of a 73°
angle is 107°.   **29.** 35°   **31.** 20°   **33.** 53°   **35.** 121°   **37.** 15°   **39.** 18°
41. 45°   **43.** 49°   **45.** 12°   **47.** False   **49.** True   **51.** $\angle a = 122°$, $\angle b = 58°$
53. $\angle a = 44°$, $\angle b = 136°$ **55.** 20°   **57.** 40°   **59.** 128°   **61.** Vertical; 180°; 50°; 85°; 135°; 45°
63. $\angle x = 160°$, $\angle y = 145°$ **65.** $\angle a = 40°$, $\angle b = 140°$ **67.** $75° − x$ **69.** The measure of the third
angle is 45°.   **71.** The measure of the third angle is 73°.   **73.** The measure of the third angle is 43°.
75. The angles measure 38°, 38°, and 104°.   **77.** The angles measure 60°, 30°, and 90°.
79. True   **81.** True   **83.** The length is 9 cm. The width is 4 cm.

CONCEPT REVIEW 4.4
1. Always true   **3.** Never true   **5.** Always true

SECTION 4.4
3. 40; unknown; 0.25   **5.** The selling price is $56.   **7.** The selling price is $565.64.   **9.** The markup
rate is 75%.   **11.** The markup rate is 44.4%.   **13.** The markup rate is 60%.   **15.** The cost of the
compact disc player is $120.   **17.** The cost of the basketball is $59.   **19.** The cost of the computer is $1750.
21. True   **25.** 318.75; 375; unknown   **27.** The sale price is $101.25.   **29.** The discount price is
$218.50.   **31.** The discount rate is 25%.   **33.** The discount rate is 23.2%.   **35.** The markdown rate is
38%.   **37.** The regular price is $510.   **39.** The regular price is $300.   **41.** The regular price is $275.
43. True   **45.** The markup is $18.   **47.** The markup rate is 40%.   **49.** The cost of the camera is $230.
51. The regular price is $80.   **53.** No. The single discount that would give the same sale price is 28%.

CONCEPT REVIEW 4.5
1. Always true   **3.** Always true   **5.** Never true

SECTION 4.5
1. Row 1: 0.052; 0.052x; Row 2: x + 1000; 0.072; 0.072(x + 1000)   **3.** $9000 was invested at 7%, and $6000 was
invested at 6.5%.   **5.** $1500 was invested in the mutual fund.   **7.** $200,000 was deposited at 10%, and
$100,000 was deposited at 8.5%.   **9.** Teresa has $3000 invested in bonds that earn 8% annual simple interest.

11. She has $2500 invested at 11%.   **13.** $40,500 was invested at 8%, and $13,500 was invested at 12%.
15. The total amount invested was $650,000.   **17.** The total amount invested was $500,000.
19. a. 3% and 5%   **b.** $5000   **21.** The amount of the research consultant's investment is $45,000.
23. The total annual interest received was $3040.   **25.** The value of the investment in three years is $3831.87.
27. a. By age 55, the couple should have $170,000 saved for retirement.

CONCEPT REVIEW 4.6

1. Always true   **3.** Always true   **5.** Never true   **7.** Always true

SECTION 4.6

1. a. $10.50   **b.** $.36   **5.** The clinic should use 2 lb of dog food and 3 lb of vitamin supplement.
7. The mixture costs $6.98 per pound.   **9.** 56 oz of the $4.30 alloy and 144 oz of the $1.80 alloy were used.
11. You can add 1 lb of blueberries.   **13.** 10 kg of hard candy must be mixed with the jelly beans.
15. To make the mixture, 3 lb of caramel are needed.   **17.** To make the mixture, 300 lb of the $.80 meal are
needed.   **19.** 37 lb of almonds and 63 lb of walnuts were used.   **21.** The cost per pound is $1.40.
23. The cost per ounce is $3.   **25. c, e,** and **f**   **27.** 0.09; 225   **31.** The percent concentration is 24%.
33. 20 gal of the 15% solution must be mixed with 5 gal of the 20% solution.   **35.** 30 lb of 25% wool yarn is
used.   **37.** 6.25 gal of the plant food that is 9% nitrogen are combined with the plant food that is 25% nitrogen.
39. The percent concentration is 19%.   **41.** 30 oz of the potpourri that is 60% lavender are used.
43. To make the solution, 100 ml of the 7% solution and 200 ml of the 4% solution are used.   **45.** 150 oz of
pure chocolate are added.   **47.** The percent concentration is 12%.   **49.** 1.2 oz of dried apricots must be
added.   **51.** False   **53.** The cost is $3.65 per ounce.   **55.** 10 oz of water evaporated from the
solution.   **57.** 75 g of pure water must be added.   **59.** 85 adults and 35 children attended the performance.

CONCEPT REVIEW 4.7

1. Never true   **3.** Never true   **5.** Always true

SECTION 4.7

1. a. Row 1: $3r$; 5; $15r$; Row 2: 5; $5r$ **b.** $15r$; $5r$; 3520   **3. a**   **5.** The speed of the first plane is
105 mph. The speed of the second plane is 130 mph.   **7.** The second skater overtakes the first skater after 40 s.
9. Michael's boat will be alongside the tour boat in 2 h.   **11.** The airport is 120 mi from the corporate offices.
13. The sailboat traveled 36 mi in the first 3 h.   **15.** The passenger train is traveling at 50 mph. The freight
train is traveling at 30 mph.   **17.** It takes the second ship 1 h to catch up to the first ship.   **19.** The two
trains will pass each other in 4 h.   **21.** The average speed on the winding road was 34 mph.   **23.** The car
overtakes the cyclist 48 mi from the starting point.   **25.** The rate of the cyclist is 13 mph.   **27.** The rate of
the car is 60 mph.   **29.** The joggers will meet at 7:48 A.M.   **31.** The cyclist's average speed is $13\frac{1}{3}$ mph.

CONCEPT REVIEW 4.8

1. Never true   **3.** Always true   **5.** Never true

SECTION 4.8

1. $n \le 50$ **3.** $500 > 0.12n$ **5.** The smallest integer is 2.   **7.** The amount of income tax to be paid is
$3150 or more.   **9.** The organization must collect more than 440 lb.   **11.** The student must score 78 or
better.   **13.** The dollar amount in sales must be more than $5714.   **15.** The dollar amount the agent
expects to sell is $20,000 or less.   **17.** A person must use this service for more than 60 min.   **19.** 8 ounces
or less must be added.   **21.** The ski area is more than 38 mi away.   **23.** The maximum number of miles
you can drive is 166.   **25. b, c,** and **e**   **27.** The integers are 1, 3, and 5 or 3, 5, or 7.   **29.** The crew
can prepare 8 to 12 aircraft in this period of time.   **31.** The minimum number is 467 calendars.

CHAPTER 4 REVIEW EXERCISES

1. $2x - 7 = x$; 7 [4.1.1] **2.** The length of the shorter piece is 14 in. [4.1.2] **3.** The two numbers are 8 and 13. [4.1.2] **4.** $2x + 6 = 4(x - 2)$; 7 [4.1.1] **5.** The discount rate is $33\frac{1}{3}\%$. [4.4.2] **6.** $8000 is invested at 6%, and $7000 is invested at 7%. [4.5.1] **7.** The angles measure 65°, 65°, and 50°. [4.3.3] **8.** The rate of the motorcyclist is 45 mph. [4.7.1] **9.** The measures of the three angles are 16°, 82°, and 82°. [4.3.3] **10.** The markup rate is 80%. [4.4.1] **11.** The concentration of butterfat is 14%. [4.6.2] **12.** The length is 80 ft. The width is 20 ft. [4.3.1] **13.** A minimum of 1151 copies can be ordered. [4.8.1] **14.** The regular price is $32. [4.4.2] **15.** 7 qt of cranberry juice and 3 qt of apple juice were used. [4.6.1] **16.** The cost is $25.95. [4.4.1] **17.** The two numbers are 6 and 30. [4.1.2] **18.** $5600 is deposited in the 12% account. [4.5.1] **19.** The cards are the 7 and 8 of hearts. [4.2.1] **20.** One liter of pure water should be added. [4.6.2] **21.** The lowest score the student can receive is 72. [4.8.1] **22.** $-7 = \frac{1}{2}x - 10$; 6 [4.1.1] **23.** The height is 1063 ft. [4.1.2] **24.** The measures of the three angles are 75°, 60°, and 45°. [4.3.3] **25.** There are 128 one-dollar bills. [4.2.2] **26.** The length of the longer piece is 7 ft. [4.1.2] **27.** The number of hours of consultation was 8. [4.1.2] **28.** There are 77 12¢ stamps and 37 17¢ stamps. [4.2.2] **29.** The cost is $671.25. [4.4.1] **30.** They will meet after 4 min. [4.7.1] **31.** The measures of the three sides are 8 in., 12 in., and 15 in. [4.3.1] **32.** The integers are -17, -15, and -13. [4.2.1] **33.** The maximum width is 10 ft. [4.8.1] **34.** $\angle a = 138°$, $\angle b = 42°$ [4.3.2]

CHAPTER 4 TEST

1. $6n + 13 = 3n - 5$; $n = -6$ [4.1.1] **2.** $3n - 15 = 27$; $n = 14$ [4.1.1] **3.** The numbers are 8 and 10. [4.1.2] **4.** The lengths are 6 ft and 12 ft. [4.1.2] **5.** The cost is $200. [4.4.1] **6.** The discount rate is 20%. [4.4.2] **7.** 20 gal of the 15% solution must be added. [4.6.2] **8.** The length is 14 m. The width is 5 m. [4.3.1] **9.** The integers are 5, 7, and 9. [4.2.1] **10.** Five or more residents are in the nursing home. [4.8.1] **11.** $5000 is invested at 10%, and $2000 is invested at 15%. [4.5.1] **12.** 8 lb of the $7 coffee and 4 lb of the $4 coffee should be used. [4.6.1] **13.** The rate of the first plane is 225 mph. The rate of the second plane is 125 mph. [4.7.1] **14.** The measures of the three angles are 48°, 33°, and 99°. [4.3.3] **15.** There are 15 nickels and 35 quarters in the bank. [4.2.2] **16.** The amounts to be deposited are $1400 at 6.75% and $1000 at 9.45%. [4.5.1] **17.** The minimum length is 24 ft. [4.8.1] **18.** The sale price is $79.20. [4.4.2]

CUMULATIVE REVIEW EXERCISES

1. $-12, -6$ [1.1.1] **2.** 6 [1.2.2] **3.** $-\frac{1}{6}$ [1.4.1] **4.** $-\frac{11}{6}$ [1.4.2] **5.** -18 [1.1.2] **6.** -24 [2.1.1] **7.** $9x + 4y$ [2.2.2] **8.** $-12 + 8x + 20x^3$ [2.2.4] **9.** $4x + 4$ [2.2.5] **10.** $6x^2$ [2.2.2] **11.** No [3.1.1] **12.** -3 [3.2.1] **13.** -15 [3.1.3] **14.** 3 [3.2.1] **15.** -10 [3.2.3] **16.** $\frac{2}{5}$ [1.3.4] **17.** $x \geq 4$ [3.3.2] **18.** $x \geq -3$ [3.3.2] **19.** $x > 18$ [3.3.3] **20.** $x \geq 4$ [3.3.3] **21.** 2.5% [1.3.4] **22.** 12% [1.3.4] **23.** 3 [3.1.5] **24.** 45 [3.1.5] **25.** $8n + 12 = 4n$; $n = -3$ [4.1.1] **26.** The area of the garage is 600 ft². [4.1.2] **27.** The number of hours of labor is 5. [4.1.2] **28.** 20% of the libraries had the reference book. [3.1.5] **29.** The amount of money deposited is $2000. [4.5.1] **30.** The markup rate is 75%. [4.4.1] **31.** 60 g of the gold alloy must be used. [4.6.1] **32.** 30 oz of pure water must be added. [4.6.2] **33.** The measure of one of the equal angles is 47°. [4.3.3] **34.** The middle even integer is 14. [4.2.1] **35.** There are 7 dimes in the bank. [4.2.2]

Answers to Chapter 5 Selected Exercises

PREP TEST

1. -3 [1.4.2]   **2.** -1 [2.1.1]   **3.** $-3x + 12$ [2.2.4]   **4.** -2 [3.2.1]   **5.** 5 [3.2.1]

6. -2 [3.2.1]   **7.** 13 [2.1.1]   **8.** $\frac{3}{4}x - 4$ [2.2.4]   **9.** **a, b, c**   [3.3.1]

CONCEPT REVIEW 5.1

1. Always true   **3.** Never true   **5.** Never true   **7.** Always true

SECTION 5.1

1. right; down   **5.**   **7.**   **9.**

11. $A(2, 3), B(4, 0), C(-4, 1), D(-2, -2)$ **13.** $A(-2, 5), B(3, 4), C(0, 0), D(-3, -2)$ **15. a.** $2; -4$
b. $1; -3$ **17. a.** I   **b.** II   **c.** IV   **d.** III   **19.** $26; 60; 31; 56; 26; 60; 31; 56$

21.   **23.**

25.   **27.** Denominator   **29.** The average rate of change is $4°$ per hour.

31. a. 10.45 cents   **b.** $9.7\overline{3}$ cents; less than   **33. a.** The average rate of change is $-2.1\overline{3}$ million people
per year.   **b.** The average rate of change is -1.3 million people per year.   **35. a.** -7.16 cents
b. 1975–1980; 4.8 cents   **37.** From 30 to 40 min   **39.** 1 unit   **41.** 0 units   **43.** 1 unit
45. $(0, 0)$

CONCEPT REVIEW 5.2

1. Never true   **3.** Always true   **5.** Never true   **7.** Never true   **9.** Always true

SECTION 5.2

1. $x; y$ **3.** $m = 4, b = 1$ **5.** $m = \frac{5}{6}, b = \frac{1}{6}$ **7.** Yes   **9.** No   **11.** No   **13.** Yes

15. No   **17.** (3, 7)   **19.** (6, 3)   **21.** (0, 1)   **23.** (−5, 0)   **25. a.** 2   **b.** Negative

27. a. −7; −1; −7   **b.** −4; 0; −4   **c.** −1; 1; −1   **29.**   **31.**

33.   **35.**   **37.**   **39.**   **41.**

43.   **45.**   **47.**   **49.**   **51.**

53.   **55.**   **57.**   **59.** x; $-2y$; -2; $\dfrac{1}{2}$; 5   **61.** horizontal

63. $y = -3x + 10$ **65.** $y = 4x - 3$ **67.** $y = -\dfrac{3}{2}x + 3$ **69.** $y = \dfrac{2}{5}x - 2$ **71.** $y = -\dfrac{2}{7}x + 2$

73. $y = -\dfrac{1}{3}x + 2$ **75.**   **77.**   **79.**   **81.**

83.   **85.**   **87.** (3, 0), (0, −3)   **89.** (3, 0), (0, −6)   **91.** (10, 0), (0, −2)

93. (−4, 0), (0, 12)   **95.** (0, 0), (0, 0)   **97.** (−6, 0), (0, 3)   **99.**   **101.**

103.   **105.**   **107.**   **109.**

111.   **113.**   **115.**   **117.**

119.   **121.** To the right   **123. a.** $y = -\dfrac{1}{2}x - 5$ **b.** $(-2, -4)$ **125.** 1 unit

CONCEPT REVIEW 5.3

1. Always true   **3.** Never true   **5.** Never true

SECTION 5.3

3. $2; -4; 3; 1$ **5.** -2 **7.** $\dfrac{1}{3}$ **9.** $-\dfrac{5}{2}$ **11.** $-\dfrac{1}{2}$ **13.** -1 **15.** Undefined   **17.** 0

19. $-\dfrac{1}{3}$ **21.** 0   **23.** -5 **25.** Undefined   **27.** $-\dfrac{2}{3}$ **29.** Yes   **31.** No

33. $m = 50$. The electronic mail sorter sorts 50 pieces of mail per minute.   **35.** $m = -0.02$. The car uses 0.02 gal of gasoline per mile driven.   **37. a.** $a = c, b \neq d$ **b.** $b = d, a \neq c$ **c.** Downward to the right

39. $5; (0, -3)$ **41.**   **43.**   **45.**   **47.**

49.   **51.**   **53.**   **55.**   **57.**

59. Above; downward to the right   **61.** Increasing the coefficient of x increases the slope.   **63.** Increasing the constant term increases the y-intercept.   **65.** i and D; ii and C; iii and B; iv and F; v and E; vi and A

67. No, not all graphs of straight lines have a y-intercept. In general, vertical lines do not have a y-intercept. For example, $x = 2$ does not have a y-intercept.

CONCEPT REVIEW 5.4

1. Always true   **3.** Sometimes true   **5.** Always true

SECTION 5.4

1. $3; 1; 3x + 1$ **3.** $y = 2x + 2$ **5.** $y = -3x - 1$ **7.** $y = \dfrac{1}{3}x$ **9.** $y = \dfrac{3}{4}x - 5$ **11.** $y = -\dfrac{3}{5}x$

13. $y = \dfrac{1}{4}x + \dfrac{5}{2}$ **15.** $y = -\dfrac{2}{3}x - 7$ **19.** $y = 2x - 3$ **21.** $y = -2x - 3$ **23.** $y = \dfrac{2}{3}x$

25. $y = \dfrac{1}{2}x + 2$ **27.** $y = -\dfrac{3}{4}x - 2$ **29.** $y = \dfrac{3}{4}x + \dfrac{5}{2}$ **31.** $y = -\dfrac{4}{3}x - 9$

33. a. $y - b = m(x - 0)$ **b.** Yes   **35.** $y = 3x + 4$ **37.** $y = -x - 4$ **39.** $y = -\dfrac{6}{5}x + 5$

41. $y = -\dfrac{2}{5}x - 7$ **43.** $y = 5$ **45.** $x = 5$ **47.** $y = \dfrac{4}{5}x + 8$ **49.** $y = -\dfrac{1}{2}x - 2$

51. $y = -\dfrac{4}{3}x - 3$ **53.** $y = 3x - 3$ **55.** $y = 3x$ **57.** $x = 3$ **59.** Yes; however, all of the points must be on the same line.   **61.** Yes; $y = -x + 6$ **63.** No   **65.** 7   **67.** -1

69. $F = \dfrac{9}{5}C + 32$ **71. a.** $y = 2.86x - 5438.4$ **b.** 324.5 million   **c.** 0.9 million

CONCEPT REVIEW 5.5

1. Always true   **3.** Never true   **5.** Always true   **7.** Always true

SECTION 5.5

1. ordered pairs; domain; range   **3.** No
5. {(87.7, 91.0), (71.4, 84.0), (79.1, 84.5), (90.1, 91.6), (82.5, 94.3), (68.4, 74.5), (82.5, 80.2)}; no
7. {(4, 411), (5, 514), (6, 618), (7, 720), (8, 823)}; Yes   **9.** {(55, 273), (65, 355), (75, 447), (85, 549)}; yes
11. Domain: {0, 2, 4, 6}; range: {0}; yes   **13.** Domain: {2}; range: {2, 4, 6, 8}; no   **15.** Domain: {0, 1, 2, 3};
range {0, 1, 2, 3}; yes   **17.** Domain: {−3, −2, −1, 1, 2, 3}; range: {−3, 2, 3, 4}; yes   **19.** 40; (10, 40)
21. −11; (−6, −11)   **23.** 12; (−2, 12)   **25.** $\dfrac{7}{2}; \left(\dfrac{1}{2}, \dfrac{7}{2}\right)$ **27.** 2; (−5, 2)   **29.** 32; (−4, 32)
31. Range: {−19, −13, −7, −1, 5}; the ordered pairs (−5, −19), (−3, −13), (−1, −7), (1, −1), and (3, 5) belong to the
function.   **33.** Range: {1, 2, 3, 4, 5}; the ordered pairs (−4, 1), (−2, 2), (0, 3), (2, 4), and (4, 5) belong to the
function.   **35.** Range: {6, 7, 15}; the ordered pairs (−3, 15), (−1, 7), (0, 6), (1, 7), and (3, 15) belong to the function.
37. $x; y; f(x)$ **39.**   **41.**   **43.**   **45.**

47.   **49.**   **51.**   **53.**   **55.**

57.   **59.**   **61.** No   **63. a.** $f(x) = 30{,}000 - 5000x$

b. 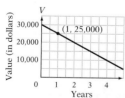   **c.** The value of the computer after 1 year is $25,000.

65. a. $f(m) = 0.18m + 50$ **b.**   **c.** The cost to drive this car 500 mi is $140.

CONCEPT REVIEW 5.6

1. Never true   **3.** Always true   **5.** Always true

SECTION 5.6

3.   **5.**   **7.**   **9.**   **11.**

13.   **15.**   **17.**   **19.** Negative   **21.** $y \geq 2x + 2$

23. $y > 2$ **25.**   **27.**

CHAPTER 5 REVIEW EXERCISES

1. $(3, 0)$ [5.2.1]   **2.** $y = 3x - 1$ [5.4.1/5.4.2]   **3.** [5.2.3]   **4.** 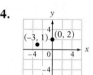 [5.1.1]

5. 79 [5.5.1]   **6.** 0 [5.3.1]   **7.** [5.2.2]   **8.** [5.2.3]

9. $y = -\dfrac{2}{3}x + \dfrac{4}{3}$ [5.4.1/5.4.2]   **10.** $(2, 0), (0, -3)$ [5.2.3]   **11.** [5.3.2]

12. [5.5.2]   **13.** $y = \dfrac{2}{3}x + 3$ [5.4.1/5.4.2]   **14.** 2 [5.3.1]   **15.** -4 [5.5.1]

16. Domain: $\{-20, -10, 0, 10\}$; range: $\{-10, -5, 0, 5\}$; yes [5.5.1]   **17.** [5.2.2]

18. [5.3.2]   **19.** [5.1.1]   **20.** [5.5.2]

21. $(6, 0), (0, -4)$ [5.2.3]   **22.** $y = 2x + 2$ [5.4.1/5.4.2]   **23.** [5.2.3]

24. [5.6.1]   **25.** Yes [5.3.1]   **26.** $y = \dfrac{5}{4}x + 9$ [5.4.3]   **27.** [5.3.2]

28. [5.2.3]   **29.** $(-2, -5)$ [5.2.1]   **30.** $y = -3x + 2$ [5.4.1/5.4.2]

31. [5.5.2]   **32.** 0 [5.5.1]   **33.** $y = -\dfrac{1}{3}x - 2$ [5.4.3]   **34.** $y = \dfrac{1}{2}x - 2$ [5.4.1/5.4.2]

35. Yes [5.2.1]   **36.** $(2, -1)$ [5.2.1]   **37.** $(0, 0); (0, 0)$ [5.2.3]   **38.** $y = 3$ [5.4.1/5.4.2]

39. [5.6.1]   **40.** [5.3.2]   **41.** $y = 3x - 4$ [5.4.1/5.4.2]

42. [5.2.3]   **43.** Domain: $\{-10, -5, 5\}$; range $\{-5, 0\}$; no [5.5.1]

44. Range: $\{-53, -23, 7, 37, 67\}$ [5.5.1]   **45.** Range: $\{2, 3, 4, 5, 6\}$ [5.5.1]

46. [5.1.2]   **47.** 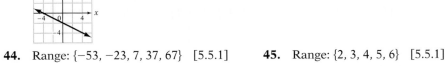 [5.1.2]

48. $\{(25, 4.8), (35, 3.5), (40, 2.1), (20, 5.5), (45, 1.0)\}$; yes [5.5.1]

49. **a.** $f(s) = 70s + 40{,}000$ **b.**   **c.** The contractor's cost to build a house of 1500 ft² is $145,000. [5.5.2]

50. The average hourly rate of change was 46 cents per year. [5.1.3]

CHAPTER 5 TEST

1. $y = -\dfrac{1}{3}x$ [5.4.1/5.4.2] **2.** $\dfrac{7}{11}$ [5.3.1] **3.** $(8, 0); (0, -12)$ [5.2.3] **4.** $(9, -13)$ [5.2.1]

5. [5.2.3] **6.** [5.2.2] **7.** 10 [5.5.1] **8.** No [5.2.1]

9. [5.3.2] **10.** [5.6.1] **11.** [5.1.1]

12. [5.3.2] **13.** $y = \dfrac{3}{5}x + 8$ [5.4.3] **14.** $y = -\dfrac{2}{5}x + 7$ [5.4.1/5.4.2]

15. $y = 4x - 7$ [5.4.1/5.4.2] **16.** 13 [5.5.1] **17.** [5.2.2] **18.** [5.6.1]

19. [5.2.3] **20.** [5.3.2] **21.** [5.5.2]

22. [5.5.2] **23.** 25 [5.5.1] **24.** $\{-22, -7, 5, 11, 26\}$ [5.5.1] **25.** No [5.3.1]

26. The average annual rate of change was 0.5 million drivers per year. [5.1.3]

27. [5.1.2] **28. a.** $f(t) = 8t + 1000$ **b.**

c. The cost to manufacture 340 toasters is $3720. [5.5.2]

29. $\{(8.5, 64), (9.4, 68), (10.1, 76), (11.4, 87), (12.0, 92)\}$; yes [5.5.1] **30.** The slope is 36. The cost of lumber has been increasing by $36 per month. [5.3.1]

CUMULATIVE REVIEW EXERCISES

1. -12 [1.4.2] **2.** $-\dfrac{5}{8}$ [2.1.1] **3.** $-17x + 28$ [2.2.5] **4.** $\dfrac{3}{2}$ [3.2.1] **5.** 1 [3.2.3]

6. $\dfrac{1}{15}$ [1.3.4] **7.** $\{1, 2, 3, 4, 5, 6, 7, 8\}$ [1.1.1] **8.** $-4, 0, 5$ [1.1.1] **9.** $a \geq -1$ [3.3.3]

10. $y = \frac{4}{5}x - 3$ [5.2.3]   **11.** $(-2, -7)$ [5.2.1]   **12.** 0 [5.3.1]   **13.** $(4, 0); (0, 10)$ [5.2.3]

14. $y = -x + 5$ [5.4.1/5.4.2]   **15.** [5.2.2]   **16.** [5.2.3]

17. [5.5.2]   **18.** [5.6.1]

19. Domain: {0, 1, 2, 3, 4}; range: {0, 1, 2, 3, 4}; yes [5.5.1]   **20.** -11 [5.5.1]
21. {$-7, -2, 3, 8, 13, 18$} [5.5.1]   **22.** 7 and 17 [4.1.2]   **23.** The fulcrum is 7 ft from the 80-pound
force. [3.2.4]   **24.** The length of the first side is 22 ft. [4.3.1]   **25.** The sale price is $62.30. [4.4.2]

Answers to Chapter 6 Selected Exercises

PREP TEST

1. $y = \frac{3}{4}x - 6$ [5.2.3]   **2.** 1000 [3.2.3]   **3.** $33y$ [2.2.5]   **4.** $10x - 10$ [2.2.5]   **5.** Yes [5.2.1]
6. $(4, 0)$ and $(0, -3)$ [5.2.3]   **7.** Yes [5.3.1]   **8.** [5.2.2]   **9.** 1.5 h [4.7.1]

CONCEPT REVIEW 6.1

1. Always true   **3.** Sometimes true   **5.** Never true

SECTION 6.1

3. Yes   **5.** Yes   **7.** No   **9.** No   **11.** No   **13.** Yes   **15.** Yes   **19.** Independent
21. Dependent   **23.** Inconsistent   **25.** $(2, -1)$ **27.** No solution   **29.** $(-2, 4)$ **31.** $(4, 1)$
33. $(4, 1)$ **35.** $(4, 3)$ **37.** $(3, -2)$ **39.** $(2, -2)$ **41.** The system of equations is inconsistent and
has no solution.   **43.** The system of equations is dependent. The solutions are the ordered pairs that satisfy the
equation $y = 2x - 2$.   **45.** $(1, -4)$ **47.** $(0, 0)$ **49.** The system of equations is inconsistent and has no
solution.   **51.** $(0, -2)$ **53.** $(1, -1)$ **55.** $(2, 0)$ **57.** $(-3, -2)$
59. The system of equations is inconsistent and has no solution.   **61.** Inconsistent
63. $y = 2$ **65.** $y = x$ **67. a.** Always true **b.** Never true **c.** Always true
    $y = x + 4$ $y = -x + 2$

CONCEPT REVIEW 6.2

1. Always true   **3.** Never true   **5.** Never true

SECTION 6.2

1. 2; 1; 2; 1   **3.** $(2, 1)$ **5.** $(4, 1)$ **7.** $(-1, 1)$ **9.** $(3, 1)$ **11.** $(1, 1)$ **13.** $(-1, 1)$
15. The system of equations is inconsistent and has no solution.   **17.** The system of equations is inconsistent

and has no solution. **19.** $\left(-\dfrac{3}{4}, -\dfrac{3}{4}\right)$ **21.** $\left(\dfrac{9}{5}, \dfrac{6}{5}\right)$ **23.** $(-7, -23)$ **25.** $(1, 1)$ **27.** $(2, 0)$

29. $(2, 1)$ **31.** $\left(\dfrac{9}{19}, -\dfrac{13}{19}\right)$ **33.** $(5, 7)$ **35.** $(1, 7)$ **37.** $\left(\dfrac{17}{5}, -\dfrac{7}{5}\right)$ **39.** $\left(-\dfrac{6}{11}, \dfrac{31}{11}\right)$

41. $(2, 3)$ **43.** $(0, 0)$ **45.** The system of equations is dependent. The solutions are the ordered pairs that satisfy the equation $3x + y = 4$. **47.** $\left(\dfrac{20}{17}, -\dfrac{15}{17}\right)$ **49.** $(5, 2)$ **51.** $(-17, -8)$ **53.** $\left(-\dfrac{5}{7}, \dfrac{13}{7}\right)$

55. $(3, -2)$ **57.** Dependent **59.** $\left(-\dfrac{11}{20}, \dfrac{23}{40}\right)$ **61.** $(3, -2)$ **63.** $(1, 7)$ **65.** 2 **67.** 2

CONCEPT REVIEW 6.3
1. Always true **3.** Never true **5.** Never true

SECTION 6.3
1. a 3 **b** -4 **3.** $(5, -1)$ **5.** $(1, 3)$ **7.** $(1, 1)$ **9.** $(3, -2)$ **11.** The system of equations is dependent. The solutions are the ordered pairs that satisfy the equation $2x - y = 1$. **13.** $(3, 1)$
15. The system of equations is inconsistent and has no solution. **17.** $(1, 3)$ **19.** $(2, 0)$ **21.** $(0, 0)$
23. $(5, -2)$ **25.** $(-17, 7)$ **27.** $(3, 4)$ **29.** $(1, -1)$ **31.** The system of equations is dependent. The solutions are the ordered pairs that satisfy the equation $x + 3y = 4$. **33.** $(3, 1)$ **35.** $\left(1, \dfrac{1}{3}\right)$

37. $(1, 1)$ **39.** $\left(\dfrac{1}{2}, -\dfrac{1}{2}\right)$ **41.** $\left(\dfrac{2}{3}, \dfrac{1}{9}\right)$ **43.** $\left(\dfrac{7}{25}, -\dfrac{1}{25}\right)$ **45.** $\left(\dfrac{11}{12}, -\dfrac{7}{6}\right)$ **47.** $(1, 4)$

49. $(1, 2)$ **51.** $A = 3, B = -1$ **53.** $A = 2$ **55. a.** $k \neq 1$ **b.** $k \neq \dfrac{3}{2}$ **c.** $k \neq 4$

CONCEPT REVIEW 6.4
1. Always true **3.** Never true **5.** Never true

SECTION 6.4
1. Row 1: $b + c$; 2; $2(b + c)$; Row 2: $b - c$; 3; $3(b - c)$ **3.** Greater than **5.** The speed of the whale in calm water is 35 mph. The rate of the current is 5 mph. **7.** The team's rowing rate in calm water was 14 km/h. The rate of the current was 6 km/h. **9.** The rate of the boat in calm water was 7 mph. The rate of the current was 3 mph. **11.** The speed of the jet in calm air was 525 mph. The rate of the wind was 35 mph. **13.** The rate of the plane in calm air was 100 mph. The rate of the wind was 20 mph. **15.** The speed of the helicopter in calm air was 225 mph. The rate of the wind was 45 mph. **17.** Table 1: Row 1: 4; A; 4A; Row 2: 2; C; 2C; Table 2: Row 1: 2; A; 2A; Row 2: 3; C; 3C **19.** Less than **21.** The cost is $245. **23.** The cost of the wheat is $.65 per pound. The cost of the rye is $.70 per pound. **25.** The daytime rate is $7 per hour. The nighttime rate is $9 per hour. **27.** The team scored 21 two-point baskets and 15 three-point baskets. **29.** There are 8 nickels and 10 quarters in the first bank. **31.** There are 8 dimes and 10 quarters in the bank. **33.** The two angles measure 55° and 125°. **35.** $6000 was invested in the 9% account, and $4000 was invested in the 8% account. **37.** There are 0 dimes and 5 nickels, or 1 dime and 3 nickels, or 2 dimes and 1 nickel in the bank.

CHAPTER 6 REVIEW EXERCISES
1. $(-1, 1)$ [6.2.1] **2.** $(2, -3)$ [6.1.1] **3.** $(-3, 1)$ [6.3.1] **4.** $(1, 6)$ [6.2.1] **5.** $(1, 1)$ [6.1.1]
6. $(1, -5)$ [6.3.1] **7.** $(3, 2)$ [6.2.1] **8.** The system of equations is dependent. The solutions are the ordered pairs that satisfy the equation $8x - y = 25$. [6.3.1] **9.** $(3, -1)$ [6.3.1] **10.** $(1, -3)$ [6.1.1]
11. $(-2, -7)$ [6.3.1] **12.** $(4, 0)$ [6.2.1] **13.** Yes [6.1.1] **14.** $\left(-\dfrac{5}{6}, \dfrac{1}{2}\right)$ [6.3.1]

15. $(-1, -2)$ [6.3.1] **16.** $(3, -3)$ [6.1.1] **17.** The system of equations is inconsistent and has no solution. [6.3.1] **18.** $\left(-\dfrac{1}{3}, \dfrac{1}{6}\right)$ [6.2.1] **19.** The system of equations is dependent. The solutions are the ordered pairs that satisfy the equation $y = 2x - 4$. [6.1.1] **20.** The system of equations is dependent. The solutions are the ordered pairs that satisfy the equation $3x + y = -2$. [6.3.1] **21.** $(-2, -13)$ [6.3.1] **22.** The system of equations is dependent. The solutions are the ordered pairs that satisfy the equation $4x + 3y = 12$. [6.2.1] **23.** $(4, 2)$ [6.1.1] **24.** The system of equations is inconsistent and has no solution. [6.3.1] **25.** $\left(\dfrac{1}{2}, -1\right)$ [6.2.1] **26.** No [6.1.1] **27.** $\left(\dfrac{2}{3}, -\dfrac{1}{6}\right)$ [6.3.1] **28.** The system of equations is inconsistent and has no solution. [6.2.1] **29.** $\left(\dfrac{1}{3}, 6\right)$ [6.2.1] **30.** The system of equations is inconsistent and has no solution. [6.1.1] **31.** $(0, -1)$ [6.3.1] **32.** $(-1, -3)$ [6.2.1] **33.** $(0, -2)$ [6.2.1] **34.** $(2, 0)$ [6.3.1] **35.** $(-4, 2)$ [6.3.1] **36.** $(1, 6)$ [6.2.1] **37.** The rate of the plane in calm air is 180 mph. The rate of the wind is 20 mph. [6.4.1] **38.** There were 60 adult tickets and 140 children's tickets sold. [6.4.2] **39.** The rate of the canoeist in calm water was 8 mph. The rate of the current was 2 mph. [6.4.1] **40.** There were 130 mailings requiring 33¢ in postage. [6.4.2] **41.** The rate of the boat in calm water was 14 km/h. The rate of the current was 2 km/h. [6.4.1] **42.** The customer purchased 4 compact discs at $15 each and 6 at $10 each. [6.4.2] **43.** The rate of the plane in calm air was 125 km/h. The rate of the wind was 15 km/h. [6.4.1] **44.** The rate of the paddle boat in calm water was 3 mph. The rate of the current was 1 mph. [6.4.1] **45.** There are 350 bushels of lentils and 200 bushels of corn in the silo. [6.4.2] **46.** The rate of the plane in calm air was 105 mph. The rate of the wind was 15 mph. [6.4.1] **47.** There are 4 dimes in the coin purse. [6.4.2] **48.** The rate of the plane in calm air was 325 mph. The rate of the wind was 25 mph. [6.4.1] **49.** The investor bought 1300 of the $6 shares and 200 of the $25 shares. [6.4.2] **50.** The rate of the sculling team in calm water was 9 mph. The rate of the current was 3 mph. [6.4.1]

CHAPTER 6 TEST

1. $(3, 1)$ [6.2.1] **2.** $(2, 1)$ [6.3.1] **3.** Yes [6.1.1] **4.** $(1, -1)$ [6.2.1] **5.** $\left(\dfrac{1}{2}, -1\right)$ [6.3.1] **6.** $(-2, 6)$ [6.1.1] **7.** The system of equations is inconsistent and has no solution. [6.2.1] **8.** $(2, -1)$ [6.2.1] **9.** $(2, -1)$ [6.3.1] **10.** $\left(\dfrac{22}{7}, -\dfrac{5}{7}\right)$ [6.2.1] **11.** $(1, -2)$ [6.3.1] **12.** No [6.1.1] **13.** $(2, 1)$ [6.2.1] **14.** $(2, -2)$ [6.3.1] **15.** $(2, 0)$ [6.1.1] **16.** $(4, 1)$ [6.2.1] **17.** $(3, -2)$ [6.3.1] **18.** The system of equations is dependent. The solutions are the ordered pairs that satisfy the equation $3x + 6y = 2$. [6.1.1] **19.** $(1, 1)$ [6.2.1] **20.** $(4, -3)$ [6.3.1] **21.** $(-6, 1)$ [6.2.1] **22.** $(1, -4)$ [6.3.1] **23.** The rate of the plane in calm air is 100 mph. The rate of the wind is 20 mph. [6.4.1] **24.** The rate of the boat in calm water is 14 mph. The rate of the current is 2 mph. [6.4.1] **25.** There are 40 dimes and 30 nickels in the first bank. [6.4.2]

CUMULATIVE REVIEW EXERCISES

1. $-8, -4$ [1.1.1] **2.** $\{1, 2, 3, 4, 5, 6, 7, 8, 9, 10\}$ [1.1.1] **3.** 10 [1.4.2] **4.** $40a - 28$ [2.2.5] **5.** $\dfrac{3}{2}$ [2.1.1] **6.** $-\dfrac{3}{2}$ [3.1.3] **7.** $-\dfrac{7}{2}$ [3.2.3] **8.** $-\dfrac{2}{9}$ [3.2.3] **9.** $x < -5$ [3.3.3] **10.** $x \le 3$ [3.3.3] **11.** 24% [3.1.5] **12.** $(4, 0), (0, -2)$ [5.2.3] **13.** $-\dfrac{7}{5}$ [5.3.1]

14. $y = -\dfrac{3}{2}x$ [5.4.1/5.4.2] **15.** [5.2.3] **16.** [5.2.2]

17. [5.6.1] **18.** [5.5.2] **19.** Domain: $\{-5, 0, 1, 5\}$; range: $\{5\}$; yes [5.5.1]

20. 3 [5.5.1] **21.** Yes [6.1.1] **22.** $(-2, 1)$ [6.2.1] **23.** $(0, 2)$ [6.1.1] **24.** $(2, 1)$ [6.3.1]
25. $\{-22, -12, -2, 8, 18\}$ [5.5.1] **26.** 200 cameras were produced during the month. [3.2.4]
27. $3750 should be invested at 9.6%, and $5000 should be invested at 7.2%. [4.5.1] **28.** The rate of the plane is 160 mph. The rate of the wind is 30 mph. [6.4.1] **29.** The rate of the boat in calm water is 10 mph. [6.4.1]
30. There are 40 dimes in the first bank. [6.4.2]

Answers to Chapter 7 Selected Exercises

PREP TEST

1. 1 [1.2.2] **2.** -18 [1.2.3] **3.** $\dfrac{2}{3}$ [1.2.4] **4.** 48 [2.1.1] **5.** 0 [1.2.4]
6. No [2.2.2] **7.** $5x^2 - 9x - 6$ [2.2.2] **8.** 0 [2.2.2] **9.** $-6x + 24$ [2.2.4]
10. $-7xy + 10y$ [2.2.5]

CONCEPT REVIEW 7.1

1. Always true **3.** Never true **5.** Always true

SECTION 7.1

1. Binomial **3.** Monomial **5.** No **7.** Yes **9.** Yes **11.** descending; like
13. $-2x^2 + 3x$ **15.** $y^2 - 8$ **17.** $5x^2 + 7x + 20$ **19.** $x^3 + 2x^2 - 6x - 6$
21. $2a^3 - 3a^2 - 11a + 2$ **23.** $5x^2 + 8x$ **25.** $7x^2 + xy - 4y^2$ **27.** $3a^2 - 3a + 17$
29. $5x^3 + 10x^2 - x - 4$ **31.** $3r^3 + 2r^2 - 11r + 7$ **33.** $-2x^3 + 3x^2 + 10x + 11$
35. $Q + R$ **37.** $-7x^2 - 5x + 3$ **39.** $4x$ **41.** $3y^2 - 4y - 2$ **43.** $-7x - 7$
45. $4x^3 + 3x^2 + 3x + 1$ **47.** $y^3 - y^2 + 6y - 6$ **49.** $-y^2 - 13xy$ **51.** $2x^2 - 3x - 1$
53. $-2x^3 + x^2 + 2$ **55.** $3a^3 - 2$ **57.** $4y^3 - 2y^2 + 2y - 4$ **59. a.** Positive **b.** Negative
c. Positive **61.** $-a^2 - 1$ **63.** $-4x^2 + 6x + 3$ **65.** $4x^2 - 6x + 3$ **67.** Yes. For example,
$(3x^3 - 2x^2 + 3x - 4) - (3x^3 + 4x^2 - 6x + 5) = -6x^2 + 9x - 9$

CONCEPT REVIEW 7.2

1. Never true **3.** Always true **5.** Never true

SECTION 7.2

3. 2; a^5; b^3; 10; 6; 5; 1; 3; adding; 11; 4 **5.** $2x^2$ **7.** $12x^2$ **9.** $6a^7$ **11.** x^3y^5 **13.** $-10x^9y$
15. x^7y^8 **17.** $-6x^3y^5$ **19.** x^4y^5z **21.** $a^3b^5c^4$ **23.** $-a^5b^8$ **25.** $-6a^5b$ **27.** $40y^{10}z^6$
29. $-20a^2b^3$ **31.** $x^3y^5z^3$ **33.** $-12a^{10}b^7$ **37. a.** Power **b.** Product **39. a.** Product
b. Power **41. a.** Yes **b.** No **c.** No **d.** Yes **43.** 64 **45.** 4 **47.** -64
49. x^9 **51.** x^{14} **53.** x^4 **55.** $4x^2$ **57.** $-8x^6$ **59.** x^4y^6 **61.** $9x^4y^2$ **63.** $27a^8$

65. $-8x^7$ **67.** x^8y^4 **69.** a^4b^6 **71.** $16x^{10}y^3$ **73.** $-18x^3y^4$ **75.** $-8a^7b^5$ **77.** $-54a^9b^3$
79. $-72a^5b^5$ **81.** $32x^3$ **83.** $-3a^3b^3$ **85.** $13x^5y^5$ **87.** $27a^5b^3$ **89.** $-5x^7y^4$ **91.** a^{2n}
93. a^{2n} **95.** True   **97.** False; $x^{2\cdot 5} = x^{10}$ **99.** No; $2^{(3^2)}$ is larger. $(2^3)^2 = 8^2 = 64$, whereas
$2^{(3^2)} = 2^9 = 512$.   **101.** $x = y$ when n is odd.

CONCEPT REVIEW 7.3

1. Always true   **3.** Sometimes true   **5.** Always true   **7.** Sometimes true

SECTION 7.3

1. $-3y$; $-3y$; Distributive; $-3y$; $-3y^2$; $21y$ **3.** $x^2 - 2x$ **5.** $-x^2 - 7x$ **7.** $3a^3 - 6a^2$
9. $-5x^4 + 5x^3$ **11.** $-3x^5 + 7x^3$ **13.** $12x^3 - 6x^2$ **15.** $6x^2 - 12x$ **17.** $-x^3y + xy^3$
19. $2x^4 - 3x^2 + 2x$ **21.** $2a^3 + 3a^2 + 2a$ **23.** $3x^6 - 3x^4 - 2x^2$ **25.** $-6y^4 - 12y^3 + 14y^2$
27. $-2a^3 - 6a^2 + 8a$ **29.** $6y^4 - 3y^3 + 6y^2$ **31.** $x^3y - 3x^2y^2 + xy^3$ **33.** **b** and **c**
35. $x^3 + 4x^2 + 5x + 2$ **37.** $a^3 - 6a^2 + 13a - 12$ **39.** $-2b^3 + 7b^2 + 19b - 20$
41. $-6x^3 + 31x^2 - 41x + 10$ **43.** $x^4 - 4x^3 - 3x^2 + 14x - 8$ **45.** $15y^3 - 16y^2 - 70y + 16$
47. $5a^4 - 20a^3 - 15a^2 + 62a - 8$ **49.** $y^4 + 4y^3 + y^2 - 5y + 2$ **51. a.** 4   **b.** 5
53. $4x$; x; $4x$; 5; -3; x; -3; 5 **55. a.** $3d$; d **b.** $3d$; -1 **c.** 4; d **d.** 4; -1 **57.** $x^2 + 4x + 3$
59. $a^2 + a - 12$ **61.** $y^2 - 5y - 24$ **63.** $y^2 - 10y + 21$ **65.** $2x^2 + 15x + 7$ **67.** $3x^2 + 11x - 4$
69. $4x^2 - 31x + 21$ **71.** $3y^2 - 2y - 16$ **73.** $9x^2 + 54x + 77$ **75.** $21a^2 - 83a + 80$
77. $15b^2 + 47b - 78$ **79.** $2a^2 + 7ab + 3b^2$ **81.** $6a^2 + ab - 2b^2$ **83.** $2x^2 - 3xy - 2y^2$
85. $10x^2 + 29xy + 21y^2$ **87.** $6a^2 - 25ab + 14b^2$ **89.** $2a^2 - 11ab - 63b^2$ **91.** $100a^2 - 100ab + 21b^2$
93. $15x^2 + 56xy + 48y^2$ **95.** $14x^2 - 97xy - 60y^2$ **97.** $56x^2 - 61xy + 15y^2$ **99.** Positive
101. $5x$; 1; $25x^2$; 1 **103.** $y^2 - 25$ **105.** $4x^2 - 9$ **107.** $x^2 + 2x + 1$ **109.** $9a^2 - 30a + 25$
111. $9x^2 - 49$ **113.** $4a^2 + 4ab + b^2$ **115.** $x^2 - 4xy + 4y^2$ **117.** $16 - 9y^2$
119. $25x^2 + 20xy + 4y^2$ **121.** Zero   **123.** Positive   **125.** $2x + 5$; $2x - 5$; $4x^2 - 25$
127. The area is $(10x^2 - 35x)$ ft².   **129.** The area is $(18x^2 + 12x + 2)$ in².   **131.** The area is
$(4x^2 + 4x + 1)$ km².   **133.** The area is $(4x^2 + 10x)$ m².   **135.** The area is $(\pi x^2 + 8\pi x + 16\pi)$ cm².
137. The area is $(90x + 2025)$ ft².   **139.** $4ab$ **141.** $9a^4 - 24a^3 + 28a^2 - 16a + 4$ **143.** $24x^3 - 3x^2$
145. $x^{2n} + x^n$ **147.** $x^{2n} + 2x^n + 1$ **149.** $x^2 - 1$ **151.** $x^4 - 1$ **153.** $x^6 - 1$ **155.** 1024
157. $12x^2 - x - 20$ **159.** $7x^2 - 11x - 8$

CONCEPT REVIEW 7.4

1. Never true   **3.** Always true   **5.** Never true   **7.** Never true

SECTION 7.4

1. $\dfrac{1}{25}$ **3.** 64   **5.** $\dfrac{1}{27}$ **7.** 1   **11.** 4; 10; 3; $4x^7$ **13.** y^4 **15.** a^3 **17.** p^4

19. $2x^3$ **21.** $2k$ **23.** m^5n^2 **25.** $\dfrac{3r^2}{2}$ **27.** $-\dfrac{2a}{3}$ **29.** $\dfrac{1}{x^2}$ **31.** a^6 **33.** $\dfrac{4}{x^7}$

35. $5b^8$ **37.** $\dfrac{x^2}{3}$ **39.** 1   **41.** $\dfrac{1}{y^5}$ **43.** $\dfrac{1}{a^6}$ **45.** $\dfrac{1}{3x^3}$ **47.** $\dfrac{2}{3x^5}$ **49.** $\dfrac{y^4}{x^2}$

51. $\dfrac{2}{5m^3n^8}$ **53.** $\dfrac{1}{p^3q}$ **55.** $\dfrac{1}{2y^3}$ **57.** $\dfrac{7xz}{8y^3}$ **59.** $\dfrac{p^2}{2m^3}$ **61.** $-\dfrac{8x^3}{y^6}$ **63.** $\dfrac{9}{x^2y^4}$

65. $\dfrac{2}{x^4}$ **67.** $-\dfrac{5}{a^8}$ **69.** $-\dfrac{a^5}{8b^4}$ **71.** $\dfrac{10y^3}{x^4}$ **73.** $\dfrac{1}{2x^3}$ **75.** $\dfrac{3}{x^3}$ **77.** $\dfrac{1}{2x^2y^6}$

79. $-\dfrac{1}{6x^3}$ **81. a.** False   **b.** True   **85.** 8; left; 8 **87.** No. 39.4 is not between 1 and 10.

89. No. 2.4 is not an integer.   **91.** 2.37×10^6 **93.** 4.5×10^{-4} **95.** 3.09×10^5 **97.** 6.01×10^{-7}
99. 710,000   **101.** 0.000043   **103.** 671,000,000   **105.** 0.00000713   **107.** 1×10^{21}
109. 4×10^{-10} **111.** 1.2×10^{10} **113.** 2.45×10^9 **115.** 6.65×10^{19} **117.** 3.22×10^{-14}

119. 3.6×10^5 **121.** 1.8×10^{-18} **123.** Less than   **125.** $\dfrac{3}{64}$ **127.** For 2^x: $\dfrac{1}{4}, \dfrac{1}{2}$, 1, 2, 4. For

2^{-x}: 4, 2, 1, $\dfrac{1}{2}, \dfrac{1}{4}$.   **129.** 0.0625   **131.** xy^2 **133.** $\dfrac{x^6 z^6}{4y^5}$ **135.** 1   **137.** 0

139. False; $(2a)^{-3} = \dfrac{1}{8a^3}$ **141.** False; $(2 + 3)^{-1} = 5^{-1} = \dfrac{1}{5}$

CONCEPT REVIEW 7.5

1. Always true   **3.** Never true

SECTION 7.5

1. $3y$; $3y$; $6y^4$; 1   **3.** $x + 1$ **5.** $2a - 5$ **7.** $3a + 2$ **9.** $4b^2 - 3$ **11.** $x - 2$
13. $-x + 2$ **15.** $x^2 + 3x - 5$ **17.** $x^4 - 3x^2 - 1$ **19.** $xy + 2$ **21.** $-3y^3 + 5$
23. $3x - 2 + \dfrac{1}{x}$ **25.** $-3x + 7 - \dfrac{6}{x}$ **27.** $4a - 5 + 6b$ **29.** $9x + 6 - 3y$ **31.** Multiply $4x$ and

$2x^2 - 3x - 1$. $4x(2x^2 - 3x - 1) = 8x^3 - 12x^2 - 4x$ **33.** **a.** $3x^2$; x **b.** $3x$; $x - 2$ **c.** $-4x$; $-6x$

d. $3x + 2$; 11   **35.** $x + 2$ **37.** $2x + 1$ **39.** $2x - 4$ **41.** $x + 1 + \dfrac{2}{x - 1}$

43. $2x - 1 - \dfrac{2}{3x - 2}$ **45.** $5x + 12 + \dfrac{12}{x - 1}$ **47.** $a + 3 + \dfrac{4}{a + 2}$ **49.** $y - 6 + \dfrac{26}{2y + 3}$

51. $2x + 5 + \dfrac{8}{2x - 1}$ **53.** $5a - 6 + \dfrac{4}{3a + 2}$ **55.** $3x - 5$ **57.** $x^2 + 2x + 3$ **59.** $x^2 - 3$

61. False   **63.** $(x + 2), (x - 3)$ **65.** $3a^2$ **67.** $4x^2 - 6x + 3$

CHAPTER 7 REVIEW EXERCISES

1. $21y^2 + 4y - 1$ [7.1.1]   **2.** $-20x^3y^5$ [7.2.1]   **3.** $-8x^3 - 14x^2 + 18x$ [7.3.1]
4. $10a^2 + 31a - 63$ [7.3.3]   **5.** $6x^2 - 7x + 10$ [7.5.1]   **6.** $2x^2 + 3x - 8$ [7.1.2]   **7.** -729 [7.2.2]
8. $x^3 - 6x^2 + 7x - 2$ [7.3.2]   **9.** $a^2 - 49$ [7.3.4]   **10.** 1296 [7.4.1]   **11.** $x - 6$ [7.5.2]
12. $2x^3 + 9x^2 - 3x - 12$ [7.1.1]   **13.** $18a^8 b^6$ [7.2.1]   **14.** $3x^4 y - 2x^3 y + 12x^2 y$ [7.3.1]
15. $8b^2 - 2b - 15$ [7.3.3]   **16.** $-4y + 8$ [7.5.1]   **17.** $13y^3 - 12y^2 - 5y - 1$ [7.1.2]

18. 64 [7.2.2]   **19.** $6y^3 + 17y^2 - 2y - 21$ [7.3.2]   **20.** $4b^2 - 81$ [7.3.4]   **21.** $\dfrac{b^6 c^2}{a^4}$ [7.4.1]

22. $2y - 9$ [7.5.2]   **23.** 3.97×10^{-6} [7.4.2]   **24.** $x^4 y^8 z^4$ [7.2.1]   **25.** $-12y^5 + 4y^4 - 18y^3$ [7.3.1]
26. $18x^2 - 48x + 24$ [7.3.3]   **27.** 0.0000623 [7.4.2]   **28.** $-7a^2 - a + 4$ [7.1.2]   **29.** $9x^4 y^6$ [7.2.2]

30. $12a^3 - 8a^2 - 9a + 6$ [7.3.3]   **31.** $25y^2 - 70y + 49$ [7.3.4]   **32.** $\dfrac{x^4 y^6}{9}$ [7.4.1]

33. $x + 5 + \dfrac{4}{x + 12}$ [7.5.2]   **34.** 240,000 [7.4.2]   **35.** $a^6 b^{11} c^9$ [7.2.1]
36. $8a^3 b^3 - 4a^2 b^4 + 6ab^5$ [7.3.1]   **37.** $6x^2 - 7xy - 20y^2$ [7.3.3]   **38.** $4b^4 + 12b^2 - 1$ [7.5.1]
39. $-4b^2 - 13b + 28$ [7.1.2]   **40.** $100a^{15} b^{13}$ [7.2.2]   **41.** $12b^5 - 4b^4 - 6b^3 - 8b^2 + 5$ [7.3.2]

42. $36 - 25x^2$ [7.3.4]   **43.** $\dfrac{2y^3}{x^3}$ [7.4.1]   **44.** $a^2 - 2a + 6$ [7.5.2]   **45.** $4b^3 - 5b^2 - 9b + 7$ [7.1.1]

46. $-54a^{13} b^5 c^7$ [7.2.1]   **47.** $-18x^4 - 27x^3 + 63x^2$ [7.3.1]   **48.** $30y^2 - 109y + 30$ [7.3.3]
49. 9.176×10^{12} [7.4.2]   **50.** $-2y^2 + y - 5$ [7.1.2]   **51.** $144x^{14} y^{18} z^{16}$ [7.2.2]

52. $-12x^4 - 17x^3 - 2x^2 - 33x - 27$ [7.3.2]   **53.** $64a^2 + 16a + 1$ [7.3.4]   **54.** $\dfrac{2}{ab^6}$ [7.4.1]

55. $b^2 + 5b + 2 + \dfrac{7}{b-7}$ [7.5.2]   **56.** The area is $(20x^2 - 35x)$ m².   [7.3.5]

57. The area is $(25x^2 + 40x + 16)$ in².   [7.3.5]   **58.** The area is $(9x^2 - 4)$ ft².   [7.3.5]   **59.** The area is $(\pi x^2 - 12\pi x + 36\pi)$ cm².   [7.3.5]   **60.** The area is $(15x^2 - 28x - 32)$ mi².   [7.3.5]

CHAPTER 7 TEST

1. $3x^3 + 6x^2 - 8x + 3$ [7.1.1]   **2.** $-4x^4 + 8x^3 - 3x^2 - 14x + 21$ [7.3.2]   **3.** $4x^3 - 6x^2$ [7.3.1]

4. $-8a^6b^3$ [7.2.2]   **5.** $-4x^6$ [7.4.1]   **6.** $\dfrac{6b}{a}$ [7.4.1]   **7.** $-5a^3 + 3a^2 - 4a + 3$ [7.1.2]

8. $a^2 + 3ab - 10b^2$ [7.3.3]   **9.** $4x^4 - 2x^2 + 5$ [7.5.1]   **10.** $2x + 3 + \dfrac{2}{2x-3}$ [7.5.2]

11. $-6x^3y^6$ [7.2.1]   **12.** $6y^4 - 9y^3 + 18y^2$ [7.3.1]   **13.** $\dfrac{9}{x^3}$ [7.4.1]   **14.** $4x^2 - 20x + 25$ [7.3.4]

15. $10x^2 - 43xy + 28y^2$ [7.3.3]   **16.** $x^3 - 7x^2 + 17x - 15$ [7.3.2]   **17.** $\dfrac{a^4}{b^6}$ [7.4.1]

18. 2.9×10^{-5} [7.4.2]   **19.** $16y^2 - 9$ [7.3.4]   **20.** $3y^3 + 2y^2 - 10y$ [7.1.2]   **21.** $9a^6b^4$ [7.2.2]

22. $10a^3 - 39a^2 + 20a - 21$ [7.3.2]   **23.** $9b^2 + 12b + 4$ [7.3.4]   **24.** $-\dfrac{1}{4a^2b^5}$ [7.4.1]

25. $4x + 8 + \dfrac{21}{2x-3}$ [7.5.2]   **26.** a^3b^7 [7.2.1]   **27.** $a^2 + ab - 12b^2$ [7.3.3]

28. 0.000000035 [7.4.2]   **29.** The area is $(4x^2 + 12x + 9)$ m².   [7.3.5]   **30.** The area is $(\pi x^2 - 10\pi x + 25\pi)$ in².   [7.3.5]

CUMULATIVE REVIEW EXERCISES

1. $\dfrac{1}{144}$ [1.3.3]   **2.** $\dfrac{25}{9}$ [1.4.1]   **3.** $\dfrac{4}{5}$ [1.4.2]   **4.** 87 [1.1.2]   **5.** 0.775 [1.3.1]

6. $-\dfrac{27}{4}$ [2.1.1]   **7.** $-x - 4xy$ [2.2.2]   **8.** $-12x$ [2.2.3]   **9.** $-22x + 20$ [2.2.5]

10. 8 [2.2.1]   **11.** -18 [3.1.3]   **12.** 16 [3.2.2]   **13.** 12 [3.2.3]

14. 80 [3.2.2]   **15.** 24% [3.1.5]   **16.** $x \geq -3$ [3.3.3]   **17.** $-\dfrac{9}{5}$ [5.3.1]

18. $y = -\dfrac{3}{2}x - \dfrac{3}{2}$ [5.4.1/5.4.2]   **19.** [5.2.3]   **20.** 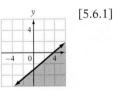 [5.6.1]

21. Domain: $\{-8, -6, -4, -2\}$; range: $\{-7, -5, -2, 0\}$; yes   [5.5.1]   **22.** -2 [5.5.1]   **23.** $(4, 1)$ [6.2.1]

24. $(1, -4)$ [6.3.1]   **25.** $5b^3 - 7b^2 + 8b - 10$ [7.1.2]   **26.** $15x^3 - 26x^2 + 11x - 4$ [7.3.2]

27. $20b^2 - 47b + 24$ [7.3.3]   **28.** $25b^2 + 30b + 9$ [7.3.4]   **29.** $-\dfrac{b^4}{4a}$ [7.4.1]   **30.** $5y - 4 + \dfrac{1}{y}$ [7.5.1]   **31.** $a - 7$ [7.5.2]   **32.** $\dfrac{9y^2}{x^6}$ [7.4.1]   **33.** $\{1, 9, 17, 21, 25\}$ [5.5.1]

34. $5(n - 12)$; $5n - 60$ [2.3.2]   **35.** $8n - 2n = 18$; $n = 3$ [4.1.1]   **36.** The length is 15 m. The width is 6 m.   [4.3.1]   **37.** The selling price is $43.20.   [4.4.1]   **38.** The concentration of orange juice is 28%.   [4.6.2]

39. The car overtakes the cyclist 25 mi from the starting point.   [4.7.1]   **40.** The area is $(9x^2 + 12x + 4)$ ft².   [7.3.5]

Answers to Chapter 8 Selected Exercises

PREP TEST

1. $2 \cdot 3 \cdot 5$ [1.3.3]   **2.** $-12y + 15$ [2.2.4]   **3.** $-a + b$ [2.2.4]   **4.** $-3a + 3b$ [2.2.5]

5. 0 [3.1.3]   **6.** $-\dfrac{1}{2}$ [3.2.1]   **7.** $x^2 - 2x - 24$ [7.3.3]   **8.** $6x^2 - 11x - 10$ [7.3.3]

9. x^3 [7.4.1]   **10.** $3x^3y$ [7.4.1]

CONCEPT REVIEW 8.1

1. Always true   **3.** Always true   **5.** Never true   **7.** Never true

SECTION 8.1

3. a. z **b.** 3 **c.** x **d.** y^2 **e.** $3xy^2$ **5.** x^3 **7.** xy^4 **9.** xy^4z^2 **11.** $7a^3$ **13.** 1
15. $3a^2b^2$ **17.** ab **19.** $2x$ **21.** $3x$ **23.** $5(a + 1)$ **25.** $8(2 - a^2)$ **27.** $4(2x + 3)$
29. $6(5a - 1)$ **31.** $x(7x - 3)$ **33.** $a^2(3 + 5a^3)$ **35.** $y(14y + 11)$ **37.** $2x(x^3 - 2)$
39. $2x^2(5x^2 - 6)$ **41.** $xy(x - y^2)$ **43.** $2a^5b + 3xy^3$ **45.** $6b^2(a^2b - 2)$ **47.** $2abc(3a + 2b)$
49. $9(2x^2y^2 - a^2b^2)$ **51.** $6x^3y^3(1 - 2x^3y^3)$ **53.** $x(x^2 - 3x - 1)$ **55.** $2(x^2 + 4x - 6)$
57. $b(b^2 - 5b - 7)$ **59.** $4(2y^2 - 3y + 8)$ **61.** $5y(y^2 - 4y + 2)$ **63.** $3y^2(y^2 - 3y - 2)$
65. $3y(y^2 - 3y + 8)$ **67.** $a^2(6a^3 - 3a - 2)$ **69.** $x^2(8y^2 - 4y + 1)$ **71.** $x^3y^3(4x^2y^2 - 8xy + 1)$
73. x^a **75. a.** $4(3x - 2); 3x - 2$ **b.** $5x; 4$ **77.** $(a + b)(x + 2)$ **79.** $(b + 2)(x - y)$
81. $(y - 4)(a - b)$ **83.** $a(x - 2) + b(x - 2)$ **85.** $b(a - 7) - 3(a - 7)$ **87.** $x(a - 2b) + y(a - 2b)$
89. $(x - 2)(a - 5)$ **91.** $(y - 3)(b - 3)$ **93.** $(x - y)(a + 2)$ **95.** $(c + 5)(z - 8)$
97. $(3x - 4)(w + 1)$ **99.** $(x + 4)(x^2 + 3)$ **101.** $(y + 2)(2y^2 + 3)$ **103.** $(a + 3)(b - 2)$
105. $(a - 2)(x^2 - 3)$ **107.** $(a - b)(3x - 2y)$ **109.** $(x - 3)(x + 4a)$ **111.** $(x - 5)(y - 2)$
113. $(7x + 2y)(3x - 7)$ **115.** $(2r + a)(a - 1)$ **117.** $(4x + 3y)(x - 4)$ **119.** $(2y - 3)(5xy + 3)$
121. II   **123. a.** $(x + 3)(2x + 5)$ **b.** $(2x + 5)(x + 3)$ **125. a.** $(a - b)(2a - 3b)$
b. $(2a - 3b)(a - b)$ **127.** 28 **129.** P doubles

CONCEPT REVIEW 8.2

1. Never true   **3.** Always true   **5.** Never true

SECTION 8.2

1.

Factors of 18	Sum
1, 18	19
2, 9	11
3, 6	9

3.

Factors of −21	Sum
1, −21	−20
−1, 21	20
3, −7	−4
−3, 7	4

5.

Factors of −28	Sum
1, −28	−27
−1, 28	27
2, −14	−12
−2, 14	12
4, −7	−3
−4, 7	3

7. $(x + 1)(x + 2)$ **9.** $(x + 1)(x - 2)$ **11.** $(a + 4)(a - 3)$ **13.** $(a - 1)(a - 2)$ **15.** $(a + 2)(a - 1)$
17. $(b - 3)(b - 3)$ **19.** $(b + 8)(b - 1)$ **21.** $(y + 11)(y - 5)$ **23.** $(y - 2)(y - 3)$
25. $(z - 5)(z - 9)$ **27.** $(z + 8)(z - 20)$ **29.** $(p + 3)(p + 9)$ **31.** $(x + 10)(x + 10)$
33. $(b + 4)(b + 5)$ **35.** $(x + 3)(x - 14)$ **37.** $(b + 4)(b - 5)$ **39.** $(y + 3)(y - 17)$
41. $(p + 3)(p - 7)$ **43.** Nonfactorable over the integers   **45.** $(x - 5)(x - 15)$ **47.** $(x - 7)(x - 8)$

49. $(x + 8)(x - 7)$ **51.** $(a + 3)(a - 24)$ **53.** $(a - 3)(a - 12)$ **55.** $(z + 8)(z - 17)$
57. $(c + 9)(c - 10)$ **59. a.** Positive   **b.** Positive   **61. a.** common   **b.** 5   **c.** $x^2 - 2x - 8$
d. $x + 2; x - 4$ **63.** $2(x + 1)(x + 2)$ **65.** $3(a + 3)(a - 2)$ **67.** $a(b + 5)(b - 3)$
69. $x(y - 2)(y - 3)$ **71.** $z(z - 3)(z - 4)$ **73.** $3y(y - 2)(y - 3)$ **75.** $3(x + 4)(x - 3)$
77. $5(z + 4)(z - 7)$ **79.** $2a(a + 8)(a - 4)$ **81.** $(x - 2y)(x - 3y)$ **83.** $(a - 4b)(a - 5b)$
85. $(x + 4y)(x - 7y)$ **87.** Nonfactorable over the integers   **89.** $z^2(z - 5)(z - 7)$
91. $b^2(b - 10)(b - 12)$ **93.** $2y^2(y + 3)(y - 16)$ **95.** $x^2(x + 8)(x - 1)$ **97.** $4y(x + 7)(x - 2)$
99. $8(y - 1)(y - 3)$ **101.** $c(c + 3)(c + 10)$ **103.** $3x(x - 3)(x - 9)$ **105.** $(x - 3y)(x - 5y)$
107. $(a - 6b)(a - 7b)$ **109.** $(y + z)(y + 7z)$ **111.** $3y(x + 21)(x - 1)$ **113.** $3x(x + 4)(x - 3)$
115. $4z(z + 11)(z - 3)$ **117. a.** Yes   **b.** Yes   **119.** $(c + 4)(c + 5)$ **121.** $a^2(b - 5)(b - 9)$
123. $36, 12, -12, -36$ **125.** $22, 10, -10, -22$ **127.** $3, 4$ **129.** $5, 8, 9$ **131.** 2

CONCEPT REVIEW 8.3

1. Never true   **3.** Sometimes true   **5.** Always true

SECTION 8.3

1. a. $2; -15; 15; -5; 5$ **b.** $-29x; 29x; -7x; 7x$ **c.** $x - 5; 2x + 3$ **3.** $(x + 1)(2x + 1)$
5. $(y + 3)(2y + 1)$ **7.** $(a - 1)(2a - 1)$ **9.** $(b - 5)(2b - 1)$ **11.** $(x + 1)(2x - 1)$
13. $(x - 3)(2x + 1)$ **15.** Nonfactorable over the integers   **17.** $(2t - 1)(3t - 4)$
19. $(x + 4)(8x + 1)$ **21.** $(b - 4)(3b - 4)$ **23.** $(z - 14)(2z + 1)$ **25.** $(p + 8)(3p - 2)$
27. $(2x - 3)(3x - 4)$ **29.** $(b + 7)(5b - 2)$ **31.** $(2a - 3)(3a + 8)$ **33.** $(3t + 1)(6t - 5)$
35. $(3a + 7)(5a - 3)$ **37.** $(2y - 5)(4y - 3)$ **39.** $(2z + 3)(4z - 5)$ **41.** $(x + 5)(3x - 1)$
43. $(3x + 4)(4x + 3)$ **45.** Nonfactorable over the integers   **47.** $(x + y)(3x - 2y)$ **49.** $(4 + z)(7 - z)$
51. $(1 - x)(8 + x)$ **53.** $3(x + 5)(3x - 4)$ **55.** $4(2x - 3)(3x - 2)$ **57.** $a^2(5a + 2)(7a - 1)$
59. $5(b - 7)(3b - 2)$ **61.** $2x(x + 1)(5x + 1)$ **63.** $2y(y - 4)(5y - 2)$ **65.** $yz(z + 2)(4z - 3)$
67. $b^2(4b + 5)(5b + 4)$ **69.** $xy(3x + 2)(3x + 2)$ **71.** m and p **73.** $-18; -17; 18; 17; -9; -7; 9; 7;$
$-6; -3; 6; 3$ **75.** $(t + 2)(2t - 5)$ **77.** $(p - 5)(3p - 1)$ **79.** $(3y - 1)(4y - 1)$ **81.** Nonfactorable
over the integers   **83.** $(3y + 1)(4y + 5)$ **85.** $(a + 7)(7a - 2)$ **87.** $(z + 2)(4z + 3)$
89. $(2p + 5)(11p - 2)$ **91.** $(y + 1)(8y + 9)$ **93.** $(2b - 3)(3b - 2)$ **95.** $(3b + 5)(11b - 7)$
97. $(3y - 4)(6y - 5)$ **99.** Nonfactorable over the integers   **101.** $(2z - 5)(5z - 2)$
103. $(6z + 5)(6z + 7)$ **105.** $(2y - 3)(7y - 4)$ **107.** $(x + 6)(6x - 1)$ **109.** $3(x + 3)(4x - 1)$
111. $10(y + 1)(3y - 2)$ **113.** $x(x + 1)(2x - 5)$ **115.** $(a - 3b)(2a - 3b)$ **117.** $(y + z)(2y + 5z)$
119. $(1 + x)(18 - x)$ **121.** $4(9y + 1)(10y - 1)$ **123.** $8(t + 4)(2t - 3)$ **125.** $p(2p + 1)(3p + 1)$
127. $3(2z - 5)(5z - 2)$ **129.** $3a(2a + 3)(7a - 3)$ **131.** $y(3x - 5y)(3x - 5y)$
133. $xy(3x - 4y)(3x - 4y)$ **135.** Two positive   **137.** Two negative   **139.** $2y(y - 3)(4y - 1)$
141. $ab(a + 4)(a - 6)$ **143.** $5t(3 + 2t)(4 - t)$ **145.** $(y + 3)(2y + 1)$ **147.** $(2x - 1)(5x + 7)$
149. $7, -7, 5, -5$ **151.** $7, -7, 5, -5$ **153.** $11, -11, 7, -7$ **155.** $(x + 2)(x - 3)(x - 1)$

CONCEPT REVIEW 8.4

1. Never true   **3.** Sometimes true   **5.** Always true   **7.** Never true

SECTION 8.4

1. a. $3x; 2$ **b.** $3x + 2; 3x - 2$ **3.** Answers will vary.   **a.** $x^2 - 16$ **b.** $(x + 7)(x - 7)$ **c.** $x^2 + 10x + 25$
d. $(x - 3)^2$ **e.** $x^2 + 36$ **5.** $4; 25x^6; 100x^4y^4$ **7.** $(x + 2)(x - 2)$ **9.** $(a + 9)(a - 9)$
11. $(2x + 1)(2x - 1)$ **13.** $(y + 1)^2$ **15.** $(a - 1)^2$ **17.** Nonfactorable over the integers
19. $(x^3 + 3)(x^3 - 3)$ **21.** $(5x + 1)(5x - 1)$ **23.** $(1 + 7x)(1 - 7x)$ **25.** $(x + y)^2$ **27.** $(2a + 1)^2$

29. $(8a - 1)^2$ **31.** Nonfactorable over the integers **33.** $(x^2 + y)(x^2 - y)$ **35.** $(3x + 4y)(3x - 4y)$
37. $(4b + 1)^2$ **39.** $(2b + 7)^2$ **41.** $(5a + 3b)^2$ **43.** $(xy + 2)(xy - 2)$ **45.** $(4 + xy)(4 - xy)$
47. $(2y - 9z)^2$ **49.** $(3ab - 1)^2$ **51.** $(m^2 + 16)(m + 4)(m - 4)$ **53.** $(x + 1)(9x + 4)$
55. $(y^4 + 9)(y^2 + 3)(y^2 - 3)$ **57.** **a** and **c** **59.** common **61.** $2(x + 3)(x - 3)$
63. $x^2(x + 7)(x - 5)$ **65.** $5(b + 3)(b + 12)$ **67.** Nonfactorable over the integers
69. $2y(x + 11)(x - 3)$ **71.** $x(x^2 - 6x - 5)$ **73.** $3(y^2 - 12)$ **75.** $(2a + 1)(10a + 1)$
77. $y^2(x + 1)(x - 8)$ **79.** $5(a + b)(2a - 3b)$ **81.** $2(5 + x)(5 - x)$ **83.** $ab(3a - b)(4a + b)$
85. $2(x - 1)(a + b)$ **87.** $3a(2a - 1)^2$ **89.** $3(81 + a^2)$ **91.** $2a(2a - 5)(3a - 4)$
93. $(x - 2)(x + 1)(x - 1)$ **95.** $a(2a + 5)^2$ **97.** $3b(3a - 1)^2$ **99.** $6(4 + x)(2 - x)$
101. $(x + 2)(x - 2)(a + b)$ **103.** $x^2(x + y)(x - y)$ **105.** $2a(3a + 2)^2$ **107.** $b(2 - 3a)(1 + 2a)$
109. $(x - 5)(2 + x)(2 - x)$ **111.** $8x(3y + 1)^2$ **113.** $y^2(5 + x)(3 - x)$ **115.** $y(y + 3)(y - 3)$
117. $2x^2y^2(x + 1)(x - 1)$ **119.** $x^5(x^2 + 1)(x + 1)(x - 1)$ **121.** $2xy(3x - 2)(4x + 5)$
123. $x^2y^2(2x - 5)^2$ **125.** $(x - 2)^2(x + 2)$ **127.** $4xy^2(1 - x)(2 - 3x)$ **129.** $2ab(2a - 3b)(9a - 2b)$
131. $x^2y^2(1 - 3x)(5 + 4x)$ **133.** $(4x - 3 + y)(4x - 3 - y)$ **135.** $(x - 2 + y)(x - 2 - y)$ **137.** 4
139. $12, -12$ **141.** $12, -12$ **143.** 9 **145.** 1 **147.** 4 **149.** 3
151. $(x + 2)(x^2 - 2x + 4)$ **153.** $(y - 3)(y^2 + 3y + 9)$ **155.** $(y + 4)(y^2 - 4y + 16)$
157. $(2x - 1)(4x^2 + 2x + 1)$

CONCEPT REVIEW 8.5

1. Always true **3.** Always true **5.** Never true

SECTION 8.5

3. $0 = x^2 + x - 2$ **5.** $-3, -2$ **7.** $7, 3$ **9.** $0, 5$ **11.** $0, 9$ **13.** $0, -\dfrac{3}{2}$ **15.** $0, \dfrac{2}{3}$

17. $-2, 5$ **19.** $9, -9$ **21.** $\dfrac{7}{4}, -\dfrac{7}{4}$ **23.** $3, 5$ **25.** $8, -9$ **27.** $-\dfrac{1}{2}, 1$ **29.** $-\dfrac{2}{3}, -4$

31. $-7, 3$ **33.** $0, 7$ **35.** $-1, -4$ **37.** $2, 3$ **39.** $\dfrac{1}{2}, -4$ **41.** $\dfrac{1}{3}, 4$ **43.** $3, 9$

45. $9, -2$ **47.** $-1, -2$ **49.** $5, -9$ **51.** $4, -7$ **53.** $-2, -3$ **55.** $-8, -5$ **57.** $1, 3$

59. $-12, 5$ **61.** $3, 4$ **63.** $-\dfrac{1}{2}, -4$ **65.** Less than **67.** One

69. $x + 1; x^2 + (x + 1)^2; x^2; (x + 1)^2; 113$ **71.** The number is 6. **73.** The numbers are 2 and 4.
75. The integers are 4 and 5. **77.** The integers are 15 and 16. **79.** The base is 18 ft. The height is 6 ft.
81. The length is 18 ft. The width is 8 ft. **83.** The length of a side of the original square is 4 m.
85. The radius of the original circle is 3.81 in. **87.** The dimensions are 4 in. by 7 in. **89.** The object will
hit the ground 10 s later. **91.** 12 consecutive natural numbers beginning with 1 will give a sum of 78.
93. There are 8 teams in the league. **95.** The ball will be 16 ft above the ground 1 s after it hits home plate.
97. $-\dfrac{3}{2}, -5$ **99.** $9, -3$ **101.** $0, 9$ **103.** $-6, 3$ **105.** 48 or 3 **107.** The length is 10 cm.
The width is 7 cm.

CHAPTER 8 REVIEW EXERCISES

1. $7y^3(2y^6 - 7y^3 + 1)$ [8.1.1] **2.** $(a - 4)(3a + b)$ [8.1.2] **3.** $(c + 2)(c + 6)$ [8.2.1]
4. $a(a - 2)(a - 3)$ [8.2.2] **5.** $(2x - 7)(3x - 4)$ [8.3.1/8.3.2] **6.** $(y + 6)(3y - 2)$ [8.3.1/8.3.2]
7. $(3a + 2)(6a - 5)$ [8.3.1/8.3.2] **8.** $(ab + 1)(ab - 1)$ [8.4.1] **9.** $4(y - 2)^2$ [8.4.2]

10. $0, -\dfrac{1}{5}$ [8.5.1]   **11.** $3ab(4a + b)$ [8.1.1]   **12.** $(b - 3)(b - 10)$ [8.2.1]

13. $(2x + 5)(5x + 2y)$ [8.1.2]   **14.** $3(a + 2)(a - 7)$ [8.2.2]   **15.** $n^2(n + 1)(n - 3)$ [8.2.2]

16. Nonfactorable over the integers [8.3.1/8.3.2]   **17.** $(2x - 1)(3x - 2)$ [8.3.1/8.3.2]

18. Nonfactorable over the integers [8.4.1]   **19.** $2, \dfrac{3}{2}$ [8.5.1]   **20.** $7(x + 1)(x - 1)$ [8.4.2]

21. $x^3(3x^2 - 9x - 4)$ [8.1.1]   **22.** $(x - 3)(4x + 5)$ [8.1.2]   **23.** $(a + 7)(a - 2)$ [8.2.1]
24. $(y + 9)(y - 4)$ [8.2.1]   **25.** $5(x - 12)(x + 2)$ [8.2.2]   **26.** $-3, 7$ [8.5.1]
27. $(a + 2)(7a + 3)$ [8.3.1/8.3.2]   **28.** $(x + 20)(4x + 3)$ [8.3.1/8.3.2]   **29.** $(3y^2 + 5z)(3y^2 - 5z)$ [8.4.1]

30. $5(x + 2)(x - 3)$ [8.2.2]   **31.** $-\dfrac{3}{2}, \dfrac{2}{3}$ [8.5.1]   **32.** $2b(2b - 7)(3b - 4)$ [8.3.1/8.3.2]

33. $5x(x^2 + 2x + 7)$ [8.1.1]   **34.** $(x - 2)(x - 21)$ [8.2.1]   **35.** $(3a + 2)(a - 7)$ [8.1.2]
36. $(2x - 5)(4x - 9)$ [8.3.1/8.3.2]   **37.** $10x(a - 4)(a - 9)$ [8.2.2]   **38.** $(a - 12)(2a + 5)$ [8.3.1/8.3.2]
39. $(3a - 5b)(7x + 2y)$ [8.1.2]   **40.** $(a^3 + 10)(a^3 - 10)$ [8.4.1]   **41.** $(4a + 1)^2$ [8.4.1]

42. $\dfrac{1}{4}, -7$ [8.5.1]   **43.** $10(a + 4)(2a - 7)$ [8.3.1/8.3.2]   **44.** $6(x - 3)$ [8.1.1]

45. $x^2y(3x^2 + 2x + 6)$ [8.1.1]   **46.** $(d - 5)(d + 8)$ [8.2.1]   **47.** $2(2x - y)(6x - 5)$ [8.4.2]
48. $4x(x + 1)(x - 6)$ [8.2.2]   **49.** $-2, 10$ [8.5.1]   **50.** $(x - 5)(3x - 2)$ [8.3.1/8.3.2]
51. $(2x - 11)(8x - 3)$ [8.3.1/8.3.2]   **52.** $(3x - 5)^2$ [8.4.1]   **53.** $(2y + 3)(6y - 1)$ [8.3.1/8.3.2]
54. $3(x + 6)^2$ [8.4.2]   **55.** The length is 100 yd. The width is 50 yd. [8.5.2]   **56.** The length is 100 yd.
The width is 60 yd. [8.5.2]   **57.** The two integers are 4 and 5. [8.5.2]   **58.** The distance is 20 ft. [8.5.2]
59. The width of the larger rectangle is 15 ft. [8.5.2]   **60.** The length of a side of the original square was
20 ft. [8.5.2]

CHAPTER 8 TEST
1. $3y^2(2x^2 + 3x + 4)$ [8.1.1]   **2.** $2x(3x^2 - 4x + 5)$ [8.1.1]   **3.** $(p + 2)(p + 3)$ [8.2.1]

4. $(x - 2)(a - b)$ [8.1.2]   **5.** $\dfrac{3}{2}, -7$ [8.5.1]   **6.** $(a - 3)(a - 16)$ [8.2.1]   **7.** $x(x + 5)(x - 3)$ [8.2.2]

8. $4(x + 4)(2x - 3)$ [8.3.1/8.3.2]   **9.** $(b + 6)(a - 3)$ [8.1.2]   **10.** $\dfrac{1}{2}, -\dfrac{1}{2}$ [8.5.1]

11. $(2x + 1)(3x + 8)$ [8.3.1/8.3.2]   **12.** $(x + 3)(x - 12)$ [8.2.1]   **13.** $2(b + 4)(b - 4)$ [8.4.2]
14. $(2a - 3b)^2$ [8.4.1]   **15.** $(p + 1)(x - 1)$ [8.1.2]   **16.** $5(x^2 - 9x - 3)$ [8.1.1]
17. Nonfactorable over the integers [8.3.1/8.3.2]   **18.** $(2x + 7y)(2x - 7y)$ [8.4.1]   **19.** $3, 5$ [8.5.1]
20. $(p + 6)^2$ [8.4.1]   **21.** $2(3x - 4y)^2$ [8.4.2]   **22.** $2y^2(y + 1)(y - 8)$ [8.2.2]
23. The length is 15 cm. The width is 6 cm. [8.5.2]   **24.** The length of the base is 12 in. [8.5.2]
25. The two integers are -13 and -12. [8.5.2]

CUMULATIVE REVIEW EXERCISES
1. -8 [1.2.2]   **2.** -8.1 [1.3.2]   **3.** 4 [1.4.2]   **4.** -7 [2.1.1]   **5.** The Associative Property of

Addition [2.2.1]   **6.** $18x^2$ [2.2.3]   **7.** $-6x + 24$ [2.2.5]   **8.** $\dfrac{2}{3}$ [3.1.3]   **9.** 5 [3.2.3]

10. $\dfrac{7}{4}$ [3.2.2]   **11.** 3 [3.2.3]   **12.** 35 [3.1.5]   **13.** $x \le -3$ [3.3.3]   **14.** $x < \dfrac{1}{5}$ [3.3.3]

15. [5.2.2]   **16.** [5.5.2]

17. Domain: $\{-5, -3, -1, 1, 3\}$; range: $\{-4, -2, 0, 2, 4\}$; yes [5.5.1]   **18.** 61 [5.5.1]

19. [graph] [5.6.1]   **20.** $(2, -5)$ [6.2.1]   **21.** $(1, 2)$ [6.3.1]   **22.** $3y^3 - 3y^2 - 8y - 5$ [7.1.1]

23. $-27a^{12}b^6$ [7.2.2]   **24.** $x^3 - 3x^2 - 6x + 8$ [7.3.2]   **25.** $4x + 8 + \dfrac{21}{2x - 3}$ [7.5.2]

26. $\dfrac{y^6}{x^{12}}$ [7.4.1]   **27.** $(a - b)(3 - x)$ [8.1.2]   **28.** $(x + 5y)(x - 2y)$ [8.2.2]

29. $2a^2(3a + 2)(a + 3)$ [8.3.1/8.3.2]   **30.** $(5a + 6b)(5a - 6b)$ [8.4.1]   **31.** $3(2x - 3y)^2$ [8.4.2]

32. $\dfrac{4}{3}, -5$ [8.5.1]   **33.** $\{-11, -7, -3, 1, 5\}$ [5.5.1]   **34.** The average daily high temperature

was $-3°C$. [1.2.5]   **35.** The length is 15 cm. The width is 6 cm. [4.3.1]   **36.** The pieces measure 4 ft and
6 ft. [4.1.2]   **37.** The maximum distance you can drive a Company A car is 359 mi. [4.8.1]
38. $6500 must be invested at an annual simple interest rate of 11%. [4.5.1]
39. The discount rate is 40%. [4.4.2]   **40.** The three integers are 10, 12, and 14. [4.2.1]

Answers to Chapter 9 Selected Exercises

PREP TEST

1. 36 [1.3.3]   **2.** $\dfrac{3x}{y^3}$ [7.4.1]   **3.** $-\dfrac{5}{36}$ [1.3.3]   **4.** $-\dfrac{10}{11}$ [1.3.2]   **5.** No. $\dfrac{0}{a} = 0$ but $\dfrac{a}{0}$ is

undefined. [1.2.4]   **6.** $\dfrac{19}{8}$ [3.2.1]   **7.** $130°$ [4.3.2]   **8.** $(x - 6)(x + 2)$ [8.2.1]

9. $(2x - 3)(x + 1)$ [8.3.1/8.3.2]   **10.** Jean will catch up to Anthony at 9:40 A.M. [4.7.1]

CONCEPT REVIEW 9.1

1. Always true   **3.** Never true   **5.** Always true   **7.** Never true

SECTION 9.1

5. a. $3; x^2; y^2$ **b.** $3y^3; x$ **7.** $\dfrac{3}{4x}$ **9.** $\dfrac{1}{x + 3}$ **11.** -1 **13.** $\dfrac{2}{3y}$ **15.** $-\dfrac{3}{4x}$ **17.** $\dfrac{a}{b}$

19. $-\dfrac{2}{x}$ **21.** $\dfrac{y - 2}{y - 3}$ **23.** $\dfrac{x + 5}{x + 4}$ **25.** $\dfrac{x + 4}{x - 3}$ **27.** $-\dfrac{x + 2}{x + 5}$ **29.** $\dfrac{2(x + 2)}{x + 3}$ **31.** $\dfrac{2x - 1}{2x + 3}$

33. False   **35.** $\dfrac{2}{3xy}$ **37.** $\dfrac{8xy^2ab}{3}$ **39.** $\dfrac{2}{9}$ **41.** $\dfrac{y^2}{x}$ **43.** $\dfrac{y(x + 4)}{x(x + 1)}$ **45.** $\dfrac{x^3(x - 7)}{y^2(x - 4)}$

47. $-\dfrac{y}{x}$ **49.** $\dfrac{x + 3}{x + 1}$ **51.** $\dfrac{x - 5}{x + 3}$ **53.** $-\dfrac{x + 3}{x + 5}$ **55.** $\dfrac{12x^4}{(x + 1)(2x + 1)}$ **57.** $-\dfrac{x + 3}{x - 12}$

59. $\dfrac{x + 2}{x + 4}$ **61.** $\dfrac{2x - 5}{2x - 1}$ **63.** $\dfrac{3x - 4}{2x + 3}$ **65.** 1   **67.** x^d **69.** $a - 5; 5a$ **71.** $\dfrac{2xy^2ab^2}{9}$

73. $\dfrac{5}{12}$ **75.** $3x$ **77.** $\dfrac{y(x + 3)}{x(x + 1)}$ **79.** $\dfrac{x + 7}{x - 7}$ **81.** $-\dfrac{4ac}{y}$ **83.** $\dfrac{x - 5}{x - 6}$ **85.** 1

87. $-\dfrac{x+6}{x+5}$ **89.** $\dfrac{2x+3}{x-6}$ **91.** $\dfrac{4x+3}{2x-1}$ **93.** $\dfrac{(2x+5)(4x-1)}{(2x-1)(4x+5)}$ **95.** Yes **97.** Yes

99. $-6, 1$ **101.** $-1, 1$ **103.** $3, -2$ **105.** -3 **107.** $\dfrac{4}{3}, -\dfrac{1}{2}$ **109.** $\dfrac{4a}{3b}$ **111.** $\dfrac{8}{9}$

113. $\dfrac{x-4}{y^4}$ **115.** $\dfrac{(x-2)(x-2)}{(x-4)(x+4)}$ **117.** $\dfrac{x}{x+8}$

CONCEPT REVIEW 9.2

1. Always true **3.** Never true **5.** Always true

SECTION 9.2

1. a. $4; 5$ **b.** $3; 4; 5; 60$ **c.** $60x^4y^5$ **3.** $24x^3y^2$ **5.** $30x^4y^2$ **7.** $8x^2(x+2)$
9. $6x^2y(x+4)$ **11.** $40x^3(x-1)^2$ **13.** $4(x-3)^2$ **15.** $(2x-1)(2x+1)(x+4)$
17. $(x-7)^2(x+2)$ **19.** $(x+4)(x-3)$ **21.** $(x+5)(x-2)(x+7)$ **23.** $(x-7)(x-3)(x-5)$
25. $(x+2)(x+5)(x-5)$ **27.** $(2x-1)(x-3)(x+1)$ **29.** $(2x-5)(x-2)(x+3)$ **31.** $(x+3)(x-5)$
33. $(x+6)(x-3)$ **35. a.** One **b.** Zero **c.** Two **37.** $y(y-3)^2$ **39.** y
41. $\dfrac{4x}{x^2}; \dfrac{3}{x^2}$ **43.** $\dfrac{4x}{12y^2}; \dfrac{3yz}{12y^2}$ **45.** $\dfrac{xy}{x^2(x-3)}; \dfrac{6x-18}{x^2(x-3)}$ **47.** $\dfrac{9x}{x(x-1)^2}; \dfrac{6x-6}{x(x-1)^2}$
49. $\dfrac{3x}{x(x-3)}; \dfrac{5}{x(x-3)}$ **51.** $\dfrac{3}{(x-5)^2}; -\dfrac{2x-10}{(x-5)^2}$ **53.** $\dfrac{3x}{x^2(x+2)}; \dfrac{4x+8}{x^2(x+2)}$
55. $\dfrac{x^2-6x+8}{(x+3)(x-4)}; \dfrac{x^2+3x}{(x+3)(x-4)}$ **57.** $\dfrac{3}{(x+2)(x-1)}; \dfrac{x^2-x}{(x+2)(x-1)}$ **59.** $\dfrac{5}{(2x-5)(x-2)}; \dfrac{x^2-3x+2}{(2x-5)(x-2)}$
61. $\dfrac{x^2-3x}{(x+3)(x-3)(x-2)}; \dfrac{2x^2-4x}{(x+3)(x-3)(x-2)}$ **63.** $-\dfrac{x^2-3x}{(x-3)^2(x+3)}; \dfrac{x^2+2x-3}{(x-3)^2(x+3)}$
65. $\dfrac{3x^2+12x}{(x-5)(x+4)}; \dfrac{x^2-5x}{(x-5)(x+4)}; -\dfrac{3}{(x-5)(x+4)}$ **67.** $\dfrac{300}{10^4}; \dfrac{5}{10^4}$ **69.** $\dfrac{b^2}{b}; \dfrac{5}{b}$ **71.** $\dfrac{y-1}{y-1}; \dfrac{y}{y-1}$
73. $\dfrac{x^2+1}{(x-1)^3}; \dfrac{x^2-1}{(x-1)^3}; \dfrac{x^2-2x+1}{(x-1)^3}$ **75.** $\dfrac{2b}{8(a+b)(a-b)}; \dfrac{a^2+ab}{8(a+b)(a-b)}$
77. $\dfrac{x-2}{(x+y)(x+2)(x-2)}; \dfrac{x+2}{(x+y)(x+2)(x-2)}$

CONCEPT REVIEW 9.3

1. Never true **3.** Never true **5.** Always true

SECTION 9.3

1. numerators; $8a$; factors **3.** $\dfrac{11}{y^2}$ **5.** $-\dfrac{7}{x+4}$ **7.** $\dfrac{8x}{2x+3}$ **9.** $\dfrac{5x+7}{x-3}$ **11.** $\dfrac{2x-5}{x+9}$
13. $\dfrac{-3x-4}{2x+7}$ **15.** $\dfrac{1}{x+5}$ **17.** $\dfrac{1}{x-6}$ **19.** $\dfrac{3}{2y-1}$ **21.** $\dfrac{1}{x-5}$ **23.** common denominator;
LCM **25.** False **27.** $\dfrac{4y+5x}{xy}$ **29.** $\dfrac{19}{2x}$ **31.** $\dfrac{5}{12x}$ **33.** $\dfrac{19x-12}{6x^2}$ **35.** $\dfrac{52y-35x}{20xy}$
37. $\dfrac{13x+2}{15x}$ **39.** $\dfrac{7}{24}$ **41.** $\dfrac{x+90}{45x}$ **43.** $\dfrac{x^2+2x+2}{2x^2}$ **45.** $\dfrac{2x^2+3x-10}{4x^2}$ **47.** $\dfrac{3y^2+8}{3y}$
49. $\dfrac{x^2+4x+4}{x+4}$ **51.** $\dfrac{4x+7}{x+1}$ **53.** $\dfrac{-3x^2+16x+2}{12x^2}$ **55.** $\dfrac{x^2-x+2}{x^2y}$
57. $\dfrac{16xy-12y+6x^2+3x}{12x^2y^2}$ **59.** $\dfrac{3xy-6y-2x^2-14x}{24x^2y}$ **61.** $\dfrac{9x+2}{(x-2)(x+3)}$ **63.** $\dfrac{2(x+23)}{(x-7)(x+3)}$

65. $\dfrac{2x^2 - 5x + 1}{(x + 1)(x - 3)}$ **67.** $\dfrac{4x^2 - 34x + 5}{(2x - 1)(x - 6)}$ **69.** $\dfrac{2a - 5}{a - 7}$ **71.** $\dfrac{4x + 9}{(x + 3)(x - 3)}$ **73.** $\dfrac{-x + 9}{(x + 2)(x - 3)}$

75. $\dfrac{14}{(x - 5)^2}$ **77.** $\dfrac{-2(x + 7)}{(x + 6)(x - 7)}$ **79.** $\dfrac{x - 2}{2x}$ **81.** $\dfrac{x^2 + x + 4}{(x - 2)(x + 1)(x - 1)}$ **83.** $\dfrac{x - 4}{x - 6}$

85. $\dfrac{2x + 1}{x - 1}$ **87.** 2   **89.** $\dfrac{b^2 + b - 7}{b + 4}$ **91.** $\dfrac{4n}{(n - 1)^2}$ **93.** $-\dfrac{3(x^2 + 8x + 25)}{(x - 3)(x + 7)}$ **95.** 1

97. $\dfrac{x^2 - x + 2}{(x + 5)(x + 1)}$ **99.** $\dfrac{2}{3}; \dfrac{3}{4}; \dfrac{4}{5}; \dfrac{50}{51}; \dfrac{100}{101}; \dfrac{1000}{1001}$ **101.** $\dfrac{6}{y} + \dfrac{7}{x}$ **103.** $\dfrac{2}{m^2n} + \dfrac{8}{mn^2}$

CONCEPT REVIEW 9.4

1. Sometimes true   **3.** Never true   **5.** Always true

SECTION 9.4

1. $\dfrac{5}{x}; \dfrac{6}{x^2}; \dfrac{4}{x^2}; x^2$ **3.** $x^2 - 4; x + 2; x - 2$ **5.** $\dfrac{x}{x - 3}$ **7.** $\dfrac{2}{3}$ **9.** $\dfrac{y + 3}{y - 4}$ **11.** $\dfrac{2(2x + 13)}{5x + 36}$

13. $\dfrac{3}{4}$ **15.** $\dfrac{x - 2}{x + 2}$ **17.** $\dfrac{x + 2}{x + 3}$ **19.** $\dfrac{x - 6}{x + 5}$ **21.** $-\dfrac{x - 2}{x + 1}$ **23.** $x - 1$ **25.** $\dfrac{1}{2x - 1}$

27. $\dfrac{x - 3}{x + 5}$ **29.** $\dfrac{x - 7}{x - 8}$ **31.** $\dfrac{2y - 1}{2y + 1}$ **33.** $\dfrac{x - 2}{2x - 5}$ **35.** $\dfrac{x - 2}{x + 1}$ **37.** $\dfrac{x - 1}{x + 4}$ **39.** $\dfrac{-x - 1}{4x - 3}$

41. $\dfrac{x + 1}{2(5x - 2)}$ **43.** $\dfrac{b + 11}{4b - 21}$ **45.** True   **47.** $\dfrac{5}{3}$ **49.** $-\dfrac{1}{x - 1}$ **51.** $\dfrac{ab}{b + a}$

53. $\dfrac{y + 4}{2(y - 2)}$

CONCEPT REVIEW 9.5

1. Always true   **3.** Always true   **5.** Sometimes true   **7.** Always true

SECTION 9.5

3. $x; x - 4; x(x - 4)$ **5.** $7(x - 4); 3x; 7$ **7.** $-5; 3$ **9.** $-1; 2$ **11.** 4   **13.** -3 **15.** $\dfrac{3}{4}$

17. -1 **19.** No solution   **21.** $-6; 2$ **23.** $-\dfrac{2}{3}; 5$ **25.** $6; -1$ **27.** $-7; 3$ **29.** $\dfrac{2}{3}; 4$

31. proportion   **33.** 9   **35.** 36   **37.** 10   **39.** 113   **41.** -2 **43.** 15   **45.** 4
47. True   **49.** 10 mi; 3 cm; 3 cm; 10 mi   **51.** Yes   **53.** 20,000 people voted in favor of the
amendment.   **55.** The office building requires 140 air vents.   **57.** For 2 c of boiling water, 6 c of sugar are
required.   **59.** There are about 800 fish in the lake.   **61.** Yes, the shipment will be accepted.   **63.** The
person's height is 67.5 in.   **65.** The distance between the two cities is 750 mi.   **67.** The recommended area
of a window is 40 ft^2.   **69.** There are 160 ml of carbonated water in 280 ml of soft drink.   **71.** For an
annual yield of 1320 bushels, 10 additional acres must be planted.   **73.** To serve 70 people, 2 additional gallons
are necessary.   **75. a.** YZ **b.** $\angle R$ **77.** The measure of side DE is 12.8 in.   **79.** The height of
triangle DEF is 4.7 ft.   **81.** The perimeter of triangle ABC is 18 m.   **83.** The area of triangle ABC is 48 cm^2.
85. False   **87. a.** PQO **b.** OM **89.** The length of BC is 15 m.   **91.** The length of QO is 10 ft.
93. The perimeter of triangle OPQ is 12 m.   **95.** The height of the flagpole is 14.375 ft.   **97.** 1

99. $0; -\dfrac{2}{3}$ **101.** -3 and -4 **103.** The first person's share of the winnings was $1.25 million.

105. The cost would be $18.40.   **107. a.** He calculated the circumference to be 24,960 mi.
b. The difference is 160 mi.

CONCEPT REVIEW 9.6

1. Always true **3.** Always true **5.** Always true

SECTION 9.6

1. $h = \dfrac{2A}{b}$ **3.** $t = \dfrac{d}{r}$ **5.** $T = \dfrac{PV}{nR}$ **7.** $L = \dfrac{P - 2W}{2}$ **9.** $b_1 = \dfrac{2A - hb_2}{h}$ **11.** $h = \dfrac{3V}{A}$

13. $S = C - Rt$ **15.** $P = \dfrac{A}{1 + rt}$ **17.** $w = \dfrac{A}{S + 1}$ **19.** Yes **21. a.** $h = \dfrac{S - 2\pi r^2}{2\pi r}$ **b.** 5 in.

c. 4 in. **23. a.** $r = \dfrac{S - C}{C}$ **b.** $66.\overline{6}\%$ **c.** $43.\overline{3}\%$

CONCEPT REVIEW 9.7

1. Never true **3.** Always true **5.** Never true

SECTION 9.7

3. Row 1: $\dfrac{1}{10}; t; \dfrac{t}{10}$; Row 2: $\dfrac{1}{12}; t; \dfrac{t}{12}$ **5.** It will take 2 h to fill the fountain with both sprinklers operating.

7. It would take 3 h to move the earth. **9.** It would take the computers 30 h. **11.** It would take 24 min to cool the room 5°F. **13.** It would take the second welder 15 h. **15.** It would take the second pipeline 90 min to fill the tank. **17.** It would take 3 h to harvest the field using only the older reaper. **19.** It will take the second technician 3 h. **21.** It would take the small unit $14\frac{2}{3}$ h. **23.** It would have taken one of the welders 40 h. **25.** Less than k **27. a.** Row 1: 1440; $380 - r$; $\dfrac{1440}{380 - r}$; Row 2: 1600; $380 + r$; $\dfrac{1600}{380 + r}$

b. $\dfrac{1440}{380 - r}; \dfrac{1600}{380 + r}$ **29.** The camper hiked at a rate of 4 mph. **31.** The rate of the jet was 360 mph.

33. The rate of the boat for the first 15 mi was 7.5 mph. **35.** The family can travel 21.6 mi down the river.

37. The technician traveled at a rate of 20 mph through the congested traffic. **39.** The rate of the river's current was 5 mph. **41.** The rate of the freight train was 30 mph. The rate of the express train was 50 mph.

43. The rate of the car is 48 mph. **45.** The rate of the jet stream was 50 mph. **47.** The rate of the current is 5 mph. **49.** It would take $1\frac{1}{19}$ h to fill the tank. **51.** The amount of time spent traveling by canoe was 2 h. **53.** The bus usually travels at a rate of 60 mph.

CHAPTER 9 REVIEW EXERCISES

1. $\dfrac{by^3}{6ax^2}$ [9.1.2] **2.** $\dfrac{22x - 1}{(3x - 4)(2x + 3)}$ [9.3.2] **3.** $x = -\dfrac{3}{4}y + 3$ [9.6.1] **4.** $\dfrac{2x^4}{3y^7}$ [9.1.1]

5. $\dfrac{1}{x^2}$ [9.1.3] **6.** $\dfrac{x - 2}{3x - 10}$ [9.4.1] **7.** $72a^3b^5$ [9.2.1] **8.** $\dfrac{4x}{3x + 7}$ [9.3.1]

9. $\dfrac{3x}{16x^2}; \dfrac{10}{16x^2}$ [9.2.2] **10.** $\dfrac{x - 9}{x - 3}$ [9.1.1] **11.** $\dfrac{x - 4}{x + 3}$ [9.1.3] **12.** $\dfrac{2y - 3}{5y - 7}$ [9.3.2]

13. $\dfrac{1}{x}$ [9.1.2] **14.** $\dfrac{1}{x + 3}$ [9.3.1] **15.** $15x^4(x - 7)^2$ [9.2.1] **16.** 10 [9.5.2]

17. No solution [9.5.1] **18.** $-\dfrac{4a}{5b}$ [9.1.1] **19.** $\dfrac{1}{x + 3}$ [9.3.1] **20.** 24 in. [9.5.4]

21. 5 [9.5.1] **22.** $\dfrac{x + 9}{4x}$ [9.4.1] **23.** $\dfrac{3x - 1}{x - 5}$ [9.3.2] **24.** $\dfrac{x - 3}{x + 3}$ [9.1.3]

25. $-\dfrac{x+6}{x+3}$ [9.1.1]   **26.** 2 [9.5.1]   **27.** $x-2$ [9.4.1]   **28.** $\dfrac{x+3}{x-4}$ [9.1.2]   **29.** 15 [9.5.2]

30. 12 [9.5.2]   **31.** $\dfrac{x}{x-7}$ [9.4.1]   **32.** $x=2y+15$ [9.6.1]   **33.** $\dfrac{3(3a+2b)}{ab}$ [9.3.2]

34. $(5x-3)(2x-1)(4x-1)$ [9.2.1]   **35.** $c=\dfrac{100m}{i}$ [9.6.1]   **36.** 40 [9.5.2]   **37.** 3 [9.5.2]

38. $\dfrac{7x+22}{60x}$ [9.3.2]   **39.** $\dfrac{8a+3}{4a-3}$ [9.1.2]   **40.** $\dfrac{3x^2-x}{(6x-1)(2x+3)(3x-1)};\dfrac{24x^3-4x^2}{(6x-1)(2x+3)(3x-1)}$ [9.2.2]

41. $\dfrac{2}{ab}$ [9.3.1]   **42.** 62 [9.5.2]   **43.** 6 [9.5.1]   **44.** $\dfrac{b^3y}{10ax}$ [9.1.3]   **45.** It would take the apprentice 6 h. [9.7.1]   **46.** The spring would stretch 8 in. [9.5.3]   **47.** The rate of the wind is 20 mph. [9.7.2]   **48.** To make 10 gal of the garden spray will require 16 additional ounces. [9.5.3]   **49.** Using both hoses, it would take 6 h to fill the pool. [9.7.1]   **50.** The rate of the car is 45 mph. [9.7.2]

CHAPTER 9 TEST

1. $\dfrac{x+5}{x+4}$ [9.1.3]   **2.** $\dfrac{2}{x+5}$ [9.3.1]   **3.** $3(2x-1)(x+1)$ [9.2.1]   **4.** -1 [9.5.2]

5. $\dfrac{x+1}{x^3(x-2)}$ [9.1.2]   **6.** $\dfrac{x-3}{x-2}$ [9.4.1]   **7.** $\dfrac{3x+6}{x(x-2)(x+2)};\dfrac{x^2}{x(x-2)(x+2)}$ [9.2.2]

8. $x=-\dfrac{5}{3}y-5$ [9.6.1]   **9.** 2 [9.5.1]   **10.** $\dfrac{5}{(2x-1)(3x+1)}$ [9.3.2]   **11.** 1 [9.1.3]

12. $\dfrac{3}{x+8}$ [9.3.1]   **13.** $6x(x+2)^2$ [9.2.1]   **14.** $-\dfrac{x-2}{x+5}$ [9.1.1]   **15.** 4 [9.5.1]

16. $t=\dfrac{f-v}{a}$ [9.6.1]   **17.** $\dfrac{2x^3}{3y^5}$ [9.1.1]   **18.** $\dfrac{3}{(2x-1)(x+1)}$ [9.3.2]   **19.** 3 [9.5.2]

20. $\dfrac{x^3(x+3)}{y(x+2)}$ [9.1.2]   **21.** $-\dfrac{3xy+3y}{x(x+1)(x-1)};\dfrac{x^2}{x(x+1)(x-1)}$ [9.2.2]   **22.** $\dfrac{x+3}{x+5}$ [9.4.1]

23. For 15 gal of water, 2 additional pounds of salt will be required. [9.5.3]   **24.** The rate of the wind is 20 mph. [9.7.2]   **25.** It would take both pipes 6 min to fill the tank. [9.7.1]

CUMULATIVE REVIEW EXERCISES

1. -17 [1.1.2]   **2.** -6 [1.4.1]   **3.** $\dfrac{31}{30}$ [1.4.2]   **4.** 21 [2.1.1]   **5.** $5x-2y$ [2.2.2]

6. $-8x+26$ [2.2.5]   **7.** -20 [3.2.1]   **8.** -12 [3.2.3]   **9.** 10 [3.1.5]   **10.** $x<\dfrac{9}{5}$ [3.3.2]

11. $x\le15$ [3.3.3]   **12.** [5.2.2]   **13.** [5.5.2]   **14.** [5.2.3]

15. [5.6.1]   **16.** $\{-3,5,11,19,27\}$ [5.5.1]   **17.** 37 [5.5.1]   **18.** $\left(\dfrac{2}{3},3\right)$ [6.2.1]

19. $\left(\dfrac{1}{2},-1\right)$ [6.3.1]   **20.** $-6x^4y^5$ [7.2.1]   **21.** $a^{20}b^{15}$ [7.2.2]   **22.** $\dfrac{a^3}{b^2}$ [7.4.1]

23. $a^2 + ab - 12b^2$ [7.3.3]   **24.** $3b^3 - b + 2$ [7.5.1]   **25.** $x^2 + 2x + 4$ [7.5.2]

26. $(4x + 1)(3x - 1)$ [8.3.1/8.3.2]   **27.** $(y - 6)(y - 1)$ [8.2.1]   **28.** $a(2a - 3)(a + 5)$ [8.3.1/8.3.2]

29. $4(b + 5)(b - 5)$ [8.4.2]   **30.** -3 and $\frac{5}{2}$ [8.5.1]   **31.** $-\frac{x + 7}{x + 4}$ [9.1.1]   **32.** 1 [9.1.3]

33. $\frac{8}{(3x - 1)(x + 1)}$ [9.3.2]   **34.** 1 [9.5.1]   **35.** $a = \frac{f - v}{t}$ [9.6.1]

36. $5x - 18 = -3; x = 3$ [4.1.1]   **37.** $5000 must be invested at an annual simple interest rate of 11%. [4.5.1]

38. There is 70% silver in the 120-gram alloy. [4.6.2]   **39.** The base is 10 in. The height is 6 in. [8.5.2]

40. It would take both pipes 8 min to fill the tank. [9.7.1]

Answers to Chapter 10 Selected Exercises

PREP TEST

1. -14 [1.1.2]   **2.** $-2x^2y - 4xy^2$ [2.2.2]   **3.** 14 [3.1.3]   **4.** $\frac{7}{5}$ [3.2.2]   **5.** x^6 [7.2.1]

6. $x^2 + 2xy + y^2$ [7.3.4]   **7.** $4x^2 - 12x + 9$ [7.3.4]   **8.** $a^2 - 25$ [7.3.4]   **9.** $4 - 9v^2$ [7.3.4]

10. $\frac{x^2y^2}{9}$ [7.4.1]

CONCEPT REVIEW 10.1

1. Never true   **3.** Always true   **5.** Sometimes true

SECTION 10.1

3. $2, 20, 50$ **7.** radical sign; radicand   **9.** 4 **11.** 7 **13.** $4\sqrt{2}$ **15.** $2\sqrt{2}$ **17.** $18\sqrt{2}$

19. $10\sqrt{10}$ **21.** $\sqrt{15}$ **23.** $\sqrt{29}$ **25.** $-54\sqrt{2}$ **27.** $3\sqrt{5}$ **29.** 0 **31.** $48\sqrt{2}$

33. $\sqrt{105}$ **35.** 30 **37.** $30\sqrt{5}$ **39.** $5\sqrt{10}$ **41.** $4\sqrt{6}$ **43.** 18 **45. a.** Rational

b. Irrational   **c.** Irrational   **d.** Not a real number   **47.** 15.492 **49.** 16.971 **51.** 15.652

53. 18.762 **57.** $4; x^3; y^4$ **59.** x^3 **61.** $y^7\sqrt{y}$ **63.** a^{10} **65.** x^2y^2 **67.** $2x^2$

69. $2x\sqrt{6}$ **71.** $xy^3\sqrt{xy}$ **73.** $ab^5\sqrt{ab}$ **75.** $2x^2\sqrt{15x}$ **77.** $7a^2b^4$ **79.** $3x^2y^3\sqrt{2xy}$

81. $2x^5y^3\sqrt{10xy}$ **83.** $4a^4b^5\sqrt{5a}$ **85.** $8ab\sqrt{b}$ **87.** x^3y **89.** $8a^2b^3\sqrt{5b}$ **91.** $6x^2y^3\sqrt{3y}$

93. $4x^3y\sqrt{2y}$ **95.** $5a + 20$ **97.** $2x^2 + 8x + 8$ **99.** $x + 2$ **101.** $y + 1$ **103.** Rational

105. Irrational   **107. a.** The speed of the car is $12\sqrt{15}$ mph.   **b.** The speed of the car is approximately

46 mph.   **109.** $0.05ab^2\sqrt{ab}$ **111. a.** 1 **b.** 3 **c.** $3\sqrt{3}$ **113.** The length of a side of the

square is 8.7 cm.   **115.** $x \geq 0$ **117.** $x \geq -5$ **119.** $x \leq \frac{5}{2}$ **121.** All real numbers

CONCEPT REVIEW 10.2

1. Never true   **3.** Always true   **5.** Always true

SECTION 10.2

1. $5; 8; -3$ **3.** $11\sqrt{5}$ **5.** $-6\sqrt{5}$ **7.** $-8\sqrt{3}$ **9.** $5\sqrt{y}$ **11.** $-3\sqrt{2a}$ **13.** $-12\sqrt{5a}$

15. $-7y\sqrt{3}$ **17.** $-7b\sqrt{3x}$ **19.** $2\sqrt{xy}$ **21.** $-3\sqrt{2}$ **23.** $20\sqrt{2}$ **25.** $25\sqrt{3} - 6\sqrt{2}$

27. $41\sqrt{y}$ **29.** $-12x\sqrt{3}$ **31.** $2xy\sqrt{x} - 3xy\sqrt{y}$ **33.** $-9x\sqrt{3x}$ **35.** $-13y^2\sqrt{2y}$

37. $4a^2b^2\sqrt{ab}$ **39.** $7\sqrt{2}$ **41.** $6\sqrt{x}$ **43.** $-3\sqrt{y}$ **45.** $-45\sqrt{2}$ **47.** $13\sqrt{3} - 12\sqrt{5}$

49. $32\sqrt{3} - 3\sqrt{11}$ **51.** $6\sqrt{x}$ **53.** $-34\sqrt{3x}$ **55.** $10a\sqrt{3b} + 10a\sqrt{5b}$ **57.** $-2xy\sqrt{3}$

59. $-7b\sqrt{ab} + 4a^2\sqrt{b}$ **61.** $3ab\sqrt{2a} - ab + 4ab\sqrt{3b}$ **63. a.** False   **b.** True

c. False   **d.** True   **65.** $8\sqrt{x+2}$ **67.** $2x\sqrt{2y}$ **69.** $2ab\sqrt{6ab}$
71. $-11\sqrt{2x+y}$ **73.** The perimeter is $(6\sqrt{3}+2\sqrt{15})$ cm.   **75.** The perimeter is 22.4 cm.

CONCEPT REVIEW 10.3

1. Always true   **3.** Always true   **5.** Sometimes true

SECTION 10.3

1. 9; 3   **3.** 5   **5.** 6   **7.** x **9.** x^3y^2 **11.** $3ab^6\sqrt{2a}$ **13.** $12a^4b\sqrt{b}$ **15.** $2-\sqrt{6}$
17. $x-\sqrt{xy}$ **19.** $5\sqrt{2}-\sqrt{5x}$ **21.** $4-2\sqrt{10}$ **23.** $x-6\sqrt{x}+9$ **25.** $3a-3\sqrt{ab}$
27. $10abc$ **29.** $15x-22y\sqrt{x}+8y^2$ **31.** $x-y$ **33.** $10x+13\sqrt{xy}+4y$ **35.** Less than
39. a. No   **b.** Yes   **c.** No   **d.** No   **41.** 4   **43.** 7   **45.** 3   **47.** $x\sqrt{5}$
49. $\dfrac{a^2}{7}$ **51.** $\dfrac{\sqrt{3}}{3}$ **53.** $\sqrt{3}$ **55.** $\dfrac{\sqrt{3x}}{x}$ **57.** $\dfrac{\sqrt{2x}}{x}$ **59.** $\dfrac{3\sqrt{x}}{x}$ **61.** $\dfrac{2\sqrt{y}}{xy}$
63. $\dfrac{4\sqrt{b}}{7b}$ **65.** $\dfrac{5\sqrt{6}}{27}$ **67.** $\dfrac{\sqrt{y}}{3xy}$ **69.** $\dfrac{2\sqrt{3x}}{3y}$ **71.** $-\dfrac{\sqrt{2}+3}{7}$ **73.** $\dfrac{15-3\sqrt{5}}{20}$
75. $\dfrac{x\sqrt{y}+y\sqrt{x}}{x-y}$ **77.** $\dfrac{\sqrt{3xy}}{3y}$ **79.** $-2-\sqrt{6}$ **81.** $-\dfrac{\sqrt{10}+5}{3}$ **83.** $\dfrac{x-3\sqrt{x}}{x-9}$ **85.** $-\dfrac{1}{2}$
87. 7   **89.** -5 **91.** $\dfrac{7}{4}$ **93.** $-\dfrac{42-26\sqrt{3}}{11}$ **95.** $\dfrac{14-9\sqrt{2}}{17}$ **97.** $\dfrac{a-5\sqrt{a}+4}{2a-2}$
99. $\dfrac{y+5\sqrt{y}+6}{y-9}$ **101.** -1.3 **103.** $-\dfrac{4}{9}$ **105.** $\dfrac{3}{2}$ **107.** The area is 59 m^2.
109. a. True   **b.** True   **c.** False; $x+2\sqrt{x}+1$ **d.** True   **111.** No

CONCEPT REVIEW 10.4

1. Sometimes true   **3.** Always true   **5.** Sometimes true

SECTION 10.4

1. **b** and **c**   **3.** 2; 2; $x-2$; 25; 27; 2   **5.** 25   **7.** 144   **9.** 5   **11.** 16   **13.** 8
15. No solution   **17.** 6   **19.** 24   **21.** -1 **23.** $-\dfrac{2}{5}$ **25.** $\dfrac{4}{3}$ **27.** 15   **29.** 5
31. 1   **33.** 1   **35.** 1   **37.** 2   **39.** No solution   **41.** **c**   **43.** The number is 1.
45. The number is 11.   **47.** 90°; legs   **51.** The length of the hypotenuse is 10.30 cm.   **53.** The length
of the other leg of the triangle is 9.75 ft.   **55.** The length of the diagonal is 12.1 mi.   **57. a.** Yes
b. Yes   **c.** Yes   **d.** Yes   **59.** The depth of the water is 12.5 ft.   **61.** The pitcher's mound is
more than halfway between home plate and second base.   **63.** The periscope has to be 10.67 ft above the water.
65. Yes, the ladder will be long enough to reach the gutters.   **67.** The length of the pendulum is 7.30 ft.
69. The distance to the memorial is 250 ft.   **71.** The bridge is 64 ft high.   **73.** The height of the screen is
21.6 in.   **75.** 5   **77.** 8   **79. a.** The perimeter is $12\sqrt{2}$ cm.   **b.** The area is 12 cm^2.
81. The area is 244.78 ft^2.

CHAPTER 10 REVIEW EXERCISES

1. $-11\sqrt{3}$ [10.2.1]   **2.** $-x\sqrt{3}-x\sqrt{5}$ [10.3.2]   **3.** $x+8$ [10.1.2]   **4.** No solution [10.4.1]
5. 1 [10.3.2]   **6.** $7\sqrt{7}$ [10.2.1]   **7.** $12a+28\sqrt{ab}+15b$ [10.3.1]   **8.** $7x^2+42x+63$ [10.1.2]
9. 12 [10.1.1]   **10.** 16 [10.4.1]   **11.** $4x\sqrt{5}$ [10.2.1]   **12.** $5ab-7$ [10.3.1]
13. 3 [10.4.1]   **14.** $\sqrt{35}$ [10.1.1]   **15.** $7x^2y\sqrt{15xy}$ [10.2.1]   **16.** $\dfrac{x}{3y^2}$ [10.3.2]
17. $9x-6\sqrt{xy}+y$ [10.3.1]   **18.** $a+4$ [10.1.2]   **19.** $20\sqrt{3}$ [10.1.1]   **20.** $26\sqrt{3x}$ [10.2.1]

21. $\dfrac{8\sqrt{x}+24}{x-9}$ [10.3.2]   **22.** $3a\sqrt{2}+2a\sqrt{3}$ [10.3.1]   **23.** $9a^2\sqrt{2ab}$ [10.1.2]

24. $-6\sqrt{30}$ [10.1.1]   **25.** $-4a^2b^4\sqrt{5ab}$ [10.2.1]   **26.** $7x^2y^4$ [10.3.2]   **27.** $\dfrac{3}{5}$ [10.4.1]

28. c^9 [10.1.2]   **29.** $15\sqrt{2}$ [10.1.1]   **30.** $18a\sqrt{5b}+5a\sqrt{b}$ [10.2.1]   **31.** $\dfrac{16\sqrt{a}}{a}$ [10.3.2]

32. 8 [10.4.1]   **33.** $a^5b^3c^2$ [10.3.1]   **34.** $21\sqrt{70}$ [10.1.1]   **35.** $2y^4\sqrt{6}$ [10.1.2]
36. 5 [10.3.2]   **37.** 5 [10.4.1]   **38.** $8y+10\sqrt{5y}-15$ [10.3.1]   **39.** 99.499 [10.1.1]
40. 7 [10.3.1]   **41.** $25x^4\sqrt{6x}$ [10.1.2]   **42.** $-6x^3y^2\sqrt{2y}$ [10.2.1]   **43.** $3a$ [10.3.2]

44. $20\sqrt{10}$ [10.1.1]   **45.** 20 [10.4.1]   **46.** $\dfrac{7a}{3}$ [10.3.2]   **47.** 10 [10.3.1]

48. $6x^2y^2\sqrt{y}$ [10.1.2]   **49.** $36x^8y^5\sqrt{3xy}$ [10.1.2]   **50.** 3 [10.4.1]   **51.** 20 [10.1.1]
52. $-2\sqrt{2x}$ [10.2.1]   **53.** 6 [10.4.1]   **54.** 3 [10.3.1]   **55.** The larger integer is 51. [10.4.2]
56. The explorer's weight on the surface of Earth is 144 lb. [10.4.2]   **57.** The length of the other leg is
14.25 cm. [10.4.2]   **58.** The radius of the sharpest corner is 25 ft. [10.4.2]
59. The depth is 100 ft. [10.4.2]   **60.** The length of the guy wire is 26.25 ft. [10.4.2]

CHAPTER 10 TEST
1. $11x^4y$ [10.1.2]   **2.** $-5\sqrt{2}$ [10.2.1]   **3.** $6x^2\sqrt{xy}$ [10.3.1]   **4.** $3\sqrt{5}$ [10.1.1]
5. $6x^3y\sqrt{2x}$ [10.1.2]   **6.** $6\sqrt{2y}+3\sqrt{2x}$ [10.2.1]   **7.** $y+8\sqrt{y}+15$ [10.3.1]   **8.** $\sqrt{2}$ [10.3.2]
9. 9 [10.3.2]   **10.** 11 [10.4.1]   **11.** 22.361 [10.1.1]   **12.** $4a^2b^5\sqrt{2ab}$ [10.1.2]
13. $a-\sqrt{ab}$ [10.3.1]   **14.** $4x^2y^2\sqrt{5y}$ [10.3.1]   **15.** $7ab\sqrt{a}$ [10.3.2]   **16.** 25 [10.4.1]
17. $8x^6y^2\sqrt{3xy}$ [10.1.2]   **18.** $4ab\sqrt{2ab}-5ab\sqrt{ab}$ [10.2.1]   **19.** $a-4$ [10.3.1]
20. $-6-3\sqrt{5}$ [10.3.2]   **21.** 5 [10.4.1]   **22.** $3\sqrt{2}-x\sqrt{3}$ [10.3.1]   **23.** $-6\sqrt{a}$ [10.2.1]
24. $6\sqrt{3}$ [10.1.1]   **25.** 7.937 [10.1.1]   **26.** $6ab\sqrt{a}$ [10.3.2]   **27.** No solution [10.4.1]
28. The smaller integer is 40. [10.4.2]   **29.** The length of the pendulum is 5.07 ft. [10.4.2]
30. The ladder reaches 15.2 ft high on the building. [10.4.2]

CUMULATIVE REVIEW EXERCISES
1. $-\dfrac{1}{12}$ [1.4.2]   **2.** $2x+18$ [2.2.5]   **3.** $\dfrac{1}{13}$ [3.2.3]   **4.** $x\le-\dfrac{9}{2}$ [3.3.3]   **5.** $-\dfrac{4}{3}$ [5.3.1]

6. $y=\dfrac{1}{2}x-2$ [5.4.1/5.4.2]   **7.** -18 [5.5.1]   **8.** [5.5.2]   **9.** [5.6.1]

10. $(2,-1)$ [6.1.1]   **11.** $(1,1)$ [6.2.1]   **12.** $(3,-2)$ [6.3.1]   **13.** $\dfrac{6x^5}{y^3}$ [7.4.1]

14. $-2b^2+1-\dfrac{1}{3b^2}$ [7.5.1]   **15.** $3x^2y^2(4x-3y)$ [8.1.1]   **16.** $(3b+5)(3b-4)$ [8.3.1/8.3.2]

17. $2a(a-3)(a-5)$ [8.2.2]   **18.** $\dfrac{1}{4(x+1)}$ [9.1.2]   **19.** $\dfrac{x-5}{x-3}$ [9.4.1]   **20.** $\dfrac{x+3}{x-3}$ [9.3.2]

21. $\dfrac{5}{3}$ [9.5.1]   **22.** $38\sqrt{3a}-35\sqrt{a}$ [10.2.1]   **23.** 8 [10.3.2]   **24.** 14 [10.4.1]

25. The largest integer that satisfies the inequality is -33. [4.8.1]   **26.** The cost is $24.50. [4.4.1]
27. 56 oz of pure water must be added. [4.6.2]   **28.** The two numbers are 6 and 15. [4.1.2]
29. It would take the small pipe 48 h to fill the tank. [9.7.1]   **30.** The smaller integer is 24. [10.4.2]

Answers to Chapter 11 Selected Exercises

PREP TEST

1. 41 [2.1.1]   **2.** $-\dfrac{1}{5}$ [3.2.1]   **3.** $(x + 4)(x - 3)$ [8.2.1]   **4.** $(2x - 3)^2$ [8.4.1]

5. Yes [8.4.1]   **6.** 3 [9.5.2]   **7.**   [5.2.2]   **8.** $2\sqrt{7}$ [10.1.1]

9. $|a|$ [10.1.2]   **10.** The hiking trail is 3.6 mi long. [9.7.2]

CONCEPT REVIEW 11.1

1. Never true   **3.** Sometimes true   **5.** Always true

SECTION 11.1

1. $a = 3, b = -4, c = 1$ **3.** $a = 2, b = 0, c = -5$ **5.** $a = 6, b = -3, c = 0$ **7.** $x^2 - 3x - 8 = 0$
9. $x^2 - 16 = 0$ **11.** $2x^2 + 12x + 13 = 0$ **17.** standard; $x + 6$; $x - 6$; 0; 0; Zero Products; -6; 6

19. -3 and 5   **21.** 0 and 7   **23.** $-\dfrac{5}{2}$ and $\dfrac{1}{3}$ **25.** -5 and 3   **27.** 1 and 3   **29.** -1 and -2

31. 3   **33.** 0 and $\dfrac{3}{2}$ **35.** -2 and 5   **37.** $\dfrac{2}{3}$ and 1   **39.** -3 and $\dfrac{1}{3}$ **41.** $-\dfrac{3}{2}$ and $\dfrac{4}{3}$

43. -3 and $\dfrac{4}{5}$ **45.** $\dfrac{1}{3}$ **47.** -4 and 4   **49.** $-\dfrac{2}{3}$ and $\dfrac{2}{3}$ **51.** $\dfrac{2}{3}$ and 2   **53.** -6 and $\dfrac{3}{2}$

55. $\dfrac{2}{3}$ **57.** -3 and 6   **59.** 0 and 12   **61. a.** Two positive   **b.** One positive and one negative

c. One positive and one negative   **63.** 3; -3 **65.** -6 and 6   **67.** -1 and 1   **69.** $-\dfrac{7}{2}$ and $\dfrac{7}{2}$

71. $-\dfrac{2}{3}$ and $\dfrac{2}{3}$ **73.** $-\dfrac{3}{4}$ and $\dfrac{3}{4}$ **75.** There is no real number solution.   **77.** $2\sqrt{6}$ and $-2\sqrt{6}$

79. -5 and 7   **81.** -7 and -3 **83.** -6 and 4   **85.** -9 and -1 **87.** 2 and 16   **89.** $-\dfrac{9}{2}$

and $-\dfrac{3}{2}$ **91.** $-\dfrac{1}{3}$ and $\dfrac{7}{3}$ **93.** $-\dfrac{12}{7}$ and $-\dfrac{2}{7}$ **95.** $4 + 2\sqrt{5}$ and $4 - 2\sqrt{5}$ **97.** There is no real

number solution.   **99.** $\dfrac{1}{2} + \sqrt{6}$ and $\dfrac{1}{2} - \sqrt{6}$ **101.** $-\dfrac{4}{3}$ and $\dfrac{8}{3}$ **103.** Zero   **105.** Two

107. 66 and 110   **109.** $\sqrt{2}$ and $-\sqrt{2}$ **111.** 0 and 1   **113.** $\dfrac{\sqrt{ab}}{a}$ and $-\dfrac{\sqrt{ab}}{a}$ **115.** The speed is
10 m/s.

CONCEPT REVIEW 11.2

1. Always true   **3.** Always true   **5.** Never true

SECTION 11.2

1. a. perfect-square; x; 18; 81   **b.** 81; $x + 9$ **3.** $x^2 + 12x + 36$; $(x + 6)^2$ **5.** $x^2 + 10x + 25$; $(x + 5)^2$
7. $x^2 - x + \dfrac{1}{4}$; $\left(x - \dfrac{1}{2}\right)^2$ **9.** -3 and 1   **11.** $-2 + \sqrt{3}$ and $-2 - \sqrt{3}$ **13.** There is no real number

solution. **15.** $-3 + \sqrt{14}$ and $-3 - \sqrt{14}$ **17.** 2 **19.** $1 + \sqrt{2}$ and $1 - \sqrt{2}$ **21.** $\dfrac{-3 + \sqrt{13}}{2}$ and

$\dfrac{-3 - \sqrt{13}}{2}$ **23.** -8 and 1 **25.** $-3 + \sqrt{5}$ and $-3 - \sqrt{5}$ **27.** $4 + \sqrt{14}$ and $4 - \sqrt{14}$

29. 1 and 2 **31.** $\dfrac{3 + \sqrt{29}}{2}$ and $\dfrac{3 - \sqrt{29}}{2}$ **33.** $\dfrac{1 + \sqrt{5}}{2}$ and $\dfrac{1 - \sqrt{5}}{2}$ **35.** $\dfrac{5 + \sqrt{13}}{2}$ and $\dfrac{5 - \sqrt{13}}{2}$

37. $\dfrac{-1 + \sqrt{13}}{2}$ and $\dfrac{-1 - \sqrt{13}}{2}$ **39.** $-5 + 4\sqrt{2}$ and $-5 - 4\sqrt{2}$ **41.** $\dfrac{-3 + \sqrt{5}}{2}$ and $\dfrac{-3 - \sqrt{5}}{2}$

43. $\dfrac{1 + \sqrt{17}}{2}$ and $\dfrac{1 - \sqrt{17}}{2}$ **45.** There is no real number solution. **47.** $\dfrac{1}{2}$ and 1 **49.** -3 and $\dfrac{1}{2}$

51. $\dfrac{1 + \sqrt{2}}{2}$ and $\dfrac{1 - \sqrt{2}}{2}$ **53.** $\dfrac{2 + \sqrt{5}}{2}$ and $\dfrac{2 - \sqrt{5}}{2}$ **55.** $3 + \sqrt{2}$ and $3 - \sqrt{2}$ **57.** $1 + \sqrt{13}$ and

$1 - \sqrt{13}$ **59.** $\dfrac{3 + 3\sqrt{3}}{2}$ and $\dfrac{3 - 3\sqrt{3}}{2}$ **61.** $4 + \sqrt{7}$ and $4 - \sqrt{7}$ **63.** Both negative **65.** 1.193

and -4.193 **67.** 2.766 and -1.266 **69.** 0.151 and -1.651 **71.** $22 + 12\sqrt{2}$ and $22 - 12\sqrt{2}$

73. -3 **75.** $6 + \sqrt{58}$ and $6 - \sqrt{58}$

CONCEPT REVIEW 11.3

1. Always true **3.** Never true **5.** Never true

SECTION 11.3

3. $4x$; 2; $x^2 - 4x - 2$; 1; -4; -2 **5.** -7 and 1 **7.** -3 and 6 **9.** $1 + \sqrt{6}$ and $1 - \sqrt{6}$
11. $-3 + \sqrt{10}$ and $-3 - \sqrt{10}$ **13.** There is no real number solution. **15.** $2 + \sqrt{13}$ and $2 - \sqrt{13}$

17. 0 and 1 **19.** $\dfrac{1 + \sqrt{2}}{2}$ and $\dfrac{1 - \sqrt{2}}{2}$ **21.** $-\dfrac{3}{2}$ and $\dfrac{3}{2}$ **23.** $\dfrac{3 + \sqrt{3}}{3}$ and $\dfrac{3 - \sqrt{3}}{3}$

25. $\dfrac{1 + \sqrt{10}}{3}$ and $\dfrac{1 - \sqrt{10}}{3}$ **27.** There is no real number solution. **29.** $\dfrac{4 + \sqrt{10}}{2}$ and $\dfrac{4 - \sqrt{10}}{2}$

31. $-\dfrac{2}{3}$ and 3 **33.** $\dfrac{5 + \sqrt{73}}{6}$ and $\dfrac{5 - \sqrt{73}}{6}$ **35.** $\dfrac{1 + \sqrt{37}}{6}$ and $\dfrac{1 - \sqrt{37}}{6}$ **37.** $\dfrac{1 + \sqrt{41}}{5}$ and $\dfrac{1 - \sqrt{41}}{5}$

39. -3 and $\dfrac{4}{5}$ **41.** $-3 + 2\sqrt{2}$ and $-3 - 2\sqrt{2}$ **43.** $\dfrac{3 + 2\sqrt{6}}{2}$ and $\dfrac{3 - 2\sqrt{6}}{2}$ **45.** There is no real

number solution. **47.** $\dfrac{-1 + \sqrt{2}}{3}$ and $\dfrac{-1 - \sqrt{2}}{3}$ **49.** $-\dfrac{1}{2}$ and $\dfrac{2}{3}$ **51.** $\dfrac{-4 + \sqrt{5}}{2}$ and $\dfrac{-4 - \sqrt{5}}{2}$

53. $\dfrac{1 + 2\sqrt{3}}{2}$ and $\dfrac{1 - 2\sqrt{3}}{2}$ **55.** $-\dfrac{3}{2}$ **57.** $\dfrac{-5 + \sqrt{2}}{3}$ and $\dfrac{-5 - \sqrt{2}}{3}$ **59.** $\dfrac{1 + \sqrt{19}}{3}$ and $\dfrac{1 - \sqrt{19}}{3}$

61. $\dfrac{5 + \sqrt{65}}{4}$ and $\dfrac{5 - \sqrt{65}}{4}$ **63.** $6 + \sqrt{11}$ and $6 - \sqrt{11}$ **65.** True **67.** 5.690 and -3.690

69. 7.690 and -1.690 **71.** 4.589 and -1.089 **73.** 0.118 and -2.118 **75.** 1.105 and -0.905

77. $3 + \sqrt{13}$ and $3 - \sqrt{13}$ **79.** **a.** False **b.** False **c.** False **d.** True

CONCEPT REVIEW 11.4

1. Always true **3.** Never true **5.** Never true

SECTION 11.4

1. **a.** 5 **b.** -8 **3.** -1; -1; i; 10 **5.** $9i$ **7.** $35i$ **9.** $i\sqrt{13}$ **11.** $5i\sqrt{3}$
13. $-12i\sqrt{6}$ **15.** $a - \sqrt{-b^2}$ **17.** $5 + 2i$ **19.** $-7 - 12i$ **21.** $5 + 12i\sqrt{3}$ **23.** $7 - 12i\sqrt{7}$

25. $3 + 5i$ **27.** $-1 + i\sqrt{6}$ **29.** $-\dfrac{2}{5} - \dfrac{12\sqrt{10}}{5}i$ **31.** $-2; 3; 4 - 5i$ **33.** $10i$ **35.** $-9i$

37. $7 + 9i$ **39.** $-8 + 7i$ **41.** $13 + 2i$ **43.** $2 - 10i$ **45.** $-8 - 2i$ **47.** 6 **49.** 0

51. False **53.** Negative **55.** $-8i; -8i; -8i; 56; -1; -1; 56; -8i$ **57.** -20 **59.** 18

61. $-20 + 10i$ **63.** $2 + 23i$ **65.** $-9 - 7i$ **67.** $-41 - i$ **69.** $-21 + 20i$ **71.** $-3 - 4i$

73. $29i$ **75.** 20 **77.** 17 **79.** False **81.** $1 + 4i$ **83.** $1 - 6i$ **85.** $-7 - 2i$

87. $5 + 3i$ **89.** $\dfrac{3}{2} - \dfrac{3}{4}i$ **91.** $-\dfrac{2}{3} - \dfrac{5}{3}i$ **93.** $\dfrac{3}{2} - \dfrac{3}{2}i$ **95.** $-1 - 3i$ **97.** $5 - 3i$

99. $3 - 5i$ **101.** $2 + 4i$ **103.** True **105.** $4i, -4i$ **107.** $7i, -7i$ **109.** $3i\sqrt{3}, -3i\sqrt{3}$

111. $2i\sqrt{3}, -2i\sqrt{3}$ **113.** $-1 + 6i, -1 - 6i$ **115.** $2 + 2i\sqrt{3}, 2 - 2i\sqrt{3}$

117. $-2 + 5i\sqrt{2}, -2 - 5i\sqrt{2}$ **119.** $-\dfrac{3}{2} + i, -\dfrac{3}{2} - i$ **121.** $1 + i, 1 - i$ **123.** $-2 + i, -2 - i$

125. $3 + 2i, 3 - 2i$ **127.** $1 + i\sqrt{2}, 1 - i\sqrt{2}$ **129.** $-1 + \dfrac{1}{2}i, -1 - \dfrac{1}{2}i$ **131.** $\dfrac{1}{2} - i\sqrt{3}, \dfrac{1}{2} + i\sqrt{3}$

133. One real solution **135.** -1 **137.** $5 + 25i$ **139.** $-46 - 9i$ **141.** $3 + i$

143. $2i\sqrt{2}, -2i\sqrt{2}$ **145.** $2 + i\sqrt{5}, 2 - i\sqrt{5}$ **147.** $3 + i\sqrt{5}, 3 - i\sqrt{5}$

CONCEPT REVIEW 11.5

1. Always true **3.** Never true **5.** Never true

SECTION 11.5

5. Up **7.** Up **9.** Up **11. a.** $-1; 0; 9$ **b.** parabola; down **c.** $2; -4; 5$ **d.** $2; 5$

13. 4 **15.** -5 **17.** -42 **19.** **21.** **23.**

25. **27.** **29.** **31.** **33.**

35. **37.** False **39.** The x-intercepts are $(2, 0)$ and $(3, 0)$. The y-intercept is $(0, 6)$.

41. The x-intercepts are $(-3, 0)$ and $(3, 0)$. The y-intercept is $(0, 9)$. **43.** The x-intercepts are $\left(-1 + \sqrt{7}, 0\right)$ and $\left(-1 - \sqrt{7}, 0\right)$. The y-intercept is $(0, -6)$. **45.** The x-intercepts are $\left(\dfrac{3}{2}, 0\right)$ and $(-1, 0)$. The y-intercept is $(0, -3)$.

47. The x-intercepts are $\left(\dfrac{1 + \sqrt{17}}{-2}, 0\right)$ and $\left(\dfrac{1 - \sqrt{17}}{-2}, 0\right)$. The y-intercept is $(0, 4)$. **49.**

51.   **53.**   **55.**   **57.**   **59.**

61. $y = x^2 - 8x + 15$ **63.** $y = 2x^2 - 12x + 22$ **65.** $(-2, 0), (0, 0),$ and $(3, 0)$ **67.** $(-2, 0), (-1, 0),$ and $(2, 0)$ **69.** Linear function   **71.** Neither   **73.** Quadratic function   **75.** The model predicts the cost will be 54¢.   **77.** -2

CONCEPT REVIEW 11.6

1. Never true   **3.** Always true   **5.** Always true

SECTION 11.6

1. a. $2w - 2$ **b.** $w(2w - 2)$ **c.** $w(2w - 2)$; 84   **3.** The two integers are 7 and 9.
5. The integers are 6 and 10, or -10 and -6.   **7.** The length is 6 ft. The width is 4 ft.
9. The length is 100 ft. The width is 50 ft.   **11.** It would take the first computer 35 min and the second computer 14 min.   **13.** It would take the first engine 12 h and the second engine 6 h.
15. The rate of the plane in calm air was 100 mph.   **17.** The cyclist's rate during the first 150 mi was 50 mph.
19. The arrow will be 32 ft above the ground at 1 s and at 2 s.   **21.** The maximum speed is 151.6 km/h.
23. The water from the hose is 244.1 ft from the tugboat.   **25.** The ball hits the basket 1.88 s after it is released.
27. False   **29.** The radius of the base is 5.64 cm.   **31.** The integers are $-6, -5, -4,$ and -3, or 3, 4, 5, and 6.
33. The radius of the large pizza is 7 in.   **35.** The dimensions of the cardboard are 20 in. by 20 in.

CHAPTER 11 REVIEW EXERCISES

1. 4 and -4 [11.1.1/11.1.2]   **2.** $\dfrac{1 + \sqrt{13}}{2}$ and $\dfrac{1 - \sqrt{13}}{2}$ [11.2.1/11.3.1]   **3.** $\dfrac{3 + \sqrt{29}}{2}$ and $\dfrac{3 - \sqrt{29}}{2}$

[11.2.1/11.3.1]   **4.** $\dfrac{5}{7}$ and $-\dfrac{5}{7}$ [11.1.1/11.1.2]   **5.** [11.5.1]   **6.** [11.5.1]

7. $6i\sqrt{7}$ [11.4.1]   **8.** $-\dfrac{1}{2}$ and $-\dfrac{1}{3}$ [11.1.1]   **9.** $\dfrac{3}{2}i, -\dfrac{3}{2}i$ [11.4.5]

10. $\dfrac{-10 + 2\sqrt{10}}{5}$ and $\dfrac{-10 - 2\sqrt{10}}{5}$ [11.2.1/11.3.1]   **11.** $2 - 4i$ [11.4.2]   **12.** 6 and -5 [11.1.1]

13. $\dfrac{4}{3}$ and $-\dfrac{7}{2}$ [11.1.1]   **14.** $2\sqrt{10}$ and $-2\sqrt{10}$ [11.1.2]   **15.** $-3 + 5i$ [11.4.2]

16. $1 + \sqrt{11}$ and $1 - \sqrt{11}$ [11.2.1/11.3.1]   **17.** 3 and 9 [11.1.1]   **18.** 16 and -2 [11.1.2]

19. [11.5.1]   **20.** [11.5.1]

21. 1 and -9 [11.1.2]   **22.** $\dfrac{-4 + \sqrt{23}}{2}$ and $\dfrac{-4 - \sqrt{23}}{2}$ [11.2.1/11.3.1]   **23.** $-\dfrac{1}{6}$ and $-\dfrac{5}{4}$ [11.1.1]

24. $2 + 2i$ and $2 - 2i$ [11.4.5]   **25.** $20 + 12i$ [11.4.3]   **26.** $\dfrac{4}{7}$ [11.1.1]   **27.** 2 and -1 [11.1.2]

28. $-2 + 14i$ [11.4.3]   **29.** $\dfrac{-7 + \sqrt{61}}{2}$ and $\dfrac{-7 - \sqrt{61}}{2}$ [11.2.1/11.3.1]   **30.** 2 and $\dfrac{5}{12}$ [11.1.1]

31. $3 + \sqrt{5}$ and $3 - \sqrt{5}$ [11.1.2]   **32.** $-4 + \sqrt{19}$ and $-4 - \sqrt{19}$ [11.2.1/11.3.1]

33.   [11.5.1]   **34.**   [11.5.1]   **35.** -7 and -10 [11.1.1]

36. $\dfrac{1}{2} + \dfrac{1}{2}i$ [11.4.4]   **37.** $-3 + i\sqrt{3}$ and $-3 - i\sqrt{3}$ [11.4.5]   **38.** $-3 + \sqrt{11}$ and $-3 - \sqrt{11}$ [11.2.1/

[11.3.1]   **39.** 3 and $-\dfrac{1}{9}$ [11.1.1]   **40.** $\dfrac{-5 + \sqrt{33}}{4}$ and $\dfrac{-5 - \sqrt{33}}{4}$ [11.2.1/11.3.1]   **41.**

[11.5.1]   **42.** $-3 - i$ [11.4.4]   **43.** 1 and $\dfrac{5}{2}$ [11.1.1]   **44.**   [11.5.1]

45. The rate of the air balloon is 25 mph. [11.6.1]   **46.** The height is 10 m. The base is 4 m. [11.6.1]
47. The two integers are 3 and 5. [11.6.1]   **48.** The rate of the boat in still water is 5 mph. [11.6.1]
49. The object will be 12 ft above the ground at $\dfrac{1}{2}$ s and $1\dfrac{1}{2}$ s. [11.6.1]   **50.** It would take the smaller drain
12 h and the larger drain 4 h. [11.6.1]

CHAPTER 11 TEST

1. $-4 + 2\sqrt{5}$ and $-4 - 2\sqrt{5}$ [11.1.2]   **2.** $\dfrac{-4 + \sqrt{22}}{2}$ and $\dfrac{-4 - \sqrt{22}}{2}$ [11.2.1/11.3.1]

3. -4 and $\dfrac{5}{3}$ [11.1.1]   **4.** $12i\sqrt{5}$ [11.4.1]   **5.** $-2 + 2\sqrt{5}$ and $-2 - 2\sqrt{5}$ [11.2.1/11.3.1]

6.   [11.5.1]   **7.** $-2 + \sqrt{2}$ and $-2 - \sqrt{2}$ [11.2.1/11.3.1]   **8.** $-8 + 13i$ [11.4.2]

9. $-\dfrac{1}{2}$ and 3 [11.1.1]   **10.** $\dfrac{3 + \sqrt{7}}{2}$ and $\dfrac{3 - \sqrt{7}}{2}$ [11.2.1/11.3.1]   **11.** $24 + 30i$ [11.4.3]

12. $5 + 3\sqrt{2}$ and $5 - 3\sqrt{2}$ [11.1.2]   **13.** $3 + \sqrt{14}$ and $3 - \sqrt{14}$ [11.2.1/11.3.1]   **14.** $-18 + 13i$

[11.4.3]   **15.** $\dfrac{5 + \sqrt{33}}{2}$ and $\dfrac{5 - \sqrt{33}}{2}$ [11.2.1/11.3.1]   **16.** $\dfrac{5}{2}$ and $\dfrac{1}{3}$ [11.1.1]

17. $\dfrac{-3 + \sqrt{37}}{2}$ and $\dfrac{-3 - \sqrt{37}}{2}$ [11.2.1/11.3.1]   **18.** $-\dfrac{1}{2} - \dfrac{3}{2}i$ [11.4.4]   **19.** $4 + i$ and $4 - i$ [11.4.5]

20.   [11.5.1]   **21.** $3 + i$ [11.4.4]   **22.** The length is 8 ft. The width is 5 ft. [11.6.1]

23. The rate of the boat in calm water is 11 mph. [11.6.1]   **24.** The middle odd integer is 5 or -5. [11.6.1]

25. The rate for the last 8 mi was 4 mph. [11.6.1]

CUMULATIVE REVIEW EXERCISES

1. $-28x + 27$ [2.2.5]   **2.** $\dfrac{3}{2}$ [3.1.3]   **3.** 3 [3.2.3]   **4.** $x > \dfrac{1}{9}$ [3.3.3]   **5.** $(3, 0)$ and $(0, -4)$

[5.2.3]   **6.** $y = -\dfrac{4}{3}x - 2$ [5.4.1/5.4.2]   **7.** Domain: $\{-2, -1, 0, 1, 2\}$; range: $\{-8, -1, 0, 1, 8\}$; yes [5.5.1]

8. 37 [5.5.1]   **9.**   [5.2.2]   **10.**   [5.6.1]   **11.** $(2, 1)$ [6.2.1]

12. $(2, -2)$ [6.3.1]   **13.** $-\dfrac{4a}{3b^2}$ [7.4.1]   **14.** $x + 2 - \dfrac{4}{x - 2}$ [7.5.2]   **15.** $(x - 4)(4y - 3)$ [8.1.2]

16. $x(3x - 4)(x + 2)$ [8.3.1/8.3.2]   **17.** $\dfrac{9x^2(x - 2)(x - 4)}{(2x - 3)^2(x + 2)}$ [9.1.3]   **18.** $\dfrac{x + 2}{2(x + 1)}$ [9.3.2]

19. $\dfrac{x - 4}{2x + 5}$ [9.4.1]   **20.** -3 and 6 [9.5.2]   **21.** $a - 2$ [10.3.1]   **22.** 5 [10.4.1]

23. $\dfrac{1}{2}$ and 3 [11.1.1]   **24.** $2 + 2\sqrt{3}$ and $2 - 2\sqrt{3}$ [11.1.2]   **25.** $\dfrac{2 + \sqrt{19}}{3}$ and $\dfrac{2 - \sqrt{19}}{3}$ [11.2.1/11.3.1]

26.   [11.5.1]   **27.** The cost is \$72. [3.1.5]   **28.** The cost is \$4.50 per pound. [4.6.1]

29. To earn a dividend of \$752.50, 250 additional shares are required. [9.5.2]   **30.** The rate of the plane in calm air is 200 mph. The rate of the wind is 40 mph. [6.4.1]   **31.** The student must receive a score of 77 or better. [4.8.1]   **32.** The length of the guy wire is 31.62 m. [10.4.2]   **33.** The middle odd integer is -7 or 7. [11.6.1]

Answers to Final Exam

1. -3 [1.1.2]   **2.** -6 [1.2.2]   **3.** 12.5% [1.3.4]   **4.** -256 [1.4.1]   **5.** -11 [1.4.2]

6. $-\dfrac{15}{2}$ [2.1.1]   **7.** $9x + 6y$ [2.2.2]   **8.** $6z$ [2.2.3]   **9.** $16x - 52$ [2.2.5]   **10.** -50 [3.1.3]

11. -3 [3.2.3]   **12.** 15.2 [3.1.5]   **13.** $x \le -3$ [3.3.3]   **14.** $y \ge \dfrac{5}{2}$ [3.3.3]   **15.** $\dfrac{2}{3}$ [5.3.1]

16. $y = -\dfrac{2}{3}x - 2$ [5.4.1/5.4.2]   **17.** [5.3.2]   **18.** [5.5.2]

19. $\{-1, 2, 5, 8, 11\}$ [5.5.1]   **20.**   [5.6.1]   **21.** $(6, 17)$ [6.2.1]   **22.** $(2, -1)$ [6.3.1]

23. $-3x^2 - 3x + 8$ [7.1.2]   **24.** $81x^4y^{12}$ [7.2.2]   **25.** $6x^3 + 7x^2 - 7x - 6$ [7.3.2]

26. $-\dfrac{x^8y}{2}$ [7.4.1]   **27.** $\dfrac{16y^7}{x^8}$ [7.4.1]   **28.** $3x^2 - 4x - \dfrac{5}{x}$ [7.5.1]   **29.** $5x - 12 + \dfrac{23}{x + 2}$ [7.5.2]

30. $3.9 \cdot 10^{-8}$ [7.4.2]   **31.** $2(4 - x)(a + 3)$ [8.1.2]   **32.** $(x - 6)(x + 1)$ [8.2.1]

33. $(2x - 3)(x + 1)$ [8.3.1/8.3.2]   **34.** $(3x + 2)(2x - 3)$ [8.3.1/8.3.2]   **35.** $4x(2x - 1)(x - 3)$

[8.3.1/8.3.2]   **36.** $(5x + 4)(5x - 4)$ [8.4.1]   **37.** $3y(5 + 2x)(5 - 2x)$ [8.4.2]   **38.** $\dfrac{1}{2}$ and 3

[8.5.1/11.1.1]   **39.** $\dfrac{2(x + 1)}{x - 1}$ [9.1.2]   **40.** $\dfrac{-3x^2 + x - 25}{(2x - 5)(x + 3)}$ [9.3.2]   **41.** $x + 1$ [9.4.1]

42. 2 [9.5.1]   **43.** $a = b$ [9.6.1]   **44.** $7x^3$ [10.1.2]   **45.** $38\sqrt{3a}$ [10.2.1]

46. $\sqrt{15} + 2\sqrt{3}$ [10.3.2]   **47.** 5 [10.4.1]   **48.** $3 + \sqrt{7}$ and $3 - \sqrt{7}$ [11.1.2]

49. $\dfrac{1 + \sqrt{5}}{4}$ and $\dfrac{1 - \sqrt{5}}{4}$ [11.2.1/11.3.1]   **50.**   [11.5.1]   **51.** $2x + 3(x - 2)$; $5x - 6$ [2.3.2]

52. The original value of the machine was $3000.   [3.1.5]   **53.** There are 60 dimes in the bank.   [4.2.2]

54. The angles measure 60°, 50°, and 70°.   [4.3.3]   **55.** The markup rate is 65%.   [4.4.1]

56. An additional $6000 must be invested at 11%.   [4.5.1]   **57.** The cost is $3 per pound.   [4.6.1]

58. The percent concentration is 36%.   [4.6.2]   **59.** The plane traveled 215 km during the first hour.   [4.7.1]

60. The rate of the boat is 15 mph. The rate of the current is 5 mph.   [6.4.1]   **61.** The length is 10 m. The width

is 5 m.   [8.5.2]   **62.** 16 oz of dye are required.   [9.5.3]   **63.** It would take them 0.6 h to prepare the dinner.

[9.7.1]   **64.** The length of the other leg is 11.5 cm.   [10.4.2]   **65.** The rate of the wind is 25 mph.   [11.6.1]

Glossary

abscissa The first number in an ordered pair. It measures a horizontal distance and is also called the first coordinate. (Sec. 5.1)

absolute value of a number The distance of the number from zero on the number line. (Sec. 1.1)

acute angle An angle whose measure is between $0°$ and $90°$. (Sec. 4.3)

addend In addition, a number being added. (Sec. 1.2)

addition The process of finding the total of two numbers. (Sec. 1.2)

addition method An algebraic method of finding an exact solution of a system of linear equations. (Sec. 6.3)

additive inverses Numbers that are the same distance from zero on the number line, but on opposite sides; also called opposites. (Sec. 1.1, 2.2)

adjacent angles Two angles that share a common side. (Sec. 4.3)

alternate exterior angles Two nonadjacent angles that are on opposite sides of the transversal and outside the parallel lines. (Sec. 4.3)

alternate interior angles Two nonadjacent angles that are on opposite sides of the transversal and between the parallel lines. (Sec. 4.3)

analytic geometry Geometry in which a coordinate system is used to study the relationships between variables. (Sec. 5.1)

angle Figure formed when two rays start from the same point; it is measured in degrees. (Sec. 1.5)

area A measure of the amount of surface in a region. (Sec. 1.5)

arithmetic mean of values Average determined by calculating the sum of the values and then dividing that result by the number of values. (Sec. 1.2)

average of a set of numbers The sum of the numbers divided by the number of numbers in the set. (Sec. 1.2)

average rate of change The average rate of change of y with respect to x is the change in y divided by the change in x. (Sec. 5.1)

axes The two number lines that form a rectangular coordinate system; also called coordinate axes. (Sec. 5.1)

axis of symmetry of a parabola A line of symmetry that passes through the vertex of the parabola and is parallel to the y-axis for an equation of the form $y = ax^2 + bx + c$. (Sec. 11.5)

base In exponential notation, the factor that is multiplied the number of times shown by the exponent (Sec. 1.4)

base of a parallelogram One of the parallel sides of the parallelogram. (Sec. 1.5)

base of a triangle The side of a triangle that the triangle rests on. (Sec. 1.5)

binomial A polynomial of two terms. (Sec. 7.1)

binomial factor A factor that has two terms. (Sec. 8.1)

center of a circle The point from which all points on the circle are equidistant. (Sec. 1.5)

circle Plane figure in which all points are the same distance from its center. (Sec. 1.5)

circumference The distance around a circle. (Sec. 3.2)

clearing denominators Removing denominators from an equation that contains fractions by multiplying each side of the equation by the LCM of the denominators. (Sec. 3.2, 9.5)

coefficient The number part of a variable term. (Sec. 2.1)

combine like terms Use the Distributive Property to add the coefficients of like variable terms; add like terms of a variable expression. (Sec. 2.2)

complementary angles Two angles whose sum is $90°$. (Sec. 1.5, 4.3)

complete the square Add to a binomial the constant term that makes it a perfect-square trinomial. (Sec. 11.2)

complex conjugates Complex numbers of the form $a + bi$ and $a - bi$. (Sec. 11.4)

complex fraction A fraction whose numerator or denominator contains one or more fractions. (Sec. 9.4)

complex number A number of the form $a + bi$, where a and b are real numbers and $i = \sqrt{-1}$. (Sec. 11.4)

conjugates Binomial expressions that differ only in the sign of a term. The expressions $a + b$ and $a - b$ are conjugates. (Sec. 10.3)

consecutive even integers Even integers that follow one another in order. (Sec. 4.2)

consecutive integers Integers that follow one another in order. (Sec. 4.2)

G2   Glossary

consecutive odd integers   Odd integers that follow one another in order. (Sec. 4.2)

constant term   A term that includes no variable part; also called a constant. (Sec. 2.1)

coordinate axes   The two number lines that form a rectangular coordinate system; also simply called axes. (Sec. 5.1)

coordinates of a point   The numbers in an ordered pair that is associated with a point. (Sec. 5.1)

corresponding angles   Two angles that are on the same side of the transversal and are both acute angles or are both obtuse angles. (Sec. 4.3)

cost   The price that a business pays for a product. (Sec. 4.4)

decimal notation   Notation in which a number consists of a whole-number part, a decimal point, and a decimal part. (Sec. 1.3)

degree   A unit used to measure angles. (Sec. 1.5, 4.3)

degree of a polynomial in one variable   In a polynomial, the largest exponent that appears on the variable. (Sec. 7.1)

dependent system of equations   A system of equations that has an infinite number of solutions. (Sec. 6.1)

dependent variable   In a function, the variable whose value depends on the value of another variable known as the independent variable. (Sec. 5.5)

descending order   The terms of a polynomial in one variable arranged so that the exponents on the variable decrease from left to right. The polynomial $9x^5 - 2x^4 + 7x^3 + x^2 - 8x + 1$ is in descending order. (Sec. 7.1)

diameter of a circle   A line segment that has endpoints on the circle and goes through the circle's center. (Sec. 1.5)

difference of two squares   A polynomial of the form $a^2 - b^2$. (Sec. 8.4)

discount   The amount by which a retailer reduces the regular price of a product for a promotional sale. (Sec. 4.4)

discount rate   The percent of the regular price that the discount represents. (Sec. 4.4)

domain   The set of first coordinates of the ordered pairs in a relation. (Sec. 5.5)

double root   The two equal roots of a quadratic equation. (Sec. 11.1)

element of a set   One of the objects in a set. (Sec. 1.1)

equation   A statement of the equality of two mathematical expressions. (Sec. 3.1)

equilateral triangle   A triangle in which all three sides are of equal length. (Sec. 1.5, 4.3)

evaluate a function   Replace x in $f(x)$ with some value and then simplify the numerical expression that results. (Sec. 5.5)

evaluate a variable expression   Replace each variable by its value and then simplify the resulting numerical expression. (Sec. 2.1)

even integer   An integer that is divisible by 2. (Sec. 4.2)

exponent   In exponential notation, the elevated number that indicates how many times the base occurs in the multiplication. (Sec. 1.4)

exponential form   The expression 2^5 is in exponential form. Compare *factored form*. (Sec. 1.4)

exterior angle of a triangle   An angle adjacent to an interior angle of the triangle. (Sec. 4.3)

factor   In multiplication, a number being multiplied. (Sec. 1.2)

factor a polynomial   To write the polynomial as a product of other polynomials. (Sec. 8.1)

factor a trinomial of the form $ax^2 + bx + c$ To express the trinomial as the product of two binomials. (Sec. 8.3)

factor by grouping   Group and factor terms in a polynomial in such a way that a common binomial factor is found. (Sec. 8.1)

factor completely   Write a polynomial as a product of factors that are nonfactorable over the integers. (Sec. 8.2)

factored form   The expression $2 \cdot 2 \cdot 2 \cdot 2 \cdot 2$ is in factored form. Compare *exponential form*. (Sec. 1.4)

FOIL method   A method of finding the product of two binomials in which the sum of the products of the first terms, of the outer terms, of the inner terms, and of the last terms is found. (Sec. 7.3)

formula   A literal equation that states rules about measurements. (Sec. 9.6)

simplest form of a fraction   A fraction in which the numerator and denominator have no common factors other than 1. (Sec. 9.1)

function   A relation in which no two ordered pairs that have the same first coordinate have different second coordinates. (Sec. 5.5)

function notation   Notation used for those equations that define functions. (Sec. 5.5)

graph of a function   A graph of the ordered pairs (x, y) of the function. (Sec. 5.5)

graph of a relation   The graph of the ordered pairs that belong to the relation. (Sec. 5.5)

graph of an equation in two variables A graph of the ordered-pair solutions of the equation. (Sec. 5.2)

graph of an integer A heavy dot directly above that number on the number line. (Sec. 1.1)

graph of an ordered pair The dot drawn at the coordinates of the point in the plane. (Sec. 5.1)

graph a point in the plane Place a dot at the location given by the ordered pair; plot a point in the plane. (Sec. 5.1)

graph of $x = a$ A vertical line passing through the point whose coordinates are $(a, 0)$. (Sec. 5.2)

graph of $y = b$ A horizontal line passing through the point whose coordinates are $(0, b)$. (Sec. 5.2)

greater than A number a is greater than another number b, written $a > b$, if a is to the right of b on the number line. (Sec. 1.1)

greater than or equal to The symbol $\geq$ means "is greater than or equal to." (Sec. 1.1)

greatest common factor of two numbers The greatest number that is a factor of the two numbers. (Sec. 8.1)

greatest common factor of two monomials The product of the GCF of the coefficients of the monomials and the common variable factors. (Sec. 8.1)

half-plane The solution set of an inequality in two variables. (Sec. 5.6)

height of a triangle A line segment perpendicular to the base of the triangle from the opposite vertex. (Sec. 1.5)

height of a parallelogram The distance between the base of the parallelogram and the opposite parallel side. It is perpendicular to the base. (Sec. 1.5)

hypotenuse In a right triangle, the side opposite the 90° angle. (Sec. 10.4)

imaginary number A number of the form ai, where a is a real number and $i = \sqrt{-1}$. (Sec. 11.4)

imaginary part of a complex number For the complex number $a + bi$, b is the imaginary part. (Sec. 9.4)

imaginary unit The number whose square is -1, designated by the letter i. (Sec. 11.4)

inconsistent system of equations A system of equations that has no solution. (Sec. 6.1)

independent system of equations A system of equations that has one solution. (Sec. 6.1)

independent variable In a function, the variable that varies independently and whose value determines the value of the dependent variable. (Sec. 5.5)

inequality An expression that contains the symbol $>, <, \geq$ (is greater than or equal to), or $\leq$ (is less than or equal to). (Sec. 3.3)

integers The numbers $\ldots, -3, -2, -1, 0, 1, 2, 3, \ldots$. (Sec. 1.1)

interior angle of a triangle An angle within the region enclosed by the triangle. (Sec. 4.3)

intersecting lines Lines that cross at a point in the plane. (Sec. 1.5)

irrational number A number that cannot be written in the form a/b, where a and b are integers and b is not equal to zero. (Sec. 1.3, 10.1)

isosceles triangle A triangle that has two equal angles and two equal sides. (Sec. 1.5, 4.3)

least common multiple of two numbers The smallest number that contains the prime factorization of each number. (Sec. 1.3, 9.2)

least common multiple of two polynomials The polynomial of least degree that contains the factors of each polynomial. (Sec. 9.2)

legs In a right triangle, the sides opposite the acute angles, or the two shortest sides of the triangle. (Sec. 10.4)

legs than A number a is less than another number b, written $a < b$, if a is to the left of b on the number line. (Sec. 1.1)

less than or equal to The symbol $\leq$ means "is less than or equal to." (Sec. 1.1)

like terms Terms of a variable expression that have the same variable part. (Sec. 2.2)

line A line extends indefinitely in two directions in a plane; it has no width. (Sec. 1.5)

linear equation in two variables An equation of the form $y = mx + b$, where m is the coefficient of x and b is a constant; also called a linear function. (Sec. 5.2)

linear function An equation of the form $f(x) = mx + b$ or $y = mx + b$, where m is the coefficient of x and b is a constant; also called a linear equation in two variables. (Sec. 5.5)

line segment Part of a line; it has two endpoints. (Sec. 1.5)

literal equation An equation that contains more than one variable. (Sec. 9.6)

lowest common denominator The smallest number that is a multiple of each denominator in question. (Sec. 1.3)

markup The difference between selling price and cost. (Sec. 4.4)

markup rate The percent of a retailer's cost that the markup represents. (Sec. 4.4)

monomial A number, a variable, or a product of numbers and variables; a polynomial of one term. (Sec. 7.1)

multiplication The process of finding the product of two numbers. (Sec. 1.2)

multiplicative inverse of a number The reciprocal of the number. (Sec. 2.2)

natural numbers The numbers 1, 2, 3, ... (Sec. 1.1)

negative integers The numbers . . . , $-4, -3, -2, -1$. (Sec. 1.1)

negative slope A property of a line that slants downward to the right. (Sec. 5.3)

nonfactorable over the integers A description of a polynomial that does not factor when only integers are used. (Sec. 8.1)

numerical coefficient The number part of a variable term. When the numerical coefficient is 1 or -1, the 1 is usually not written. (Sec. 2.1)

obtuse angle An angle whose measure is between $90°$ and $180°$. (Sec. 4.3)

odd integer An integer that is not divisible by 2. (Sec. 4.2)

opposite of a polynomial The polynomial created when the sign of each term of the original polynomial is changed. (Sec. 7.1)

opposites Numbers that are the same distance from zero on the number line, but on opposite sides; also called additive inverses. (Sec. 1.1)

ordered pair A pair of numbers, such as (a, b), that can be used to identify a point in the plane determined by the axes of a rectangular coordinate system. (Sec. 5.1)

Order of Operations Agreement A set of rules that tells us in what order to perform the operations that occur in a numerical expression. (Sec. 1.4)

ordinate The second number in an ordered pair. It measures a vertical distance and is also called the second coordinate. (Sec. 5.1)

origin The point of intersection of the two coordinate axes that form a rectangular coordinate system. (Sec. 5.1)

parabola The name given to the graph of a quadratic equation in two variables. (Sec. 11.4)

parallel lines Lines that never meet; the distance between them is always the same. (Sec. 1.5, 4.3)

parallelogram A four-sided plane figure with opposite sides parallel. (Sec. 1.5)

percent Parts of 100. (Sec. 1.3)

perfect cube The cube of an integer. (Sec. 8.4)

perfect square The square of an integer. (Sec. 10.1)

perfect-square trinomial A trinomial that is a product of a binomial and itself. (Sec. 8.4)

perimeter The distance around a plane geometric figure. (Sec. 1.5, 4.3)

perpendicular lines Intersecting lines that form right angles. (Sec. 1.5, 4.3)

plane Flat surface determined by the intersection of two lines. (Sec. 1.5)

plane figures Figures that lie entirely in a plane. (Sec. 1.5)

plot a point in the plane Place a dot at the location given by the ordered pair; graph a point in the plane. (Sec. 5.1)

point-slope formula If (x_1, y_1) is a point on a line with slope m, then $y - y_1 = m(x - x_1)$. (Sec. 5.4)

polynomial A variable expression in which the terms are monomials. (Sec. 7.1)

positive integers The integers 1, 2, 3, 4 . . . . (Sec. 1.1)

positive slope A property of a line that slants upward to the right. (Sec. 5.3)

principal square root The positive square root of a number. (Sec. 10.1)

product In multiplication, the result of multiplying two numbers. (Sec. 1.2)

proportion An equation that states the equality of two ratios or rates. (Sec. 9.5)

Pythagorean Theorem If a and b are the lengths of the legs of a right triangle and c is the length of the hypotenuse, then $c^2 = a^2 + b^2$. (Sec. 10.4)

quadrant One of the four regions into which the two axes of a rectangular coordinate system divide the plane. (Sec. 5.1)

quadratic equation An equation of the form $ax^2 + bx + c, a \neq 0$; also called a second-degree equation. (Sec. 8.5, 11.1)

quadratic equation in two variables An equation of the form $y = ax^2 + bx + c$, where a is not equal to zero. (Sec. 11.4)

quadratic function A function of the form $f(x) = ax^2 + bx + c$, where a is not equal to zero. (Sec. 11.4)

radical equation An equation that contains a variable expression in a radicand. (Sec. 10.4)

radical sign The symbol $\sqrt{}$, which is used to indicate the positive, or principal, square root of a number. (Sec. 10.1)

radicand In a radical expression, the expression under the radical sign. (Sec. 10.1)

radius of a circle A line segment from the center of a circle to a point on the circle. (Sec. 1.5)

range The set of second coordinates of the ordered pairs in a relation. (Sec. 5.5)

rate The quotient of two quantities that have different units. (Sec. 9.5)

rate of work That part of a task that is completed in one unit of time. (Sec. 9.7)

ratio The quotient of two quantities that have the same unit. (Sec. 9.5)

rational expression A fraction in which the numerator and denominator are polynomials. (Sec. 9.1)

rational number A number that can be written in the form a/b, where a and b are integers and b is not equal to zero. (Sec. 1.3)

rationalize the denominator Remove a radical from the denominator of a fraction. (Sec. 10.3)

ray A figure that starts at a point and extends indefinitely in one direction. (Sec. 1.5)

real numbers The rational numbers and the irrational numbers. (Sec. 1.3)

real part of a complex number For the complex number $a + bi$, a is the real part. (Sec. 11.4)

reciprocal of a fraction The fraction that results when the numerator and denominator of a fraction are interchanged. (Sec. 1.3, 2.2)

reciprocal of a rational expression The rational expression that results when the numerator and denominator of a rational expression are interchanged. (Sec. 9.1)

rectangle A parallelogram that has four right angles. (Sec. 1.5)

rectangular coordinate system System formed by two number lines, one horizontal and one vertical, that intersect at the zero point of each line. (Sec. 5.1)

relation Any set of ordered pairs. (Sec. 5.5)

repeating decimal A decimal formed when dividing the numerator of a fraction by its denominator, in which a digit or a sequence of digits in the decimal repeats infinitely. (Sec. 1.3)

right angle An angle whose measure is 90°. (Sec. 1.5, 4.3)

right triangle A triangle that contains a 90° angle. (Sec. 10.4)

roster method Method of writing a set by enclosing a list of the elements in braces. (Sec. 1.1)

scatter diagram A graph of collected data as points in a coordinate system. (Sec. 5.1)

scientific notation Notation in which a number is expressed as the product of two factors, one a number between 1 and 10 and the other a power of 10. (Sec. 7.4)

second-degree equation An equation of the form $ax^2 + bx + c = 0$, $a \neq 0$; also called a quadratic equation. (Sec. 11.1)

selling price The price for which a business sells a product to a customer. (Sec. 4.4)

set A collection of objects. (Sec. 1.1)

similar objects Objects that have the same shape but not necessarily the same size. (Sec. 9.5)

similar triangles Triangles that have the same shape but not necessarily the same size. (Sec. 9.5)

slope The measure of the slant of a line. The symbol for slope is m. (Sec. 5.3)

slope-intercept form The slope-intercept form of an equation of a straight line is $y = mx + b$. (Sec. 5.3)

solids Objects in space. (Sec. 1.5)

solution of a system of equations in two variables An ordered pair that is a solution of each equation of the system. (Sec. 6.1)

solution of an equation A number that, when substituted for the variable, results in a true equation. (Sec. 3.1)

solution of a linear equation in two variables An ordered pair whose coordinates make the equation a true statement. (Sec. 5.2)

solution set of an inequality A set of numbers, each element of which, when substituted for the variable, results in a true inequality. (Sec. 3.3)

solve an equation Find solutions of the equation. (Sec. 3.1)

square A rectangle that has four equal sides. (Sec. 1.5)

square root A square root of a positive number x is a number a for which $a^2 = x$. (Sec. 10.1)

standard form of a quadratic equation A quadratic equation written with the polynomial in descending order and equal to zero. $ax^2 + bx + c = 0$ is in standard form. (Sec. 8.5, 11.1)

straight angle An angle whose measure is 180°. (Sec. 1.5, 4.3)

substitution method An algebraic method of finding an exact solution of a system of equations. (Sec. 6.2)

subtraction The process of finding the difference between two numbers. (Sec. 1.2)

sum In addition, the total of two or more numbers. (Sec. 1.2)

supplementary angles Two angles whose sum is 180°. (Sec. 1.5, 4.3)

system of equations Equations that are considered together. (Sec. 6.1)

terminating decimal   A decimal that is formed when dividing the numerator of its fractional counterpart by the denominator results in a remainder of zero. (Sec. 1.3)

terms of a variable expression   The addends of the expression. (Sec. 2.1)

transversal   A line intersecting two other lines at two different points. (Sec. 4.3)

triangle   A three-sided closed figure. (Sec. 1.5, 4.3)

trinomial   A polynomial of three terms. (Sec. 7.1)

undefined slope   A property of a vertical line. (Sec. 5.3)

uniform motion   The motion of a moving object whose speed and direction do not change. (Sec. 3.1, 4.7, 9.7)

value of a function   The result of evaluating a variable expression, represented by the symbol $f(x)$. (Sec. 5.5)

variable   A letter of the alphabet used to stand for a number that is unknown or that can change. (Sec. 1.1, 2.1)

variable expression   An expression that contains one or more variables. (Sec. 2.1)

variable part   In a variable term, the variable or variables and their exponents. (Sec. 2.1)

variable term   A term composed of a numerical coefficient and a variable part. (Sec. 2.1)

vertex of an angle   Point at which the two rays that form the angle meet. (Sec. 1.5)

vertex of a parabola   The lowest point on the graph of a parabola if the parabola opens up. The highest point on the graph of a parabola if the parabola opens down. (Sec. 11.4)

vertical angles   Two angles that are on opposite sides of the intersection of two lines. (Sec. 4.3)

whole numbers   The whole numbers are 0, 1, 2, 3 . . . . (Sec. 1.1)

x-axis   The horizontal axis in an xy-coordinate system. (Sec. 5.1)

x-coordinate   The abscissa in an xy-coordinate system. (Sec. 5.1)

x-intercept   The point at which a graph crosses the x-axis. (Sec. 5.2)

y-axis   The vertical axis in an xy-coordinate system. (Sec. 5.1)

y-coordinate   The ordinate in an xy-coordinate system. (Sec. 5.1)

y-intercept   The point at which a graph crosses the y-axis. (Sec. 5.2)

zero slope   A property of a horizontal line. (Sec. 5.3)

Index

Index of Applications

Table of Equations and Formulas

Slope of a Straight Line

$$\text{Slope} = m = \frac{y_2 - y_1}{x_2 - x_1}, \ x_1 \neq x_2$$

Slope-intercept Form of a Straight Line

$$y = mx + b$$

Point-slope Formula for a Line

$$y - y_1 = m(x - x_1)$$

Quadratic Formula

$$x = \frac{-b \pm \sqrt{b^2 - 4ac}}{2a}$$

Perimeter and Area of a Triangle, and Sum of the Measures of the Angles

$$P = a + b + c$$
$$A = \frac{1}{2}bh$$
$$\angle A + \angle B + \angle C = 180°$$

Pythagorean Theorem

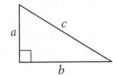

$$a^2 + b^2 = c^2$$

Perimeter and Area of a Rectangle

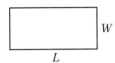

$$P = 2L + 2W$$
$$A = LW$$

Perimeter and Area of a Square

$$P = 4s$$
$$A = s^2$$

Circumference and Area of a Circle

$$C = 2\pi r \quad \text{or} \quad C = \pi d$$
$$A = \pi r^2$$

Area of a Trapezoid

$$A = \frac{1}{2}h(b_1 + b_2)$$

Volume and Surface Area of a Rectangular Solid

$$V = LWH$$
$$SA = 2LW + 2LH + 2WH$$

Volume and Surface Area of a Cube

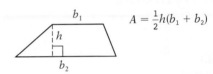

$$V = s^3$$
$$SA = 6s^2$$

Volume and Surface Area of a Right Circular Cylinder

$$V = \pi r^2 h$$
$$SA = 2\pi r^2 + 2\pi rh$$

Volume and Surface Area of a Right Circular Cone

$$V = \frac{1}{3}\pi r^2 h$$
$$SA = \pi r^2 + \pi rl$$

Volume and Surface Area of a Sphere

$$V = \frac{4}{3}\pi r^3$$
$$SA = 4\pi r^2$$

Table of Measurement Abbreviations

U.S. Customary System

Length		Capacity		Weight		Area	
in.	inches	oz	fluid ounces	oz	ounces	in^2	square inches
ft	feet	c	cups	lb	pounds	ft^2	square feet
yd	yards	qt	quarts				
mi	miles	gal	gallons				

Metric System

Length		Capacity		Weight/Mass		Area	
mm	millimeters (0.001 m)	ml	milliliters (0.001 L)	mg	milligrams (0.001 g)	cm^2	square
cm	centimeters (0.01 m)	cl	centiliters (0.01 L)	cg	centigrams (0.01 g)		centimeters
dm	decimeters (0.1 m)	dl	deciliters (0.1 L)	dg	decigrams (0.1 g)	m^2	square meters
m	meters	L	liters	g	grams		
dam	decameters (10 m)	dal	decaliters (10 L)	dag	decagrams (10 g)		
hm	hectometers (100 m)	hl	hectoliters (100 L)	hg	hectograms (100 g)		
km	kilometers (1000 m)	kl	kiloliters (1000 L)	kg	kilograms (1000 g)		

Time

h	hours	min	minutes	s	seconds

Table of Symbols

$+$	add
$-$	subtract
$\cdot$, $(a)(b)$	multiply
$\frac{a}{b}$, $\div$	divide
( )	parentheses, a grouping symbol
[ ]	brackets, a grouping symbol
π	pi, a number approximately equal to $\frac{22}{7}$ or 3.14
$-a$	the opposite, or additive inverse, of a
$\frac{1}{a}$	the reciprocal, or multiplicative inverse, of a
$=$	is equal to
$\approx$	is approximately equal to
$\neq$	is not equal to
$<$	is less than
$\leq$	is less than or equal to
$>$	is greater than
$\geq$	is greater than or equal to
(a, b)	an ordered pair whose first component is a and whose second component is b
$\circ$	degree (for angles and temperature)
$\sqrt{a}$	the principal square root of a
$|a|$	the absolute value of a

TI-30X IIS

Operations on fractions
$6\frac{2}{3} + \frac{3}{4} = 7\frac{5}{12}$

6 [Ab/c] 2 [Ab/c] 3 [+] 3 [Ab/c] 4 [ENTER]

6⌐2⌐3+3⌐4
　　　　7⌐5/12

The value of π

π
3.141592654

Power of a number (See Note 1 below.)

13 [∧] 4 [ENTER]

13⁴
　　　28561

Square root of a number

2nd [√] 36 [)] [ENTER]

√(36)
　　　　6

Square a number

7 [x²] [ENTER]

7²
　　　49

Photo courtesy of Texas Instruments Incorporated

Access operations in blue

Change decimal to fraction or fraction to decimal

.4 [2nd] [F◆D] [ENTER]

.4▸F◆D
　　　2/5

Operations with parentheses

3 [+] 2 [(] 10 [−] 6 [)] [ENTER]

3+2(10−6)
　　　11

Operations with percent

11 [×] 25 [2nd] [%] [ENTER]

11*25%
　　　2.75

Used to complete an operation

Enter a negative number (See Note 2 below.)

[(−)] 12 [÷] 6 [ENTER]

−12/6
　　　−2

---

fx-300MS

Square root of a number

[√] 36 [=]

√36
　　　6

Operations on fractions
$6\frac{2}{3} + \frac{3}{4} = 7\frac{5}{12}$

6 [ab/c] 2 [ab/c] 3 [+] 3 [ab/c] 4 [=]

6⌐2⌐3+3⌐4
　　　7⌐5⌐12

Square a number

7 [x²] [=]

7²
　　　49

Enter a negative number (See Note 2 below.)

[(−)] 12 [÷] 6 [=]

−12÷6
　　　−2

Photo courtesy of Casio, Inc.

Access operations in gold

Change decimal to fraction

.4 [=] [SHIFT] [d/c]

.4
　　　2⌐5

Power of a number (See Note 1 below.)

13 [∧] 4 [=]

13⁴
　　　28561

Operations with parentheses

3 [+] 2 [(] 10 [−] 6 [)] [=]

3+2(10−6)
　　　11

Operations with percent

11 [×] 25 [SHIFT] [%] [=]

11x25%
　　　2.75

Used to complete an operation

The value of π

[SHIFT] [π] [=]

π
3.141592654

NOTE 1: Some calculators use the [yˣ] key to calculate a power.
　　　　For those calculators, enter 13 [yˣ] 4 [=] to evaluate 13⁴.

NOTE 2: Some calculators use the [+/−] key to enter a negative number.
　　　　For those calculators, enter 12 [+/−] [÷] 6 [=] to calculate −12 ÷ 6.

TI-83 Plus/84 Plus*

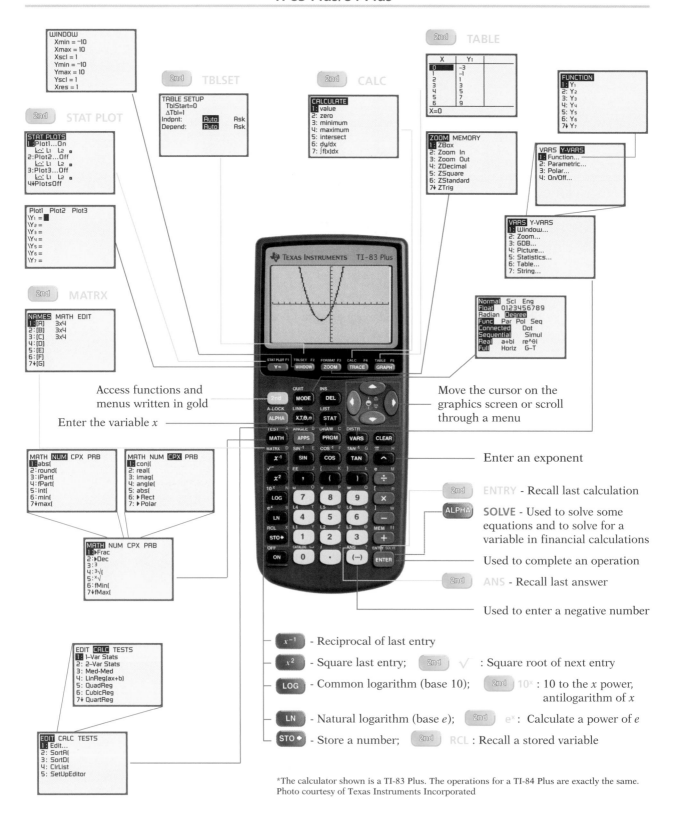

WINDOW
Xmin = -10
Xmax = 10
Xscl = 1
Ymin = -10
Ymax = 10
Yscl = 1
Xres = 1

2nd TBLSET

TABLE SETUP
TblStart=0
ΔTbl=1
Indpnt: Auto Ask
Depend: Auto Ask

2nd CALC

CALCULATE
1: value
2: zero
3: minimum
4: maximum
5: intersect
6: dy/dx
7: ∫f(x)dx

2nd TABLE

X	Y1
0	-3
1	-1
2	1
3	3
4	5
5	7
6	9
X=0	

FUNCTION
1: Y1
2: Y2
3: Y3
4: Y4
5: Y5
6: Y6
7↓ Y7

2nd STAT PLOT

STAT PLOTS
1: Plot1...On
    ∟ L1 L2
2: Plot2...Off
    ∟ L1 L2
3: Plot3...Off
    ∟ L1 L2
4↓ PlotsOff

Plot1 Plot2 Plot3
\Y1 = ■
\Y2 =
\Y3 =
\Y4 =
\Y5 =
\Y6 =
\Y7 =

ZOOM MEMORY
1: ZBox
2: Zoom In
3: Zoom Out
4: ZDecimal
5: ZSquare
6: ZStandard
7↓ ZTrig

VARS Y-VARS
1: Function...
2: Parametric...
3: Polar...
4: On/Off...

VARS Y-VARS
1: Window...
2: Zoom...
3: GDB...
4: Picture...
5: Statistics...
6: Table...
7: String...

2nd MATRX

NAMES MATH EDIT
1: [A]   3x4
2: [B]   3x4
3: [C]   3x4
4: [D]
5: [E]
6: [F]
7↓ [G]

Normal Sci Eng
Float 0123456789
Radian Degree
Func Par Pol Seq
Connected Dot
Sequential Simul
Real a+bi re^θi
Full Horiz G-T

Access functions and
menus written in gold

Enter the variable x

Move the cursor on the
graphics screen or scroll
through a menu

MATH NUM CPX PRB
1: abs(
2: round(
3: iPart(
4: fPart(
5: int(
6: min(
7↓ max(

MATH NUM **CPX** PRB
1: conj(
2: real(
3: imag(
4: angle(
5: abs(
6: ▶Rect
7: ▶Polar

MATH NUM CPX PRB
1: ▶Frac
2: ▶Dec
3: ³
4: ³√(
5: ˣ√(
6: fMin(
7↓ fMax(

Enter an exponent

2nd ENTRY - Recall last calculation

ALPHA SOLVE - Used to solve some
equations and to solve for a
variable in financial calculations

Used to complete an operation

2nd ANS - Recall last answer

Used to enter a negative number

EDIT CALC TESTS
1: 1-Var Stats
2: 2-Var Stats
3: Med-Med
4: LinReg(ax+b)
5: QuadReg
6: CubicReg
7↓ QuartReg

EDIT CALC TESTS
1: Edit...
2: SortA(
3: SortD(
4: ClrList
5: SetUpEditor

x^{-1} - Reciprocal of last entry

x^2 - Square last entry; **2nd** √ : Square root of next entry

LOG - Common logarithm (base 10); **2nd** 10^x : 10 to the x power,
antilogarithm of x

LN - Natural logarithm (base e); **2nd** e^x : Calculate a power of e

STO▶ - Store a number; **2nd** RCL : Recall a stored variable

*The calculator shown is a TI-83 Plus. The operations for a TI-84 Plus are exactly the same.
Photo courtesy of Texas Instruments Incorporated

The Pythagorean Theorem

The Pythagorean Theorem

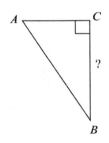

A **right triangle** contains one right angle. The side across from the right angle is called the **hypotenuse**. The other two sides are called **legs**.

Question: For the triangle at the left, which side is the hypotenuse? [1]

The angles in a right triangle are usually labeled with the capital letters A, B, and C, with C reserved for the right angle. The side opposite angle A is side a, the side opposite angle B is side b, and c is the hypotenuse.

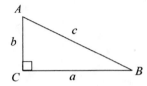

Question: Using the convention stated in the above paragraph, what letter should replace the question mark in the triangle at the left? [2]

The Pythagorean Theorem states an important relationship that exists among the sides of a right triangle. The theorem is named after Pythagoras, a Greek mathematician and philosopher who lived from about 572–501 B.C. Although Pythagoras is generally credited with the discovery, there is evidence that it was known years before his birth. There is reference to this theorem in Chinese writings from about 1100 B.C., and it is believed that the Egyptians and Babylonians knew of it as early as 2000 B.C.

Point of Interest
Historians believe that surveyors in ancient Egypt used stretched ropes with 12 equally spaced knots to measure right angles when laying out land boundaries. The surveyors knew that a triangle with sides measuring 3, 4, and 5 units was a right triangle.

The **Pythagorean Theorem** states that the square of the hypotenuse of a right triangle is equal to the sum of the squares of the two legs.

In the figure at the right is a right triangle with legs measuring 3 units and 4 units and a hypotenuse measuring 5 units. Each side of the triangle is also the side of a square. The number of square units in the area of the largest square is equal to the sum of the areas of the smaller squares.

Square of the hypotenuse	=	sum of the squares of the two legs

$$5^2 = 3^2 + 4^2$$
$$25 = 9 + 16$$
$$25 = 25$$

---

1. Side c is the hypotenuse because it is the side across from the right angle.
2. The letter a (lower case a) should replace the question mark because it is the side opposite angle A.

Pythagorean Theorem

If a and b are the lengths of the legs of a right triangle and c is the length of the hypotenuse, then $c^2 = a^2 + b^2$.

If the lengths of two sides of a right triangle are known, the Pythagorean Theorem can be used to find the length of the third side.

Consider a right triangle with legs that measure 5 cm and 12 cm. Use the Pythagorean Theorem, with $a = 5$ and $b = 12$, to find the length of the hypotenuse. (If you let $a = 12$ and $b = 5$, the result is the same.)

$$c^2 = a^2 + b^2$$
$$c^2 = 5^2 + 12^2$$
$$c^2 = 25 + 144$$
$$c^2 = 169$$

This equation states that the square of c is 169. Since $13^2 = 169$, $c = 13$, and the length of the hypotenuse is 13 cm. We can find c by taking the square root of 169: $\sqrt{169} = 13$. This suggests the following property.

The Principal Square Root Property

If $r^2 = s$, then $r = \sqrt{s}$, and r is called the square root of s.

The Principal Square Root Property and its application are illustrated as follows:

Because $4^2 = 16$, $4 = \sqrt{16}$. Therefore, if $c^2 = 16$, $c = \sqrt{16} = 4$.

Because $8^2 = 64$, $8 = \sqrt{64}$. Therefore, if $c^2 = 64$, $c = \sqrt{64} = 8$.

Question: If $c^2 = 81$, what is the value of c? [3]

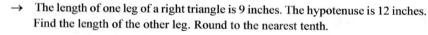

→   The length of one leg of a right triangle is 9 inches. The hypotenuse is 12 inches. Find the length of the other leg. Round to the nearest tenth.

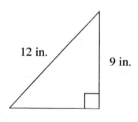

Use the Pythagorean Theorem.

$a = 9$ and $c = 12$.

$$a^2 + b^2 = c^2$$
$$9^2 + b^2 = 12^2$$

Square 9 and square 12.

$$81 + b^2 = 144$$

We want to solve for b^2. Subtract 81 from each side of the equation.

$$81 - 81 + b^2 = 144 - 81$$
$$b^2 = 63$$

Use the Principal Square Root Property.

$$b = \sqrt{63}$$

Use a calculator to approximate $\sqrt{63}$.

$$b \approx 7.9$$

The length of the other leg is approximately 7.9 inches.

Take Note
In this example, if you let $b = 9$ and solve for a^2, the result is the same.

---

3. $c = \sqrt{81} = 9$

Example 1   The two legs of a right triangle measure 5 meters and 13 meters. Find the hypotenuse of the right triangle. Round to the nearest hundredth.

Solution

$c^2 = a^2 + b^2$ • Use the Pythagorean Theorem.

$c^2 = 5^2 + 13^2$ • $a = 5$ and $b = 13$.

$c^2 = 25 + 169$ • Square 5 and square 13.

$c^2 = 194$

$c = \sqrt{194}$ • Use the Principal Square Root Property.

$c \approx 13.93$

The length of the hypotenuse is 13.93 meters.

You-Try-It 1   The two legs of a right triangle measure 7 meters and 14 meters. Find the hypotenuse of the right triangle. Round to the nearest hundredth.

Solution   See page S1.

Example 2   The hypotenuse of a right triangle measures 14 feet, and one leg measures 11 feet. Find the measure of the other leg. Round to the nearest tenth.

Solution

$a^2 + b^2 = c^2$ • Use the Pythagorean Theorem.

$11^2 + b^2 = 14^2$ • $a = 11$ and $c = 14$.

$121 + b^2 = 196$ • Square 11 and square 14.

$121 - 121 + b^2 = 196 - 121$ • Solve for b^2. Subtract 121 from

$b^2 = 75$ each side of the equation.

$b = \sqrt{75}$ • Use the Principal Square Root Property.

$b \approx 8.7$

The measure of the other leg is approximately 8.7 feet.

You-Try-It 2   The hypotenuse of a right triangle measures 16 feet, and one leg measures 5 feet. Find the measure of the other leg. Round to the nearest hundredth.

Solution   See page S1.

The hypotenuse is always the longest side of a right triangle. This fact can be used as a quick check when you are solving a right triangle for the length of one of the sides. For example, in Example 2, we found that the length of a leg was 8.7 feet. Since 8.7 < 14 (the hypotenuse), we know that the answer is "in the right ballpark."

Question: Two legs of a right triangle measure 3 meters and 9 meters. Is the length of the hypotenuse less than 3 meters, between 3 and 9 meters, or greater than 9 meters? [4]

4. The length of the hypotenuse is longer than either leg, so the length is greater than 9 meters.

Example 3   High Definition Television (HDTV) gives consumers a wider viewing area, more like a film seen in a movie theater. A regular television with a 27-inch diagonal measurement has a screen 16.2 inches tall. An HDTV screen with the same 16.2-inch height would have a diagonal measuring 33 inches. How many inches wider is the HDTV screen? Round to the nearest tenth.

State the goal.

The goal is to find the difference between the width of an HDTV screen and a regular television screen given that both have a height of 16.2 inches, the diagonal of the HDTV screen is 33 inches, and the diagonal of the regular TV is 27 inches.

Describe a strategy.

• Use the Pythagorean Theorem to find the width of an HDTV screen that has a 16.2-inch height an a 33-inch diagonal.
• Use the Pythagorean Theorem to find the width of a regular TV screen that has a 16.2-inch height an a 27-inch diagonal.
• Subtract the width of the regular television screen from the width of the HDTV screen.

Solve the problem.

$$a^2 + b^2 = c^2$$
$$(16.2)^2 + b^2 = 33^2$$ • For the HDTV, $a = 16.2$ and $c = 33$.
$$262.44 + b^2 = 1089$$
$$b^2 = 826.56$$ • Solve for b^2. Subtract 262.44 from each side of the equation.

$$b = \sqrt{826.56}$$ • Use the Product Property of Square Roots.
$$b \approx 28.7$$ • The width of the HDTV screen is 28.7 inches.

$$a^2 + b^2 = c^2$$
$$(16.2)^2 + b^2 = 27^2$$ • For the regular TV, $a = 16.2$ and $c = 27$.
$$262.44 + b^2 = 729$$
$$b^2 = 466.56$$ • Solve for b^2. Subtract 262.44 from each side of the equation.

$$b = \sqrt{466.56}$$ • Use the Product Property of Square Roots.
$$b = 21.6$$ • The width of the regular TV screen is 21.6 inches.

$$28.7 - 21.6 = 7.1$$ • Find the difference between the two widths.

The width of the HDTV screen is 7.1 inches wider than the width of the regular TV screen.

Check your work.   ✓

You-Try-It 3   Dave Marshall needs to clean the gutters of his home. The gutters are 28 feet above the ground. For safety, the distance a ladder reaches up a wall should be four times the distance from the bottom of the ladder to the base of the side of the house. Therefore, the ladder must be 7 feet from the base of the house. Will a 30-foot ladder be long enough to reach the gutters?

Solution   See page S1.

EXERCISES

Topics for Discussion

1. Label the right triangle shown at the right. Include the right angle symbol, the three angles, and the three sides.

2. What does the Pythagorean Theorem state?

3. Can the Pythagorean Theorem be used to find the length of side *c* of the triangle at the right? If so, determine *c*. If not, explain why the theorem cannot be used.

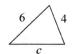

4. What does the Principal Square Root Property state?

The Pythagorean Theorem

Determine whether the triangle is a right triangle.

5.

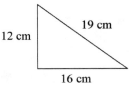

12 cm

19 cm

16 cm

No

6.

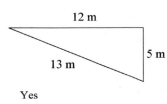

12 m

5 m

13 m

Yes

7.

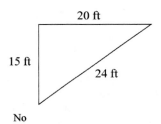

20 ft

15 ft

24 ft

No

8. The two legs of a right triangle measure 5 centimeters and 9 centimeters. Find the length of the hypotenuse. Round to the nearest tenth.

9. The two legs of a right triangle measure 8 inches and 4 inches. Find the length of the hypotenuse. Round to the nearest tenth.

10. The hypotenuse of a right triangle measures 12 feet. One leg of the triangle measures 7 feet. Find the length of the other leg of the triangle. Round to the nearest hundredth.

11. The hypotenuse of a right triangle measures 20 centimeters. One leg of the triangle measures 16 centimeters. Find the length of the other leg of the triangle.

12. The diagonal of a rectangle is a line drawn from one vertex to the opposite vertex. Find the length of the diagonal in the rectangle shown at the right. Round to the nearest tenth.

7.45 mi

11.7 mi

13. The infield of a baseball diamond is a square. The distance between successive bases is 90 feet. The pitcher's mound is on the diagonal between home plate and second base at a distance of 60.5 feet from home plate. Is the pitcher's mound more or less than halfway between home plate and second base?

14. The infield of a softball diamond is a square. The distance between successive bases is 60 feet. The pitcher's mound is on the diagonal between home plate and second base at a distance of 46 feet from home plate. Is the pitcher's mound more or less than halfway between home plate and second base?

15. An L–shaped sidewalk from the parking lot to a memorial is shown in the figure at the right. The distance directly across the grass to the memorial is 650 feet. The distance to the corner is 600 feet. Find the distance from the corner to the memorial.

16. A commuter plane leaves an airport traveling due south at 400 mph. Another plane leaving at the same time travels due east at 300 mph. Find the distance between the two planes after 2 hours.

17. The measure of a television screen is given by the length of a diagonal across the screen. A 36-inch television has a width of 28.8 inches. Find the height of the screen. Round to the nearest tenth.

18. The measure of a television screen is given by the length of a diagonal across the screen. A 33-inch big screen television has a width of 26.4 inches. Find the height of the screen. Round to the nearest tenth.

19. A guy wire is to be attached to a telephone pole at a point 20 meters above the ground. The wire is anchored to the ground at a point 8 meters from the base of the telephone pole. How long a guy wire is required? Round to the nearest tenth.

20. Melissa leaves a dock in her sailboat and sails 4 mi due east. She then tacks and sails 2.5 mi due south. The walkie-talkie Melissa has on board has a range of 5 mi. Will she be able to call a friend on the dock from her location using the walkie-talkie?

Introduction to Trigonometry

Trigonometric Functions of an Acute Angle

Using the Pythagorean theorem, given two sides of a right triangle, it is possible to determine the length of the third side. In some situations, however, it may not be practical or possible to know two of the sides of a right triangle.

Consider, for example, the problem of an engineer trying to determine the distance across a ravine so that a bridge can be built connecting the two sides. Look at the triangle drawn below.

It would be fairly easy to measure the length of the side of the triangle that is on the land (100 feet), but measuring the lengths of sides a and c cannot be accomplished easily because of the ravine.

To solve problems similar to this one, relationships between the sides and angles of a triangle were explored. This study became know as *trigonometry* which comes from two Greek words meaning "triangle measurement."

Given triangle ABC and $A'B'C'$, in which $\angle A = \angle A'$, $\angle B = \angle B'$, and $\angle C = \angle C'$, then triangle ABC is similar to $A'B'C'$.

 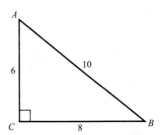

The lengths of the corresponding sides of these triangles are different; however, the *ratios* of the lengths of the corresponding sides are equal.

For example,

$$\frac{a}{c} = \frac{4}{5} \text{ and } \frac{a'}{c'} = \frac{8}{10} = \frac{4}{5}. \quad \text{Therefore, } \frac{a}{c} = \frac{a'}{c'}.$$

$$\frac{b}{a} = \frac{3}{4} \text{ and } \frac{b'}{a'} = \frac{6}{8} = \frac{3}{4}. \quad \text{Therefore, } \frac{b}{a} = \frac{b'}{a'}.$$

These ratios remain constant regardless of the lengths of the sides of the triangles. They depend only on the sizes of the acute angles in any two similar triangles.

Using the three sides, a, b, and c, of a right triangle, three ratios can be written. These ratios are used to define three trigonometric functions: sine, cosine, and tangent (abbreviated sin, cos, and tan, respectively).

In defining these trigonometric functions, "opposite" is used to mean the length of the leg opposite the given angle, and "adjacent" is used to mean the length of the leg adjacent to (next to) the given angle.

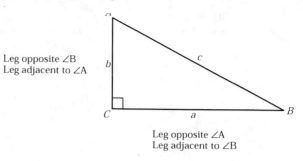

Leg opposite ∠B
Leg adjacent to ∠A

Leg opposite ∠A
Leg adjacent to ∠B

The Trigonometric Functions

If α is either acute angle of a right triangle (A or B), then

$$\sin \alpha = \frac{\text{opposite}}{\text{hypotenuse}}$$

$$\cos \alpha = \frac{\text{adjacent}}{\text{hypotenuse}}$$

$$\tan \alpha = \frac{\text{opposite}}{\text{adjacent}}$$

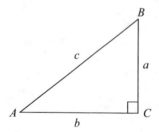

Question: Which trigonometric function is defined by each of the following ratios? [1]

a. $\dfrac{\text{adjacent}}{\text{hypotenuse}}$ **b.** $\dfrac{\text{opposite}}{\text{adjacent}}$ **c.** $\dfrac{\text{opposite}}{\text{hypotenuse}}$

For the right triangle shown at the left, which side is:

d. adjacent to $\angle A$ **e.** opposite $\angle A$

f. adjacent to $\angle B$ **g.** opposite $\angle B$

Going back to our 3-4-5 right triangle, we note the following:

$$\sin A = \frac{opp}{hyp} = \frac{4}{5} \qquad \sin B = \frac{opp}{hyp} = \frac{3}{5}$$

$$\cos A = \frac{adj}{hyp} = \frac{3}{5} \qquad \cos B = \frac{adj}{hyp} = \frac{4}{5}$$

$$\tan A = \frac{opp}{adj} = \frac{4}{3} \qquad \tan B = \frac{opp}{adj} = \frac{3}{4}$$

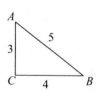

Take Note

Notice how $\sin A = \cos B$ and $\sin B = \cos A$. Since $A + B = 90°$, A and B are "complementary." The "co" in cosine stands for complement. Hence, cosine is short for "complement's sine." Also note the reciprocal relationship between $\tan A$ and $\tan B$.

So when the sides of a right triangle are known, values can be determined for the sine, cosine, and tangent of either acute angle. Most often, however, what is known about an angle is its measure in degrees. How is the tangent of an angle, measured in degrees, determined? Let's choose an angle of 35° to illustrate.

---

1. **a.** cosine (abbreviated cos) **b.** tangent (abbreviated tan) **c.** sine (abbreviated sin) **d.** b **e.** a **f.** a **g.** b

To find the tangent of 35° using the definitions above, we would need to carefully construct a right triangle containing an angle of 35°. Since any two right triangles containing an angle of 35° would be similar, by the arguments above, <u>the value for tan 35° would be the same no matter what triangle we draw.</u> A carefully constructed triangle, as described below, will give a value for tan 35° of approximately 0.7.

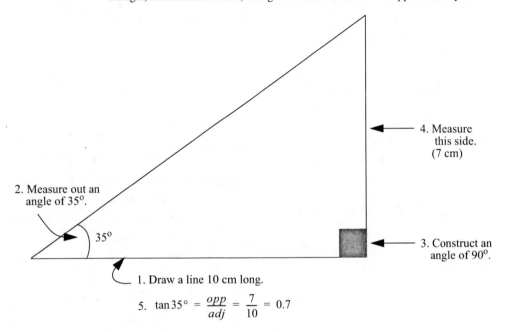

4. Measure this side. (7 cm)

2. Measure out an angle of 35°.

35°

3. Construct an angle of 90°.

1. Draw a line 10 cm long.

5. $\tan 35° = \dfrac{opp}{adj} = \dfrac{7}{10} = 0.7$

Take Note

The hypotenuse, c, is never referred to as the side opposite angle A or B, and it is never referred to as the leg adjacent to angle A or angle B. It is only referred to as the hypotenuse.

From this same triangle, we could also obtain values for sin 35° and cos 35°. The important thing is that, once these values have been determined, <u>they never change</u> and could therefore be recorded in a table of values. Similar work could be done for every angle from 1° to 89° with results recorded. Mathematicians have done this work and organized the results as shown in the table at the end of this section.

Fortunately for us, calculators have also been programmed to allow us to obtain these values.

→   Use a calculator to find tan 35°.

   Confirm that your calculator is in "degree mode." (Look for the "deg" on the display.)

   Press the tan button and key in 35

   Press Enter.   tan 35° = 0.700207538

Despite the fact that the values of the trigonometric functions are approximate, it is customary to use the equal sign rather than the approximately equal sign when writing these function values.

Example 1   Use a calculator to find sin 43.8° to the nearest ten-thousandth.

Solution   sin 43.8° = 0.6921

• The calculator must be in degree
You-Try-It 1   Use a calculator to find tan ~~mode. Press the sin key followed by~~ 43.8° to the nearest ten-thousandth.
43.8. Press Enter.

Solution   See page S1.

Using trigonometry, the engineer mentioned at the beginning of this section could determine the distance across the ravine after determining the measure of $\angle A$. Suppose the engineer measures the angle as $33.8°$. Now the engineer would ask, "Which trigonometric function involves the leg opposite an angle and the leg adjacent to that angle?" Knowing that the tangent function is the required function, the engineer could write and solve the equation $\tan 33.8° = \dfrac{a}{100}$.

$$\tan 33.8° = \frac{a}{100}$$

$100(\tan 33.8°) = a$ • Multiply each side of the equation by 100.

$66.9 \acute{Y} a$ • Use a calculator to find $\tan 33.8°$. Multiply the result in the display by 100.

The length of the bridge must be approximately 66.9 feet.

Example 2   For the right triangle shown at the left, find the length of side a. Round to the nearest hundredth.

Solution   We are given the measure of $\angle A$ and the hypotenuse. We want to find the length of side a. Side a is opposite $\angle A$. The trigonometric function that involves the leg opposite an angle and the hypotenuse is the sine function.

$$\sin A = \frac{\text{opposite}}{\text{hypotenuse}}$$

$$\sin 24° = \frac{a}{14}$$

$14(\sin 24°) = a$ • Multiply each side by 14.

$5.69 \acute{Y} a$ • Key in 14 sin(14°).

The length of side a is approximately 5.69 meters.

You-Try-It 2   For the right triangle shown at the left, find the length of side a. Round to the nearest hundredth.

Solution   See page S1.

Inverse Trigonometric Functions

Sometimes it is necessary to find one of the acute angles in a right triangle. For instance, suppose it is necessary to find $\angle A$ in the figure at the right. Because the leg adjacent to $\angle A$ is known and the hypotenuse is known, we can write:

$$\cos A = \frac{\text{adjacent}}{\text{hypotenuse}}$$

$$\cos A = \frac{24}{30}$$

The solution of this equation is the angle whose cosine is $24/30$. This angle can be found by using the $\cos^{-1}$ key on a calculator.

$$\cos^{-1}(24/30) = 36.86989765$$

To the nearest tenth, $\angle A$ is $36.9°$.

The function $\cos^{-1}$ is called the *inverse cosine function*.[2]

> **Definition of the Inverse Sine, Inverse Cosine, and Inverse Tangent Functions**
>
> For $0° < x < 90°$:
> $y = \sin^{-1}(x)$ can be read "y is the angle whose sine is x."
> $y = \cos^{-1}(x)$ can be read "y is the angle whose cosine is x."
> $y = \tan^{-1}(x)$ can be read "y is the angle whose tangent is x."

Note that $\sin^{-1}(x)$ is used to denote the inverse of the sine function. It is not the reciprocal of $\sin x$ but the notation used for its inverse. The same is true for $\cos^{-1}$ and $\tan^{-1}$.

The expression $y = \sin^{-1}(x)$ is sometimes written $y = \arcsin(x)$. The two expressions are equivalent. The expressions $y = \cos^{-1}(x)$ and $y = \arccos(x)$ are equivalent, as are $y = \tan^{-1}(x)$ and $y = \arctan(x)$.

To find an inverse function on a calculator, usually the INV or 2nd key is pressed prior to pushing the function key. Some calculators have $\sin^{-1}$, $\cos^{-1}$, and $\tan^{-1}$ keys. Consult the manual of instruction for your calculator.

Example 3   Use a calculator to find $\sin^{-1}(0.9171)$. Round to the nearest tenth.

Solution $\sin^{-1}(0.9171) = 66.5°$ • The calculator must be in degree mode. Press the keys for the inverse sine function followed by .9171. Press Enter.

You-Try-It 3   Use a calculator to find $\tan^{-1}(0.3165)$. Round to the nearest tenth.

Solution   See page S1.

Example 4   Given $\sin \theta = 0.7239$, find θ. Use a calculator. Round to the nearest tenth.

Solution   The calculator must be in the degree mode. This is equivalent to finding $\sin^{-1}(0.7239)$.

$\sin^{-1}(0.7239) \approx 46.3774°$.

Therefore, to the nearest tenth, $\theta = 46.4°$.

You-Try-It 4   Given $\tan \theta = 0.5681$, find θ. Use a calculator. Round to the nearest tenth.

Solution   See page S1.

Example 5   For the right triangle shown at the left, find $\angle B$. Round to the nearest tenth.

2. This angle could also be found by looking for $\frac{24}{30} = 0.8$ in the cosine column in the table on page 20.

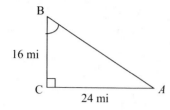

Solution   We want to find the measure of $\angle B$, and we are given the length of the leg opposite $\angle B$ and the leg adjacent to $\angle B$. The trigonometric function that involves the leg opposite an angle and the leg adjacent to that angle is the tangent function.

$$\tan B = \frac{\text{opposite}}{\text{adjacent}}$$

$$\tan B = \frac{24}{16}$$

$$B = \tan^{-1}\left(\frac{24}{16}\right)$$

$$B = 56.3° \qquad \bullet \text{ Use the tan}^{-1} \text{ key on a calculator.}$$

The measure of $\angle B$ is approximately 56.3°.

You-Try-It 5   For the right triangle shown at the left, find $\angle A$. Round to the nearest tenth.

Solution   See page S1.

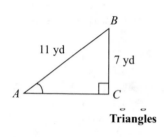

Triangles

To solve a right triangle means to use the information given about it to find the unknown sides and angles. A right triangle can be solved when two sides are known or when one acute angle and one side of the triangle are known. In either case, begin by drawing a diagram of the right triangle and labeling the given parts.

In Example 6 and You-Try-It 6 below, two sides of the triangle are given. In Example 7 and You-Try-It 7, one acute angle and one side are given.

Example 6   Solve right triangle ABC given $b = 12$ centimeters and $c = 15$ centimeters. Round to the nearest whole number.

Solution

• Draw a diagram, labeling the given parts. Remember that $\angle C$ is always the right angle.

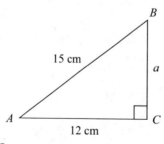

• Use the Pythagorean Theorem to find the third side.

$$a$$
$$a^2$$
$$a^2 + 144 = 225$$
$$a^2 = 81$$
$$a = 9$$

$$\sin B = \frac{\text{opposite}}{\text{hypotenuse}}$$

$$\sin B = \frac{12}{15}$$

$$b = \sin^{-1}\left(\frac{12}{15}\right)$$

$$B \approx 53°$$

• Write a trigonometric function which relates the two given sides and one unknown angle. Solve for the unknown angle by finding $\sin^{-1}(12/15)$.

$$\angle A = 90° - 53°$$
$$= 37°$$

• Angle A and angle B are complementary angles.

Side $a = 9$ meters, $\angle A = 37°$, and $\angle B = 53°$.

You-Try-It 6   Solve right triangle ABC given $a = 8$ centimeters and $b = 10$ centimeters. Round to the nearest whole number.

Solution   See page S2.

Example 7   Solve right triangle ABC given $c = 24$ meters and $\angle A = 35°$. Round to the nearest whole number.

Solution

• Draw a diagram, labeling the given parts. Remember that $\angle C$ is always the right angle.

$$\angle B = 90° - 35°$$
$$= 55°$$

• Find $\angle B$, the complement of $\angle A$.

$$\sin A = \frac{\text{opposite}}{\text{hypotenuse}}$$

$$\sin 35° = \frac{a}{24}$$

$$a = 24(\sin 35°)$$
$$a \doteq 14$$

• Write a trigonometric function which relates the given angle and the given side to one of the unknown sides.

• Solve the equation for the unknown side.
• Key in 24 sin(35).

Take Note
Remember to put the calculator in the degree mode.

$$\cos A = \frac{\text{adjacent}}{\text{hypotenuse}}$$

$$\cos 35° = \frac{b}{24}$$

$$b = 24(\cos 35°)$$
$$b \doteq 20$$

• Write a trigonometric function which relates the given angle and the given side to the other unknown side.

• Solve the equation for the unknown side.
• Key in 24 cos(35).

$\angle B = 55°$, side $a = 14$ meters, and side $b = 20$ meters.

You-Try-It 7   Solve right triangle ABC given $b = 18$ centimeters and $\angle B = 25°$. Round to the nearest whole number.

Solution   See page S2.

Angles of Elevation and Depression

The use of trigonometry is necessary in a variety of situations. One application, called **line of sight problems**, concerns an observer looking at an object.

Angles of elevation and depression are measured with respect to a horizontal line. If the object being sighted is above the observer, the acute angle formed by the line of sight and the horizontal line is an **angle of elevation**. If the object being sighted is below the observer, the acute angle formed by the line of sight and the horizontal line is an **angle of depression**.

Example 8   The angle of elevation of the top of a flagpole 62 feet away is 34°. Find the height of the flagpole. Round to the nearest tenth.

State the goal.   The goal is to find the height of the flagpole given the horizontal distance to the flagpole and the angle from the horizontal to the top of the flagpole.

Describe a strategy.   Draw a diagram. To find the height, write a trigonometric function that relates the given information and the unknown side of the triangle.

Solve the problem.

$$\tan 34° = \frac{h}{62}$$
$$62(\tan 34°) = h$$
$$41.8 \acute{Y} h$$

The height of the flagpole is 41.8 feet.

Check your work.   Đ

You-Try-It 8   The angle of depression from the top of a lighthouse that is 20 meters high of a boat on the water is 25°. How far is the boat from the lighthouse? Round to the nearest tenth.

Solution   See page S2.

EXERCISES

Topics for Discussion

1. For the right triangle at the right, use the sides a, b, and c to:
    a. name the ratio for sin A
    b. name the ratio for sin B
    c. name the ratio for cos A
    d. name the ratio for cos B
    e. name the ratio for tan A
    f. name the ratio for tan B

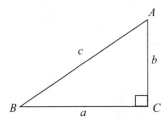

2. Explain the meaning of the notation $y = \sin^{-1}(x)$, $y = \cos^{-1}(x)$, and $y = \tan^{-1}(x)$.

Use your calculator to find the value of each of the following. Round to the nearest ten-thousandth.

3. cos 47°	**4.** sin 62°	**5.** tan 55°	**6.** cos 11°
7. sin 85.6°	**8.** cos 21.9°	**9.** tan 63.4°	**10.** sin 7.8°
11. tan 41.6°	**12.** cos 73°	**13.** sin 57.7°	**14.** tan 39.2°
15. sin 58.3°	**16.** tan 35.1°	**17.** cos 46.9°	**18.** sin 50°

Inverse Trigonometric Functions

Use a calculator. Round to the nearest tenth.

19. Given sin $\theta = 0.6239$, find θ.

20. Given cos $\phi = 0.9516$, find ϕ.

21. Find $\cos^{-1}(0.7536)$.

22. Find $\sin^{-1}(0.4478)$.

23. Given tan $\phi = 0.3899$, find ϕ.

24. Given sin $\theta = 0.7349$, find θ.

25. Find $\tan^{-1}(0.7815)$.

26. Find $\cos^{-1}(0.6032)$.

27. Given cos $\theta = 0.3007$, find θ.

28. Given tan $\phi = 1.588$, find ϕ.

29.   Find $\sin^{-1}(0.0105)$.

30.   Find $\tan^{-1}(0.2438)$.

31.   Given $\sin \beta = 0.9143$, find β.

32.   Given $\cos \theta = 0.4756$, find θ.

33.   Find $\cos^{-1}(0.8704)$.

34.   Find $\sin^{-1}(0.2198)$.

Solving Right Triangles

35.   For right triangle ABC, the hypotenuse is 9 meters and $\angle A = 38^\circ$ as shown at the right. Find the length of side a. Round to the nearest hundredth.

36.   For right triangle ABC, the hypotenuse is 15 centimeters and $\angle B = 52^\circ$. Find the length of side a. Round to the nearest hundredth.

37.   In right triangle ABC, side a is 16 meters and side b is 18 meters. Find $\angle A$. Round to the nearest tenth.

38.   For right triangle ABC, the hypotenuse is 6 inches and $\angle A = 26^\circ$. Find the length of side b. Round to the nearest hundredth.

39.   In right triangle ABC, shown at the right, side a is 32 centimeters and side b is 21 centimeters. Find $\angle B$. Round to the nearest tenth.

40.   In right triangle ABC, side a is 10 inches and the hypotenuse is 14 inches. Find $\angle B$. Round to the nearest tenth.

41.   For right triangle ABC, the hypotenuse is 14 feet and $\angle B = 70^\circ$, as shown at the right. Find the length of side b. Round to the nearest hundredth.

42. For right triangle *ABC*, side *a* is 20 centimeters and ∠*B* = 41°. Find the length of the hypotenuse. Round to the nearest hundredth.

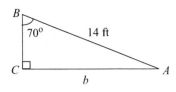

43. In right triangle *ABC*, side *b* is 25 yards and the hypotenuse is 40 yards. Find ∠*A* . Round to the nearest tenth.

44. For right triangle *ABC*, side *a* is 8 yards and ∠*A* = 63°. Find the length of the hypotenuse. Round to the nearest hundredth.

45. In right triangle *ABC*, shown at the right, side *b* is 12 miles and the hypotenuse is 15 miles. Find ∠*B* . Round to the nearest tenth.

46. In right triangle *ABC*, side *a* is 7 feet and the hypotenuse is 9 feet. Find ∠*A* . Round to the nearest tenth.

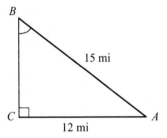

47. For right triangle *ABC*, side *a* is 12 meters and ∠*A* = 37°, as shown at the right. Find the length of side *b*. Round to the nearest hundredth.

48. For right triangle *ABC*, side *b* is 5 miles and ∠*A* = 24°. Find the length of side *a*. Round to the nearest hundredth.

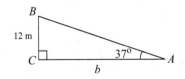

For problems 49 - 62, draw a picture and label. Set up an equation and solve. Show all work. **Round all angles to nearest tenth degree and all sides to 3 significant digits.**

49. A captive balloon, fastened by a cable 997 feet long, was blown by a wind so that the cable made an angle of 57.6° with the ground. Find the height of the balloon.

50.   A road is inclined at an angle of 9.8° with the horizontal. Find the distance which must be driven on this road in order to be elevated 14.8 feet above the horizontal.

51.   A ladder 30.8 feet long leans against a building. If the foot of the ladder is 7.25 feet from the base of the building, find the angle the ladder makes with the building.

52.   A plane takes off from a field and rises at an angle of 11.4° with the horizontal. Find the height of the plane after it has traveled a horizontal distance of 1250 feet.

53.   A guy wire whose grounded end is 16 feet from the pole it supports makes an angle of 56.7° with the ground. How long is the wire?

54.   A lighthouse built at sea level is 169 feet high. From its top, the angle of depression to a boat below measures 25. 1°. Find the distance from the boat to the foot of the lighthouse.

55.   At a point 39.3 feet from the base of a tree, the angle of elevation of its top measures 53.4°. Find the height of the tree.

56.   An artillery spotter in a plane at an altitude of 978 feet observes the angle of depression of an enemy tank to measure 28.5°. How far is the enemy tank from the point on the ground directly below the spotter?

57.   A 20.6 foot ladder leans against the house. The ladder make an angle of 65.1° with the ground. How far up the side of the house does the ladder reach?

58.   Find the angle of elevation of the sun when a tree 40.5 feet high casts a shadow 28.3

feet long.

59.   A television transmitter antenna is 600 feet high. If the angle between the guy wire (attached at the top) and the antenna is 55.4°, how long is the guy wire?

60.   A ramp used to load a racing car onto a flatbed carrier is 5.25 meters long, and its upper end is 1. 74 meters above the lower end. Find the angle between the ramp and the horizontal.

61.   The angle of elevation of the sun is 51.3° at a time when a tree casts a shadow 23.7 yards long. Find the height of the tree.

62.   From the top of a building 312 feet tall the angle of depression to a flower bed on the ground below is 12.0°. What is the distance between the base of the building and the flower bed?

Table of Trigonometric Ratios

Angle	Sine	Cosine	Tangent	Angle	Sine	Cosine	Tangent
0°	0.0000	1.0000	0.0000	45°	0.7071	0.7071	1.0000
1°	0.0175	0.9998	0.0175	46°	0.7193	0.6947	1.0355
2°	0.0349	0.9994	0.0349	47°	0.7314	0.6820	1.0724
3°	0.0523	0.9986	0.0524	48°	0.7431	0.6691	1 1106
4°	0.0698	0.9976	0.0699	49°	0.7547	0.6561	1 1504
5°	0.0872	0.9962	0.0875	50°	0.7660	0.6428	1.1918
6°	0.1045	0.9945	0.1051	51°	0.7771	0.6293	1.2349
7°	0.1219	0.9925	0.1228	52°	0.7880	0.6157	1.2799
8°	0.1392	0.9903	0.1405	53°	0.7986	0.6018	1.3270
9°	0.1564	0.9877	0.1584	54°	0.8090	0.5878	1.3764
10°	0.1736	0.9848	0.1763	55°	0.8193	0.5736	1.4281
11°	0.1908	0.9816	0.1944	56°	0.8290	0.5592	1.4826
12°	0.2079	0.9781	0.2126	57°	0.8387	0.5446	1.5399
13°	0.2250	0.9744	0.2309	58°	0.8480	0.5299	1.6003
14°	0.2419	0.9703	0.2493	59°	0.8572	0.5150	1.6643
15°	0.2588	0.9659	0.2679	60°	0.8660	0.5000	1.7321
16°	0.2756	0.9613	0.2867	61°	0.8746	0.4848	1.8040
17°	0.2924	0.9563	0.3057	62°	0.8829	0.4695	1.8807
18°	0.3090	0.9511	0.3249	63°	0.8910	0.4540	1.9626
19°	0.3256	0.9455	0.3443	64°	0.8988	0.4384	2.0503
20°	0.3420	0.9397	0.3640	65°	0.9063	0.4226	2.1445
21°	0.3584	0.9336	0.3839	66°	0.9135	0.4067	2.2460
22°	0.3746	0.9272	0.4040	67°	0.9205	0.3907	2.3559
23°	0.3907	0.9205	0.4245	68°	0.9272	0.3746	2.4751
24°	0.4067	0.9135	0.4452	69°	0.9336	0.3584	2.6051
25°	0.4226	0.9063	0.4663	70°	0.9397	0.3420	2.7475
26°	0.4384	0.8988	0.4877	71°	0.9455	0.3256	2.9042
27°	0.4540	0.8910	0.5095	72°	0.9511	0.3090	3.0777
28°	0.4695	0.8829	0.5317	73°	0.9563	0.2924	3.2709
29°	0.4848	0.8746	0.5543	74°	0.9613	0.2756	3.4874
30°	0.5000	0.8660	0.5774	75°	0.9659	0.2588	3.7321
31°	0.5150	0.8572	0.6009	76°	0.9703	0.2419	4.0108
32°	0.5299	0.8480	0.6249	77°	0.9744	0.2250	4.3315
33°	0.5446	0.8387	0.6494	78°	0.9781	0.2079	4.7046
34°	0.5592	0.8290	0.6745	79°	0.9816	0.1908	5.1446
35°	0.5736	0.8192	0.7002	80°	0.9848	0.1736	5.6713
36°	0.5878	0.8090	0.7265	81°	0.9877	0.1564	6.3138
37°	0.6018	0.7986	0.7536	82°	0.9903	0.1392	7.1154
38°	0.6157	0.7880	0.7813	83°	0.9925	0.1219	8.1443
39°	0.6293	0.7771	0.8098	84°	0.9945	0.1045	9.5144
40°	0.6428	0.7660	0.8391	85°	0.9962	0.0872	11.4301
41°	0.6561	0.7547	0.8693	86°	0.9976	0.0698	14.3007
42°	0.6691	0.7431	0.9004	87°	0.9986	0.0523	19.0811
43°	0.6820	0.7314	0.9325	88°	0.9994	0.0349	28.6363
44°	0.6947	0.7193	0.9657	89°	0.9998	0.0175	57.2900
45°	0.7071	0.7071	1.0000	90°	1.0000	0.0000	undefined

SOLUTIONS to You-Try-Its

Pythagorean Theorem

You-Try-It 1

$c^2 = a^2 + b^2$

$c^2 = 7^2 + 14^2$

$c^2 = 49 + 196$

$c^2 = 245$

$c = \sqrt{245}$

$c \approx 15.65$

The length of the hypotenuse is 15.65 meters.

You-Try-It 2

$a^2 + b^2 = c^2$

$5^2 + b^2 = 16^2$

$25 + b^2 = 256$

$25 - 25 + b^2 = 256 - 25$

$b^2 = 231$

$b = \sqrt{231}$

$b \approx 15.20 \ \text{feet}$

The measure of the other leg is approximately 15.20 feet.

You-Try-It 3

Goal

The goal is to determine if the 30-foot ladder is long enough to reach the gutters when the gutters are 28 feet above the ground and the bottom of the ladder is 7 feet from the base of the side of the house.

Strategy

- Use the Pythagorean Theorem to find the hypotenuse of a right triangle with legs that measure 7 feet and 28 feet.
- Compare the length of the hypotenuse with 30 feet. If the hypotenuse is shorter than 30 feet, the ladder is long enough to reach the gutters. If the hypotenuse is longer than 30 feet, the ladder will not reach the gutters.

Solution

$c^2 = a^2 + b^2$

$c^2 = 7^2 + 28^2$

$c^2 = 49 + 784$

$c^2 = 833$

$c = \sqrt{833}$

$c \approx 28.9$

$28.9 < 30$ The hypotenuse is shorter than 30 feet.

The ladder will reach the gutters.

Check   Check your work.

Introduction to Trigonometry

You-Try-It 1

$\tan 37.1^\circ = 0.7563$

You-Try-It 2

We are given the measure of $\angle B$ and the hypotenuse. We want to find the length of side a Side a is adjacent to $\angle B$. The trigonometric function that involves the side adjacent to an angle and the hypotenuse is the cosine function.

$$\cos B = \frac{\text{adjacent}}{\text{hypotenuse}}$$

$$\cos 48^\circ = \frac{a}{12}$$

$$12(\cos 48^\circ) = a$$

$$8.03 \approx y$$

The length of side a is approximately 8.03 feet.

You-Try-It 3

$\tan^{-1} 0.3165 = 17.6^\circ$

You-Try-It 4

Ensure that the calculator is in degree mode.   Solving $\tan \theta = 0.5681$ for θ is equivalent to finding $\tan^{-1} 0.5681$.

$\tan^{-1}(0.5681) \approx 29.6009^\circ$

Therefore, to the nearest tenth of a degree, $\theta = 29.6^\circ$.

You-Try-It 5

We want to find the measure of $\angle A$. and we are given the length of the side opposite $\angle A$ and the hypotenuse. The trigonometric function that involves the side opposite an angle and the hypotenuse is the sine function.

$$\sin A = \frac{\text{opposite}}{\text{hypotenuse}}$$

$$\sin A = \frac{7}{11}$$

$$\sin A = 0.\overline{63}$$

$$A = \sin^{-1}(0.\overline{63}) \approx 39.5^\circ$$

The measure of $\angle A$ is approximately 39.5°.

You-Try-It 6

$$c^2 = a^2 + b^2$$
$$c^2 = 8^2 + 10^2$$
$$c^2 = 64 + 100$$
$$c^2 = 164$$
$$c = \sqrt{164}$$
$$c \approx 13$$

$$\sin A = \frac{\text{opposite}}{\text{hypotenuse}}$$

$$\sin A = \frac{8}{10}$$

$$\sin A = \frac{4}{5}$$

$$\sin A = 0.8$$

$$A \approx 53^\circ$$

$$\angle B = 90^\circ - 53^\circ = 37^\circ$$

Side $c = 13$ centimeters, $\angle A = 53^\circ$, and $\angle B = 37^\circ$.

You-Try-It 7

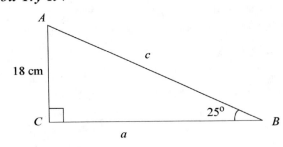

$$\angle A = 90^\circ - 25^\circ = 65^\circ$$

$$\sin B = \frac{\text{opposite}}{\text{hypotenuse}}$$

$$\sin 25^\circ = \frac{18}{c}$$

$$c = \frac{18}{\sin 25^\circ}$$

$$c \approx 43$$

$$\tan B = \frac{\text{opposite}}{\text{adjacent}}$$

$$\tan 25^\circ = \frac{18}{a}$$

$$a = \frac{18}{\tan 25^\circ}$$

$$a \approx 39$$

$\angle A = 65^\circ$, side $c = 43$ centimeters, and side $a = 39$ centimeters.

You-Try-It 8

Goal

The goal is to find how far the boat is from the lighthouse given that the lighthouse is 10 meters high and the angle of depression from the top of the lighthouse is 25°.

Strategy

- Draw a diagram. Label the unknown distance d.
- Find the complement of the angle of depression.
- Write a trigonometric function that relates the given information and side d of the triangle.

Solution

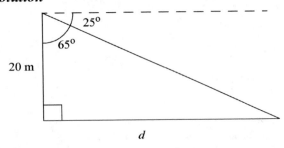

$$90^\circ - 25^\circ = 65^\circ$$

$$\tan 65^\circ = \frac{d}{20}$$

$$20(\tan 65^\circ) = d$$

$$42.9 \approx d$$

The boat is 42.9 meters from the lighthouse.

Check ✓

Pythagorean Theorem

5. No   **7.** No   **9.** 8.9 in.   **11.** 12 cm   **13.** Less than   **15.** 250 ft   **17.** 21.6 in.

19. 21.5 m

Introduction to Trigonometry

3. 0.6820   **5.** 1.4281   **7.** 0.9971   **9.** 1.9970   **11.** 0.8879   **13.** 0.4852   **15.** 0.8453

17. 0.6833   **19.** 38.6° **21.** 41.1° **23.** 21.3° **25.** 38.0° **27.** 72.5° **29.** 0.6°

31. 66.1° **33.** 29.5° **35.** 5.54 m   **37.** 41.6° **39.** 33.3° **41.** 13.16 ft   **43.** 51.3°

45. 53.1° **47.** 15.92 m   **49.** 842 ft   **51.** 13.6° **53.** 29.1 ft   **55.** 52.9 ft   **57.** 18.7 ft

59. 1060 ft   **61.** 19.0 yd